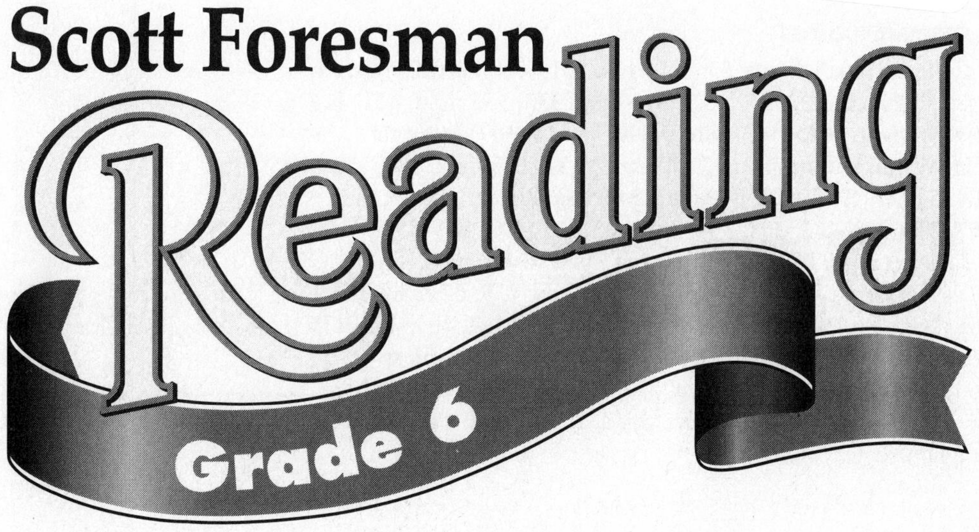

Teacher's Resource Book

Scott Foresman

Editorial Offices: Glenview, Illinois • Parsippany, New Jersey • New York, New York
Sales Offices: Parsippany, New Jersey • Duluth, Georgia • Glenview, Illinois
Coppell, Texas • Ontario, California

Credits

Illustrations

Rondi Collette: pp. 313 left, 335 left, 404, 561, 630; **Patti Corcoran:** pp. 65, 85, 132, 178, 220, 242, 267, 315 right, 333, 335 right, 414, 424, 497 left, 566 right, 584, 614; **Nelle Davis:** pp. 18, 109, 249 right, 541 right; **Waldo Dunn:** pp. 63, 75, 82, 89, 131, 136 right, 139, 145 left, 151, 219, 274, 522, 649, 662; **Morissa Geller:** pp. 87, 125, 170, 197, 238, 252, 283, 308, 384, 387, 405, 431, 492, 544, 552; **Vickie Learner:** pp. 168, 448; **Mapping Specialists:** pp. 21, 67, 612; **Laurie O'Keefe:** pp. 134, 217; **Joel Snyder:** pp. 4, 9, 67 right, 114, 144, 145, 158, 180, 249 left, 271, 315 left, 340, 406 left, 409, 453, 475, 541 left, 566 left, 610 right, 627, 632, 635, 654; **TSI Graphics:** pp. 136 left, 227 left, 264, 406 right, 539, 588, 610 left; **N. Jo Tufts:** pp. 195, 286; **Jessica Wolk-Stanley:** pp. 352, 487, 650; **Lisa Zucker:** pp. 45 right, 202, 227 right, 519.

ISBN 0-328-02235-7
ISBN 0-328-04062-2

3 4 5 6 7 8 9 10 - V039 - 10 09 08 07 06 05 04 03 02
3 4 5 6 7 8 9 10 - V039 - 10 09 08 07 06 05 04 03

Table of Contents

Unit 1

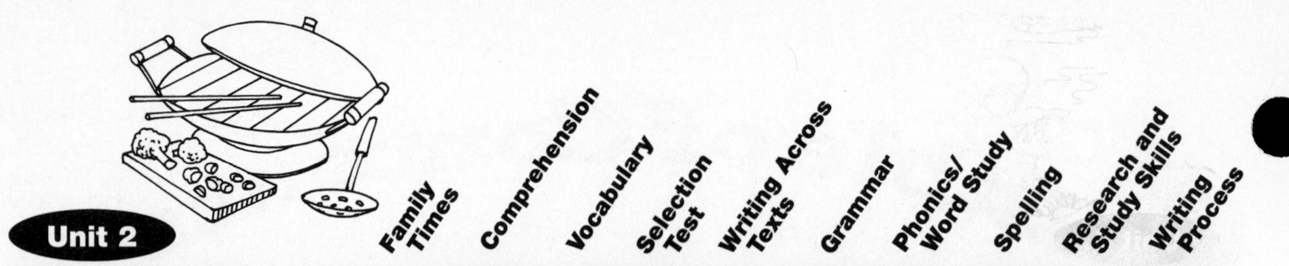

Unit 2

The Living Earth	Family Times	Comprehension	Vocabulary	Selection Test	Writing Across Texts	Grammar	Phonics/ Word Study	Spelling	Research and Study Skills	Writing Process
A Trouble-Making Crow	114–115	116, 118, 121–122	117	119–120	123	124–128	129	130–133	134–135	
From a Spark	136–137	138, 140, 143–144	139	141–142	145	146–150	151	152–155	156–157	
Storm-a-Dust	158–159	160, 162, 165–166	161	163–164	167	168–172	173	174–177	178–179	
The Day of the Turtle	180–181	182, 184, 187–188	183	185–186	189	190–194	195	196–199	200–201	
Saving the Sound	202–203	204, 206, 209–210	205	207–208	211	212–216	217	218–221	222–223	224–226

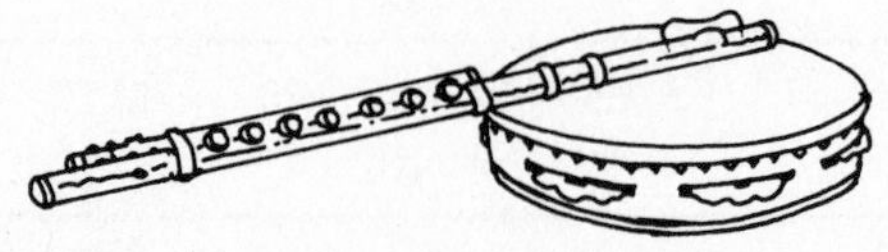

Unit 3

Goals Great and Small	Family Times	Comprehension	Vocabulary	Selection Test	Writing Across Texts	Grammar	Phonics/ Word Study	Spelling	Research and Study Skills	Writing Process
Elizabeth Blackwell: Medical Pioneer	227–228	229, 231, 234–235	230	232–233	236	237–241	242	243–246	247–248	
Born Worker	249–250	251, 253, 256–257	252	254–255	258	259–263	264	265–268	269–270	
Wilma Unlimited	271–272	273, 275, 278–279	274	276–277	280	281–285	286	287–290	291–292	
Casey at the Bat	293–294	295, 297, 300–301	296	298–299	302	303–307	308	309–312	313–314	
The Night of the Pomegranate	315–316	317, 319, 322–323	318	320–321	324	325–329	330	331–334	335–336	337–339

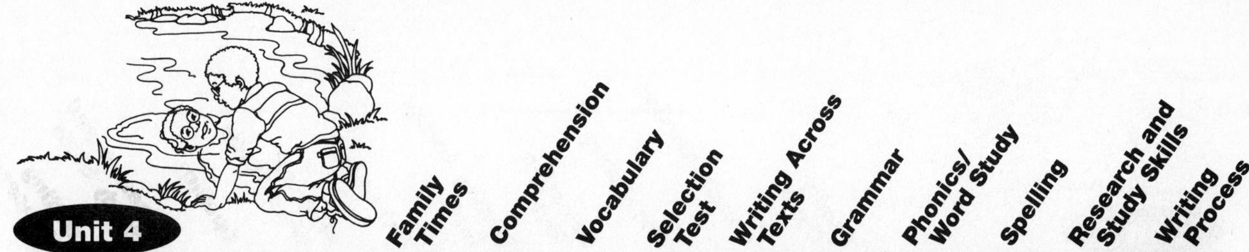

Unit 4

The Way We Were—The Way We Are	Family Times	Comprehension	Vocabulary	Selection Test	Writing Across Texts	Grammar	Phonics/ Word Study	Spelling	Research and Study Skills	Writing Process
Spring Paint	340–341	342, 344, 347–348	343	345–346	349	350–354	355	356–359	360–361	
A Brother's Promise	362–363	364, 366, 369–370	365	367–368	371	372–376	377	378–381	382–383	
from Catching the Fire	384–385	386, 388, 391–392	387	389–390	393	394–398	399	400–403	404–405	
The Seven Wonders of the Ancient World	406–407	408, 410, 413–414	409	411–412	415	416–420	421	422–425	426–427	
The Gold Coin	428–429	430, 432, 435–436	431	433–434	437	438–442	443	444–447	448–449	450–452

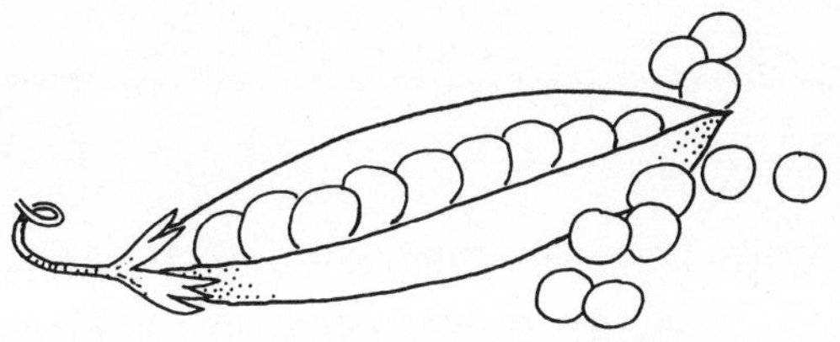

Unit 5

Into the Unknown	Family Times	Comprehension	Vocabulary	Selection Test	Writing Across Texts	Grammar	Phonics/ Word Study	Spelling	Research and Study Skills	Writing Process
To the Pole	453–454	455, 457, 460–461	456	458–459	462	463–467	468	469–472	473–474	
from El Güero	475–476	477, 479, 482–483	478	480–481	484	485–489	490	491–494	495–496	
Destination: Mars	497–498	499, 501, 504–505	500	502–503	506	507–511	512	513–516	517–518	
The Land of Expectations	519–520	521, 523 526–527	522	524–525	528	529–533	534	535–538	539–540	
The Trail Drive	541–542	543, 545 548–549	544	546–547	550	551–555	556	557–560	561–562	563–565

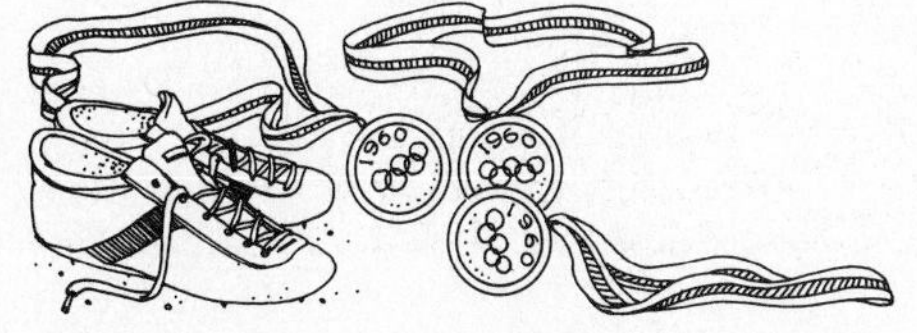

Unit 6

I've Got It!	Family Times	Comprehension	Vocabulary	Selection Test	Writing Across Texts	Grammar	Phonics/ Word Study	Spelling	Research and Study Skills	Writing Process
Noah Writes a B & B Letter	566–567	568, 570 573–574	569	571–572	575	576–580	581	582–585	586–587	
Louis Braille	588–589	590, 592 595–596	591	593–594	597	598–602	603	604–607	608–609	
The Librarian Who Measured the Earth	610–611	612, 614 617–618	613	615–616	619	620–624	625	626–629	630–631	
Tyree's Song	632–633	634, 636 639–640	635	637–638	641	642–646	647	648–651	652–653	
Cutters, Carvers, and the Cathedral	654–655	656, 658 661–662	657	659–660	663	664–668	669	670–673	674–675	676–678

Name____

Summary

Tony Sails—On the Sea and Into the Past

After eleven-year-old Tony saves $300, his first idea is to buy a motorbike. But since the legal driving age is fifteen, he buys a sailboat instead. Tony takes sailing lessons from Chris. Tony capsizes once, but he doesn't give up. As Tony learns to sail, he also learns about himself, his family, and the history of his grandmother's seaside hometown.

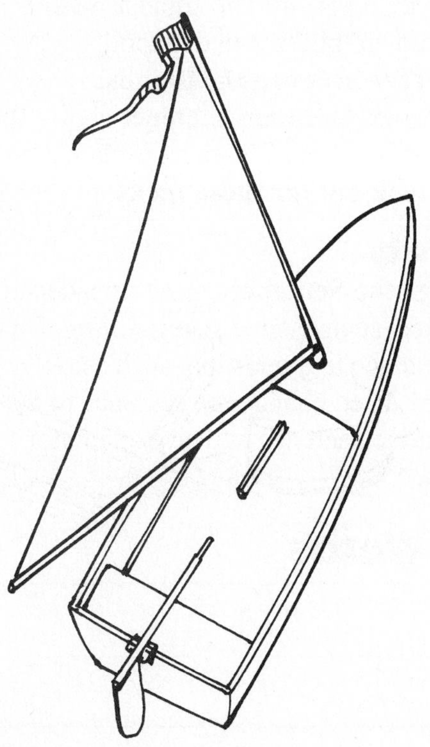

Activity

Act Out the Story. Have your child describe the scene in which Tony convinces his parents to let him buy the boat. Using your child's description, act out the scene together.

Reading Skills

Sequence

To understand a story or an article, it helps to understand the **sequence**—the order in which things happen or characters perform actions. Clue words such as *when, first, then,* and *next* can help you follow the order in which things happen. When Chris teaches Tony to sail, she first teaches him the names of items on the boat, then she demonstrates how to sail, and finally she lets Tony sail. Which three clue words are used in this example to signal the sequence? *(first, then,* and *finally)*

Activity

Make a Story Board. Choose a favorite story. On five index cards, draw five different scenes from the story. Include captions, speech balloons, or thought balloons if you wish. When you are done, arrange the index cards so that they show the correct sequence of events.

Family Times

Tested Vocabulary

Words to Know

Knowing the meanings of these words is important to reading "Tony and the Snark." Practice using these words to learn their meanings.

cove a small, sheltered bay

disaster a very unpleasant event

jolt a sudden jerk or shock

peninsula land nearly surrounded by water

submerged underwater; covered by water

Grammar

Kinds of Sentences

Some sentences tell and some ask. Other sentences give commands or show strong feeling. Each kind of sentence begins with a capital letter and ends with a special mark.

- ❖ A **declarative sentence** makes a statement. It ends with a period.
  I know how to sail.
- ❖ An **interrogative sentence** asks a question. It ends with a question mark.
  Have you ever been on a sailboat?
- ❖ An **imperative sentence** gives a command or makes a request. It ends with a period. The subject *(you)* is not shown, but it is understood.
  Steer between the islands.
- ❖ An **exclamatory sentence** shows strong feeling. It ends with an exclamation point.
  Look out for those rocks!

Activity

Change the Sentence. Make up a declarative sentence, such as *He's going sailing.* Change the sentence to a question, such as: *Is he going sailing?* Then change the sentence to an imperative sentence and an exclamatory sentence.

Tested Spelling Words

____________	____________	____________	____________
____________	____________	____________	____________
____________	____________	____________	____________
____________	____________	____________	____________
____________	____________	____________	____________

Name ______________________________

Sequence

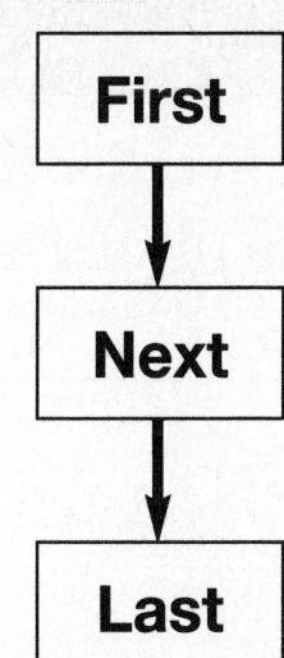

- **Sequence** refers to the order of events in both fiction and nonfiction. Sequence can also refer to steps in a process.
- Clue words such as *when, first, then,* and *next* will help you follow the order in which events happen. Dates and times of day are other clues to the order of events.

Directions: Reread "Jerry Takes Off." Then complete the flow chart. Write the story events from the box in the flow chart in order.

Story Events

Tanya and Tony churned up water as Jerry demonstrated his backstroke.

After Jerry perfected his flip turn, he learned how to dive properly.

When Jerry touched the opposite edge of the pool, Wayne Cabot shouted down to the three of them.

When Tony arrived at the shallow end, Coach Fulton described the way he wanted Jerry to practice his turns.

Then Jerry demonstrated how well he learned to start off in a backstroke race.

During the next week, Jerry managed to work in some extra coaching.

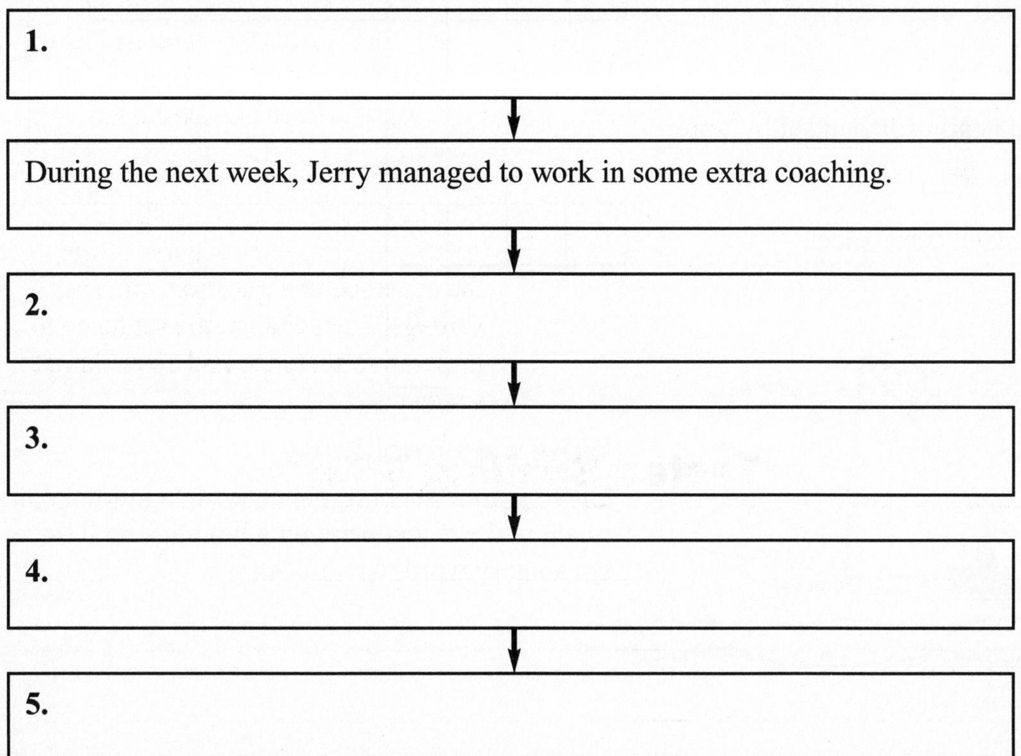

Notes for Home: Your child read a story and listed events from the story in the order in which they happened. ***Home Activity:*** Have your child describe five things that he or she did today in the order in which they happened.

Name ____________________________

Vocabulary

Directions: Choose the word from the box that best completes each sentence. Write the word on the line to the left.

Check the Words You Know
__ cove
__ disaster
__ jolt
__ peninsula
__ submerged

____________ **1.** Michelle's boat had to change direction in order to sail around the longest side of the _____.

____________ **2.** Finally, she sailed the boat into a small _____.

____________ **3.** With a _____, the boat hit something hard.

____________ **4.** It was a _____ rock just under the surface of the water.

____________ **5.** Luckily, the rock did not harm the boat, and Michelle avoided a _____!

Directions: Choose the word from the box that best matches each clue. Write the word in the puzzle.

Down

6. a very unpleasant event

8. a small, sheltered bay

Across

7. land nearly surrounded by water

9. under water

10. a sudden jar or shock

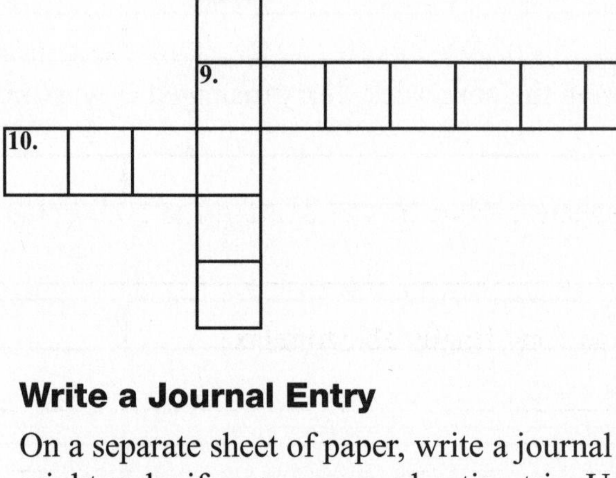

Write a Journal Entry

On a separate sheet of paper, write a journal entry you might make if you were on a boating trip. Use as many vocabulary words as you can.

Notes for Home: Your child identified and used vocabulary words from "Tony and the Snark." ***Home Activity:*** Together, make up a story about troubles on board a ship. Encourage your child to suggest ways the vocabulary words can be used in the story.

Name ______________________________

Sequence

- **Sequence** is the order in which things happen or characters perform actions.
- **Sequence** can also refer to the steps in a process.
- Sometimes events happen at the same time. Clue words like *while, as,* and *during* signal two events happening at the same time.

Directions: Reread what happens in "Tony and the Snark" when the boat capsizes. Then answer the questions below. Notice that some story events happen at the same time.

The mast careened. Tony, frightened, let go of everything. The next second the boat capsized.

As Tony hit the water he lost his breath. Struggling, he began to sink. Even as he did he felt the upward pull of his life jacket. Spitting, flailing arms and legs, he broke through to the water's surface.

"Let your jacket hold you!" he heard Chris shout. "Don't fight! Get your breath!"

Tony stopped thrashing. And when he realized the jacket would hold him, he relaxed.

1. What happened when Tony hit the water?

____

2. What happened as he struggled and began to go under?

____

3. What happened while he was spitting and flailing his arms and legs?

____

4. When was Tony finally able to relax?

____

____

5. On a separate sheet of paper, list what you consider to be the five main events of "Tony and the Snark." Check to be sure that your events are in the right sequence.

Notes for Home: Your child read a story and used details to understand sequence—the order of events in the story. ***Home Activity:*** Encourage your child to make a schedule of his or her evening activities on a typical school night. Help your child list the events in sequential order.

Name ______________________________

Selection Test

Directions: Choose the best answer to each item. Mark the letter for the answer you have chosen.

Part 1: Vocabulary

Find the answer choice that means about the same as the underlined word in each sentence.

1. Homes on that <u>peninsula</u> are very expensive.
A. steep hill
B. cleared land in a forest
C. low, grassy land near a stream
D. land almost surrounded by water

2. Diane practiced sailing in the <u>cove</u>.
F. a small, sheltered bay
G. a small pond
H. a lake
J. a slow-moving river

3. Watch out for the <u>submerged</u> rocks!
A. under the surface of the water
B. floating on the water
C. falling
D. overhead

4. Sam thought his first date was a <u>disaster</u>.
F. a surprise
G. an event that causes much suffering
H. a sad moment
J. a joyous event

5. The car stopped with a <u>jolt</u>.
A. loud noise
B. gradual slowing
C. jerk or sudden jarring movement
D. smell of something burning

Part 2: Comprehension

Use what you know about the story to answer each item.

6. Before Tony's parents said he could buy the *Snark*, they—
F. went to the Mart to see it.
G. bought a life jacket.
H. discussed it with his grandmother.
J. made him clean and wax the car.

7. At the beginning of the story, Tony had money saved up from—
A. selling a motor scooter.
B. having a birthday party.
C. opening a bank account.
D. delivering newspapers.

8. Tony promised his parents that whenever he sailed, he would—
F. wash and wax the car.
G. wear a life jacket.
H. go with a teacher.
J. take swimming lessons.

9. Where does most of this story take place?
A. at Tony's house
B. at the Mart
C. on the Connecticut shore
D. in Jamal's driveway

10. Why did Tony's face get hot after he capsized the *Snark?*
F. He scraped his face on a rock.
G. His face felt hot compared to the cold water.
H. He was embarrassed.
J. He was scared.

11. What happened after Tony and Chris got all the water out of the *Snark?*
A. Tony sailed it back to the harbor.
B. Tony's father drove them to the harbor.
C. They waded back to the harbor.
D. Chris and Tony went swimming.

GO ON

Name ______________________________

12. Chris most likely started the sailing lesson by explaining words like "port" and "dagger board" so that Tony would—
- F. sound like a sailor when he talked to other people.
- G. lose his confidence and listen to her.
- H. realize that sailing is not easy.
- J. understand her directions when she told him what to do.

13. Which words best describe Chris?
- A. loud and bossy
- B. confident and encouraging
- C. daring and pushy
- D. shy and unsure

14. When Tony first arrived at Carluci's Fish Store, he assumed that—
- F. Chris was a boy.
- G. sailboats were faster than speedboats.
- H. Chris knew where treasure was buried.
- J. he could learn to sail in one afternoon.

15. You can tell that Chris thinks Swallows Bay Harbor is—
- A. too dangerous for sailing.
- B. a boring place to live.
- C. too crowded with people.
- D. a good place to learn sailing.

STOP

Sequence

- **Sequence** is the order in which things happen or characters perform actions.
- **Sequence** can also refer to the steps in a process.
- Sometimes events happen at the same time. Clue words such as *while, as,* and *during* signal that two events happen at the same time.

Directions: Read the story below.

Tarik felt the fear hit him while he waited for the curtain to go up. When he saw the audience in front of him, he grew even more scared. "What if I forget my lines? What if I trip on my costume?"

However, when it was his turn to speak, all nervous thoughts flew away. He felt the story take over as he spoke, moved, and acted. He went through the scene perfectly.

When the curtain came down, Tarik felt proud of himself. He boasted to his classmates, "We did it! We were a hit!" while they waited together to take a bow.

Directions: Use the flow chart below to place the listed story events in correct order. Events that happen at the same time can be listed side by side. Some have been done for you.

Story Events

Tarik felt proud of himself.
They waited to take a bow.
Tarik saw the audience in front of him.
It was Tarik's turn to speak.
Tarik felt a jolt of fear.
Tarik forgot his fear.
The curtain came down.
Tarik boasted to his classmates.

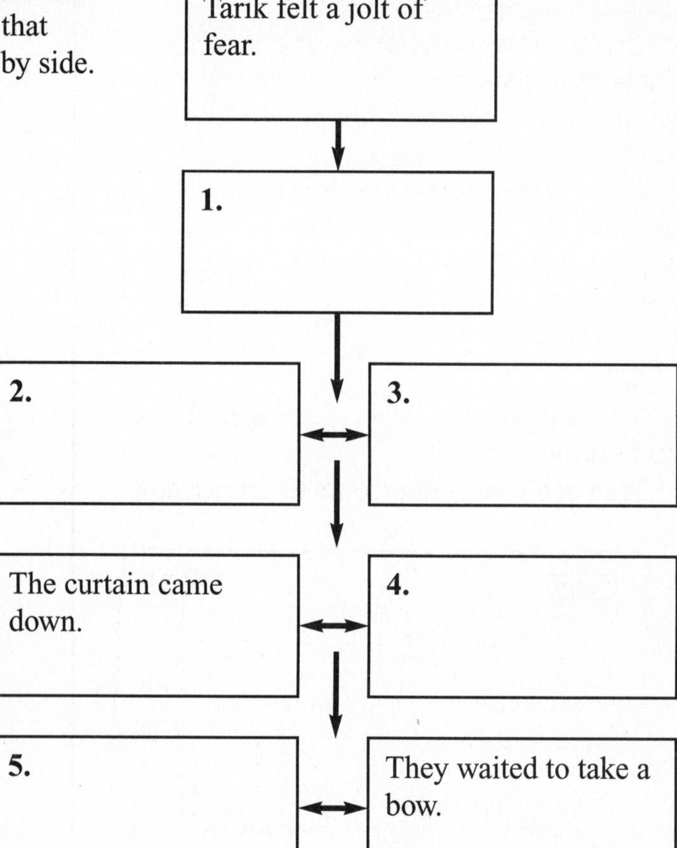
Tarik felt a jolt of fear.
1.
2.
3.
The curtain came down.
4.
5.
They waited to take a bow.

Notes for Home: Your child read a story and used its details to understand the sequence of events, including events that happen at the same time. ***Home Activity:*** With your child, discuss the order of the steps for making and serving breakfast.

Name ______________________________

REVIEW

Cause and Effect

Directions: Read the story. Then read each question about the story. Choose the best answer to each question. Mark the letter for the answer you have chosen.

The Dark Day

Mira woke with a jolt. Dad was shaking her by the shoulder, saying, "Mira, wake up! You overslept."

"Oh, no," groaned Mira. "I'm going to be late for school. I'll miss math review. This day is a disaster already!"

Her father looked concerned. "I'm sorry, honey. How quickly can you get ready? I'll drive you to school. I'm sure I can get you there in time."

Mira jumped into her blue jeans and raced to the kitchen, buttoning her shirt as she ran. She put two frozen waffles—her favorite breakfast treats—into the toaster. She flipped the light switch as she gulped down her juice, but nothing happened. "Everything's going wrong today. Now the light has burned out too."

Mira popped up her waffles, planning to eat them on the way to school. They were as cold and pale as before. "Hey, wait a minute!" She dashed to the window. No lights shone from other houses. The cars were still, buried under mounds of snow.

Then she saw her father shaking his head and smiling.

Mira could see tomorrow's headlines now:

MAJOR SNOWSTORM CAUSES
POWER FAILURE!!
LINES DOWN,
TRAFFIC HALTED!

1. Mira is going to be late for school because—
   - **A.** she overslept.
   - **B.** she made waffles for breakfast.
   - **C.** she'll miss math review.
   - **D.** it was a dark morning.

2. Mira's waffles are pale and cold because—
   - **F.** she's late for school.
   - **G.** she likes them that way.
   - **H.** she can't see their color in the darkened kitchen.
   - **J.** there's no electric power.

3. The kitchen light doesn't work because—
   - **A.** it burned out.
   - **B.** she didn't turn it on.
   - **C.** the snowstorm caused a power failure.
   - **D.** everything's going wrong that day.

4. What was the first cause that set off the chain of effects in this story?
   - **F.** a snowstorm
   - **G.** no electricity
   - **H.** Mira oversleeping
   - **J.** Mira's father oversleeping

5. What was the storm's most serious effect?
   - **A.** The morning was gray, and Mira overslept.
   - **B.** Mira's waffles were cold.
   - **C.** There was no electricity, and people couldn't travel.
   - **D.** People needed shovels and boots.

Notes for Home: Your child read a story and noted the causes and effects of events in the story. ***Home Activity:*** Watch a television news program with your child. Ask her or him to explain what happened and why. See if your child can identify more than one cause or effect.

Name ______________________________

Writing Across Texts

Directions: Consider what you learned from the fiction selection, "Tony and the Snark" and the nonfiction article, "Swimming for the Gold." Complete the table with information about story events and the characters Tony Souza and Amy Van Dyken.

	Tony Souza	Amy Van Dyken
Type of Activity	**1.**	**6.**
Amount of Experience	**2.**	**7.**
Preparation	**3.**	**8.**
Keys to Success	**4.**	**9.**
What Happens	**5.**	**10.**

Write a Paragraph

Both "Tony and the Snark" and "Swimming for the Gold" tell about learning experiences. Write a paragraph that compares and contrasts the experiences the two young people had. Use the information you recorded in the table above. Write your paragraph on a separate sheet of paper.

Notes for Home: Your child used information from different sources to write a comparison-contrast paragraph. ***Home Activity:*** As you read stories and articles with your child, discuss ways the ideas connect to other literature, informational articles, and television shows.

REVIEW

Grammar: Sentences

Directions: Read each group of words. Write **S** if it is a sentence. Write **NS** if it is not a sentence.

__________ **1.** During my summer vacation, I visited the United Nations for the first time.

__________ **2.** Located in New York City.

__________ **3.** It began with 50 member countries.

__________ **4.** Now has a total of 185 member countries.

__________ **5.** The UN has its own flag and stamps!

__________ **6.** Even a web site of its own!

__________ **7.** I was very impressed by the building.

__________ **8.** All the flags from all the nations.

__________ **9.** People from many countries, many in colorful native clothing.

__________ **10.** I really enjoy learning new things.

Directions: Add a word or group of words to complete each sentence. Write the complete sentence on the line. Remember to start each sentence with a capital letter.

11. For the first time, I _____.

____

12. _____ was very exciting!

____

13. I could hardly wait to _____.

____

14. _____ was the best experience of all!

____

15. I recommend _____.

____

Notes for Home: Your child identified and wrote complete sentences. ***Home Activity:*** Together, write a letter or postcard to a family member or friend. Use complete sentences.

Name ______________________________

Grammar: Kinds of Sentences—Declarative, Interrogative, Imperative, and Exclamatory

There are four kinds of sentences. Each begins with a capital letter and ends with a special end mark.

A **declarative sentence** makes a statement. It ends with a period.

The rudder on any boat is a steering device.

An **interrogative sentence** asks a question. It ends with a question mark.

Doesn't an airplane have a rudder too?

An **imperative sentence** gives a command or request. It ends with a period. The subject *(you)* is not shown, but it is understood.

Fasten your life jacket, please.

An **exclamatory sentence** expresses strong feeling. It ends with an exclamation mark.

So many facts about boats are new to me!

Directions: Write whether each sentence is **declarative, interrogative, imperative,** or **exclamatory.**

_______________ **1.** I'm planning to take up sailing.

_______________ **2.** What fun it would be to sail the ocean blue!

_______________ **3.** Are there still pirates lurking around the ocean?

_______________ **4.** Read this true story about piracy.

_______________ **5.** I have a dream of sailing around the world.

Directions: Write the correct end punctuation to complete each sentence.

6. Sailing lessons can be confusing _____

7. You have to understand about wind, currents, and angles _____

8. Try not to become discouraged _____

9. Did you know that even famous navigators had some troubles _____

10. Focus on one thing at a time _____

Notes for Home: Your child identified four kinds of sentences and added end punctuation to sentences. ***Home Activity:*** Read with your child and work together to identify different kinds of sentences. Ask your child to tell you about different end punctuation marks.

Name ______________________________

Grammar: Kinds of Sentences—Declarative, Interrogative, Imperative, and Exclamatory

Directions: Add the correct end punctuation to each sentence.

1. Tami was sure she was braver than anyone else _____
2. Isn't she afraid of anything _____
3. She should be careful around strange animals _____
4. What a narrow escape I had yesterday _____
5. I mistakenly thought a wild animal was tame _____
6. Climb the cliff with us _____
7. Don't forget the mountain climbers' rules _____
8. I was absolutely terrified _____
9. Some people are afraid of heights _____
10. Aren't you ever afraid _____

Directions: Read each sentence and decide which kind of sentence it is. Then change it to the kind of sentence named in ( ). Write the new sentence on the line, using correct end punctuation.

11. Do we believe in using common sense? (declarative)

____

12. You can ask the Appalachian Mountain Club for advice. (imperative)

____

13. Think about climbing Mount Everest. (interrogative)

____

14. Would that be a wonderful adventure? (exclamatory)

____

15. You haven't ever climbed Mount Washington. (interrogative)

____

Write a Paragraph

On a separate sheet of paper, write a paragraph about an event you remember. Use at least one of each of the four kinds of sentences in your paragraph.

Notes for Home: Your child identified and wrote different kinds of sentences. ***Home Activity:*** Say different kinds of sentences aloud. Have your child use hand signs to show the end punctuation for each one. For example, point a forefinger for a period.

Name ______________________

RETEACHING

Grammar: Kinds of Sentences—Declarative, Interrogative, Imperative, and Exclamatory

Read the directions below. Write your responses in complete sentences.

1. Make a statement that tells what is pictured. Use a period at the end of your sentence.

   ____

2. Tell exactly how you feel about the spider. Express yourself strongly with an exclamation mark.

   ____

3. Give the spider a command. Use a period.

   ____

4. Ask the spider why it did not obey you. Use a question mark.

   ____

A **declarative sentence** makes a statement. An **interrogative sentence** asks a question. An **imperative sentence** gives a command or makes a request. An **exclamatory sentence** expresses strong feeling.

Directions: Write **declarative, interrogative, exclamatory,** or **imperative** to describe each sentence.

______________ **1.** Tell me about your nature walk.

______________ **2.** Did you see the bright orange salamander?

______________ **3.** What a beautiful beetle that is!

______________ **4.** Are earthworms good for the soil?

______________ **5.** Ants are very strong for their size.

______________ **6.** Listen for the crickets on summer evenings.

______________ **7.** How slowly those snails move!

______________ **8.** Lightning bugs glow in the dark.

Notes for Home: Your child identified declarative, interrogative, imperative, and exclamatory sentences. ***Home Activity:*** Have your child look at advertisements in newspapers and magazines and identify each type of sentence he or she finds.

Grammar: Kinds of Sentences—Declarative, Interrogative, Imperative, and Exclamatory

Directions: Add end punctuation. Circle any letters that need capitalization.

1. how interesting the solar system is ________
2. venus is covered with thick clouds ________
3. Jupiter, the largest planet, has the shortest day ________
4. which planet would you visit first ________
5. Look through a telescope at the craters on the moon ________
6. Did you know that Mercury is closest to the sun ________
7. what a great distance Pluto is from the sun ________
8. Watch for meteor showers in June, August, and December ________
9. the polar caps on Mars change with the seasons ________
10. What are the lines on the surface of Mars ________
11. How vast the Milky Way is ________
12. it has more than 100 billion stars ________

Directions: Use the sentence below to write new sentences about Saturn. Write the kind of sentence asked for in ( ).

Saturn is a bright planet with beautiful rings.

13. ______________________________ (interrogative)
14. ______________________________ (exclamatory)
15. ______________________________ (imperative)
16. ______________________________ (declarative)
17. ______________________________ (imperative)

Write a Letter

On a separate sheet of paper, write a letter to the President. Tell why you should be one of the first students chosen to take a trip to the moon. Explain your motivations, and ask questions about space. Add variety to your writing by using different kinds of sentences.

Notes for Home: Your child punctuated and wrote four types of sentences. ***Home Activity:*** Write a declarative sentence. (For example: *We walked out the door.*) Together, change the sentence into an imperative sentence, an interrogative sentence, and an exclamatory sentence.

Name ______________________________

Phonics: Common Word Patterns

Directions: Read each word below. Some words have a word pattern **consonant-vowel-consonant-e (CVCe)** as in **gave.** Most CVCe words have a **long vowel** sound. Other words have a word pattern **vowel-consonant-consonant-vowel (VCCV)** as in **pocket.** Often, the first vowel in VCCV words has a **short vowel** sound. Sort the words according to their word patterns. Write each word in the correct column.

listen	drove	bladelike	fifteen	home
smile	history	windows	life	jacket

CVCe gave	VCCV pocket
1. ______________	6. ______________
2. ______________	7. ______________
3. ______________	8. ______________
4. ______________	9. ______________
5. ______________	10. ______________

Directions: You can use word patterns to help you pronounce words. Read each sentence. Say the underlined word to yourself. Which pattern do you see and hear? Circle the correct pattern in ( ). Some words might have both.

11. Learning a new skill makes us feel confident inside. (CVCe/VCCV)
12. It is not always easy to avoid disaster when trying something new. (CVCe/VCCV)
13. Even though the boat capsized, the sailing student did not give up. (CVCe/VCCV)
14. It is probably best not to be alone when trying something new for the first time. (CVCe/VCCV)
15. History shows us that only those who take a chance come out a winner. (CVCe/VCCV)

Notes for Home: Your child sorted and wrote words based on letter patterns such as *gave (CVCe)* and *pocket (VCCV)*. ***Home Activity:*** Write *gave* and *pocket*. Take turns changing one letter of each word to make a new word without changing the *CVCe* or *VCCV* patterns.

Name ______________________________

Spelling: Short Vowels

Pretest Directions: Fold back the page along the dotted line. On the blanks, write the spelling words as they are dictated. When you have finished the test, unfold the page and check your words.

1. ______________
2. ______________
3. ______________
4. ______________
5. ______________
6. ______________
7. ______________
8. ______________
9. ______________
10. ______________
11. ______________
12. ______________
13. ______________
14. ______________
15. ______________
16. ______________
17. ______________
18. ______________
19. ______________
20. ______________

1. We **admire** beautiful sunsets.
2. The **canyon** was very deep.
3. Use a microscope to **magnify** it.
4. The old ship has a **cannon**.
5. Offer him a glass of **lemonade**.
6. What new **method** did you use?
7. The bakers **decorate** the cake.
8. She ran the longest **distance**.
9. Let's go **swimming** tomorrow.
10. His parents are not very **strict**.
11. Her **injury** was not too serious.
12. I need a **tissue**.
13. My sister studies **modern** dance.
14. This movie is a **comedy**.
15. He is known for his **honesty**.
16. This land is private **property**.
17. Her **husband** gave her a ring.
18. I get **clumsy** when I am tired.
19. The **hundredth** customer wins.
20. The castle has an old **dungeon**.

Notes for Home: Your child took a pretest on words that have short vowel sounds. ***Home Activity:*** Help your child learn misspelled words before the final test. Your child should look at the word, say it, spell it aloud, and then spell it with eyes shut.

Name ______________________________

Spelling: Short Vowels

Word List

admire	method	injury	property
canyon	decorate	tissue	husband
magnify	distance	modern	clumsy
cannon	swimming	comedy	hundredth
lemonade	strict	honesty	dungeon

Directions: Choose the words from the box that have a short **u, a,** or **i** vowel sound. Write each word in the correct column.

Short u as in under

1. ____________________
2. ____________________
3. ____________________
4. ____________________

Short a as in land

5. ____________________
6. ____________________
7. ____________________
8. ____________________

Short i as in fit

9. ____________________
10. ____________________
11. ____________________
12. ____________________
13. ____________________

Directions: Choose the word from the box that contains each word below. Write the word on the line.

____________________ **14.** rate

____________________ **15.** prop

____________________ **16.** mode

____________________ **17.** lemon

____________________ **18.** one

____________________ **19.** met

____________________ **20.** come

Notes for Home: Your child spelled words with short vowel sounds: *a* as in *apple, e* as in *leg, i* as in *tin, o* as in *concert, u* as in *hunt*. ***Home Activity:*** Write each word on a slip of paper. Take turns choosing a word and using it in a sentence.

Name ______________________________

Spelling: Short Vowels

Directions: Proofread this diary entry. Find five spelling mistakes. Use the proofreading marks to correct each mistake.

≡	Make a capital.
/	Make a small letter.
∧	Add something.
℘	Take out something.
⊙	Add a period.
¶	Begin a new paragraph.

August 19th

This is my first time sailing at night. The dark seems to magnfy each sound. I can hear the surf in the distence booming like a canon. I think I like sailing at night because I can lie on deck and admire the stars, which decarate the sky like so many tiny lights.

I'd better get some sleep. Tomorrow we are sailing to our friend's beach property to go swiming at her house.

Spelling Tip

swimming

Remember to double the final consonant of one-syllable words that end with **consonant-vowel-consonant.**

Word List

admire	method	injury	property
canyon	decorate	tissue	husband
magnify	distance	modern	clumsy
cannon	swimming	comedy	hundredth
lemonade	strict	honesty	dungeon

Write a Diary Entry

Imagine you are the captain of a large ship. On a separate sheet of paper, write a diary entry from the captain's personal log. Try to use at least five of your spelling words.

Notes for Home: Your child spelled words with short vowel sounds: *a* as in *apple, e* as in *leg, i* as in *tin, o* as in *concert, u* as in *hunt.* ***Home Activity:*** Have your child demonstrate the difference between a short *e* sound and a long *e* sound, using a variety of words.

Name ______________________

Spelling: Short Vowels

REVIEW

Word List

admire	lemonade	swimming	modern	husband
canyon	method	strict	comedy	clumsy
magnify	decorate	injury	honesty	hundredth
cannon	distance	tissue	property	dungeon

Directions: Choose the word from the box that best completes each sentence. Write the word on the line to the left.

______________________ 1. My favorite drink on a hot day is _____.

______________________ 2. My brother-in-law is my sister's _____.

______________________ 3. A bicycle helmet may protect you from an _____.

______________________ 4. Every Fourth of July, a ball is fired from the old _____.

______________________ 5. Wendy and I are on our way to the lake to go _____.

______________________ 6. The jail in a castle is called a _____.

______________________ 7. We laughed and laughed at a television _____.

______________________ 8. I am going to sneeze; please hand me a _____.

______________________ 9. I called it a valley, but Sue said it is a _____.

______________________ 10. One out of one hundred is one _____.

Directions: Choose the word from the box that has the same or nearly the same meaning as each word below. Write the word on the line.

11. possession ______________________

12. truthfulness ______________________

13. rigid ______________________

14. adorn ______________________

15. respect ______________________

16. enlarge ______________________

17. way ______________________

18. length ______________________

19. current ______________________

20. awkward ______________________

Notes for Home: Your child spelled words with short vowel sounds: *a* as in *apple, e* as in *leg, i* as in *tin, o* as in *concert, u* as in *hunt.* ***Home Activity:*** Scramble the letters of each spelling word. Have your child unscramble each word.

Name ______________________________

Map/Atlas

A **map** is a drawing of a place. A **map key** shows what the symbols used on a map mean. A **compass** shows the directions north, south, east, and west. The **scale** shows distances. An **atlas** is a book of maps.

Directions: The map below shows the route taken by the explorers Meriwether Lewis and William Clark from 1804 to 1806. President Thomas Jefferson believed it was possible to sail across North America from the Mississippi River to the Pacific Ocean, and he sent Lewis and Clark to look for this water route. Use the map to answer the questions on the next page.

Lewis and Clark Exploration of the Northwest, 1804–1806

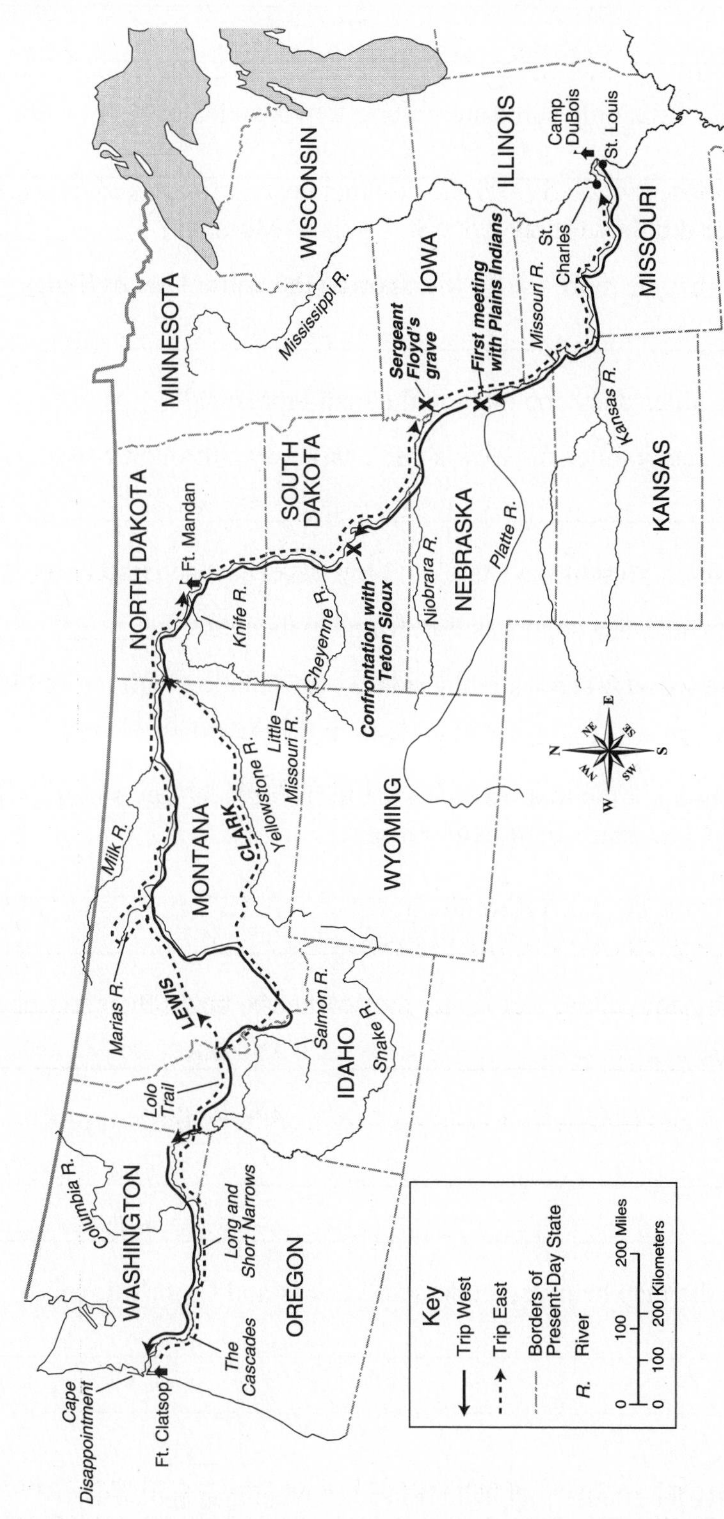

Name ______________________________

1. How does the map key help you understand the map? ______________________________

____

2. What do the dashed lines with arrows represent? What do the solid lines with arrows represent?

____

____

3. Why do you think only some sites along Lewis and Clark's trips are labeled?

____

4. Which river did they follow from St. Louis to Montana? ______________________________

5. Would the map be more useful if it showed the entire United States? Explain.

____

6. How many miles does one inch on the map represent? ______________________________

7. About how many miles did Lewis and Clark travel through Missouri as they went west?

____

8. Through which present-day state did they travel east separately? ______________________________

9. In which present-day state was Fort Mandan located? ______________________________

10. In which present-day state did they have a confrontation with the Teton Sioux? ______________________________

11. In which present-day western state is the Lolo Trail? ______________________________

12. Why do you think the map key uses the term "present-day states"? Hint: Think about when Lewis and Clark made their explorations.

____

____

13. What is the name of the fort where they turned to begin their trip back east?

____

14. Were Lewis and Clark able to sail directly from the Mississippi River to the Pacific Ocean?

____

____

15. How does the map help you understand Lewis and Clark's travels? ______________________________

____

____

Notes for Home: Your child read a historical map and answered questions about it. ***Home Activity:*** Show your child a weather map from the newspaper. Take turns asking one another questions about it, such as: *Where is it going to rain? What does this symbol represent?*

Family Times

Name______________________________

Summary

Jackie Robinson Breaks the Color Barrier

In the 1940s, all Major League baseball players were white. Branch Rickey, the general manager of the Brooklyn Dodgers, wanted to change that. He searched the Negro Leagues for a talented baseball player who could meet the challenge. He found his man in Jackie Robinson.

Robinson's job was not easy. Fans often yelled hateful things when he was on the field. But Robinson didn't give up. Over time, his teammates grew more and more impressed by his talent and courage. During a game in Cincinnati, Ohio, Dodger shortstop Pee Wee Reese publicly demonstrated his support for Jackie Robinson. Fans still remember his gesture as one of the most moving moments in sports history.

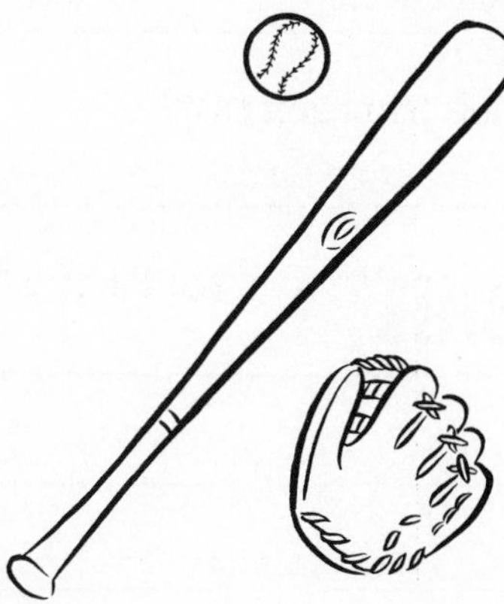

Activity

Narrate the Event. Imagine that you are a radio announcer at the game in Cincinnati. Describe what happens as Pee Wee Reese walks to first base to stand with Jackie Robinson.

Reading Skills

Author's Viewpoint

Author's viewpoint is the way an author thinks about the subject of his or her writing. An author's viewpoint may be one of fear, admiration, pity, or some other strong feeling. You can identify an author's viewpoint by thinking about the words he or she uses to describe a subject. The author Peter Golenbock uses words like *bravery, courage,* and *strong beliefs* to tell you that he admires Jackie Robinson.

Baseball *is* America's Favorite Pastime

To the Editor:

Baseball is the greatest game in the world! There's no better way to spend a long summer afternoon. The bright sunlight, the roar of the crowd, the crack of the bat, the delicious taste of hot dogs and lemonade—everything you need for a good time! What other sport gives you such a long season of wonderful memories?

Activity

Read Letters to the Editor. Together, read some letters to the editor in your local newspaper and cut them out. Underline words or phrases that reveal the author's viewpoint. Sum up this viewpoint in a sentence or two.

Family Times

Tested Vocabulary

Words to Know

Knowing the meanings of these words is important to reading *Teammates.* Practice using these words to learn their meanings.

abuse rough or cruel treatment

dedication devotion to a purpose

hateful showing strong dislike

hostility extreme unfriendliness

prejudice unfounded dislike

racial of or about races of people

tremendous incredible; extraordinary

Grammar

Subjects, Predicates, and Fragments

A sentence must have both a subject and a predicate. The **complete subject** is all of the words that tell whom or what the sentence is about. The **complete predicate** is all of the words that tell what the subject is or does.

A **sentence fragment** is a group of words that looks like a sentence but does not express a complete thought. You can correct some fragments by adding words to make them a complete sentence.

Fragment: Loves to go to baseball games!
Complete Sentence: My aunt loves to go to baseball games!

Activity

Find the Fragments. Identify some sentence fragments that you hear on a radio or television show. Change the fragments to complete sentences.

Tested Spelling Words

______	______	______	______
______	______	______	______
______	______	______	______
______	______	______	______
______	______	______	______

Name ______________________

Author's Viewpoint

- An **author's viewpoint** is the way an author looks at the subject he or she is writing about.
- An author's viewpoint may be one of anger, admiration, pity, or some other feeling.
- You can identify an author's viewpoint by thinking about the words an author uses to describe a subject.

Directions: Reread "Play Ball!" Complete the table by providing phrases from the story that reveal the author's viewpoint about the main character. Then identify the author's viewpoint about the story's subject using details given in the story.

Character or Subject	Phrases that Describe Character/Subject	Author's Viewpoint
Kenny	Kenny hops up.	The author admires Kenny. He thinks that Kenny is quick, alert, and responsible.
	1.	
	2.	
	3.	
	4.	
Baseball	The team's three doctors are also in the dugout, watching how the players' bodies are working during the game.	**5.**
	. . . that sacred moment. . . .	
	. . . a tense batter throws his helmet and bat. . . .	

Notes for Home: Your child read a story and used words from the story to identify the author's viewpoint. ***Home Activity:*** Describe a person, place, or thing. Then ask your child to describe how you feel about that person, place, or thing, based on your description.

Vocabulary

Directions: Choose the word from the box that best matches each definition. Write the word on the line.

Check the Words You Know
__ abuse
__ dedication
__ hateful
__ hostility
__ prejudice
__ racial
__ tremendous

__________________ **1.** showing or causing hate

__________________ **2.** rough or cruel treatment

__________________ **3.** very great; enormous

__________________ **4.** devotion to a purpose

__________________ **5.** unfounded dislike

Directions: Choose a word from the box that best matches each clue. Write the word on the line to the left.

__________________ **6.** During the Civil Rights movement of the 1950s and 1960s, many men and women were working and fighting for _____ equality for all Americans.

__________________ **7.** These Civil Rights workers often had to face the _____ of angry crowds.

__________________ **8.** Despite these obstacles, the _____ of the workers paid off as unfair laws were overturned.

__________________ **9.** Since the 1950s, there have been some _____ changes in the way people of different races relate to one another.

__________________ **10.** Although _____ against others still exists, the Civil Rights movement was successful in getting laws passed to protect against unfair treatment of others based on their race.

Write an Opinion

Think about a time you felt others had treated you unfairly because you were "different" from them. How did this make you feel? On a separate sheet of paper, write an opinion on how prejudice affects the way people treat one another. Use as many vocabulary words as you can.

Notes for Home: Your child identified and used vocabulary words from the story *Teammates.* ***Home Activity:*** Select five words from a story you and your child read together. Take turns telling each other what the word means and using it in a sentence.

Name ______________________

Author's Viewpoint

- **Author's viewpoint** is the way an author thinks about the subject of his or her writing.
- An author's viewpoint may be one of fear, admiration, pity, amusement, or other feeling.
- You can identify an author's viewpoint by thinking about the words an author uses to describe a subject.

Directions: Reread the part of *Teammates* in which Pee Wee Reese takes a stand. Then answer the questions below. Think about how the author shows his viewpoint.

With his head high, Pee Wee walked directly from his shortstop position to where Jackie was playing first base. The taunts and shouting of the fans were ringing in Pee Wee's ears. It saddened him, because he knew it could have been his friends and neighbors. Pee Wee's legs felt heavy, but he knew what he had to do.

As he walked toward Jackie wearing the gray Dodger uniform, he looked into his teammate's bold, pained eyes. The first baseman had done nothing to provoke the hostility except that he sought to be treated as an equal. Jackie was grim with anger. Pee Wee smiled broadly as he reached Jackie. Jackie smiled back.

Stepping beside Jackie, Pee Wee put his arm around Jackie's shoulders.

1. How does the author signal that Pee Wee is going to do something important?

____

2. Why is it difficult for Pee Wee to listen to the taunts of the crowd?

____

3. How does the author show his opinion of the crowd?

____

____

4. What is the author's opinion of Jackie Robinson?

____

____

5. What does the author think of Pee Wee Reese? Explain your thinking on a separate sheet of paper. Give examples from the selection to support your answer.

Notes for Home: Your child read a selection and used its details to identify the author's viewpoint. ***Home Activity:*** Read a newspaper or magazine letter to the editor with your child. Ask your child to tell you the writer's viewpoint.

Name ______________________________

Selection Test

Directions: Choose the best answer to each item. Mark the letter for the answer you have chosen.

Part 1: Vocabulary

Find the answer choice that means about the same as the underlined word in each sentence.

1. The <u>hostility</u> between them is obvious.
   A. cooperation
   B. dislike; unfriendliness
   C. respect
   D. strong affection

2. Jack wished he could take back his <u>hateful</u> comments.
   F. showing strong dislike
   G. clever
   H. not correct
   J. silly

3. Marty has the <u>dedication</u> needed to win the award.
   A. lack of interest
   B. ill will
   C. determination to reach a goal
   D. talent

4. That law has put a stop to the <u>abuse</u> of animals.
   F. movement
   G. cruel treatment
   H. housing
   J. daily care

5. The truck carried a <u>tremendous</u> load.
   A. important
   B. very old
   C. huge
   D. valuable

6. Margo talked about her <u>racial</u> background.
   F. of or about jobs
   G. related to history
   H. of or about art
   J. of or about a race of people

7. I'll never understand Daisy's <u>prejudice</u>.
   A. way of expressing oneself
   B. interest in something
   C. dislike without a reason
   D. attraction to something

Part 2: Comprehension

Use what you know about the selection to answer each item.

8. Before Jackie Robinson tried out for the Dodgers, he—
   F. became friends with Pee Wee Reese.
   G. played in the Negro Leagues.
   H. played against the Cincinnati Reds.
   J. played in the Major Leagues.

9. African Americans gathered in crowds to watch Jackie Robinson at his first tryout with the Dodgers because they—
   A. hoped he would become the first African American player in the Major Leagues.
   B. thought he should play in the Negro Leagues.
   C. did not know if he was a very good player.
   D. wanted to protect him from people who threatened him.

10. The author most likely wrote this selection to—
   F. persuade readers to learn more about baseball.
   G. describe the people of the 1940s.
   H. inform readers about a hero.
   J. compare Jackie Robinson and Pee Wee Reese.

GO ON

11. Branch Rickey and Pee Wee Reese both thought that Jackie Robinson—
- A. could end segregation in America.
- B. should not play for the Dodgers.
- C. might take their jobs.
- D. could help the Dodgers win games.

12. What is the main idea of this selection?
- F. There were many extraordinary baseball players in the Negro Leagues.
- G. Branch Rickey was not afraid of change.
- H. Pee Wee Reese and Jackie Robinson played on the same team.
- J. Jackie Robinson overcame prejudice to become the first African American player in Major League baseball.

13. Which sentence states a generalization that is valid?
- A. Everyone in the Major Leagues supported racial segregation.
- B. Many players in the Negro Leagues were good baseball players.
- C. Everyone hoped Jackie Robinson would become a star player for the Dodgers.
- D. Most players in the Negro Leagues became famous.

14. The author of this selection believes that all baseball players should be—
- F. treated equally, regardless of race.
- G. paid exactly the same salary.
- H. made famous throughout the world.
- J. yelled at by fans.

15. The author of this selection would most likely agree that—
- A. people should not be concerned about racial problems.
- B. Jackie Robinson's skills were more important to Branch Rickey than his self-control.
- C. Branch Rickey was a smart and courageous man.
- D. Pee Wee Reese was just like the rest of Robinson's teammates.

STOP

Name ______________________________

Author's Viewpoint

- **Author's viewpoint** is the way an author thinks about the subject of his or her writing.
- An author's viewpoint may be one of fear, admiration, pity, amusement, or other feeling.
- You can identify an author's viewpoint by thinking about the words an author uses to describe a subject.

Directions: Read the passage below.

When it comes to pets, leave the dogs in their kennels! Give me a lizard any time.

Dogs, whose moist eyes and wide grins appear to show affection for their owners, fool people. They know what their easily tricked owners want to see.

Dogs need their owners to amuse them and keep them company. So they make huge efforts to warm their masters' hearts. They fetch and roll over to get what they want—an extra doggie treat or a cozy spot in the bedroom.

Lizards have no need to hide who they are. "Love me or leave me," they say. They let you know right away, "We can be friends if you see that we're equals. But don't expect me to perform for you or put on a happy face just because you're around. I've got my own life."

They're not being hateful, only honest and independent. Who can resist a lizard?

Directions: The table below shows evidence of the author's viewpoint about lizards. Fill in the other half of the table with evidence of the author's viewpoint about dogs. Below the table, state your conclusions about the author's viewpoint about both animals.

Lizards	Dogs
Lizards don't hide who they are.	**1.**
Lizards think they are their owners' equals.	**2.**
Lizards have their own lives.	**3.**
Lizards are honest and independent.	**4.**

5. ______________________________

____

____

Notes for Home: Your child read a selection and used its details to identify the author's viewpoint. ***Home Activity:*** Read a news article with your child. Have him or her circle words and phrases that reveal an author's thoughts or feelings about a subject.

Main Idea and Supporting Details

REVIEW

Directions: Read the passage. Then read each question about the passage. Choose the best answer to each question. Mark the letter for the answer you have chosen.

A Sport Unlike Any Other

Baseball is a sport unlike any other. It is a team sport that depends largely on individual effort. The pitcher must make his pitch and get it in the spot he wants to hit—until he releases the ball, his teammates can do nothing to help him. Teammates back one another up on all plays, but each fielder has to catch the balls within his reach and make accurate throws to get runners out. Each player is responsible for covering his own territory.

In no other sport does the defense hold the ball. The idea of basketball, football, and hockey is to take the ball (or puck) away from the opponent; the two teams fight for possession of the ball throughout the game. In baseball, the point is to cross home plate more often than the other team.

When the first batter comes up in a game, he is his team's only active player, against the nine active players in the field for the other team. In no other sport are the sides designed to be uneven at all times. The greatest number of active players on the offensive team is four—if the bases are loaded and a man is up to bat.

Professional baseball teams play a 162-game season—more than twice as many games as basketball teams, and more than ten times as many as football. The season lasts for six months, with a game almost every day.

1. What is the main idea of the passage?
   - **A.** Baseball is the best sport.
   - **B.** Baseball is just like any other sport.
   - **C.** Baseball is unlike any other sport.
   - **D.** Baseball is duller than any other sport.

2. The main idea of the first paragraph is that—
   - **F.** the pitcher's teammates cannot help him until he throws the ball.
   - **G.** baseball depends on individual effort.
   - **H.** outfielders cover a lot of territory.
   - **J.** fielders have to make accurate throws.

3. The main idea of the second paragraph is—
   - **A.** that football is similar to basketball.
   - **B.** that baseball is not a battle for possession of the ball.
   - **C.** that hockey is played with a puck.
   - **D.** that a football has a shape all its own.

4. The main idea of the third paragraph is—
   - **F.** that there are never more than four offensive players at one time.
   - **G.** that there can never be more than three runners on base.
   - **H.** that the first batter faces nine opponents.
   - **J.** that in baseball, the sides are never even.

5. Which of the following is **not** a supporting detail of the last paragraph?
   - **A.** Baseball is the most popular sport.
   - **B.** Professional basketball has fewer games in a season than baseball.
   - **C.** Teams play every day for six months.
   - **D.** Professional baseball has a 162-game season.

Notes for Home: Your child has identified the main ideas of a passage and the details that support those ideas. ***Home Activity:*** Review a magazine advertisement with your child. Challenge him or her to identify the main idea and supporting details.

Writing Across Texts

Directions: Think about what you learned about the "Negro Leagues" from the story *Teammates* and the selection "Legends." Then fill out the chart below with information from the selections about the players in those leagues.

Player	Team(s) He Played On	One Fact About Him
Josh Gibson	**1.**	**6.**
Leroy "Satchel" Paige	**2.**	**7.**
James "Cool Papa" Bell	**3.**	**8.**
Jackie Robinson	**4.**	**9.**
Oscar Charleston	**5.**	**10.**

Write an Essay

Our relationships with others help us learn more about ourselves. In *Teammates,* you read about the first African American to play in the Major Leagues, Jackie Robinson. Write an essay about what you think Jackie Robinson may have learned through his experiences with baseball fans, teammates, and friends, before and after he joined the Major Leagues. Write your essay on a separate sheet of paper.

Notes for Home: Your child compared a selection with the unit theme, "Myself and Others." ***Home Activity:*** As you read stories and articles with your child, discuss ways the ideas connect to what your child knows about himself or herself and others.

Name ______________________________

Grammar: Four Kinds of Sentences

REVIEW

Directions: Add the correct punctuation mark to the end of each sentence. Then tell whether the sentence is **declarative, interrogative, imperative,** or **exclamatory.**

________________ **1.** Intolerance usually results from a lack of information _____

________________ **2.** Do you feel uncomfortable, for example, around a person with a disability _____

________________ **3.** Don't let this feeling make you ignore the person _____

________________ **4.** A good friend may be right in front of you _____

________________ **5.** Make the effort to find out more about this person _____

Directions: Write five sentences about someone who has experienced prejudice from others. It can be a real person or an imaginary character. Write the kind of sentence shown in ( ). Remember to start each sentence with a capital letter and end each one with the correct end punctuation.

6. (declarative)

____

____

7. (interrogative)

____

____

8. (declarative)

____

____

9. (imperative)

____

____

10. (exclamatory)

____

____

Notes for Home: Your child identified and wrote the four different kinds of sentences and added the correct punctuation mark at the end of each of them. ***Home Activity:*** Challenge your child to use the same word—such as *dog* or *school*—in each of the four kinds of sentences.

Name ______________________________

Grammar: Subjects and Predicates

The **subject** is the word or group of words about which something is said in the sentence. All the words in the subject are called the **complete subject.** The most important word in the complete subject is called the **simple subject.** It is usually a noun or a pronoun. Some simple subjects, such as *Jackie Robinson,* are more than one word.

All citizens can enjoy one another's talents and ideas.

The **predicate** is the word or group of words that tells something about the subject. All the words in the predicate make up the **complete predicate.** The most important word in the complete predicate is the verb. It is called the **simple predicate.** Some simple predicates can have more than one word.

People from other countries may bring us new music and foods.

A sentence fragment is a group of words that looks like a sentence but does not express a complete thought. Correct sentence fragments by adding words to make a complete sentence or by joining the fragment to a related sentence.

Sentence fragment: The names of immigrants' music and foods.

Sentence: The names of immigrants' music and foods add words to American English.

Directions: Decide if the underlined group of words is the complete subject, the complete predicate, or a sentence fragment. Circle **CS, CP,** or **SF** to show your answer.

1. The five girls enjoyed the overnight trip. CS CP SF
2. The clear blue lake was beautiful. CS CP SF
3. Set up their tents at night. CS CP SF
4. Millions of stars sparkled overhead. CS CP SF
5. Each girl had brought some homemade food. CS CP SF
6. Alanna O'Brian offered Irish bread. CS CP SF
7. The happy girls ate Denise's Greek baklava for dessert. CS CP SF
8. The girls in the group. CS CP SF
9. They packed up their tents. CS CP SF
10. Climbed into their van again. CS CP SF

Notes for Home: Your child has learned to identify complete subjects, complete predicates, and sentence fragments. ***Home Activity:*** Play a game in which you or your child gives a complete subject and the other person adds a complete predicate to form a complete sentence.

Name ______________________

Grammar: Subjects and Predicates

Directions: For each sentence, underline the complete subject once. Underline the complete predicate twice. Then, circle the simple subject and simple predicate.

1. Banneker Middle School had a fine glee club.
2. It was holding auditions last week.
3. Dominic wanted to join that musical group.
4. Mr. Dixon, the glee club director, gave him a voice test.
5. The boy was singing way off key.
6. Some students in the glee club were snickering.
7. Their unkind behavior displeased the director.
8. However, Dominic simply shrugged his shoulders.
9. He said something to Mr. Dixon.
10. The surprised director waved a hand toward the piano.

Directions: Correct each sentence fragment by adding words to make it a complete sentence. Write the new sentence on the line.

11. Some sheet music.

____

12. Could read the music and was playing it!

____

13. The singers in the glee club.

____

14. Asked Dominic to be the glee club pianist.

____

15. At glee club practice after that.

____

Write an Invitation

On a separate sheet of paper, write an invitation to a friend to go to a concert with you. Use complete sentences. Identify the simple subject and predicate in each.

Notes for Home: Your child identified simple and complete subjects and predicates in sentences and corrected sentence fragments. ***Home Activity:*** Ask your child to explain these terms, using the exercises above as examples.

Name ______________________

RETEACHING

Grammar: Subjects and Predicates

In each of the complete sentences, underline the complete subject once and the complete predicate twice. Circle the simple subject and the simple predicate. Draw a line through the sentence fragment.

1. Six members of the team looked for a good place to watch the animals.
2. Plenty of sunlight to see the lions.
3. We all worked together to reach our common goal.

The **subject** is the word or group of words about which something is said in a sentence. The most important part of the subject is called the **simple subject.** It is usually a noun or a pronoun. All the words in the subject make up the **complete subject.** The **predicate** is the word or group of words that tells something about the subject. The most important part of the predicate is the verb. It is called the **simple predicate.** All the words in the predicate make up the **complete predicate.** A **sentence fragment** is an incomplete sentence.

Directions: Draw a line through each sentence fragment. In each complete sentence, underline the complete subject once. Circle the simple subject. Then underline the complete predicate twice and circle the simple predicate.

1. Some lions live in the wild.
2. Most male lions are larger than female lions.
3. Cubs are young lions.
4. Live together in a group called a pride.
5. A group of lions may include over ten animals.
6. The diet of lions is mostly meat.
7. Sleep many more hours per day than humans do.
8. All wild lions hunt other animals.
9. Children of many countries.
10. Special people train lions for the circus.
11. The fascinated crowds admire the beauty and strength of lions.
12. Some wild animals live freely in Africa and Asia.
13. The powerful lion is known as "the king of beasts."
14. Of a lion in a zoo is twenty to twenty-five years.

Notes for Home: Your child identified sentence fragments and simple subjects and predicates. ***Home Activity:*** Together, read a movie review. Then read the subject of one sentence. Have your child write a new predicate. Read a predicate and have your child write a subject.

Name ______________________________

Grammar: Subjects and Predicates

Directions: Draw a line between the complete subject and the complete predicate in each sentence. Circle each simple subject and simple predicate.

1. Several cities served as the capital before 1800.
2. The national government moved away from Philadelphia.
3. Washington, D.C., has been the capital since then.
4. George Washington chose a location in 1791.
5. His choice included land in both Maryland and Virginia.
6. Those states gave their land to the government.
7. Congress located the capital near a river.
8. The capital was built on ten square miles of government land.
9. Pierre L'Enfant was the designer of the project.
10. This famous engineer planned the city.

Directions: Circle the simple subject in each sentence. Then complete the puzzle with those words. (Hint: Each word can fit correctly in only one place.)

11. Many tourists visit Washington, D.C., every year.
12. This city with its famous buildings has many attractions.
13. The President's home is called the White House.
14. Visitors tour its many public rooms.
15. The first President in the White House was John Adams.

Notes for Home: Your child identified subjects and predicates in sentences and added information to form complete sentences from sentence fragments. ***Home Activity:*** Say some sentence fragments to your child. *(Answered a question.)* Have him or her add information to form complete sentences.

Name ______________________________

Phonics: Vowel Digraphs

Directions: The **long e** sound heard in **feet** can be spelled: **ea, ee, ei,** or **ie.** The **long a** sound heard in **wait** can be spelled **ai.** Read the newspaper story below. Say the underlined words to yourself. Match each underlined word with a word to the right that rhymes. Write the word on the correct line.

SPORTS

Yesterday was an amazing day in sports. Athletes from all over the world took the <u>field</u>. If the athletes were <u>afraid</u> of the competitions that were about to begin, it never showed. They <u>received</u> thunderous applause from the fans who had come to <u>see</u> them compete. <u>Indeed</u>, everyone who attended the games <u>believed</u> they were about to witness performances by the world's greatest athletes. They couldn't wait for the sports <u>series</u> to begin.

1. wearies ______________
2. heaved ______________
3. be ______________
4. relieved ______________
5. pealed ______________
6. stayed ______________
7. bead ______________

Directions: Read each sentence. Say each underlined word to yourself. Listen for the word with the **long e** sound as in **feet,** or the **long a** sound as in **wait.** Write the word with the long vowel sound on the line.

______________ 8. <u>When</u> playing a <u>team</u> sport, everybody is responsible for a win or a loss.

______________ 9. The <u>pain</u> of losing is bearable if you <u>have</u> the thrill of winning too.

______________ 10. A dedicated athlete could, if she or he <u>wished</u>, play a sport during each <u>season</u>.

______________ 11. Often communities have local sports <u>leagues</u> for <u>amateur</u> athletes.

______________ 12. It is an <u>unbelievable</u> feeling when all players work <u>together</u> on a team.

______________ 13. <u>Often</u> athletes <u>aim</u> to be number one in their sport.

______________ 14. Most athletes <u>love</u> the challenge they <u>feel</u> from competing against others.

______________ 15. Many <u>consider</u> playing sports to be their <u>field</u> of dreams.

Notes for Home: Your child worked with words with long *e* (*<u>see</u>, <u>sea</u>, <u>fie</u>ld, rec<u>ei</u>ve*) and long *a* (*w<u>ai</u>t*) vowel sounds. ***Home Activity:*** Read a sports story with your child. Try to find other words with these vowel sounds and spelling patterns.

Name ________________________________

Spelling: Words with *ei* and *ie*

Pretest Directions: Fold back the page along the dotted line. On the blanks, write the spelling words as they are dictated. When you have finished the test, unfold the page and check your words.

Pretest

1. ____________________
2. ____________________
3. ____________________
4. ____________________
5. ____________________
6. ____________________
7. ____________________
8. ____________________
9. ____________________
10. ____________________
11. ____________________
12. ____________________
13. ____________________
14. ____________________
15. ____________________
16. ____________________
17. ____________________
18. ____________________
19. ____________________
20. ____________________

1. There is a cobweb on the **ceiling**.
2. The cashier gave him a **receipt**.
3. I did not mean to **deceive** you.
4. **Neither** John nor Jamila will go.
5. You may do it at your **leisure**.
6. Many foods provide **protein**.
7. He is the team's wide **receiver**.
8. **Seize** the opportunity.
9. He is very **conceited**.
10. The cows graze in the **field**.
11. You can **achieve** your dreams.
12. That is a farfetched **belief**.
13. Let's keep this talk **brief**.
14. The rain was a welcome **relief**.
15. We made four dollars **apiece**.
16. The knight picks up his **shield**.
17. I am my aunt's only **niece**.
18. The truck runs on **diesel** fuel.
19. Accidents can cause **grief**.
20. Cars must **yield** to pedestrians.

Notes for Home: Your child took a pretest on words with the letters *ei* and *ie*. ***Home Activity:*** Help your child learn misspelled words before the final test. Your child can underline the word parts that caused the problems and concentrate on those parts.

Name ______________________________

Spelling: Words with *ei* and *ie*

Word List

ceiling	leisure	conceited	brief	niece
receipt	protein	field	relief	diesel
deceive	receiver	achieve	apiece	grief
neither	seize	belief	shield	yield

Directions: Choose the words from the box that rhyme with each word below. Write the words on the lines.

wield

1. ______________
2. ______________
3. ______________

piece

4. ______________
5. ______________

either

6. ______________

thief

7. ______________
8. ______________
9. ______________
10. ______________

believe

11. ______________
12. ______________

Directions: Choose the word from the box that best completes each sentence. Write the word on the line to the left.

______________ **13.** Luis's pride in his home runs made him seem _____ to some people.

______________ **14.** However, Luis worked hard, practicing even during _____ time on days off.

______________ **15.** The _____ from Mighty Mike's Batting Cages showed the number of hours Luis spent practicing.

______________ **16.** Luis had to _____ the moment before they lost the game.

______________ **17.** It was a good thing they played in an outdoor stadium, because the ball Luis hit would have broken any _____ overhead.

______________ **18.** Luis ran around the bases as if on _____ fuel.

______________ **19.** Luis was the proud _____ of his teammates' congratulations.

______________ **20.** "It was the _____ in the hot dogs that did it!" Luis joked.

Notes for Home: Your child spelled words with *ei* and *ie*. ***Home Activity:*** Have your child name two words, one with *ei* and one with *ie,* that have the long *e* sound as in *believe.* Make sure your child can spell each word correctly.

Name ______________________________

Spelling: Words with *ei* and *ie*

Directions: Proofread this poem. Find five spelling mistakes. Use the proofreading marks to correct each mistake.

≡	Make a capital.
/	Make a small letter.
∧	Add something.
℘	Take out something.
⊙	Add a period.
¶	Begin a new paragraph.

Good greif! That barking is beyond belief!
The dog is ruining my well-earned liesure!
Hmm. I should sieze him to get some relief!
Or maybe shield myself with soothing music?
I could decieve myself and call it singing.
I only hope that his song will be breif!

Spelling Tip

seize **diesel**

It is easy to misspell words in which the long **e** sound is spelled **ei** or **ie.** Check the poem carefully to be sure the **ei** and **ie** words are spelled correctly.

Word List

ceiling	leisure	conceited	brief	niece
receipt	protein	field	relief	diesel
deceive	receiver	achieve	apiece	grief
neither	seize	belief	shield	yield

Write a Poem

On a separate sheet of paper, write a poem in which you describe how your tolerance was tested. How did you handle the situation? What did it teach you about being tolerant? Try to use at least three of your spelling words.

Notes for Home: Your child spelled words with *ei* and *ie.* ***Home Activity:*** Take turns saying and spelling each word from the box. Continue adding and practicing other hard-to-spell *ei* and *ie* words.

Name ______________________________

Spelling: Words with *ei* and *ie*

REVIEW

Word List

ceiling	protein	achieve	shield
receipt	receiver	belief	niece
deceive	seize	brief	diesel
neither	conceited	relief	grief
leisure	field	apiece	yield

Directions: Choose the word from the box that has the same or nearly the same meaning as each word below. Write the word on the line.

1. sales slip ____________________

2. gain ____________________

3. comfort ____________________

4. lie ____________________

5. relaxation ____________________

6. grab ____________________

7. give way ____________________

8. thought ____________________

9. vain ____________________

10. fuel ____________________

11. each ____________________

12. sorrow ____________________

Directions: Choose the word from the box that best completes each statement. Think about the relationship of the pairs of words being compared. Write the word on the line to the left. See the example below.

Woman is to *man* as *lioness* is to *lion.*

____________________ **13.** *Uncle* is to *aunt* as *nephew* is to _____.

____________________ **14.** *Earth* is to *sky* as *floor* is to _____.

____________________ **15.** *Catcher* is to *mask* as *knight* is to _____.

____________________ **16.** *Pitcher* is to *catcher* as *sender* is to _____.

____________________ **17.** *Fish* is to *stream* as *sheep* is to _____.

____________________ **18.** *All* is to *none* as *both* is to _____.

____________________ **19.** *Spinach* is to *iron* as *meat* is to _____.

____________________ **20.** *Tall* is to *short* as *lasting* is to _____.

Notes for Home: Your child spelled words with *ei* and *ie.* ***Home Activity:*** Point out that if you can spell *belief,* you can spell *believe.* Then have your child name other words you can spell if you can spell *receipt, deceive,* and *relief* correctly.

Name ______________________ Teammates

Technology: Newspaper

You can find current **newspapers** and **news magazines** online using a computer and the Internet. When you connect to the Internet, you may see a welcome screen with choices such as "news" or "newsstand." If you click on this kind of button, you might get a screen like the one below. The underlined words at the bottom of the screen are links to other web pages. If you click on a link, you'll get a new web page.

Directions: Use the computer screen to answer the questions that follow.

1. Explain how you can get to the web page for *The New York News*. ______________________

2. How might you be able to get to other newspapers not listed on this screen? ______________________

3. What should you do if you need help? ______________________

4. How is an online "newsstand" similar to a real newsstand? How is it different? ______________________

Name ______________________

After you get to an online newspaper or magazine, you may be able to search by a specific section of the newspaper, such as sports. There will probably also be a search box in which you can type key words. Use "AND" between each key word.

Directions: Use the computer screen to answer the questions that follow.

5. In which section would you search for information about a museum exhibit? ______

6. In which section would you search for information about current news about Europe?

______

7. In which section would you search for information about the people running for mayor?

______

8. In which section would you search for information about decorating your living room?

______

9. Give two ways to find a list of upcoming baseball games. ______

______

10. If you wanted to find an article that had been printed in the newspaper a few months ago, would you search an online newspaper or go to the library to look for a print newspaper or a microfilm of a newspaper? Explain.

______

______

Notes for Home: Your child answered questions about finding infomation in a newspaper or magazine on the Internet. ***Home Activity:*** Look through your local newspaper with your child or search for one on the Internet. Discuss the different sections of the paper.

Family Times

Name______________________________

Summary

The Ellis Family Gets Muddy—and Is Proud of It!

What's normal for April Ellis and her family isn't necessarily normal for other people. The Ellises live in a converted school bus while they build a house out of adobe—dried mud! April is sometimes embarrassed about her family and is relieved that her classmates don't know where she lives.

When April's father offers to lead a class project, she worries about how her friends will react to him. But when Tom Ellis finally comes to class, he teaches more than just a skill. He teaches April that she should be proud of her family.

Reading Skills

Cause and Effect

An **effect** is something that happens. A **cause** is why something happens. Understanding cause-and-effect relationships can help you understand the characters and events in stories.

To find an effect, ask yourself "What happened?" To find a cause, ask yourself "Why did this happen?" or "What caused this to happen?"

By the end of "April's Mud," April has changed her mind about having friends visit her home. What caused this change? When Tom Ellis came to class, April's classmates respected and liked him. This helped April learn to take pride in her family's unique qualities, rather than wish that she lived like everyone else.

Activity

Draw a Picture. Help your child draw a floor plan that shows the inside of your home. Label each room with its function (bedroom, kitchen, etc.) and its size. Remember to indicate the doors and windows.

Activity

Discuss Causes and Effects. Choose an event, such as a favorite team winning or losing a championship, and discuss its causes. Then choose another event, such as a heavy rainstorm, and discuss its effects.

Family Times

Tested Vocabulary

Words to Know

Knowing the meanings of these words is important to reading "April's Mud." Practice using these words to learn their meanings.

adobe brick made of dried clay, used in building

authentic genuine; real

concrete a mixture of crushed stone, sand, cement, and water, used in building

converted changed into a different form or used in a different way

heritage traditions, skills, and so on, passed down from one generation to the next

normal usual; common; accepted

Grammar

Independent and Dependent Clauses

An **independent clause** is any part of a sentence that has a subject and a predicate and can stand alone as a sentence. A **dependent clause** has a subject and a predicate but cannot stand alone as a sentence.

In the following sentences, the independent clauses are underlined once and the dependent clauses are underlined twice.

The children liked the adobe house because it was different.

When we looked at the plans, we decided that the project was too difficult.

Activity

Constructing Sentences. Pair up family members. Take turns making up sentences that contain independent and dependent clauses. One person gives an independent or dependent clause, and the other person completes the sentence. Use conjunctions such as *or, and,* or *but* to join two independent clauses. Use words like *because, when,* or *if* to join a dependent clause to an independent clause.

Tested Spelling Words

Name ______________________________

Cause and Effect

- An **effect** is something that happens. A **cause** is why something happens.
- To find an effect, ask yourself, "What happened?" To find a cause, ask yourself "Why did it happen?"
- An effect may have more than one cause, and a cause may have more than one effect.
- Sometimes an author does not state a cause, and you need to draw your own conclusions about why something happens.

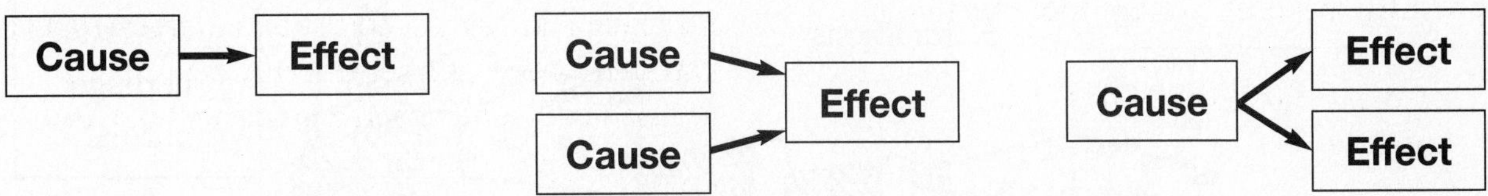

Directions: Reread "Leaving Home." Then complete the table. Provide each missing cause or effect.

Cause (Why did it happen?)	Effect (What happened?)
1.	Pa felt it was too crowded where they lived.
2.	Pa decided to move the family out West.
They would have to leave family and friends behind.	**3.**
4.	Mama's friends gathered to say farewell.
Mama was sad to leave.	**5.**

Notes for Home: Your child identified causes and effects in a story. ***Home Activity:*** Ask your child to relate the events of the day. Discuss the events together, encouraging your child to identify any cause-effect relationships among the day's events.

Name ______________________________

Vocabulary

Directions: Choose the word from the box that has the same or nearly the same meaning as each word or words below. Write the word on the line.

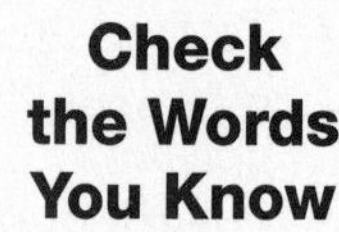

Check the Words You Know

__ adobe
__ authentic
__ concrete
__ converted
__ heritage
__ normal

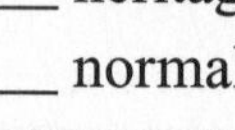

________________ **1.** building mixture of crushed stone, sand, cement, and water

________________ **2.** real

________________ **3.** changed

________________ **4.** usual

________________ **5.** traditions

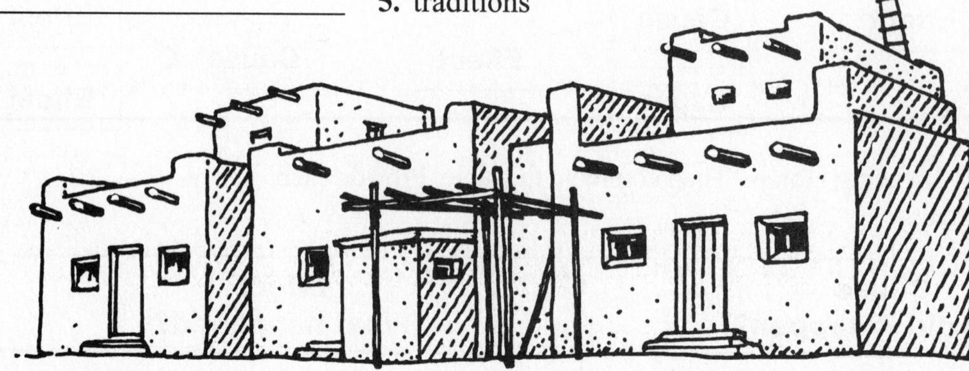

Directions: Choose the word from the box that best completes each sentence. Write the word on the line to the left.

________________ **6.** With hard work, the Pueblo people _____ clay, straw, and water into a place to live.

________________ **7.** They made _____ bricks to build the walls.

________________ **8.** It was _____ for them to use these natural materials for building their homes.

________________ **9.** It was part of the _____ passed down from their elders.

________________ **10.** There are still people today who would much rather live in an _____ adobe home than in one built with newer materials.

Write a Description

On a separate sheet of paper, write a description of something a family member taught you to do or make. It could be a skill like woodcarving, playing an instrument, or cooking a special meal. Use as many vocabulary words as you can in your description.

Notes for Home: Your child identified and used vocabulary words from "April's Mud." ***Home Activity:*** Challenge your child to make up a story about building a place to live, using the vocabulary words listed above.

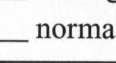

Name ______________________

Cause and Effect

- An **effect** is something that happens. A **cause** is why something happens.
- An effect may have more than one cause, and a cause may have more than one effect.
- Sometimes you need to draw your own conclusions about what happens and why.

Directions: Reread the passage of "April's Mud" that describes what happens when the Ellises try to make adobe bricks. Then answer the questions below. Look for effects that have more than one cause.

At the end of the day they were all so sore and tired they could hardly move. But they forgot to cover the finished adobes, and when a rainstorm came up suddenly during the night, the adobes melted right back to mud again. Then, because the clay was so dense and Tom hadn't mixed in enough straw, their next batch cracked.

1. Why are the Ellises hardly able to move?

____

2. Name two causes of the adobes melting back into mud.

____

____

3. Name two causes of the adobes cracking.

____

____

4. What might the family do next time to save the adobe bricks from melting?

____

5. On a separate sheet of paper, list the causes and effects of Tom's decision to build an adobe house. Remember that the author may not always state causes and effects directly.

Notes for Home: Your child read part of a story and used its details to identify causes and effects. ***Home Activity:*** Read a story or watch a TV drama or comedy with your child. Take turns challenging each other to identify what happens (effects) and why (causes).

Selection Test

Directions: Choose the best answer to each item. Mark the letter for the answer you have chosen.

Part 1: Vocabulary

Find the answer choice that means about the same as the underlined word in each sentence.

1. Luke does not lead a <u>normal</u> life.
- A. healthful
- B. special
- C. usual; like most other people's
- D. exciting; filled with interesting events

2. The bed was a <u>converted</u> sofa.
- F. changed into another form
- G. expensive
- H. decorated with bright colors
- J. repainted

3. Dad has an <u>authentic</u> 1956 race car.
- A. one of a kind
- B. fake; copied
- C. in the latest style
- D. real; genuine

4. It was cool inside the <u>adobe</u> house.
- F. made of wood
- G. building material made of baked clay
- H. new
- J. shaded

5. Mr. Alvarez made <u>concrete</u> stairs.
- A. mixture of sand, cement, and water
- B. wood
- C. plaster that sets in a hard coat
- D. dried mud

6. Sam wanted to learn about his <u>heritage</u>.
- F. neighborhood
- G. friends from school
- H. childhood
- J. beliefs and traditions handed down from earlier generations

Part 2: Comprehension

Use what you know about the story to answer each item.

7. The first adobes that April's family made were ruined because they—
- A. dried out too fast.
- B. were washed away by rain.
- C. baked in the sun.
- D. did not have enough straw.

8. In this story, April learns that—
- F. her parents are hippies.
- G. she is going to attend a new school.
- H. her classmates think her father is interesting.
- J. she has classmates who live in old buses.

9. Which event from the story happened before April saw the floor plan?
- A. April's father taught her class to build a *horno*.
- B. April's family made adobe bricks.
- C. April's father visited her class at school.
- D. April decided to invite her classmates to visit her home.

10. In his plans for the house, Tom seems to feel that it is most important to—
- F. make sure April and Susan have their own rooms.
- G. make the house bigger than Mr. Flores's house.
- H. make the house very much like houses of the old days.
- J. make the house as modern as possible.

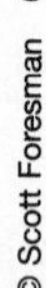

11. Compared to the beginning of the story, at the end April is more—
    A. embarrassed.
    B. shy.
    C. lonely.
    D. confident.

12. The finished shape of the *horno* is like the shape of—
    F. an igloo.
    G. a bus.
    H. an adobe house.
    J. a teepee.

13. Why did April feel better about the school project by the end of the story?
    A. She always enjoyed working with her father.
    B. Her classmates did not know she lived in a bus.
    C. Her friends already knew how to work with adobe mud.
    D. Her classmates enjoyed making the *horno*.

14. The author's main purpose in this selection is to—
    F. tell an entertaining story about April.
    G. explain how to make adobe bricks.
    H. persuade people not to build adobe houses.
    J. compare adobe houses with wooden houses.

15. When their adobe house is built, April will most likely—
    A. decide to build a room for herself.
    B. feel proud of her family's work.
    C. be embarrassed by the dirt floor.
    D. try to keep people from seeing it.

STOP

Name ___________________________

Cause and Effect

- An **effect** is something that happens. A **cause** is why something happens.
- An effect may have more than one cause, and a cause may have more than one effect.
- Sometimes you need to draw your own conclusions about what happens and why.

Directions: Read the story below.

Mitch had no idea that ice skating would change his life. At first, he practiced at the rink a couple of times a week.

The more he practiced, the better he got at skating. Mitch decided he wanted to take figure skating lessons and buy new skates, so he worked on weekends to save the money.

His parents noticed Mitch's growing dedication and took him to see a championship performance. The exciting shows made Mitch curious about past skaters. He began combing the library shelves to learn something about the history of skating. He also searched the Internet for information. It didn't take long for him to get connected with other figure skaters, including some champions!

Directions: Write causes and effects in the boxes to complete the table.

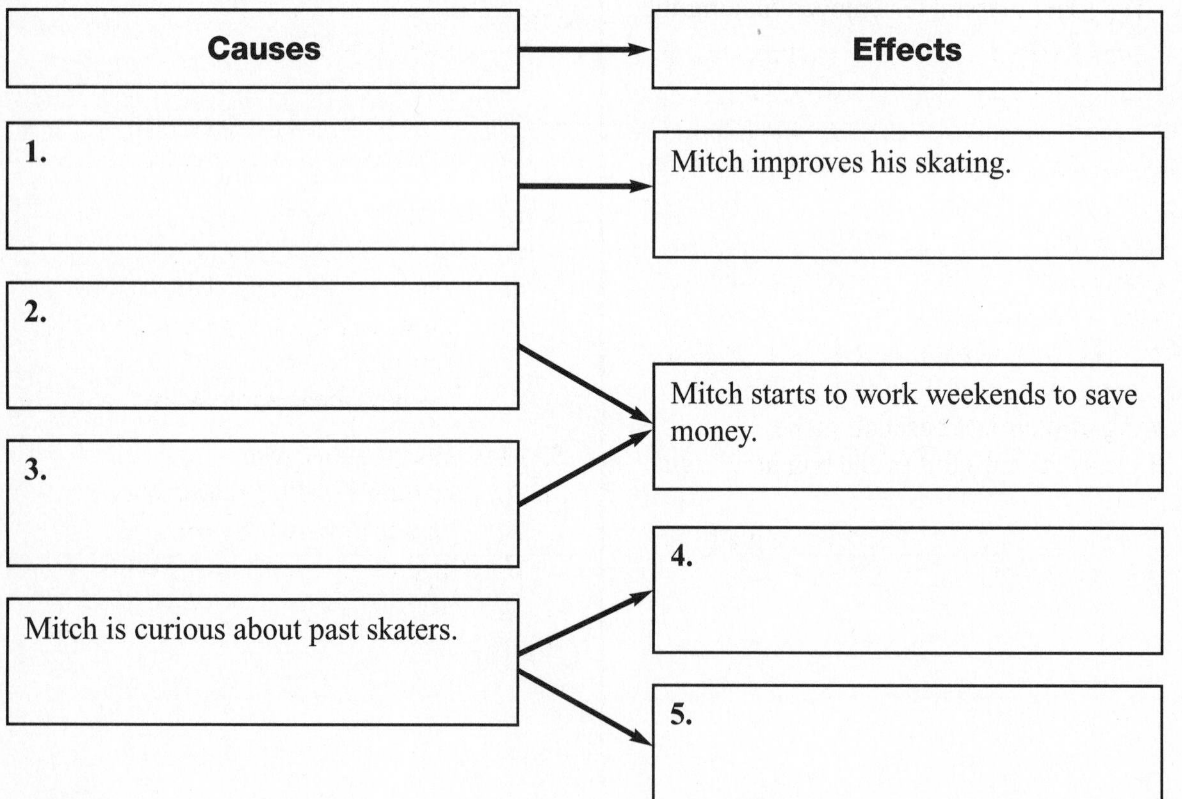

Causes	Effects
1.	Mitch improves his skating.
2.	Mitch starts to work weekends to save money.
3.	Mitch starts to work weekends to save money.
Mitch is curious about past skaters.	4.
Mitch is curious about past skaters.	5.

Notes for Home: Your child read a story and used its details to identify causes and effects. ***Home Activity:*** Talk with your child about events that happened at school or at home. For each event, discuss why it happened. Consider whether there is more than one cause for each effect.

Name ______________________________

Making Judgments and Plot

REVIEW

Directions: Read the story. Then read each question about the story. Choose the best answer to the question. Mark the letter for the answer you have chosen.

Undercover Artist

No one paid much attention to the new kid, Max. Who would? He didn't talk much. At lunch, Max just about disappeared. Some of his new classmates thought he was homesick. Others just thought he was boring.

One morning a cartoon of Mr. Foley's sixth grade class appeared on the chalkboard. You could easily identify people in it. The artist had caught the personalities of everyone in the class. It showed Joey gazing out the window. Kathy was waving her hand to answer a question. Keisha was shown taking lots of notes. It captured Mr. Foley perfectly with his glasses on top of his head and chalk marks all over his suit.

Almost everybody laughed and praised the drawing. Mr. Foley didn't erase it. Max said nothing. He didn't seem very interested.

By lunch time, the class was dying to discover who the mystery artist was. No one in the sixth grade had such talent.

Then Rosa remembered that Max always doodled while the rest of the class talked and joked. She went to look over Max's shoulder. Sure enough, he was deep into a funny drawing of their last baseball game.

"I guess the cat's out of the bag now," said Max.

"It sure is," said Lou, "and we're glad. We need you on the class newspaper!"

1. The rising action of this story begins when—
- **A.** we first read about Max.
- **B.** the cartoon appears on the board.
- **C.** the class is at lunch.
- **D.** the newspaper comes out.

2. The climax of the story occurs when—
- **F.** Lou says, "We need you on the class newspaper!"
- **G.** Max just about disappears at lunch.
- **H.** the class sees the drawing on the chalkboard.
- **J.** the class realizes that Max is the artist.

3. At first, the class assumed Max was
- **A.** very talented.
- **B.** an athlete.
- **C.** very involved in schoolwork.
- **D.** uninteresting or homesick.

4. By the story's end, the class
- **F.** thinks Rosa is very smart.
- **G.** wants to frame a picture by Max.
- **H.** wants to print the next issue of the newspaper.
- **J.** has new ideas about Max.

5. Max was quiet because—
- **A.** he didn't like his classmates.
- **B.** he was always busy drawing.
- **C.** he didn't know the answers.
- **D.** he was doing his homework.

Notes for Home: Your child read a story and used its details to identify important characters and events and to make judgments about them. ***Home Activity:*** Ask your child to outline the main events of a story you both know. Talk together about your judgments of the main characters.

Name ______________________________

Writing Across Texts

Directions: Consider what you learned about working with adobe in "April's Mud" and "El Horno." Complete the table below by recording facts that you learned about adobe.

Adobe
Adobe is a mixture of mud, straw, and water.
1.
2.
3.
4.
5.
6.
7.
8.
9.
10.

Write an Encyclopedia Article

Pretend you work for a book publisher. Your job is to write an encyclopedia article about adobe. Use details from "April's Mud" and "El Horno" to help you create the article. Use a separate piece of paper for your writing.

Notes for Home: Your child listed details from a fiction story and a nonfiction selection to write an encyclopedia article. ***Home Activity:*** As you read stories and nonfiction selections with your child, ask your child how the reading connects to other texts he or she has read.

Name ____________________

Grammar: Subjects and Predicates

REVIEW

Directions: In each sentence below, underline the complete subject once and the complete predicate twice.

1. Some people think that what you wear says a lot about who you are.
2. Students in my school seem to believe these ideas about clothes.
3. They think the latest styles identify a "cool" person.
4. The fads are sometimes expensive and uncomfortable.
5. Many people wear them anyway.
6. I don't think clothes are all that important.
7. I believe that clothing tells only about the outside of a person.
8. Some schools have dress codes that tell what students can wear.
9. Students in other schools wear uniforms that all look alike.
10. Students in those schools may focus more on what's inside the people they meet.

Directions: Write sentences that include the following simple subjects and predicates. Remember to begin each sentence with a capital letter and end each one with a punctuation mark.

11. style is

____

____

12. people spend

____

____

13. rules would be

____

____

14. friends dress

____

____

15. I would like

____

____

Notes for Home: Your child identified simple and complete subjects and predicates and wrote sentences using simple subjects and predicates. ***Home Activity:*** Challenge your child to complete a sentence that is missing a subject or a predicate.

Name ______________________________

Grammar: Independent and Dependent Clauses

A sentence part that has a subject and a predicate and makes sense by itself is called an **independent clause.**

Hal likes to dive, and he is also a good swimmer.
independent clause — independent clause

A **dependent clause** also has a subject and a predicate, but it does not make sense by itself. It cannot stand alone as a sentence.

Before he dives in an unfamiliar spot, he checks it for depth and for other safety factors.
dependent clause

Directions: Write **I** if the underlined words are an independent clause. Write **D** if the underlined words are a dependent clause.

_______ **1.** Carlos bought new shoes, but he didn't really like them.

_______ **2.** Since the shoes had high backs, they were just like other kids' shoes.

_______ **3.** Because they were so high, the backs of the shoes hurt Carlos's feet.

_______ **4.** The other kids would laugh at him if he didn't wear shoes like theirs.

_______ **5.** Blisters develop when your shoes rub the wrong place.

_______ **6.** Try on a lot of shoes before you buy a pair.

_______ **7.** Choose carefully, and don't buy anything uncomfortable.

_______ **8.** Think for yourself, or you'll wish you had!

_______ **9.** If you don't think for yourself, you're acting like a sheep.

_______ **10.** A sheep will follow another sheep, even if it walks into danger.

Notes for Home: Your child identified independent clauses, which make complete sentences by themselves, and dependent clauses, which must be part of a longer sentence. ***Home Activity:*** Have your child mark and identify clauses in a newspaper article.

Grammar: Independent and Dependent Clauses

Directions: Write **I** if the underlined words are an independent clause. Write **D** if the underlined words are a dependent clause.

__________ **1.** Lily made a wish that her casts would come off soon.

__________ **2.** Lily would practice before autumn came.

__________ **3.** After school started, she could play again.

__________ **4.** Lily watched the game, but she was feeling sad.

__________ **5.** Before she was injured, she had been a very active girl.

Directions: Add an independent clause to complete each sentence. Write the new sentence on the line.

6. If Lily looks eager to talk,

____

____

7. She could coach other players now, or

____

____

8. Lily can move around on crutches, and

____

____

9. When she calls friends on the phone,

____

____

10. Because she likes mystery films,

____

____

Write a Description

On a separate sheet of paper, write a description of a good friend. Use at least three sentences that contain independent clauses.

Notes for Home: Your child identified independent clauses, which can be sentences by themselves, and dependent clauses, which must be part of a longer sentence. ***Home Activity:*** Write some simple sentences. Have your child add a dependent clause to each one.

Name ______________________________

Grammar: Independent and Dependent Clauses

Underline each independent clause once. Underline each dependent clause twice.

1. Although our house might seem strange, my family lives a happy life.
2. We grow our own food, and we read lots of books.
3. I've thought about moving back into an apartment, but I would miss being outside.

An **independent clause** is a sentence part that has a subject and a predicate. It can make sense as a complete sentence. A **dependent clause** is a sentence part that has a subject and a predicate, but it cannot make sense as a complete sentence.

Directions: Write **I** if the underlined group of words is an independent clause. Write **D** if the underlined group of words is a dependent clause.

______________ 1. It was my first day at the new school, and I wasn't sure how other kids would react to my name.

______________ 2. When I sat down at my new desk, I looked around at my classmates' faces.

______________ 3. Everyone looked pretty nice, but no one had spoken to me.

______________ 4. Because I was a little shy, I hoped someone would introduce herself or himself to me.

______________ 5. My teacher started taking attendance, and I listened to her.

Directions: Add an independent clause to complete each sentence. Write each new sentence on the line.

6. When the teacher said, "Sunshine Bluebird McGuire,"

____

____

7. Although I was nervous about what my new classmates might say,

____

____

Notes for Home: Your child used independent clauses, which make complete sentences by themselves, and dependent clauses, which must be parts of longer sentences. ***Home Activity:*** Together, listen to a news report on the radio. Have your child identify independent and dependent clauses.

Name ______________________________

Grammar: Independent and Dependent Clauses

Directions: Add an independent clause to complete each sentence. Write each new sentence on the lines.

1. As soon as I was old enough,

____

____

2. When I have my next birthday,

____

____

3. Although I would rather be with my friends,

____

____

4. Because I like to do my best in school,

____

____

Directions: Add a dependent clause to complete each sentence. Write each new sentence on the lines.

5. ______________________, I will probably go on to college.

____

____

6. ______________________, I like to spend time thinking about my day.

____

____

7. ______________________, we travel or spend time doing work around the house.

____

____

8. ______________________, my sister and I have become very good at sharing.

____

____

Notes for Home: Your child wrote independent and dependent clauses in sentences. ***Home Activity:*** Together, look at "April's Mud." Have your child identify independent and dependent clauses in sentences in the story.

Name ______________________________

Phonics: Diphthongs and Digraphs

Directions: Each sentence contains an underlined word with the letter combination **au, aw, ew,** or **ou.** Say the underlined word to yourself. Listen to the sounds that the letters **au, aw, ew,** and **ou** represent. Circle the word in ( ) that has the same vowel sound as the underlined word.

1. The class knew that building the playhouse would be a lot of hard work. (knee/new)
2. It takes many people to build a house. (hound/hoot)
3. They paused to inspect the land on which the house would be built. (pace/paw)
4. The builders showed the plans they had drawn to their supervisor. (author/away)
5. The carpenter tried to figure out about how much wood she would need. (soup/round)
6. Then she made a list of other raw materials she needed to get. (say/sauce)

Directions: Read the sentences below. Each sentence contains a word with a vowel sound heard in **saw, new,** or **loud.** Underline this word and write it on the line.

______________ 7. Today, some people still live in authentic adobe homes.

______________ 8. It is best to build an adobe home on level ground.

______________ 9. Examine your space outdoors to see where a home can be built.

______________ 10. Before building, most people draw a plan of their home so they have an idea of what it will look like.

______________ 11. A basic plan for constructing the home is usually an outline that shows where each room will be and how big it will be.

______________ 12. The adobe will be made with a few simple materials.

______________ 13. One of the ingredients in an adobe brick is straw.

______________ 14. An adobe brick measures about half a foot long.

______________ 15. The completion of an adobe home is often cause for celebration.

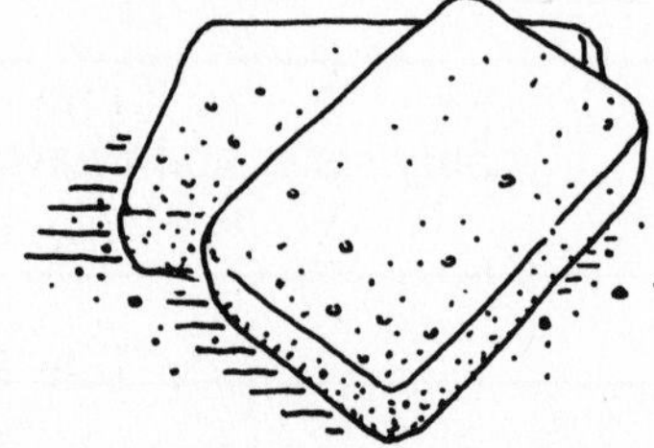

Notes for Home: Your child identified the vowel sounds of words with *au (sauce), aw (saw), ew (few),* and *ou (out). **Home Activity:*** Read a story with your child. Try to find other words with these vowel sounds and spelling patterns. Make a list of these words together.

Name ____________________

Spelling: Vowel Sounds in *rule* and *view*

Pretest Directions: Fold back the page along the dotted line. On the blanks, write the spelling words as they are dictated. When you have finished the test, unfold the page and check your words.

1. ____________	1. The store must **reduce** its staff.
2. ____________	2. She has a casual **attitude**.
3. ____________	3. It will be a **costume** party.
4. ____________	4. The night was **absolutely** dark.
5. ____________	5. I **assume** you know each other?
6. ____________	6. The **sewer** flooded in the storm.
7. ____________	7. They moved to **New York** City.
8. ____________	8. I must **renew** my membership.
9. ____________	9. Let us **review** today's lesson.
10. ____________	10. He has a detached **viewpoint**.
11. ____________	11. The reporters **interview** the star.
12. ____________	12. We went to a **preview** of the film.
13. ____________	13. Which cereal is the better **value**?
14. ____________	14. **Continue** with your game.
15. ____________	15. The **rescue** team arrived in time.
16. ____________	16. It's **humid** by the seashore.
17. ____________	17. The **universe** must be vast.
18. ____________	18. The soldier put on his **uniform**.
19. ____________	19. She went to her class **reunion**.
20. ____________	20. The **United States** is a country.

Notes for Home: Your child took a pretest on words with vowel sounds such as those in *rule* and *view*. ***Home Activity:*** Help your child learn misspelled words before the final test. Dictate the word and have your child spell the word aloud for you or write it on paper.

Name ______________________

Spelling: Vowel Sounds in *rule* and *view*

Word List

reduce	assume	review	value	United States
attitude	sewer	viewpoint	continue	universe
costume	New York	interview	rescue	uniform
absolutely	renew	preview	humid	reunion

Directions: Choose the words from the box that have the same vowel sound as **rule.** Write each word in the correct column.

Spelled u-consonant-e

1. ______________________
2. ______________________
3. ______________________
4. ______________________
5. ______________________

Spelled ew

6. ______________________
7. ______________________
8. ______________________

Directions: Choose the words from the box that have the same vowel sound as **view** spelled **iew.** Write the words on the lines.

9. ______________________
10. ______________________
11. ______________________
12. ______________________

Directions: Find eight words from the box in the puzzle. They may be printed across or down. Circle the words in the puzzle. Then write them on the lines. Hint: Each word has the same vowel sound as **view** spelled **ue** or **u.**

13. ______________
14. ______________
15. ______________
16. ______________
17. ______________
18. ______________
19. ______________
20. ______________

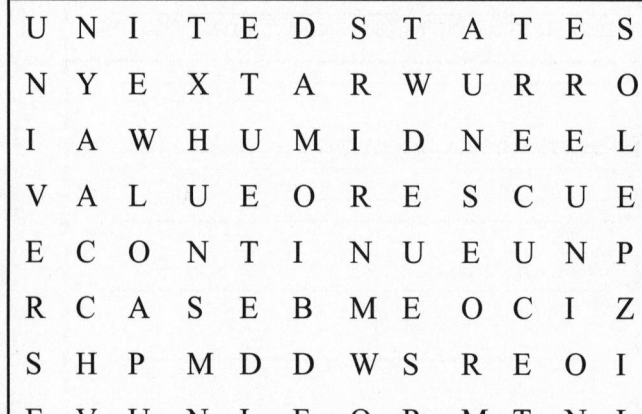

U	N	I	T	E	D	S	T	A	T	E	S
N	Y	E	X	T	A	R	W	U	R	R	O
I	A	W	H	U	M	I	D	N	E	E	L
V	A	L	U	E	O	R	E	S	C	U	E
E	C	O	N	T	I	N	U	E	U	N	P
R	C	A	S	E	B	M	E	O	C	I	Z
S	H	P	M	D	D	W	S	R	E	O	I
E	V	U	N	I	F	O	R	M	T	N	L

Notes for Home: Your child spelled words with the vowel sounds in *rule* (spelled *u-consonant-e* and *ew*) and *view* (spelled *iew, ue,* and *u*). ***Home Activity:*** Ask your child to name some words that rhyme with *view.* Discuss how each rhyming word is spelled.

Name ______________________________

Spelling: Vowel Sounds in *rule* and *view*

Directions: Proofread this advertisement. Find five spelling mistakes. Use the proofreading marks to correct each mistake.

≡	Make a capital.
/	Make a small letter.
∧	Add something.
⸗	Take out something.
⊙	Add a period.
¶	Begin a new paragraph.

Build Your Own Home!

Why live in a unifrom house like everyone else's?

Redeuce the expense of hiring builders!

Build it yourself!

A place you have built yourself will have far greater valiew than a place made for other people!

It's fun! It's easy! Read all about it!

Prevue, interview, and consultation absoluetly free!

Spelling Tip

New York **United States**

Remember to capitalize both words in place names such as **New York** and **United States.**

Word List

reduce	interview
attitude	preview
costume	value
absolutely	continue
assume	rescue
sewer	humid
New York	United States
renew	universe
review	uniform
viewpoint	reunion

Write an Advertisement

On a separate sheet of paper, write an advertisement to sell a product of your choice. Try to use at least three of your spelling words.

Notes for Home: Your child spelled words with the vowel sounds in *rule* (spelled *u-consonant-e* and *ew*) and *view* (spelled *iew, ue,* and *u*). ***Home Activity:*** Write each spelling word, deliberately misspelling some words. Have your child check and correct the words.

Name ______________________________

Spelling: Vowel Sounds in *rule* and *view*

REVIEW

Word List

reduce	sewer	interview	humid
attitude	New York	preview	United States
costume	renew	value	universe
absolutely	review	continue	uniform
assume	viewpoint	rescue	reunion

Directions: Choose the word from the box that best completes each sentence. Write the word on the line to the left.

__________ **1.** "The _____ is as much fun as Italy!" exclaimed Tony.

__________ **2.** Here he did not have to wear a _____ to school.

__________ **3.** From Tony's _____, his temporary new home looked good.

__________ **4.** Tony visited the famous city of _____ in the fall.

__________ **5.** He wore a fancy _____ to march in the San Genaro parade.

__________ **6.** It was so crowded that it seemed as if everyone in the _____ must be there.

__________ **7.** The _____ weather made Tony so warm he almost fainted.

__________ **8.** Another marcher had to _____ Tony from being trampled.

__________ **9.** Tony decided to _____ his layers of clothing to stay cooler.

__________ **10.** Later, he sent his little sister a newspaper _____ of the parade.

Directions: Choose the word from the box that best matches each definition. Write the word on the line.

11. positively; certainly __________

12. talk with; question __________

13. a gathering after separation __________

14. a pipe for carrying waste __________

15. manner __________

16. make like new; restore __________

17. view or show in advance __________

18. take for granted __________

19. keep on; not stop __________

20. worth or importance __________

Notes for Home: Your child spelled words with the vowel sounds in *rule* (spelled *u-consonant-e* and *ew*) and *view* (spelled *iew, ue,* and *u*). ***Home Activity:*** Help your child use the spelling words in sentences.

Name ______________________________

Research Process

The **research process** involves locating information and organizing findings from that information. First, choose a research topic. Then list questions about the topic that you want to answer through your research. Next, locate and collect information from different sources. Take careful notes as you read the information you've collected. Use your notes to interpret, summarize, and organize information for your audience, revising your questions and answers as you proceed in the research process.

Directions: Use the description of the research process above and the resources pictured below to answer the questions that follow.

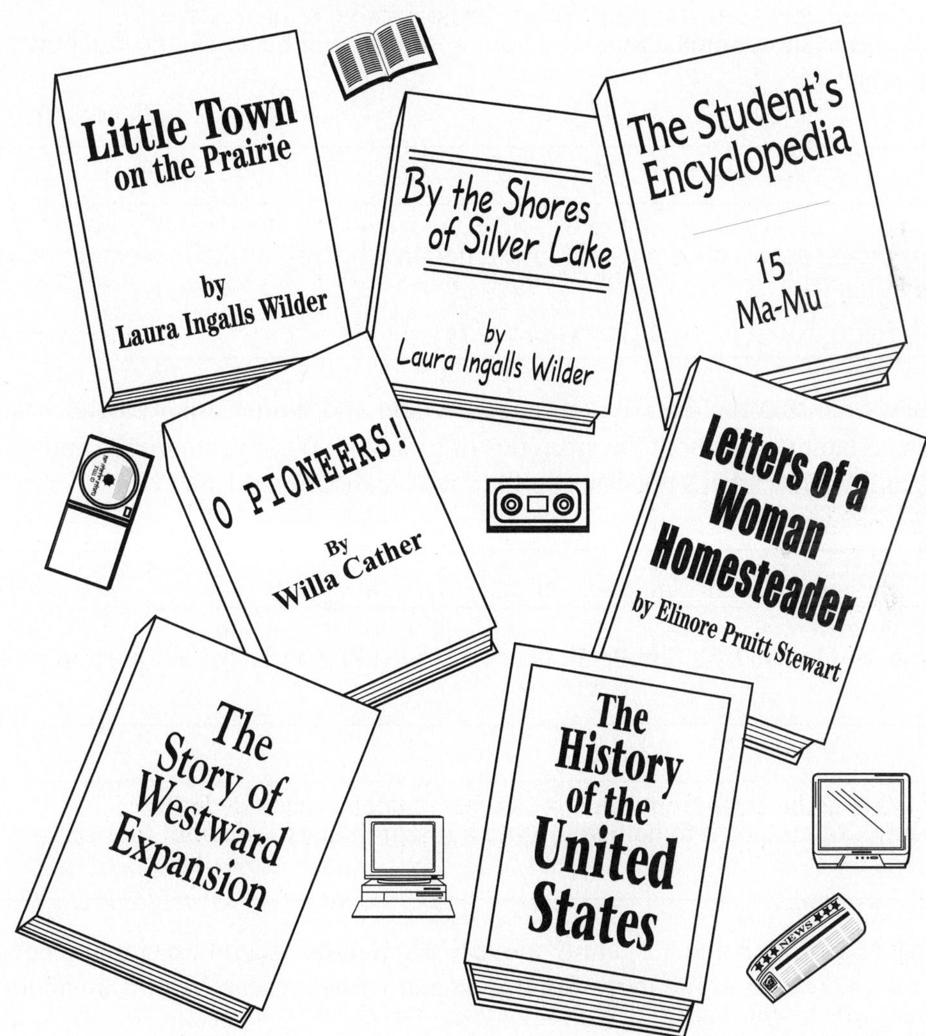

1. Why is it important to choose your topic as the first step in the research process?

____

2. How can forming questions about your topic help you begin your research?

____

____

3. Name several print and electronic media resources you might use to do research for a report.

4. You can use outlines, time lines, tables, diagrams, and graphs to organize information. Choose one of these and explain why it is helpful for organizing information.

5. Why is it important to think about who your audience will be as you decide how to present your research?

6. Which of the resources shown would give a detailed history of the movement of settlers to the West?

7. When they were children, both Laura Ingalls Wilder and Willa Cather moved west with their families and later wrote about the struggles of pioneers. What value might Laura Ingalls Wilder's and Willa Cather's novels have for a report about pioneers?

8. Why might old letters by a female pioneer be a useful resource for a report on pioneers?

9. Use the book titles shown to help you write a research question about pioneers.

10. In "April's Mud," April and her family move to the Southwest and learn many new things. Choose a topic related to life in the Southwest and write a research question about it.

Notes for Home: Your child learned about the research process. ***Home Activity:*** Together with your child, brainstorm a list of research topics. Discuss questions you could ask about each topic and possible sources of information for each topic.

Family Times

Name______________________________

Summary

One Woman, Two Homelands

In "Hot Dogs and Bamboo Shoots," Yoshiko Uchida writes about her two grandmothers. One grandmother lives in Los Angeles, and Ms. Uchida sees her regularly. The other grandmother lives in Japan. At age twelve, Yoshiko Uchida visits Japan and sees her grandmother for the first time in ten years. The trip teaches Ms. Uchida that she isn't really American or Japanese but a mixture of the two cultures.

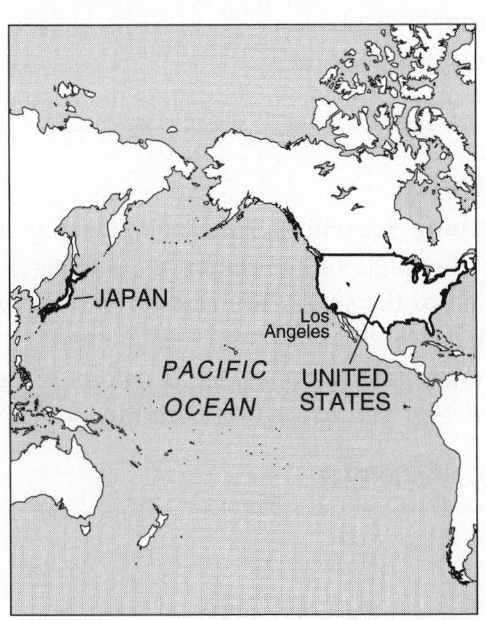

Activity

Write a Letter. Help your child write a letter from Yoshiko Uchida to her Japanese grandmother after she returns to California. In the letter, Yoshiko Uchida should share her reactions to the trip.

Reading Skills

Generalizing

A broad statement about what several people or things have in common is called a **generalization.** When Yoshiko Uchida describes her father's habit of always lingering on board ships before they depart, she is making a generalization about a repeated event that happens several times.

Clue words such as *most, many, all, sometimes, generally, always,* and *never* can help you identify generalizations.

A generalization that is supported by facts and agrees with what you already know is valid. A generalization not supported by facts is faulty.

Activity

Make Generalizations. Use clue words to make generalizations about traveling. Challenge your child to decide whether each generalization is valid or faulty, and why.

Family Times

Tested Vocabulary

Words to Know

Knowing the meanings of these words is important to reading "Hot Dogs and Bamboo Shoots." Practice using these words to learn their meanings.

anguish great pain or grief

correspondence an exchange of letters

exotic strange and unusual

foreigner person from another country

gratitude thankfulness

homeland a person's native land

traditional handed down from one generation to the next

uprooted removed from a place

Grammar

Compound and Complex Sentences

A **compound sentence** contains two simple sentences. When you write a compound sentence, use a comma and a conjunction such as *and, but*, or *or* to join the two simple sentences.

A **complex sentence** has one independent clause and one or more dependent clauses.

Simple Sentences
She was afraid of the boat.
She sailed to Japan anyway.
Compound Sentence
She was afraid of the boat, but she sailed to Japan anyway.
Complex Sentence
She must bow when she enters the room.

Activity

Combine Sentences. Have one person give a pair of related simple sentences, such as: **I will go to the store. You can come with me.** Then another person combines the two sentences into one sentence. **I will go to the store, and you can come with me.**

Tested Spelling Words

______	______	______	______
______	______	______	______
______	______	______	______
______	______	______	______
______	______	______	______

Name ______________________________

Generalizing

- **A generalization** is a broad statement about what several people or things have in common.
- Clue words such as *most, many, all, sometimes, generally, always,* and *never* can help you identify generalizations in what you read

Directions: Reread "The Key." Then complete the table. Tell whether each of the statements is a generalization. Explain your answers.

Statement	Generalization?	How do you know?
Lek was a collector.	**1.** Yes No	**2.**
Many children in rural Thailand are collectors.	**3.** Yes No	**4.**
Collecting made sense to Nong.	**5.** Yes No	**6.**
Collectors sometimes collect items of great value.	**7.** Yes No	**8.**
Nong kept hunting for things to collect.	**9.** Yes No	**10.**

Notes for Home: Your child identified generalizations—statements that tell what several people or things have in common ***Home Activity:*** Ask your child to look around a room in your house and make a generalization about it, such as *All the walls are painted white.*

Name ____

Vocabulary

Directions: Draw a line to connect each word on the left with its definition on the right.

1. anguish	your native land
2. correspondence	an exchange of letters
3. exotic	great pain or grief
4. gratitude	thankfulness
5. homeland	very different or unusual

Check the Words You Know

__ anguish
__ correspondence
__ exotic
__ foreigner
__ gratitude
__ homeland
__ traditional
__ uprooted

Directions: Choose the word from the box that best completes each sentence. Write the word on the matching numbered line to the right.

The twins' first day at school was difficult. The other children thought the twins' clothes looked **6.** _____, although these were **7.** _____ clothes worn by many young girls in their culture. They felt **8.** _____ from their friends, and they missed their **9.** _____very much. Each of the girls felt strange knowing that others saw her as a **10.** _____ living in a new country and culture.

6. ____________________
7. ____________________
8. ____________________
9. ____________________
10. ____________________

Write an E-mail Message

On a separate sheet of paper, write an e-mail message to a friend. Imagine you are traveling in some distant or exotic place. How does it feel to be a stranger in a new land? What new things might you see and do? Use as many vocabulary words as you can to describe what you see or how you feel.

Notes for Home: Your child identified and used vocabulary words from "Hot Dogs and Bamboo Shoots." ***Home Activity:*** Challenge your child to name objects that are ordinary to him or her but that might be exotic to someone from another place or culture.

Name ____________________

Generalizing

- A broad statement about what several people or things have in common is a **generalization.**
- Clue words such as *most, many, all, sometimes, generally, always,* and *never* can help you identify generalizations in what you read.
- Valid generalizations are supported by facts and agree with what you already know. Faulty generalizations are not.

Directions: Reread the part of "Hot Dogs and Bamboo Shoots" that tells about Obah San. Then answer the questions below. Look for generalizations that show actions that happen many times the same way.

We all went to the Japanese Union Church on Sundays, and Obah San was always the first one ready. Dressed in her best clothes, wearing her hat and gloves, she would sit on the sofa, patiently waiting for the rest of us to get ready.

She did the same thing if we invited her to go with us to see a movie. Obah San loved going out, and was always ready to have a good time with her grandchildren.

Because she'd never had much in life, she was always frugal and careful. She never let any food go to waste, and any fruit that was beginning to spoil had to be eaten before we could touch the good fruit.

1. Is "We all went to the Japanese Union Church on Sundays" a generalization?

____

____

2. What generalization can you make about Obah San and her grandchildren?

____

3. How is this generalization supported?

____

4. List all the clue words you can find in the passage that signal generalizations.

____

5. What generalization can you make about the importance of family among the Uchidas? Explain your thinking on a separate sheet of paper.

Notes for Home: Your child used story details to recognize and form generalizations. ***Home Activity:*** Challenge your child to state a generalization that shows what several people have in common. Encourage him or her to use clue words such as *always* or *most.*

Selection Test

Directions: Choose the best answer to each item. Mark the letter for the answer you have chosen.

Part 1: Vocabulary

Find the answer choice that means about the same as the underlined word in each sentence.

1. Lester felt like a person who was uprooted.
- A. old and slow
- B. removed from a place
- C. smart and clever
- D. hard-working

2. Her neighbors thought of Liz as a foreigner.
- F. baby
- G. one who leads a group
- H. person from another country
- J. troublemaker

3. I would like to try those exotic foods.
- A. strange and unusual
- B. hot and spicy
- C. expensive
- D. tasty

4. Dad and Granddad keep up their correspondence.
- F. bitter disagreement
- G. garden or small farm
- H. contest against each other
- J. exchange of letters

5. Mom expressed her gratitude.
- A. thankfulness
- B. hopes
- C. plans
- D. beliefs

6. Alana wore a traditional dress.
- F. reddish blue
- G. long and white with lace
- H. very expensive; costly
- J. reflecting old beliefs or customs

7. Mr. Pearson planned a visit to his homeland.
- A. any gift of property
- B. place where people share a language
- C. subdivision
- D. original or native land

8. The old man cried in anguish.
- F. surprise
- G. great pain or grief
- H. joy or gladness
- J. excitement

Part 2: Comprehension

Use what you know about the selection to answer each item.

9. At the time of this selection, most young Japanese Americans did not know their grandparents because—
- A. their families were separated by war.
- B. their grandparents had died.
- C. their grandparents lived in Japan.
- D. they could not speak Japanese.

10. The first time Yoshiko Uchida understood that her mother was also a daughter was when—
- F. her mother saw Grandmother Umegaki on the pier in Japan.
- G. her family's ship left San Francisco.
- H. she saw her uncle and cousins in Union Station.
- J. her family gathered for the New Year's feast.

GO ON

11. Why was Yoshiko Uchida in such awe of her cousins?
- A. She had never been to Los Angeles before.
- B. They were more sophisticated and worldly.
- C. She had never been to the movies before.
- D. They traveled more than she did.

12. Which generalization based on this selection is most likely valid?
- F. Children cannot have fun during a Japanese New Year's feast.
- G. Everyone likes all the dishes served at a Japanese New Year's feast.
- H. The Japanese New Year's feast is a very serious and quiet time.
- J. It usually takes several days to prepare a Japanese New Year's feast.

13. From the information in the selection, you can tell that most people in Japan—
- A. greet one another by bowing.
- B. forget about family who have moved away.
- C. have American names.
- D. cannot read Japanese.

14. Why did the author feel like an outsider when she was in Japan?
- F. She blended in with the other people in Japan.
- G. She did not like to eat the Japanese foods.
- H. She looked Japanese but did not know the language and culture.
- J. She did not like wearing Japanese clothes.

15. Yoshiko Uchida concludes that she is both American and Japanese because she—
- A. reads and writes both Japanese and English.
- B. wears Japanese clothes in America.
- C. speaks English in Japan.
- D. grew up in America, but with many Japanese customs.

STOP

Name ______________________

Generalizing

- A broad statement about what several people or things have in common is a **generalization.**
- Clue words such as *most, many, all, sometimes, generally, always,* and *never* can help you identify generalizations in what you read.
- Valid generalizations are supported by facts and agree with what you already know. Faulty generalizations are not.

Directions: Read the story below.

"The samovar is ready. Have some tea, Sasha," called Baba. My great-grandparents didn't speak Russian often, but *samovar,* the urn for tea, was a familiar word. When they were growing up in Russia, just about every home had a samovar. They brought the urn with them from their homeland. Like many other people, my great-grandparents liked to keep ties to their past.

They hardly ever made their tea in the samovar anymore. In America, they found teabags quicker and easier to use. But even then they drank their tea as they always had. Baba put a sugar cube between her teeth, sweetening her drink as she sipped. Dada stirred jam into his tea glass. "That's the way people in my village always drank their tea," he explained.

Baba said, "We like to keep some of the old ways in our life here."

Directions: Complete the table by deciding whether the generalization is valid or faulty. Use evidence from the passage to explain why it is valid or not.

Generalization	Valid or Faulty?	Evidence from Text
In the past, samovars were found in most Russian homes.	1.	2.
Sasha's great-grandparents never brew tea anymore.	3.	4.
Great-grandparents never try new things.	5.	6.
Some Russians sweeten their tea with jam.	7.	8.
Some people enjoy holding onto things from the past.	9.	10.

Notes for Home: Your child used details from a story to decide if certain generalizations were valid. ***Home Activity:*** Read a news article with your child. Look for generalizations that use clue words such as *sometimes, always, many, most,* or *never*.

REVIEW

Sequence

Directions: Read the story. Then read each question about the story. Choose the best answer to each question. Mark the letter for the answer you have chosen.

A Day-Long Celebration

Connie and Joe arrived at the annual Fourth of July parade as the flag bearer and the drummers came into view. Then came the high school marching band. The musicians looked handsome in their navy uniforms and tall plumed hats.

The parade's highlight was next. The mayor, dressed in colonial costume, read the Declaration of Independence aloud. Afterwards, a boy rang a model of the Liberty Bell. People waved small American flags. Everyone cheered and clapped when a large, colorful float came into view.

After the parade, Connie and Joe went to a picnic. While everyone was eating, the Glee Club sang.

Later that evening, the mayor made a speech about America, giving thanks for the freedoms Americans enjoy. After dark, the day's celebration ended with a thrilling fireworks display. Connie and Joe went home, tired but excited and happy.

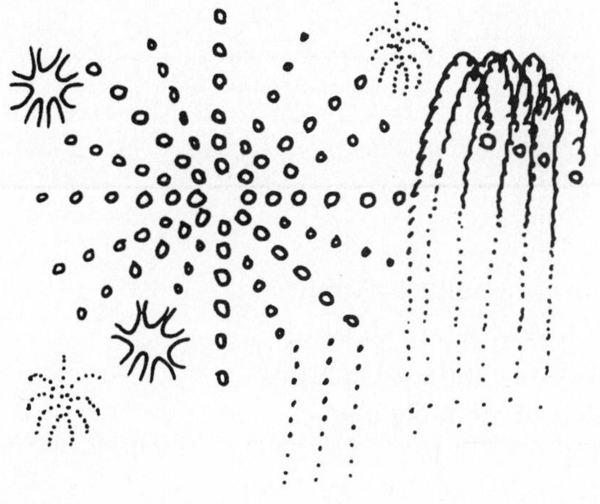

1. Directly after the flag bearer and drummers marched by, Connie and Joe saw—
   A. the Liberty Bell float.
   B. the mayor.
   C. the Glee Club.
   D. the marching band.

2. When a large, colorful float passed by—
   F. people cheered.
   G. the Glee Club sang.
   H. fireworks went off.
   J. the mayor gave a speech.

3. While people picnicked, they—
   A. heard speeches.
   B. watched fireworks.
   C. heard the Glee Club.
   D. listened to the mayor.

4. The mayor gave a speech—
   F. to start the day's celebration.
   G. just before the band came by.
   H. before the fireworks.
   J. while striking the model Liberty Bell.

5. The final event of the day's celebration was—
   A. a picnic.
   B. the mayor's speech.
   C. a fireworks display.
   D. the Glee Club performance.

Notes for Home: Your child recalled the order of events in a short story. ***Home Activity:*** Talk with your child about the events of a family tradition or preparations for the start of the school year. Challenge your child to list the events in order.

Name ______________________________

Writing Across Texts

Directions: Reread "Society and Culture" to find the definitions of the characteristics of a culture that are listed in the first column of the table below. Find examples of these characteristics of culture in "Hot Dogs and Bamboo Shoots" to explain how Yoshiko Uchida was influenced by both American and Japanese cultures. The first one is done for you.

	American Culture	Japanese Culture
Work and Rewards	Father worked for the railroad; he got passes for his family to travel.	**1.**
Organized Groups	**2.**	**3.**
Norms and Customs	**4.**	**5.**

Write a Paragraph

Reread "Society and Culture" to find the characteristics of a culture. Apply these definitions to "Hot Dogs and Bamboo Shoots." On a separate sheet of paper, write a paragraph or two that explains how Yoshiko Uchida was part of two different cultures. Use the information you recorded in the table above.

Notes for Home: Your child used information from different sources to write an explanatory paragraph. ***Home Activity:*** As you read stories and articles with your child, talk about how different characteristics of a culture are reflected in the writing.

Name ______________________________

REVIEW

Grammar: Independent and Dependent Clauses

Directions: Read each sentence. Underline all the independent clauses once. Underline all the dependent clauses twice.

1. If you like learning about different cultures, museums are a great place to start.
2. Some museums show the culture and history of one group of people, but others show many different groups.
3. When you visit California, stop by the California African American Museum in Los Angeles.
4. You can learn about African American culture at this museum, because it has many exhibits by and about African Americans.
5. After you visit there, you could also go to the Museum of African American History in Detroit, Michigan.
6. This museum includes a large model of a slave ship, but it also has modern displays.

Directions: Add an independent clause to each dependent clause below.

7. If you are interested in cultural history, ______________________________
____
____

8. Whenever I visit there, ______________________________
____
____

9. Because I'm interested in American Indian history, ______________________________
____
____

10. As I learn more about different cultures, ______________________________
____
____

Notes for Home: Your child identified dependent and independent clauses and wrote independent clauses. ***Home Activity:*** Ask your child to write sentences about a favorite tradition, and then identify the dependent and independent clauses in the sentences.

Practice

Grammar: Compound and Complex Sentences

Compound sentences and **complex sentences** help make writing more interesting.

A **compound sentence** contains two independent clauses joined with a comma and a word such as *or, and,* or *but.*

A woman wove rugs, and her husband made drums.
(independent clause) (independent clause)

A **complex sentence** contains one independent clause and one or more dependent clauses. The independent and dependent clauses are joined with words such as *if, because,* or *when.*

Because she dyes her own yarn, she weaves brightly colored rugs.
(dependent clause) (independent clause)

Directions: Write whether each sentence is **compound** or **complex.**

______________ **1.** Kit likes to cook, and she likes to travel.

______________ **2.** Wherever she goes, she collects recipes.

______________ **3.** Her collection is huge, but the recipes are all different.

______________ **4.** After Kit comes home, her friends love to visit.

______________ **5.** Since Kit loves company, she cooks her own favorite foods, which are very tasty.

______________ **6.** Kit buys spices from around the world, and she brings them home.

______________ **7.** She likes spicy food, but her friends don't care for it.

______________ **8.** If she cooks for herself, Kit uses many spices.

______________ **9.** Whenever she travels, she eats spicy food.

______________ **10.** While she's here at home, Kit will write a cookbook.

Notes for Home: Your child identified compound and complex sentences. ***Home Activity:*** Give your child a simple sentence, and challenge him or her to change it into a compound sentence or a complex sentence.

Name ______________________________

Grammar: Compound and Complex Sentences

Directions: Write whether each sentence is **compound** or **complex.**

__________ **1.** Anthropologists are scientists, and human beings are their field of study.

__________ **2.** Since each culture is different, a scientist may explore just one.

__________ **3.** Some cultures are known for their music, but no culture is known for music alone.

__________ **4.** When I see a piece of art, I think about who made it.

__________ **5.** You can learn about a culture, if you look at its food, music, and art.

Directions: Choose the group of words in ( ) that will complete each sentence. Write the complete sentence on the line, adding a comma if necessary.

6. Try Vietnamese beef stew _____.
(and enjoy its spicy flavor/although I don't have a recipe)

____

7. If a feast is held, _____.
(and at certain other times/a culture may have a special dance)

____

8. Cultures new to you are interesting, _____.
(because someone invites you/and learning about them is fun)

____

9. When we study another culture, _____.
(and its people study us, in turn/we also learn about ourselves)

____

10. When you try another culture's specialties, _____.
(some dishes may seem different/but never do this in a hurry)

____

Write an E-mail Message

Write an e-mail message to tell a friend about a culture you find interesting. Include both compound and complex sentences.

Notes for Home: Your child identified compound sentences and complex sentences. ***Home Activity:*** Ask your child to point out compound and complex sentences in newspaper or magazine articles.

Name ______________________________

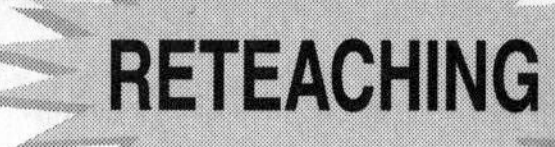

RETEACHING

Grammar: Compound and Complex Sentences

Underline each independent clause.

1. Jonathan wants to travel to Milan, but he is too busy this month.

Underline the dependent clause once and the independent clause twice.

2. Although I felt nervous, I took the test anyway.

A **compound sentence** contains two independent clauses joined with a comma and a word such as *and, or,* or *but.* A **complex sentence** contains one dependent clause and one independent clause joined by a word such as *if, because,* or *although.*

Directions: Write whether each sentence is **compound** or **complex.**

______________ 1. The sign goes here, and the banner goes there.

______________ 2. While you direct traffic, John can do his job.

______________ 3. Sue is in charge of books, but she's not here yet.

______________ 4. If you cover for her, I'll give you a hand.

______________ 5. This is a big event, and nothing must go wrong.

______________ 6. I'm weary too, but we don't have time to rest.

______________ 7. Did Mrs. Ellis donate the hat, or was it Mr. West?

______________ 8. Because we are doing so well, we may be able to close early.

______________ 9. The shoes are selling fast, but no one's buying ties.

______________ 10. This suit cost ten dollars, but it's worth more.

______________ 11. That red hat looks good, but that one looks better.

______________ 12. You should go home if you aren't going to help.

______________ 13. May I help you, or are you just browsing?

______________ 14. Although we haven't marked the price on that one, we'll sell it to you for five dollars.

______________ 15. We have done very well, but let's stay open for another half an hour.

Notes for Home: Your child identified compound and complex sentences. ***Home Activity:*** Have your child use this page to explain to you the differences between compound and complex sentences.

Name ______________________________

Grammar: Compound and Complex Sentences

Directions: Write whether each sentence is **compound** or **complex.**

______________ **1.** Math is my favorite subject, but my grades are often low.

______________ **2.** My teacher helps and encourages me when I come to her with questions.

______________ **3.** If I spend a little extra time on my math homework each night, I will understand more of the discussion in class the next day.

______________ **4.** Memorizing is hard for me, and I forget important rules.

______________ **5.** I must study hard, or my grades will not improve.

______________ **6.** Because I am a hard worker, I know I will get better in time.

Directions: Add a word such as *and, or,* or *but* and more information to complete each compound sentence.

7. It is important to do your work carefully ______________________________

____

8. I like to write stories ______________________________

____

9. My teacher is very patient ______________________________

____

Directions: Add a dependent clause to complete each complex sentence. Write the new sentence on the lines.

10. ______________________, we can skip doing homework one night.

____

____

11. ______________________, my friends went to the movie without me.

____

____

12. ______________________, I will be very happy.

____

____

Notes for Home: Your child identified and completed compound and complex sentences. ***Home Activity:*** Have your child read a newspaper or magazine article and mark two compound sentences and two complex sentences. Then have him or her make up another one of each.

Phonics: *r*-Controlled Vowels

Directions: The letters **or** can have two different sounds. The **or** in **work** sounds different than the **or** in **for.** Read the words in the box. Say the words to yourself. Listen to the different sounds that the letters **or** represent. Sort the words by their sounds. Write each word in the correct column.

according	worry	boring	worse	world
porthole	sorts	worthy	morning	worship

work	**for**
1. ______________	6. ______________
2. ______________	7. ______________
3. ______________	8. ______________
4. ______________	9. ______________
5. ______________	10. ______________

Directions: Read each sentence. Read the words in ( ). Both words fit the sentence, but only one has the vowel sound you hear in **work.** Circle the word that has the vowel sound you hear in **work.** Write the word on the matching numbered line. Underline the letters that represent the **r-controlled vowel** sound.

Some people feel an **11.** (urgent/immediate) need to travel. Their curiosity about the world is **12.** (bubbling/bursting) within them. They are so excited, they never know what to look at **13.** (first/fully). A ruined castle? An old fortress? A famous **14.** (cathedral/church)? Someone should tell them there is no need to be in such **15.** (distress/turmoil).These buildings aren't going anywhere!

11. ______________
12. ______________
13. ______________
14. ______________
15. ______________

Notes for Home: Your child sorted and wrote words with *r*-controlled vowels, such as *for, world, first,* and *church.* ***Home Activity:*** Read a story with your child. As you find words spelled with *or, ir,* and *ur,* cover the words. Have your child tell you the correct spelling.

Name ______________________________

Spelling: Vowel Sounds with *r*

Pretest

Pretest Directions: Fold back the page along the dotted line. On the blanks, write the spelling words as they are dictated. When you have finished the test, unfold the page and check your words.

1. ______________________________
2. ______________________________
3. ______________________________
4. ______________________________
5. ______________________________
6. ______________________________
7. ______________________________
8. ______________________________
9. ______________________________
10. ______________________________
11. ______________________________
12. ______________________________
13. ______________________________
14. ______________________________
15. ______________________________
16. ______________________________
17. ______________________________
18. ______________________________
19. ______________________________
20. ______________________________

1. She finished the book **report**.
2. The soldiers obeyed his **order**.
3. I need a **sword** for my costume.
4. They do **forty** laps in the pool.
5. This is an **enormous** sandwich.
6. Let's **explore** the forest.
7. It was hard to **ignore** the sound.
8. I get hungry; **therefore** I eat.
9. She is an **expert** skier.
10. The **service** station was closed.
11. Skill will **determine** the winner.
12. This is a **permanent** marker.
13. This project requires **research**.
14. I am **earning** enough money.
15. That book is **worth** reading.
16. The **worst** part is over.
17. Your research is very **thorough**.
18. Shania's mother is an **attorney**.
19. Do not **disturb** the residents.
20. Are you ready to **purchase** it?

Notes for Home: Your child took a pretest on words that have vowel sounds with the letter *r*. ***Home Activity:*** Help your child learn misspelled words before the final test. Have your child divide misspelled words into parts (such as syllables) and concentrate on each part.

Spelling: Vowel Sounds with *r*

Word List				
report	enormous	expert	research	thorough
order	explore	service	earning	attorney
sword	ignore	determine	worth	disturb
forty	therefore	permanent	worst	purchase

Directions: Choose the words from the box that have the same vowel sound as **fort.** Write each word in the correct column.

Spelled or	Spelled ore
1. ____________	6. ____________
2. ____________	7. ____________
3. ____________	8. ____________
4. ____________	
5. ____________	

Directions: Choose the words from the box that have the same vowel sound as **work.** Write each word in the correct column.

Spelled or	Spelled ur
9. ____________	13. ____________
10. ____________	14. ____________
11. ____________	
12. ____________	

Directions: Choose the word from the box that best completes each sentence. Write the word on the line to the left.

____________ **15.** My friend Yanni is an _____ who knows everything about gardens.

____________ **16.** His first book took years of study and _____.

____________ **17.** Some garden designs are _____; others change every year.

____________ **18.** Books provide an important _____ for home gardeners.

____________ **19.** Yanni has the chance of _____ a great prize if his book is selected by the judges.

____________ **20.** To _____ who will win, judges have to read all the books.

Notes for Home: Your child spelled words with the vowel sound heard in *report* and *explore,* and the vowel sound heard in *expert, research,* and *disturb.* ***Home Activity:*** Challenge your child to find other words with these two vowel sounds. Discuss how these words are spelled.

Name ____________________

Spelling: Vowel Sounds with *r*

Directions: Proofread these two Japanese *haiku* (short poems about simple images). Find five spelling mistakes. Use the proofreading marks to correct each mistake.

≡	Make a capital.
/	Make a small letter.
∧	Add something.
℘	Take out something.
⊙	Add a period.
¶	Begin a new paragraph.

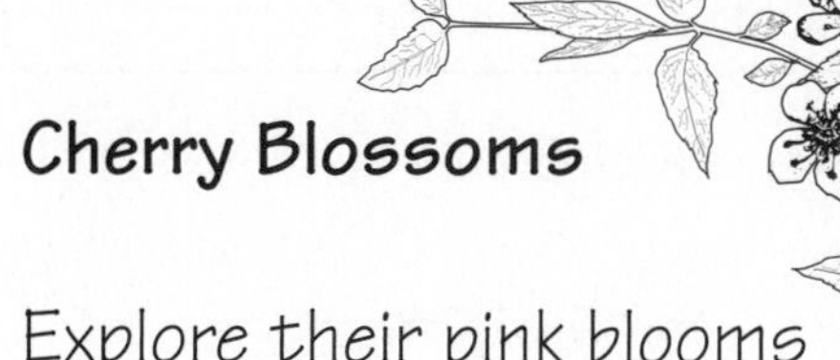

Cherry Blossoms

Explore their pink blooms

See their premanent order

Wurth of fourty trees

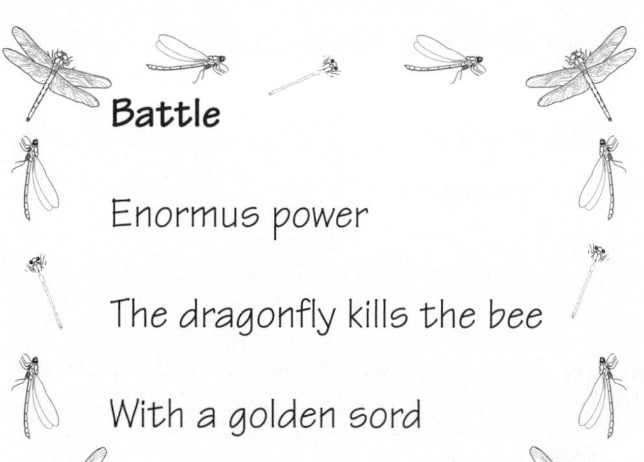

Battle

Enormus power

The dragonfly kills the bee

With a golden sord

Spelling Tip

report **worth**

Watch for letter pairs that represent different vowel sounds. The letters **or** can represent two different vowel sounds, as heard in **report** and **worth.**

Word List

report	determine
order	permanent
sword	research
forty	earning
enormous	worth
explore	worst
ignore	thorough
therefore	attorney
expert	disturb
service	purchase

Write a Haiku

On a separate sheet of paper, write a haiku of your own. A haiku always has three lines. The first and third lines have five syllables each. The second line has seven syllables. A haiku usually focuses on a single, simple image. Try to use at least three of your spelling words.

Notes for Home: Your child spelled words with the vowel sound heard in *report* and *explore,* and the vowel sound heard in *expert, research,* and *disturb. **Home Activity:*** Encourage your child to describe the haiku he or she has written. Discuss the image in the haiku.

Name ______________________________

Spelling: Vowel Sounds with *r*

REVIEW

Word List

report	enormous	expert	research	thorough
order	explore	service	earning	attorney
sword	ignore	determine	worth	disturb
forty	therefore	permanent	worst	purchase

Directions: Write the word from the box that belongs in each group.

1. article, story, ________________
2. blade, knife, ________________
3. value, importance, ________________
4. overlook, disregard, ________________
5. consequently, thus, ________________
6. help, aid, ________________
7. twenty, thirty, ________________
8. decide, conclude, ________________

Directions: Choose the word from the box that is the most opposite in meaning for each word below. Write the word on the line.

9. sell ______________
10. best ______________
11. spending ______________
12. beginner ______________
13. temporary ______________
14. tiny ______________

Directions: Choose the word from the box that best replaces the underlined word. Write the word on the line.

______________ 15. Arrange the coins by value.

______________ 16. The biologist's study may help find a cure for a disease.

______________ 17. I am taking my cat in for a complete health check.

______________ 18. Ben is sleeping; please do not bother him.

______________ 19. Connie has an appointment with her lawyer.

______________ 20. I want to investigate where the mouse could have gone.

Notes for Home: Your child spelled words with the vowel sound heard in *report* and *explore*, and the vowel sound heard in *expert, research,* and *disturb*. ***Home Activity:*** Have your child choose a spelling word and find another word with the same vowel sound spelled the same way.

Name ______________________

Parts of a Book

The main **parts of a book** include its cover, title page, copyright page, table of contents, chapter titles, section heads, captions, footnotes, index, bibliography, and appendix.

Directions: Use the table of contents from a book of folk tales to answer the questions below and on the next page.

Folk Tales from Japan, China, and India

1. How are the folk tales organized in this book? How do you know?

____

____

2. From what country is the folk tale *The Five Sparrows?* ______________________

3. On which page does the first of the Indian folk tales begin? ______________________

4. Name two folk tales that are from India. ____________________

5. Which part of the book would you look at to find information about other folk tales to read?

6. Suppose you wanted to compare the fairy tale *Cinderella* with a similar folk tale from another country. Would this book be helpful? Explain.

7. Suppose you wanted to see if any of these folk tales included a story about a tiger. Which section of the book would help you figure this out? Explain.

8. Suppose you were writing a research report on jackals to tell facts about this animal. Would *The Blue Jackal* on page 66 be useful for your report? Explain.

9. Can you judge a book by its cover? What information will you find on a book cover?

10. A copyright page tells when a book was published. Why might this information be important when you are doing research?

Notes for Home: Your child answered questions about different parts of a book. ***Home Activity:*** Examine some fiction and nonfiction books with your child. Have your child point out different parts of each book and explain what information it shows.

Family Times

Name____

Summary

Jet Crash Changes the Lives of the Austin Family

On a normal, noisy Saturday night, the Austins' telephone rings. The call changes everything. Uncle Hal, a pilot, has died in a jet crash. His copilot has also died. Aunt Elena and the copilot's daughter, Maggy, come to stay with the Austins. Vicky, John, and their mother help their visitors and each other cope with the news.

Activity

Describe the Situation. Encourage your child to describe the Austins' household before and after Aunt Elena and Maggy come to stay. What has changed? How do the people behave differently?

Reading Skills

Character

Characters are the people or animals in stories. You can learn about characters by noticing what they think, say, and do. When Vicky looks at Aunt Elena and feels unable to speak, you learn that Vicky is sensitive to others and feels things deeply.

You can also learn about characters by paying attention to how other characters in the story treat them and what those characters say about them. Through what Uncle Douglas says, we learn that Vicky has an artistic temperament and feels what other people feel.

Activity

Play a Guessing Game. Sit in a circle. The first player describes a famous person. The other players guess who is being described. Include details about how the person looks, speaks, and behaves, and what others say about him or her.

Family Times

Tested Vocabulary

Words to Know

Knowing the meanings of these words is important to reading "The Telephone Call." Practice using these words to learn their meanings.

bewilderment great confusion

cope deal or struggle with successfully

objective not influenced by emotion

orphan a child whose parents are dead

tactful having or showing an ability to say and do the right thing

Grammar

Correcting Run-on Sentences

Run-on sentences occur when writers mistakenly combine sentences without any punctuation. They also occur if you combine sentences with just a comma and leave out the necessary conjunction.

The examples below show two ways to correct a run-on sentence.

Run-on Sentence: Aunt Kate is a scientist, she also likes art.

Corrected Sentence:
Aunt Kate is a scientist, but she also likes art.
Aunt Kate is a scientist. She also likes art.

Activity

Let's Get It Right! Write run-on sentences on slips of paper. Take turns choosing and correcting each run-on sentence. Remember, there is more than one way to correct each sentence.

Tested Spelling Words

Name ______________________

Character

- **Characters** are the people or animals who take part in the events of a short story, novel, play, or other form of fiction.
- You can learn about characters from their thoughts, words, and actions.
- You can also learn about characters by paying attention to how other characters in the story treat them and what other characters say about them.

Directions: Reread "Granny's Chair." Then complete the table. Provide the missing phrases or sentences to tell what Rachel is like, how she is feeling, and how you know.

What is Rachel like? How is she feeling?	How do you know?
Rachel feels uncertain.	**1.**
Rachel's thoughts are wandering.	**2.**
3.	She remembers Granny's hands in detail.
4.	She stays inside with the grownups. She smiles at her uncle. She doesn't complain, and she tries to imitate the rhythm of their hands.
Rachel feels left out.	**5.**

Notes for Home: Your child used details from a story to describe a character. ***Home Activity:*** Choose a character from a book or television show. Have your child describe what the character is like and provide details to support his or her description.

Name ______________________________

Vocabulary

Directions: Choose the word from the box that best replaces the underlined word or words. Write the word on the line.

Check the Words You Know
__ bewilderment
__ cope
__ objective
__ orphan
__ tactful

__________ **1.** Sandy can <u>handle difficult situations</u> well.

__________ **2.** She takes an <u>open, unprejudiced</u> approach when conflicts arise.

__________ **3.** When people get angry, Sandy is <u>polite</u>, saying and doing just the right thing.

__________ **4.** When she is in a state of <u>confusion</u>, she looks for facts that will help her solve the problem.

__________ **5.** Her common sense and kindness were just what the <u>parentless child</u> needed.

Directions: Choose the word from the box that best matches each clue. Write the letters of the word on the blanks. The boxed letters spell a synonym for *crisis*.

6. not influenced by emotion

7. great confusion

8. a child who has no living parents

9. deal or struggle with

10. able to say and do the right thing

6. ___ ___ ___ [ ] ___ ___ ___ ___ ___

[m]

7. ___ ___ ___ ___ ___ ___ [ ] ___ ___ ___ ___ ___

8. ___ [ ] ___ ___ ___ ___

[g]

9. ___ ___ ___ [ ]

[n]

10. ___ ___ [ ] ___ ___ ___ ___

[y]

A synonym for *crisis:* __________________

Write a Narrative

On a separate sheet of paper, write about an event or time in your life that was funny, sad, exciting, or interesting. Describe what happened in the order that it happened. Make sure your narrative has a beginning, middle and end. Use as many vocabulary words as you can.

Notes for Home: Your child identified and used vocabulary words from "The Telephone Call." ***Home Activity:*** With your child, explore different ways to describe feelings, using as many of the listed vocabulary words as you can.

Name ________________________________

Character

- **Characters** are the people or animals who take part in the events of a short story, novel, play, or other form of fiction.
- You can learn about characters through their thoughts, words, and actions.
- You can also learn about characters by paying attention to how other characters in the story treat them and what others say about them.

Directions: Reread what happens in "The Telephone Call" when Uncle Douglas explains empathy. Then answer the questions below. Use the information in the passage to tell about the characters.

"But why does John know what to say, and how to say it, and all I can do is act stupid, as though it didn't matter?"

"Just because it matters too much. Have you ever heard of *empathy?*"

I shook my head.

"John can show Aunt Elena how sorry he is because he has a scientific mind and he can see what has happened from the outside. All good scientists have to know how to be observers. He can be deeply upset about Uncle Hal and deeply sorry for Aunt Elena, but he can be objective about it. You can't."

"Why?"

"Because you have an artistic temperament, Vicky, and I've never seen you be objective about anything yet. When you think about Aunt Elena and how she must be feeling right now, it is for the moment as though you *were* Aunt Elena; you get right inside her suffering, and it becomes your suffering, too. That's empathy. . . ."

1. How does Vicky think she handles the situation?

____

2. What does Uncle Douglas think of Vicky?

____

3. What does Uncle Douglas think of John?

____

4. Based on what he has said, what do you think of Uncle Douglas?

____

5. Later in the story, Mother takes John and Vicky to watch the night sky. What does this action tell you about Mother? Explain your thinking on a separate sheet of paper.

Notes for Home: Your child read a short story and learned about the characters. ***Home Activity:*** Read a story together or watch a TV program together. Then encourage your child to explain what he or she has learned about each character.

Selection Test

Directions: Choose the best answer to each item. Mark the letter for the answer you have chosen.

Part 1: Vocabulary

Find the answer choice that means about the same as the underlined word in each sentence.

1. Grandma tries to <u>cope</u> with her illness.
A. heal
B. rest
C. deal with
D. fight against

2. Aunt Margaret is the most <u>tactful</u> person I have ever known.
F. warm and loving
G. skilled at saying the right thing in difficult situations
H. graceful and beautiful
J. direct and to the point

3. Elsie tried to write an <u>objective</u> letter.
A. long and detailed
B. clear and easy to understand
C. personal or friendly
D. not affected by personal feelings

4. Alexa looked at us in <u>bewilderment</u>.
F. great confusion
G. fear
H. eager excitement
J. wonder

5. Marie is an <u>orphan</u>.
A. a child whose parents are dead
B. an infant
C. a person who is married
D. a woman

Part 2: Comprehension

Use what you know about the story to answer each item.

6. What made the Saturday evening at the beginning of the story unusual?
F. Suzy was playing doctor with her dolls.
G. The house was filled with noise.
H. Aunt Elena called about an accident.
J. Daddy had to see a sick patient.

7. Maggy came to live with the Austins because she—
A. no longer had a family of her own.
B. was Suzy's best friend.
C. wanted to spend more time with other children.
D. did not like Aunt Elena.

8. How did Vicky feel when she first learned that Maggy would be staying with them?
F. excited about having a new friend
G. upset because she did not like Maggy
H. confused about how the changes would affect her
J. sorry that she could not help Maggy feel better

GO ON

9. What happened just after Vicky found Aunt Elena trying to make coffee in the kitchen?
- A. John came in and hugged Aunt Elena.
- B. Uncle Douglas drove up to the house.
- C. Suzy and Maggy set the table.
- D. The telephone rang.

10. You can tell from the story that Vicky preferred people around her to be—
- F. misleading.
- G. secretive.
- H. loud.
- J. calm.

11. Compared with John, Vicky had a harder time trying to—
- A. feel sorry for other people.
- B. understand how Aunt Elena felt.
- C. feel her mother's pain.
- D. say the right things to people.

12. What was one way Aunt Elena dealt with losing Uncle Hal?
- F. She prayed that Hal would come back to her.
- G. She cried hard and felt no hope.
- H. She remembered the good times they had together.
- J. She kept busy so she could forget him.

13. The author's main purpose in this selection is to—
- A. describe how to make other people feel better.
- B. tell a story about how a family deals with a crisis.
- C. persuade people not to fly planes.
- D. explain why change is necessary.

14. Why did Vicky feel more sympathy for Aunt Elena than for Maggy?
- F. Vicky had known Maggy longer.
- G. Vicky liked and understood Aunt Elena.
- H. Vicky did not feel sorry for Aunt Elena.
- J. Vicky was closer to Maggy in age.

15. Why was Mother more patient with Maggy when she knocked over chairs than she would have been with her own children or their friends?
- A. Maggy was having a hard time and did not yet know what was expected of her.
- B. Maggy was too young to know any better.
- C. Maggy was always so well behaved that Mother assumed it was an accident.
- D. Maggy could not control the movements of her body.

STOP

Name ______________________________

Character

- **Characters** are the people or animals who take part in the events of a short story, novel, play, or other form of fiction.
- You can learn about characters through their thoughts, words, and actions.
- You can also learn about characters by paying attention to how other characters in the story treat them and what others say about them.

Directions: Read the story below.

Anita's mother had been rushed to the hospital last night. Anita felt lost without her.

Her father didn't know how he was going to manage. He worked long hours, and he wanted to be at the hospital. He needed someone else to take care of Anita. He asked Aunt Martine, Uncle Sid, and Aunt Fran.

"I'd love to have you, but my expensive glass collection is in the only extra room," said Aunt Martine. "I'm not used to having children around."

"I'm always willing to do my duty," Uncle Sid said with tight lips. "Of course I'll take the child if it's necessary."

Aunt Fran smiled warmly and put her arm around Anita. "Anita, I could use some company in the house. What do you think?" Anita smiled back.

Directions: Write words or phrases to describe Anita's relatives in the four blank boxes below. The box for Anita has been done for you.

Anita	Dad	Aunt Martine
lost frightened	1.	2.

Uncle Sid	Aunt Fran
3.	4.

5. Which relative should Anita stay with? Explain your choice.

____

____

Notes for Home: Your child used story details to describe different characters. ***Home Activity:*** Take turns describing the traits of family members or close friends. Challenge your child to sum up each character description with a few key words.

Name ______________________

REVIEW

Cause and Effect

Directions: Read the story. Then read each question about the story. Choose the best answer to each question. Mark the letter for the answer you have chosen.

The Lucky Return

Steve couldn't wait to grow old enough to take care of his cousin's dog! Steve's cousin Sandy had a beautiful dog named Rex. Steve often visited Sandy because he enjoyed caring for and playing with her dog.

Imagine Steve's joy when Sandy asked him to care for Rex for an entire weekend. The first day that Steve was caring for Rex it was raining lightly, but Steve decided to take Rex outside to play.

Steve walked several blocks to a nearby park. Suddenly, the rain shower turned into a heavy rain and the wind began to blow.

As Steve was leaving the park with Rex, another dog ran in front of them. Rex surprised Steve by lunging after the large dog. Steve's hand was so wet from the rain that he couldn't hold the leash. Rex bolted after the other dog and the two animals ran swiftly through the park. Steve ran as fast as he could, but the dogs got farther and farther away.

When he realized that he couldn't catch Rex, Steve sat down, right in a puddle of rain, and began to cry. He was afraid that he had lost Sandy's beautiful dog forever.

As he was crying, Steve heard a familiar bark and looked up to see Rex running toward him. Steve gave Rex a big hug as Rex licked his face. "Please forgive me, Rex. I'll never take you out in bad weather again."

As the rain began to stop, Steve started to walk Rex home. This time he held the leash firmly with both hands.

1. Steve often visited Sandy because—
- **A.** she is his cousin.
- **B.** his parents were away a lot.
- **C.** he enjoyed caring for her cat.
- **D.** he enjoyed playing with her dog.

2. Steve was unable to hold the leash because—
- **F.** the wind was blowing.
- **G.** he was scared.
- **H.** his hand was wet and slippery.
- **J.** he couldn't see in the rain.

3. Steve begins to cry because—
- **A.** he didn't want to care for Rex.
- **B.** he sat in a rain puddle.
- **C.** he was afraid that he had lost Rex for good.
- **D.** he was afraid of the other dog.

4. Which of the following is **not** an effect of losing Rex?
- **F.** Steve promises not to take Rex out in bad weather again.
- **G.** The rainstorm makes it difficult for Steve to hold the leash.
- **H.** Steve cries.
- **J.** Steve sits in a rain puddle.

5. Steve might not have lost Rex if—
- **A.** the weather had been nice.
- **B.** the park wasn't so far away.
- **C.** he had not sat in the puddle.
- **D.** he had not cried.

Notes for Home: Your child used details to identify causes and effects in a story. ***Home Activity:*** Help your child identify some of the things she or he does to get good results, such as practicing for sports, setting aside enough time for homework, or studying for a test.

Name ________________________________

Writing Across Texts

Directions: Consider how the experiences of Vicky from "The Telephone Call" and Yoshiko Uchida, author of "Hot Dogs and Bamboo Shoots," are alike and different. Complete the table below to compare and contrast these selections.

	The Telephone Call	Hot Dogs and Bamboo Shoots
Characters	Vicky	Yoshiko Uchida
Setting	Rural America today	**3.**
Events	Uncle Hal dies. **1.**	**4.**
Ending	**2.**	**5.**

Write a Letter

"The Telephone Call" and "Hot Dogs and Bamboo Shoots" are two selections about young girls who experience changes in their lives. How are their experiences alike? How are they different? Write a friendly letter from one of the characters to the other discussing the changes that have occurred and how the character feels about them. Use a separate sheet of paper for your letter.

Notes for Home: Your child compared and contrasted information from two selections. ***Home Activity:*** As you read stories with your child, discuss the changes that the characters face and how those changes may be similar to or different from changes your child has experienced.

Name ______________________________

REVIEW

Grammar: Compound and Complex Sentences

Directions: Write whether each sentence is compound or complex.

__________ **1.** While a customer is eating, he suddenly cannot breathe.

__________ **2.** He turns blue, and his finger points to his throat.

__________ **3.** The Heimlich maneuver could save his life, and fortunately the waitress knows how to perform the maneuver.

__________ **4.** As she stands behind the customer, she wraps her arms around his waist.

__________ **5.** When she presses quickly on his stomach, the stuck piece of food finally comes out.

Directions: Add an independent clause to the first two sentences to make them compound sentences. Add independent clauses to the last three sentences to make them complex sentences. Write the complete sentences on the lines.

6. (compound sentence) Life is full of emergencies, and _____.

____

____

7. (compound sentence) You should learn CPR and the Heimlich maneuver, but _____.

____

____

8. (complex) _____, if you couldn't help someone in need.

____

____

9. (complex) If you can swim, _____.

____

____

10. (complex) When there is an emergency, _____.

____

____

Notes for Home: Your child identified and wrote compound and complex sentences. ***Home Activity:*** Give your child two simple sentences and challenge him or her to combine them into a compound sentence.

Name ______________________________

Grammar: Combining Sentences

If two sentences have different subjects but the same predicate, you can combine the subjects to form a **compound subject** by using the word *and.*

Simple sentences: Jason gazed at the stars above. His sister gazed at the stars above.

Compound subject: Jason and his sister gazed at the stars above.

If two sentences have the same subject and different predicates, you can combine the predicates to form a **compound predicate** by using the word *and.*

Simple sentences: Marika waited for the bus. Marika watched the darkening sky.

Compound predicate: Marika waited for the bus and watched the darkening sky.

If two sentences have related ideas, you can combine the sentences to form a **compound sentence** by using a comma and words like *or, but,* or *and.*

Simple sentences: I was nervous. My knees were knocking.

Compound sentence: I was nervous, and my knees were knocking.

Directions: Combine each pair of sentences to form a compound subject, a compound predicate, or a compound sentence. Use the joining word *and.*

1. Sook and Lin Yu were frightened. Sook and Lin Yu wanted to go home.

____

____

2. They were in the woods. They saw how dark it was.

____

____

3. Sook saw a mysterious shape. Lin Yu saw a mysterious shape too.

____

____

4. The shape came forward. It was huge.

____

____

5. Sook shivered. Lin Yu shook.

____

____

Notes for Home: Your child has learned to combine sentences. ***Home Activity:*** Using a favorite book, ask your child to show you how to combine sentences.

Extra Practice

Grammar: Combining Sentences

Directions: Combine each pair of sentences to form a compound subject, a compound predicate, or a compound sentence. Use the joining words *or, and,* or *but.*

1. Tara smiled happily. Tara hummed a little song.

____

2. Tara planned to have fun. Her friends planned to have fun.

____

3. They would swim. They would dive.

____

4. The parking lot was empty. The beach was empty.

____

5. Huge waves came in. Huge waves broke on the sand.

____

6. Tara felt nervous. Her friends yelled happily.

____

7. The waves were big. Tara stepped backward.

____

8. Tara sat down on the sand. Her friends went wading.

____

9. A wave crashed down. Angie disappeared.

____

10. The water grew calmer. Angie stood up.

____

Write a Paragraph

Write a paragraph to finish the story of Tara and her friends. Then look for sentences you can combine to make your writing more interesting.

Notes for Home: Your child combined short sentences to form longer, more interesting sentences. ***Home Activity:*** Ask your child to explain various ways of combining sentences. Then, together, examine newspaper ads, looking for sentences that can be combined.

Grammar: Combining Sentences

RETEACHING

Combine each pair of sentences. Write each new sentence.

1. Margaret walked home. Peter walked home.

____

2. Margaret went to the library. Margaret stopped by the store.

____

3. They left for the airport early. They got stuck in traffic.

____

Form a **compound subject** by combining two sentences with the same predicate but different subjects. Form a **compound predicate** by combining two sentences that have the same subject but different predicates. Form a **compound sentence** by combining two simple sentences that have related ideas.

Directions: Combine each pair of sentences to form a sentence with a compound subject or a compound predicate, or to form a compound sentence. Use the joining word *or, and,* or *but.* Write each new sentence on the line.

1. Jane Wilkinson is new at Kennedy School this year. Ray Wilkinson is new at Kennedy School this year.

____

____

2. Jane and Ray don't know anyone at school. They would like to make new friends.

____

____

3. My brother invites Ray to club meetings. My brother's friends invite Ray to club meetings.

____

4. Carole opened the newspaper. Carole read about Taylor and Ushma.

____

5. They had entered a literary contest. They had tied for first prize.

____

Notes for Home: Your child wrote compound sentences and sentences with compound subjects and compound predicates. ***Home Activity:*** Write simple sentences about your family. Have your child combine them to form compound sentences or sentences with compound subjects or predicates.

Name ______________________

Grammar: Combining Sentences

Directions: Combine each pair of sentences to form a sentence with a compound subject or a compound predicate, or to form a compound sentence. Use the joining word *and, but,* or *or.* Write each new sentence.

1. I am the oldest child in my family. I am not the tallest.

____

2. My younger brother Josh is taller than I am. My younger brother Sam is taller than I am.

____

3. I have more responsibilities than my brothers and sister. I do more chores than my brothers and sister.

____

4. My mother expects me to make snacks for my siblings after school. I have to make sure they start their homework right away.

____

____

5. I return our library books on my way home from school. I buy fresh bread for dinner.

____

____

6. My dad broke his leg last year. He wasn't able to do many of the things around the house that he normally does.

____

____

7. The doctor said he had to stay in bed. He could sit in a chair with his leg elevated and watch TV.

____

____

8. My brothers wanted to be helpful to our dad. They weren't sure how.

____

9. We had a big celebration for my dad the day his cast was taken off. We made a cake for my dad the day his cast was taken off.

____

____

Notes for Home: Your child wrote compound sentences and sentences with compound subjects and predicates. ***Home Activity:*** Have your child look at a story that he or she enjoyed as a young child. Have your child combine simple sentences from the story to form compound sentences.

Name ______________________

Phonics: Complex Spelling Patterns

Directions: Read the words in the box. They may look alike, but they have very different vowel sounds. Read the words to the left. Match each word to the left with a word from the box that has the same vowel sound. Write the word on the line.

through	thought	though

1. taught ______________
2. throw ______________
3. threw ______________

Directions: Read the words in the box. Match them with the words below that have the same vowel sound. Write the words on the lines.

bought	dough	sought	soup	soul	coupon

4. thought ______________ ______________
5. though ______________ ______________
6. through ______________ ______________

Directions: Read each sentence. Say the underlined word to yourself. Circle the word in ( ) that has the same vowel sound as the underlined word.

7. Although it was getting late, they didn't want to leave Marcie alone. (bought/boulder)
8. She thought everyone was kind for trying to make her feel better. (caught/count)
9. After the death of her uncle, her emotions went through many changes. (though/rule)
10. No one thought she was insensitive for not being able to express her feelings. (foul/fought)
11. Everyone tried to be a little cheerful, even though the occasion was a somber one. (bowl/brought)
12. It helps to have friends around to get you through the good times and the bad times. (know/knew)

Directions: Write a sentence for each of these words: **through, thought, though.**

13. ______________________________
14. ______________________________
15. ______________________________

Notes for Home: Your child identified the different vowel sounds for words with *ough,* such as *through, thought,* and *though.* ***Home Activity:*** Write several *ough* words on separate slips of paper. Have your child read each word and use it in a sentence.

Name ____________________

Pretest

Spelling: Getting Letters in Correct Order

Pretest Directions: Fold back the page along the dotted line. On the blanks, write the spelling words as they are dictated. When you have finished the test, unfold the page and check your words.

1. ____________________
2. ____________________
3. ____________________
4. ____________________
5. ____________________
6. ____________________
7. ____________________
8. ____________________
9. ____________________
10. ____________________
11. ____________________
12. ____________________
13. ____________________
14. ____________________
15. ____________________
16. ____________________
17. ____________________
18. ____________________
19. ____________________
20. ____________________

1. Her **poetry** is wonderful.
2. I smelled a **beautiful** flower.
3. His sister is **thirteen** years old.
4. The cat has a scratchy **tongue**.
5. Some **pieces** of candy were left.
6. I've saved two **thousand** dollars.
7. We walked **through** the park.
8. What an **unusual** story!
9. The **building** was torn down.
10. Mrs. Patel got a fishing **license**.
11. They will **remodel** the house.
12. She was **grateful** for the help.
13. I'm your friend, not your **enemy**.
14. What **instrument** do you play?
15. A jazz band will **perform**.
16. Do you **prefer** milk or juice?
17. My mother **judged** the dog show.
18. He **adjusted** the recliner.
19. The **soldier** laid down his gun.
20. My **neighborhood** is nearby.

Notes for Home: Your child took a pretest on words with difficult letter combinations. ***Home Activity:*** Help your child learn misspelled words before the final test. See if there are any similar errors and discuss a memory trick that could help.

Name ______________________________

Spelling: Getting Letters in Correct Order

Word List			
poetry	neighborhood	license	perform
beautiful	thousand	remodel	prefer
thirteen	through	grateful	judged
tongue	unusual	enemy	adjusted
pieces	building	instrument	soldier

Directions: Choose the word from the box that is the base word of each word below. Write the word on the line.

1. preferably ______________
2. gratefulness ______________
3. licensed ______________
4. performance ______________
5. instrumental ______________
6. beautifully ______________
7. remodeling ______________
8. thirteenth ______________

Directions: Choose the word from the box that completes each equation. Write the word on the line.

9. thought – ght + sand = ______________
10. un + use – e + ual = ______________
11. poem – m + try = ______________
12. ad + justify – ify + ed = ______________
13. pie + crust – rust + es = ______________
14. judgment – ment + ed = ______________
15. neigh + boring – ing + hood = ______________
16. sole – e + diet – t + r = ______________
17. tongs – s + ue = ______________
18. the – e + rough = ______________
19. energy – rgy + my = ______________
20. built – t + ding = ______________

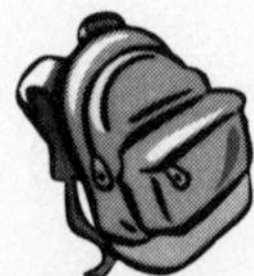

Notes for Home: Your child spelled words with letter combinations that are hard to keep in order. ***Home Activity:*** Have your child spell each spelling word aloud. If your child mixes up some letters, give a spelling hint that will help him or her remember the correct spelling.

Name ______________________

Spelling: Getting Letters in Correct Order

Directions: Proofread this letter about a family crisis. Find seven spelling mistakes. Use the proofreading marks to correct each mistake.

≡	Make a capital.
/	Make a small letter.
∧	Add something.
℘	Take out something.
⊙	Add a period.
¶	Begin a new paragraph.

Dear Jane,

You won't believe what happened. My father decided to remodal the bedroom himself. "You don't need a lisence to put in a couple of windows," he said.

I perfer not to think about it. I can still hear the unuzual sound he made as he fell. The sound echoed right thorugh our building. We are greatful to the people in the nieghborhood who came running. The window had broken into a thousand pieces. Luckily, the only thing seriously hurt was Dad's pride.

Write soon,

Rafael

Spelling Tip

through **prefer**

Your spelling words contain letters that are hard to keep in order. Study the Word List carefully before proofreading the letter.

Word List

poetry
beautiful
thirteen
tongue
pieces
neighborhood
thousand
through
unusual
building
license
remodel
grateful
enemy
instrument
perform
prefer
judged
adjusted
soldier

Write a Letter

Imagine you are Jane. On a separate sheet of paper, write a letter to Rafael describing a family crisis and how it was solved. Try to use at least five of your spelling words.

Notes for Home: Your child spelled words with letter combinations that are hard to keep in order. ***Home Activity:*** Help your child to make up sentences that contain the words *perform* and *pieces.* Have your child check his or her sentences to see that all words are correctly spelled.

Name ______________________________

Spelling: Getting Letters in Correct Order

REVIEW

Word List

poetry	pieces	unusual	grateful	prefer
beautiful	neighborhood	building	enemy	judged
thirteen	thousand	license	instrument	adjusted
tongue	through	remodel	perform	soldier

Directions: Choose the word from the box that best matches each clue. Write the word on the line.

______________________ **1.** I am what the parts of a jigsaw puzzle are called.

______________________ **2.** I am ten hundreds.

______________________ **3.** I am a person who serves in the army.

______________________ **4.** I am always between twelve and fourteen.

______________________ **5.** I am needed for speech.

______________________ **6.** I am something or someone who tries to harm.

______________________ **7.** I am a permit that allows a person to drive.

______________________ **8.** I am a group of words that sometimes rhyme.

______________________ **9.** I am both a place to live and a game played with blocks.

______________________ **10.** I am something with which you can make music.

Directions: Choose the word from the box that best matches each definition. Write the word on the line.

______________________ **11.** community or area

______________________ **12.** strange

______________________ **13.** decided or concluded from evidence

______________________ **14.** like better

______________________ **15.** thankful

______________________ **16.** lovely

______________________ **17.** make over

______________________ **18.** act or carry out

______________________ **19.** in one side and out the other

______________________ **20.** changed or fixed slightly

Notes for Home: Your child spelled words with combinations of letters that are hard to keep in order. ***Home Activity:*** Encourage your child to find as many shorter words within the words in the list as possible. For example, *instrument* contains *in* and *strum.*

Name ______________________________

Telephone Directory

A **telephone directory** is a book with entries listed alphabetically by last name of a person or by the name of a business. The **white pages** lists telephone numbers and addresses of individuals and businesses. The **yellow pages** lists phone numbers, addresses, and advertisements of businesses. It is arranged alphabetically by category of business.

Directions: Use the following section of the yellow pages to answer the questions on the next page.

145 Movers—Newspapers

Movers

Great Bear Moving and Storage
30 Morocco St 555-5645

Jack and Jill Movers
315 3rd St 555-9080

Moonstone Movers Inc
82 College Ave 555-1309

Two Guys Movers
200 4th St 555-9008

Where or When Movers Inc
3 College Ave 555-5536

Music Instruction

Arbor Music School
321 7th St 555-6710

Music—Sheet

Napoleon's Guitars
67 7th St 555-8971

Phantom Music Inc
333 7th St 555-4439

Scores and More
352 2nd St 555-1130

Musical Instruments—Repairs

Napoleon's Guitars
67 7th St 555-7322

Poliuto's Pianos
69 7th St 555-1083

Musical Instruments—Sales

Napoleon's Guitars
67 7th St 555-4445

Poliuto's Pianos
69 7th St 555-0102

We've Got Rhythm

No one has a larger selection of rhythm and percussion instruments than we do!

Monday–Friday, 10 A.M. to 6 P.M.
Saturday, 1:00 P.M. to 8 P.M.

Free drum lesson, Saturdays at 1 P.M.

208 Garfield Place
(near Westwood Mall)
555-1782

Newspapers

The Daily Yell
74 College Avenue 555-6543

The Mirror
85 College Avenue 555-3548
Advertisements 555-0762
Arts Desk 555-9398
City Desk 555-8285
Copy Chief 555-5301
Sports Desk 555-5324

The Tribune
99 College Avenue 555-9021

Name ______________________

1. What business categories are listed?

2. Are these entries near the beginning, middle, or end of the yellow pages? Explain.

3. Which of the newspapers listed is probably the largest? Why do you think so?

4. Would you turn ahead or back in the directory to find a plumber? Why?

5. Can you purchase a guitar and have one repaired at the same shop? Explain.

6. Which business uses an advertisement? What information does the advertisement give that the other listings do not give?

7. Would Vicky Austin's phone number be in the white pages or the yellow pages? Explain.

8. Would you look in the white pages or the yellow pages if you needed the phone number for a locksmith? Explain.

9. If you lived on Third Street, where would you go to buy sheet music? Why?

10. Many directories will list emergency numbers at the front of the directory in a separate section. Why do you think this information is listed this way?

Notes for Home: Your child answered questions about a telephone directory. ***Home Activity:*** Take turns saying a person's name or a name or type of business. Use the white pages or yellow pages to find each listing.

Name ______________________________

Story Organizer

Directions: Fill in the graphic organizer with information about the event or experience that you plan to write about.

Possible title: ______________________________

Event: ______________________________

When? ______________________________

Where? ______________________________

Details

1. ______________________________

2. ______________________________

3. ______________________________

4. ______________________________

How did it end? ______________________________

Notes for Home: Your child planned a personal narrative. ***Home Activity:*** Have your child tell you about the experience he or she is writing about. Ask for details and explore the range of emotions.

Name ______________________________

Elaboration
Add Details

- When you write, you can elaborate by **adding vivid and specific details** that help readers picture your subject more clearly.
- You can provide precise details by telling how things look, sound, feel, taste, and smell.

Directions: Read the sentences about a basketball game. Then use vivid, precise words to add details to each sentence. Use the phrases from the box for ideas for your sentences. Write the new sentences on the lines.

grabbed	charged	ticks of the clock
roared with excitement	three-point shot	sky high
like a glove	swished	jump shot

1. There were only six seconds left.

____

2. Kathy jumped for the ball.

____

3. I caught the rebound.

____

4. On defense, she covered me closely.

____

5. She ran right into me.

____

6. She made a long shot at the buzzer.

____

7. The ball went through the net.

____

8. The crowd cheered.

____

Notes for Home: Your child used vivid, precise words to add details to sentences. ***Home Activity:*** Invite your child to give you an oral description of the end of this game, pretending he or she is a sports announcer.

Name ____

Self-Evaluation Guide

Personal Narrative Checklist

Directions: Think about the final draft of your personal narrative. Then answer each question below.

	Yes	No	Not sure
1. Does my narrative flow smoothly from beginning to middle to end?			
2. Did I use enough details to let my audience know how I feel about the event?			
3. Did I keep my audience and purpose in mind?			
4. Did I use vivid words to express myself?			
5. Did I proofread and edit carefully to avoid errors?			

6. Which sentence of your personal narrative uses the most precise, vivid words? Copy it here.

____

____

____

7. If you were asked to write a sequel, or continuation, of your personal narrative, what would you write about?

____

____

____

____

____

Notes for Home: Your child has just completed a self-evaluation of a personal narrative. ***Home Activity:*** Discuss with your child what he or she would do differently if he or she could rewrite this personal narrative.

Family Times

Name________________________________

Summary

Crows May Be Smarter Than You Think!

Some people think that crows are nothing more than birds that eat farmers' crops. But in "A Trouble-Making Crow," Jean Craighead George shows that crows are not just simple birds. She tells about her pet crows and scientific studies. Crows are clever. They can hide, count, and can communicate with other crows. They can also learn to talk, just as parrots do.

Activity

Draw a Comic Strip. Have your child tell you what he or she learned about crows from reading "A Trouble-Making Crow." Encourage your child to draw a comic strip that shows one of Crowbar George's adventures, such as stealing picnic food or playing with the children. Help your child to include captions, speech balloons, or thought balloons.

Reading Skills

Making Judgments

When you read, you often **make judgments.** In other words, you form opinions about characters, actions, or ideas. You also read judgments that the author makes.

Test judgments by looking for supporting evidence in the story. For instance, Jean Craighead George makes the judgment that crows are clever. She presents evidence to support this judgment, such as the behavior of her pet crows and studies of crows. What judgment would you make about crows after reading the story? What evidence supports your judgment?

Activity

You Be the Judge! Select a list of activities, such as household chores, shopping, working in the garden, or watching movies. Together, judge the activities according to enjoyability on a scale of one to five. Discuss the reasons for your judgments. Add and judge other activities.

Family Times

Tested Vocabulary

Words to Know

Knowing the meanings of these words is important to reading "A Trouble-Making Crow." Practice using these words to learn their meanings.

aggressive ready to attack or to take by force

attributes qualities or characteristics

outwit outsmart

persisted refused to stop

secretive not open; sneaky

tolerated put up with

vengeance revenge

Grammar

Proper Nouns and Common Nouns

Nouns that name particular persons, places, and things are called **proper nouns.** Each important word in a proper noun begins with a capital letter.

Nouns that do not refer to any particular person, place, or thing are called **common nouns.**

Common Noun	Proper Noun
pet	Crowbar George
country	United States of America
uncle	Uncle Karl

Activity

Who, What, Where? Give your child a common noun, such as *doctor, planet,* or *stadium.* Challenge him or her to come up with a matching proper noun, such as *Dr. Martinez, Mars,* or *Comiskey Park.*

Tested Spelling Words

____________	____________	____________	____________
____________	____________	____________	____________
____________	____________	____________	____________
____________	____________	____________	____________
____________	____________	____________	____________

Name ______________________________

Making Judgments

- **Making a judgment** means forming an opinion about someone or something.
- When you make a judgment, you think about your own experiences and beliefs, as well as the information the author provides.
- When an author expresses a judgment about someone or something, test the author's judgment by looking for evidence to support it.

Directions: Reread "The Truth About Wolves." Then complete the table. Tell what judgments the author expresses about lions and wolves and the evidence he provides to support each judgment. Then answer the question below.

The Author's Judgment About . . .	Supporting Evidence
Dogs: Dogs are humans' best friends.	Dogs are friendly, loyal, intelligent, and playful.
Lions: 1.	**2.**
Wolves: 3.	**4.**

5. Do you agree with the author's judgment about wolves? Does the author support his judgment well?

____

____

____

Notes for Home: Your child identified judgments made by an author, and then made his or her own judgments about the author's ideas. ***Home Activity:*** Help your child identify the judgments expressed in a newspaper editorial. Check whether the judgments are supported.

Name ______________________________

Vocabulary

Directions: Choose the word from the box that best matches each definition. Write the word on the line.

Check the Words You Know
___ aggressive
___ attributes
___ outwit
___ persisted
___ secretive
___ tolerated
___ vengeance

______________________ **1.** refused to stop

______________________ **2.** very active; not passive

______________________ **3.** revenge

______________________ **4.** qualities or characteristics

______________________ **5.** not open; having secrets

Directions: Choose the word from the box that best completes each sentence. Write the word on the line to the left. Then find and circle the words in the puzzle below. Words may appear across, down, or diagonally.

______________________ **6.** Tom Cat knew that the package on the counter contained fish. An experienced cat burgular like himself knew well the delicious _____ of fresh fish.

______________________ **7.** He did not want Teeter, the kitten, in on the heist, so he was very _____.

______________________ **8.** Tom planned to _____ the kitten and get the fish all for himself.

______________________ **9.** He wasn't afraid of Teeter's _____.

______________________ **10.** He was patient and _____ Teeter, but he didn't think the kitten was very smart.

Q U J A L F P F S R E A B B M
A T T R I B U T E S V Z T J U
I D E B T V F I C A T I O N W
L U I A X Y J E R R O I L H N
P Z H I Q J T C E G V I E B Z
B K E O U T W I T F L A R X E
I W H J D T U I I X S S A H K
N Y I R B E A L V H Z E T T O
T I J Z V E N G E A N C E E Q
A J U W I M L Y Z G F D D L D

Write a Story

On a separate sheet of paper, write a story about a character (an animal or imaginary person) who wants something so badly that he or she is willing to trick others to get it. Use as many vocabulary words as you can.

Notes for Home: Your child identified and used vocabulary words from "A Trouble-Making Crow." ***Home Activity:*** Think of fictional characters from a book or a movie that you or your child can describe using the vocabulary words.

Name ____________________

Making Judgments

- **Making a judgment** means forming an opinion about someone or something.
- When you make a judgment, you think about your own experiences and beliefs, as well as the information the author provides.
- As you read, look for evidence to support your judgments or the author's judgments.

Directions: Reread what happens in "A Trouble-Making Crow" after Craig's mother tells him that the crow New York has to go. Then answer the questions below. Think about what happens in the story to help you make judgments.

"People come first," I said. "How would you feel if Hilde was blinded by our crow?"

His eyes widened as he understood the seriousness of New York's vengeance.

"I don't want to kill him," I said. "I want to take him far away and let him go—far from Hilde."

"Will he dive at anyone else's eyes?"

"No. Hilde must have kicked him or hurt him somehow, and he's taking it out on her. He won't forget. Crows are like that."

Craig ran into the yard to find New York, and I went to the cellar for an animal carrying case.

1. Do you think it would make sense to kill New York? Explain your answer.

____

2. Do you think that the mother's decision to let New York go free is fair? Explain.

____

____

3. Do you think Craig's mother understands animal behavior? Why?

____

____

4. Does Craig understand his mother's decision? How do you know?

____

____

5. Think about the story of Dr. Kalmbach's crow at the end of "A Trouble-Making Crow." On a separate sheet of paper, explain how the story affected your opinion of what Craig's mother did about New York.

Notes for Home: Your child used story details to make judgments about characters and actions. ***Home Activity:*** With your child, make judgments about characters or actions in a movie you've seen or a book you've read together.

Selection Test

Directions: Choose the best answer to each item. Mark the letter for the answer you have chosen.

Part 1: Vocabulary

Find the answer choice that means about the same as the underlined word in each sentence.

1. The old dog tolerated the puppy.
- A. chased after
- B. looked for
- C. played with
- D. put up with

2. Sharon persisted for five days.
- F. got better
- G. refused to stop
- H. went away
- J. studied hard

3. Margo has many good attributes.
- A. faults
- B. feelings or emotions
- C. qualities or characteristics
- D. ways to help others

4. Sam cannot outwit his brother.
- F. be more clever than
- G. act friendly toward
- H. catch by surprise
- J. run faster than

5. Members of the club are very secretive.
- A. talking for a long time
- B. special in a certain way
- C. not open; keeping things hidden from others
- D. proud of themselves

6. The dog seemed to want vengeance.
- F. revenge
- G. comfort
- H. warmth
- J. safety

7. The tennis player made an aggressive move toward his opponent.
- A. friendly
- B. ready to attack
- C. brief
- D. quiet or shy

Part 2: Comprehension

Use what you know about the selection to answer each item.

8. New York got into trouble because he—
- F. stole some food.
- G. took money from children.
- H. tore cabbage leaves.
- J. dived at a child's eyes.

9. According to this selection, crows know how to—
- A. sing songs with words.
- B. polish shoes.
- C. avoid danger.
- D. give directions.

10. The George family began to teach Crowbar to talk just after—
- F. Crowbar said hello at a picnic.
- G. they read about how crows are like parrots.
- H. the man delivering milk heard him say hello.
- J. a police officer tried to scare him away.

11. Who is Hilde?
- A. a pet crow
- B. one of the author's children
- C. one of the author's pet salamanders
- D. a girl who lives in the neighborhood

GO ON

12. Which example offers the best proof that crows are intelligent?
- F. A crow that caws three times is identifying itself.
- G. Crowbar ate a piece of cold cheeseburger.
- H. New York flew into Baird Park and did not return.
- J. Crowbar used a lid to slide with the children.

13. Crows do not make good pets because they—
- A. seek revenge against those who hurt them.
- B. can pick out one person in a crowd.
- C. can learn to talk.
- D. are able to count.

14. Most of the time, the author describes and reacts to the pets in her house as if they were—
- F. wild animals.
- G. friends.
- H. scientific experiments.
- J. celebrities.

15. At the end of the story, the author feels sad because she—
- A. is afraid of the large flock of crows.
- B. is happy that Crowbar will not bother her anymore.
- C. will miss Crowbar.
- D. worries that the wild crows will hurt Crowbar.

STOP

Making Judgments

- **Making a judgment** means forming an opinion about someone or something.
- When you make a judgment, you think about your own experiences and beliefs, as well as the information the author provides.
- As you read, look for evidence to support your judgments or the author's judgments.

Directions: Read the story below.

Like most dogs, Myra is gentle and quiet. But recently she developed a problem. Every once in a while, she would start to bark and run around the living room as if something were driving her crazy.

Grandpa worried that Myra might hurt the baby. He thought we should keep Myra in a separate room. But Mom, Dad, and I didn't think there was danger.

I watched Myra carefully. I noticed that every time she acted strangely, Grandpa was in the house listening to his favorite CD of loud marching bands. It was the music that was upsetting Myra! So we asked Grandpa not to play that CD when Myra was in the house. Grandpa cheerfully agreed.

Directions: Complete the table by finishing the judgments made or by giving reasons to support a judgment.

Judgment	Reason for Judgment
I think the narrator of the story is intelligent and observant.	**1.**
2. I think Grandpa's idea about keeping Myra out was:	Myra only barked when the music was on.
3. I think the solution of not playing the music when Myra is in the house is:	**4.**
I think that Grandpa is reasonable.	**5.**

Notes for Home: Your child used story details to make judgments about characters and actions. ***Home Activity:*** Have your child choose a favorite story. Together, decide whether a character's actions and ideas are fair or good.

Name ______________________________

REVIEW

Paraphrasing

Directions: Read the passage. Then read each question about the passage. Choose the best answer to each question. Mark the letter for the answer you have chosen.

The Crow Family

The crow family is a group of large black birds. Crows, jays, jackdaws, magpies, ravens, and rooks are all members of this family.

The common crow has glossy black feathers and a strong bill with a sharp point. Crows have strong feet that are good for walking. Male and female crows look very much alike, but the female is a little bit smaller.

Crows are highly intelligent. A crow can be a good pet if the owner obtains the crow when the crow is young. Most people recognize a crow's harsh cry, *"Caw! Caw!"* The crow can make many other noises. Sometimes people can teach crows to speak a few words.

Crows are attracted by shiny objects. They pick up stray coins, lost earrings, and any other small shiny things they find. Crows will keep these small treasures forever. They always have places where they hide their growing collections. They are famous for their habit of hoarding things.

Crows are found all over the world, except in New Zealand. The common crow is seen in many parts of North America. In recent years, crows have even become more common in big cities like New York City.

1. Which of the following statements accurately paraphrases information in the passage?
- **A.** There is only one kind of crow.
- **B.** Magpies, ravens, rooks are the only kinds of crows.
- **C.** There are many kinds of crows.
- **D.** No crows make good pets.

2. Which of the following statements accurately paraphrases information in the passage?
- **F.** Crows can't walk.
- **G.** Male and female crows are the same size.
- **H.** The common crow has black feathers.
- **J.** The crow's bill isn't pointed.

3. A crow—
- **A.** can't be a good pet.
- **B.** can make a good pet if disciplined.
- **C.** can be trained to be a pet at any age.
- **D.** can be a good pet if you get it when it is young.

4. A crow—
- **F.** can sometimes have a large vocabulary.
- **G.** can sometimes learn to say a few words.
- **H.** cannot imitate sounds.
- **J.** makes one noise.

5. The common crow—
- **A.** lives everywhere but New Zealand.
- **B.** lives everywhere but North America.
- **C.** lives only in New Zealand.
- **D.** lives only in North America.

Notes for Home: Your child chose statements that paraphrased information in a nonfiction article. ***Home Activity:*** With your child, read a few paragraphs of a newspaper or magazine article. Have your child restate each paragraph in his or her own words.

Name ____________________

Writing Across Texts

Directions: Consider what you learned about crows in the two selections "A Trouble-Making Crow" and "The Crow and the Pitcher." What are some of the characteristics of a crow? Add five examples to the web below.

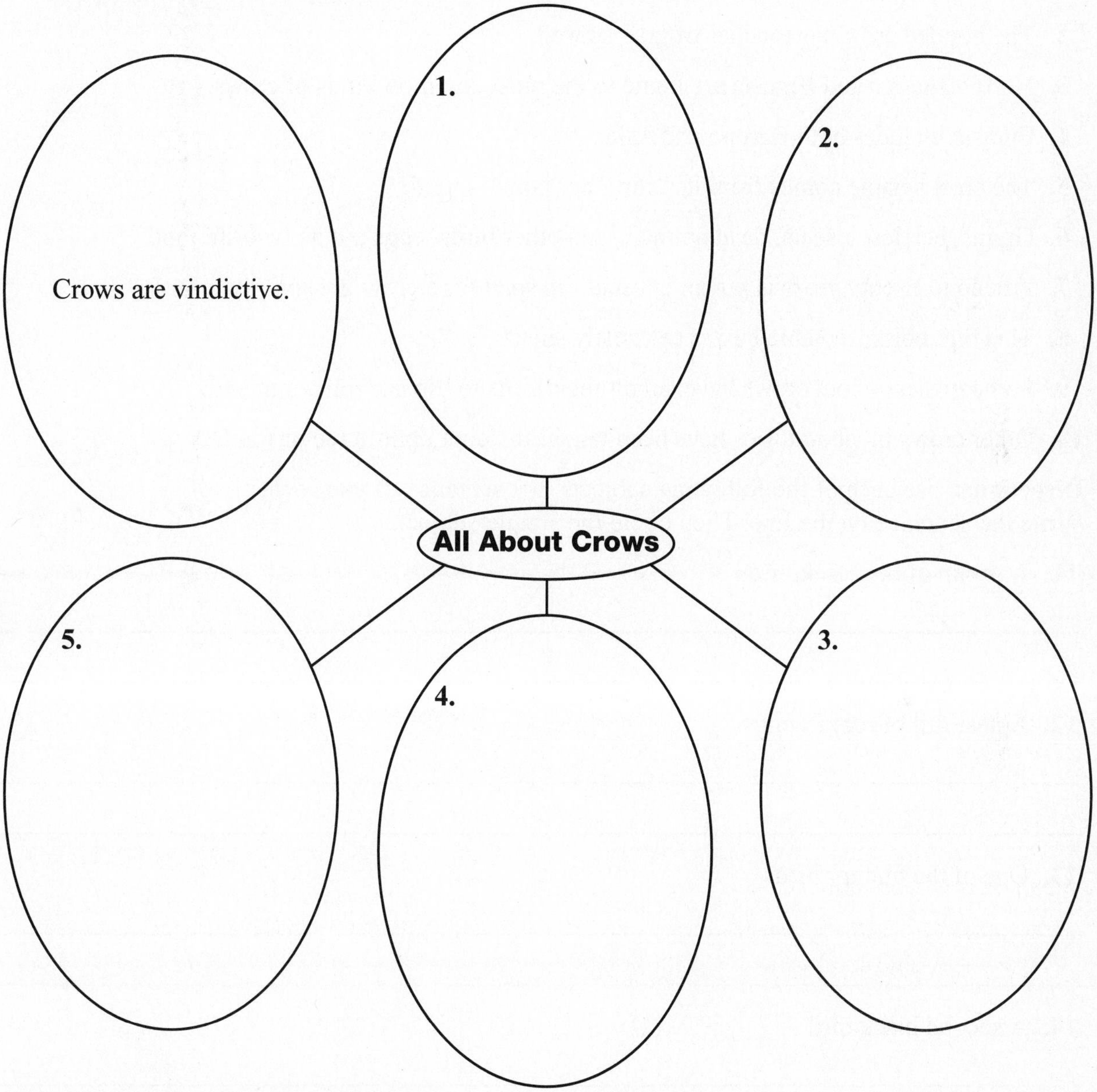

All About Crows

Crows are vindictive.

1.

2.

3.

4.

5.

Write an Encyclopedia Article

Use the completed web and the selections "A Trouble-Making Crow" and "The Crow and the Pitcher" to write an encyclopedia article about the characteristics of crows. Write your article on a separate sheet of paper.

Notes for Home: Your child has used two different sources to complete a web and write an encyclopedia article. ***Home Activity:*** Read other stories or articles about animals. Encourage your child to create a similar web and use it to name the characteristics of other animals.

Name ______________________________

Grammar: Subjects

REVIEW

Directions: Underline the complete subject in each sentence. Then circle the simple subject. (There may be more than one simple subject in a sentence.)

1. All crows have feathers of a glossy black color.
2. The hooded crow has touches of gray as well.
3. North America and Eurasia are home to the most common kinds of crows.
4. Eurasia includes both Europe and Asia.
5. The crow's name comes from its "caw" or "craw" sound.
6. Grains, berries, insects, dead animals, and other birds' eggs are its favorite food.
7. Fifteen to twenty years is not an unusual life span for a crow in captivity.
8. This big, noisy, sociable bird is extremely smart.
9. Some owners of pet crows have taught their birds to "speak" on command.
10. Other crows in laboratories have been taught to count up to three or four.

Directions: Use each of the following subjects in a sentence of your own. Write the sentence on the line. Then circle the simple subject.

11. A group of big black birds

____

____

12. A nest full of robin's eggs

____

____

13. One of the hungry birds

____

____

14. A second black bird

____

____

15. A female robin and then the male

____

____

Notes for Home: Your child recognized simple and complete subjects and used them in sentences. ***Home Activity:*** Look through a newspaper, magazine, or book with your child. Encourage your child to find the simple and complete subjects of sentences.

Practice

Grammar: Proper Nouns and Common Nouns

A noun names one or more persons, places, or things (Things include ideas.). A **proper noun** is the name of a *particular* person, place, or thing: *Anne D. Gray, Texas, Tuesday,* and *Dr. Fiorenza* are proper nouns.

A proper noun, such as *Martin Luther King Jr. School,* may consist of more than one word. Begin each important word in a proper noun with a capital letter.

Nouns that are not proper nouns are called **common nouns.** A common noun does not name any particular person, place, or thing. The words *sister, state,* and *day,* are common nouns. Common nouns are not capitalized.

Directions: Underline the nouns in each sentence. If a noun is a proper noun, underline it twice.

1. A flock of crows lives near the open meadow.

2. Each morning joggers can hear these birds all over Central Park.

3. When Mrs. Wall is walking her terrier nearby, the crows sound an alarm.

4. "Mr. Jet" is my name for the crow with the harshest voice.

5. His nest is high in the tallest evergreen near Turtle Pond.

6. Students from Barnard College check their guides to local birds.

7. Roger Tory Peterson wrote five guides for birdwatchers.

8. Do ravens really live at the Tower of London?

9. In Manhattan, falcons lay their eggs on the ledges of skyscrapers.

10. Gyrfalcons are found at the Arctic Circle, not in New York City.

Directions: Write **C** if the noun is a common noun. Write **P** if the noun is a proper noun. If it is a proper noun, rewrite it correctly on the line.

11. field ____________

12. hoyt park ____________

13. labor day ____________

14. binoculars ____________

15. mr. a. p. finney ____________

Notes for Home: Your child identified proper nouns and common nouns. ***Home Activity:*** Just for fun, challenge your child to try to speak for five minutes without using *any* nouns.

Extra Practice

Grammar: Proper Nouns and Common Nouns

Directions: Underline the nouns in each sentence. If a noun is a proper noun, underline it twice.

1. Our family visited Maine this summer.
2. The trip began with a drive up the coast to a town called Camden.
3. Kennebunkport and Bangor are full of shops and restaurants.
4. The next stop was at Acadia National Park.
5. Outstanding features of the trip were Thunder Hole and Cadillac Mountain.

Directions: Rewrite each sentence on the lines below. Capitalize all proper nouns.

6. The ocean was spectacular that day, and acadia park was beautiful.

____

____

7. Dad drove through washington county to nova scotia.

____

____

8. The bay of fundy is an unusual body of water.

____

____

9. Because of the shape of this bay, which is in canada, the tide comes in suddenly.

____

____

10. A 42-foot wall of water rushes in from the atlantic ocean in just minutes!

____

____

Write About a Place

Write a paragraph or two describing the town or city where you live. Name a few points of interest, such as parks or buildings, and explain why they are important. Use at least three common nouns and three proper nouns.

Notes for Home: Your child identified proper nouns and common nouns and capitalized proper nouns. ***Home Activity:*** Together, write a variety of common and proper nouns on slips of paper. Take turns with your child drawing slips and using the noun in a sentence.

Name ______________________________

Grammar: Proper Nouns and Common Nouns

RETEACHING

Draw a line to join each common noun on the left with a proper noun on the right.

Common Noun	Proper Noun
inventor	New Jersey
month	Thomas Alva Edison
state	February

A **common noun** names any of a kind of person, place, or thing. A **proper noun** names a particular person, place, or thing. Proper nouns always begin with capital letters.

Directions: Write **common noun** or **proper noun** to describe the underlined word.

1. Thomas Edison invented the lightbulb. ______________
2. Thomas Alva Edison was born in Ohio in 1847. ______________
3. He was educated at home by his mother. ______________
4. At age twelve he was a newsboy. ______________
5. Edison later worked on a train in Michigan. ______________

Directions: Underline the common nouns and proper nouns in each sentence.

6. Edison patented over a thousand inventions.
7. Where did the busy inventor work in America?
8. The laboratory was in New Jersey.
9. His phonograph was famous in Europe.
10. Thomas Edison helped to invent movies.

Directions: Copy the nouns you underlined in items 6–10. Write each one in the correct column.

Common Nouns	Proper Nouns
11. ______________	12. ______________
13. ______________	14. ______________
15. ______________	16. ______________
17. ______________	18. ______________
19. ______________	20. ______________

Notes for Home: Your child identified and categorized common nouns and proper nouns. ***Home Activity:*** Together, write a list of nouns that name persons, places, and things in your home. Have your child capitalize proper nouns correctly.

Name ______________________________

Grammar: Proper Nouns and Common Nouns

Directions: Read the paragraph. Write each underlined noun in the correct column.

Do you know about the huge statues of heads on Easter Island? Easter Island is located in the South Pacific west of Chile. Scientists do not know much about the background of the statues. There are more than 600 of these giant heads with long ears. Jacob Roggeven first saw the carved giants in 1722. The heads weigh fifty tons and do not look like the Polynesians on this Pacific island.

Common Nouns	Proper Nouns
1. ____________	2. ____________
3. ____________	4. ____________
5. ____________	6. ____________
7. ____________	8. ____________
9. ____________	10. ____________

Directions: Underline each common noun once and each proper noun twice.

11. The statues on Easter Island are made of red stone.

12. Some statues are over 40 feet and weigh 90 tons.

13. Islanders carved the statues from the rock of extinct volcanoes.

14. The builders of these figures are still unknown to the experts.

15. Thor Heyerdahl sailed to Easter Island on a raft.

16. This explorer from Norway studied the currents of the Pacific Ocean.

17. Heyerdahl wrote an interesting book about the monuments.

18. This book contains ideas about the mystery of the lonely island in the Pacific.

19. Today its population includes many Chileans.

20. The librarian will find the book for the class.

Write an Announcement

On a separate sheet of paper, write an announcement about a discovery you made, such as an unusual stone or a special place. Before you begin writing, think about what you were doing right before you made the discovery. Then start to write. Tell what you discovered and where you found it. Use common and proper nouns.

Notes for Home: Your child has identified common nouns and proper nouns and capitalized proper nouns correctly. ***Home Activity:*** Have your child read his or her announcement. Then have him or her underline common nouns and circle proper nouns.

Name ______________________

Phonics: Consonant Sounds for *c* and *g*

Directions: Read the sentences below. Two words in each sentence have the letter **c.** Circle the word with the **hard-c** sound as in **cold.** Underline the word with the **soft-c** sound as in **place.**

1. We were certain the country would be a great spot for our day off.
2. We saw a large bird sitting on the fence while we had our picnic.
3. Seeing a wild crow was a new experience for our family.
4. The bird eventually escaped our stares by flying to a nearby spruce tree.
5. No matter how we coaxed, the bird would not leave its place up high.

Directions: Read the sentences below. Two words in each sentence have the letter **g.** One has a **hard-g** sound as in **go.** The other word has a **soft-g** sound as in **gentle.** Circle the words with the **hard-g** sound. Underline the words with the **soft-g** sound.

6. Sometimes several crows would hide in the garden among the cabbages.
7. The crows gathered around looking for food like scavengers.
8. The birds seemed to beg urgently with their loud squawks.
9. It appeared as if the huge crow was the leader of the group.
10. Large crows can be very aggressive sometimes.

Directions: Read the sentences below. Each underlined word has both a **c** and a **g.** Circle the two words in each group that have the same consonant sounds as the **c** and **g** in the underlined word.

11. I did not <u>recognize</u> the calls of the little crow when I first heard it.

    cat trance goat giant

12. The baby bird had fallen between the <u>cabbage</u> leaves and was calling for help.

    fence frantic good giant

13. We <u>encouraged</u> the crow to fly off on its own.

    cellar complex forgive page

14. It took a few hops, then it <u>gracefully</u> flew to a tree branch.

    gate gem corn stance

15. Although some people may not like crows, it's hard to imagine that the gentle bird we saw would ever seek <u>vengeance</u>.

    frog stage certain picnic

Notes for Home: Your child identified the sounds that the letters *c* and *g* can represent, such as *go, cabbage* (hard g, soft g), *crow, fence* (hard c, soft c). ***Home Activity:*** Read a book about animals with your child. Find words with these letters and have your child say them aloud.

Name ____________________

Pretest

Spelling: Words from Many Cultures

Pretest Directions: Fold back the page along the dotted line. On the blanks, write the spelling words as they are dictated. When you have finished the test, unfold the page and check your words.

1. ____________	1. The **moose** has huge antlers.
2. ____________	2. We saw a **cobra** at the zoo.
3. ____________	3. The **alligator** lives in a swamp.
4. ____________	4. I want **vanilla** ice cream.
5. ____________	5. He has never eaten a **banana**.
6. ____________	6. **Tomato** sauce can stain clothing.
7. ____________	7. Please use a lot of **mustard**.
8. ____________	8. Her parents learned the **hula**.
9. ____________	9. What's in your **picnic** basket?
10. ____________	10. Let's have a **barbecue**.
11. ____________	11. It isn't wise to pet a **crocodile**.
12. ____________	12. The **coyote** barked at the birds.
13. ____________	13. A **koala** lives in this big tree.
14. ____________	14. She likes **macaroni** and cheese.
15. ____________	15. Please pass me the **catsup**.
16. ____________	16. They danced the **polka** all night.
17. ____________	17. We are going to the **ballet**.
18. ____________	18. My parents like to **waltz**.
19. ____________	19. We ate at a **banquet** hall.
20. ____________	20. I made two trips to the **buffet**.

Notes for Home: Your child took a pretest on words that come from other languages. ***Home Activity:*** Help your child learn misspelled words before the final test. Your child should look at the word, say it, spell it aloud, and then spell it with eyes shut.

Think and Practice

Spelling: Words from Many Cultures

Word List				
moose	banana	picnic	koala	ballet
cobra	tomato	barbecue	macaroni	waltz
alligator	mustard	crocodile	catsup	banquet
vanilla	hula	coyote	polka	buffet

Directions: Write the words from the box that belong in each group.

Animals	Things to Eat	Dances
1. ________	7. ________	13. ________
2. ________	8. ________	14. ________
3. ________	9. ________	15. ________
4. ________	10. ________	16. ________
5. ________	11. ________	
6. ________	12. ________	

Directions: Choose the word from the box that best matches each clue. Write the word on the line.

________ **17.** It is both an open grill and meat cooked in a spicy sauce.

________ **18.** It is a meal eaten outdoors. Hint: Ants love them.

________ **19.** It is a meal at which people serve themselves from a sideboard or counter.

________ **20.** It is a feast or large meal with many courses.

Notes for Home: Your child spelled words that come from other languages. ***Home Activity:*** Challenge your child to use the spelling words to write several sentences. Have him or her check the sentences to be sure all the words are spelled correctly.

Spelling: Words from Many Cultures

Directions: Proofread these minutes from a meeting. Find seven spelling mistakes. Use the proofreading marks to correct each mistake.

≡	Make a capital.
/	Make a small letter.
∧	Add something.
ᔕ	Take out something.
⊙	Add a period.
¶	Begin a new paragraph.

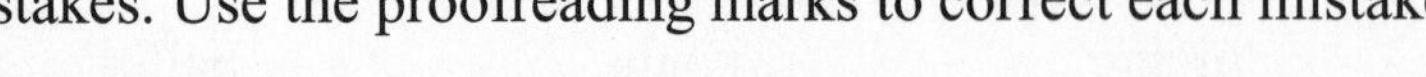

Minutes from August Meeting

- This summer's picnick was great. We'll plan to have another one next June.
- We ran short of catsup, musterd, relish, macaronie salad, and meat. We'll need more food, more barbaque grills, and extra cooks.
- The vanila ice cream melted. Let's try strawberry shortcake next time.
- Next year we should set up the food on a buffett table.
- The guests really enjoyed dancing, especially the waltz and poka. Let's include those dances and add others.

Word List

moose
cobra
alligator
vanilla
banana
tomato
mustard
hula
picnic
barbecue
crocodile
coyote
koala
macaroni
catsup
polka
ballet
waltz
banquet
buffet

Spelling Tip

ballet **buffet**

Many English words come from other languages and may have unexpected spellings. **Ball<u>et</u>** and **buff<u>et</u>** are French words, so they follow the French rule that **-et** sounds like the English long **a.**

Write Minutes from a Meeting

Imagine that you are the head caretaker of a wild animal park. You hold a meeting to discuss ways to keep the animals healthy and happy. On a separate piece of paper, make a list of plans for the park. Use at least five spelling words.

Notes for Home: Your child spelled words that come from other languages. ***Home Activity:*** Work with your child to create a crossword puzzle using several of the spelling words.

Name ____________________

Spelling: Words from Many Cultures

REVIEW

Word List

moose	banana	picnic	koala	ballet
cobra	tomato	barbecue	macaroni	waltz
alligator	mustard	crocodile	catsup	banquet
vanilla	hula	coyote	polka	buffet

Directions: Choose the word from the box that best matches each definition. Write the word on the line.

____________ **1.** a lizard-like reptile with a narrow head (Greek)

____________ **2.** a large reptile with a short, flat head (Spanish)

____________ **3.** a theatrical dance (French, from Italian)

____________ **4.** a red or yellow juicy fruit (Nahuatl [Aztec])

____________ **5.** a tube-shaped type of pasta (Italian)

____________ **6.** a meal at which people serve themselves (French)

____________ **7.** a large mammal with broad antlers (Algonquin)

____________ **8.** a smooth, gliding dance in triple time (German)

____________ **9.** a curved yellow or red tropical fruit (Spanish)

____________ **10.** a yellow seasoning (French)

____________ **11.** a spicy sauce made from tomatoes (Malay)

____________ **12.** a lively folk dance (Polish)

Directions: Choose the word from the box that best completes each command. Write the word on the line to the left.

____________ **13.** Roast the meat on the outdoor _____.

____________ **14.** Hear the howling of the wild _____.

____________ **15.** Plan to eat several courses at the ceremonial _____.

____________ **16.** Stir the cake batter and then add the _____.

____________ **17.** Please avoid stepping on that poisonous _____!

____________ **18.** Look at the furry Australian _____ in the tree.

____________ **19.** Put the _____ basket on that blanket under the tree.

____________ **20.** Dance the graceful Hawaiian _____.

Notes for Home: Your child spelled words that come from other languages. ***Home Activity:*** With your child, write tongue twisters for the spelling words, such as *Minnie the Moose munched many mangoes.*

Name ___________________________________

Questions for Inquiry

Formulating and revising **questions for inquiry** about a topic can help you set a purpose for your reading and help you focus your research. Before you begin your research, think about the questions you want answered about the topic. As you read, you may need to revise your questions to focus more specifically on the topic.

Directions: Before you read the encyclopedia entry below, answer the first two questions on the next page. Then read the entry and use it to answer the rest of the questions.

Common Crow

Family: *Corvidae* (includes jays, ravens, magpies, rooks, and jackdaws)

Scientific name: *Corvus brachyrhynchos*

Size: 17–21 inches long (43 to 53 centimeters)

Color: black

Diet: corn, wheat, insects, spiders, small birds, eggs, rodents, dead flesh

Common crow, also called the American crow, or *corvus brachyrhynchos,* is probably, with the robin and the pigeon, one of the three most easily-recognized birds in the United States. Crows are medium-sized, coal-black birds, much larger than robins and other songbirds, but much smaller than eagles, gulls, or hawks. This bird can be found in many parts of the world, although there are no crows in New Zealand, the Antarctic, or South America.

Crows use more than 23 different calls to communicate with one another. They cooperate with one another much more than other birds do. Both parents look after the nestling crows, and crows in the same flock will take turns keeping watch for enemies, gathering food, and attacking intruders. Flocks of crows can number in the thousands.

Name ______________________________

1. List information that you already know about crows. ______________________________

2. Write two questions of inquiry that you want answered about crows. ______________________________

3. Did the encyclopedia entry help answer your questions? If so, what answers did you find? If not, how might you revise your questions?

4. After reading the encyclopedia entry, what other questions of inquiry might you have about crows?

5. In what kinds of sources could you research to answer your questions of inquiry?

Notes for Home: Your child formulated questions for inquiry about crows. ***Home Activity:*** Have your child write a list of questions about an interesting animal. Work together to answer these questions using a nature program, an encyclopedia, a nonfiction book, or the Internet.

Family Times

Name____

Summary

A Spark of Hope for Brian

Brian is stranded in the Canadian wilderness. He needs a fire for warmth and for protection from animals, but how can he make one with no matches or lighter? Brian soon realizes he has the tools that he needs—he has already made a spark! He will keep on experimenting until he makes a fire.

Activity

Finish the Story. Encourage your child to tell you the rest of "From a Spark," including how Brian actually makes the fire. Then work together to write out the steps of the process. Illustrate each step to show how a fire can be started.

Reading Skills

Predicting

A **prediction** is a statement about what might happen next in a story or article. To make a prediction, think about what you already know and what has already happened in the story or article. After you read the first few pages of "From a Spark," would you have predicted that Brian would make a fire? Would you have predicted that he would survive?

After you make a prediction, continue reading to check its accuracy. Revise your prediction if it does not agree with new information.

Activity

Make a TV Prediction. Watch a TV show or movie with your family. During commercial breaks, each person writes a prediction about what will happen in the next segment. Read the predictions aloud at the next break to see how accurate they were.

Family Times

Tested Vocabulary

Words to Know

Knowing the meanings of these words is important to reading "From a Spark." Practice using these words to learn their meanings.

hatchet a small ax with a short handle

ignite to set on fire

painstaking requiring careful effort or attention

smoldered burned and smoked without flames

survival the act of staying alive

Grammar

Plural Nouns

Plural nouns name more than one person, place, or thing. Most plural nouns are formed by adding **-s** or **-es** to the singular form: **birds, watches.** With other nouns, you must make a spelling change before you add **-es.** Use the following rules for plurals that need spelling changes before adding **-es.**

- ❖ If a noun ends in a **consonant** and **y,** change the **y** to **i** and then add **-es: cities, libraries, babies.**
- ❖ Change **f** or **fe** to **v** and add **-es** to many singular nouns that end in **f** or **fe: halves, wives, leaves.**

Activity

Name That Object. Take turns naming objects in the room, such as *piano* and *shelf.* Tell how to spell the plural version of each object named, such as *pianos* and *shelves.* Encourage your child to check a dictionary for correct spellings as needed.

Tested Spelling Words

______	______	______	______
______	______	______	______
______	______	______	______
______	______	______	______
______	______	______	______

Name ________________________________

Predicting

- To **predict** means to state what might happen next in a story or article. To make a prediction, think about what you know and what has already happened.
- After making a prediction, continue reading to check its accuracy. Revise your prediction if it does not agree with new information.

Directions: Reread "At the Water's Edge." Then complete each box. Read each question and tell what logical prediction can be made based on what you have read up to that point in the story. Give a reason for each prediction.

Question: What do you predict Alec might see from the high rock?
1. Prediction:
2. Reason:

Question: What do you predict Alec might do after he first tastes the moss?
3. Prediction:
4. Reason:

Question: What might Alec do next? Why do you think so?
5. Prediction:
6. Reason:

Notes for Home: Your child read a story and made predictions about what would happen next. ***Home Activity:*** Tell your child a story about a real-life experience. Pause throughout the story to have your child make and/or revise predictions about what will happen next.

Name ______________________________

Vocabulary

Directions: Choose the word from the box that best completes each sentence. Write the word on the line to the left.

Check the Words You Know
___ hatchet
___ ignite
___ painstaking
___ smoldered
___ survival

______________ **1.** In winter, a person's _____ depends on having a source of heat.

______________ **2.** A _____ is a handy tool to cut small pieces of dry wood for the fire.

______________ **3.** Dry matches are needed to _____ a campfire.

______________ **4.** Without matches, it is a _____ job to get a fire started.

______________ **5.** Safety rules are very important with fires. Many forest fires have begun from an untended campfire that _____ and then burst into flames.

Directions: Choose the word from the box that best matches each clue. Write the word in the puzzle.

Down

6. small ax with a short handle

8. to set on fire

Across

7. requiring careful effort or attention

9. the act of staying alive

10. burned and smoked without flames

Write an Essay

On a separate sheet of paper, write one or two paragraphs explaining the uses of fire in everyday life. Do you think fire is as imporant to our lives today as to people in the past? Explain your thinking using as many vocabulary words as you can.

Notes for Home: Your child identified and used vocabulary words from "From a Spark." ***Home Activity:*** With your child, make up a story of having to survive in the woods. Use as many of the vocabulary words as you can.

Predicting

- To **predict** means to state what you think might happen next in a story or article.
- To make a prediction, think about what you already know and what has already happened.
- Check and change your prediction as you encounter new information.

Directions: Reread what happens in "From a Spark" after Brian wakes up from the dream about his father and Terry. Then answer the questions below. Think about the predictions you made as you were reading the story.

Fire. The hatchet was the key to it all. When he threw the hatchet at the porcupine in the cave and missed and hit the stone wall it had showered sparks, a golden shower of sparks in the dark, as golden with fire as the sun was now.

The hatchet was the answer. That's what his father and Terry had been trying to tell him. Somehow he could get fire from the hatchet. The sparks would make fire.

Brian went back into the shelter and studied the wall. . . . It only took him a moment to find where the hatchet had struck. The steel had nicked into the edge of one of the darker stone pieces.

1. What do you think Brian will do with the hatchet?

____

2. Which clues helped you make this prediction?

____

____

3. How will Brian use the wall to help him make fire?

____

4. Which clues helped you make this prediction?

____

____

5. Do you think Brian will survive? Explain your thinking on a separate sheet of paper.

Notes for Home: Your child used story details to predict what would happen next in a story. ***Home Activity:*** With your child, read the first paragraph of an article or a story. Work together to predict what will happen next or what the article or story will be about.

Name ____________________

Selection Test

Directions: Choose the best answer to each item. Mark the letter for the answer you have chosen.

Part 1: Vocabulary

Find the answer choice that means about the same as the underlined word in each sentence.

1. Restoring an old house is <u>painstaking</u> work.
- A. fast
- B. very successful
- C. uncomfortable
- D. requiring careful attention

2. He made a list of what he needed for <u>survival</u>.
- F. staying alive
- G. happiness
- H. success in business
- J. homework

3. The ranger made kindling with a <u>hatchet</u>.
- A. small ax
- B. sharp knife
- C. large boot
- D. kind of saw

4. The trash pile <u>smoldered</u> behind the barn.
- F. spread to the trees
- G. grew out of control
- H. burned without flames
- J. made an awful smell

5. Mr. Dennison was afraid to <u>ignite</u> the wood.
- A. blow on
- B. set on fire
- C. break up
- D. cut into pieces

Part 2: Comprehension

Use what you know about the story to answer each item.

6. At the beginning of the story, Brian wakes up to the smell of—
- F. pine trees.
- G. an animal.
- H. smoke.
- J. raspberries.

7. A porcupine slapped Brian with its tail because Brian—
- A. had a hatchet.
- B. thought it was a bear.
- C. kicked it.
- D. was asleep in the cave.

8. After removing the quills from his leg, Brian feels—
- F. relieved.
- G. sick to his stomach.
- H. very discouraged.
- J. sure that someone will come to help him.

9. When Brian dreams of Terry lighting the charcoal, a reader is most likely to predict that—
- A. the porcupine will return.
- B. Brian will soon have a fever.
- C. Brian will die in the cave.
- D. Brian will make a fire.

10. Why does Brian think of the fire as "hungry"?
- F. It needs air.
- G. He is starving.
- H. He must keep feeding it with fuel.
- J. It reminds him of the barbecue in his dreams.

11. Based on what he has learned, if Brian's fire goes out he is most likely to—
- A. give up on having a fire.
- B. make a new fire.
- C. look for matches.
- D. cry in self-pity.

GO ON

12. Brian's experience in getting the fire going shows that—

F. Brian is able to remember and use things he has learned.
G. most fires don't need oxygen.
H. Brian should have taken a survival course.
J. most animals will approach a fire if they need to get warm.

13. What is Brian most concerned about in this story?

A. controlling the fire
B. finding Terry
C. saving his money
D. staying alive

14. Brian threw the hatchet because he thought that—

F. a porcupine would be scared by a shower of sparks.
G. he had to protect himself from a large animal.
H. a snake would not be moving around at night.
J. a bad dream was coming true.

15. Which statement best describes Brian?

A. He has not had much experience living outdoors.
B. He does not like his family.
C. He does not have much patience.
D. He cannot think clearly because of his injury.

Name ______________________________

Predicting

- To **predict** means to state what you think might happen next in a story or article.
- To make a prediction, think about what you already know and what has already happened.
- Check and change your prediction as you encounter new information.

Directions: Read the story below.

Shocked, Matt looked at the footprints in the snow. They were his footprints! He had been wandering in circles. Matt began to panic. He would never find his way back to camp! He would freeze out in the wild!

Matt took a deep breath. He knew he had to stay calm. He thought of other times when he had been scared. He never got scared when his father was there. When his father wasn't there, it helped Matt just to think about him.

Ahead of Matt, there were many rocks and hollows in the hill. Matt suddenly remembered that if you could get inside a little cave or hollow, you could build a wall of snow by the entrance to keep warm.

Directions: Complete the table by answering the questions below.

Question	Prediction	Story Clues Used to Make Prediction
What will Matt do to calm himself?	**1.**	**2.**
How will Matt keep warm?	**3.**	**4.**
		5.

Notes for Home: Your child used story details to make predictions about what could happen next. ***Home Activity:*** With your child, observe characters in television shows or movies. Make predictions together about what they will do next.

Name ______________________________

Setting and Steps in a Process

REVIEW

Directions: Read the passage. Then read each question about the passage. Choose the best answer to each question. Mark the letter for the answer you have chosen.

A Cold Journey

Roald Amundsen left Norway secretly. He wanted to beat the British explorer Robert Scott to the South Pole. No explorer had traveled so far.

Amundsen and his team reached the edge of Antarctica in January. They took a few trips inland to set up supplies of food and fuel. Then they waited for spring to arrive so they could travel.

In October, spring arrived. Amundsen's team began its trip through Antarctica to the South Pole. The trip was painstaking. They ran out of the food they had brought. In order to survive, they had to kill and eat the weaker sled dogs. But on December 14, 1911, Amundsen and his team became the first people to reach the South Pole. Soon Amundsen was famous throughout the world.

1. Most of this story is set—
- **A.** in Norway.
- **B.** in Britain.
- **C.** in Antarctica.
- **D.** all over the world.

2. How would this story be different if Robert Scott had already reached the South Pole?
- **F.** Amundsen would not have left secretly.
- **G.** Amundsen could have traveled in January.
- **H.** Amundsen could have gotten food from Scott.
- **J.** Amundsen would have been as famous as Scott.

3. What did Amundsen do first?
- **A.** He set up camp at the edge of Antarctica.
- **B.** He left Norway secretly.
- **C.** He set up supplies.
- **D.** He began his trip through the Antarctic.

4. Before Amundsen left the edge of the Antarctic, he—
- **F.** killed weaker sled dogs.
- **G.** set up supplies of food and fuel.
- **H.** met with Robert Scott.
- **J.** traveled to the South Pole.

5. How does the Antarctic setting affect Amundsen's actions?
- **A.** Dogs have to be killed and eaten when food runs out.
- **B.** He has to get more dogs to keep traveling.
- **C.** He has to send far away for help.
- **D.** He has to travel alone.

Notes for Home: Your child identified the time and place in which a story takes place, and the order in which story events happened. ***Home Activity:*** Have your child choose a favorite story. With your child, identify the time and place in which the story takes place.

Name ______________________________

Writing Across Texts

Directions: Consider the selections "A Trouble-Making Crow" and "From a Spark." Complete the table by listing the problems the characters experienced.

From a Spark	A Trouble-Making Crow
Brian is alone in the Canadian wilderness.	New York, their pet crow, started diving at Hilde Black's eyes.
1.	**6.**
2.	**7.**
3.	**8.**
4.	**9.**
5.	**10.**

Write a Paragraph

Use the information from the table above to write a paragraph that compares and contrasts the problems that Brian has with the problems of the family in "A Trouble-Making Crow." Write your paragraph on a separate sheet of paper.

Notes for Home: Your child used details from two different selections to write a comparison/contrast paragraph. ***Home Activity:*** As you read other stories or articles, encourage your child to point out their likenesses and differences.

Name ______________________________

REVIEW

Grammar: Nouns

Directions: Underline each noun in the sentences that follow. Underline proper nouns twice.

1. My Aunt Fay and her children, Alana and Nathan, were taking a bus from New Hampshire to Cape Cod.
2. From the bus, Nathan pointed out Boston and Plymouth.
3. Of course, Plymouth and Plymouth Rock are famous as the landing place of the Pilgrims in the seventeenth century.
4. The passengers felt a sudden jolt, and the bus went into a skid along Route 95.
5. Fortunately, Officer Eileen Regan and Officer Jamal Davis were on the scene quickly, and no one suffered serious injury.

Directions: Write each sentence correctly. Remember to capitalize all proper nouns.

6. The famous mt. everest lies in the himalayan mountains in asia.

____

____

7. In 1953, edmund hillary and tenzing norgay became the first climbers to reach the soaring peak.

____

____

8. Thousands have climbed mt. mcKinley in north america and mt. kilimanjaro in africa.

____

____

9. Hundreds of climbers from europe, the americas, japan, and other parts of the world have died in these attempts.

____

____

10. A chilling book by jon krakauer tells of the twelve climbers who died climbing mt. everest in may 1996.

____

____

Notes for Home: Your child identified and used common and proper nouns in sentences. ***Home Activity:*** Take a walk with your child. Encourage your child to list the people, places, and things you see, using common and proper nouns.

Name ______________________

Grammar: Plural Nouns

A noun that names more than one person, place, thing, or idea is a **plural noun.**

Regular Nouns

- Add **-s** or **-es** to most nouns to make them plural: fork, forks.
- Add **-es** to nouns ending in **ch, sh, x, z, s** or **ss:** match, matches; wish, wishes; box, boxes; buzz, buzzes; bus, buses; success, successes.
- If a noun ends in a **vowel** followed by **y,** add **-s.** If a noun ends in a **consonant** and **y,** change the **y** to **i** and add **-es:** journey, journeys; lady, ladies.

Irregular Nouns

- Some nouns have the same singular and plural form: elk/elk; deer/deer.
- Some nouns change the spelling of the word to form the plural: child, children; ox, oxen.
- You can form the plurals of some nouns ending in **f** or **fe** by changing **f** or **fe** to **v** and adding **-es:** wolf, wolves; knife, knives.
- Add **-s** to certain nouns that end in **f:** roof, roofs; chief, chiefs.
- Add **-s** to nearly all nouns that end in **ff:** sheriff, sheriffs.
- Add **-s** to nouns ending in a **vowel** and **o:** patio, patios; stereo, stereos.
- Check the dictionary for plurals of nouns ending in a consonant followed by **o:** photo, photos; piano, pianos; hero, heroes; tomato, tomatoes.

Directions: Write the plural form of each underlined noun or nouns. Use a dictionary if you need help.

______________ **1.** Kelly saw a thief, but not the kind a sheriff would arrest.

______________ **2.** The fox was holding a large mouse in its jaw.

______________ **3.** The bandit couldn't unlock the latch of the gate.

______________ **4.** It managed to slip under the fence.

______________ **5.** It ran across the vegetable garden.

______________ **6.** The fox would feed its baby before eating.

______________ **7.** The sheep in the field was alarmed.

______________ **8.** It stamped its hoof in fear.

______________ **9.** It wished a hero would come to the rescue!

______________ **10.** High above the roof, an osprey wished it had caught the mouse.

Notes for Home: Your child wrote plural nouns. ***Home Activity:*** Look through a catalog or an illustrated encyclopedia with your child. Ask your child to tell you how to form plurals of the names of objects pictured.

Name ______________________________

Grammar: Plural Nouns

Directions: Write the plural form of each noun in ( ). Use a dictionary if you need help.

_______________ **1.** The (cliff) towered above the two climbers.

_______________ **2.** (Patch) of blue could be seen between the rocky slopes.

_______________ **3.** Were those (elk) scrambling over the rocks?

_______________ **4.** Even as (child), the climbers had dreamed about this mountain!

_______________ **5.** They also had heard many (story) about its dangers.

_______________ **6.** They were not (hero), just two people trying to reach its peak.

_______________ **7.** Therefore, they were well equipped with (ax) and other tools.

_______________ **8.** Some unpleasant (surprise) awaited them, however.

_______________ **9.** Soon their (life) would be in great danger.

_______________ **10.** Would they reach camp before the (sky) turned dark?

Directions: Write five sentences. Use the plural form of each noun in the box in each sentence.

journey	foot	challenge	spy	knife

11. ______________________________

12. ______________________________

13. ______________________________

14. ______________________________

15. ______________________________

Write a TV News Report

Think of a real or fictional person who was caught in a dangerous situation and survived. On a separate sheet of paper, write a short report for the TV evening news. Include at least three plural nouns in your report.

Notes for Home: Your child wrote the plural form of various nouns. ***Home Activity:*** Ask your child to use a book or a magazine to find plural nouns and tell you the singular form of each one.

Name ______________________

Grammar: Plural Nouns

RETEACHING

Draw a line to connect each noun pair in each box.

Singular	Plural
clock	shelves
watch	watches
knife	clocks
shelf	men
man	knives

Singular	Plural
child	trays
lady	deer
tray	ladies
hero	children
deer	heroes

A **plural noun** names more than one person, place, thing, or idea. Most nouns add **-s** to make the plural form. Some nouns change their spellings in the plural forms. A few have the same singular and plural spellings.

Directions: Write the plural form of each noun.

1. girl ______________________ **2.** birch ______________________

3. glass ______________________ **4.** fox ______________________

5. pony ______________________ **6.** lash ______________________

7. tomato ______________________ **8.** monkey ______________________

9. elf ______________________ **10.** sheep ______________________

11. tooth ______________________ **12.** hobby ______________________

Directions: Write each sentence. Use the plural form of the noun in ( ).

13. (Clock) and (watch) are timepieces.

____

14. Many (person) observed their (shadow).

____

15. (Century) ago Egyptian (child) used shadow clocks.

____

Notes for Home: Your child used plural forms of nouns in sentences. ***Home Activity:*** Have your child cut out pictures from magazines and make a collage that represents himself or herself. Your child should label pictures with plural and singular nouns.

Name ______________________________ From a Spark

Grammar: Plural Nouns

Directions: Write the plural form of each word in ( ).

1. six ______________ (mouse) **2.** a few ______________ (tomato)

3. two ______________ (man) **4.** several ______________ (shelf)

5. many ______________ (monkey) **6.** young ______________ (child)

7. several ______________ (batch) **8.** three ______________ (thief)

9. red ______________ (balloon) **10.** big ______________ (city)

11. four ______________ (plate) **12.** eight ______________ (elf)

13. five ______________ (fish) **14.** some ______________ (match)

Directions: Write each sentence. Use the plural form of each noun in ( ).

15. Our school gave all the (child) (pass) to the state fair.

____

16. We saw (booth) with (display) of prize-winning vegetables.

____

17. Two (tomato) and four (squash) won ribbons.

____

18. We tasted several (variety) of delicious (pie).

____

19. (Box) of homemade jams and (jelly) lined the (shelf).

____

20. We visited the 4-H Club exhibit of (calf) and (sheep).

____

21. Have you ever seen (cowboy) ride (pony) in (rodeo)?

____

Write a Paragraph

On a separate sheet of paper, write a paragraph about what you would like to see at a state fair. Try to use as many plural nouns as possible in your sentences.

Notes for Home: Your child identified plural forms of nouns and used them in sentences. ***Home Activity:*** Have your child make a list of items needed to do a particular task. Then have him or her write the plural forms of the names of those items.

Name ______________________________

Phonics: Silent Consonants

Directions: Some words have consonants that you don't hear. Say each word to yourself. Circle the word in each group that has the **silent consonant.** Underline the consonant that is silent.

1. liken list liter listening	**2.** not knee kept kite	**3.** bury raspberries raisin laundry
4. drop distance dumb disturb	**5.** signal sign signature sister	**6.** complete compound combine comb
7. wrist win work waist	**8.** fasten faster finally frantic	**9.** design desert dusty duplicate

Directions: Read the travel guide. Find seven words with **silent consonants.** Write each word on the lines, and circle the consonant that is silent.

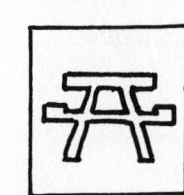

Glenview Park

Located just a half hour from downtown, Glenview Park is a place known to hikers as the best park in town. You won't find any loud radios there. Bring a knapsack with a nice treat and a good book. Climb the old gnarled trees to get a better view. If you listen very closely, you can hear the quiet of the outdoors. Deer come at dusk to the side of a clearing, so bring your binoculars!

10. ____________

11. ____________

12. ____________

13. ____________

14. ____________

15. ____________

16. ____________

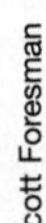

Notes for Home: Your child reviewed silent consonants, such as the *w* in *write*. ***Home Activity:*** Read a travel guide with your child. Help your child identify words with silent consonants. Have your child write the words and circle the silent letters.

Pretest

Name ____________________

Spelling: Unexpected Consonant Spellings

Pretest Directions: Fold back the page along the dotted line. On the blanks, write the spelling words as they are dictated. When you have finished the test, unfold the page and check your words.

1. ____________	**1.** I don't **doubt** your excuse.
2. ____________	**2.** Strange movies **fascinate** her.
3. ____________	**3.** He enjoys his **science** classes.
4. ____________	**4.** We drove along a **scenic** route.
5. ____________	**5.** Leaves change colors in **autumn**.
6. ____________	**6.** He writes a daily **column**.
7. ____________	**7.** The defendant is not **guilty**.
8. ____________	**8.** Our soccer **league** is a big one.
9. ____________	**9.** Her brother was her **guardian**.
10. ____________	**10.** The spy wore a clever **disguise**.
11. ____________	**11.** His jokes are very **subtle**.
12. ____________	**12.** They were in **debt** to the bank.
13. ____________	**13.** I enjoy **reminiscent** music.
14. ____________	**14.** The cliff makes a steep **descent**.
15. ____________	**15.** I **condemn** cruelty to animals.
16. ____________	**16.** This is a **solemn** occasion.
17. ____________	**17.** Sometimes you need **guidance**.
18. ____________	**18.** Your meaning is **vague**.
19. ____________	**19.** The hikers battled **fatigue**.
20. ____________	**20.** I like books filled with **intrigue**.

Notes for Home: Your child took a pretest on words with unexpected combinations of consonants. ***Home Activity:*** Help your child learn misspelled words before the final test. Your child can underline the word parts that caused the problems and concentrate on those parts.

Name ______________________

Spelling: Unexpected Consonant Spellings

Word List				
doubt	autumn	guardian	reminiscent	guidance
fascinate	column	disguise	descent	vague
science	guilty	subtle	condemn	fatigue
scenic	league	debt	solemn	intrigue

Directions: Choose the words from the box spelled with **bt, gue,** and **gu.** Listen for the consonant sound each group of letters represents. Write each word in the correct column.

Words spelled bt	Words spelled gue	Words spelled gu
1. ______	4. ______	8. ______
2. ______	5. ______	9. ______
3. ______	6. ______	10. ______
	7. ______	11. ______

Directions: Choose the word from the box that best completes each sentence. Write the word on the line to the left.

______ **12.** The desert sunrise provided a _____ view as we entered the mine.

______ **13.** We went exploring this _____ to avoid the colder temperatures of winter.

______ **14.** Gradually, we began the _____ down the steep slope.

______ **15.** Fred looked serious and _____ as daylight faded behind us.

______ **16.** We had read the studies in the _____ journals about the atmosphere inside old mine shafts.

______ **17.** Our group had to decide whether to _____ the property as unsuitable for future use.

______ **18.** The mine was _____ of a scene from an old movie.

______ **19.** Each sturdy _____ helped hold up the rough ceiling.

______ **20.** The complexity of the mine would amaze and _____ anyone.

Notes for Home: Your child spelled words with unexpected letter combinations. ***Home Activity:*** Help your child sort the spelling words into groups that contain the letters *sc, bt, gu* or *gue,* and *mn.* Each letter group represents one consonant sound.

Name ____________________

Spelling: Unexpected Consonant Spellings

Directions: Proofread this journal entry. Find six spelling mistakes. Use the proofreading marks to correct each mistake.

- ≡ Make a capital.
- / Make a small letter.
- ∧ Add something.
- Take out something.
- ⊙ Add a period.
- ¶ Begin a new paragraph.

Day 3. It's great to be back up top again. We just finished the hardest desent into the caves to date, and all my muscles ache with fatige. But today we found a cavern sure to fascinat even the most experienced explorer! After hours of climbing and crawling through mud in temperatures reminiscint of a refrigerator, I began to dout my abilities. Finally, I squeezed my way through a narrow passage into a huge chamber. Our lights shone on an enormous limestone colum. Now I understand the intrigue of cave exploration!

Word List

doubt
fascinate
science
scenic
autumn
column
guilty
league
guardian
disguise
subtle
debt
reminiscent
descent
condemn
solemn
guidance
vague
fatigue
intrigue

Spelling Tip

fascinate **fatigue**

Fascinate, fatigue, and other spelling words use two or more letters to stand for one consonant sound. Make sure they are spelled correctly in the journal entry.

Write a Journal Entry

On a separate sheet of paper, write a journal entry describing a wilderness adventure. Imagine that you are exploring a new territory. Have you had any narrow escapes? How did you survive? How did you feel when you finally reached your goal? Try to use at least five of your spelling words.

Notes for Home: Your child spelled words with unexpected letter combinations. ***Home Activity:*** Have your child read the spelling words for you to write. Then have your child check your spelling.

Name ____________________

Spelling: Unexpected Consonant Spellings

REVIEW

Word List

doubt	autumn	guardian	reminiscent	guidance
fascinate	column	disguise	descent	vague
science	guilty	subtle	condemn	fatigue
scenic	league	debt	solemn	intrigue

Directions: Write the word from the box that belongs in each group.

1. pillar, post, ____________________
2. unclear, not distinct, ____________________
3. beautiful, natural, ____________________
4. costume, mask, ____________________
5. grave, serious, ____________________
6. direction, leadership, ____________________
7. caretaker, protector, ____________________
8. plot, scheme, ____________________
9. judge, convict, ____________________
10. remembered, suggestive, ____________________
11. interest, charm, ____________________

Directions: Choose the word from the box that best matches each clue. Write the word on the line.

____________________ **12.** It's not obvious so you might just overlook me.

____________________ **13.** It's the season between summer and winter.

____________________ **14.** It includes the subjects chemistry, biology, and physics.

____________________ **15.** It's a group of people or a division in sports.

____________________ **16.** It's what you feel when you don't know for sure.

____________________ **17.** It's the opposite of *innocent.*

____________________ **18.** It's how you would describe a beautiful view.

____________________ **19.** It's money or other items owed to someone.

____________________ **20.** It's a trip downstairs, down a hill, or down a mountain.

Notes for Home: Your child spelled words with unexpected letter combinations. ***Home Activity:*** Give your child clues about each spelling word. Have your child identify and spell each word. For example: *You use a costume to do this. (disguise)*

Name ______________________

Thesaurus

A **thesaurus** is a kind of dictionary that lists synonyms (words with the same or similar meanings), antonyms (words with opposite meanings), and other related words. Parts of speech are listed to show how a word is used. If a word has multiple meanings, synonyms for each type of meaning are given.

You can use a thesaurus to help you find new and interesting words so you don't repeat the same words too often in your writing. An index lists all the entry words in alphabetical order so you can look them up quickly.

Directions: Use these thesaurus entries to answer the questions that follow.

soundless (adj) still, mute, quiet. See SILENT.

spark (n) **1. flash:** flicker, flare, sparkle, glow, glint, glimmer; **2. stimulus:** goad, spur, motivation, inspiration.

spark (v) **1. flash:** flicker, flare, sparkle, glint; **2. stimulate:** goad, spur, motivate, inspire, ignite, start, activate. (ant) extinguish, douse.

sparkle (v) **1. with light:** glitter, shine, flicker, glint, glimmer, glow, dazzle, shimmer: *The silver ornaments sparkle in the firelight.* **2. with intelligence:** be lively, be vivacious, be the life of the party, shine, dazzle: *Her stories sparkle with clever humor.*

sparse (adj) scanty, meager, slight, scarce, thin, poor, spare, skimpy, few and far between. (ant) thick, abundant, plentiful.

1. What part of speech is *soundless?* How do you know? ______________________

____

2. What are the synonyms for *soundless?* ______________________

Name ______________________________

3. Why do you think the entry for *soundless* includes the cross-reference for *silent?*

____

____

____

4. Why does this thesaurus show two entries for *spark?* ______________________________

____

5. Rewrite the following sentence using a synonym for *spark*.
He saw a brief spark of light when the hatchet hit the rock.

____

____

6. Which meaning of *sparkle* is used in the following sentence? Which synonyms would you use to replace the word *sparkled?* Pick the synonyms that would make the most sense in the sentence.
The stars sparkled like tiny diamonds scattered across the night sky.

____

____

____

7. Write a sentence using any of the antonyms listed. Hint: You can use the list of synonyms to help you figure out the meaning of an antonym.

____

____

8. How is a thesaurus like a dictionary? How is it different? ______________________________

____

____

____

9. How can you find the synonyms for a word in a thesaurus? Describe the steps.

____

____

10. Why is a thesaurus a useful reference source when you are writing something?

____

____

Notes for Home: Your child used entries from a thesaurus to answer questions. ***Home Activity:*** Make a list of ten common words. Take turns with your child listing as many synonyms as you can for each word. Use the thesaurus, if one is available, to help you.

Family Times

Name______________________________

Summary

Dust Storm Blows Mysterious Stranger into Lindy's House

Lindy and her family are battling a drought and struggling to keep their crops alive. One day, Lindy and her father see a storm approaching. But it isn't a rainstorm. It's a wall of dust. Along with the dust, the storm brings a strange boy named Drylongso to Lindy's house. Drylongso knows a lot about droughts and what causes them.

Activity

Act Out a Scene. Have your child describe Lindy and Drylongso. Then act out the scene between Lindy and Drylongso when they first meet. Encourage your child, as Drylongso, to tell you about the droughts and their causes.

Reading Skills

Setting

The **setting** of a story is the place and time in which it occurs.

Sometimes the author tells you exactly where and when the story takes place. In "Storm-a-Dust," Mamalou tells us that it is 1975.

Sometimes the author uses details to reveal the setting. In "Storm-a-Dust," the characters are taking care of crops. This suggests that the story is set on a farm.

The setting of a story can influence what happens to a character and how the character behaves. The setting can also contribute to an overall feeling or mood. In "Storm-a-Dust," the characters' actions and the mood are affected by the setting: they protect themselves from the dust, and feel unsure about their future.

Activity

Describe a Setting. Imagine your home is the setting for a story. Describe the rooms, and tell how each room can affect the characters' actions and moods.

Family Times

Tested Vocabulary

Words to Know

Knowing the meanings of these words is important to reading "Storm-a-Dust." Practice using these words to learn their meanings.

eerie scary in a weird or strange way

grasslands a large expanse of land covered with grass

gritty containing small bits of dust, sand, and so on

hazy not clear; murky

peculiar odd; strange; unusual

spindly very long and slender

Grammar

Possessive Nouns

Possessive nouns show ownership. You form possessive nouns by adding an **apostrophe** and **s** or by adding only an apostrophe. Here are some rules for forming possessive nouns:

- ❖ Add **'s** to form the possessive of most singular nouns.

  the farmer's truck
  Chris's rake
- ❖ Add only an apostrophe to form the possessive of plural nouns that end in **s.**

  three days' work
- ❖ Add **'s** to form the possessive of plural nouns that do not end in **s.**

  the oxen's stable

Activity

Whose Is It? Play "Whose Is It?" Choose something that can belong to a person or to some people, such as a pen, a house, or a student project. Then use a possessive noun to tell who owns the object, for example: *Maria's pen, the Joneses' house, the students' project.* Spell out the phrase and tell where the apostrophe belongs.

Tested Spelling Words

Setting

- The **setting** of a story is the place and time in which the story occurs.
- Sometimes the author tells you the setting. Other times, the author reveals the setting through details.
- The setting can influence what happens to a character or how a character behaves. It can also contribute to the overall feeling, or mood.

Directions: Reread "The Glittering Cloud." Then complete the tables. Identify the place in which the story occurs. Then list story details that describe the setting and tell how the setting influences the characters and mood.

Story Setting	
Time: the 1800s	**Place: 1.**

Story Details About Setting	Influence on Characters and Mood
2. The prairie	The mood is one of discomfort caused by such strong heat.
3. The schoolhouse	**4.** The school children
5. The wheat	**6.** Pa
7. A cloud	**8.** The dog
9. Large brown grasshoppers	**10.** The mood

Notes for Home: Your child identified the details that reveal the setting of a story and described its effects on the characters. ***Home Activity:*** Choose a favorite story that has an interesting setting. Use details from the story to help your child draw a picture illustrating the setting.

Name ______________________________________

Vocabulary

Directions: Choose the word from the box that has the same or nearly the same meaning as each word below. Write the word on the line.

Check the Words You Know
___ eerie
___ grasslands
___ gritty
___ hazy
___ peculiar
___ spindly

____________________ **1.** odd; strange; unusual

____________________ **2.** having bits of sand and dust

____________________ **3.** scary; weird

____________________ **4.** very long and slender

____________________ **5.** unclear; murky

Directions: Choose the word from the box that best completes each sentence. Write the word on the matching numbered line below.

The dry **6.** ____ stretched for miles and miles. The dusty air made the setting sun look **7.** ____ and unclear. In the dust storm, the air was **8.** ____ with sand. Tall, **9.** ____ stalks of grass bowed and waved. In the light of the rising moon, the moving grass seemed to come alive. The whole scene was very spooky and **10.** ____. I was glad when the sun rose bright and clear the next day.

6. ____________________ **9.** ____________________

7. ____________________ **10.** ____________________

8. ____________________

Write a Weather Report

On a separate sheet of paper, write a weather report describing a dust storm or some other kind of extreme weather. Use as many of the vocabulary words as you can.

Notes for Home: Your child identified and used vocabulary words from "Storm-a-Dust." ***Home Activity:*** With your child, name as many weather words that have similar meaning as you can, such as *hazy, murky, unclear,* and *misty.*

Name ________________________

Setting

- The **setting** is the place and time in which a story occurs. It may be directly identified or only suggested through story details.
- The setting of a story can influence what happens to a character and how a character behaves.

Directions: Reread what happens at the beginning of "Storm-a-Dust," when Lindy is wiping the red dust off. Then answer the questions below. Think about the story details to help you identify the setting.

She must wipe each plant and flower clean. For red dust covered everything. Dust spotted her cheeks reddish brown. It covered her hands in red dust mittens. She took a last swipe at a stunted sunflower. "How are you this morning, yellow fella?" she asked the sunflower.

"Oh, but I need some water," Lindy answered in a sunflower-high voice.

"I'll water you at sundown, yellow fella," she told the flower.

She tied her wiper around her waist. Her tank top and jeans were dusty. Lindy climbed up on the old wood fence and shook her head at their pie-shaped field. "Don't think the corn will make it," she called over to her dad.

1. Where do you think the story takes place? What details suggest this?

____

____

2. What is the weather like where Lindy lives? How do you know?

____

____

3. Why is the weather important where Lindy lives?

____

4. What season of the year is it? How do you know?

____

5. How does the setting affect Lindy and her parents? How might their lives be different in a different setting? Explain your thinking on a separate sheet of paper.

Notes for Home: Your child identified the setting of the story and explained why the setting is important to the story. ***Home Activity:*** Work with your child to describe your home as though it is the setting for a story. Discuss how each room is the setting for different activities.

Name ______________________________

Selection Test

Directions: Choose the best answer to each item. Mark the letter for the answer you have chosen.

Part 1: Vocabulary

Find the answer choice that means about the same as the underlined word in each sentence.

1. Mom did not want to use the <u>gritty</u> rag on the windshield.
- A. covered with oil or grease
- B. old; worn out
- C. containing small bits of dirt or sand
- D. having many holes

2. The sky was <u>hazy</u>.
- F. bright blue
- G. sparkling
- H. filled with black clouds
- J. not clear

3. The gardener watered the <u>spindly</u> bush.
- A. covered with flowers
- B. very long and slender
- C. huge
- D. young or newly planted

4. An <u>eerie</u> quiet filled the house.
- F. scary in a strange way
- G. happy and exciting
- H. complete; total
- J. cozy and comforting

5. The air had a <u>peculiar</u> odor.
- A. odd
- B. terrible
- C. lovely
- D. fruity

6. Alfonse hiked across the <u>grasslands</u>.
- F. low hills at the base of mountains
- G. lands covered with grass
- H. narrow strips of rocky pathways
- J. lands that rise up high

Part 2: Comprehension

Use what you know about the story to answer each item.

7. The "wall" that Lindy sees is actually a—
- A. dust storm.
- B. big flock of birds.
- C. snowstorm.
- D. line of thunderstorms.

8. Lindy's father watches the sky because he hopes he will see—
- F. a rainbow.
- G. rain clouds.
- H. flocks of birds.
- J. grasshoppers.

9. Throughout the story, Lindy sneezes and coughs because she is—
- A. getting sick.
- B. having a reaction to the plants.
- C. breathing dusty air.
- D. allergic to cats.

10. This story begins at what time of day?
- F. late afternoon
- G. morning
- H. sundown
- J. night

11. Which detail about the setting best conveys the mood of the story?
- A. "They stayed in the house with Drylongso."
- B. "This is 1975; we know more."
- C. "They all stared out at an eerie blue world."
- D. "Every window had little drifts in the corners."

GO ON

12. When Drylongso arrives, the family—
F. is afraid of him.
G. cleans his face and gives him water.
H. asks him to tell them stories.
J. has him clean up their house.

13. From this story you can conclude that—
A. farmers should never use plows.
B. young seedlings cannot be saved with water during a drought.
C. overusing grasslands can cause dust storms.
D. dust storms do very little damage.

14. Lindy's family invites Drylongso to stay with them because—
F. they want Lindy to have a brother.
G. he has been separated from his family and has nowhere to go.
H. they need his help on the farm.
J. he is the only one who can make them laugh during hard times.

15. Drylongso tells Lindy some dust-storm stories in order to—
A. teach her lessons about farming.
B. convince her that he is her brother.
C. make her stay in the house.
D. keep her spirits up.

Name ______________________________

Setting

- The **setting** is the place and time in which a story occurs. It may be directly identified or only suggested through story details.
- The setting can influence what happens to a character and how a character behaves.

Directions: Read the story below.

The sound of the wind against the hut woke Marta early. When she looked outside, she saw nothing except the huge waves crashing on the shore. The waves had been high for the past four months.

Marta thought her island home was beautiful. But the huge waves were making life harder for Marta and the 100 others who lived there.

The ship that came once every three months had been unable to reach the island since fall. Marta and her people needed supplies from that ship. Marta had heard of a new kind of boat, a huge boat powered by steam. That boat might do better in the sea. But for now, Marta and her people would have to find another way to survive.

Directions: Complete the circles in the web. Circle your answer to each question, and then give supporting evidence from the story.

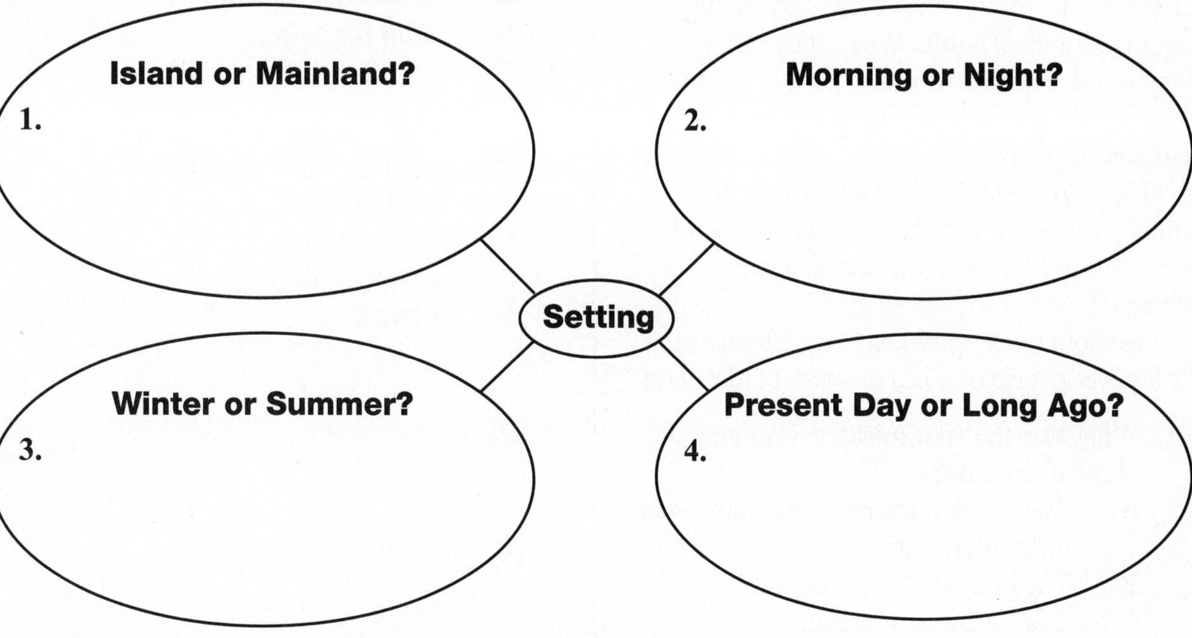

5. How does the setting affect Marta and her people?

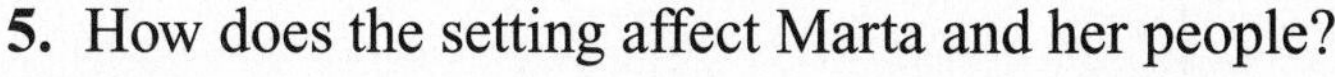

____

Notes for Home: Your child read a story and identified its setting—where and when the story takes place. ***Home Activity:*** Have your child choose a favorite story and describe the setting of that story. Then suggest a change in the setting and ask how that might change the story.

REVIEW

Sequence

Directions: Read the story. Then read each question about the story. Choose the best answer to each question. Mark the letter for the answer you have chosen.

On the Map

When Tom and Stephanie looked at the map, they thought they had an easy hike. But they soon found out that a map doesn't show everything.

On the second day of the hike, Tom wanted to change the route they had planned. He and Stephanie looked at the map and found a shortcut. The trees were beautiful, and they saw several animals. But the shortcut was so hilly that their packs began to feel heavy. They got rid of everything they didn't want to carry. Unfortunately, this included one of their water bottles.

By the third day, they had drunk all the water from the bottle they had kept. Looking at the map, Stephanie found a detour that would take her and Tom past a stream, where they could refill their bottle. When they got there, they made a terrible discovery—the stream was dry! In the end, they had to radio the rangers for help.

"I'm sorry, Stephanie," said Tom. "If I hadn't wanted to change the hike, we would have followed a flat path near a strong stream."

"We both made mistakes," said Stephanie. "I'll never get rid of a heavy water bottle again!"

1. What was the first mistake Tom and Stephanie made?
- **A.** They took a shortcut that they were unfamiliar with.
- **B.** They decided to go on a hike.
- **C.** They went to a stream.
- **D.** They got lost.

2. Which of these events happened first?
- **F** Tom took a detour to go to a stream.
- **G.** Tom and Stephanie got rid of everything they didn't want to carry.
- **H.** They went to a dry stream.
- **J.** They radioed for help.

3. If Stephanie had not thrown out her water bottle, they might have—
- **A.** avoided the first shortcut.
- **B.** been unable to radio for help.
- **C.** been able to climb the hills.
- **D.** avoided the detour to the dry stream.

4. The last thing that Tom and Stephanie did was to—
- **F.** talk about how they might have avoided their mistakes.
- **G.** go to a dry stream.
- **H.** radio for help.
- **J.** get rid of a water bottle.

5. If they had stayed on their original course, they probably would not have—
- **A.** needed help.
- **B** needed a map.
- **C** gotten tired.
- **D** argued.

Notes for Home: Your child read a story and answered questions about the order of events. ***Home Activity:*** Have your child think of a favorite story and list a few important events. Ask your child to explain how the story would have been different if one event had not happened.

Name ____

Writing Across Texts

Directions: Consider what you learned about dust storms and droughts from the selections "Storm-a-Dust" and "What Is a Drought?" Complete the table below by writing five effects of a dust storm and five effects of a drought.

"Storm-a-Dust"	"What Is a Drought?"
1.	**6.**
2.	**7.**
3.	**8.**
4.	**9.**
5.	**10.**

Write a Comparative Essay

Refer to the two reading selections and the completed table above to write an essay in which you compare and contrast the effects of a dust storm and a drought. Write your essay on a separate sheet of paper.

Notes for Home: Your child compared and contrasted information about natural disasters from two sources. ***Home Activity:*** As you read stories and articles, have your child compare and contrast the effects of events described in the reading materials.

Name ______________________________

Grammar: Plural Nouns

REVIEW

Directions: Write the plural form of each of the following nouns. Use a dictionary if you need help.

1. month ______________
2. lunch ______________
3. foot ______________
4. butterfly ______________
5. alley ______________
6. ox ______________
7. tomato ______________
8. dish ______________
9. pencil ______________
10. loaf ______________

Directions: Use the plural form of the noun in ( ) to complete each sentence. Write the plural noun on the line to the left. Use a dictionary if you need help.

______________ **11.** Dust storms blow huge _____ of dust or sand over a large area. (quantity)

______________ **12.** In the 1930s, some _____ of the country suffered terribly. (region)

______________ **13.** Many cows, _____, pigs, and other animals died. (sheep)

______________ **14.** Human _____ were lost as well. (life)

______________ **15.** The powerful _____ blew millions of tons of topsoil into the ocean. (wind)

______________ **16.** As a result, _____ could not farm the land. (person)

______________ **17.** _____ were covered in dust. (Roof)

______________ **18.** Schools were forced to close, and _____ stayed home. (child)

______________ **19.** In many cases, _____ were the only link to the outside world. (radio)

______________ **20.** Great _____ of people moved to other parts of the country to escape devastation. (mass)

Notes for Home: Your child wrote regular and irregular plural nouns. ***Home Activity:*** List singular nouns from the newspaper on slips of paper. Have your child write the plural forms of these nouns.

Name ______________________________

Grammar: Possessive Nouns

Possessive nouns show that one or more persons, places, or things have or own something. They are formed with an **apostrophe (')** and **-s** or with only an **apostrophe (').** Here are three rules to help you write possessive nouns:

- Add **'s** to form the possessive of most singular nouns: the barn's silo.
- Add **'s** to form the possessive of plural nouns that do not end in **-s:** the children's shoes.
- Add only **(')** to form the possessive of plural nouns that end in **-s:** the horses' trough.

Directions: Underline the possessive noun in each sentence. If the possessive noun is plural, circle it as well.

1. The kitchen's warmth was welcome.

2. The children's boots dripped on the floor.

3. Outside, the storm's fury increased.

4. Snow and pellets of ice hit the windows' small, old-fashioned panes.

5. The wind's howl swept down the chimney.

6. The downstairs rooms of the house looked eerie, lit only by the candles' glow.

7. Outside, steam rose from the three sheep's backs.

8. Each sheep's head was away from the wind.

9. The barn's shape was blurred by snow.

10. Some animals' tracks formed small valleys in the snow.

Directions: Rewrite each underlined phrase to show possession. Write the new phrase on the line.

______________________ **11.** Look at the patterns the feet of animals have been making in the snow.

______________________ **12.** Wind has certainly roughened the surface of the ice.

______________________ **13.** Danielle plans to measure the depths of those snowdrifts.

______________________ **14.** Boughs of evergreens can often bear heavy loads of snow.

______________________ **15.** What does the sound of hailstones remind you of?

Notes for Home: Your child identified and formed possessive nouns. ***Home Activity:*** Ask your child to explain how to make singular and plural nouns possessive. Take turns thinking of examples of possessive nouns.

Extra Practice

Grammar: Possessive Nouns

Directions: Rewrite each underlined phrase to show possession. Write the new phrase on the line.

______________ 1. The noses of the animals were lifted to the wind.

______________ 2. Heavy with leaves, the branches of trees creaked and swayed.

______________ 3. Even the tails of the squirrels twitched nervously.

______________ 4. All the animals could sense the threat of the storm.

______________ 5. The waters of the river flowed fast and powerfully.

______________ 6. A frightened deer ran to the edge of the water and tried to cross.

______________ 7. The legs of the deer became caught in a swirling branch.

______________ 8. Soon the cries of the creature rang through the forest.

______________ 9. Fortunately, a cabin for campers stood near the river.

______________ 10. Because of the bravery of the people, the life of the deer was saved.

Write a Description

On a separate sheet of paper, write a description of a storm and how it makes you feel. Use colorful words in your description. Use at least three possessive nouns in your description.

Notes for Home: Your child wrote the possessive forms of nouns. ***Home Activity:*** Write a variety of nouns on small slips of paper. Take turns with your child, choosing the slips and spelling or writing the singular and plural possessive forms of the nouns.

Name ____

Grammar: Possessive Nouns

RETEACHING

Underline the possessive nouns. Write the nouns.

1. Sue's smile was joyful. ______________________
2. The seals' barks were heard outside. ______________________
3. Children's laughter rang in the air. ______________________

A **possessive noun** shows ownership. Add an apostrophe (**'**) and **-s** to spell the possessive form of a singular noun. Add only an apostrophe to spell the possessive form of a plural noun that ends with **-s.** Add an apostrophe and **-s** to spell the possessive form of a plural noun that does not end in **-s.**

Directions: Underline the possessive nouns.

1. The bear's food is being prepared.
2. Lions' roars could be heard throughout the zoo.
3. The keeper's pride in the big cats was clear.
4. The girls ran quickly to the alligators' pits.
5. The boys laughed at the hippopotamus's big yawn.
6. Mr. Morris was fascinated by the monkey's actions.
7. He drew the children's attention to the bears.
8. The sleeping cub's face shone with contentment.
9. The tourists' guide pointed to the cub.

Directions: Write the possessive form of the noun in ( ).

10. The ______________ laughter woke the bear. (men)
11. Look at the ______________ sharp claw. (animal)
12. The ______________ eyes opened wide. (visitors)
13. It walked to the ______________ corner for a nap. (cage)
14. The ______________ directions helped us. (guide)
15. The ______________ cage has a tree trunk with branches. (snake)
16. The ______________ habitat has a lake. (deer)

Notes for Home: Your child used possessive forms of singular and plural nouns. ***Home Activity:*** Have your child make a list of friends, family members, and families' last names. Have him or her write sentences, using the lists to write possessive nouns.

Name ______________________________

Grammar: Possessive Nouns

Directions: Write in the blank the posessive form of the noun in ( ).

1. ______________ population is enormous. (China)
2. China is the ______________ third largest country in land area. (world)
3. This ______________ history dates from 3500 years ago. (country)
4. Early ______________ name for China was "Zhonghua." (scholars)
5. The ______________ meaning is "central land." (word)
6. Their homeland seemed like the ______________ center. (Earth)
7. The ______________ height protected the land. (mountains)
8. The ______________ shores formed its eastern border. (seas)
9. We listened eagerly to the ______________ stories about China. (travelers)

Directions: Rewrite each underlined phrase so that it contains a possessive noun.

10. Chinese civilization was influenced by <u>the ideas of many philosophers</u>.

____

11. Confucius was <u>the son of a noble</u>.

____

12. <u>The beliefs of this man</u> taught love, wisdom, and sincerity.

____

13. Respect for parents was important in <u>the lessons of his students</u>.

____

14. Today his ideas still influence <u>the customs of China</u>.

____

15. <u>The education of children</u> is based on Confucius's teaching.

____

Write a Travel Brochure

On a separate sheet of paper, write a travel brochure for a country you would like to visit. Describe the weather, the people, and must-see places to explore. Use possessive nouns in some of your sentences.

Notes for Home: Your child used possessive forms of singular and plural nouns in sentences. ***Home Activity:*** Together, make a list of places your child often goes. Have your child use possessive forms of the place names to write sentences about what can be found there.

Name ______________________________

Word Study: Compound Words

Directions: Compound words are words formed by combining two other words. Compound words can be **closed** *(sunburn),* **open** *(ice cream),* or **hyphenated** *(half-time).* Combine a word from the left box with a word from the right box to form a compound word that makes sense. Write both words and the resulting compound word on the lines below.

pan	bare
snow	table
fence	sun
beach	dead
baby	through

footed	cloth
cakes	post
flake	out
end	umbrella
sit	burn

1. ____________ + ____________ = ____________
2. ____________ + ____________ = ____________
3. ____________ + ____________ = ____________
4. ____________ + ____________ = ____________
5. ____________ + ____________ = ____________
6. ____________ + ____________ = ____________
7. ____________ + ____________ = ____________
8. ____________ + ____________ = ____________
9. ____________ + ____________ = ____________
10. ____________ + ____________ = ____________

Directions: Read the paragraph. Find five compound words. Write each compound word on the line.

The storm came up out of nowhere. Dresses and shirts on the clothesline flapped in the wind. The scarecrow looked like a stick-fella dancing in the field. A cloudburst of rain came pouring down. Then, as quickly as it had begun, the storm was over.

11. ____________
12. ____________
13. ____________
14. ____________
15. ____________

Notes for Home: Your child wrote compound words, such as *sunburn, ice cream,* and *half-time.* ***Home Activity:*** Play a game with your child. Say one part of a compound word. Challenge your child to complete the compound word.

Pretest

Spelling: Compound Words 1

Pretest Directions: Fold back the page along the dotted line. On the blanks, write the spelling words as they are dictated. When you have finished the test, unfold the page and check your words.

1. ______________________
2. ______________________
3. ______________________
4. ______________________
5. ______________________
6. ______________________
7. ______________________
8. ______________________
9. ______________________
10. ______________________
11. ______________________
12. ______________________
13. ______________________
14. ______________________
15. ______________________
16. ______________________
17. ______________________
18. ______________________
19. ______________________
20. ______________________

1. I went to the library by **myself**.
2. They always enjoy **themselves**.
3. The **hallway** was long.
4. Who is your **homeroom** teacher?
5. They want to know **everything**.
6. I have a **teenage** brother.
7. One **teammate** was late.
8. She has a new **skateboard**.
9. **Everybody** came to the party.
10. Your dog ate my **doughnut**.
11. **Ice cream** is best on hot days.
12. I changed in the **locker room**.
13. I bought a new **tape recorder**.
14. Let's have **root beer** floats.
15. This street is a **dead end**.
16. Can you fix the **air conditioner**?
17. His father has a **polka dot** tie.
18. I love the new **roller coaster**.
19. Put an **ice pack** on your bruise.
20. What is the **solar system**?

Notes for Home: Your child took a pretest on compound words written as one word and as two words. ***Home Activity:*** Help your child learn misspelled words before the final test. Dictate the word and have your child spell the word aloud for you or write it on paper.

Name ______________________________

Spelling: Compound Words 1

Word List

myself	teenage	ice cream	air conditioner
themselves	teammate	locker room	polka dot
hallway	skateboard	tape recorder	roller coaster
homeroom	everybody	root beer	ice pack
everything	doughnut	dead end	solar system

Directions: Add a word to each word below to form a compound word from the box. Write the compound word on the line.

1. root ______________
2. my ______________
3. air ______________
4. dead ______________
5. roller ______________
6. body ______________
7. polka ______________
8. them ______________
9. cream ______________
10. team ______________

Directions: Find the two words in each sentence that make up a compound word from the box. Write the compound word on the line.

______________ 11. My locker is near the weight room.

______________ 12. Boxes blocked the hall, but he found a way past.

______________ 13. Fill the cooler with ice before you pack the food and drinks.

______________ 14. We listened to a tape of a recorder, flute, and guitar.

______________ 15. He had to go home and clean his room.

______________ 16. The solar panel was near the heating system.

______________ 17. She loved to skate fast down the big wooden board.

______________ 18. After shaping the dough into small pieces, place a nut on each piece.

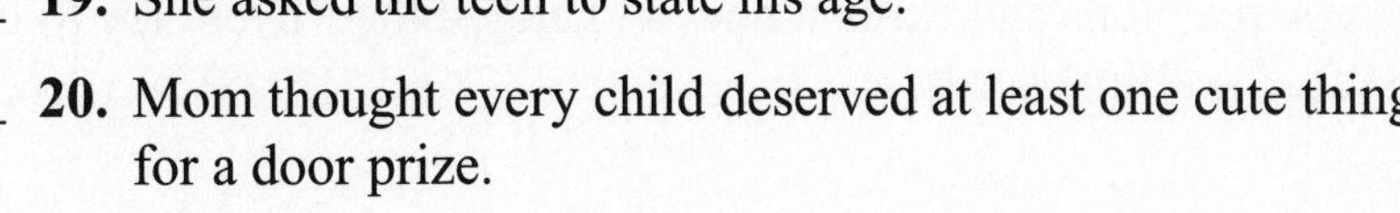

______________ 19. She asked the teen to state his age.

______________ 20. Mom thought every child deserved at least one cute thing for a door prize.

Notes for Home: Your child spelled compound words written as one word and as two words. ***Home Activity:*** Take turns saying one part of one of the compound words from the Word List. The other person names the compound word and spells it.

Spelling: Compound Words 1

Directions: Proofread this story. Find six spelling mistakes. Use the proofreading marks to correct each mistake.

≡	Make a capital.
/	Make a small letter.
∧	Add something.
ℊ	Take out something.
⊙	Add a period.
¶	Begin a new paragraph.

Danny and his family had crouched in their halway closet as the tornado passed by. After the storm, Danny went outside and joined all the neighbors who lived on their ded end street. They were talking among themselves about the damage. It seemed as if evrything had been tossed around. Wet papers made polkadot patterns everywhere. An air conditioner had been blown through a window at the home of Danny's teamate Willie. Luckily, no one had been hurt. And amazingly, a skate board still sat in the yard where someone had left it before the storm.

Spelling Tip

Some compounds are closed and are written as one word: **everything.** Others are open and are written as two words: **air conditioner.**

Word List

myself
themselves
hallway
homeroom
everything
teenage
teammate
skateboard
everybody
doughnut
ice cream
locker room
tape recorder
root beer
dead end
air conditioner
polka dot
roller coaster
ice pack
solar system

Write a Short Story

On a separate sheet of paper, write a short story that describes the effects of a flood, a blizzard, or other violent storm. Include the characters' reactions and explain how it changed their lives. Try to use at least five spelling words.

Notes for Home: Your child spelled compound words written as one word and as two words, such as *everybody* and *tape recorder*. ***Home Activity:*** Encourage your child to find the compound words in a short newspaper article. Make a list of these compound words.

Name ______________________________

Spelling: Compound Words 1

REVIEW

Word List

myself	teenage	ice cream	air conditioner
themselves	teammate	locker room	polka dot
hallway	skateboard	tape recorder	roller coaster
homeroom	everybody	root beer	ice pack
everything	doughnut	dead end	solar system

Directions: Write the word from the box that belongs in each group.

1. pastry, turnover, ______________________

2. bike, roller skates, ______________________

3. galaxy, universe, ______________________

4. gym, stadium, ______________________

5. Ferris wheel, carousel, ______________________

6. lobby, corridor, ______________________

7. freezer, refrigerator, ______________________

8. stripe, plaid, ______________________

9. turntable, CD player, ______________________

10. choir room, assembly room, ______________________

Directions: Choose the word from the box that best completes each song title. Write the word on the line to the left. Be sure to capitalize each important word.

______________________ **11.** "A Bandage for My Heart and an _____ for My Soul"

______________________ **12.** "Two Straws Sticking in a _____ Float"

______________________ **13.** "Why Does _____ Clown Around in Class?"

______________________ **14.** "Just Too Young to Be a _____ Superstar"

______________________ **15.** "Scoop Me Up Another _____ Cone!"

______________________ **16.** "I'm Lonesome and Lonely All by _____"

______________________ **17.** "Just One More _____ Street"

______________________ **18.** "They'll Have to Move It by _____"

______________________ **19.** "_____ Is Better Now That You're Here"

______________________ **20.** "My _____ and I Can Win Any Game"

Notes for Home: Your child spelled compound words written as one word and as two words, such as *everybody* and *tape recorder*. ***Home Activity:*** Write each part of a compound word on a slip of paper. Draw two slips and try to form a compound word.

Locate/Collect Information

You can **locate and collect information** about a topic using a variety of sources. Sources of information include print (textbooks, reference books, trade books, magazines/periodicals, newspapers, photographs), electronic media (computer: CD-ROMs, Internet websites; non-computer: audiotapes, videotapes, films, microfilms), and people (librarians, teachers, experts, eyewitnesses).

Directions: Suppose you are writing a report about volcanic eruptions. Use the sources of information below to answer the questions that follow.

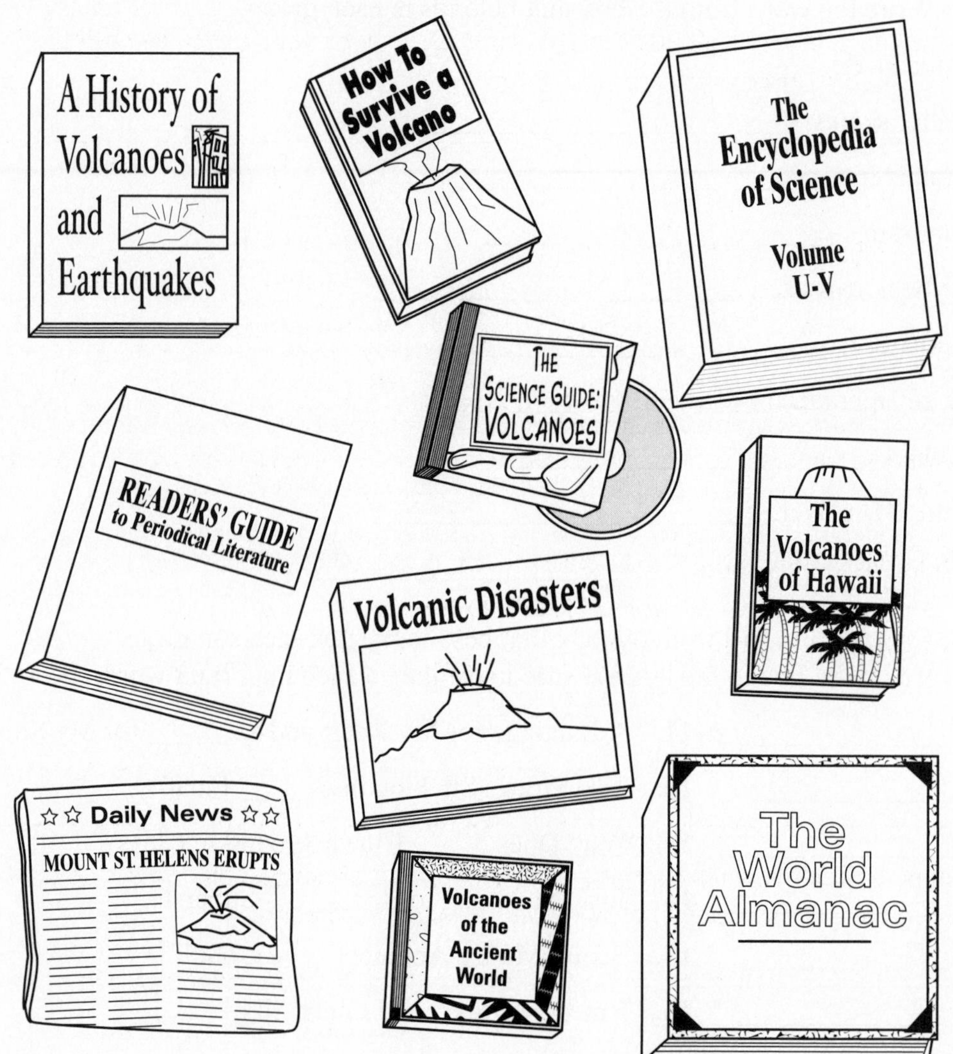

1. Why might the encyclopedia be a good place to start your research? ______________________________

____

____

2. Which key words might you look up in an encyclopedia to find the information you need?

____

____

3. Which kind of sources would be best if you were looking for information about a volcano that erupted yesterday? Why?

____

____

4. What information can you find using *Readers' Guide to Periodical Literature?*

____

____

5. If you wanted to include pictures in your research report, which sources might include visual material that you could use?

____

____

6. What are some sources other than the ones shown that you might use to locate information for your research report?

____

____

7. Suppose you wanted to show information about famous volcanic disasters over a long period of time. Which of the sources shown might be the most helpful? Why?

____

____

8. What would be the best way to keep track of information if you interviewed an expert on volcanoes? Why?

____

____

9. An almanac often gives charts and tables listing facts about specific events. What kind of information might an almanac provide on volcanic eruptions?

____

10. Write your own question of inquiry about volcanoes. Then tell which source of information you might use to try to find the answer for your question. Explain why this source of information would be helpful.

____

____

Notes for Home: Your child learned to locate and collect information on a research topic. ***Home Activity:*** Give your child a topic for research. Have him or her suggest a number of sources that might contain useful information about that topic.

Family Times

Name______________________________

Summary

Girl Saves Stranded Sea Turtle

Laura would always remember the day she set out to save a giant sea turtle. He was stuck in the sand, far too heavy to push or carry to the sea, and steadily growing weaker. Laura's rescue attempts failed to free him, but the look in the turtle's eyes kept her from giving up. Finally, with help from Granny May, Laura discovered how to give the turtle enough strength to return to the open sea. In the process, she learned a valuable lesson about life and hope.

Activity

A New Point of View. Ask your child to retell the story from the turtle's point of view. Suggest that he or she include the turtle's thoughts about his life-threatening situation and about Laura's attempts to help.

Reading Skills

Visualizing

Visualizing means creating a mental image as you read. To help you visualize a scene, an author may use the following:

- ❖ Imagery, or vivid words and phrases that create clear, detailed pictures.
  The green net bulged with small, red, jumping shrimp.
- ❖ Sensory details, or words that describe how something looks, sounds, smells, tastes, or feels:
  The turtle's shell was round and smooth. It made a rasping sound as the turtle hurried to the gentle waves.

Activity

Describe a Scene. Cut out several magazine photos that show interesting and picturesque places. Display the photos so others can see them clearly. Take turns describing one of the photos using imagery and sensory details. Other family members should try to guess which photo is being described.

Family Times

Tested Vocabulary

Words to Know

Knowing the meanings of these words is important to reading "The Day of the Turtle." Practice using these words to learn their meanings.

driftwood wood that has washed upon the shore

jellyfish a sea animal made up of jellylike tissue

spar a wooden pole used as part of a ship's sail

tentacle a long, slender growth on a jellyfish

wary cautious; careful

Grammar

Commas with Nouns in a Series

A **comma** is a punctuation mark used to separate three or more nouns in a series, or list. Use a comma after each noun except the last one.

The waves contained shrimp, lobster, and jellyfish.

If a word pair is part of the series, treat it as if it were one word.

The deeper water contained sharks, <u>sea turtles</u>, tuna, and barracuda.

Activity

Write Captions. Write captions for photographs in a photo album. Identify people and items in the photos. Remember to use commas to separate three or more nouns. Example: *Adam, Dale, and I are standing in front of a huge aquarium full of fish, sharks, and coral.*

Tested Spelling Words

Name ______________________________

Visualizing

- To **visualize** is to create a mental image as you read.
- An author may help you visualize by using imagery, words that produce strong images, or sensory details, words that describe how something looks, sounds, smells, tastes, or feels.

Directions: Reread "The Wexford Doe." Then complete each box. List the words from the story that help you visualize what Deirdre experiences.

The Woods	The Stone Wall	The Doe
at the end of Scarlet Oak	low	**7.**
damp air	**4.**	**8.**
1.	**5.**	**9.**
2.	one web cradled a sleeping spider	scampered away
3.	**6.**	**10.**

Notes for Home: Your child identified words that appeal to the senses and create strong mental images. ***Home Activity:*** Challenge your child to visualize a familiar place and then describe it to you by using imagery and sensory details.

Name ___________________________

Vocabulary

Directions: Choose the word from the box that best completes each sentence. Write the word on the line to the left.

Check the Words You Know
___ driftwood
___ jellyfish
___ spar
___ tentacle
___ wary

___________________ **1.** While we were sailing, we saw a large _____ floating past, just under the surface of the water.

___________________ **2.** Swimmers need to be _____ of jellyfish.

___________________ **3.** Touching a single jellyfish _____ can be very painful and even dangerous.

___________________ **4.** We set anchor near a beach, furled the sail, and fastened it to the _____.

___________________ **5.** We gathered _____ for a small fire and watched the sun set.

Directions: Choose the word from the box that best matches each clue. Write the word in the puzzle.

Down

6. a sea animal made of jellylike tissue

7. cautious; careful

Across

8. a long, slender growth of a jellyfish

9. wood that has been washed up on the shore

10. a wooden pole used as part of a ship's sail

Write a Description

On a separate sheet of paper, write a description of an imaginary sea creature. Is it friendly or dangerous? What does it look like? How does it move? Use vivid details and your vocabulary words to make your writing interesting.

Notes for Home: Your child identified and used vocabulary words from "The Day of the Turtle." ***Home Activity:*** Work together to create a sea story, using the listed vocabulary words. Share your story with other family members.

Name ___________________________

Visualizing

- To **visualize** is to create a mental image as you read.
- Imagery and sensory details help you visualize scenes from stories.

Directions: Reread what happens in "The Day of the Turtle" when Granny May tries to feed shrimp to the turtle. Then answer the questions below. Use imagery and sensory details from the story to help you visualize.

She told me to dig a bowl in the sand right under the turtle's chin, and then she shook out her net. He looked mildly interested for a moment and then looked away. It was no good. Granny May was looking out to sea, shielding her eyes against the glare of the sun.

"I wonder," she murmured. "I wonder. I won't be long." And she was gone down to the sea. She was wading out up to her ankles, then up to her knees, with her shrimping net scooping through the water around her. I stayed behind with the turtle and threw more stones at the gulls. When she came back, her net was bulging with jellyfish, blue jellyfish. She emptied them into the turtle's sandy bowl. At once he was at them like a vulture, snapping, crunching, swallowing, until there wasn't a tentacle left.

1. Picture the day in your mind. Is it sunny, cloudy, hot, or cold? How do you know?

____

____

2. Describe how you think Granny May looks as she wades into the sea.

____

3. What details does the author use to help you picture the net with jellyfish?

____

____

4. Visualize the turtle as he eats the jellyfish. How does eating the jellyfish change his behavior?

____

____

5. Select another scene from the story, such as the turtle trudging toward the water. On a separate sheet of paper, describe the mental image you create from the story details.

Notes for Home: Your child used imagery and sensory details from the story to create a mental image of a scene. ***Home Activity:*** Have your child choose a favorite story. Work with your child to visualize and describe characters and places from the story using story details.

Selection Test

Directions: Choose the best answer to each item. Mark the letter for the answer you have chosen.

Part 1: Vocabulary

Find the answer choice that means about the same as the underlined word in each sentence.

1. Alfred filled a pail with <u>jellyfish</u>.
A. fish eggs
B. sea animals with soft, often clear, tissue
C. sea animals with shells
D. sea animals that look like horses

2. Jenny would not touch the <u>tentacle</u>.
F. part of the body by which an animal sees
G. organ in which digestion occurs
H. the outer surface of an animal
J. long, slender growth on an animal; feeler

3. When she saw the large dog, Liz felt <u>wary</u>.
A. cautious; careful
B. surprised
C. interested; curious
D. friendly

4. The crew returned with a new <u>spar</u>.
F. floor of a ship
G. door on a ship
H. wooden pole used to support a sail on a ship
J. a platform used by a lookout on a ship

5. Mr. Hong had a pile of <u>driftwood</u>.
A. wood washed up on the shore
B. highly polished wood
C. wood found under trees in an orchard
D. expensive wood

Part 2: Comprehension

Use what you know about the story to answer each item.

6. Why does Laura have such a hard time getting the turtle to the water?
F. It struggles against her.
G. It has lost its shell.
H. It likes lying in the sun.
J. It is very big and heavy.

7. What does Laura do first?
A. tries to turn the turtle over
B. digs a hole beside the turtle
C. digs a channel to the sea
D. piles seaweed on top of the turtle

8. What has happened to Granny May's house?
F. It is filled with water.
G. The roof has blown off.
H. It has burned down.
J. The doors and windows are broken.

9. On the beach, the gulls are waiting for—
A. a ship to appear.
B. the tide to come in.
C. a chance to eat the turtle.
D. the tide to go out.

10. Laura digs a channel to the sea to—
F. help the turtle return to the water.
G. hide the turtle.
H. keep the gulls away from the turtle.
J. collect food for the turtle.

11. Why doesn't the turtle return to the sea the first day?
A. It cannot breathe.
B. It is very young.
C. It is too weak.
D. It cannot walk on land.

12. Laura thinks that the turtle—
- F. wants to be her pet.
- G. will always remember her.
- H. is afraid of Granny May.
- J. understands what she says.

13. Which sentence from the story best helps you visualize what the turtle looks like lying in the sand?
- A. "I think it's called a leatherback turtle."
- B. "After a while I gave up and sat down beside him on the sand."
- C. "His flippers were quite still and held out to the clouds above as if he was worshiping them."
- D. "That turtle would just be food to him, and to anyone else who finds him."

14. Granny May most likely helps Laura with the turtle because she—
- F. understands why Laura wants to save it.
- G. does not like turtle soup.
- H. can always catch plenty of shrimp.
- J. likes having secrets from Laura's father.

15. Based on what Laura says about her father, how will he probably react when he finds out that Laura and Granny May helped the turtle go back to the sea?
- A. He will go down to the beach to look for it.
- B. He will be angry because they need the food.
- C. He will understand their concern for the turtle.
- D. He will tell them to go catch another turtle.

Name ______________________________

Visualizing

- To **visualize** is to create a mental image as you read.
- Imagery and sensory details help you visualize scenes from stories.

Directions: Read the story below.

The desert is a good home for my family, but it isn't fit for a dog. That's the thought that went through my mind when I came across the dog that I now call Elmo.

I don't know where Elmo came from. But the trip through the burning desert had not been kind to him. His fur felt like strips of old paper. He moved more like a broken bicycle than a dog. Elmo was careful not to let his left hind foot step solidly on the ground. His leg must have hurt, because he would flinch when he stepped on it as if he had stepped on a needle.

For about a month, we kept Elmo inside, away from the harsh winds and heavy heat. Now, Elmo's fur is a glossy black color, and it feels like a thick rug. His leg is like a healthy tree trunk, and he gallops like a horse. Elmo is now as much at home in the desert as we are.

Directions: Complete the sentences in the boxes. Think about the details in the story. Use your own words to write descriptions.

At the Beginning		By the End
Elmo's fur is dry and thin.	→	**1.** Elmo's fur is:
2. Elmo's walk is:	→	**3.** Elmo's walk is:
4. Elmo's leg is:	→	**5.** Elmo's leg is:

Notes for Home: Your child read a story and used imagery and sensory details from the story to visualize its elements. ***Home Activity:*** Encourage your child to visualize a favorite place. Then have your child describe what the place looks like.

Making Judgments

REVIEW

Directions: Read the passage. Then read each question about the passage. Choose the best answer to each question. Mark the letter for the answer you have chosen.

Letters to the Editor

The Problem of Palmer's Pond

To the Editor,

The issue about what to do with Palmer's Pond has arisen once more. Some people think we should allow motorboats on Palmer's Pond. But independent studies have shown that oil from the boats would put fish in danger. So we should keep motorboats *out* of the pond.

We should also be wary of the plan to build a hotel near the pond. A hotel would destroy the quiet that we love. For the same reason, we should not build a new beach. No matter what the mayor's study says, we don't need a new beach yet.

My family has lived on Palmer's Pond for 120 years. I know what the pond needs. To save the pond, we need to keep it the same.

Sincerely,

Gillian Boswell

1. When the author says that motorboats should be kept off the pond, she—
- **A.** does not support her opinion.
- **B.** uses an independent study to support her opinion.
- **C.** is only stating facts.
- **D.** is ignoring facts.

2. The author's opinion about a new hotel is—
- **F.** supported by a study.
- **G.** supported by facts.
- **H.** not supported.
- **J.** contradicted by other statements in the article.

3. When the author says that a new beach should not be built, she—
- **A.** uses a study to support her opinion.
- **B.** seems free of bias.
- **C.** lists facts.
- **D.** ignores a study.

4. Which statement shows that the author might **not** be a fair judge of plans for the pond?
- **F.** She ignores the mayor's study.
- **G.** She ignores an independent study.
- **H.** She doesn't want motorboats.
- **J.** Her family has lived on the pond for 120 years.

5. Because the author wants the pond to stay the same, she probably—
- **A.** will not consider anything that might change it.
- **B.** considers all opposing opinions carefully.
- **C.** gives a balanced account of the situation.
- **D.** supports all of her opinions.

Notes for Home: Your child made judgments about the statements in a letter and how well the arguments are supported. ***Home Activity:*** With your child, read an editorial column. Discuss how well the author presents and supports his or her opinions.

Name ______________________

Writing Across Texts

Directions: You read two selections about the living earth in "The Day of the Turtle" and "Storm-a-Dust." Think about the characters, setting, and plot. How are the selections alike? How are they different? Write your responses in the Venn diagram below.

The Day of the Turtle	Both Stories	Storm-a-Dust
The story is about an animal.	A young girl is the main character in both stories.	The story is about a dust storm.
2. ______________________	1. ______________________	4. ______________________
3. ______________________		5. ______________________

Write a Comparative Paragraph

In a paragraph or two, compare and contrast the problems faced by Laura with the problems faced by Lindy. Use the selections, what you know, and the completed Venn diagram to write your paragraph on a separate sheet of paper.

Notes for Home: Your child has compared and contrasted information from two different stories. ***Home Activity:*** As you read other stories or articles, encourage your child to point out how events are alike and different.

Name ______________________________

Grammar: Sentence Punctuation

REVIEW

Directions: Write **C** if the sentence has correct end punctuation. If the punctuation is incorrect, write the correct punctuation on the line.

1. Do you have an animal shelter in your town. _____
2. What a great job those shelters do! _____
3. They rescue and take in animals of all kinds, especially cats and dogs? _____
4. Please answer this question? _____
5. Did you adopt your cat from the local shelter? _____
6. The shelter was full of adorable animals. _____
7. How hard it must have been to choose one animal? _____
8. How long did it take you to make up your mind? _____

Directions: Read each sentence. Add a comma to each compound sentence. Then add the correct end punctuation.

9. The day was hot and we decided to drive to the beach
10. We packed our bathing suits and a delicious picnic lunch
11. We had to wait for Leroy and Anna was a little late too
12. Finally we were in the car and on our way
13. How excited we were about going to the beach
14. What is in the middle of the road ahead
15. It might be a small horse or a sheep or it could be a large dog
16. My mom slowed the car and we saw a big, dirty, tired dog
17. Should we stop or should we continue driving
18. We wanted to keep going but we could not abandon that poor animal
19. What a smart decision we made
20. We never got to the beach but we did eventually get the best pet in the world

Notes for Home: Your child added punctuation marks to the ends of sentences and added commas between parts of compound sentences. ***Home Activity:*** Challenge your child to explain the reason for the punctuation in several sentences in favorite books or magazines.

Practice

Grammar: Commas with Nouns in Series and in Direct Address

A **comma** is a punctuation mark that is used to set off a word or a group of words from other words in the same sentence. In this way, a comma helps to make the meaning of a sentence clear.

Three or more words (such as nouns) or groups of words listed together in a sentence are called a **series.** A comma is used after each item in the series except the last.

Mike, Sam, and Tammy went to Stewart Beach Aquarium.
The three friends had peanut butter and jelly sandwiches, apples, and juice for lunch.

One or two commas are used to set off the names of people who are directly addressed in speech or writing. This use of a noun is called **direct address.**

Mike, do you know which bus goes to the aquarium?
I think, Tammy, that it is the M17 bus.
Do you know for sure, Sam?

Directions: Add commas to each sentence to set off nouns used in a series or in direct address.

1. Eleanor Joe and Terry work at Stewart Beach Aquarium.
2. Eleanor gives tours on Fridays Saturdays and Sundays.
3. Joe arranges for lectures films and shows.
4. Did you think Terry that my last lecture was clear?
5. The aquarium has been attracting students teachers and tourists.
6. When is the next showing of the film about dolphins Joe?
7. Terry is one of the people who feed the dolphins porpoises and seals.
8. Joe please finish the new schedule by Friday.
9. Stingrays sharks manatees and squids are just a few of the creatures that you can see at the aquarium.
10. Stewart Beach Aquarium is easy to reach by train bus or car.

Notes for Home: Your child added commas to nouns in a series and in direct address. ***Home Activity:*** Say sentences in which people are spoken to directly by name. Ask your child which word the comma should follow.

Name ______________________________

Grammar: Commas with Nouns in Series and in Direct Address

Directions: Add commas to each sentence to set off nouns used in a series or in a direct address.

1. Paul do you remember that terrible storm three summers ago?
2. It rained on Monday Tuesday Wednesday and Thursday.
3. Water got into the attic the cellar and the garage.
4. Were you here that summer Jamal?
5. The storm damaged the house the garden and the new deck.

Directions: Rewrite each sentence below to include a noun of direct address. Use commas as needed.

6. Did I tell you about one downpour that lasted nine days?

____

____

7. TV news stories showed rescuers rowing through flooded areas.

____

____

8. Rivers at flood level threatened people's homes.

____

____

9. The nonstop rain was part of the El Niño effect.

____

10. Yes, this occurred in the spring of 1998.

____

Write a News Article

On a separate sheet of paper, write a brief news article about a strong force in nature, such as a blizzard, hurricane, tornado, or flood. The force can be one that you have experienced or one that you have read about or heard about. Include items in a series. Remember to use commas correctly.

Notes for Home: Your child used commas to separate words listed in a series and to set off the names of people being addressed directly. ***Home Activity:*** Invite your child to write several sentences in which three or more items are listed in a series, using commas to separate them.

Name ______________________________

RETEACHING

Grammar: Commas with Nouns in Series and in Direct Address

Circle the commas in the sentences below.

1. Alicia, what is an aqueduct?
2. It is a water canal, tunnel, or pipe.
3. I am going to Italy to see them, Veronica.

When you write, use commas:
- to separate words or groups of words in a series;
- to set off the name of a person directly addressed.

Directions: Insert commas where they are needed in the following sentences.

1. Jena what is an aqueduct bridge?
2. It is a structure with arches a road and a canal.
3. It carried water people and goods across a valley.
4. Nancy what is the Aqua Appia?
5. It was the first Roman aqueduct Darla.
6. Nine Roman aqueducts were built in all Judy.
7. Some of them John are still in use.

Directions: Use each set of words to write a new sentence. Use the words as items in a series. Add commas where they belong.

8. June July August

____

____

9. pizza ice cream potato chips

____

____

Notes for Home: Your child used commas in sentences with nouns in series and names directly addressed. ***Home Activity:*** Watch a television news program together. Have your child write sentences in which nouns are used in a series or people are directly addressed. Use sentences from the news program.

Grammar: Commas with Nouns in Series and in Direct Address

Directions: Add commas where needed to the sentences below.

1. Sharon who are the Inuit?
2. They are a group of people who live in areas of Greenland North America and Siberia.
3. They inhabit Baffin Island Banks Island and Victoria Island.
4. Inuit is their name for themselves Gerald.
5. Lisa it means "the people."
6. They arrived in North America after the Native Americans Sandra.
7. Kim do the Inuit people have many dialects?
8. Many stories legends and myths are told in the Inuit language.

Directions: Rewrite each sentence below to include a noun in direct address. You may wish to add other information as well. Use commas as needed.

9. Learning another language is easiest when a person is very young.

____

____

10. Why do you think that is true?

____

____

11. If you would like to understand more about a particular culture and its customs, learning some of the language can be helpful.

____

____

Write a Paragraph

On a separate sheet of paper, write a paragraph about a people or culture you would like to study. Describe some of their customs that you find interesting. You may use an encyclopedia to find information, if you wish.

Notes for Home: Your child used commas in sentences in which people are directly addressed by name. ***Home Activity:*** Have your child write commands for toys or stuffed animals in your home, directly addressing them by name. Your child should use commas in his or her written commands.

Name ______________________________

Word Study: Base Words

Directions: Many words are formed by adding letters to the beginning or end of a word. The word you start with is called the **base word.** Read each sentence. Find the base word in the underlined word. Write the base word on the line.

_______________ **1.** The turtle lay gasping for air.

_______________ **2.** It seemed as if it could not move an inch.

_______________ **3.** The turtle kept shutting its mouth.

_______________ **4.** I shouted at the turtle to get into the water.

_______________ **5.** But the creature was too exhausted to move.

_______________ **6.** The turtle lay uncovered and exposed.

_______________ **7.** It looked at me with unblinking eyes.

_______________ **8.** The turtle's wrinkled skin was becoming dry.

_______________ **9.** The birds made a threatening noise.

_______________ **10.** I honestly didn't know how to help the turtle.

Directions: Combine each base word and ending to make a new word. You might need to add, drop, or change letters to spell the word correctly. Write the new word on the line.

11. nudge + -ing = _______________

12. drag + -ing = _______________

13. noisy + -ly = _______________

14. hungry + -er = _______________

15. jump + -ing = _______________

Notes for Home: Your child identified base words in longer words, such as *think* in *unthinking,* and used base words to write longer words. ***Home Activity:*** Read a news article with your child. Look for words that are formed from base words.

Name ______________________

Pretest

Spelling: Compound Words 2

Pretest Directions: Fold back the page along the dotted line. On the blanks, write the spelling words as they are dictated. When you have finished the test, unfold the page and check your words.

1. ______________________
2. ______________________
3. ______________________
4. ______________________
5. ______________________
6. ______________________
7. ______________________
8. ______________________
9. ______________________
10. ______________________
11. ______________________
12. ______________________
13. ______________________
14. ______________________
15. ______________________
16. ______________________
17. ______________________
18. ______________________
19. ______________________
20. ______________________

1. The **basketball** game was close.
2. We looked **everywhere** for him.
3. The cat went **outside**.
4. **Summertime** is always nice.
5. I forgot **something** at home.
6. She said it as an **afterthought**.
7. My sister is a **cheerleader**.
8. The **quarterback** was tackled.
9. This old **bookstore** is wonderful.
10. He works at the **courthouse**.
11. She had to **baby-sit** her brother.
12. Let's go **roller-skating** tomorrow.
13. The old **drive-in** theater closed.
14. You must learn **self-control**.
15. He has a **part-time** job.
16. We **ice-skated** for an hour.
17. My aunt is **ninety-five** years old.
18. Her **brother-in-law** is a pilot.
19. We **water-skied** all day.
20. I like **old-fashioned** clothing.

Notes for Home: Your child took a pretest on compound words with and without hyphens. ***Home Activity:*** Help your child learn misspelled words. He or she can divide misspelled words into parts (such as syllables), concentrate on each part, and notice if there is a hyphen.

Name ______________________

Spelling: Compound Words 2

Word List				
basketball	something	bookstore	drive-in	ninety-five
everywhere	afterthought	courthouse	self-control	brother-in-law
outside	cheerleader	baby-sit	part-time	water-skied
summertime	quarterback	roller-skating	ice-skated	old-fashioned

Directions: Choose a word from the box that best answers each question. Write the word on the line.

______________ **1.** What is the opposite of *modern?*

______________ **2.** What would be an excellent test score?

______________ **3.** When do schoolchildren have lots of free time?

______________ **4.** What helps a person keep his or her temper?

______________ **5.** What do you have if you have more than nothing?

______________ **6.** How do you describe a job you only go to on weekends?

______________ **7.** Which word names an idea that comes too late?

Directions: Write the words from the box that belong in each group.

Places	People	Activities
8. ______	**13.** ______	**16.** ______
9. ______	**14.** ______	**17.** ______
10. ______	**15.** ______	**18.** ______
11. ______		**19.** ______
12. ______		**20.** ______

Notes for Home: Your child spelled compound words with and without hyphens and compounds made up of a noun and a verb. ***Home Activity:*** Read a newspaper with your child. Make a list of compound words you find.

Proofread and Write

Spelling: Compound Words 2

Directions: Proofread this news story. Find six spelling mistakes. Use the proofreading marks to correct each mistake.

≡	Make a capital.
/	Make a small letter.
∧	Add something.
℘	Take out something.
⊙	Add a period.
¶	Begin a new paragraph.

Local Students Save Dog

A small dog named Wylie had a quarter-back and a cheer-leader to thank for saving his life. According to Stan Nagy, the dog's owner and brother-in law to the mayor, Wylie chased something into a pipe on a street. As temperatures out side soared above ninety-five degrees, the little dog couldn't get out. Luckily, Paul Woud and Yassi Levine were roller-skating to a nearby drivin restaurant when they heard Wylie bark. Levine, a partime clerk's intern at the courthouse, alerted the police, who freed Wylie.

Word List
basketball
everywhere
outside
summertime
something
afterthought
cheerleader
quarterback
bookstore
courthouse
baby-sit
roller-skating
drive-in
self-control
part-time
ice-skated
ninety-five
brother-in-law
water-skied
old-fashioned

Spelling Tip

Remember to keep all the letters when writing a closed compound word. Use hyphens for numbers twenty-one to ninety-nine, compounds ending with **in-law,** compounds beginning with **self,** and compounds made up of a noun and a verb.

Write a News Story

On a separate sheet of paper, write a news story about an animal rescue. Try to use at least five of your spelling words.

Notes for Home: Your child spelled compound words with and without hyphens and compounds made up of a noun and a verb. ***Home Activity:*** Take turns naming other compounds that contain one of the shorter words that make up the compounds in the Word List.

Name ______________________________

Spelling: Compound Words 2

REVIEW

Word List

basketball	something	bookstore	drive-in	ninety-five
everywhere	afterthought	courthouse	self-control	brother-in-law
outside	cheerleader	baby-sit	part-time	water-skied
summertime	quarterback	roller-skating	ice-skated	old-fashioned

Directions: Choose the word from the box that includes the underlined part of each word below. Write the word on the line.

1. twenty-five ____________
2. law-abiding ____________
3. afternoon ____________
4. self-pity ____________
5. nowhere ____________
6. wastebasket ____________
7. everything ____________
8. drive-through ____________
9. shutout ____________
10. storybook ____________

Directions: Choose a word from the box that best completes each person's statement. Write the word on the line to the left.

____________ **11.** Big brother: "Sure, Mom. I'll _____ the kids tonight."

____________ **12.** Football player: "If the _____ passes me the ball, I'll run."

____________ **13.** Judge: "My office can be found in the county _____."

____________ **14.** Little girl: "I want to go to the _____ party at the rink."

____________ **15.** Coach: "To be a _____, you must have pep and team spirit."

____________ **16.** Boater: "We _____ up and down the lake all afternoon."

____________ **17.** Antique dealer: "People really love _____ gadgets."

____________ **18.** Student: "To earn a little money, I work _____ in the fall."

____________ **19.** Lifeguard: "The outdoor pool is open daily in the _____."

____________ **20.** Hockey player: "I've _____ since the day I learned to walk."

Notes for Home: Your child spelled compound words with and without hyphens and compounds made up of a noun and a verb. ***Home Activity:*** Challenge your child to write the hyphenated compounds from the list in alphabetical order.

Name ______________________________

Technology: Study Strategies

CD-ROM resources can help you gather information on a particular topic. You might use a CD-ROM dictionary, encyclopedia, or a topic-related CD-ROM. You can use search CD-ROMs to find specific information or click on underlined links to find related information.

Directions: Use the three CD-ROM sample screens to answer the questions that follow.

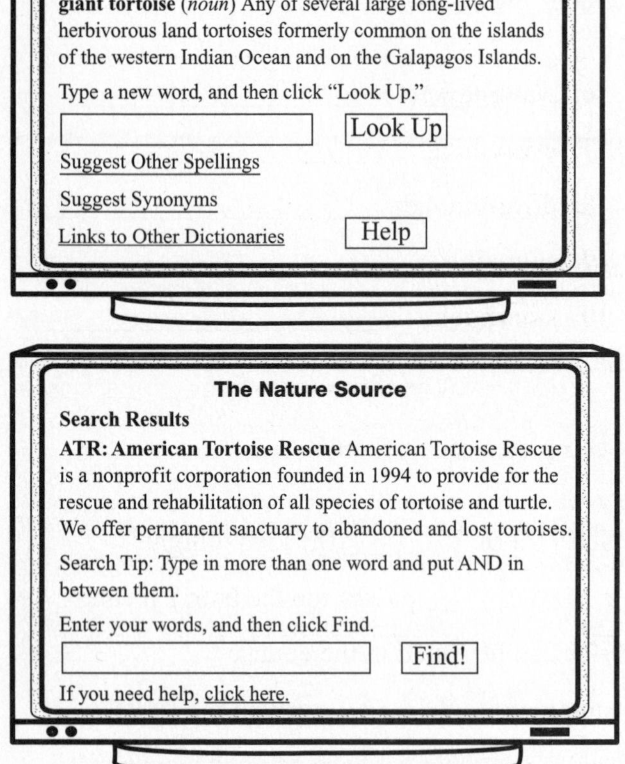

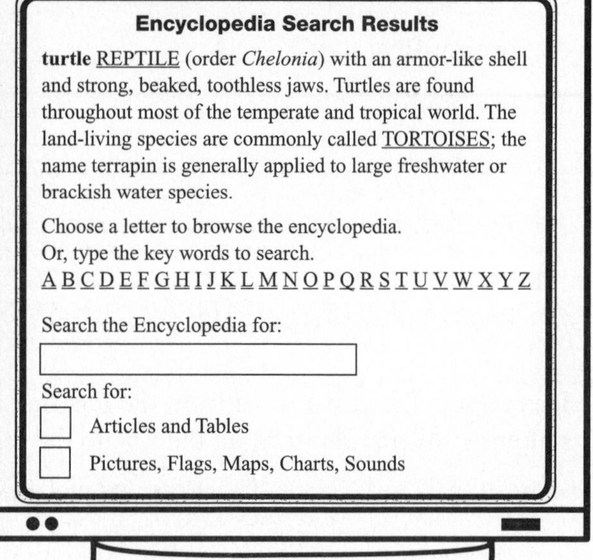

1. How would you find the meaning of "herbivorous" using the CD-ROM dictionary?

____

2. How would you find examples of the sounds turtles make in the CD-ROM encyclopedia?

____

3. How could you use the CD-ROM encyclopedia to find related information about tortoises?

____

4. What key words could you use to find information about a turtle's diet in "The Nature Source" CD-ROM? Hint: Use AND between key words.

____

Name ______________________________

Use **study strategies** to help you save time and avoid reading irrelevant information. You can make a **K-W-L table,** follow the steps of **SQ2R,** or **skim and scan** text to focus your research.

Directions: Use the study strategies below and the three CD-ROM samples to answer the questions that follow.

K What I Know	W What I Want to Know	L What I Learned

SQ2R

- **Survey** the text
- Formulate **questions** about it.
- **Read** the text.
- **Recite** what you have learned.

Skim a text to see if it is appropriate.

Scan a text using key words to locate specific information.

5. Why would writing questions about what you want to know help you save research time?

____

____

6. Pick one of the CD-ROM samples. Write one question about something more you would want to know after reading the information on the CD-ROM.

____

7. When you're surveying or skimming a text, why is it important to look at titles, heads, and boldfaced or underlined words?

____

8. Why are the underlined words in the CD-ROM encyclopedia entry important?

____

9. Scan the information in "The Nature Source" CD-ROM to find out what ATR stands for and when this group was formed.

____

10. Which of the three study strategies would you be most likely to use? Why?

____

____

Notes for Home: Your child used CD-ROM resources to practice using different study strategies. ***Home Activity:*** With your child, pick one of the three study strategies described above. Help your child use one of these strategies to prepare for an upcoming test or research report.

Family Times

Name________________________________

Summary

Huge Oil Spill Kills Countless Wild Creatures

In March 1989, the *Exxon Valdez* struck a reef. The result was the largest oil spill in U.S. history. The oil damaged thousands of miles of coastline and killed countless birds, fish, and other animals. Rescuers rushed to stop the oil from spreading and save what wildlife they could, but they faced many challenges. Scientists continue to study the area and its recovery.

Activity

Act Out the Part. Encourage your child to share with you information he or she learned about the *Exxon Valdez* oil spill. Ask your child to act out the part of a rescue worker. Have him or her describe the cleanup process and explain how the oil spill affects the local wildlife.

Reading Skills

Persuasive Devices

Persuasive devices are the special techniques an author uses to influence the way you think or feel.

One type of persuasive device is the use of **loaded words.** Authors use loaded words to bring out an emotional response in readers and to convince readers of their ideas and views. For example, an author who describes our environment as *fragile* wants to bring out a feeling of concern and protectiveness in the reader.

As you read persuasive writing, think about whether the author is appealing to your reason through facts and ideas or to your emotions through loaded words.

Activity

Write an Announcement. Write a public service announcement that you might broadcast on the radio or television about the harmful effects of an oil spill or other disaster on the environment. Use loaded words.

Family Times

Tested Vocabulary

Words to Know

Knowing the meanings of these words is important to reading "Saving the Sound."

Practice using these words to learn their meanings.

cleanup the act of cleaning up

contaminated polluted

environment the air, water, soil, and so on

fragile delicate; easily damaged

muck filth

toll a thing lost or suffered

widespread occuring in many places

Grammar

Subject-Verb Agreement

The subject and verb in a sentence must work together, or agree in number. If a singular noun subject is used in a sentence, then the verb form that agrees with that subject must be used. The same is true for plural noun subjects.

Words that come between the subject and the verb do not affect the number of the subject or the form of the verb. In the following sentences, the subjects are underlined once and the verbs are underlined twice.

The tanker in the bay hits the reef.

The feathers on all the birds stick together.

The men arrive in all kinds of boats.

Activity

Agreement Game. Have one player name a singular or plural subject. Have the other player give a verb that agrees with the subject named and make up a sentence using the subject and verb. Switch roles, using other subjects and verbs.

Tested Spelling Words

______	______	______	______
______	______	______	______
______	______	______	______
______	______	______	______
______	______	______	______

Name ______________________________

Persuasive Devices

- **Persuasive devices** are the special techniques an author uses to influence the way you think or feel.
- One type of persuasive device is the use of *loaded words.* Authors use *loaded words* to bring out an emotional response in readers and to convince readers of their ideas and views.

Directions: Reread "Why Care?" Then read the following paraphrases of the article. Complete the table by underlining the loaded word or words in each paraphrase. Then describe the response that readers are likely to have to the loaded words.

Paraphrase	Emotional Response
Humankind dominates the environment.	Readers feel sympathy for the weak and vulnerable environment.
We affect plants and animals negatively.	Readers feel ashamed of the way humans have affected plants and animals.
We shouldn't be bullying the rest of Earth's creatures.	**1.**
Plants and animals are important sources of beauty and fun.	**2.**
Many species enrich our lives just by existing.	**3.**
Our actions may force species into extinction.	**4.**
We are violating other living things' right to exist.	**5.**

Notes for Home: Your child identified loaded words, a persuasuve device used by writers to persuade readers of their point of view. ***Home Activity:*** Help your child identify loaded words in a newspaper editorial or letter to the editor.

Name ______________________________

Vocabulary

Directions: Draw a line to connect each word on the left with its definition on the right.

1. contaminated	the air, water, soil, and so on
2. toll	polluted
3. environment	delicate; easily damaged
4. muck	filth
5. fragile	something paid, lost, or suffered

Check the Words You Know

__ cleanup
__ contaminated
__ environment
__ fragile
__ muck
__ toll
__ widespread

Directions: Choose the word from the box that best completes each sentence. Write the letters of the word on the blanks. The boxed letters spell a problem that humans have created.

6. Some problems with our air are so _____ that they extend for miles.

7. Chemicals released into our air and water take a _____ on all of Earth's life forms.

8. Harmful waste from factories mixes with soil and water and creates a _____ that no one wants to touch!

9. Businesses that dump this type of waste can cause great damage to Earth's _____ ecosystems.

10. If we all work together, can we do a complete _____ of our environment?

6. __ __ __ __ __ [ ] __ __ __ __
[o]
7. __ __ __ [ ]
[l]
8. __ [ ] __ __
[t]
9. __ __ __ __ [ ] __ __
[o]
10. __ __ __ __ [ ] __ __

A problem humans have created: ______________________________

Write an Editorial

On a separate sheet of paper, write an editorial in which you state your opinion on an environmental issue or a law, such as recycling or noise pollution. Talk about how the issue affects your neighbors and your community. Use as many vocabulary words as you can.

Notes for Home: Your child identified and used vocabulary words from the selection "Saving the Sound." ***Home Activity:*** With your child, discuss the environment and how it could be made better. Encourage your child to use the listed vocabulary words as you talk.

Name ______________________________

Persuasive Devices

- **Persuasive devices** are the special techniques an author uses to influence the way you think or feel.
- One type of persuasive device is the use of loaded words. Authors use loaded words to bring out an an emotional response in readers and to convince readers of their ideas and views.

Directions: Reread the section of "Saving the Sound" in which the author describes the coming of spring to Prince William Sound. Then answer the questions below. Look for loaded words that the author uses to influence your thinking.

In the springtime, the Sound is waking from winter. Ice and snow are melting. Bears emerge from their hibernation dens. Fish and birds that winter elsewhere begin to return. Prince William Sound is coming to life.

The wreck of the *Exxon Valdez,* however, changed all that. The oil spill turned a time of awakening and beauty into a time of nightmare and death. The Sound awoke on March 24, 1989, to find itself the victim of a disaster unlike anything that had occurred before in the United States.

1. Which sentences are statements of simple facts? Underline these facts.
2. Write some loaded words from the selection that are positive. Explain what the author's purpose is in using these words.

____

____

3. Write some loaded words from the selection that are strongly negative. Explain what the author's purpose is in using these words.

____

____

4. The author writes "The Sound awoke. . ." as if the place were a person. Why do you think the author makes this suggestion?

____

____

5. On a separate sheet of paper, describe the author's main purpose of "Saving the Sound" and explain whether or not you think the author influenced your thinking.

Notes for Home: Your child read a work of nonfiction and looked at ways the author might try to influence readers. ***Home Activity:*** With your child, look at an advertisement. Discuss ways in which it tries to persuade you to make a decision.

Selection Test

Directions: Choose the best answer to each item. Mark the letter for the answer you have chosen.

Part 1: Vocabulary

Find the answer choice that means about the same as the underlined word in each sentence.

1. Cleanup began right away.
- A. act of removing dirt and filth
- B. use of bright lights
- C. act of building something
- D. the burning of oil

2. Karen works hard to save the environment.
- F. bird's nest
- G. large trees
- H. body shape
- J. natural surroundings

3. There is a fragile balance among living things in the sea.
- A. delicate; easily damaged
- B. lasting forever
- C. new; invented recently
- D. changing quickly

4. That red barrel holds contaminated water.
- F. clear
- G. polluted
- H. used for drinking
- J. nearly frozen

5. Alison scooped muck into the pail.
- A. clear water
- B. dirt; filth
- C. sea animals
- D. white sand

6. The accident took a heavy toll on the local economy.
- F. benefits resulting from an event
- G. warning sign
- H. something lost, paid, or suffered
- J. cause

7. The storm had widespread effects.
- A. local
- B. felt immediately
- C. minor; not very large
- D. distributed over a large area

Part 2: Comprehension

Use what you know about the selection to answer each item.

8. Where did the *Exxon Valdez* spill its oil?
- F. Anchorage
- G. Kodiak Island
- H. Cook Inlet
- J. Prince William Sound

9. The first step in the cleanup was to—
- A. try to contain the spill.
- B. rescue birds and animals.
- C. scoop up oil and take it to shore.
- D. build walls to protect fishing grounds.

10. In the first few days after the spill, why did nice weather hamper the cleanup efforts?
- F. Oil washed over the containment booms.
- G. Chemicals used to break up the oil require rough seas.
- H. It made the oil slick spread faster.
- J. Workers were slow to respond to the disaster.

11. In this selection, the author is trying to persuade readers to—
- A. support the fishing industry.
- B. visit Alaska to see the effects of the spill.
- C. help protect the natural environment.
- D. send money to organizations that rescue wildlife.

GO O

12. The author of this selection makes the effects of the oil spill seem terrible by—
- F. noting that other spills have occurred since then.
- G. comparing the size of the Sound with New Jersey.
- H. naming the company that spilled the oil.
- J. using words that bring out an emotional response in the reader.

13. "Loaded words" are used as a persuasive device in which of the following sentences from the selection?
- A. "The wreck of the *Exxon Valdez*, however, changed all that."
- B. "The oil spill turned a time of awakening and beauty into a time of nightmare and death."
- C. "One of the worst parts of the first few hours of the spill is that no one was prepared for it."
- D. "The oil-spill response plan calls for spill-fighting equipment to be on hand five hours after a spill occurs."

14. To make this selection more balanced, the writer could have included the point of view of—
- F. commercial fishermen.
- G. wildlife biologists.
- H. oil-company employees.
- J. local residents.

15. Which sentence states an opinion?
- A. "The Sound's most appealing sea creature is the playful sea otter."
- B. "Much smaller than sea lions, they [sea otters] usually weigh less than 250 pounds (113 kg)."
- C. "Otters live in the region year-round."
- D. "Bears wander the forests and mountains, searching for food."

STOP

Name ______________________________

Persuasive Devices

- **Persuasive devices** are the special techniques an author uses to influence the way you think or feel.
- One type of persuasive device is the use of loaded words. Authors use loaded words to bring out an emotional response in readers and to convince readers of their ideas and views.

Directions: Read the article below.

In the past 30 years, our government and some industries have tried to fight air pollution. For example, most cars in America now have special equipment to cut down on pollution.

Unfortunately, these efforts have not been enough. In some places, the air is too foul to breathe. Though scientists have not yet proven it, it is obvious that air pollution contributes to global warming and to the ruining of our climate. Some people claim that it costs too much to fight pollution. But more and more people agree that we should spend as much money as it takes to make our air clean.

Directions: Complete the table. For each statement, write **yes** or **no** to indicate whether the statement includes loaded words. Then write a sentence explaining your answer.

Statement	Persuasive Device Yes or No?	Reason for Answer
The air is too foul to breathe.	**1.**	"Foul" is a loaded word.
Most cars in America now have special equipment to cut down on pollution.	**2.**	**3.**
Though scientists have not yet proven it, it is obvious that air pollution contributes to global warming and to the ruining of our climate.	**4.**	**5.**

Notes for Home: Your child read a passage and identified whether or not the author uses loaded words. ***Home Activity:*** Help your child write an editorial about an issue of his or her choice. Work together to include loaded words to influence readers.

REVIEW

Fact and Opinion and Graphic Sources

Directions: Look at the table and read the caption. Then read each question about the table and caption. Choose the best answer to each question. Mark the letter for the answer you have chosen.

Air Quality of U.S. Cities, 1991–1994				
	1991	**1992**	**1993**	**1994**
Chicago	8	7	1	8
Dallas	1	3	5	1
Los Angeles	182	185	146	136
New York	22	4	6	8
San Francisco	0	0	0	0

This table shows the number of days in a year that the air in five American cities failed to meet acceptable air-quality standards. The source of the data is the U.S. Environmental Protection Agency.

1. Which of the following is a statement of opinion?
   A. Los Angeles had 185 days with unacceptable air quality in 1992.
   B. The source of the data is the U.S. Environmental Protection Agency.
   C. Los Angeles is the worst place to live in the U.S.
   D. San Francisco had the fewest days of unacceptable air quality.

2. Which is an incorrect statement of fact?
   F. San Francisco has better air quality than any other city in the table.
   G. Los Angeles has the most polluted air of the five cities.
   H. The air quality in New York improved greatly after 1991.
   J. 1994 had more days of unacceptable air quality than 1992.

3. Which statement of opinion is supported by data in the table?
   A. Air quality in the U.S. is improving.
   B. No one likes poor air quality.
   C. The author is the best authority on air quality.
   D. The U.S. Environmental Protection Agency is working hard to improve air quality.

4. Which statement of opinion is supported by data in the table.
   F. San Francisco is a very pretty city.
   G. The trend shown in the table is encouraging.
   H. The air will improve because we need to make a difference.
   J. Air pollution is still a problem because of corrupt city governments.

5. If the trend continues, 2004 will have—
   A. no days with bad air.
   B. the same number of days with bad air as 1994.
   C. more days with bad air than 1994.
   D. fewer days with bad air than 1994.

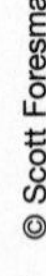

Notes for Home: Your child read a table and a caption and used it to identify related statements of fact and opinion. ***Home Activity:*** With your child, look through a newspaper for a graphic source, such as a graph or a table. Identify statements of fact and opinion in it.

Name ______________________________

Writing Across Texts

Directions: Refer to "Saving the Sound" and "How Do People Help Provide a Clean Environment?" to complete the Compare/Contrast diagram below. Use examples from the selections to describe the different kinds of pollution.

Central Issues

Sewage

1. ______________________________

2. ______________________________

Alike

Human actions cause pollution.

3. ______________________________

4. ______________________________

Different

Many animals die.

5. ______________________________

6. ______________________________

Conclusions

Humans must protect the environment from pollutants.

7. ______________________________

8. ______________________________

9. ______________________________

10. ______________________________

Write an Explanation

Use the selections and the completed Compare/Contrast diagram to write an explanation in which you compare and contrast the kinds of pollution described in the selections. Write your explanation on a separate sheet of paper.

Notes for Home: Your child has combined information from two sources to compare and contrast different kinds of pollution. ***Home Activity:*** As you read stories and articles, ask your child to explain how ideas in the reading materials are alike and different.

Name ______________________________

Grammar: Subjects and Predicates

REVIEW

Directions: Draw a line between the complete subject and the complete predicate in each sentence. Then underline the simple subject and the simple predicate.

1. Pollution of the oceans occurs in many different ways.
2. Oceanographers are needed in increasing numbers.
3. Such experts possess interests in science, the sea, and adventure.
4. Jacques Costeau was the most famous oceanographer of all.
5. This daring, brilliant scientist exposed the ocean's problems to the world.
6. The field of oceanography includes a number of different specialties.
7. The living creatures of the ocean are studied by marine biologists.
8. Pollution problems might be solved someday by a chemical oceanographer.
9. Underwater photographers record the mysteries below the water.
10. Your special interests will lead you to the fascinating study of the world's oceans.

Directions: Write **S** on the line to the left if the group of words can be a sentence subject. Write **P** if the group of words can be a sentence predicate. Then use each group of words to write a sentence of your own.

_________ **11.** animals in the ocean

____

____

_________ **12.** can cause terrible damage to the seas

____

____

_________ **13.** may be changed forever

____

____

_________ **14.** recovery from an oil spill

____

____

_________ **15.** the secrets of the ocean

____

Notes for Home: Your child identified and used simple and complete subjects and simple and complete predicates. ***Home Activity:*** Have your child write some sentences about events at school, and highlight each simple subject and predicate.

Name ____________________

Grammar: Subject-Verb Agreement

To work together, the subject of a sentence and the verb must agree in number. The following rules are for sentences that tell what is happening now, at the present time.

For a singular noun subject, add **-s** or **-es** to most verbs.

Tim lives in Alaska.
His brother writes to him from college.

For a plural noun subject, do **not** add **-s** or **-es** to the verb.

Many people visit Tim.
His grandparents travel to Alaska every year.

For compound subjects joined by *and* or *both,* use the verb form for a plural subject.

Carla and Mary want some of Tim's photos of glaciers.
Both his Alaskan friends and his father collect slides of Alaskan wildlife.

For a singular and a plural noun subject joined by *or, either . . . or,* or *neither . . . nor,* the verb must agree with the subject closer to it.

Neither Tim's friends in Washington nor Mary wants to live in the far north.

Directions: Circle the correct form of the verb in ( ) to complete each sentence.

1. Tim (spend/spends) much of his time working.
2. He (guide/guides) tours through the Alaskan wilderness.
3. Tim and his sister (work/works) together.
4. Four guides (share/shares) the work.
5. Each guide (own/owns) an equal part of the company.

Directions: Write the correct form of the verb in ( ) to complete each sentence.

____________________ **6.** On one tour, visitors (sail) through the Gulf of Alaska.

____________________ **7.** Sometimes, a humpback whale (swim) into view.

____________________ **8.** Bald eagles often (soar) above the water.

____________________ **9.** Many small islands (lie) in the Gulf of Alaska.

____________________ **10.** Sometimes a tour ship or a cabin cruiser (stop) near one of the islands.

Notes for Home: Your child chose and wrote the verb forms that agree with singular subjects and plural subjects. ***Home Activity:*** Have your child choose a verb. Then ask him or her to use the verb in a sentence with a singular subject and in a sentence with a plural subject.

Grammar: Subject-Verb Agreement

Directions: Circle the correct form of the verb in ( ) to complete each sentence.

1. Treasure Salvages Inc. (search/searches) the seas for old sunken ships.
2. The company (find/finds) special maps.
3. First, people (look/looks) for clues to find ships that were lost.
4. Next, boats (survey/surveys) likely areas.
5. Usually, a boat (use/uses) a metal detector to find iron objects left by sunken ships.

Directions: Write the correct form of the verb in ( ) to complete each sentence.

__________ **6.** When divers (locate) a sunken ship, they are very careful.

__________ **7.** A diver (take) an interest in more than just gold and silver.

__________ **8.** Both valuable coins and others relics of the past (interest) the searchers.

__________ **9.** Can either a company or individuals (collect) these artifacts and put them into museums?

__________ **10.** People (study) these artifacts for clues about the past.

__________ **11.** Scientists (examine) any navigational instruments from the old ship.

__________ **12.** Passengers' clothing and personal possessions (tell) much about the owners' social position.

__________ **13.** The ship's furnishings or cargo also (provide) information.

__________ **14.** A museum exhibit usually (include) items such as dishes and knives.

__________ **15.** What cargo of ancient times (seem) most interesting to you?

Write a Job Description

Choose one outdoor job, such as forest ranger or lifeguard. On a separate sheet of paper, write three or four sentences that describe ways someone in that job might help to protect our environment. Remember to make your subjects and verbs agree.

Notes for Home: Your child learned how to make verbs agree with subjects. ***Home Activity:*** Say a sentence with a singular subject, such as *Ben cleans up the store.* Then give your child a plural subject and have him or her change the verb to make it agree with the subject.

Name ______________________________

RETEACHING

Grammar: Subject-Verb Agreement

Subject	Some Verbs That Agree
I	am, was, walk, search
singular nouns and **she, he, it**	is, was, walks, searches
plural nouns and **we, you, they**	are, were, walk, search

Complete the sentence. Write a subject and a verb that agree. Use words from the chart.

______________________ ______________________ in the park.
(subject) (verb)

A verb must agree with its subject. Add **-s** or **-es** to most verbs with singular subjects. Do **not** add **-s** or **-es** to verbs with plural subjects.

Directions: Complete each sentence. Write the correct form of the verb in ( ).

1. Mountains ________________ from pressure under the Earth's surface. (forms/form)
2. Some mountains ________________ as volcanoes. (starts/start)
3. Molten rock ________________ through the Earth. (pushes/push)
4. The rock ________________ into lava on the surface of the land. (cools/cool)
5. Sometimes underground forces ________________ folds. (causes/cause)
6. The force ________________ areas of land together. (presses/press)
7. The folds ________________ above the land around them. (projects/project)
8. Trees ________________ smaller near the top. (becomes/become)
9. Foggy mornings ________________ often in the mountains. (occurs/occur)
10. A mountain lion ________________ among the high rocks. (hides/hide)
11. A major mountain range called the Alps ________________ in Europe. (exists/exist)
12. Snow usually ________________ high mountains all year long. (covers/cover)
13. The Himalayas ________________ climbers. (challenges/challenge)
14. I ________________ Edmund Hillary was the first to climb Mt. Everest. (thinks/think)

Notes for Home: Your child practiced subject-verb agreement by writing verbs in sentences. ***Home Activity:*** Together, make a list of verbs that are involved in your child's favorite activity. Have him or her write sentences, making sure subjects and verbs agree.

Name ______________________________

Grammar: Subject-Verb Agreement

Directions: Circle the simple subject. Write the correct form of the verb in ( ) to agree with the subject.

1. Three primary colors __________ all of the other colors. (creates/create)

2. I __________ red and blue. (prefers/prefer)

3. The light of every color __________ in waves. (travel/travels)

4. Red's waves __________ the furthest. (stretch/stretches)

5. The human eye __________ the different waves. (distinguish/distinguishes)

6. Objects __________ light into the human eye. (reflects/reflect)

Directions: Write the correct present-tense form of each verb in ( ) on the line.

__________ **7.** Warm colors (include) red, orange, and yellow.

__________ **8.** Most often, a rainbow (appear) after rain has fallen.

__________ **9.** My younger brother (splash) in puddles after storms.

__________ **10.** He also (look) up at rainbows and (smile).

__________ **11.** Then our grandparents (photograph) us.

Directions: Complete the sentences. Include a verb in the present tense that agrees with each subject.

12. Sometimes a rainbow ______________________________.

13. The paint on the wall ______________________________.

14. Some modern cameras ______________________________.

15. The school colors ______________________________.

16. A large color photograph ______________________________.

17. The trees in summer ______________________________.

Write a Poem

On a separate sheet of paper, write a poem about a beautiful sunset or autumn landscape. Make sure your verbs agree with your subjects.

Notes for Home: Your child used verbs in sentences to make subjects and verbs agree. ***Home Activity:*** Say a verb to your child *(run, sing, play)* and have him or her use the verb in sentences with a singular subject and a plural subject. Switch roles.

Name ______________________________

Phonics: Complex Spelling Patterns

Directions: The vowels **ou** can have several different sounds. Match each **ou** word on the left with a word from the box that has the same vowel sound. Write the matching word on the line.

storm	power	bubble	secure

________ **1.** trouble ________ **2.** hour ________ **3.** pour ________ **4.** tourist

Directions: Read each sentence below. Circle the word that has the same vowel sound as the underlined word.

5. Prince William Sound in Alaska is a great source of fish.
sound sour sir sore

6. Mountains rim the edge of the Sound.
mounds mold months mute

7. But disaster struck in 1989 when a large amount of oil was spilled into the water.
about almost above absorb

8. People in countries around the world were shocked by the oil spill.
count cook cup cool

9. Many tourists used to visit before the spill.
shout sure sour some

10. Four hundred workers were flown to the site.
north fought naught found

11. The oil kept pouring out of the ship.
odd ox pout punt

12. Southern shores were also affected.
court cousin count sour

13. Volunteers worked around the clock to try to save the wildlife.
sought road rot sound

14. Thousands of birds died as a result of the spill.
hound though through thought

15. Many sea otters were also found dead on the shores.
first frog pound pond

Notes for Home: Your child matched the different *ou* vowel sounds, such as *sound, southern, source,* and *tourist* to words with similar vowel sounds. ***Home Activity:*** Ask your child to read a chapter of a book to you. Help your child look for words with *ou* vowels.

Pretest

Spelling: Words with No Sound Clues

Pretest Directions: Fold back the page along the dotted line. On the blanks, write the spelling words as they are dictated. When you have finished the test, unfold the page and check your words.

1. ____________	**1.** I'm **interested** in beekeeping.
2. ____________	**2.** They **usually** arrive early.
3. ____________	**3.** She drove an **American** car.
4. ____________	**4.** We walked **toward** the ocean.
5. ____________	**5.** The café is a family **business**.
6. ____________	**6.** I had **vegetable** soup for lunch.
7. ____________	**7.** This book is **really** mine.
8. ____________	**8.** His house stood **opposite** theirs.
9. ____________	**9.** The hike up the hill was **difficult**.
10. ____________	**10.** Will it be **Christmas** soon?
11. ____________	**11.** She bought a sports **magazine**.
12. ____________	**12.** Please **apologize** to him.
13. ____________	**13.** Try to **multiply** the figures.
14. ____________	**14.** **Jealousy** is a strong emotion.
15. ____________	**15.** The conclusion was **elementary**.
16. ____________	**16.** We cannot live without **oxygen**.
17. ____________	**17.** He grew up in **Maryland**.
18. ____________	**18.** This is a **sensitive** matter.
19. ____________	**19.** **Laughter** can be contagious.
20. ____________	**20.** Cancer is a terrible **disease**.

Notes for Home: Your child took a pretest on words that give no sound clues as to their spelling. ***Home Activity:*** Help your child learn misspelled words before the final test. Your child should look at the word, say it, spell it aloud, and then spell it with eyes shut.

Name ______________________________

Spelling: Words with No Sound Clues

Word List			
interested	vegetable	magazine	oxygen
usually	really	apologize	Maryland
American	opposite	multiply	sensitive
toward	difficult	jealousy	laughter
business	Christmas	elementary	disease

Directions: Choose the word from the box that contains each word below. Write the word on the line. Use each word only once.

1. site ______________
2. sit ______________
3. usual ______________
4. real ______________
5. bus ______________
6. ease ______________
7. can ______________
8. log ______________
9. tip ______________
10. tar ______________

Directions: Choose the word from the box that best matches each definition. Write the word on the line.

______________ 11. a publication with stories and articles

______________ 12. envy

______________ 13. happy sound

______________ 14. attentive; not bored

______________ 15. in the direction of

______________ 16. an east-coast state

______________ 17. December 25

______________ 18. an edible plant

______________ 19. hard

______________ 20. a gas in the air

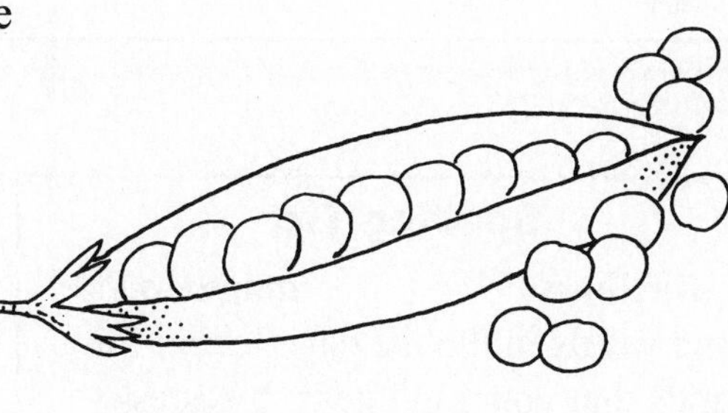

Notes for Home: Your child spelled words with letters that give no sound clues as to their spelling, such as *vegetable, business,* and *opposite. **Home Activity:*** Challenge your child to sort words from the list into groups according to the number of syllables the words contain.

Name ______________________________

Spelling: Words with No Sound Clues

Directions: Proofread these interview questions for a news article. Find five spelling mistakes. Use the proofreading marks to correct each mistake.

≡	Make a capital.
/	Make a small letter.
∧	Add something.
℘	Take out something.
⊙	Add a period.
¶	Begin a new paragraph.

1. Why should the American public still be intrested in the oil spill after more than ten years?
2. Which animals do not usully recover from the spill?
3. Magezine articles have said that some plants were more likely to die from dusease than others. Please explain.
4. Is the oil spill affecting the fishing busnes in the region? If so, in what way?

Word List

interested
usually
American
toward
business
vegetable
really
opposite
difficult
Christmas
magazine
apologize
multiply
jealousy
elementary
oxygen
Maryland
sensitive
laughter
disease

Spelling Tip

business **magazine**

Some words in the list have letters for sounds that you don't hear: **bus<u>i</u>ness.** Other words in the list have vowel sounds that give no clue to their spelling: **mag<u>a</u>zine.**

Write Interview Questions

Imagine that you need to interview experts who are cleaning up an oil spill. On a separate sheet of paper, write several questions you would ask to find out more about the accident and cleanup efforts. Try to use at least five of your spelling words.

Notes for Home: Your child spelled words with letters that give no sound clues as to their spelling. ***Home Activity:*** Hold a spelling bee with family and friends, taking turns spelling each word aloud.

Name ______________________

Spelling: Words with No Sound Clues REVIEW

Word List				
interested	business	difficult	multiply	Maryland
usually	vegetable	Christmas	jealousy	sensitive
American	really	magazine	elementary	laughter
toward	opposite	apologize	oxygen	disease

Directions: Choose the word from the box that is the most opposite in meaning for each word below. Write the word on the line.

1. health ______________
2. hard-hearted ______________
3. divide ______________
4. rarely ______________
5. insult ______________
6. away ______________
7. bored ______________
8. easy ______________
9. pleasure ______________
10. same ______________

Directions: Choose the word from the box that best matches each clue. Write the letters of the word on the blanks. The boxed letters tell why the bee went to see a doctor.

11. a weekly or monthly publication ___ ___ ___ ___ ___ [ ] ___ ___
12. grade school ___ ___ ___ ___ ___ ___ [ ] ___ ___ ___
13. a reaction to a good joke ___ ___ ___ ___ [ ] ___ ___ ___
14. actually; truly ___ ___ [ ] ___ ___ ___
15. one of the fifty states ___ ___ ___ ___ ___ ___ ___ [ ]
16. a December holiday ___ [ ] ___ ___ ___ ___ ___ ___ ___
17. a United States citizen ___ ___ ___ ___ [ ] ___ ___ ___
18. grown in a garden [ ] ___ ___ ___ ___ ___ ___ ___ ___
19. the gas we breathe ___ ___ ___ ___ [ ] ___
20. envy ___ ___ ___ ___ ___ ___ [ ] ___

Why did the bee go to see a doctor? ______________________

Notes for Home: Your child spelled words with letters that give no sound clues as to their spelling. ***Home Activity:*** Help your child create a crossword puzzle using as many spelling words as possible.

Graphs

Graphs display data in visual form. They can quickly show how one piece of information compares to other pieces or how something changes over time. There are several types of graphs. **Bar graphs** use vertical and horizontal bars to show amounts that you can compare easily. **Circle graphs** have a pie shape. They show how a whole is divided into parts. **Line graphs** are named for the lines that connect a series of points on a graph. They show how things change over time.

Directions: Use the graphs to answer the questions that follow.

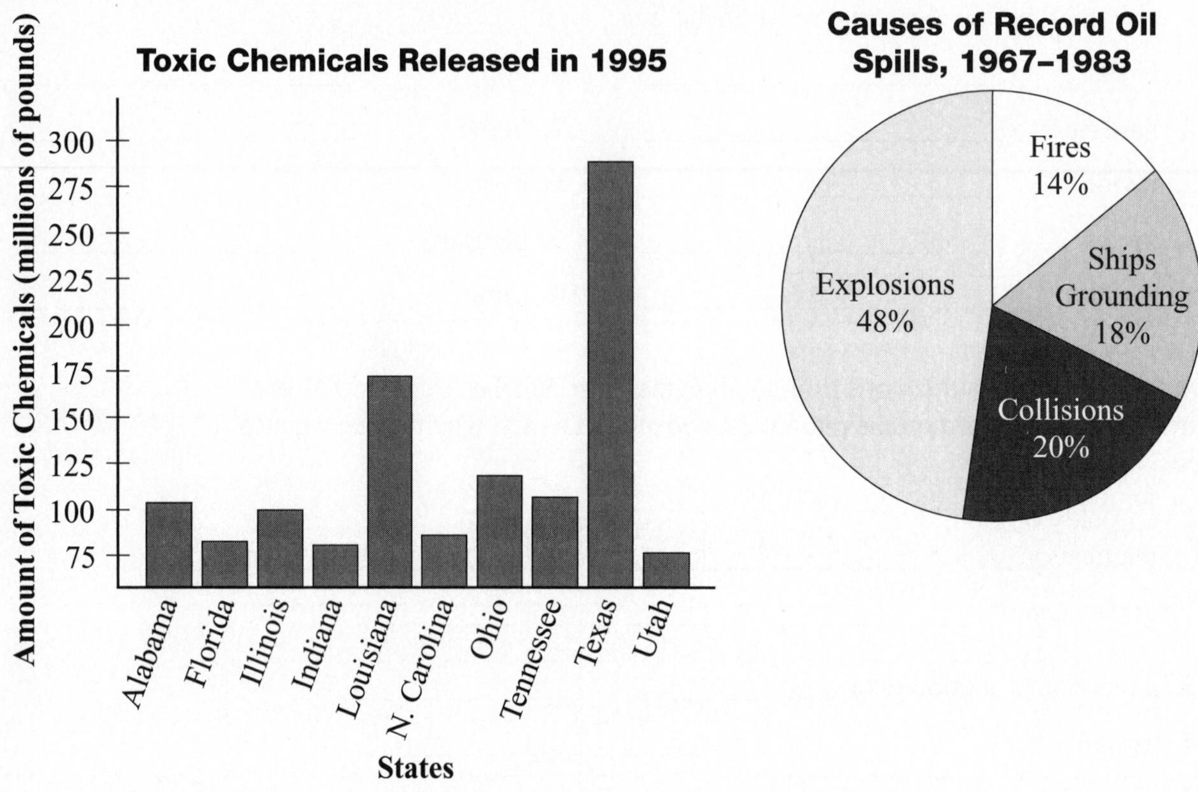

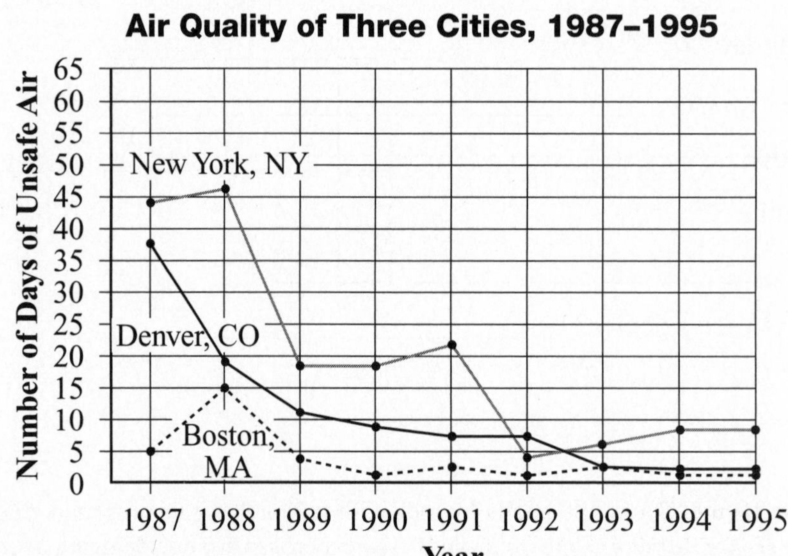

Name ___________________________________

1. According to the bar graph, which state released the greatest amount of toxic chemicals in 1995? How do you know?

____

2. What unit is used to measure the amount of toxic chemicals released? ___________

____

3. How does a bar graph help you compare the amounts of toxic chemicals released by different states?

____

____

4. What information does the circle graph represent? ___________________

____

5. What type of accident caused most of the record oil spills from 1967 to 1983? Explain.

____

____

____

6. Based on the data in the circle graph, would it be true to say that almost half of the record oil spills from 1967 to 1983 were caused by explosions? Explain.

____

____

7. On the line graph, what unit is used to measure the unsafe air in the three cities?

____

8. For about how many days in 1988 was the air not safe in New York? For how many days in 1989 was the air not safe in New York?

____

____

9. Does the line graph for New York for the period 1988 to 1989 show that the number of days of unsafe air has increased, decreased, or stayed the same?

____

____

10. Which graph is most effective in showing changes over time? ___________________

Notes for Home: Your child answered questions about circle, bar, and line graphs. ***Home Activity:*** Show your child some graphs from a magazine or newspaper. Discuss with your child what information each graph shows. Take turns asking one another questions about the graphs.

Name ____________________

Description Web

Directions: Write your topic (the animal you will describe) on the line in the Topic circle. Then organize details about this animal by writing them in the Details circles.

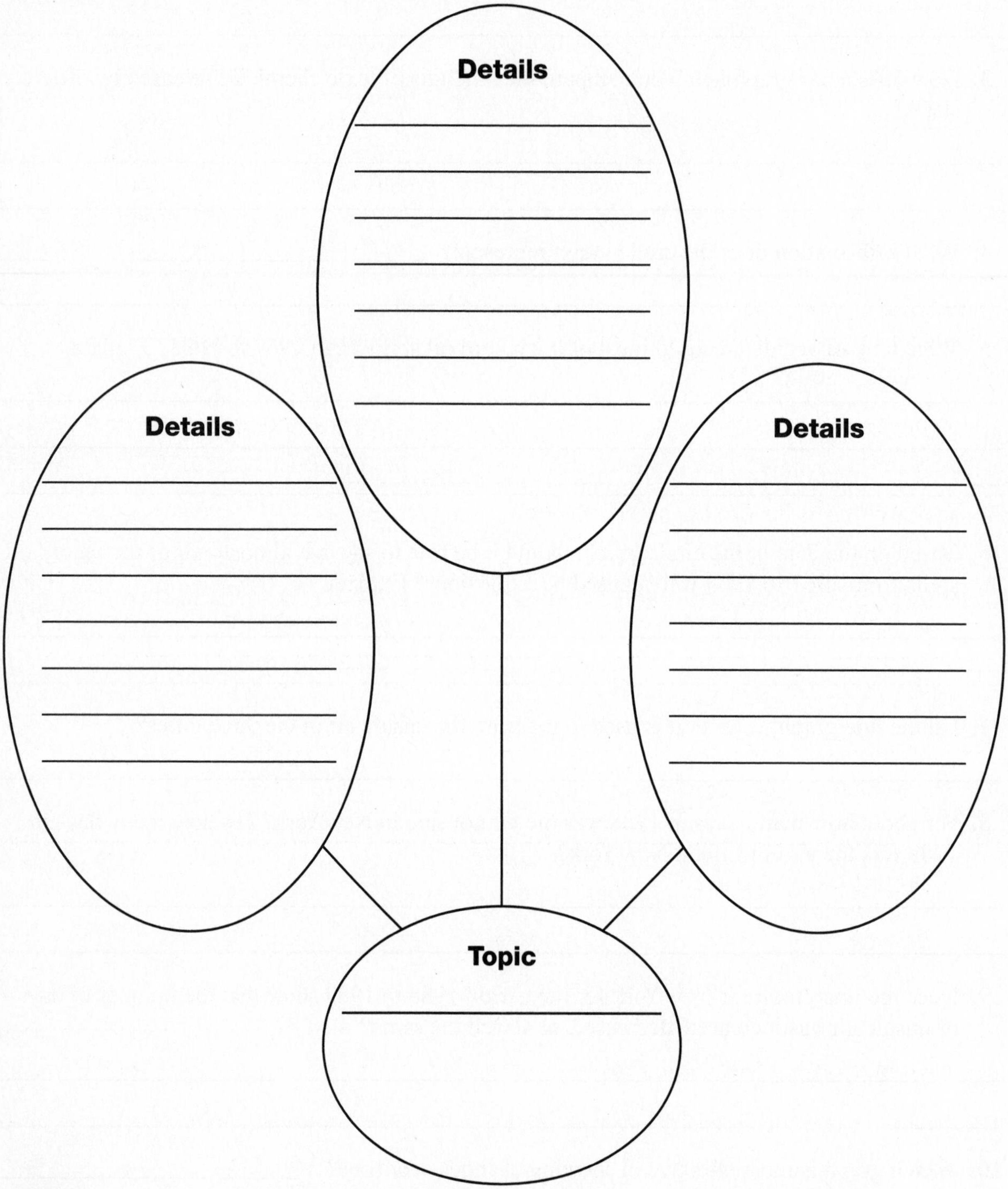

Details

______
______
______
______
______
______
______

Details

______
______
______
______
______
______
______

Details

______
______
______
______
______
______
______

Topic

______

Notes for Home: Your child filled out a Description Web with details about an animal he or she will describe. ***Home Activity:*** Encourage your child to describe a room in the house using different organizational approaches–for example: from top to bottom, or by order of importance.

Name ______________________

Elaboration

Sense Words

- When you write, you can elaborate by **adding sense words** that help readers imagine things more clearly.
- You can provide vivid images by sharing how things look, sound, feel, taste, and smell.

wild	white	golden	brown
wonderful	huge	roaring	sleek
slithery	excited	tall	long
coil	limber	big	noisy
black	colorful	wrinkly	playful

Directions: Read each sentence below. Then pick a word from the box to make each sentence more vivid and interesting. Write the sentences using these new words. Hint: Some sentences need more than one word.

1. Many animals live in the zoo.

____

2. The python snakes wrap around the trees.

____

3. Three pandas played in the grass.

____

4. Two African elephants showered us with water.

____

5. The monkeys swung from limb to limb.

____

6. A tiger with stripes stalked in his cage.

____

7. The lions' den was full of kingly beasts.

____

8. Their manes were thick and long.

____

Notes for Home: Your child elaborated on sentence ideas by adding sense words. ***Home Activity:*** After going outside with your child, have him or her use sentences with sense words to describe the sights, smells, and sounds in your neighborhood.

Name ______________________________

Self-Evaluation Guide

Description

Directions: Think about the final draft of your description. Then answer each question below.

	Yes	No	Not sure
1. Does my description tell about my topic animal?			
2. Did I use descriptive words to give readers a good picture of this animal?			
3. Did I keep my audience and purpose in mind?			
4. Did I present my ideas in an organized way?			
5. Did I proofread and edit carefully to avoid errors?			

6. What part of your description do you think gives the best picture of your topic animal?

____

____

____

____

7. Write one thing that you could change to make this description even better (a word, phrase, or sentence).

____

____

____

____

Notes for Home: Your child completed a self-evaluation of a description he or she wrote about an animal *Home Activity:* Encourage your child to tell you one way he or she tried to make this description vivid.

Family Times

Name________________________________

Summary

The First Woman Doctor

Elizabeth Blackwell fought the prejudices of her times to become the first woman in the United States to receive a medical degree. While training in Paris, she caught a serious eye infection that left her blind in one eye. Even this setback did not make her give up; eventually she opened her own clinic in a poor New York City neighborhood. Here she provided medical care for immigrants and continued her battle to prove her abilities and open people's minds to change.

Activity

Discuss Attitudes. Encourage your child to share with you what he or she discovered about the lives of women in the 1800s by reading the biography "Elizabeth Blackwell: Medical Pioneer." Ask your child to explain how people's attitudes about women's abilities affected their decisions in the 1800s. Then discuss how times and attitudes have changed.

Reading Skills

Drawing Conclusions

To **draw a conclusion** means to make a decision or form an opinion about what you are reading.

Each conclusion should make sense based on the facts and details in the writing. Thinking about your own experience can also help you draw sensible conclusions.

In the play, Elizabeth Blackwell asked the doctor if she would regain the sight in her left eye. In reply, he shook his head and said he had done all he could. A sensible conclusion to draw from these clues is that she will not regain her sight in that eye.

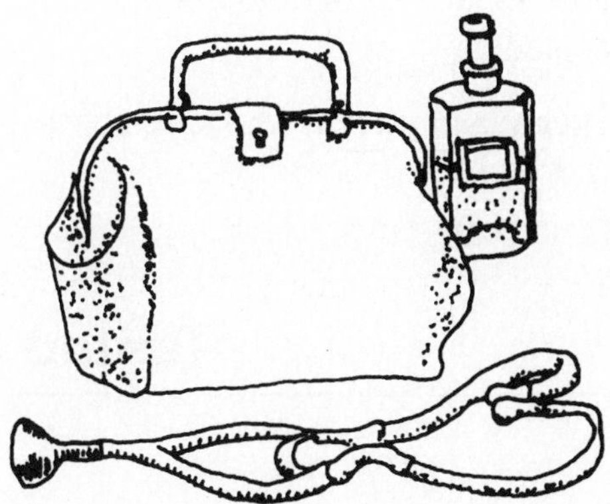

Activity

Guessing Game. Describe the skills and tools needed for a certain profession. Have your child guess which profession you are describing. Switch roles and repeat.

Family Times

Tested Vocabulary

Words to Know

Knowing the meanings of these words is important to reading "Elizabeth Blackwell: Medical Pioneer." Practice using these words to learn their meanings.

application a written request for something

clinic a place where people can receive medical treatment at a reduced cost

diploma a certificate recognizing completion of a given course of study

independent able to act or function without help from others

infection disease caused by contact with germs, viruses, fungi, and so on

qualified having the necessary skills, abilities, and so on

rejection act or condition of not being accepted

surgeon a physician who specializes in surgery

Grammar

Linking Verbs

A **linking verb** does not show action. Instead, it links, or joins, the subject to another word or words in the predicate. A linking verb tells something about what the subject is or how the subject feels.

Linking verbs include forms of the verb *to be,* such as *am, is, was,* or *were.* They also include verbs like *seem, feel,* and *become.* Note how the verbs in the following sentences link the subject to a word or group of words in the predicate.

Elizabeth Blackwell <u>became</u> a doctor.

Sometimes she <u>felt</u> discouraged.

She <u>was</u> a hard worker.

Activity

Describe Qualities. Use linking verbs to describe the qualities or characteristics of friends and neighbors. Examples: *Kris is talkative. Mrs. Lynn seems happy today.*

Tested Spelling Words

Name ________________________________

Drawing Conclusions

- To **draw a conclusion** means to make a decision or form an opinion about what you read.
- A conclusion should be sensible. It should make good sense based on the facts and details in the piece of writing and your own experience.

Directions: Reread "To the Rescue." Then complete the table. Write a conclusion for each piece of evidence. Write evidence that supports each conclusion.

Evidence (Story Details and What I Already Know)	Conclusions
1.	Clara Barton is risking her life by coming to Sharpsburg.
2.	The doctors at Sharpsburg do not have enough medical supplies.
Clara Barton has spent more than a year gathering medical supplies from friends and concerned citizens.	**3.**
4.	The doctors appreciate Clara Barton's help.
Clara Barton sees a bullet hole in her in sleeve. Undaunted, she keeps on working.	**5.**

Notes for Home: Your child read a passage and drew conclusions from its details. ***Home Activity:*** With your child, discuss a familiar book, movie, or television show. Work with your child to draw conclusions about what the characters did and why.

Name ______________________________

Vocabulary

Directions: Choose the word from the box that best completes each sentence. Write the word on the line to the left.

Check the Words You Know
__ application
__ clinic
__ diploma
__ independent
__ infection
__ qualified
__ rejection
__ surgeon

______________________ **1.** After she graduated, she framed her ____ and hung it with her other certificates of study.

______________________ **2.** It is hard for anyone to deal with ____ because everyone wants to be accepted.

______________________ **3.** Anyone may go to a ____ for inexpensive medical treatment.

______________________ **4.** The doctor cleaned the patient's wound carefully to avoid the risk of an ____ spreading.

______________________ **5.** A ____ is a physician who performs surgical operations.

Directions: Choose the word from the box that best fits each definition. Write the word on the line. Then find and circle the words in the puzzle. Words may appear across, down, or diagonally.

____________ **6.** having the necessary skills and abilities

____________ **7.** a written request for something

____________ **8.** able to act without help from others

____________ **9.** a refusal of an attempt to gain acceptance

____________ **10.** a place to get medical treatment

T G I V A H N A P W J O R
X F M E P S S U B N O K E
I N D E P E N D E N T D J
B I L Q L V I A C L T J E
H N A Z I T Y L X Z V B C
C S D I C L I N I C N A T
J G H O A W F V T A I N I
S B E O T X I I C D U V O
Q U A L I F I E D L L U N
M I X X O S V K A I B L A
Y T Z A N J N Q U A F I D

Write a Conversation

On a separate sheet of paper, write a conversation between a doctor and a patient. The doctor could be asking about a patient's health. The patient could be checking on the doctor's qualifications. Use as many vocabulary words as you can.

Notes for Home: Your child identified and used vocabulary words from "Elizabeth Blackwell: Medical Pioneer." ***Home Activity:*** Work with your child to write a definition for each of the listed vocabulary words. Use a dictionary as needed.

Name ______________________________

Drawing Conclusions

- To **draw a conclusion** means to make a decision or form an opinion about what you read.
- A **conclusion** should make good sense based on the facts and details in the piece of writing.

Directions: Reread what happens in "Elizabeth Blackwell: Medical Pioneer," when Elizabeth tries to go to medical school. Then answer the questions below. Use story details to think about the characters and to draw conclusions of your own.

DR. BARNES: No woman has ever gone to medical school!
ELIZABETH: You told me I had the ability.
DR. BARNES: You do! But it's 1847, Miss Blackwell. There isn't a college in the country that will accept you.
ELIZABETH: Times won't change unless we make them change!
DR. BARNES *(Slowly.)*: There is one way.
ELIZABETH: What? What?
DR. BARNES: Disguise yourself as a man, and go study in Paris.
ELIZABETH *(Shocked.)*: How can I help other women, if I'm in disguise?

1. Why does Dr. Barnes think no college will accept Elizabeth?

____

____

2. Why does Elizabeth think it won't help other women if she disguises herself as a man to attend medical school?

____

____

3. Why do you think Elizabeth asks Dr. Barnes for help?

____

4. How would you describe Elizabeth's character?

____

5. On a separate sheet of paper, explain how Elizabeth helps to get women accepted as doctors. Use details from the story to support your answer.

Notes for Home: Your child has read part of a play and used details to draw conclusions. ***Home Activity:*** Describe some of your recent actions. Challenge your child to draw logical conclusions about why you did what you did.

Name ______________________________

Selection Test

Directions: Choose the best answer to each item. Mark the letter for the answer you have chosen.

Part 1: Vocabulary

Find the answer choice that means about the same as the underlined word in each sentence.

1. Mrs. Ashland took her children to the <u>clinic</u>.
- A. school for nurses
- B. place where people receive medical care
- C. hospital for blind people
- D. shopping mall

2. The baby's <u>infection</u> was gone in several days.
- F. discomfort or pain
- G. sneezing caused by dust
- H. sadness or extreme loneliness
- J. condition caused by disease-producing germs

3. The <u>surgeon</u> checked her knee.
- A. business manager
- B. doctor who performs operations
- C. type of lawyer
- D. person who specializes in teeth

4. My sister framed her <u>diploma</u>.
- F. realistic image such as a photograph
- G. self-portrait
- H. certificate awarded for completing a course of study
- J. oil painting

5. She is an <u>independent</u> person.
- A. well-traveled
- B. wealthy
- C. self-employed
- D. able to act without help from others

6. The writer got a letter of <u>rejection</u>.
- F. praise
- G. act of giving thanks
- H. condition of not being accepted
- J. criticism

7. Brian sent in his <u>application</u>.
- A. written request for admission
- B. essay
- C. homework
- D. order to appear in court

8. He was certainly <u>qualified</u> for the job.
- F. having the necessary training or skills
- G. nervous; shaky
- H. receiving praise
- J. not prepared

Part 2: Comprehension

Use what you know about the play to answer each item.

9. Why did Elizabeth Blackwell have difficulty getting into medical school?
- A. She was not very well prepared.
- B. No woman had ever gone to medical school.
- C. She was not very highly recommended.
- D. The medical schools did not need any new students.

10. Elizabeth Blackwell took a job as a student nurse because she—
- F. was not yet trained to be a doctor.
- G. needed to learn to work with poor eyesight.
- H. thought she could learn more from being a nurse than from being a doctor.
- J. could not find a hospital that would hire her as a doctor.

GO ON

Name ____________________

11. You can conclude that Dr. Blackwell's eyesight improved because she—
   A. became a practicing doctor in New York.
   B. wanted to become a surgeon.
   C. was accepted to study at St. Bartholomew's.
   D. changed her dream.

12. Dr. Blackwell did not become a surgeon because—
   F. there had never been a female surgeon before.
   G. she could not get into a medical school.
   H. her eyesight was not good enough.
   J. she was more interested in practical medicine.

13. You can conclude that Sean confronted the mob outside Dr. Blackwell's clinic because he—
   A. did not want to pay medical bills.
   B. thought all doctors should be women.
   C. appreciated her work.
   D. had been saved by her.

14. Which of these goals became most important to Elizabeth Blackwell after she set up her clinic in New York?
   F. overcoming prejudice
   G. making a good living
   H. having a family
   J. becoming a surgeon

15. From the end of the play you can conclude that Elizabeth Blackwell—
   A. thought women were designed to help men.
   B. believed that very few doctors would ever be women.
   C. argued that women were better doctors than men.
   D. believed more women would become doctors.

STOP

Name ______________________________

Drawing Conclusions

- To **draw a conclusion** means to make a decision or form an opinion about what you read.
- A **conclusion** should make good sense based upon the facts and details in the piece of writing.

Directions: Read the play excerpt below.

ENRIQUE: Did you like my story? Do you think I have the talent to be a writer?
MS. CHEN *(Smiling.):* I think you may be a great writer someday if you work hard. Our "Clinic for New Writers" may be just the class you need.
ENRIQUE *(Surprised.):* There's a class for writers?
MS. CHEN: All your classmates will be writers like yourself. You will help each other by sharing your reactions to each other's work.
ENRIQUE: I will work so hard in that class! It will be great to have other writers to talk to. I've always been the only one I know who writes stories.
MS. CHEN: The class will help you look critically at your own work and try different kinds of writing. By the end of the year, you'll know whether you really want to be a writer.
ENRIQUE: If I ever become famous, Ms. Chen, it will be thanks to you!

Directions: Complete the table. Draw conclusions based on details from the play or provide details to support conclusions given.

What I Read	What I Conclude
Ms. Chen thinks Enrique may become a great writer.	1.
2.	Enrique is different from his friends.
Enrique will work hard in writing class.	3.
4.	Enrique can learn a lot from a writer's class.
If Enrique becomes famous, he will thank Ms. Chen.	5.

Notes for Home: Your child read part of a play and used details to draw conclusions. ***Home Activity:*** Watch a television drama or comedy with your child. Together, draw conclusions about the main characters, why they act as they do, and how true-to-life they seem.

Name ______________________________

REVIEW

Compare and Contrast/ Text Structure

Directions: Read the story. Then read each question about the story. Choose the best answer to each question. Mark the letter for the answer you have chosen.

Two Peas in a Pod

Neil and Nancy are brother and sister, but you wouldn't know it to look at them. Neil's face is serious. His eyes seem to see all the way into your thoughts. He is not especially tall, but broad-shouldered and strongly built. In contrast, Nancy is very tall and slender, with long arms and legs. Her eyes always twinkle. When you hear her laugh, you have to laugh too!

Underneath the surface, though, they are as alike as identical twins. When they make up their minds to do something, nothing stops them. They have different talents and interests, but similar ways of doing things.

All through the fall and winter, Nancy practiced daily to break the school's sprint racing record. Rain or shine, Nancy was out on the track, working to run faster each week. She competed with herself as much as with other runners. When the spring track meet was held, Nancy was the fastest runner on her team.

Neil was in charge of designing and building the sets for the December class play. Even when his crew all came down with the flu and he was on his own, Neil didn't give up. He got some friends to help, and he worked late into the night for several days to finish the sets on time. When the play was performed, everyone praised his work.

In their different ways, Nancy and Neil show the value of staying focused. Brother and sister work hard to achieve their goals.

1. Nancy and Neil—
- **A.** are alike inside and out.
- **B.** look like brother and sister.
- **C.** don't act alike.
- **D.** don't look alike.

2. Neil and Nancy are both—
- **F.** hard-working.
- **G.** talkative.
- **H.** unfocused.
- **J.** solemn.

3. Neil and Nancy—
- **A.** never have setbacks.
- **B.** work hard to get what they want.
- **C.** change their goals when problems arise.
- **D.** focus only on their setbacks.

4. The title and the second paragraph tell that Nancy and Neil—
- **F.** are very similar, despite appearances.
- **G.** are identical twins.
- **H.** make up their minds easily.
- **J.** are more different than alike.

5. The passage is organized to show how Neil and Nancy are—
- **A.** related.
- **B.** different.
- **C.** alike.
- **D.** different in some ways and similar in other ways.

Notes for Home: Your child has read a story, compared and contrasted characters, and described the story's organization. ***Home Activity:*** Read a short story to your child. Challenge him or her to identify similarities and differences among the characters.

Name ______________________________

Writing Across Texts

Directions: In "Elizabeth Blackwell: Medical Pioneer," Elizabeth Blackwell encountered many obstacles in reaching her goal of becoming a doctor. In "She's the Boss," Kathleen McGrath probably faced obstacles on her way to becoming the Navy's first female warship commander. Compare and contrast some of the difficulties these women faced in the selections. Complete the table below.

Obstacles Elizabeth Blackwell Faced	Obstacles Kathleen McGrath Might Have Faced
Goal: She wanted to be a doctor.	**Goal:** She wanted to be a Navy Commander.
1.	**6.**
2.	**7.**
3.	**8.**
4.	**9.**
5.	**10.**

Write an Essay

Compare and contrast the obstacles Elizabeth Blackwell faced to those Kathleen McGrath may have faced while trying to reach difficult goals. Write your essay on a separate sheet of paper.

Notes for Home: Your child read about the first woman to attend medical school and become a doctor in the United States. ***Home Activity:*** With your child, discuss potential careers that interest him or her and possible obstacles your child may face while trying to achieve that goal.

Name ______________________________

REVIEW

Grammar: Predicates

Directions: Underline the complete predicate in each sentence. Then circle the simple predicate. (There may be more than one simple predicate in a sentence.)

1. Susan B. Anthony fought for women's rights for 55 years.
2. As a young woman, she worked in the anti-slavery movement.
3. Her efforts helped the passage of the 14th Amendment to the Constitution.
4. That amendment forbid slavery and made citizens of all slaves.
5. At the time, however, women possessed very few rights.
6. Susan B. Anthony saw the similarity between the issues of women's rights and slavery.
7. She met Elizabeth Stanton in 1851 and planned a course of action.
8. They created the National Women's Suffrage Association in 1869.
9. Both women campaigned throughout the country and lobbied members of Congress to allow women to vote.
10. The 19th Amendment to the Constitution passed in Congress 14 years after Susan B. Anthony's death.

Directions: Add a predicate to each subject to form a sentence. Write the complete sentence on the line.

11. Women in the past ____________.

____

12. Women today ____________.

____

13. Women in the future ____________.

____

14. Laws ____________.

____

15. My mother ____________.

____

Notes for Home: Your child identified simple and complete predicates. ***Home Activity:*** To reinforce this lesson, have your child identify the simple predicates in the five sentences he or she wrote above.

Practice

Grammar: Verbs

A **verb** is the main word in the predicate of a sentence. An **action verb** tells what action the subject performs. Sometimes the action takes place in someone's mind.

Ruri worked hard for many years.
She wanted to save as much money as she could.

A **linking verb** links, or joins, the subject with a word or group of words in the predicate that tells something about the subject, such as what the subject is or how the subject feels.

Linking verbs are either forms of *be,* such as *am, is, are, was,* and *were,* or verbs like *feel, seem,* and *become.*

Ruri's new restaurant is great.

She seems very happy about the results of her work.

Directions: Underline the action verb in each sentence.

1. Ruri designed the entire restaurant.
2. She chose the furniture and the lighting.
3. Sometimes Ruri worried about her goals.
4. Often, she asked her sister for advice.
5. Ruri trusts her sister more than anyone else.
6. Ruri and her sister planned the menus for the restaurant.
7. They wanted a mix of different types of foods.
8. Ruri always uses fresh produce and meats.
9. She buys them from the local farmers.
10. Her customers appreciate all of Ruri's efforts.

Directions: Underline the linking verb in each sentence.

11. Ruri's business certainly seems successful.
12. The restaurant is almost always full.
13. I am a regular customer at the restaurant.
14. The servers are polite and helpful.
15. Diners always feel good at Ruri's.

Notes for Home: Your child identified action verbs, such as *run* or *think,* and linking verbs, such as *was* or *feel.* ***Home Activity:*** Have your child write three sentences that describe things he or she did in school. Help your child identify each action verb or linking verb.

Grammar: Verbs

Directions: Underline the verb in each sentence. Write **A** if the verb is an action verb. Write **L** if it is a linking verb.

__________ **1.** Ken and Liam picked a project for the school fair.

__________ **2.** They made a short videotape about the history of the school.

__________ **3.** The two friends interviewed many former teachers and students.

__________ **4.** Some people felt shy about talking on camera.

__________ **5.** Ken and Liam also found old photographs and pictures of the school.

__________ **6.** The boys worked on the videotape for six weeks.

__________ **7.** Despite the difficulties, the final, edited tape was wonderful.

Directions: Write a sentence for each word from the box that tells about a person or a group of people you admire.

admire	excels	encourages

8. ______________________________

____

9. ______________________________

____

10. ______________________________

____

Write a Letter

On a separate sheet of paper, write a letter to a friend telling about a task that was difficult. Include details to explain why the task was hard and how you completed it. When you are finished, underline all action verbs and circle all linking verbs.

Notes for Home: Your child identified action verbs, such as *run* or *think,* and linking verbs, such as *was* or *feel*. ***Home Activity:*** Have your child write three sentences that describe a favorite book. Help your child identify the action verbs or linking verbs in each sentence.

Name ______________________________

Grammar: Verbs

RETEACHING

Read each sentence. The complete predicate is underlined. Write each simple predicate.

1. A bird is a pretty creature. ___________
2. Plovers are one kind of bird. ___________
3. They eat insects and worms. ___________

An **action verb** expresses action the subject performs. Linking verbs, such as **is, was, being, am, are, were,** and **been,** join the subject to a word or group of words in the predicate.

Directions: Write the verb in each sentence on the line.

1. All plovers migrate from place to place. ___________
2. They run with energy. ___________
3. They build nests in a safe spot on the ground. ___________
4. Some make their homes along the seashore. ___________
5. Some live in fields or on plains. ___________
6. The golden plover migrates long distances. ___________
7. It breeds in Arctic regions. ___________
8. Some plovers stay in Florida during winter months. ___________
9. The bird flies about 2,400 miles over open ocean. ___________
10. We have a picture of a plover in our living room. ___________
11. They are small birds with long legs. ___________

Directions: Circle the verb in each sentence. Write **action** or **linking** on the line.

12. The killdeer is a type of plover. ___________
13. People recognize its shrill cry of "kill-deer." ___________
14. Two black bands mark its white breast. ___________
15. The feathers on its back are grayish-brown. ___________
16. The female lays four black-spotted eggs. ___________

Notes for Home: Your child identified action verbs and linking verbs in sentences. ***Home Activity:*** Have your child use this page to explain the differences between action and linking verbs. Ask him or her to provide other examples of action and linking verbs in sentences.

Name ____________________

Grammar: Verbs

Directions: Underline the verb in each sentence. Write each one. Then write **A** if it is an action verb or **L** if it is a linking verb.

1. Ants live together in large communities. ____________
2. The queen ant lays eggs. ____________
3. Worker ants feed the young. ____________
4. The nests contain many chambers. ____________
5. Many ant homes are in mounds of earth. ____________
6. Ants develop in several stages. ____________
7. Tiny white eggs hatch in a few weeks. ____________
8. Some ants live for several years. ____________
9. A few reach the age of fifteen years. ____________
10. Carpenter ants were destructive to human homes. ____________
11. One kind of hunter ant destroys harmful pests. ____________
12. All ants belong to the same family of insects. ____________

Directions: Circle the verb in each sentence. Write **action** or **linking** on the line.

13. Ants store food in their nest. ____________
14. Some kinds of ants eat grass seed. ____________
15. Another gathers grain for food. ____________
16. Another insect is an important partner of ants. ____________
17. This insect produces a sweet honeydew. ____________
18. This fluid nourishes the ants. ____________
19. Some ants are dormant in the winter. ____________
20. Other kinds of ants destroy harmful pests. ____________

Write a Funny Song

On a separate sheet of paper, write a funny song about your least favorite insect. Use precise and colorful verbs to describe the insect's behavior.

Notes for Home: Your child identified action and linking verbs in sentences. ***Home Activity:*** Say a sentence with two verbs. Have your child say another sentence, using one of those verbs and another of his or her choosing. Continue with other verbs.

Name ______________________________

Word Study: Regular Plurals

Directions: To make most nouns plural, add **-s.** For nouns that end in **x, s, ss, ch,** or **sh,** add **-es.** For nouns that end in a **consonant** and **y,** change the **y** to **i** and add **-es.** Read the paragraph below. Make each word in ( ) plural. Write the plural word on the line.

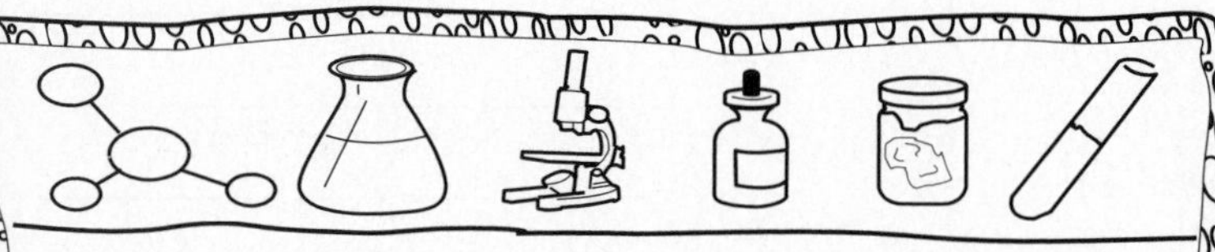

(Doctor) and (nurse) must attend school and complete special training before they are ready to help others. They listen to (lecture) presented by people who are important in the medical field. They must achieve excellent (grade) in most of their (class). They spend hours in (library) and (laboratory). With all these (experience), these highly-trained men and women are ready to handle most (emergency). Many of these dedicated professionals work to become the (leader) in their field.

1. ______________
2. ______________
3. ______________
4. ______________
5. ______________
6. ______________
7. ______________
8. ______________
9. ______________
10. ______________

Directions: Write the plural of each word. For some words, you will add **-s.** For others, you will add **-es.** You may need to change **y** to **i** before adding **-es.**

11. study ______________
12. pioneer ______________
13. canary ______________
14. league ______________
15. officer ______________
16. beach ______________
17. sympathy ______________
18. circus ______________
19. pickax ______________
20. lady ______________
21. narrator ______________
22. eyelash ______________
23. hobby ______________
24. monkey ______________
25. tax ______________
26. dictionary ______________
27. charlatan ______________
28. messenger ______________
29. mystery ______________
30. eyeglass ______________

Notes for Home: Your child formed plural nouns by adding *-s,* or *-es.* ***Home Activity:*** Choose individual items from around your home. Have your child write the names of the items. Help your child to write the plural form of each item.

Name ______________________________

Pretest

Spelling: Suffixes *-ance, -ence, -ant, -ent*

Pretest Directions: Fold back the page along the dotted line. On the blanks, write the spelling words as they are dictated. When you have finished the test, unfold the page and check your words.

1. ______________________
2. ______________________
3. ______________________
4. ______________________
5. ______________________
6. ______________________
7. ______________________
8. ______________________
9. ______________________
10. ______________________
11. ______________________
12. ______________________
13. ______________________
14. ______________________
15. ______________________
16. ______________________
17. ______________________
18. ______________________
19. ______________________
20. ______________________

1. Where is the main **entrance**?
2. Their **performance** starts soon.
3. I admire your car's **appearance**.
4. We went to the **clearance** sale.
5. Car **insurance** can be expensive.
6. We celebrate **Independence** Day.
7. What's the **difference**?
8. I envy her **excellence** in art.
9. He speaks with great **confidence**.
10. The friends met by **coincidence**.
11. What a **brilliant** idea!
12. My family is **important** to me.
13. Car exhaust is an air **pollutant**.
14. He made an **ignorant** remark.
15. At first, I was **hesitant** to go.
16. Dolphins are **intelligent** animals.
17. Her anger was very **apparent**.
18. The salesman was **persistent**.
19. What time's **convenient** for you?
20. He's a very **consistent** student.

Notes for Home: Your child took a pretest on words ending in the suffixes *-ance, -ence, -ant,* and *-ent.* ***Home Activity:*** Help your child learn misspelled words before the final test. Your child should look at the word, say it, spell it aloud, and then spell it with eyes shut.

Think and Practice

Spelling: Suffixes *-ance, -ence, -ant, -ent*

Word List			
entrance	independence	brilliant	intelligent
performance	difference	important	apparent
appearance	excellence	pollutant	persistent
clearance	confidence	ignorant	convenient
insurance	coincidence	hesitant	consistent

Directions: Choose the words from the box that have the suffixes **-ance** or **-ence.** Write each word in the correct column.

Words Ending -ance	Words Ending -ence
1. ____________	6. ____________
2. ____________	7. ____________
3. ____________	8. ____________
4. ____________	9. ____________
5. ____________	10. ____________

Directions: Choose the word from the box that best matches each definition. Write the word on the line.

____________ **11.** significant; meaningful

____________ **12.** not giving up

____________ **13.** always the same

____________ **14.** lacking knowledge

____________ **15.** doubtful; undecided

____________ **16.** something that dirties

____________ **17.** handy; nearby

____________ **18.** sparkling; dazzling

____________ **19.** obvious

____________ **20.** smart

Notes for Home: Your child spelled words ending in the suffixes *-ance, -ence, -ant,* and *-ent.* ***Home Activity:*** Have your child tell which three words are the most difficult to remember how to spell. Help her or him think up memory clues such as *You don't need an A to spell excellence.*

Name ________________________________

Spelling: Suffixes *-ance, -ence, -ant, -ent*

Directions: Proofread this profile of aviation pioneer Amelia Earhart. Find six spelling mistakes. Use the proofreading marks to correct each mistake.

≡	Make a capital.
/	Make a small letter.
∧	Add something.
☡	Take out something.
⊙	Add a period.
¶	Begin a new paragraph.

Amelia Earhart is one pilot who made an important diferance for women everywhere. Her independance of spirit inspired women all over the country to have more confidance in their abilities to try new things. Despite early setbacks, Amelia Earhart was persitant in her efforts to make her dreams of flying come true. She was the first woman to fly solo across the Atlantic Ocean and she did it in record time! Because of her brillant performence as a pilot, it became apparent to many people that women could do whatever they had the courage to try.

Word List

entrance
performance
appearance
clearance
insurance
independence
difference
excellence
confidence
coincidence
brilliant
important
pollutant
ignorant
hesitant
intelligent
apparent
persistent
convenient
consistent

Spelling Tip

apparent

There are often no sound clues to let you know whether to use an **a** or an **e** when adding the suffixes **-ance, -ence, -ant,** and **-ent.** Make up clues to help you remember the correct spelling, such as: There is always a **parent** in **apparent.**

Write a Paragraph

On a separate sheet of paper, write a description of a real or imaginary female pioneer. Try to use at least five of your spelling words.

Notes for Home: Your child spelled words ending in the suffixes *-ance, -ence, -ant,* and *-ent.* ***Home Activity:*** Have your child name additional words that are spelled with *-ence,* such as *sentence.* Together, make a list of these words and check their spellings in a dictionary.

Name ______________________________

Spelling: Suffixes *-ance, -ence, -ant, -ent*

REVIEW

Word List				
entrance	insurance	confidence	pollutant	apparent
performance	independence	coincidence	ignorant	persistent
appearance	difference	brilliant	hesitant	convenient
clearance	excellence	important	intelligent	consistent

Directions: Choose the word from the box that best completes each sentence. Write the words on the matching numbered lines to the right.

It was not a **1.** _____ that the opening **2.** _____ of Andrew McCoy's new play was on Friday the thirteenth. Early misfortunes, including the discovery of a toxic **3.** _____ in the theater's cooling system, undermined people's **4.** _____ that the play would ever open. **5.** _____ rumors that the play was jinxed have plagued the producers from the start. They also had to wait for the money from the **6.** _____ company to cover costs of water damage to the sets. At last, they were given **7.** _____ to go ahead with the performance. The **8.** _____ of the sets and costumes when the curtain was raised made the audience praise the **9.** _____ of the design. The next **10.** _____ job that remains is to bring in large crowds.

1. ______________________
2. ______________________
3. ______________________
4. ______________________
5. ______________________
6. ______________________
7. ______________________
8. ______________________
9. ______________________
10. ______________________

Directions: Choose a word from the box that is the most opposite in meaning for each word or words below. Write the word on the line. Use each word only once.

11. dull ______________

12. dependence ______________

13. similarity ______________

14. always changing ______________

15. out of the way ______________

16. exit ______________

17. knowing ______________

18. certain ______________

19. dumb ______________

20. hidden ______________

Notes for Home: Your child reviewed words ending in the suffixes *-ance, -ence, -ant,* and *-ent. **Home Activity:*** Challenge your child to use words ending in *-ance* to make up a rhyme.

Name ______________________________

Technology: Card Catalog/Library Database

You can use a **card catalog** or **library database** to find books, magazines, audiotapes, videotapes, CD-ROMs, and other materials in the library. You can search for materials by author, title, or subject. If you don't know exactly what you are searching for in the library database, you can use key words. Be sure to type and spell words carefully. If you use more than one key word in your search, put the word "AND" between the key words.

Directions: Look at the starting search screen for a library database below. Tell which box and key words you would use to search for the book or books listed below.

Search Kempe High Library

- ☐ Title (exact search)
- ☐ Title (key words)
- ☐ Author (last name, first name)
- ☐ Author (key words)
- ☐ Subject (exact search)
- ☐ Subject (key words)

Check a box and type your key words in the box below. Press return.

[   ]

1. books about Elizabeth Blackwell ______________________________

2. books written by Joanna Halpert Kraus ______________________________

3. a book titled *Women in Nineteenth-Century America* ______________________________

4. books about famous women in medicine ______________________________

5. a book titled *Elizabeth Blackwell: First Woman Doctor* ______________________________

6. books about the history of medicine ______________________________

If you search with a broad subject such as "medicine," the database may give you more choices. These might be arranged according to more specific topics.

Directions: Use the list of specific topics to answer the questions that follow.

Subject: medicine

Search Results	**Number of Items**
1 Medicine - history	(13)
2 Medicine - women	(4)
3 Medicine - drugs	(12)
4 Medicine - fiction	(8)
5 Medicine - hospitals	(13)
6 Medicine - preventative	(7)
7 Medicine - disease	(23)
8 Medicine - schools	(6)

Type a number or press return to enter a new search.

7. Which topics might be useful to find out more about women and medicine in the 1800s?

____

8. Which number would you type to find a fictional story about medicine? ____________

9. What are some ways to find information on Marie Curie, another medical pioneer?

____

____

____

10. How is searching a library database like and unlike using a card catalog?

____

____

____

Notes for Home: Your child answered questions about using a card catalog and a library database. ***Home Activity:*** Ask your child to name two topics to research. Together, make a list of subject key words for each topic that you could use to search the database at the library.

Family Times

Name________________________________

Summary

Hard Work and Good Rewards

José's cousin Arnie promises to line up odd jobs and help José in exchange for some of the wages. This partnership soon turns sour when all Arnie does is watch, criticize, and take the credit for all of José's hard work. When the owner of a pool José is cleaning injures himself, José helps him while Arnie runs away. When José later discovers Arnie taking credit, José learns something about himself: he is a hard worker and a good person.

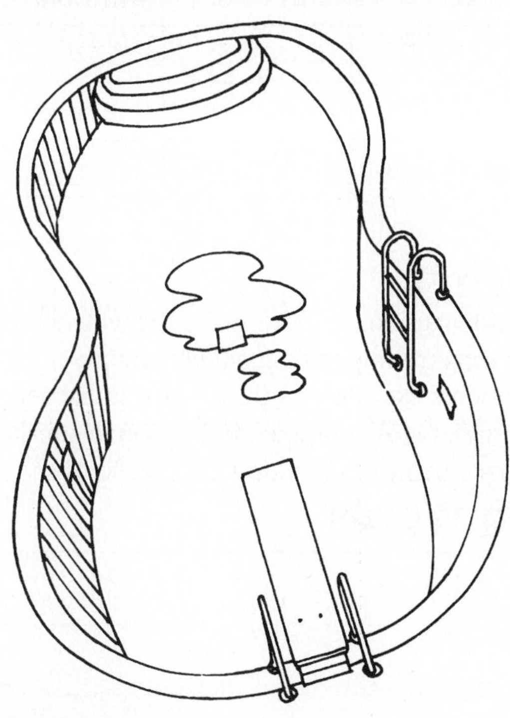

Activity

Interview a Witness. Prompt your child to play the part of Mr. Clemens, the man who injured himself. Interview your child to find out about the accident and what Mr. Clemens thinks of José and Arnie.

Reading Skills

Compare and Contrast

To **compare** means to tell how two or more things are alike. Clue words for likenesses include *like, similarly, as, in addition, likewise,* and *in the same way.*

José was afraid at first, just like Arnie.

To **contrast** means to tell how two or more things are different. Clue words for differences include *but, however, different, although, in spite of,* and *on the other hand.*

José stayed to help, but Arnie ran away.

Activity

Compare and Contrast. Think of pairs that have something in common, such as two people, two pets, two activities, or two objects. Write each pair on a slip of paper. Take turns choosing a slip and comparing and contrasting the items named.

Family Times

Tested Vocabulary

Words to Know

Knowing the meanings of these words is important to reading "Born Worker." Practice using these words to learn their meanings.

accompanied went along with

attitude a way of thinking, acting, or feeling

collapsed fell down suddenly

grime deeply-embedded surface dirt

laborer a person who does work requiring strength rather than skill

solution a liquid mixture

supervise to oversee the work or activity of others

Grammar

Verb Tenses

Verbs in the **present tense** show action that is happening now. Verbs in the **past tense** show action that happened in the past. Verbs in the **future tense** show action that will happen in the future. When you write, don't shift from one tense to another unless the action shifts from one time to another.

We worked hard yesterday, and we will work hard again tomorrow.

Past	Present	Future
worked	works/work	will work
	saves/save	
scrubbed		will scrub
saw		

Activity

Make up Excuses. Complete the table above. On separate slips of paper, have family members use some of these verbs to list several excuses for avoiding work. Exchange slips and rewrite them by changing the verb tenses.

Tested Spelling Words

Name ______________________

Compare and Contrast

- To **compare** means to tell how two or more things are alike. To **contrast** means to tell how two or more things are different.
- Some common clue words for likenesses are *like, similarly, as, in addition, likewise,* and *in the same way.* Some common clue words for differences are *but, however, differing, although, in spite of,* and *on the other hand.*

Directions: Reread "One for All." Then complete the table. Compare and contrast Julio to Lucas, Cricket, and Julio's brothers. Tell how Julio is like or unlike these other characters. One has been done for you.

Julio and Lucas	Julio and Cricket	Julio and His Brothers
1. Alike:	**3. Alike:**	**5. Alike:**
2. Different:	**4. Different:**	**Different:** Julio is younger than his brothers.

Notes for Home: Your child compared and contrasted the characters in a story. ***Home Activity:*** With your child, discuss how three people you know are alike and different. Create a table similar to the one above.

Name ______________________________

Vocabulary

Directions: Choose the word from the box that best matches each definition. Write the word on the line.

Check the Words You Know
__ accompanied
__ attitude
__ collapsed
__ grime
__ laborer
__ solution
__ supervise

________________ **1.** deeply embedded surface dirt

________________ **2.** a liquid mixture

________________ **3.** a mindset; a way of thinking

________________ **4.** to oversee others' activities

________________ **5.** a worker performing manual labor

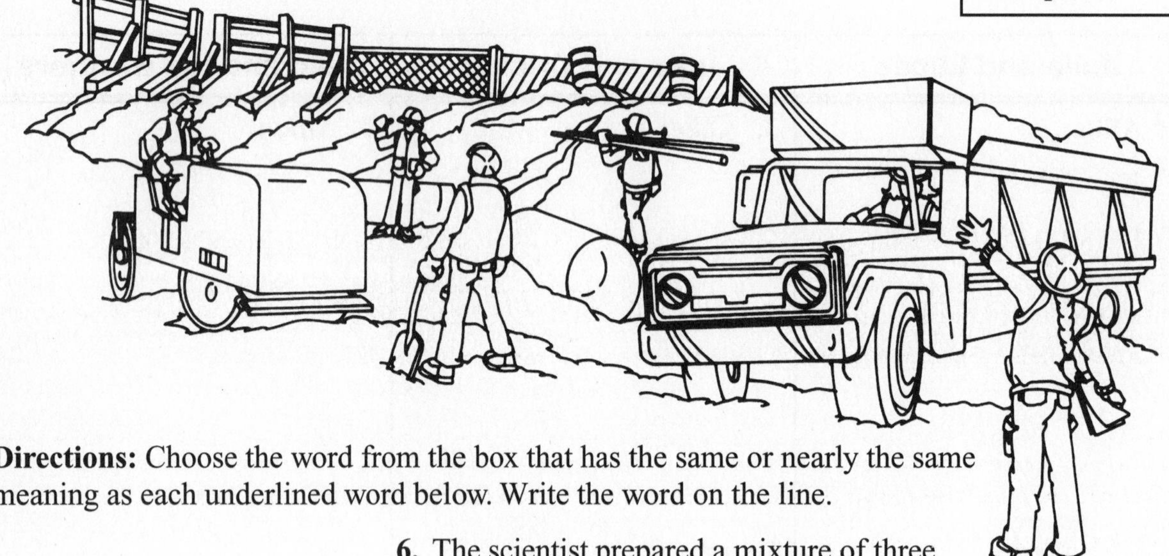

Directions: Choose the word from the box that has the same or nearly the same meaning as each underlined word below. Write the word on the line.

________________ **6.** The scientist prepared a <u>mixture</u> of three different liquids, including water.

________________ **7.** The doctor explained that the young man had <u>fainted</u> because he had been working out in the hot sun without drinking enough water.

________________ **8.** The movie star was <u>escorted</u> to the movie opening by her agent, her director, and her producer.

________________ **9.** The foreman of the construction crew thought Tom was the best <u>worker</u> of the group.

________________ **10.** The head of the sales department has to <u>oversee</u> the work of thirty customer service representatives.

Write a Thank-you Note

On a separate sheet of paper, write a note thanking someone for some work he or she has done that has made life easier for you. Use as many vocabulary words as you can.

Notes for Home: Your child learned new vocabulary words from "Born Worker." ***Home Activity:*** Play a game in which one of you describes a kind of work and the other names the worker, for example: *teaching/teacher.*

Name ______________________________

Compare and Contrast

- To **compare** means to tell how two or more things are alike. To **contrast** means to tell how two or more things are different.
- Clue words such as *like* or *as* can signal comparisons. Clue words such as *but* or *unlike* can signal contrasts.

Directions: Reread what happens in "Born Worker" when José and Arnie agree to work together. Then answer the questions below. Think about the characters in the story to help you compare and contrast.

José agreed to a seventy-thirty split, with the condition that Arnie had to help out. Arnie hollered, arguing that some people were meant to work and others to come up with brilliant ideas. He was one of the latter. Still, he agreed after José said it was that or nothing.

In the next two weeks, Arnie found an array of jobs. José peeled off shingles from a rickety garage roof, carried rocks down a path to where a pond would go, and spray-painted lawn furniture. And while Arnie accompanied him, most of the time he did nothing.

1. How are Arnie's and José's ambitions alike?

____

____

2. What does José do to get what he wants?

____

____

3. What does Arnie do to get what he wants?

____

____

4. How are their attitudes about work different?

____

____

5. On a separate sheet of paper, explain which boy you would hire and why. Give an example from the story.

Notes for Home: Your child read a short story and used details to compare and contrast its characters. ***Home Activity:*** Take turns comparing and contrasting the personalities and actions of people you and your child both know.

Name ______________________________

Selection Test

Directions: Choose the best answer to each item. Mark the letter for the answer you have chosen.

Part 1: Vocabulary

Find the answer choice that means about the same as the underlined word in each sentence.

1. Please use that green solution.
- A. type of hammer
- B. type of sponge
- C. liquid mixture
- D. powder

2. Laurel is a good laborer.
- F. follower
- G. person who remembers everything he or she reads
- H. leader
- J. person who does work that requires strength rather than skill

3. Did Mrs. DiCamillo supervise the other teachers?
- A. do the same job as
- B. oversee the work of
- C. greet in a friendly way
- D. cooperate with

4. The walls were covered with grime.
- F. dirt
- G. paint
- H. flakes of ash
- J. thin coating of water

5. After the race, Jim's attitude changed.
- A. height from the ground
- B. appearance
- C. way of thinking
- D. goal

6. Mr. Daily collapsed on the sidewalk.
- F. sat still
- G. fell down suddenly
- H. walked quickly
- J. wandered slowly

7. Yuki accompanied us to the show.
- A. followed
- B. raced
- C. led
- D. went along with

Part 2: Comprehension

Use what you know about the story to answer each item.

8. Why doesn't José like Arnie?
- F. Arnie does not earn what he gets.
- G. José is jealous of how easily Arnie makes friends.
- H. Arnie always works harder than José.
- J. José cannot ask people for work as easily as Arnie does.

9. What did Mr. Clemens do while José was scrubbing the pool?
- A. He ate loquats.
- B. He took his poodle for a walk.
- C. He got dressed.
- D. He lay in the lounge chair.

10. José shows that he is different from Arnie when he—
- F. leaves the scene of an accident.
- G. takes care of Mr. Clemens.
- H. rides a bike.
- J. acts cheerful.

11. José's attitude toward work is most like—
- A. Mr. Clemens's.
- B. Arnie's.
- C. his parents'.
- D. Mr. Bechtel's.

GO ON

12. Why does José agree to work with Arnie?
- F. He feels sorry for Arnie.
- G. He does not like asking for work.
- H. He wants to teach Arnie to be a good laborer.
- J. He wants to be rich.

13. Arnie is best described as—
- A. lazy and spoiled.
- B. sensitive and caring.
- C. talented and independent.
- D. hard-working and responsible.

14. José's opinion of Arnie is primarily based on—
- F. Mr. Clemens's reactions to him.
- G. comments neighbors have made.
- H. his parents' comments about Arnie's family.
- J. personal experience and direct observation.

15. The next time he decides to work with Arnie, José will most likely—
- A. provide transportation for Arnie.
- B. take charge of arranging the work.
- C. insist on receiving more of the pay.
- D. say he does not want to work in a backyard.

STOP

Name ______________________________

Compare and Contrast

- To **compare** means to tell how two or more things are alike. To **contrast** means to tell how two or more things are different.
- Clue words such as *like* or *as* can signal comparisons. Clue words such as *but* or *unlike* can signal contrasts.

Directions: Read the story below.

Roy turned to Sam, "Aren't you coming to the final basketball game?"

Sam looked depressed, "I wish I could, but I have to walk Wylie and start on my art project tonight."

"Oh, come on. You can take Wylie out after the game."

"I always take Wylie out at seven. He'll be upset if I'm so late. It wouldn't be fair."

Roy shrugged, "It won't matter this one time. He's only a dog!"

"I'd feel too guilty. I wouldn't enjoy the game"

"For a game as important as this, I'd worry about being fair and guilty later."

Directions: Compare and contrast Roy and Sam. In the circles below, list two things that are true about Roy, list two things that are true about Sam, and one thing that is true of both of them.

Roy

1. ______________________________

puts his own wishes first

2. ______________________________

Both Boys

3. ______________________________

Sam

takes responsibility

4. ______________________________

5. ______________________________

Notes for Home: Your child read a story and used its details to make comparisons and contrasts. ***Home Activity:*** With your child, make a list of family members' household tasks or other responsibilities. Discuss the similarities and differences among people's jobs.

Predicting and Plot

REVIEW

Directions: Read the story. Then read each question about the story. Choose the best answer to each question. Mark the letter for the answer you have chosen.

Different Directions

When we set off on our trip to Aunt Bess's that Thanksgiving, Mom teased Dad, "Are you planning to get lost again?" He never fails to lose the way. Dad has no sense of direction. Unfortunately, he doesn't know that! He is always sure he knows the way. Only as time passes does he begin a series of stops at gas stations for further directions. We are always so late that Aunt Bess has learned to tell Dad to arrive an hour earlier than she really wants us there. That way, she knows we will probably be on time.

This time, however, I was determined to get us there well before the turkey was overdone and the stuffing all gone. First, I called Aunt Bess and wrote down detailed directions. I knew it was in the final part of the trip that Dad made his worst mistakes. I read that part of the directions back to Aunt Bess to be sure I had it right. I also decided to take the road atlas.

The first time Dad got into the wrong lane, I told him I had directions, and he should go left instead of right. Dad was annoyed for a moment, but had to give in at Mom's heartfelt "Thank goodness you thought of that!" Dad swung back into the left lane.

Unfortunately, things did not go quite as I had planned. Somewhere between Lima and Elyria, my sister moaned, "I don't feel so well. Open the windows, quick!" As big gusts of air blew into the car, making Annie feel better, my careful notes blew out the window!

Mom and I stared at each other; then Mom began to laugh. All of us joined in, knowing that Aunt Bess would be as amused as we were. "I have the best solution," said Mom. "Next time, I'll drive!"

1. What conflict, or problem, do the characters in this story face?
   - **A.** Dad is always getting lost.
   - **B.** Aunt Bess cooks Thanksgiving dinner.
   - **C.** Aunt Bess lives far away.
   - **D.** The narrator gets directions from Aunt Bess.

2. What does the first paragraph lead you to expect next?
   - **F.** Mom will tease Dad.
   - **G.** Dad will not get lost this time.
   - **H.** Aunt Bess will call.
   - **J.** Dad will get lost.

3. After the instructions blow away, the narrator will probably—
   - **A.** get lost.
   - **B.** look at the road atlas.
   - **C.** arrive early at Aunt Bess's.
   - **D.** blame Dad for getting into the wrong lane.

4. The part of the story in which the instructions fly away is called the—
   - **F.** plot.
   - **G.** rising action.
   - **H.** climax.
   - **J.** conflict.

5. When Aunt Bess hears the story of the lost directions, she will probably—
   - **A.** cry.
   - **B.** laugh.
   - **C.** never invite her relatives to dinner again.
   - **D.** tell the narrator to be more careful in the future.

Notes for Home: Your child predicted events in a story and identified plot elements. ***Home Activity:*** Read a story aloud with your child. After every few paragraphs, ask your child to predict what will happen next.

Name ___________________________

Writing Across Texts

Directions: *Born Worker* and "Doing Dishes" were both written by Gary Soto. Think about what these two selections have in common. Then make five inferences about Gary Soto and his writing based on details in these two selections.

What I Can Infer About Gary Soto
1.
2.
3.
4.
5.

Write a Paragraph

Write a paragraph in which you compare Gary Soto's attitude toward work with your own. How do you feel about chores? Use information from the chart and both selections to help you. Write the paragraph on a separate sheet of paper.

Notes for Home: Your child compared two selections by the same author. ***Home Activity:*** Talk with your child about how he or she feels about work and why.

Name ______________________________

REVIEW

Grammar: Verbs

Directions: Circle the verb in each sentence. Write **A** if the verb is an action verb. Write **L** if the verb is a linking verb. Remember, an **action verb** tells what action the subject performs. Sometimes the action takes place in someone's mind. A **linking verb** links, or joins, the subject with a word or group of words in the predicate that tell something about the subject, such as what the subject is or how the subject feels.

__________ **1.** My class at school earned $200 last year.

__________ **2.** Everyone worked for neighbors or relatives.

__________ **3.** Some of the work was very hard.

__________ **4.** José raked huge piles of leaves.

__________ **5.** His hands looked sore the next day.

__________ **6.** I cleaned my grandmother's garbage cans.

__________ **7.** Whew! They were smelly!

__________ **8.** I held my nose the whole time.

__________ **9.** Others recycled newspapers and cans.

__________ **10.** Everyone felt good at the end of the day.

Directions: Use each verb in a sentence. Write the sentence on the line.

11. *looked* as an action verb

____

12. *looked* as a linking verb

____

13. *felt* as an action verb

____

14. *felt* as a linking verb

____

15. *sounded* as a linking verb

____

Notes for Home: Your child identified action and linking verbs. ***Home Activity:*** Ask your child to find a paragraph that he or she has written. Go through the paragraph together, replacing any dull, overused verbs, such as *say, go,* and *do,* with more interesting verbs.

Practice

Grammar: Verb Tenses: Present, Past, and Future

A verb in the **present tense** shows action that is happening now. Many present tense verbs that work with singular subjects end in **-s** or **-es.**

Lucas works every Saturday with me. He misses his former free time, however.

Present tense verbs that work with plural subjects do not usually add **-s** or **-es.**

Lucas and I work for Mr. Polito.

A verb in the **past tense** shows action that has already happened. Many verbs in the past tense end with **-ed.** Those that do not end with **-ed** are called **irregular verbs.** Since they do not follow a regular pattern of verb endings, you need to remember the past tense forms.

Regular verb: Lucas and I worked for Mr. Polito.
Irregular verb: We went to his house every day for three weeks.

A verb in the **future tense** shows action that will happen. Verbs in the future tense include the helping verb *will.*

Next week, we will paint Mr. Polito's fence. Light gray paint will look best.

Directions: Write **present, past,** or **future** to tell the tense of each underlined verb.

______________ **1.** Mr. Polito hired us to work in his yard.

______________ **2.** Sometimes, things are harder than they look.

______________ **3.** Our lawnmower broke, and we had to find another.

______________ **4.** We always prepare fully for each job.

______________ **5.** We know that, sometimes, accidents will happen.

______________ **6.** Recently, we painted Mrs. Warner's shed.

______________ **7.** Now, the shed looks brand new.

______________ **8.** For a while, we thought we would never finish.

______________ **9.** Mrs. Warner's dog often barks when strangers are in the yard.

______________ **10.** That dog will bother you whenever you want to do something.

Notes for Home: Your child identified whether a verb was in the present, past, or future tense. ***Home Activity:*** Choose a verb, such as *wash* or *ride*. Have your child use the verb in three sentences, using a different tense for each sentence.

Name ______________________________

Extra Practice

Grammar: Verb Tenses: Present, Past, and Future

Directions: Circle the correct tense of the verb in ( ). Write **past, present,** or **future** to name the tense you chose.

__________________ **1.** My brother (laughed/will laugh) when he finds out about my plans.

__________________ **2.** He thinks that I (will be/am) a big dreamer.

__________________ **3.** He (tells/told) me so just last week.

__________________ **4.** Next month, I (will try/tried) to join the school's swimming team.

__________________ **5.** I (learned/will learn) how to swim only last year.

__________________ **6.** Nevertheless, I think I (will succeed/succeeds).

__________________ **7.** Now, I (practice/practices) every afternoon.

__________________ **8.** Yesterday, I (swam/swim) for more than an hour.

__________________ **9.** My brother (will wonder/wonders) why I have spent so much time at the pool.

__________________ **10.** He often (will say/says) that I am like a fish.

__________________ **11.** Swimming (does/did) a person's whole body a great deal of good.

__________________ **12.** As I get better, I (will develop/developed) stronger muscles.

__________________ **13.** This sport (helps/help) me build a swimmer's heart and lungs.

__________________ **14.** Somehow, the Australian crawl never (tired/will tire) me when I was doing laps.

__________________ **15.** The swim coach (watches/will watch) the rhythm of my strokes as I swim.

Write a Paragraph

Think of something that you dream of doing, such as being a veterinarian or traveling around the world. On a separate sheet of paper, write a paragraph about your dream. As you write, remember to use the correct tense for each verb.

Notes for Home: Your child chose a verb in the past, present, or future tense to complete sentences. ***Home Activity:*** Invite your child to write sentences about something that happened yesterday and something that will happen tomorrow.

Name ______________________________

RETEACHING

Grammar: Verb Tenses: Present, Past, and Future

Write **present, past,** or **future** to show when each event happens.

1. In 1911, Roald Amundsen reached the South Pole. ______________________
2. He lived in Antarctica for a year. ______________________
3. Now we learn about his struggles. ______________________
4. We give him credit for his achievements. ______________________
5. Next week Luisa will do a report about him. ______________________
6. Someday I will read Amundsen's autobiography. ______________________

The **tense** of a verb shows when the action happens. The past-tense form of most verbs ends in **-ed.** The future tense is usually formed with the helping verb **will.**

Directions: Underline the verb in each sentence below. On the line, write **present, past,** or **future** to show the tense of the verb.

1. I will finish this book about Amundsen tomorrow. ______________
2. Amundsen's books about his adventures interest me. ______________
3. They tell the story of his explorations. ______________
4. He studied science for many years. ______________
5. From 1903 to 1906 he completed his first important expedition. ______________
6. We know of his voyage through the Northwest Passage. ______________
7. You will learn about his stay in Antarctica. ______________
8. He lived there in the bitter cold for a year. ______________
9. He finally reached the South Pole. ______________
10. His endurance of physical hardships still amazes us. ______________
11. Our class will learn about his flight over the North Pole. ______________
12. He traveled seventy hours in an airship. ______________
13. In 1928, Amundsen died during a rescue mission. ______________
14. Our class will read about his death at sea. ______________
15. I enjoy stories about heroic lives. ______________

Notes for Home: Your child identified tenses of verbs in sentences. ***Home Activity:*** Have your child choose some sentences in a favorite story and identify the tense of each verb. Then have him or her say new sentences with the verbs in different tenses.

Name ______________________

Grammar: Verb Tenses: Present, Past, and Future

Directions: Underline the verb in each sentence. On the line, write its tense.

1. Before A.D. 1100, Vikings roamed far from home. ____________
2. These freebooters practiced piracy. ____________
3. You will learn more about the Viking Age. ____________
4. They raided neighboring lands for treasure. ____________
5. Modern historians recognize their many achievements. ____________
6. They also settled new lands. ____________
7. They pioneered new trade routes. ____________
8. We know about their explorations far and wide. ____________
9. They reached North America centuries before Columbus. ____________
10. Tomorrow we will see one of their wooden long ships. ____________
11. These carried the Vikings on their ocean voyages. ____________
12. You will learn about their use as burial vessels too. ____________

Directions: Change the tense of each verb below to the tense indicated in ( ). Write each new verb on the line.

13. You enjoy Viking history. (future) ____________
14. We hear some of their great folk tales. (past) ____________
15. Museums contained many Viking treasures. (present) ____________
16. People respect their achievements. (future) ____________
17. Their explorations affect our culture. (past) ____________
18. Our word *law* came from an old Norse word. (present) ____________
19. They introduce lasting art forms. (past) ____________

Write a Tale

On a separate sheet of paper, write a tale about exploring a new land. Use the appropriate verb tense to express the time of each idea or event.

Notes for Home: Your child identified tenses of verbs in sentences. ***Home Activity:*** Have your child use some of the verbs on this page in other sentences. Encourage your child to use the verbs in different tenses.

Name ____________________

Word Study: Irregular Plurals

Directions: Most plural nouns are formed by adding **-s** and **-es.** Some plural nouns do not follow a regular spelling pattern. These are called **irregular plurals.** For some irregular plurals, you need to change the spelling of the singular noun, as in **man** and **men,** or **scarf** and **scarves.** Other irregular plurals have the same singular and plural form, such as **series.** Read each word below. Write the plural form for each word on the line.

1. tooth ________	**6.** goose ________	**11.** shelf ________
2. fireman ________	**7.** knife ________	**12.** fish ________
3. moose ________	**8.** sheep ________	**13.** ox ________
4. half ________	**9.** mouse ________	**14.** deer ________
5. foot ________	**10.** salmon ________	**15.** life ________

Directions: Find the plural nouns in the paragraph. Write each word in the correct column.

The park needed a lot of work if it was going to open soon. A gardener had been hired to clean it, and he quickly got to work. First he raked around the flower beds. It was springtime, and the flowers would need the sunlight. He knew that children would want to play near the pond and geese would come to rest on it, so he used a net to collect any floating pieces of trash. He cleared rocks from the bike path and picked up discarded cans. Lastly, he repainted the bench so men and women could picnic under the shady leaves of the old oak tree. The work had been hard, but at last the park was clean and ready.

Regular Plurals	**Irregular Plurals**
16. ____________	**21.** ____________
17. ____________	**22.** ____________
18. ____________	**23.** ____________
19. ____________	**24.** ____________
20. ____________	**25.** ____________

Notes for Home: Your child formed and identified irregular plurals, such as *mice* and *deer.* ***Home Activity:*** Read a newspaper article with your child. Help your child identify both regular and irregular plurals.

Name ________________________________

Spelling: Irregular Plurals

Pretest Directions: Fold back the page along the dotted line. On the blanks, write the spelling words as they are dictated. When you have finished the test, unfold the page and check your words.

1. ________________	**1.** These **scarfs** are made of wool.
2. ________________	**2.** Schools have teaching **staffs**.
3. ________________	**3.** This town has had ten **sheriffs**.
4. ________________	**4.** Sea animals make coral **reefs**.
5. ________________	**5.** He's met **chiefs** from many tribes.
6. ________________	**6.** The store's **shelves** are empty.
7. ________________	**7.** **Wolves** are fascinating animals.
8. ________________	**8.** We tend to keep to **ourselves**.
9. ________________	**9.** His father collects old **knives**.
10. ________________	**10.** The train was robbed by **thieves**.
11. ________________	**11.** She usually sings **solos**.
12. ________________	**12.** This store sells car **stereos**.
13. ________________	**13.** The art **studios** are downstairs.
14. ________________	**14.** **Volcanoes** erupt from time to time.
15. ________________	**15.** We bought a new set of **dominoes**.
16. ________________	**16.** The **buffaloes** grazed peacefully.
17. ________________	**17.** These spelling **quizzes** are easy!
18. ________________	**18.** Please sew up this rip in my **pants**.
19. ________________	**19.** Where did you put the **scissors**?
20. ________________	**20.** **Measles** are contagious.

Notes for Home: Your child took a pretest on words that are irregular plurals. ***Home Activity:*** Help your child learn misspelled words before the final test. Your child can underline the word parts that caused the problems and concentrate on those parts.

Spelling: Irregular Plurals

Word List			
scarfs	shelves	solos	buffaloes
staffs	wolves	stereos	quizzes
sheriffs	ourselves	studios	pants
reefs	knives	volcanoes	scissors
chiefs	thieves	dominoes	measles

Directions: Choose the words from the box where **-s** or **-es** was added to words ending in **o** and where **f** was changed to **v** before **-es** was added. Write each word in the correct column.

Plurals of Words ending in -o	Plurals ending in -ves
1. ____________________	7. ____________________
2. ____________________	8. ____________________
3. ____________________	9. ____________________
4. ____________________	10. ____________________
5. ____________________	11. ____________________
6. ____________________	

Directions: Choose the word from the box that is the plural of the word in ( ) in each sentence. Write the word on the line.

____________________ **12.** Doctor: "I'm afraid these spots look like (measles)."

____________________ **13.** Tailor: "I have to shorten these (pants) to make them fit."

____________________ **14.** Student: "Please help me study for the two (quiz) tomorrow!"

____________________ **15.** Bosses: "Both our (staff) of workers deserve raises in pay."

____________________ **16.** Governor: "The (sheriff) of those three counties are corrupt."

____________________ **17.** Seamstress: "Help! All my pairs of (scissors) are missing!"

____________________ **18.** Sioux Leaders: "The (chief) of the tribes must decide what to do."

____________________ **19.** Diver: "The coral I saw in the (reef) of Australia is beautiful."

____________________ **20.** Model: "Which of these two (scarf) goes better with this coat?"

Notes for Home: Your child spelled the plurals of words ending in *o, f,* and *ff,* and words that have the same singular and plural form, such as *pants.* ***Home Activity:*** Have your child name the spelling words whose singular and plural forms are spelled alike.

Name ______________________________

Spelling: Irregular Plurals

Directions: Proofread this interview with a Hollywood handyman. Find five spelling mistakes. Use the proofreading marks to correct each mistake.

- ≡ Make a capital.
- / Make a small letter.
- ∧ Add something.
- ℘ Take out something.
- ⊙ Add a period.
- ¶ Begin a new paragraph.

Interviewer: What are some of the everyday jobs of a handyman?

Handyman: I often sharpen knifes and scissors, put up shelfs, and repair stereoes.

Interviewer: What are some of the more unusual jobs that you have been hired to do?

Handyman: Well, working for the movie studios, I repair reefs and volcanos . . . models, that is. Once I built a four-foot-tall wall out of dominos. I think my strangest job was painting measles on plastic model heads.

Spelling Tip

stereos **volcanoes**

Some words that end in **o** are made plural by adding the **-s,** while others use **-es.** Check the interview to make sure the plural forms of words ending in **o** are spelled correctly.

Word List

scarfs	solos
staffs	stereos
sheriffs	studios
reefs	volcanoes
chiefs	dominoes
shelves	buffaloes
wolves	quizzes
ourselves	pants
knives	scissors
thieves	measles

Write an Interview

Imagine that you have to interview someone with an interesting job. On a separate sheet of paper, write the questions you will ask and make up the subject's responses. Try to use at least five of your spelling words.

Notes for Home: Your child spelled the plurals of words ending in *o, f,* and *ff,* and words that have the same singular and plural forms, such as *pants. **Home Activity:*** Give your child the singular form of each spelling word. Have your child name and spell the plural form.

Name ______________________________

Spelling: Irregular Plurals

REVIEW

Word List

scarfs	chiefs	knives	studios	quizzes
staffs	shelves	thieves	volcanoes	pants
sheriffs	wolves	solos	dominoes	scissors
reefs	ourselves	stereos	buffaloes	measles

Directions: Choose the words from the box that best complete each story. Write the words on the matching numbered lines to the right.

Theft

1. _____ and TVs are missing. The silver forks, spoons, and **2.** _____ are gone. The **3.** _____ are on their way from the station to get a list of what was taken. The **4.** _____ are on the run with the loot. Will we ever see our belongings again?

Rainy-Day Fun

We can play a game of **5.** _____ or use **6.** _____ to cut out pictures and paste them into the scrapbook. We can read about the wild **7.** _____ on the plains, or listen to the **8.** _____ Louis likes to play on his trumpet.

1. ______________________
2. ______________________
3. ______________________
4. ______________________
5. ______________________
6. ______________________
7. ______________________
8. ______________________

Directions: Choose the word from the box that best matches each clue. Write the word on the line.

______________________ **9.** We look like mountains, and we spout lava and flames.

______________________ **10.** We hold books, dishes, and other belongings.

______________________ **11.** We rule tribes and other groups of people.

______________________ **12.** We wrap around your neck and keep you warm.

______________________ **13.** We contain questions that you have to answer.

______________________ **14.** We are garments that cover your legs.

______________________ **15.** We are spots that itch.

______________________ **16.** We are groups of people who work for a boss.

______________________ **17.** We are just us.

______________________ **18.** We are the wild cousins of dogs.

______________________ **19.** We are rooms in which artists work and live.

______________________ **20.** We are underwater formations of coral.

Notes for Home: Your child spelled the plurals of words ending in *o, f,* and *ff,* and words that have the same singular and plural forms, such as *pants.* ***Home Activity:*** Help your child identify the spelling words whose plurals were formed by changing the letter *f* to *v* before adding *-es.*

Name ______________________________

Organize and Present Information

As you research and take notes, be sure to **organize information** in a logical manner that makes it easier to **present** your findings. If you have information that includes a lot of comparative quantities, you might consider using line graphs or bar graphs. Summaries, maps, time lines, illustrations, charts, and tables are other ways to organize and present information.

Thinking about text structure can also help you decide how to present your information. You may choose to organize it using chronological order, problem-solution, or cause-effect.

Directions: Read the article. Then answer the questions that follow.

In 1938, the Fair Labor Standards Act went into effect to assist people who were struggling financially because of the Great Depression. This period was a time of great poverty throughout the United States.

The most important law in the Fair Labor Standards Act was the minimum wage law. "Minimum" means "lowest," and the law made sure workers in most trades were paid no less than a set minimum amount of money per hour. In 1938, the amount was $0.25. (In 1938, a quarter was enough to buy a hearty meal at a restaurant.)

The minimum wage was reviewed in 1939 and raised to $0.30. In 1945, it went up another ten cents. In 1950, it was raised to $0.75. Six more years went by before it was raised again, this time to $1.00. Since then, the minimum wage has been raised 15 more times. The highest jump in the minimum wage took place in 1991, when it went from $3.50 to $4.25. It currently stands at $5.15.

Waiters and waitresses are not covered by the minimum wage law because they are paid "tips." Customers normally add 15% of the cost of a meal for the waiter or waitress. In addition to these tips, waiters or waitresses usually earn a certain amount of money per hour, but this wage does not have to be the minimum wage.

1. Underline or highlight the important ideas presented in this article.

2. Summarize the article briefly. ______________________________

____

____

3. Why was a minimum wage law created? ______________________________

____

4. Why aren't employers required to pay waiters and waitresses a minimum wage?

____

5. If you were giving a speech to a class about the minimum wage, what kind of graphic organizer might be a good visual aid? Why?

____

____

Directions: Study the table. Then answer the questions below.

Percentage of Female Workers in Selected Jobs, 1975 to 1997 (as a percentage of total workers)				
Job	**1975**	**1985**	**1996**	**1997**
Auto Mechanic	0.5	0.6	1.2	1.5
Cab Driver/Chauffer	8.7	10.9	10.7	8.3
Carpenter	0.6	1.2	1.3	1.6
Dentist	1.8	6.4	13.7	17.3
Dental Assistant	100.0	99.0	79.8	96.7
Journalist	44.6	51.7	55.7	51.2
Professor	31.1	35.2	43.5	42.7
Waitress	91.1	84.0	77.9	77.8
Welder	4.4	4.8	5.0	5.6

6. Explain what the number 96.7 means in the column "1997." ______________________________

____

7. Which four types of jobs showed a steady increase in the percent of female workers from 1975 to 1997? Which job shows a steady decrease?

____

____

8. How else might you organize the data in this table? Why might this be a good way to organize this data?

____

____

9. Why is it important to organize information as you do research? ______________________________

____

____

10. Why is it important to think about text structure when you are preparing to present the information you have collected?

____

____

Notes for Home: Your child read a passage, examined a table, and described ways to organize and present the information in them. ***Home Activity:*** Have your child read a newspaper or magazine article. Discuss ways your child could organize and present the information it contains.

Family Times

Name____

Summary

Against All the Odds

Before she was five, Wilma Rudolph caught polio. She recovered, but one leg was paralyzed. Wilma worked hard to strengthen her leg because she desperately wanted to go to school and play games without her leg brace. Soon, Wilma learned not just to walk but to run. Later, her running ability earned her a college scholarship and, at the age of twenty, a place on the 1960 U.S. Olympic team. Despite an ankle injury and stifling heat, Wilma Rudolph went on to win three gold medals in track and field. The once sickly child with a disability raced her way into the Olympic record books.

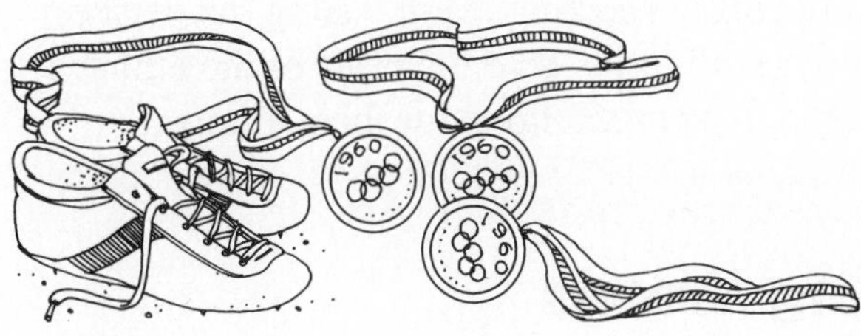

Activity

Make a Time Line. Have your child describe some of the key events in Wilma Rudolph's life. Help your child draw a time line to show the order in which events occurred.

Reading Skills

Cause and Effect

A **cause** is why something happens. An **effect** is what happens.

❖ To identify a cause, ask yourself "Why did this happen?" Clue words such as *cause, because,* and *reason* can help you to find a cause.

Wilma won the 100-meter dash because she ran better than she had run before and better than anyone else.

❖ To identify an effect, ask yourself "What happened?" Clue words such as *so, as a result, consequently,* and *therefore* can help you to find an effect.

Wilma exercised her leg all the time. As a result, she was able to go to school.

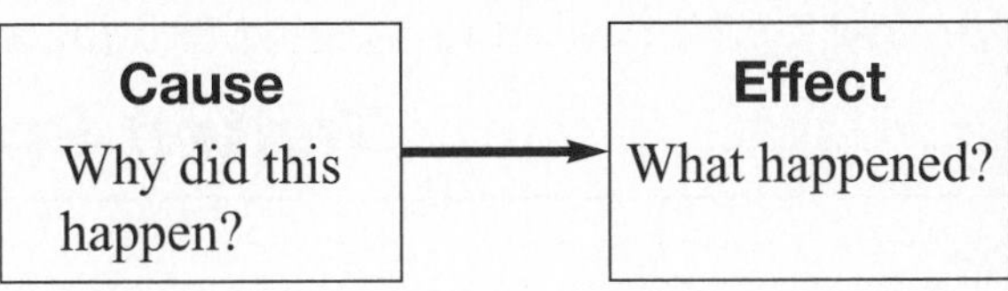

Activity

Show Relationships. Find the causes and effects of important local, national, and world events in the past year. Discuss whether each event has one or more causes and effects.

Family Times

Tested Vocabulary

Words to Know

Knowing the meanings of these words is important to reading *Wilma Unlimited.* Practice using these words to learn their meanings.

athletic of or suited to sports

competition a contest

intense extreme

memorable not to be forgotten

paralyzed unable to feel or move

unlimited endless; without limits

Grammar

Perfect Tenses of a Verb

The **perfect tense** of a verb signals that the action starts and finishes at different times.

Past Perfect: Action begun in the past and completed at another point in the past. Use *had.*

She had finished the race before all the others.

Present Perfect: Action begun in the past and completed in the present. Use *has* or *have.*

Now she has finished the race.

Future Perfect: Action to be completed at a particular time in the future. Use *will have.*

She will have finished the race by the time we get there.

Activity

Broadcast an Event. Write a broadcast of an imaginary sporting event. Using the perfect tenses of verbs, give histories of the athletes as well as predictions for their futures.

Tested Spelling Words

______	______	______	______
______	______	______	______
______	______	______	______
______	______	______	______
______	______	______	______

Name ______________________________

Cause and Effect

- An **effect** is something that happens. A **cause** is why something happens.
- To find an effect, ask yourself "What happened?" To find a cause, ask yourself "Why did it happen?"

Directions: Reread "Sunday Visitors." Then complete the table. Write the cause of each given effect. Write the effect of each given cause.

Cause (Why Did It Happen?)	Effect (What Happened?)
1.	Alice doesn't know what she wants from Peg's family.
Peg understands Alice and feels compassion for her.	**2.**
3.	The other girls are as excited about visiting day as Peg.
4.	Alice combs her hair.
5.	Dorothy blushes.

Notes for Home: Your child read a passage and linked events with their causes. ***Home Activity:*** Describe a simple event, such as a car stopping in the middle of a street. With your child, discuss possible causes of the event.

Name ___________________________________

Vocabulary

Directions: Choose the word from the box that best completes each sentence. Write the word on the line to the right.

The fall left her **1.** ____ and almost unable to move. She felt **2.** ____ grief that she would not be able to run ever again. She had always been very **3.** ____, but she knew that those days of playing sports were over. Then came a **4.** ____ day, one that she would never forget. She found that she could still enter a **5.** ____ and be an athlete.

1. ____________________

2. ____________________

3. ____________________

4. ____________________

5. ____________________

Check the Words You Know

__ athletic
__ competition
__ intense
__ memorable
__ paralyzed
__ unlimited

Directions: Choose the word from the box that best matches each clue. Write the word in the puzzle.

Down

6. a contest

7. free; not restricted

Across

8. not to be forgotten

9. something having to do with active games and sports

10. very much; extreme

Write an Awards Certificate

On a separate sheet of paper, write an awards certificate to someone who has overcome something very difficult. It can be someone you know or someone you imagine. Use as many vocabulary words as you can.

Notes for Home: Your child identified and used vocabulary words from *Wilma Unlimited.* ***Home Activity:*** Talk with your child about someone you know who has overcome an obstacle or difficult task. Make a list of words to describe that person.

Name ___________________________

Cause and Effect

- An **effect** is something that happens. A **cause** is why it happens.
- To find an effect, ask yourself "What happened?" To find a cause, ask yourself "Why did this happen?"

Directions: Reread what happens in *Wilma Unlimited* after Wilma gets polio. Then answer the questions below. Ask yourself about what happens and why to help you identify causes and effects.

Doctors and nurses at the hospital helped Wilma do exercises to make her paralyzed leg stronger. At home, Wilma practiced them constantly, even when it hurt.

To Wilma, what hurt most was that the local school wouldn't let her attend because she couldn't walk. Tearful and lonely, she watched her brothers and sisters run off to school each day, leaving her behind. Finally, tired of crying all the time, she decided she had to fight back—somehow.

Wilma worked so hard at her exercises that the doctors decided she was ready for a heavy steel brace. With the brace supporting her leg, she didn't have to hop anymore. School was possible at last.

1. Why does Wilma keep exercising her paralyzed leg even when it hurts?

____

____

2. What upsets Wilma the most about not being able to walk?

____

3. What makes Wilma stop crying and fight back?

____

4. What are the results of Wilma's hard work?

____

____

5. On a separate sheet of paper, explain what you think is the major cause of Wilma's success. Give examples from the story to support your answer.

Notes for Home: Your child read a short story and identified causes and effects. ***Home Activity:*** With your child, read or listen to a local news story. Challenge him or her to identify the causes and effects of individual news events.

Name ______________________________

Selection Test

Directions: Choose the best answer to each item. Mark the letter for the answer you have chosen.

Part 1: Vocabulary

Find the answer choice that means about the same as the underlined word in each sentence.

1. The Scott family had a memorable vacation.
- A. lengthy
- B. dull or boring
- C. not to be forgotten
- D. involving the wilderness

2. The pass gives us unlimited use of Henderson Park.
- F. without restrictions; boundless
- G. paid in advance
- H. from morning to night
- J. cheap; inexpensive

3. Those girls entered the competition.
- A. show of affection
- B. contest
- C. friendly support
- D. equipment used in track and field

4. Alano worked in intense heat.
- F. occasional
- G. mild
- H. humid
- J. extreme

5. Shem looked at his paralyzed legs.
- A. small and thin
- B. unable to move
- C. spotted
- D. covered with hair

6. Carrie joined the athletic club.
- F. having to do with sports
- G. secret
- H. related to art
- J. for girls only

Part 2: Comprehension

Use what you know about the selection to answer each item.

7. Why did the people of Clarksville think that Wilma would never walk again?
- A. The doctor had her wear a brace.
- B. She had no one to take care of her.
- C. There was no cure for polio at that time.
- D. She had always been a small and sickly child.

8. Wilma was not allowed to go to school at first because—
- F. her mother needed her help.
- G. she might make others sick.
- H. her leg was supported by a brace.
- J. she could not walk.

9. Which word best describes Wilma Rudolph throughout her life?
- A. quiet
- B. sickly
- C. determined
- D. lonely

10. What is the main idea of this selection?
- F. Wilma Rudolph overcame polio and won three Olympic gold medals.
- G. Wilma Rudolph did leg exercises until she could walk without her leg brace.
- H. Wilma Rudolph was the first person in her family to go to college.
- J. Wilma Rudolph was the fastest woman in the world.

GO ON

11. School was not as wonderful as Wilma had thought it would be because—
- A. the other kids made fun of her.
- B. she was a better basketball player than the others.
- C. there were no other African American children there.
- D. she had a hard time doing her schoolwork.

12. You can conclude that Wilma Rudolph felt supported by her community because she—
- F. did leg exercises at home.
- G. first tried to walk without her brace at church.
- H. ran in Olympic track-and-field events.
- J. went to Tennessee State University.

13. What effect did Wilma's experiences as a child overcoming polio have on her during the Olympics?
- A. She had stronger legs than the other athletes.
- B. She was well prepared to receive the baton.
- C. She was popular with the audience.
- D. She was able to really concentrate on her goal.

14. Which is a statement of opinion?
- F. It was the bravest thing she had ever done.
- G. She waited while other people filled the building.
- H. She took off her leg brace and set it by the door.
- J. She placed one foot in front of the other.

15. The biggest obstacle Wilma Rudolph had to overcome in order to become an Olympic runner was that—
- A. her mother had twenty-two children.
- B. she was African American.
- C. her leg had been paralyzed by polio.
- D. she weighed just four pounds at birth.

STOP

Name ______________________________

Cause and Effect

- An **effect** is something that happens. A **cause** is why it happens.
- To find an effect, ask yourself "What happened?" To find a cause, ask yourself "Why did this happen?"

Directions: Read the passage below.

Nelson Mandela's years of struggle and sacrifice helped to change South Africa from a deeply divided country to a land of greater racial equality.

At one time, black South Africans were only allowed to live in certain areas and work at certain low-paying jobs. Mandela led protests against these laws. In 1964, he was sentenced to life in prison for protesting. Other countries were outraged at this treatment of a man who was fighting for freedom. Their attention to his story made Mandela a powerful symbol of the fight for equality.

This worldwide anger helped convince the South African government to change things. Black South Africans now have the right to vote and the right to live where they like. In 1994, soon after he was freed from prison, Mandela was elected president of his country.

Directions: Complete the chart by writing causes and effects based on the passage.

Cause		Effect
South Africa had laws based on racial difference.	→	**1.**
Mandela protests the laws.	→	**2.**
3.	→	Mandela becomes a symbol of the fight for equality.
4.	→	The South African government begins changing the laws.
Mandela is freed and blacks are granted the right to vote.	→	**5.**

Notes for Home: Your child identified causes and effects in a passage. ***Home Activity:*** Take turns with your child naming events that happen and figuring out possible reasons why. For example: *The car won't start. Why? (It is too cold; it has no gas; it is broken.)*

Name ______________________________

REVIEW

Main Idea and Supporting Details/Context Clues

Directions: Read the passage. Then read each question about the passage. Choose the best answer to each question. Mark the letter for the answer you have chosen.

The Struggle for America

Large numbers of Chinese people came to California during the Gold Rush in the mid-1800s. They were not made welcome in their new country. They were often forced to pay special taxes and fees. Only a few jobs, such as laundry work and mining, were open to them. In some places, schools refused to accept Chinese children. No state let them argue in court against non-Chinese people, and they were not allowed to become citizens.

Prejudice against Chinese people in America was intense enough in 1882 for the U.S. to pass the Chinese Exclusion Act. This barred Chinese people from entering the country as immigrants for more than sixty years. During this time, many Chinese Americans tried to change the law by going to court.

During World War II, thousands of Chinese Americans joined the U.S. armed forces. Thousands of others went to work in defense factories. In 1943, the repeal of the Chinese Exclusion Act meant that Chinese immigrants were welcome again.

Since that time, Chinese immigration has grown rapidly. Chinese Americans have settled in many states besides California. Today, Chinese Americans have better opportunities for education and employment.

1. The main idea of this passage is that—
- **A.** Chinese people came to America after the Gold Rush.
- **B.** Chinese immigrants paid special taxes and fees.
- **C.** Chinese Americans are citizens today.
- **D.** Racial prejudice once denied opportunities to Chinese Americans.

2. The word prejudice in this passage means—
- **F.** exclusion.
- **G.** strong dislike.
- **H.** Chinese.
- **J.** immigrants.

3. Because of prejudice, Chinese people in America—
- **A.** had few rights.
- **B.** settled in California.
- **C.** became citizens.
- **D.** paid no taxes.

4. The Chinese Exclusion Act kept Chinese people from—
- **F.** going to court.
- **G.** going to school.
- **H.** entering the United States.
- **J.** becoming citizens.

5. Chinese immigration grew when—
- **A.** the Exclusion Act was overturned.
- **B.** Chinese Americans fought in court.
- **C.** World War II began.
- **D.** California became a state.

Notes for Home: Your child identified the main idea and supporting details of a passage and used context clues to understand new words. ***Home Activity:*** Have your child tell you the main idea of an article. Encourage him or her to use context clues to understand new words.

Name ___________________________

Writing Across Texts

Directions: In both *Wilma Unlimited* and "Elizabeth Blackwell: Medical Pioneer," strong women faced considerable obstacles to reach goals that were very important to them. Complete the table below to compare the obstacles faced by Wilma Rudolph and Elizabeth Blackwell in pursuing their goals.

Wilma Rudolph's Obstacles	Elizabeth Blackwell's Obstacles
Wilma was born weighing only four pounds.	Elizabeth went blind in one eye.
1.	**6.**
2.	**7.**
3.	**8.**
4.	**9.**
5.	**10.**

Write a Paragraph

Write a paragraph comparing the obstacles faced by Wilma Rudolph and Elizabeth Blackwell in realizing their potential. Write your paragraph on a separate sheet of paper.

Notes for Home: Your child compared the lives of two women who overcame many obstacles to reach their goals. ***Home Activity:*** With your child, discuss obstacles that might keep him or her from attaining specific goals. Together, figure out ways to overcome those obstacles.

Grammar: Verb Tenses: Present, Past, and Future

REVIEW

Directions: Circle the verb in each sentence. Write **present, past,** or **future** on the line to name the tense of each verb.

______ **1.** Last year Matt joined the track team at school.

______ **2.** He ran every day after school with the team.

______ **3.** Now he still runs every day—even on weekends.

______ **4.** His teammates probably will elect him captain of the team next year.

______ **5.** Matt takes this sport very seriously.

______ **6.** Before last year, Matt worked after school.

______ **7.** Now he focuses on one important goal.

______ **8.** He will participate in the Olympics one day!

______ **9.** His family will support him all the way.

Directions: Write a sentence using the verb and the verb tense given.

10. the present tense of *work*

______

11. the past tense of *work*

______

12. the future tense of *work*

______

13. the present tense of *practice*

______

14. the past tense of *practice*

______

15. the future tense of *practice*

______

Notes for Home: Your child identified the three main tenses of a verb. ***Home Activity:*** Have your child think of a familiar fairy tale or read one. Then have your child tell the same story in the present tense. If time permits, have your child make up a short fairy tale in the future tense.

Practice

Grammar: More Verb Tenses: Perfect and Progressive Tenses

The **present perfect tense** describes an action that began in the past and is completed in the present. It is formed by adding **has** or **have** to the past participle. The **past participle** of any regular verb is formed by adding **-ed** to the present tense.

The track-and-field committee has elected a new chairperson.

The **past perfect tense** describes an action begun at one point in the past and completed at another point in the past. It is formed by adding **had** to the past participle.

Until last week, Denise had attended all the committee meetings.

The **future perfect tense** describes an action to be completed at a particular time in the future. It is formed by adding **will have** to the past participle.

By next week, the committee will have created a new track schedule.

To describe an action that is ongoing, or in progress, you can use the **progressive** form of a tense. Each progressive form includes the **present participle,** the **-ing** form, of the main verb.

Roland is practicing every day. (present progressive)

Sally was recovering from a knee injury. (past progressive)

Directions: Use the correct form of the verb in ( ) to complete each sentence. Use the verb in the tense named in ( ). Write the verb on the line to the left.

________________ **1.** By last week, Tina _____ three different field events. (enter—past perfect)

________________ **2.** Tyrell _____ to improve his time in the 100-yard dash. (try—past progressive)

________________ **3.** The school _____ the new indoor track. (finish—past perfect)

________________ **4.** Our team _____ in five meets. (compete—present perfect)

________________ **5.** We _____ in twenty meets by the time the season ends. (compete—future perfect)

________________ **6.** We _____ money for new uniforms. (raise—present progressive)

________________ **7.** The fan club _____ two hundred dollars. (donate—past perfect)

________________ **8.** Soon we _____ all the money we need. (raise—future perfect)

________________ **9.** Our coach _____ a banquet. (plan—present progressive)

________________ **10.** I _____ to be chosen as the most improved athlete. (hope—present progressive)

Notes for Home: Your child wrote verbs in the perfect and progressive tenses. ***Home Activity:*** Have your child use the present progressive tense to describe actions happening now.

Grammar: More Verb Tenses: Perfect and Progressive Tenses

Directions: Use the correct form of the verb in ( ) to complete each sentence. Use the verb in the tense named in ( ). Write the verb on the line to the left.

_______________ **1.** My friends and I _____ a new outdoor track for a long time. (want—present perfect)

_______________ **2.** We _____ hundreds of signatures for our petitions. (collect—present perfect)

_______________ **3.** We _____ everything we can to get this track built. (do—present progressive)

_______________ **4.** By next year, we hope the school _____ to build the track. (agree—future perfect)

_______________ **5.** Until last month, the school board _____ our petitions and letters. (ignore—past perfect)

_______________ **6.** Our classmates _____ us advice and support. (give—past progressive)

_______________ **7.** In the past month, other board members _____ to consider our idea. (start—past perfect)

_______________ **8.** Our group _____ how to present our ideas more clearly. (learn—present progressive)

_______________ **9.** Surely, by the next board meeting, we _____ five other members. (convince—future perfect)

_______________ **10.** We _____ everyone why our plan makes sense. (show—present progressive)

Write a Short Story

On a separate sheet of paper, write a story that shares a lesson that you learned about someone or something. When you have finished, identify the tense of the verbs you used.

Notes for Home: Your child wrote verbs in present and progressive tenses. ***Home Activity:*** Have your child describe a past action using the past perfect tense. *(I had studied for that test for weeks!)*

Grammar: More Verb Tenses: Perfect and Progressive Tenses

RETEACHING

Underline the correct verb form in ( ) that best completes each sentence.

1. After a week of discussion, we (decide/have decided) not to go. **(present perfect)**
2. Until yesterday, Dan (ran/had run) two miles every day. **(past perfect)**
3. By 3:30, we (have/will have) completed the test. **(future perfect)**
4. Our book club (reading/is reading) every day. **(present progressive)**
5. June (eats/was eating) when her mother came home. **(past progressive)**

The **present perfect tense** describes an action that began in the past and ends in the present. It is formed by adding **has** or **have** to the **past participle** (the **-ed** form) of a regular verb. The **past perfect tense** describes an action that began and ended in the past. It is formed by adding **had** to the past participle. The **future perfect tense** describes an action that will be completed in the future. It is formed by adding **will have** to the past participle. Use a **progressive** form of a tense to describe an action that is in progress. This form includes the **present participle** (the **-ing** form) of the main verb.

Directions: Use the correct form of the verb in ( ) to complete each sentence. Use the verb in the tense named in ( ). Write the verb on the line.

____________________ 1. We _____ aluminum cans last month. (collect—past perfect)

____________________ 2. We _____ them to the supermarket in baskets. (carry—past perfect)

____________________ 3. The clerk _____ them carefully. (count—past perfect)

____________________ 4. We _____ our quota by tomorrow. (fill—future perfect)

____________________ 5. My brother and I _____ money to buy CDs. (save—present progressive)

____________________ 6. He _____ it all on gum and candy. (spend—past progressive)

____________________ 7. I told him that if we _____ to have a better CD collection, we needed to budget our money. (go—past progressive)

____________________ 8. So far, we _____ enough money to buy one and a half CDs. (save—present perfect)

____________________ 9. After tomorrow we _____ the right amount for two CDs. (earn—future perfect)

Notes for Home: Your child used progressive and perfect forms of verb tenses to complete sentences. ***Home Activity:*** Together, look at an article in a newspaper and have your child identify examples of sentences with progressive and perfect forms of verb tenses.

Grammar: More Verb Tenses: Perfect and Progressive Tenses

Directions: Read each sentence. Identify the tense of each underlined verb. Write the name of the tense on the line.

________________ **1.** I have located some interesting photographs.

________________ **2.** My grandmother had stored them in the attic.

________________ **3.** I was looking for an old stuffed animal when I came across them.

________________ **4.** Tonight she has shared them with me.

________________ **5.** By tomorrow I will have recorded much information.

________________ **6.** My great-grandfather had performed in many concerts.

________________ **7.** He had achieved fame as a pianist.

________________ **8.** My great-grandmother had played the violin with him.

________________ **9.** My grandmother was saving pictures of them.

________________ **10.** We will have mounted them in a book by next week.

________________ **11.** We have discovered recordings of their performances.

________________ **12.** In a year we will have donated them to the library.

________________ **13.** The library is collecting old photos and recordings for a new exhibit about our town's history.

________________ **14.** One librarian was asking for photos of people and the places they lived.

________________ **15.** My great-grandmother is smiling in many of the photographs.

Directions: Write a sentence with the verb and tense named in ( ). Write each new sentence on the line.

16. (understand—past progressive)

____

17. (try—present progressive)

____

18. (find—past perfect)

____

Notes for Home: Your child identified tenses of verbs and wrote sentences using verbs in perfect and progressive tenses. ***Home Activity:*** Together, list verbs related to your child's hobby or special skill. Have your child write sentences, using those verbs in perfect and progressive tenses.

Name ______________________________

Phonics: Schwa Sound (Within Word)

Directions: The **schwa sound** is a vowel sound heard in unstressed syllables. The **o** in **person** is an example of a schwa sound. This sound can be spelled with any vowel combination of vowels. Read each word below. Underline the vowel or vowels that stand for the schwa. Some words may contain more than one schwa sound.

1. remedies
2. television
3. several
4. celebrate
5. permanently
6. Tennessee
7. favorite
8. competition
9. against
10. stability
11. opponent
12. different

Directions: In each sentence, one of the underlined words contains the schwa sound. Write the word on the line. Underline the vowel or vowels that stand for the schwa sound.

________________ **13.** The track competition was being held in the central field area.

________________ **14.** People from dozens of states filled the stadium to watch the competitors.

________________ **15.** The racers in the relay practiced passing the baton.

________________ **16.** They were a bit nervous about the upcoming race.

________________ **17.** One runner was able to regain her balance after her initial fall at the starting line.

________________ **18.** Everyone was relieved that the athlete had not injured herself again.

________________ **19.** The winner was honored for her amazing speed and stamina at the medal ceremony.

________________ **20.** The spectators cheered all of the athletes for giving their best.

Notes for Home: Your child identified the schwa sound in words. ***Home Activity:*** Read a sports story with your child. Help your child find words with schwa sounds and check them in a dictionary. (The symbol for the schwa sound is ə.)

Name ____________________________________

Spelling: Vowels in Unstressed Syllables

Pretest Directions: Fold back the page along the dotted line. On the blanks, write the spelling words as they are dictated. When you have finished the test, unfold the page and check your words.

1. ____________________
2. ____________________
3. ____________________
4. ____________________
5. ____________________
6. ____________________
7. ____________________
8. ____________________
9. ____________________
10. ____________________
11. ____________________
12. ____________________
13. ____________________
14. ____________________
15. ____________________
16. ____________________
17. ____________________
18. ____________________
19. ____________________
20. ____________________

1. A boat is **different** from a car.
2. We're going to **register** to vote.
3. A **carnival** is coming to town.
4. I like a wide **variety** of music.
5. A party has a festive **atmosphere**.
6. This is my **favorite** book.
7. I **pattern** myself after my father.
8. We **understand** each other.
9. That **sentence** makes no sense.
10. I can think of no similar **instance**.
11. We ate at an **elegant** restaurant.
12. Our fish need a bigger **aquarium**.
13. We **communicate** by e-mail.
14. **Gasoline** is highly flammable.
15. What do they make at the **factory**?
16. Can you give a **definite** answer?
17. I grew up in **Chicago**.
18. He slumped **heavily** into his seat.
19. We had a **garage** sale last year.
20. Who will **illustrate** your book?

Notes for Home: Your child took a pretest on words that have indistinct vowel sounds in unstressed syllables. ***Home Activity:*** Help your child learn misspelled words before the final test. Dictate the word and have your child spell the word aloud for you or write it on paper.

Name ______________________________

Spelling: Vowels in Unstressed Syllables

Word List				
different	atmosphere	sentence	communicate	Chicago
register	favorite	instance	gasoline	heavily
carnival	pattern	elegant	factory	garage
variety	understand	aquarium	definite	illustrate

Directions: Write the words from the box that have two **schwa** sounds each. The **schwa** sound is an indistinct vowel sound heard in unstressed syllables, such as the **a** in **garage** or the **o** in **favorite.** Use a dictionary to check your answers.

1. ____________________ **5.** ____________________

2. ____________________ **6.** ____________________

3. ____________________ **7.** ____________________

4. ____________________

Directions: Choose the word from the box that best completes each equation. Write the word on the line.

8. favor + ite = ____________________

9. Chicken – ken + ago = ____________________

10. facts – s + ory = ____________________

11. heavy – y + ill – l + y = ____________________

12. patriot – riot + tern = ____________________

13. sensational – sational + tence = ____________________

14. il + lustre – e + ate = ____________________

15. garble – ble + age = ____________________

16. ga + solo – o + ine = ____________________

17. define – e + ite = ____________________

18. under + stand = ____________________

19. at + most – st + sphere = ____________________

20. in + stand – d + ce = ____________________

Notes for Home: Your child spelled words with indistinct vowel sounds that give no clue to their spelling, such as the *i* in *register. **Home Activity:*** Say each word aloud and have your child write it. Review the list and correct any misspellings together.

Spelling: Vowels in Unstressed Syllables

Directions: Proofread this fan letter. Find seven spelling mistakes. Use the proofreading marks to correct each mistake.

≡ Make a capital.
/ Make a small letter.
∧ Add something.
Take out something.
⊙ Add a period.
¶ Begin a new paragraph.

Dear Carl Lewis,

I undrstand that you are retiring from competition. Your absence will weigh hevily on this track and field fan!

You are my faverite athlete of all time. The varaty of diffrent events in which you competed was amazing. They all illustrate your great skill. You changed the whole atmusphere of the field when you walked onto it. You had the most elagant running style, and the pattern of exercise and hard work you followed was a great example to me.

With deepest admiration,

Jesse King

Spelling Tip

All the spelling words contain one or more **schwa** sounds, the indistinct vowel sound you hear in unstressed syllables. This vowel sound gives no clues to its spelling, so you need to check these words carefully.

Word List

different
register
carnival
variety
atmosphere
favorite
pattern
understand
sentence
instance
elegant
aquarium
communicate
gasoline
factory
definite
Chicago
heavily
garage
illustrate

Write a Fan Letter

On a separate sheet of paper, write a fan letter to an athlete you admire. Try to use at least five of your spelling words.

Notes for Home: Your child spelled words with indistinct vowel sounds that give no clue to their spelling, such as the *i* in *register. **Home Activity:*** Help your child create spelling clues. For example: *Sentence always has three e's.*

Name ______________________________

REVIEW

Spelling: Vowels in Unstressed Syllables

Directions: Choose the word from the box that best matches each clue. Write the word on the line.

Word List

different
register
carnival
variety
atmosphere
favorite
pattern
understand
sentence
instance
elegant
aquarium
communicate
gasoline
factory
definite
Chicago
heavily
garage
illustrate

______________ **1.** what someone likes best

______________ **2.** certain; positive

______________ **3.** tasteful; well-dressed; handsome

______________ **4.** with weight

______________ **5.** festival; fair

______________ **6.** sign up for; record one's name

______________ **7.** an example or a case

______________ **8.** mass of gases surrounding a star or planet

______________ **9.** convey your thoughts or ideas to someone else

______________ **10.** a regular order or design

______________ **11.** a group of different things

______________ **12.** comprehend; grasp the meaning of

Directions: Choose the word from the box that best completes each statement. Write the word on the line to the left.

______________ **13.** *Horse* is to *stable* as *car* is to _____.

______________ **14.** *Bakers* are to *bakery* as *workers* are to _____.

______________ **15.** *Letters* are to *word* as *words* are to _____.

______________ **16.** *Human* is to *food* as *motor vehicle* is to _____.

______________ **17.** *State* is to *Illinois* as *city* is to _____.

______________ **18.** *Bird* is to *cage* as *fish* is to _____.

______________ **19.** *Top* is to *bottom* as *alike* is to _____.

______________ **20.** *Leap* is to *jump* as *draw* is to _____.

Notes for Home: Your child spelled words with indistinct vowel sounds that give no clue to their spelling, such as the *i* in *register* and the *o* in *atmosphere.* ***Home Activity:*** Read some of the spelling words aloud. Challenge your child to spell the words.

Name ______________________

Almanac

An **almanac** is a yearly book that contains calendars, weather information, and dates of holidays, as well as charts and tables of current information in many different subject areas.

Directions: Study the information from an almanac. Then answer the questions that follow.

Table of Contents

General Index

Olympic Games—Summer Medals Table

Berlin, 1936		Rome, 1960		Barcelona, 1992	
Country	**Medals Won**	**Country**	**Medals Won**	**Country**	**Medals Won**
Germany	89	USSR	99	Unified Team	111
USA	56	USA	71	USA	108
Hungary	16	Italy	36	Germany	82

Medalists, Women's 100-meter race

Berlin, 1936		Rome, 1960		Barcelona, 1992	
Athlete	**Time (sec.)**	**Athlete**	**Time (sec.)**	**Athlete**	**Time (sec.)**
H. Stephens, USA	11.5	W. Rudolph, USA	11.0	G. Devers, USA	10.82
S. Walasiewicz, POL	11.7	D. Hyman, GBR	11.3	J. Cuthbert, JAM	10.83
K. Krauß, GER	11.9	G. Leone, ITALY	11.3	I. Privalova, EUN	10.84

1. Which subject area in the almanac might tell you how many miles equal one kilometer? On which page does this section of the almanac begin?

____

2. In which section would you look for information about the imports and exports of India?

____

3. In which section might you find the birth date of Albert Einstein? ______________

____

4. On which page in the almanac does the section on the arts begin? ______________

5. In which section of the almanac will you find information about the Olympics?

____

6. If you were looking for specific information on the Special Olympics, would you use the table of contents or the index? Explain.

____

____

7. How much faster did Wilma Rudolph run the 100-meter race than Dorothy Hyman?

____

8. How many medals did the United States win in the 1992 Summer Olympics? Where were these Olympic games held?

____

9. The winner of the Olympic 100-meter race is often referred to as the world's fastest runner. Suppose you were writing a report on the history of the world's fastest women. Would the data in the second table be useful? What other data might you need? Explain.

____

____

____

10. If you were making a line graph of the local high weather temperatures for the past month, would an almanac be useful? If you were making a weather map to show the highest temperatures ever recorded, would an almanac be useful? Explain.

____

____

____

Notes for Home: Your child studied an almanac and answered questions about its use. ***Home Activity:*** Look at the almanacs in a library's reference section with your child. Use the table of contents and index to find out and discuss what kinds of information can be found in almanacs.

Family Times

Name____

Summary

High Drama on the Baseball Diamond

Down by two runs in the bottom of the ninth inning, the Mudville baseball team seems sure to lose the game. The first two batters are thrown out at first. Miraculously, though, Flynn hits a single and Blake hits a double. This brings up Casey, the team's star hitter, who is certain to hit a winning home run for Mudville. Casey lets two strikes go past him. Then he swings mightily at the next pitch—and strikes out.

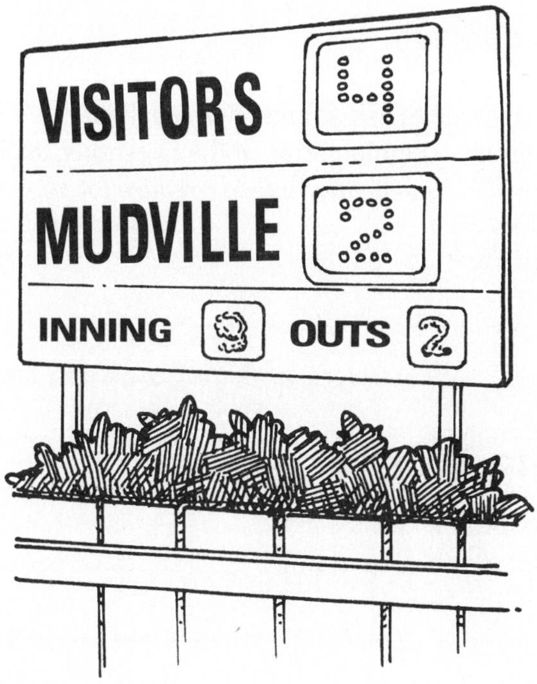

Activity

Baseball Radio Announcer. Prompt your child to pretend he or she is a sportscaster calling the last inning of the Mudville game.

Reading Skills

Summarizing

When you **summarize** a piece of writing, you give a brief statement of the main idea of an article or the most important events in a story.

When you summarize—

- ❖ **a story,** include only the main actions of the characters and the outcomes of these actions.
- ❖ **an article,** include the main idea or ideas and only the most important supporting details.

Read the summary to the left. Notice which events and details have been included, and which have been left out.

Activity

Timely Summaries. Take turns summarizing the events of a day, a week, a month, and a year. How much detail will you include? How is each summary different?

Family Times

Tested Vocabulary

Words to Know

Knowing the meanings of these words is important to reading *Casey at the Bat.* Practice using these words to learn their meanings.

defiance bold disregard of authority

despair a state of hopelessness

grandeur magnificence

haughty arrogant

scornful mocking

umpire person who rules on the plays in a game

Grammar

Irregular Verbs

Most verbs use **-ed** to form the past and past participle. Irregular verbs, however, change spelling for the past and past participle forms. Here are some irregular verbs:

Present	Past	Past Participle
begin	began	(has, have) begun
come	came	(has, have) come
do	did	(has, have) done
go	went	(has, have) gone
ring	rang	(has, have) rung
see	saw	(has, have) seen
swim	swam	(has, have) swum

Activity

Interview a Star. Make up five interview questions to ask a famous baseball star. Include irregular verbs in the questions, such as: *What have you done to prepare for this game?*

Tested Spelling Words

____	____	____	____
____	____	____	____
____	____	____	____
____	____	____	____
____	____	____	____

Name ______________________

Summarizing

- To **summarize** means to give a brief statement of the main idea of an article or the most important events in a story.
- When you summarize an article, include the main idea or ideas and only the most important supporting details.

Directions: Reread "Winners Never Quit." Summarize the main idea of the article. Then summarize the important supporting details by completing each sentence in the web. One sentence has been completed for you.

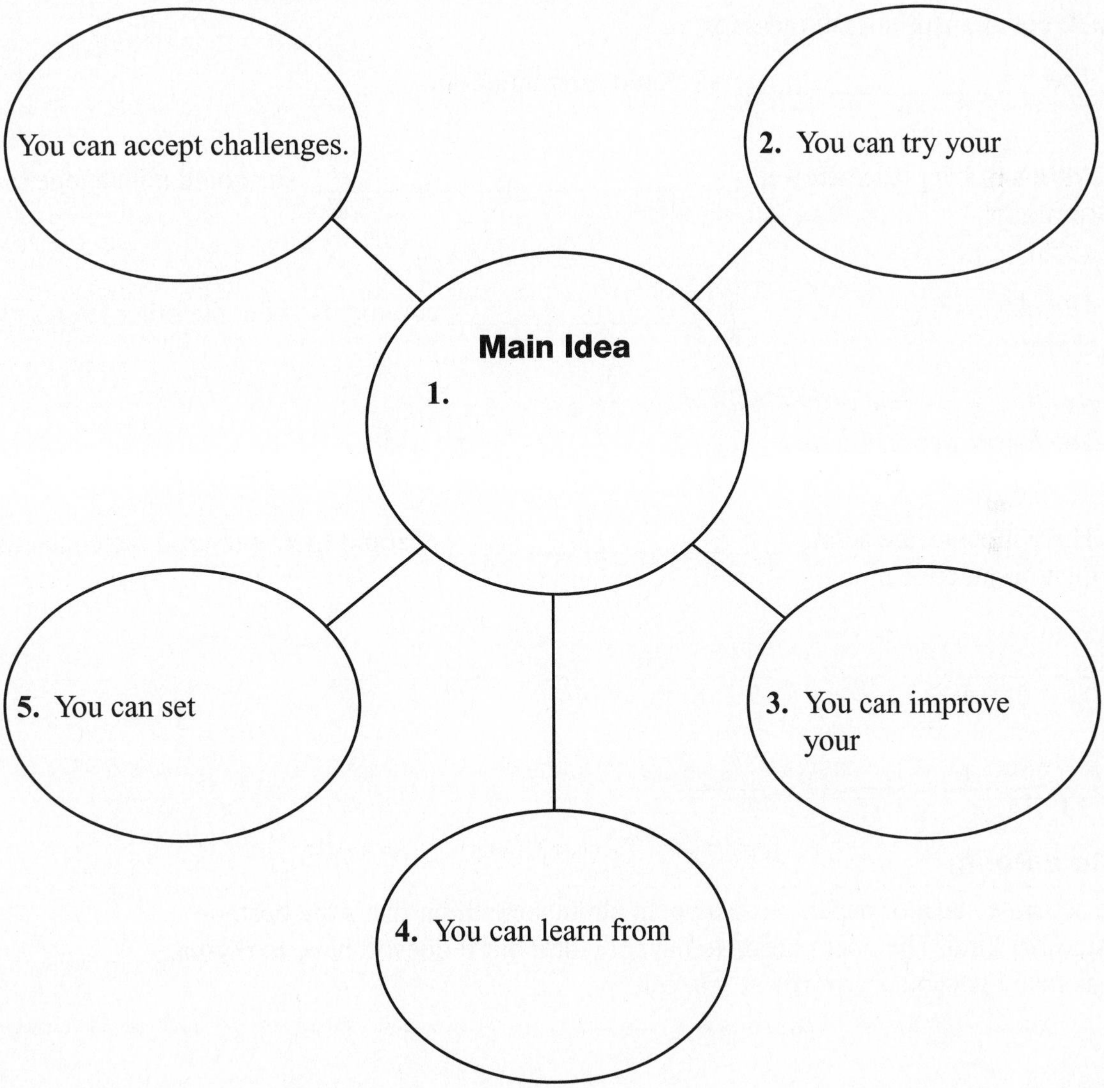

You can accept challenges.

2. You can try your

Main Idea

1.

5. You can set

3. You can improve your

4. You can learn from

Notes for Home: Your child summarized the main idea and most important supporting details of an article. ***Home Activity:*** With your child, summarize a newspaper or magazine article that you have both read. Create a web similar to the one above.

Name ______________________________

Vocabulary

Directions: Choose the word from the box that is the most opposite in meaning from each word below. Write the word on the line.

Check the Words You Know
__ defiance
__ despair
__ grandeur
__ haughty
__ scornful
__ umpire

______________ **1.** humble

______________ **2.** compliance

______________ **3.** admiring

______________ **4.** hope

______________ **5.** shabbiness

Directions: Choose the word from the box that best completes each sentence. Write the letters of the word on the blanks. Use the numbers below the blanks to spell out an inspirational message.

6. The ___ ___ ___ ___ ___ ___ declared the runner out.
(5 16 8 2 3)

7. Although the player showed ___ ___ ___ ___ ___ ___ ___ ___, she could not change the ruling.
(12 17)

8. The players made ___ ___ ___ ___ ___ ___ ___ ___ comments about the other team's many errors.
(6 13)

9. The losers went home in ___ ___ ___ ___ ___ ___ ___.
(1 9 14)

10. The winners were acting ___ ___ ___ ___ ___ ___ ___ about their win until the coach told them to practice more!
(15 4 7 11 10)

___ ___ ___ ___ ___ ___   ___ ___ v ___   ___ ___ ___
1 2 3 4 5 6   7 8   9   10 11 12

m ___ ___ t   ___ o ___ ___.
13 14   15   16 17

Write a Poem

On a separate sheet of paper, write a poem about something that's the best, or worst, of its kind. The poem needs to have rhythm, but it doesn't have to rhyme. Use as many vocabulary words as you can.

Notes for Home: Your child identified and used vocabulary words from the poem *Casey at the Bat*. ***Home Activity:*** Use the vocabulary words *defiance, scornful,* and *haughty* and challenge your child to act out each emotion. Then let your child give you similar words to act out.

Name ______________________________

Summarizing

- **Summarizing** means giving a brief statement—no more than a few sentences—of the main idea of an article or the most important events in a story.

Directions: Reread the part of *Casey at the Bat* in which Casey waits for and swings at the last pitch. Then answer the questions below. Think about Casey's actions and their outcome to help you summarize.

> The sneer is gone from Casey's lip, his teeth are clenched in hate,
> He pounds with cruel violence his bat upon the plate;
> And now the pitcher holds the ball, and now he lets it go,
> And now the air is shattered by the force of Casey's blow.
>
> Oh, somewhere in this favored land the sun is shining bright,
> The band is playing somewhere, and somewhere hearts are light;
> And somewhere men are laughing, and somewhere children shout,
> But there is no joy in Mudville—mighty Casey has struck out.
>
> From *Casey at the Bat* by Ernest Lawrence, 1888.

1. Summarize what happens in the first group of lines.

____

____

2. What happens after the first group of lines that isn't stated in the second group of lines?

____

____

3. What is the most important phrase in the second group of lines? Why?

____

____

4. Summarize the action for this part of the poem (both groups of lines).

____

____

5. On a separate sheet of paper, summarize the action of the Mudville team during the game.

Notes for Home: Your child summarized events in a poem. ***Home Activity:*** Discuss a favorite story, movie, or television show. Read another poem. Encourage your child to summarize the most important events.

Name ______________________________

Selection Test

Directions: Choose the best answer to each item. Mark the letter for the answer you have chosen.

Part 1: Vocabulary

Find the answer choice that means about the same as the underlined word in each sentence.

1. Everyone stared at the umpire.
- A. manager of a baseball team
- B. player on a professional sports team
- C. fan at a baseball game
- D. person who rules on the plays in the game

2. The fans watched in despair.
- F. state of looking forward to something
- G. state of hopelessness
- H. state of excitement
- J. state of nervousness

3. Sean had a scornful expression on his face.
- A. able to agree with others
- B. courteous; polite
- C. mocking
- D. full of teasing and fun

4. Aunt Mildred is a haughty woman.
- F. well-mannered
- G. very happy; always cheerful
- H. full of grace
- J. overly proud and self-confident

5. The house had a sense of grandeur.
- A. ability to last a long time
- B. originality; newness
- C. greatness; splendor
- D. simple style

6. Leon answered with defiance.
- F. resistance to power or authority
- G. uncontrolled energy
- H. lack of enthusiasm
- J. impatience

Part 2: Comprehension

Use what you know about the poem to answer each item.

7. The fans felt sure the Mudville team would win if—
- A. Flynn got on base.
- B. Casey got a chance to bat.
- C. Blake got a walk.
- D. the umpire was fair.

8. Why did the fans stop yelling at the umpire?
- F. They realized the calls were fair.
- G. Casey signaled for them to be quiet.
- H. Casey yelled at the umpire himself.
- J. The umpire yelled back.

9. How did Casey feel as he stepped up to the plate?
- A. confident
- B. nervous
- C. excited
- D. angry

10. Which is the best summary of the events before Casey's turn at bat?
- F. Two batters made outs.
- G. There were six points scored and two outs.
- H. The game was close until two Mudville players made outs.
- J. Mudville was losing four to two with two outs and two players on base.

GO ON

11. Which is the best summary of the events after Casey stepped up to the plate?
- A. Casey let two strikes go by, swung at and missed the third pitch, and struck out.
- B. The umpire made sure that Casey would not hit the ball.
- C. The pitcher changed the way he threw each ball, so Casey missed three pitches in a row and struck out.
- D. The pitcher threw three balls, but Casey swung at them and struck out.

12. How can you tell which team won the game?
- F. Mudville won, because Casey is a local hero.
- G. The opposing team won, because its players were more talented.
- H. Mudville won, because the narrator did not name the other team.
- J. The opposing team won, because no one is laughing or shouting.

13. Which line from the poem suggests that Casey became determined after two strikes were called?
- A. "With a smile of Christian charity great Casey's visage shone"
- B. "They saw his face grow stern and cold, they saw his muscles strain"
- C. "But Casey still ignored it, and the umpire said, 'Strike two.'"
- D. "And now the air is shattered by the force of Casey's blow."

14. Calling Flynn a "lulu" suggests that he—
- F. is a better fielder than hitter.
- G. doesn't have much experience.
- H. is a bit crazy.
- J. doesn't get along with Casey.

15. The speaker's point of view in this poem is most like that of—
- A. an umpire.
- B. an angry fan.
- C. a reporter.
- D. a judge.

STOP

Name ____

Summarizing

- **Summarizing** means giving a brief statement—no more than a few sentences—of the main idea of an article or the most important events in a story.

Directions: Read the poem. Complete the flow chart by summarizing the events of the poem.

The house is still, no one's about,
A "Welcome home, Meg!" seems much in doubt.
If no one cares that I'm back to stay,
I'll wish I'd never gone away.

It's not that I want any childish game,
Or hats, or songs. They are so lame!
Parties like that belong to the past
And I feel all grown up at last!

My parents seem to have followed my wishes.
All here is quiet; I am suspicious.
I listen at the top of the stairs,
But nothing moves. Nobody cares!

I drop my bags and my coat on the floor—
And then I hear it! The click of the door!
No one comes up. I go to find out.
"Welcome home, Meg!" my friends all shout.

Verse 1

1. Meg thinks:

Verse 2

2. Meg does not want:

Verse 3

3. Meg thinks the house is:

Verse 4

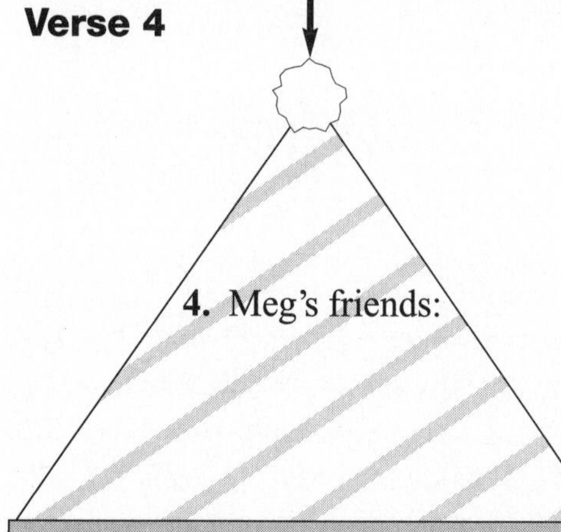

4. Meg's friends:

5. Summarize the poem in a sentence or two.

____

____

____

Notes for Home: Your child summarized key events in a poem. ***Home Activity:*** Read a magazine or newspaper article with your child. Ask your child to write a short summary, and then talk together about the main ideas summarized.

REVIEW

Predicting

Directions: Read the story. Then read each question about the story. Choose the best answer to each question. Mark the letter for the answer you have chosen.

The Humble Princess

As the two knights entered the inn, they stopped short in the doorway. A ragged young woman was scrubbing the table. She looked up at the sight of the knights and spoke in a soft and sweet voice: "Please come and sit down. Come in and hear my story." The knights sat down. If this woman were in trouble, they were ready to help.

"Once I was a princess," began the woman. "I was beautiful to look at, but I wasn't nice. My parents spoiled me. They gave me everything I wanted, and it only made me greedy for more toys and more gowns. Soon I was famous for my rudeness and selfishness. I was very unkind to my servants. I never thought about their feelings at all.

"Hoping I could learn better manners, my parents went to my wise old uncle for advice. After some thought, he said, 'Make her wear old clothes and work for a living. That way, she will learn to put other people first and stop thinking so much about herself. Let her come back to you in two years. I think by then she will have learned her lesson.'

"They sent me away as he suggested. I have done all kinds of work and traveled many miles. I have learned my lesson! The two years are up and my parents expect me to return. May I ask you to take me back to the palace?"

The knights looked at one another, then the Red Knight spoke. "Your highness, we will! But we must first continue our search for the lost prince of our Kingdom. Will you help us?"

1. The princess used to be—
- **A.** humble.
- **B.** ugly.
- **C.** rude.
- **D.** a liar.

2. The princess's punishment is fitting because—
- **F.** she wants to be a servant.
- **G.** her parents are disappointed.
- **H.** her uncle hates her.
- **J.** she treated her servants badly.

3. Stories of this kind usually—
- **A.** are in rhyme.
- **B.** have lots of jokes.
- **C.** describe characters who get away with bad behavior.
- **D.** end happily.

4. How will the princess answer the Red Knight?
- **F.** She will help him.
- **G.** She will refuse to help him.
- **H.** She will remain a servant.
- **J.** She will lead him straight to the lost prince.

5. When the princess's parents see her again, they will be—
- **A.** pleased.
- **B.** disappointed.
- **C.** angry.
- **D.** upset.

Notes for Home: Your child read a story and predicted what would happen next. ***Home Activity:*** Watch a TV show with your child. At a break, challenge her or him to predict what will happen next. Compare your child's prediction with what actually happens.

Name ___________________________

Writing Across Texts

Directions: Consider what you learned about José in "Born Worker" and Casey in *Casey at the Bat.* How does José "win" for his team? How does Casey have great responsibility placed on his shoulders? How do they handle their responsibilities? Complete the table to record some of the similarities and differences between these two characters.

José and Casey	
Alike	**Different**
Casey and José are both expected to succeed	**3.**
1.	**4.**
2.	**5.**

Write a Character Comparison

Use your completed table to help you write two paragraphs that compare and contrast the situations of José in "Born Worker" and Casey in *Casey at the Bat.* What expectations do people have of these characters? How do the characters handle the responsibility? Write your paragraphs on a separate sheet of paper.

Notes for Home: Your child wrote about how characters in two different selections handle responsibility and other people's expectations of them. ***Home Activity:*** Talk with your child about a time when two people in your family reacted differently to the same event.

Name ____________________

REVIEW

Grammar: Using Correct Verb Tenses

Directions: Circle the correct form of the verb in ( ) to complete each sentence.

1. Last year the mayor (invites/invited) a minor league team to our city.

2. No one (attended/had attended) a minor league game before.

3. My family (likes/is liking) baseball very much.

4. For years we (follow/had followed) teams like the Yankees and the Blue Jays.

5. We (will go/went) to the opening game last night.

6. We saw that everyone (is playing/was playing) as hard as possible.

7. At the end, the crowd yelled and (cheers/cheered).

8. We were excited when our team (won/wins) 7–4.

9. Now our town (will bragged/is bragging) proudly about the Santon Seagulls.

10. Next week we (will get/were getting) season tickets to the games of this minor league team.

Directions: Add a word or words to each verb to form a sentence. Write the complete sentence on the line.

11. wish

____

12. am wishing

____

13. wished

____

14. have wished

____

15. will wish

____

Notes for Home: Your child practiced using the correct tense of verbs. ***Home Activity:*** Extend the second part of this activity by having your child create sentences for the following verb tenses: *ask, am asking, asked,* and *had asked.*

Practice

Grammar: Irregular Verbs

Regular verbs are verbs that have the same spelling in the past and past participle forms. The **past form** of **regular verbs** is formed by adding **-ed** to the present tense. The **past participle** form of regular verbs is also formed by adding **-ed** to the present tense. It uses a helping verb such as *has* or *have.*

Present: We watch my little brother play baseball.

Past: We watched my little brother play baseball.

Past Participle: We have watched my little brother play baseball many times.

Irregular verbs, however, have a different spelling for the past and past participle forms.

Present: He throws the runner out at first base.

Past: He threw the runner out at first base.

Past Participle: This is the third time he has thrown the runner out at first base.

Directions: Write **regular** or **irregular** to describe each underlined verb.

______________ **1.** The Glenview Gators were one of the best teams in the league.

______________ **2.** They had a great pitcher.

______________ **3.** They usually scored at least seven runs a game.

______________ **4.** They just won against the Janesville Giants 8–2.

______________ **5.** I hoped our team would clobber them tonight.

Directions: Use the correct form of the verb shown in ( ) to complete each sentence. Write the verb on the line.

______________ **6.** Our team (play) well against the tough Gators.

______________ **7.** Our star player has (steal) home, and the score is now tied.

______________ **8.** Then, our pitcher (strike) out the lead batter.

______________ **9.** I (catch) a long fly ball to center field to make it two outs.

______________ **10.** But now the Mighty Margoles has hit a grand slam, and our team has (lose) again.

Notes for Home: Your child identified regular and irregular verbs and wrote the past and past participle forms of verbs. ***Home Activity:*** Have your child describe three things he or she did today. For each sentence, ask him or her whether the verbs are regular or irregular.

Name ______________________________

Grammar: Irregular Verbs

Directions: Write **regular** or **irregular** to describe each underlined verb.

______________ **1.** Lucy has joined the girl's softball team.

______________ **2.** She wanted to be a pitcher, but they made her a catcher instead.

______________ **3.** She has taken a lot of teasing for the bulky pads she wears.

______________ **4.** In the last game, she ran into the dugout to catch a foul ball.

______________ **5.** She tries harder than any player I have seen.

Directions: Write the correct form for each irregular verb below.

Present	**Past**	**Past Participle**
begin	**6.** ______________	**7.** has/have ______________
come	**8.** ______________	**9.** has/have ______________
eat	**10.** ______________	**11.** has/have ______________
fall	**12.** ______________	**13.** has/have ______________
ring	**14.** ______________	**15.** has/have ______________
bring	**16.** ______________	**17.** has/have ______________
swim	**18.** ______________	**19.** has/have ______________
say	**20.** ______________	**21.** has/have ______________
know	**22.** ______________	**23.** has/have ______________
drive	**24.** ______________	**25.** has/have ______________

Write a Diary Entry

On a separate sheet of paper, write a diary entry about an event that turned out differently than you had expected. The event can be either real or made up. Underline the regular verbs and circle the irregular verbs. Be careful to write the correct forms of irregular verbs.

Notes for Home: Your child identified regular verbs and irregular verbs. ***Home Activity:*** Choose several irregular verbs (such as *swing, give,* and *grow*). Have your child use each verb in a sentence that describes an action that took place in the past.

Name ______________________________

Grammar: Irregular Verbs

RETEACHING

Find the verbs in these sentences. Write them in the blanks. Be sure to include any helping verbs.

1. Luis and Liam swim this week. ______________________ (present)

2. They swam last week too. ______________________ (past)

3. The team has swum every day this month. ______________ (past participle)

The past and past participle forms of **irregular verbs** are not made by adding **-ed.** Instead, the spelling of each verb changes to make each form.

Directions: Underline the irregular verb in each sentence. Write **past** or **past participle** to tell which verb form is used.

1. Our swim team has begun regular practices. ______________

2. Some of us had swum on the team before this year. ______________

3. The coach wrote our practice schedule on a chart. ______________

4. She had given a lot of thought to the schedule. ______________

5. Then we went to the deep end of the pool. ______________

6. We have grown accustomed to the routine. ______________

7. We knew it was for our own good. ______________

Directions: Write the correct verb form in ( ) to complete each sentence.

8. The coach ______________ her whistle. (blew/blown)

9. Two of the boys had ______________ five laps. (swam/swum)

10. They had ______________ enough backstroke laps. (did/done)

11. She ______________ the boys three minutes to rest. (gave/given)

12. They ______________ towels around their shoulders. (threw/thrown)

13. The coach had ______________ down their times. (wrote/written)

14. I ______________ some milk after practice. (drank/drunk)

15. We had ______________ a good breakfast at sunrise. (ate/eaten)

Notes for Home: Your child identified irregular verbs in past and past participle forms. ***Home Activity:*** Have your child read a page from "Casey at the Bat" and identify irregular verbs in past participle forms.

Name ______________________________

Grammar: Irregular Verbs

Directions: Write the correct verb form as indicated in ( ).

1. drink (past participle) has __________ **2.** blow (past participle) has __________

3. sing (past) __________ **4.** grow (past) __________

5. eat (past) __________ **6.** go (past participle) has __________

7. throw (past participle) has __________ **8.** take (past participle) has __________

Directions: Complete each sentence by writing the past or past participle form of the verb in ( ).

9. Our visit to the state fair __________ just before lunch. (begin)

10. Everyone __________ the food at the fair was great. (know)

11. Before long we had __________ several ears of roasted corn. (eat)

12. Four-year-old Jacob __________ to find Belgian waffles. (go)

13. He had __________ very fond of these giant pastries. (grow)

14. He __________ half of his snack to his cousin Rachel. (give)

Directions: Complete each sentence with a verb form that makes sense. Write on the line the past or past participle form of one of the verbs in the box.

take	sing	give	blow	eat	fly

15. After lunch a whistle __________ to start the steer-judging competition.

16. The judges had __________ all the prizes.

17. It __________ much more time to judge the hogs and milk cows.

18. Later a famous entertainer __________ popular songs in the music tent.

19. He had __________ from Hollywood to the fairgrounds just for the day.

20. By evening Jacob had __________ two more Belgian waffles.

Write a Paragraph

On a separate sheet of paper, write a paragraph about a fair or a carnival. Use irregular verbs in some of your sentences.

Notes for Home: Your child wrote irregular verbs in past-tense and past participle forms. ***Home Activity:*** Discuss with your child what the two of you did today. Have your child give a hand signal every time one of you uses an irregular verb.

Name ______________________________________

Phonics: Schwa Sound (Final Syllable)

Directions: The **schwa sound** is a vowel sound heard in unstressed syllables. In the word **even,** the last **e** has a schwa sound. It can be spelled with any vowel or combination of vowels. Read each word below. Listen for the schwa sound in the final syllable. Underline the vowel or vowels that stand for the schwa sound.

1. silence
2. humor
3. former
4. seven
5. instant
6. Simon
7. listen
8. audience
9. rehearsal
10. random
11. anxious
12. instant
13. pretzel
14. patience
15. unravel

Directions: Circle the word with a schwa sound in each sentence. Underline the vowel or vowels that stand for the schwa sound in the final syllable.

____________ **16.** The next batter saw that the softball game was on the line.

____________ **17.** She walked to the plate, feeling the pressure to win.

____________ **18.** The players and fans yelled her name.

____________ **19.** She tried not to hear the noise, but she was only human.

____________ **20.** It was a good thing that she was the anchor of the team.

____________ **21.** The pitcher threw the ball low and fast, and she swung hard.

____________ **22.** She hit a grounder to the shortstop.

____________ **23.** The shortstop threw the ball to the person at first base.

____________ **24.** She got to first just a second before the girl at that base caught the throw.

____________ **25.** Now she could focus on stealing the next base.

Notes for Home: Your child identified the schwa sound in unstressed syllables, such as the *e* in *even. **Home Activity:*** Help your child identify words with more than one syllable that have a schwa sound in the final syllable. Ask your child to say the words aloud.

Name ______________________________

Spelling: Vowels in Final Syllables

Pretest Directions: Fold back the page along the dotted line. On the blanks, write the spelling words as they are dictated. When you have finished the test, unfold the page and check your words.

1. ______________________
2. ______________________
3. ______________________
4. ______________________
5. ______________________
6. ______________________
7. ______________________
8. ______________________
9. ______________________
10. ______________________
11. ______________________
12. ______________________
13. ______________________
14. ______________________
15. ______________________
16. ______________________
17. ______________________
18. ______________________
19. ______________________
20. ______________________

1. The store needed a new **slogan**.
2. The immigrant became a **citizen**.
3. **Urban** life can be exciting.
4. Wars **orphan** many children.
5. Have you **forgotten** something?
6. My father teaches **kindergarten**.
7. The plane's **propeller** is stuck.
8. It was a chance **encounter**.
9. Love can **conquer** hate.
10. Would you like an **appetizer**?
11. He is quite a **collector** of junk.
12. The mayor resigned in **dishonor**.
13. The farmer bought a new **tractor**.
14. A tornado can **level** a house.
15. We drove through a long **tunnel**.
16. The painter set up her **easel**.
17. I hit a **double** and a home run.
18. A spider hung by a **single** thread.
19. Can you give me an **example**?
20. We should **recycle** these cans.

Notes for Home: Your child took a pretest on words whose final syllables contain vowels that sound alike but may be spelled differently. ***Home Activity:*** Have your child divide misspelled words into parts (such as syllables) and concentrate on each part.

Name ______________________________

Spelling: Vowels in Final Syllables

Word List

slogan	forgotten	conquer	tractor	double
urban	kindergarten	appetizer	level	single
orphan	propeller	collector	tunnel	example
citizen	encounter	dishonor	easel	recycle

Directions: Choose the words from the box that end in **-en, -er, -an,** or **-or.** Listen for the vowels in the final syllables. Write each word in the correct column.

Words Ending -en

1. ______________
2. ______________
3. ______________

Words Ending -an

4. ______________
5. ______________
6. ______________

Words Ending -er

7. ______________
8. ______________
9. ______________
10. ______________

Words Ending -or

11. ______________
12 ______________
13. ______________

Directions: Find seven words from the box in the puzzle. They may be printed across or down. Circle the words in the puzzle and then write them on the lines. Hint: Their final syllables are spelled either **le** or **el.**

14. ______________
15. ______________
16. ______________
17. ______________
18. ______________
19. ______________
20. ______________

E	T	U	N	N	E	L	S
A	E	L	E	V	X	E	I
S	O	U	C	R	A	V	N
E	R	A	D	O	M	R	G
L	E	V	E	L	P	E	L
R	E	C	Y	C	L	E	E
D	O	U	B	L	E	L	D

Notes for Home: Your child spelled words whose final syllables contain vowels that often sound alike even when they are spelled differently, such as *slogan* and *citizen*. ***Home Activity:*** Challenge your child to think of two rhyming words, one ending in *-en* and one ending in *-an*.

Spelling: Vowels in Final Syllables

Directions: Proofread this sports report. Find six spelling mistakes. Use the proofreading marks to correct each mistake.

SPORTS

Today in local baseball, *The Urban Herald Rockets* will encounter its rival newspaper, *The Caspar Citizan Jets. The Urben Herald* team has not forgottan last month's single-run loss to *The Caspar Citizen,* in which a 9th inning doubel brought in the winning run. Their slogen for today's match is "Conquor *The Caspar Citizen.*" Fans should make an effort to see a good example of baseball at its best.

- ≡ Make a capital.
- / Make a small letter.
- ∧ Add something.
- ⸙ Take out something.
- ⊙ Add a period.
- ¶ Begin a new paragraph.

Word List

slogan
urban
orphan
citizen
forgotten
kindergarten
propeller
encounter
conquer
appetizer
collector
dishonor
tractor
level
tunnel
easel
double
single
example
recycle

Spelling Tip

Vowels in final syllables often sound alike even when they are spelled differently: **slogan, citizen; propeller, collector; level, double.** Check the sports report carefully to be sure words with these endings are spelled correctly.

Write a Sports Report

On a separate sheet of paper, write your own sports report. Write about an event that has just happened or is just about to happen. Try to use at least five of your spelling words.

Notes for Home: Your child spelled words whose final syllables contain vowels that often sound alike even when they are spelled differently, such as in *slogan* and *citizen. **Home Activity:*** Have your child listen to or read a short sports report and identify words with *-er* and *-or* endings.

Name ______________________

Spelling: Vowels in Final Syllables

REVIEW

Word List				
slogan	forgotten	conquer	tractor	double
urban	kindergarten	appetizer	level	single
orphan	propeller	collector	tunnel	example
citizen	encounter	dishonor	easel	recycle

Directions: Choose the word from the box that best matches each clue. Write the word on the line.

______________ **1.** This spins around on the front of the airplane.

______________ **2.** This is the grade that most five-year-olds are in.

______________ **3.** This is what you do when you return bottles for reuse.

______________ **4.** This is what a painter uses to support her canvas.

______________ **5.** This is an underground passage.

______________ **6.** This is what happens when something is not remembered.

______________ **7.** This vehicle can pull other farm machinery.

______________ **8.** This is the saying an advertiser repeats in commercials.

______________ **9.** This is a person who saves certain items, like stamps.

______________ **10.** This is a person who has lost his or her parents.

Directions: Choose the word from the box that best replaces the underlined word. Write the word on the line.

______________ **11.** The shelf is <u>flat</u> in all directions.

______________ **12.** I wouldn't want to <u>meet</u> a bear in the woods.

______________ **13.** She is the <u>city</u> planner.

______________ **14.** The <u>snack</u> was served just before the entrée.

______________ **15.** His shameful actions brought <u>disgrace</u> to his family.

______________ **16.** She expects to <u>overcome</u> her fear of flying.

______________ **17.** My savings are <u>twice</u> what they were last year.

______________ **18.** She showed me a <u>sample</u> of her work.

______________ **19.** He is a <u>native</u> of Canada.

______________ **20.** The <u>one</u> red pillow was lost in a sea of blue ones.

Notes for Home: Your child spelled words whose final syllables contain vowels that often sound alike even when they are spelled differently, such as *slogan* and *citizen*. ***Home Activity:*** Challenge your child to spell other words that end with *el* and *le*.

Name ______________________________

Announcement/Poster/Advertisement

An **announcement** is something that is made known. A **poster** is a type of announcement that gives specific facts about an event. It should answer the questions *Who?, What?, When?, Where?,* and *Why?* An **advertisement** is an announcement that tries to persuade readers, listeners, or viewers to do something, buy something, or feel a particular way.

Directions: Read the poster advertising a car wash. Use it to answer the questions that follow.

Get a Clean Car and Support Your Little League

The Rapid River Little League will be holding a car wash to raise money for much needed new uniforms and equipment.

Car Wash
Saturday, May 23rd
10:00 A.M. to 6:00 P.M.
State Fair Grounds, 2122 Lincoln Avenue
Single (wash only) $4.00
Double (wash + wax) $6.00
Grand Slam (wash, wax, windows, interior) $10.00

Rain Date:
Saturday, May 30th

You'll get a shine so bright, you'll need sunglasses!

1. What is the purpose of the poster/advertisement? ______________________________
____
____

2. What event will take place? ______________________________

3. At what time and on what day does the event take place? ______________________________
____

4. Who organized this event? ______________________________

5. What will the organizers of this event do with the money they raise? ______________________________
____

Name ______________________________

6. What will happen if it rains on May 23rd? ______________________________

____

7. What words does the poster/advertisement use to persuade readers? ______________________________

____

8. Why do you think the poster/advertisement uses different sizes and types of letters?

____

____

9. Why do you think the poster includes art? ______________________________

____

____

10. Use the space below to make your own poster to advertise the opening Little League game between the Dairy Flo Dragons and the Supreme Taco Superstars. Be sure to answer the five "W" questions.

Notes for Home: Your child answered questions about a poster advertising a fundraiser and created a poster to persuade people to attend a Little League game. ***Home Activity:*** Work with your child to create a poster about an upcoming family event.

Family Times

Name________________________________

Summary

Blame It on Mars

All month, Harriet and Mrs. Pond have spent their nights studying Mars through a telescope. That is why Harriet is so tired and why her model solar system project looks so sloppy. When Harriet tells her teacher and classmates about what she saw during her night watches, everyone realizes she has learned things by looking at the real planet that they couldn't learn from making models.

Reading Skills

Theme

The **theme** of a story is the underlying meaning or message. It can be a universal truth, such as *change is constant,* or a generalization about some aspect of life, such as *honesty is the best policy.*

To determine the theme of a story, ask yourself, "What does the author want me to learn or know by reading this story?" Stories often have more than one theme. To be valid, a statement of theme should be supported by evidence from the text.

Harriet's nightly observations of Mars teach her as much as she might learn in the classroom and are a lot of fun too. So one theme for the story might be: *Learning can take place outside the classroom.*

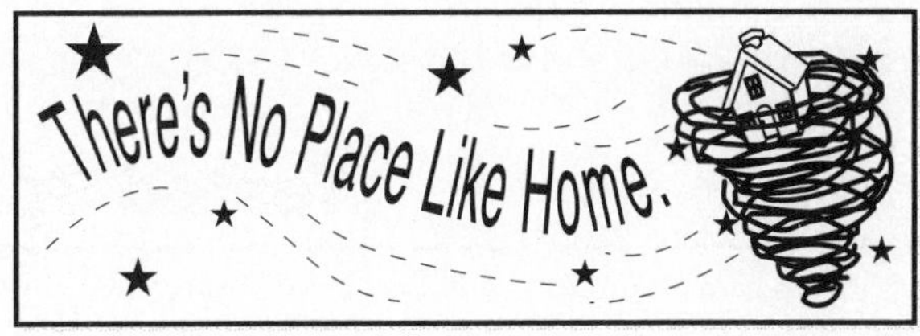

Activity

Describe a Scene. Ask your child to draw or describe a favorite scene from the story. Then ask him or her to explain how the scene fits into the remainder of the story.

Activity

Make Bumper Stickers. Think of brief statements that summarize the themes of favorite movies or videos. Write or draw your themes as bumper stickers.

Family Times

Tested Vocabulary

Words to Know

Knowing the meanings of these words is important to reading "The Night of the Pomegranate." Practice using these words to learn their meanings.

constellation a group of stars that has a recognizable shape

marveled wondered at

orbit a planet's elliptical path around another body in space

relative as compared to others

solar of the sun

universe the whole of existing things; everything there is, including all space and matter

Grammar

Direct and Indirect Objects

A sentence with an action verb may have a **direct object,** a noun or pronoun that receives the action of the verb. In the following sentences, the action verb is underlined once, and the direct object is underlined twice.

Harriet used the telescope.

She observed the planets.

The **indirect object** names the noun or pronoun to whom or for whom the action was done. In the following sentences, the indirect object is underlined once, and the direct object is underlined twice.

She showed Mrs. Pond the planets.

Activity

Design a Brochure. Write a travel brochure about Mars or another planet. See how many direct and indirect objects you can include in your sentences.

Tested Spelling Words

Theme

- The **theme** of a story is the underlying meaning or message.
- To determine the theme of a story, ask yourself, "What does the author want me to learn or know?" Your answer should be a "big idea" that can stand on its own away from the story.
- Many stories have more than one theme. To be valid, a statement of theme should be supported by evidence from the text.

Directions: Reread "A Winning Essay." Then complete the table. Write three pieces of evidence that support the first theme. Use the supporting evidence given to write a second theme and give another piece of evidence that supports it.

Theme	Evidence that Supports the Theme
Theme 1: People have different ways of expressing love.	**1.**
	2.
	3.
4. Theme 2:	**4.** Mattie has a hard time expressing her love for her mother.
	5.

Notes for Home: Your child identified the themes in a story and provided evidence to support those themes. ***Home Activity:*** Discuss a familiar book or movie with your child. Help your child identify one or more themes of the story.

Name ______________________________

Vocabulary

Directions: Draw a line to connect each word on the left with its definition on the right.

1. constellation	a planet's elliptical path around another body in space
2. marveled	the whole of existing things, including all space and matter
3. orbit	a group of stars with a recognizable shape
4. solar	wondered at
5. universe	of the sun

Check the Words You Know

__ constellation
__ marveled
__ orbit
__ relative
__ solar
__ universe

Directions: Choose the word from the box that best completes each sentence. Write the word on the line to the left. Then find and circle the words in the puzzle below. Words may appear across, down, or diagonally.

____________ **6.** Any body that goes around our Sun is part of our _____ system.

____________ **7.** Jupiter is huge _____ to Earth.

____________ **8.** The comet's _____ brought it near Earth.

____________ **9.** The _____ contains everything there is, including all space and matter.

____________ **10.** The Big Dipper is a _____ that got its name because the stars are in the shape of a dipper in the night sky.

Write a News Report

On a separate sheet of paper, write about the discovery of a new planet. Describe the planet's size, its stars, its sun(s), and so on. Use as many vocabulary words as you can.

E	V	B	A	C	S	O	R	B	I	T	Z	I	N
G	Y	J	U	Q	U	C	E	X	S	S	O	S	Y
F	C	O	N	S	T	E	L	L	A	T	I	O	N
B	W	F	I	A	C	D	A	M	I	Z	T	L	I
P	Y	A	V	J	U	A	T	I	Y	L	L	A	Z
S	N	T	E	R	R	B	I	A	T	V	X	R	E
R	J	H	R	V	S	O	V	H	N	X	D	O	F
D	N	I	S	G	M	J	E	Z	A	J	I	H	Y
N	Q	T	E	A	H	N	Y	S	S	H	D	E	M

Notes for Home: Your child identified and used vocabulary words from "The Night of the Pomegranate." ***Home Activity:*** With your child, look for names and descriptions of parts of the universe. Together, make a picture dictionary of the words you find.

Name ______________________________

Theme

- The **theme** of a story is the underlying meaning or message.
- Many stories have more than one theme.

Directions: Reread the part of "The Night of the Pomegranate" about Harriet's and Clayton's models. Then answer the questions below. Ask yourself what the author wants you to learn by reading this story.

Mars was near Earth this month. The nights had been November cold but clear as glass, and Harriet had been out to see Mars every night, which was why she hadn't gotten her solar system finished, why she was so tired, why Mom made Tom drive her to school. It was all Mars's fault.

She was using the tape on Ms. Krensky's desk when Clayton Beemer arrived with his dad. His solar system came from the hobby store. The planets were Styrofoam balls, all different sizes and painted the right colors. Saturn's rings were clear plastic painted over as delicately as insect wings.

Harriet looked down at her own Saturn. Her rings were drooping despite all the tape. They looked like a limp skirt on a . . . on a ball of scrunched-up newspaper.

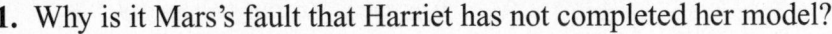

1. Why is it Mars's fault that Harriet has not completed her model?

____

2. In your own words, what is Clayton's model like? Why is it like that?

____

____

3. In your own words, what is Harriet's model like? Why is it like that?

____

____

4. What is the difference between Clayton's and Harriet's approaches to learning about the solar system?

____

____

5. On a separate sheet of paper, explain what you think the theme of this story is.

Notes for Home: Your child identified a story's theme, or the underlying meaning or message. ***Home Activity:*** Read a favorite story together. Encourage your child to explain its theme. Discuss how this theme relates to real-life experiences.

Name ______________________________

Selection Test

Directions: Choose the best answer to each item. Mark the letter for the answer you have chosen.

Part 1: Vocabulary

Find the answer choice that means about the same as the underlined word in each sentence.

1. Imagine what it would be like to travel throughout the <u>universe</u>.
- A. solar system
- B. all that exists
- C. group of stars
- D. wide desert

2. Sandra drew a picture showing Pluto's <u>orbit</u>.
- F. color
- G. planet's path around the sun
- H. size
- J. what a planet is made of

3. That <u>constellation</u> is called Orion.
- A. ring around a planet
- B. spaceship
- C. large number of planets
- D. group of stars that form a shape

4. We <u>marveled</u> at the hummingbird.
- F. had great hopes
- G. set a value for
- H. were filled with wonder
- J. refused to believe

5. The <u>relative</u> strength of steel makes it a good choice for cars.
- A. as compared with others
- B. important
- C. of or related to metal
- D. unusual

6. Heather's house uses <u>solar</u> power.
- F. of or from the sun
- G. electrical
- H. modern
- J. without heat

Part 2: Comprehension

Use what you know about the story to answer each item.

7. Why did Harriet use grape gum to construct her model of Pluto?
- A. She ran out of tape and glue.
- B. Pluto is cold.
- C. She liked the purple color.
- D. Pluto is small.

8. How did Harriet recognize Mars in the night sky?
- F. It twinkled.
- G. It was red.
- H. Mrs. Pond pointed to it.
- J. She had a map of the constellations.

9. Clayton Beemer's solar-system model—
- A. was very similar to Harriet's.
- B. made many students ask him questions.
- C. was elaborate and neatly done.
- D. used marbles and pomegranate seeds.

10. With Earth represented by Kevin's marble, Harriet compared Mars to a pomegranate seed because it—
- F. was the only thing she had with her.
- G. reminded her of Mrs. Pond.
- H. had a surprising taste.
- J. was the right color and relative size.

GO ON

11. What did Harriet learn about herself in this story?
- A. She was glad her parents were not interested in helping her with school projects.
- B. She did not know very much about any of the planets.
- C. She did not care what her classmates though about her project.
- D. She was more interested in observing Mars than in making a model.

12. What is a theme of this story?
- F. Pomegranates are tart.
- G. Sometimes Mars is visible in the sky.
- H. Sometimes we learn more from direct experience than from a school project.
- J. Work is easier if you have a partner.

13. Why did Harriet joke about her solar-system model and pull it apart?
- A. She was embarrassed by it.
- B. She was hungry.
- C. She wanted to improve it.
- D. She wanted to show off her strength.

14. Ms. Krensky's opinion of Harriet's work improved when she realized that Harriet—
- F. had a better model before she took it apart.
- G. was more interested in learning about pomegranates than planets.
- H. knew a great deal about Mars.
- J. had seen Mars in a movie.

15. Mrs. Pond tells Harriet about *The War of the Worlds* broadcast in order to—
- A. scare Harriet.
- B. share an interesting childhood memory with Harriet.
- C. show how foolish people can be.
- D. prove that Mars will someday collide with Earth.

STOP

Name ______________________________

Theme

- The **theme** of a story is the underlying meaning or message.
- Many stories have more than one theme.

Directions: Read the story below.

Sean convinced his parents he was old enough to baby-sit his little brother Paddy. He had never baby-sat before, but he'd watched his parents with the baby hundreds of times.

An hour after their parents left, Paddy woke up wailing. Sean folded the baby in his arms and rocked him, just as his parents would have done. It worked! Paddy stopped crying.

Then, just as his parents would have done, Sean gave Paddy some juice from a bottle. By then, Paddy was wide awake and wanted to play. Sean wasn't sure what his parents would do, but he decided to play peek-a-boo for a while. It wasn't long before Paddy began to yawn. Sean sang him a lullaby as he tucked him in.

Sean's parents were pleased at how well he had done. "You're a first-class baby-sitter!" they said.

Directions: Each box contains a question about important story events. Complete each box. Then use your answers to describe the story's theme.

1. Why does Sean think he can take care of Paddy?

2. Why does Sean give Paddy some juice to drink?

3. Why does Sean play peek-a-boo with Paddy?

4. Why are Sean's parents pleased?

5. This story's theme is:

Notes for Home: Your child has read a story and identified its theme. ***Home Activity:*** Read a story with your child. Help your child describe its theme. Take turns naming other stories with the same theme.

Compare and Contrast

REVIEW

Directions: Read the story. Then read each question about the story. Choose the best answer to each question. Mark the letter for the answer you have chosen.

Wish You Were Here

Helen knew all about Rome from her aunt's picture postcards. Each week a new one arrived, and Helen added it to her album. Now, visiting her aunt for the first time, she felt as if the postcards had come to life!

The postcards had made Rome seem still and calm. But the living city was filled with movement and noise. Bus passengers stuck in traffic complained as much as the people back home. Here, though, most poked their heads out the window to see what was the matter and to offer advice. Cars and motorcycles roared by and seemed to park wherever they pleased, even on sidewalks.

Pictures hadn't told Helen how different eating in Rome would be. Unlike stores in America, shops were closed for a few hours for lunch. People took a long time over their meals. Helen liked that. Lunch was always such a rush back home! Helen loved the food. Her favorite was *gelato,* Italian ice cream. It was richer and much better than ice cream at home.

Helen could not get used to the age of the buildings. Rome had many new buildings, of course, but she knew that nothing in America was as old as most of what she saw in Rome. Helen felt that every café, every house, and every sidewalk was a piece of history. She was so overwhelmed by her experiences, that when she wrote to her friend Pablo all she could say was, "Wish you were here."

1. Helen feels that her postcards have come to life because—
- **A.** things are different in Rome.
- **B.** she can see things firsthand.
- **C.** she is a tourist.
- **D.** her aunt lives in Rome.

2. Compared to Americans, Helen finds Romans —
- **F.** openly curious.
- **G.** very stuffy.
- **H.** faster eaters.
- **J.** bus riders.

3. Helen observes that when stuck in traffic, both Romans and Americans—
- **A.** get involved.
- **B.** suffer in silence.
- **C.** complain.
- **D.** get out and walk.

4. Americans eat hastily at lunch while Romans—
- **F.** eat a lot.
- **G.** take their time.
- **H.** eat *gelato*.
- **J.** eat on the run.

5. Helen observes that most buildings in Rome are—
- **A.** newer than those in America.
- **B.** about the same age as those in America.
- **C.** in worse shape than those in America.
- **D.** much older than those in America.

Notes for Home: Your child read a passage and made comparisons and contrasts. ***Home Activity:*** With your child, compare and contrast some popular ethnic foods. For instance, pizza and burritos are made of grains and vegetables, though they look and taste different.

Name ______________________

Writing Across Texts

Directions: Think about what you learned about the solar system in "The Night of the Pomegranate" and "What Is Earth's Place in Space?" Complete the Venn diagram to compare and contrast the information in each selection. Think about which explanation would help you to better understand the material.

Harriet's Explanation	Both Selections	What Is Earth's Place in Space?
She compares the sizes of Earth and Mars to a marble and a pomegranate seed.		It explains how long it takes Earth to travel around the Sun.
1. ______________________	3. ______________________	4. ______________________
2. ______________________		5. ______________________

Write a Comparison Paragraph

In "The Night of the Pomegranate," Harriet uses her personal experience to explain to her class the relative sizes and distances of the planets. Compare Harriet's explanation to what you learned in "What Is Earth's Place in Space?" Was Harriet's explanation accurate? If you were in her class, would it have been clear to you? Which way of presenting information do you consider more helpful? On a separate sheet of paper, write a paragraph discussing these issues.

Notes for Home: Your child evaluated different ways of presenting similar information. ***Home Activity:*** As you read a story or article with your child, discuss how results, or outcomes, can be interpreted in more than one way.

Name ______________________________

Grammar: Subject-Verb Agreement

REVIEW

Directions: Circle the verb in ( ) that agrees with the subject in each sentence.

1. (Does/Do) the students in your class know the names of all the planets?
2. Mercury (is/are) the closest planet to the Sun.
3. This small planet (orbits/orbit) around the Sun every 88 days.
4. The thick clouds around Venus (makes/make) the astronomer's job very difficult.
5. Mars, more than the other planets, (has/have) been the subject of many scary movies about space creatures.
6. An asteroid belt (exists/exist) between Mars and Jupiter.
7. Even amateur astronomers (enjoys/enjoy) the rings around Saturn.
8. A recent discovery by powerful telescopes (shows/show) rings around Jupiter too.
9. Jupiter, of course, (is/are) the largest planet.
10. Perhaps other planets beyond Pluto (awaits/await) our discovery.

Directions: Match each subject with a verb in the box. Then write a sentence that includes both of them.

launches	rotates	searches	shines	watches
launch	rotate	search	shine	watch

11. An astronomer ____________________.

____

12. Mission control ____________________.

____

13. Earth ____________________.

____

14. Space probes ____________________.

____

15. Stars ____________________.

____

Notes for Home: Your child identified verbs that agree with their subjects. ***Home Activity:*** Together, listen to stories on tape or a program on television. Repeat sentences aloud and discuss whether the subject-verb agreement is correct.

Practice

Grammar: Direct and Indirect Objects and Subject Complements

A **direct object** is a noun or pronoun that follows an action verb and tells who or what receives the action of the verb.

I watched a long <u>movie</u> on TV last night.

The views of Earth from outer space surprised <u>me</u>.

An **indirect object** comes after an action verb. It names the person to whom or for whom the action is done. However, the words *to* or *for* are not used before an indirect object.

I wrote <u>Maria</u> a <u>note</u> about the movie.

In this sentence, *Maria* is the indirect object of *wrote*. The word *note* is the direct object.

A **predicate noun** follows a linking verb and tells who or what the subject is.

Maria is a former <u>neighbor</u> of mine.

A **predicate adjective** follows a linking verb and describes the subject.

Maria has become <u>enthusiastic</u> about flying.

Directions: Underline each direct object once and each indirect object twice. Hint: Not every sentence has an indirect object.

1. I discovered an article about the Wright brothers.
2. The article gave me ideas about working on inventions.
3. I wrote an essay about their experiments with a glider.
4. My cousin Maxine read the paper carefully.
5. Maxine gave me her reactions in writing.

Directions: Write **PN** if the underlined word is a predicate noun. Write **PA** if it is a predicate adjective.

______________ 6. From glider flight to space flight, the progress has been <u>amazing</u>.

______________ 7. I felt <u>astonished</u> to learn that 1903 was the date of the first engine-powered flight.

______________ 8. The young Wright brothers were experienced <u>mechanics</u>.

______________ 9. Their patience with repeated failures seems <u>remarkable</u>.

______________ 10. Naturally, these two men became <u>celebrities</u>.

Notes for Home: Your child identified direct and indirect objects, as well as predicate nouns and adjectives. ***Home Activity:*** Use the examples and definitions above to help your child write additional examples.

Extra Practice

Grammar: Direct and Indirect Objects and Subject Complements

Directions: Write **DO** if the underlined word is a direct object. Write **IO** if it is an indirect object.

__________ **1.** Julia sent her relatives some letters.

__________ **2.** She wanted true stories about successful work experiences.

__________ **3.** Some of the relatives wrote notes to Julia.

__________ **4.** Uncle Bob mailed her a tape instead.

__________ **5.** Bob told Julia a fascinating story about his work with NASA's space exploration.

__________ **6.** Bob gave his niece many suggestions for her own life.

__________ **7.** Then he assigned her a little exercise.

__________ **8.** Julia described the exercise to her mother.

__________ **9.** "He has sent you many sensible ideas," Julia's mother said.

__________ **10.** Julia shared her mother's comment with her uncle.

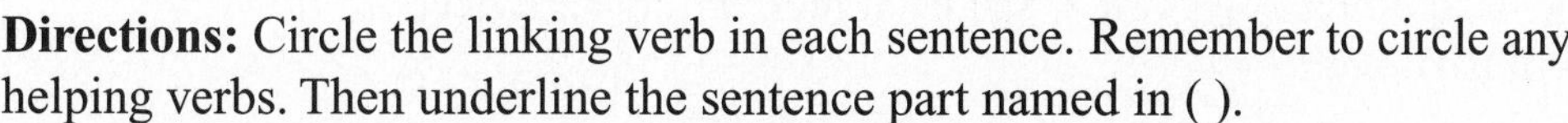

Directions: Circle the linking verb in each sentence. Remember to circle any helping verbs. Then underline the sentence part named in ( ).

11. Julia clearly felt interested in her relatives' ideas. (predicate adjective)

12. Sometimes relatives are the best advisers. (predicate noun)

13. Her uncle certainly seems kind. (predicate adjective)

14. He also has been generous with his time. (predicate adjective)

15. Uncle Bob's story will become a part of the family history. (predicate noun)

Write a Narrative Paragraph

On a separate sheet of paper, write a narrative paragraph (a very short story) about a time when you helped someone or someone helped you. Try to include one or more direct objects, indirect objects, predicate nouns, and predicate adjectives. List the direct and indirect objects and the prediate nouns and adjectives you used below your paragraph.

Notes for Home: Your child identified direct objects (Mary sent a *card*) and indirect objects *(Mary sent her a card)*, as well as predicate nouns and adjectives. ***Home Activity:*** Have your child write a sentence that includes a direct object and an indirect object.

Name ______________________________

Grammar: Direct and Indirect Objects and Subject Complements

RETEACHING

Underline the direct object in each sentence. Circle each indirect object.

1. Gloria gave me a wonderful birthday present.
2. I sent her a thank-you note yesterday.

Underline the predicate noun. Circle the predicate adjective.

3. Gloria is thoughtful about other people.
4. She became an artist after several years of work.

A **direct object** is the noun or noun phrase that follows an action verb and tells who or what receives the action of the verb. An **indirect object** is the noun or noun phrase that often directly follows an action verb and names the person to whom or for whom the action is done. A **predicate noun** follows a linking verb and tells who or what the subject is. A **predicate adjective** also follows a linking verb, and it describes the subject.

Directions: Underline each direct object once and each indirect object twice. Not every sentence will have both.

1. My friends celebrated my birthday early this year.
2. Each of them brought me a silly gift.
3. Mark gave me ten soda straws in a used milk carton.
4. Yoshi sang us a song backwards.
5. My father cooked chicken.
6. I gave each of my friends a big hug.

Directions: Write whether each underlined word is a **predicate noun** or a **predicate adjective.**

______________________ 7. Now the sun is <u>low</u> in the sky.

______________________ 8. I am a <u>photographer</u> in the city.

______________________ 9. Some people here are very <u>busy</u>.

______________________ 10. Pushing heavy bricks seems <u>easy</u> for that worker.

______________________ 11. The afternoon seemed <u>long</u> and hot.

Notes for Home: Your child identified direct and indirect objects and predicate nouns and adjectives. ***Home Activity:*** Have your child write two questions containing direct and indirect objects. Answer the questions, using direct and indirect objects. Have your child check your work.

Name ______________________________

Grammar: Direct and Indirect Objects and Subject Complements

Directions: Write **DO** if the underlined word is a direct object. Write **IO** if it is an indirect object.

______________ **1.** When my Aunt Sarah moved to Germany, she left us many <u>things</u>.

______________ **2.** One thing she gave <u>us</u> was her collection of ukuleles.

______________ **3.** Aunt Sarah collected musical <u>instruments</u> from different countries.

______________ **4.** She told my cousins <u>stories</u> about how and where the instruments were made.

______________ **5.** Some villagers in a little town in Ireland had made some <u>drums</u> she had.

______________ **6.** Aunt Sarah gave <u>me</u> her drums because she knew I liked to play them when I visited her.

______________ **7.** My brother wanted her many <u>books</u> about instruments made out of gourds.

______________ **8.** Now that she has left, we have sent her thank-you <u>cards</u> for all the gifts she gave us.

______________ **9.** In my card I told <u>her</u> what I did with the gifts.

______________ **10.** My brother and I miss the stories she told <u>us</u>.

Directions: Circle the linking verb in each sentence. Then underline each predicate adjective once and each predicate noun twice. Not every sentence will have both a predicate adjective and a predicate noun.

11. "Beth is my aunt," said my friend.

12. "I am curious about her job as a calligrapher. How should I ask her my questions?"

13. "Writing a letter seems smart," I told him.

14. "You are right!" he said.

15. Her response was very interesting.

16. She had been a calligrapher a long time ago.

17. Her entire letter was beautiful.

Notes for Home: Your child identified direct and indirect objects and predicate nouns and adjectives in sentences. ***Home Activity:*** Have your child identify in a favorite story two sentences with direct and indirect objects. Then have him or her use the direct and indirect objects in new sentences.

Name ______________________________

Word Study: Contractions

Directions: A **contraction** is a word formed by joining two words with an **apostrophe.** The apostrophe takes the place of one or more letters. Read the journal entry below. Circle each contraction. Write the contraction on the line to the left. Then write the two words that the contraction combines on the right.

> I wasn't sure what I saw the other night. As I looked up at the night sky, gazing at the stars I know so well, I spotted bright bands of light shimmering. They didn't look like stars, and I realized I hadn't seen anything like them before. Waves of greenish light rippled in the sky. "They're moving!" I thought to myself. I couldn't believe my eyes when the whole sky seemed to come alive with these lights. "It's not possible!" I said. I later found out that these bands of light are called Northern Lights. I'll never forget that sight as long as I live!

Contraction	Two Words It Combines
1. ______________	2. ______________
3. ______________	4. ______________
5. ______________	6. ______________
7. ______________	8. ______________
9. ______________	10. ______________
11. ______________	12. ______________
13. ______________	14. ______________

Directions: Combine each word pair to form a contraction. Write the contraction on the line.

15. do not ______________
16. you would ______________
17. let us ______________
18. will not ______________
19. should not ______________
20. are not ______________

Notes for Home: Your child formed contractions, such as *that's* from the words *that* and *is*. ***Home Activity:*** Listen to a radio or television program, and work with your child to identify spoken contractions. Ask your child to tell you the two words that each contraction represents.

Name ____________________

Spelling: Homophones

Pretest

Pretest Directions: Fold back the page along the dotted line. On the blanks, write the spelling words as they are dictated. When you have finished the test, unfold the page and check your words.

1. ____________________
2. ____________________
3. ____________________
4. ____________________
5. ____________________
6. ____________________
7. ____________________
8. ____________________
9. ____________________
10. ____________________
11. ____________________
12. ____________________
13. ____________________
14. ____________________
15. ____________________
16. ____________________
17. ____________________
18. ____________________
19. ____________________
20. ____________________

1. **Their** mother is a surgeon.
2. Put the groceries over **there**.
3. **They're** not coming until later.
4. I had to **wring** out my wet shirt.
5. She has a lovely diamond **ring**.
6. Please buy some **chili** pepper.
7. The wind is **chilly** tonight.
8. That cheese has a strong **scent**.
9. I **sent** a letter to my uncle.
10. I don't have a **cent** to my name.
11. Dad **oversees** our business.
12. My brother lives **overseas**.
13. My doctor sees many **patients**.
14. He has great **patience** with kids.
15. Open another box of **cereal**.
16. A **serial** is broadcast in parts.
17. This wood has a **coarse** grain.
18. I work at a local golf **course**.
19. To **counsel** is to give advice.
20. The city **council** meets today.

Notes for Home: Your child took a pretest on homophones, words that sound alike but are spelled differently and have different meanings. ***Home Activity:*** Help your child learn to connect the spelling of the word with its meaning.

Think and Practice

Spelling: Homophones

Word List

their	chili	oversees	cereal	counsel
there	chilly	overseas	serial	council
they're	scent	patients	coarse	
wring	sent	patience	course	
ring	cent			

Directions: Each word below is contained in words from the box. Write the words from the box in the correct column.

over

1. ______________________
2. ______________________

tie

3. ______________________
4. ______________________

in

5. ______________________
6. ______________________

the

7. ______________________
8. ______________________
9. ______________________

Directions: Choose the word from the box that has the same or nearly the same meaning as each word or words below. Write the word on the line.

10. cold ______________________
11. rough ______________________
12. committee ______________________
13. smell ______________________
14. penny ______________________
15. breakfast food ______________________
16. track ______________________
17. advice ______________________
18. transmitted ______________________
19. hot pepper ______________________
20. in order ______________________

Notes for Home: Your child spelled homophones—words that sound the same but have different spellings and meanings. ***Home Activity:*** Help your child write sentences using each spelling word. You may wish to use a dictionary to review the meanings of the words first.

Spelling: Homophones

Directions: Proofread this description of the solar system. Find six spelling mistakes. Use the proofreading marks to correct each mistake.

≡ Make a capital.
/ Make a small letter.
∧ Add something.
Take out something.
⊙ Add a period.
¶ Begin a new paragraph.

I see the solar system as a counsel headed by the Sun. The Sun overseas the planets and guides their course through the chili emptiness of space. Belts of rocks and other debris wring some planets, like Saturn. Their are comets that sometimes outshine the stars. You must have patience if you want to see them, because they are rarely visible. The asteroids that orbit in there belt between Mars and Jupiter are most mysterious to me.

Spelling Tip

their **there**

Because homophones sound alike, they are sometimes written incorrectly. **Their** and **there** are often mixed up. Remember **there** refers to a place and think: I looked for it **here**, but I found it **there**.

Word List

their	oversees
there	overseas
they're	patients
wring	patience
ring	cereal
chili	serial
chilly	coarse
scent	course
sent	counsel
cent	council

Write a Description

On a separate sheet of paper, write a description of the solar system. It can be a description of what you see in the night sky or what you imagine the surface of a planet would be like. Try to use at least five of your spelling words.

Notes for Home: Your child spelled homophones—words that sound the same but have different spellings and meanings. ***Home Activity:*** Begin a list of homophones, and work together to keep adding to it with examples such as *to/too/two* or *threw/through.*

Name ______________________________

Spelling: Homophones

REVIEW

Word List

their	chili	oversees	cereal	counsel
there	chilly	overseas	serial	council
they're	scent	patients	coarse	
wring	sent	patience	course	
ring	cent			

Directions: Write the word from the box that belongs in each group.

1. chronological, alphabetical, ______________
2. his, her, ______________
3. doctors, nurses, ______________
4. cold, cool, ______________
5. senate, cabinet, ______________
6. here, everywhere, ______________
7. dime, nickel, ______________
8. squeeze, twist, ______________
9. mailed, posted, ______________
10. he's, she's, ______________

Directions: Complete each comparison with a word from the box. Write the word on the line.

______________ **11.** The spices in this _____ are as hot as the desert.

______________ **12.** The cat's tongue feels as _____ as sandpaper.

______________ **13.** The milk has made this _____ as soggy as a swamp.

______________ **14.** The delays have everyone's _____ as thin as ice.

______________ **15.** The perfume's _____ is like apple blossoms in spring.

______________ **16.** The greens on this golf _____ are as smooth as glass.

______________ **17.** Patricia _____ her workers as a director does his crew.

______________ **18.** His trip _____ on the cruise ship was an adventure.

______________ **19.** Her _____ on what to do is as wise as an owl's.

______________ **20.** The _____ on her finger sparkled like a star.

Notes for Home: Your child spelled homophones—words that sound the same but have different spellings and meanings. ***Home Activity:*** Ask your child to write a sentence using the homophones *pair* and *pear.* Repeat with other pairs of homophones.

Name ______________________________

Textbook/Trade Book/Magazine/Periodical

A **textbook** teaches about a particular subject matter, such as science, social studies, or math. A **trade book** is any book that is not a textbook, periodical, or reference book. A **magazine** or **periodical** is published at set intervals (weekly, monthly, quarterly, and so on). It contains news articles, opinion columns, advertisements, cartoons, reports, and other current information. To locate information in these sources, scan the table of contents, chapter titles, headings, subheadings, captions, and index. You can also locate specific magazine articles using *The Readers' Guide to Periodical Literature.*

Directions: Use the textbook, trade book, and magazine samples below to answer the questions that follow.

The Universe Around Us • **Unit 2**

Chapter 5
Lesson 2: The Planets

Vocabulary solar, Sun, planet, moon

Study Questions: How many planets are in our solar system? What are they called? What is a moon? How many of our planets have moons?

Solar means "of the Sun." Our solar system has a sun at its center, and nine planets that orbit it. (See Fig. 1.)

The **Sun** is a giant, hot star. It gives off energy in the form of visible light, invisible light (ultraviolet and infrared light), and gamma rays.

The nine **planets** in our solar system are Mercury, Venus, Earth, Mars, Jupiter, Saturn, Uranus, Neptune, and Pluto.

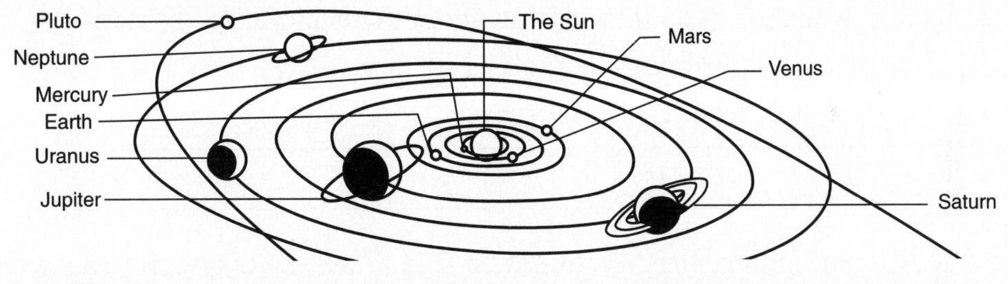

Space Exploration: Travels to the Moon and Beyond

Table of Contents

STARGAZER
• Interview with astronomer Dr. Kay Fields
• Photos of Olympus Mons—Mars's Amazing Volcano
• Keep a Stargazer Log
Which telescope is the best one for you?

Name ______________________________

1. Would you most likely find the textbook page from *The Universe Around Us* in a science, social studies, or math class? Explain.

2. Why does the textbook page include study questions near the beginning of the lesson? Read the first study question and answer it.

3. Why do you think *solar, Sun,* and *planet* on the textbook page are set in **boldfaced** type?

4. Scan the table of contents in the trade book *Space Exploration*. What is this book about? What kinds of information would you expect to find in it?

5. What was the name of the spacecraft that flew to the moon? ____________

6. Which chapter would give you information about the exploration of Mars? ____________

7. Name the topic of one article in the issue of *Stargazer* shown. ____________

8. Write a question of inquiry that you might be able to use the textbook to answer.

9. Write a question of inquiry that you might be able to use the trade book to answer.

10. Write a question of inquiry that you might be able to use the magazine to answer.

Notes for Home: Your child answered questions about a textbook, trade book, and a magazine. ***Home Activity:*** Look through one of your child's textbooks with your child. Compare the textbook to a trade book and/or a magazine. Discuss how to find information in each source.

Name ______________________________

Venn Diagram

Directions: Write the name of each person that you will compare and contrast above a circle. In the intersecting part of the circles, write similarities between the people and their paths to success. Show differences by writing points about each person in the separate parts of the two circles.

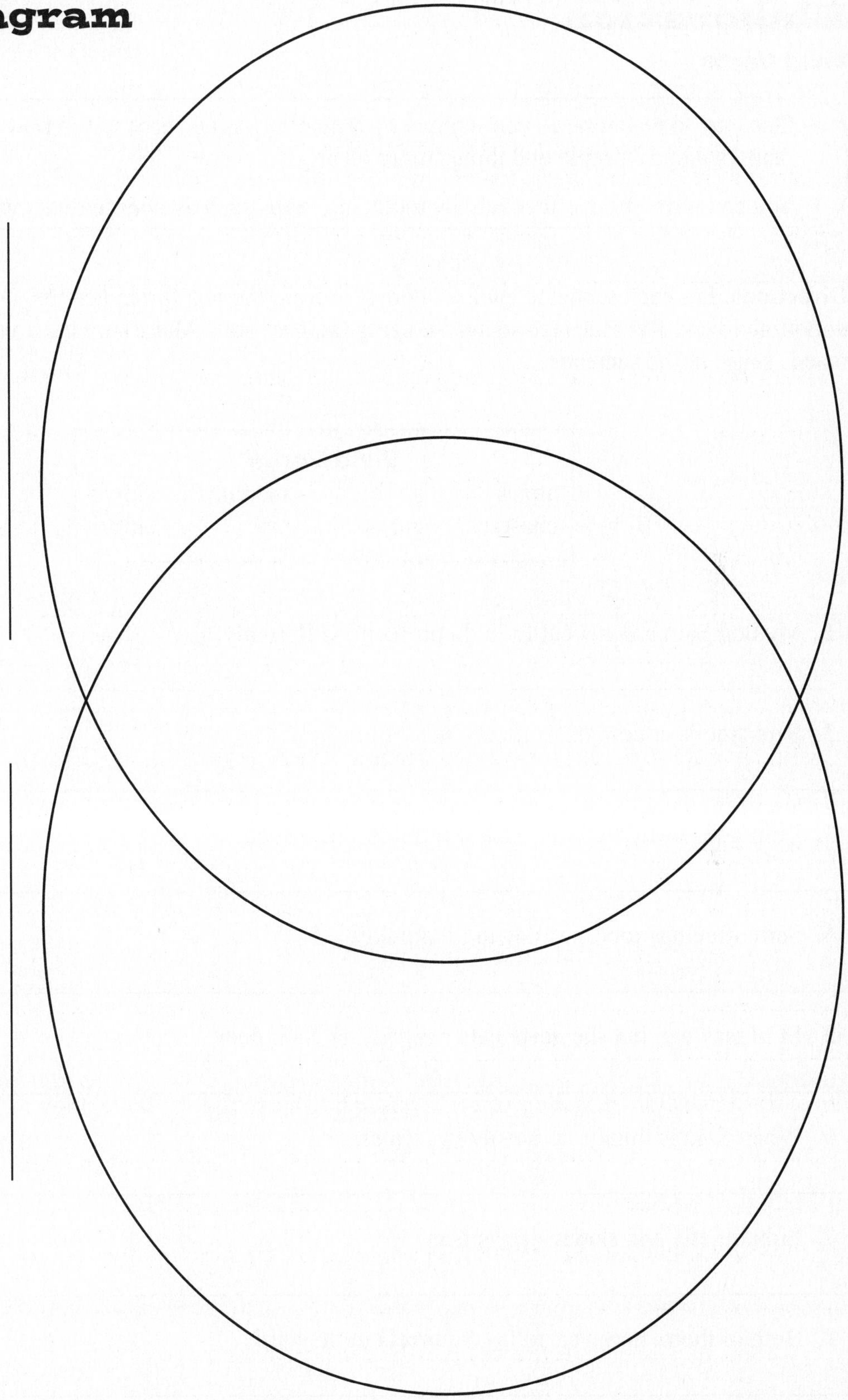

Notes for Home: Your child used this diagram to prepare information for comparing and contrasting two persons who succeeded or solved a problem. ***Home Activity:*** With your child, talk about successful people—and how they have solved problems or achieved success.

Name ______________________________

Elaboration

Vivid Verbs

- One way to elaborate as you write is by replacing vague verbs with **vivid verbs** that help readers picture people and things more clearly.
- You can write more effectively by replacing verbs such as *does* and *has* with livelier verbs.

Directions: For each sentence, pick a vivid verb from the box to replace the underlined verb. Rewrite each sentence, using the new verb. Make sure each verb makes sense in the sentence.

Vivid Verbs			
attack	gobbles	marches	slurps
chase	gulps	sips	sniffs

1. My dog Sam and my cat Lulu do problems differently.

____

2. Sam smells at new, unfamiliar kinds of food.

____

3. Lulu goes away from her dish if it holds a new food.

____

4. Sam often has food, swallowing it quickly.

____

5. Lulu may eat, but she never eats hungrily, as Sam does.

____

6. When Sam is thirsty, he noisily has water.

____

7. Lulu quietly and slowly drinks hers.

____

8. Both of them, however, follow squirrels in the yard.

____

Notes for Home: Your child improved sentences by choosing vivid verbs that express ideas more clearly. ***Home Activity:*** With your child, first make up boring sentences to tell about actions, and then replace the verbs and other words to vividly describe the same actions.

Name ______________________________

Self-Evaluation

Comparison/Contrast Essay

Directions: Think about the final draft of your comparison/contrast essay. Then answer each question in the chart.

	Yes	No	Not sure
1. Did I express a main idea and support it?			
2. Did I include similarities and differences between the two persons?			
3. Are my points of comparison and contrast expressed clearly?			
4. Did I use transition words or phrases well?			
5. Did I proofread and edit carefully to correct errors?			

6. What is the best part of my comparison/contrast essay?

____

____

____

____

7. Write one thing that you would change about this essay if you had the chance to write it again.

____

____

____

____

Notes for Home: Your child answered questions about preparing and writing a comparison/contrast essay. ***Home Activity:*** Ask your child what writing strategies he or she learned that may help in the writing of future papers.

Family Times

Name____

Summary

Grandfather Keeps Traditions Alive

In "Spring Paint," Joseph Bruchac describes the knowledge and traditions that his grandfather taught him when he was a boy. From his grandfather, Joseph Bruchac learned about his natural surroundings, the indigenous people of the American Northeast, and their tradition of spring paint. Each spring, Joseph Bruchac's grandfather would take bloodroot sap and use it to make orange markings on Joseph's face. These markings served as insect repellent for Joseph Bruchac's ancestors. For the author, they symbolize the beginning of spring and a connection to his heritage.

Reading Skills

Drawing Conclusions

When you **draw a conclusion,** you make a decision or form an opinion about what you read.

A conclusion should make sense and be based on facts and details in the writing, as well as your own experience. When you read "Spring Paint," one conclusion you might draw is that the woods are important to both Joseph and his grandfather. This conclusion is supported by the way they talk about the woods and the amount of time they spend there.

To test a conclusion, ask yourself whether the facts are accurate. Then ask yourself whether the same information might support a different conclusion. Finally, decide on the best conclusion.

Activity

Draw a Picture. Have your child draw a picture that shows a face with "spring paint" markings like the ones described in the selection.

Activity

Choose the Best Conclusion. Play a game in which one person tells a story but leaves out a crucial piece of information, such as an element of the plot or the outcome. Other players can draw conclusions about the missing element. As a group, decide which is the best conclusion.

Family Times

Tested Vocabulary

Words to Know

Knowing the meanings of these words is important to reading "Spring Paint." Practice using these words to learn their meanings.

ancestor a person from whom one is descended

boundary a line or object marking the limit of an area; border

gnarled knotted; twisted

reassuring restoring to confidence; comforting

wigwam a dome-shaped shelter made of bark

Grammar

Adjectives and Proper Adjectives

Adjectives modify, or tell more about, nouns or pronouns. Adjectives tell what kind, how many, how much, or which one.

What kind: tall tree, blue sky
How many: several geese, six plants
How much: little time, large expanse
Which one: this rock, these woods

An adjective formed from a proper noun is called a **proper adjective.** A proper adjective is capitalized.

Proper Noun	Proper Adjective
Switzerland	Swiss cheese
France	French windows
Africa	African music

Activity

Name a Country. Name a country, such as Mexico or Belgium. Then make up a phrase like the ones in the table, using the country's name as a proper adjective and adding a noun, for example, *Mexican hat dance,* or *Belgian waffles.*

Tested Spelling Words

Name ______________________

Drawing Conclusions

- When you **draw a conclusion,** you make a decision or form an opinion about what you read. Drawing conclusions is also known as *making inferences.*
- A conclusion should make sense and be based on facts and details in the writing, as well as your own experience.

Directions: Reread "Dumbfounded." Then complete the table. Read the three possible conclusions about Grandpa, choose the best conclusion, and then give evidence from the story to support your choice. Then do the same for the possible conclusions about Billy. Below the table, write your own conclusion about the relationship between Billy and Grandpa.

Possible Conclusions	Best Conclusion	Evidence (Story Details and What I Know)
Grandpa is allergic to dust. Grandpa is amazed at Billy's achievement. Grandpa always becomes emotional around Billy.	**1.**	**2.**
Billy thinks saving money is fun. Billy thinks spending money is fun. Billy is willing to work hard to get himself some dogs.	**3.**	**4.**

5. What conclusion can you draw about the relationship between Billy and Grandpa? Why?

____

____

Notes for Home: Your child drew conclusions about characters in a story. ***Home Activity:*** Discuss with your child the conclusions drawn by letter writers in the editorial section of the local newspaper. Check to see whether the writers provide supporting evidence for their conclusions.

Name ______________________________

Vocabulary

Directions: Write the word from the box that best matches each definition. Write the word on the line.

Check the Words You Know
__ ancestor
__ boundary
__ gnarled
__ reassuring
__ wigwam

______________ **1.** knotted; twisted

______________ **2.** a dome-shaped hut made of bark

______________ **3.** a distant relative from whom one is descended

______________ **4.** restoring to confidence

______________ **5.** limit; border

Directions: Choose the word from the box that best completes each sentence. Write the word on the line to the left.

______________ **6.** The _____ of our property is marked by a stone wall.

______________ **7.** Next to the stone wall is a _____ tree with branches that twist around each other.

______________ **8.** When I look at that tree, I feel calm; it is very _____.

______________ **9.** I can imagine an _____ of mine from a hundred years ago sitting under that same tree.

______________ **10.** I wonder if long ago, my family lived in a _____ near this tree and had the same view as I have now.

Write a Postcard

On a separate sheet of paper, write a postcard. Imagine you are visiting the home of one of your ancestors. Describe what you see and what you imagine life might have been like for your ancestor. Use as many vocabulary words as you can.

Notes for Home: Your child identified and used vocabulary words from "Spring Paint." ***Home Activity:*** Talk about how life was the same or different for your ancestors. Try to include the vocabulary words in your discussion.

Name ________________________________

Drawing Conclusions

- **Drawing conclusions** means making sensible decisions or forming reasonable opinions about what you read.
- A **conclusion** should be based on facts and details in the writing, as well as your own experience.

Directions: Reread the scene in "Spring Paint" in which the young man enters the lodge. Then answer the questions below. Use story details to help you draw conclusions.

"Come in, then," said the old man. He smiled a hard smile, knowing that whoever came into his lodge would freeze.

Then a young man entered the wigwam. His face was painted with red lines and circles that looked like the sun. There was a warm smile on his face; and as he sat down on the other side of the fire, the old man felt the young man's warm breath. The old man began to sweat. He felt himself growing weaker.

"Go away," said the old man.

"No," said the young man, his voice as gentle as the sound of a summer breeze. "It is you who must leave now. Your season has ended."

1. Which season of the year does the young man represent? How do you know?

____

____

2. Which season does the old man represent? How do you know?

____

____

3. Why do you think the old man tells the young man to go away?

____

____

4. The word *wigwam* suggests that the story originated in which culture or cultures?

____

____

5. On a separate sheet of paper, explain how this myth relates to the grandfather's search for bloodroot flowers.

Notes for Home: Your child formed conclusions based on story details. ***Home Activity:*** Discuss specific actions of real-life people. Challenge your child to draw conclusions about why these actions happened and what these actions reveal about each person.

Name ______________________________

Selection Test

Directions: Choose the best answer to each item. Mark the letter for the answer you have chosen.

Part 1: Vocabulary

Find the answer choice that means about the same as the underlined word in each sentence.

1. Ali's ancestor built the house.
- A. offspring, such as a child or grandchild
- B. relative by marriage
- C. relative from whom one is descended, such as a grandparent
- D. person of the same generation or age group

2. They built a wigwam.
- F. dome-shaped hut
- G. light, narrow boat
- H. cone-shaped tent
- J. large rectangular dwelling

3. A river formed the boundary.
- A. pathway; trail
- B. landscape
- C. property
- D. border line; limit

4. The branches were gnarled.
- F. rough and twisted
- G. carved with a sharp object
- H. old and weak
- J. marked with dark blotches

5. Miguel was reassuring the new student.
- A. getting to know
- B. introducing
- C. giving confidence to
- D. preparing

Part 2: Comprehension

Use what you know about the selection to answer each item.

6. When the author was a boy, his special place was—
- F. Always Winter Land.
- G. the Woods.
- H. a tree house.
- J. the old man's lodge.

7. How did the author's grandfather make a living?
- A. He hunted and gathered.
- B. He owned a store.
- C. He bred wolves as pets.
- D. He worked for a neighbor.

8. What is special about the bloodroot flower?
- F. It looks like a paintbrush.
- G. It has an especially bright color.
- H. It has a wonderful smell.
- J. It is the first flower of spring.

9. The Abenaki and the Mohawks used the juice of bloodroot stems for—
- A. repelling insects.
- B. curing headaches.
- C. flavoring foods.
- D. healing wounds.

10. In the myth about Old Man Winter, what caused the bloodroot flowers to bloom?
- F. the Great White Bear
- G. Winter's cold fire
- H. the coming of spring
- J. the songs of birds

GO ON

11. The myth explains why—
- A. some animals sleep all winter.
- B. the seasons change.
- C. flowers bloom.
- D. the sun rises and sets.

12. As a child, the author was—
- F. a good storyteller.
- G. a bit too reckless.
- H. a skillful painter.
- J. a careful observer.

13. One reason the author's grandfather painted the boy's face with bloodroot juice was to—
- A. tell an old story in a new way.
- B. make people laugh.
- C. mark the boy as a warrior.
- D. celebrate spring.

14. You can tell from this selection that the author's memories of his grandfather are closely linked with his memories of—
- F. making up games.
- G. learning about nature.
- H. becoming a writer.
- J. hunting for fossils.

15. Why did the author begin this story about his childhood by retelling a myth?
- A. The myth connects in important ways with events in his own life.
- B. The myth was one his grandfather loved to tell.
- C. The myth gives the reader an entertaining mix of fact and fiction.
- D. The myth helps the reader understand the author's family.

Name ______________________________

Drawing Conclusions

- **Drawing conclusions** means making sensible decisions or forming reasonable opinions about what you read.
- A **conclusion** should be based on facts and details in the writing, as well as your own experience.

Directions: Read the story below.

"Now I'll teach you how to make my sweet potato pie, just like my grandma taught me," said Nana. "Remember, canned filling and store-bought pie crust just won't do. Why, we've been baking these pies for six generations!"

Keesha knew Nana's pie-baking story by heart. The family recipe dated back to the days when her ancestors had grown the sweet potatoes themselves. Today Keesha was learning how to make the crisp crust and tasty filling. She smiled, thinking about the heavenly cinnamon aroma soon to fill the kitchen. One day she'd pass the recipe on to her grandchildren. She thought it would be a tasty way to honor family traditions.

Directions: Complete the table. Write evidence to support conclusions given or draw conclusions from the given evidence.

Evidence (Story Details and Personal Knowledge)	Conclusion
Nana will not use canned filling or store-bought pie crust.	**1.**
2.	Nana is proud to pass on a family tradition.
3.	Nana must have told the pie-making story many times over the years.
A heavenly cinnamon aroma would soon fill the kitchen.	**4.**
Keesha plans to pass the tradition on to her grandchildren.	**5.**

Notes for Home: Your child used story details to draw conclusions. ***Home Activity:*** Do some "people watching" during the next family gathering. Discuss possible conclusions to be drawn about people's feelings from their facial expressions and body language.

Author's Viewpoint

REVIEW

Directions: Read the passage. Then read each question about the passage. Choose the best answer to each question. Mark the letter for the answer you have chosen.

Save That Green!!

Dear Editor,

What will be built on the last green area in the center of town? Will it be an unhealthy fast-food spot or another parking lot? We don't need those! There are two diners within a few blocks of the area, and people usually don't drive into the town center. Everyone knows there are always plenty of places to park on Mattingly Avenue and on Ruth Street.

What we need is a park to protect the gnarled old oak tree growing there. Everyone knows the tree I mean, the one with the trunk that's too big to put your arms around! That tree has been there for more than 100 years. Children climb it and use it as a lookout when they play pirates. Cows used to graze in its shade. Many a pair of sweethearts met underneath its leafy branches.

The old oak tree has its small place in history too. The great American writer Mark Twain once rested under it! He told the story in a letter. His train was late and he strolled into the town. Tired from his long day's journey, he stretched out in the shade of the oak and took a nap.

That old tree and this town both need a cool, peaceful park, not another parking lot. Let's save the green and tree!

Signed,
Theresa Ver

1. The main purpose of this article is to—
   - **A.** entertain.
   - **B.** persuade.
   - **C.** explain.
   - **D.** express.

2. Which of the following is a statement of fact that the author uses to support her argument?
   - **F.** A parking lot will be built on the lot.
   - **G.** The town does not need another park.
   - **H.** Mark Twain once rested under the tree.
   - **J.** Fast-food shops are unnecessary.

3. The author hopes readers will agree that—
   - **A.** the oak tree must be saved.
   - **B.** the town needs more parking.
   - **C.** Mark Twain was a great writer.
   - **D.** cows should be allowed to graze in the center of town again.

4. Words used to influence the reader include—
   - **F.** pirates, cows
   - **G.** trunk, branches
   - **H.** train, nap
   - **J.** unhealthy, peaceful

5. The author believes that—
   - **A.** Mark Twain deserves a monument.
   - **B.** a park would be the best use of the space around the tree.
   - **C.** nothing more must be built in town.
   - **D.** oak trees are the best trees.

Notes for Home: Your child identified the author's viewpoint in a letter to the editor. ***Home Activity:*** Discuss with your child an author's viewpoint in individual letters to editors from the local newspaper.

Name ______________________________

Writing Across Texts

Directions: How are the theme, story line, and characters in the Native American legend described in "Spring Paint" like those in "Demeter's Daughter"? Complete the following table to record your ideas.

Comparing "Spring Paint" to "Demeter's Daughter"
One Way the Themes Are Alike 1.
Two Ways the Characters Are Alike 2. 3.
Two Ways the Story Lines Are Alike 4. 5.

Write a Comparison

On a separate sheet of paper, write a comparison paragraph to explain how "Spring Paint" is like "Demeter's Daughter."

Notes for Home: Your child compared legends from two different cultures. ***Home Activity:*** Together, find and read aloud a folk tale, myth, or legend from your family's ancestral culture. Discuss the story and how it shares information about the culture from which it came.

Grammar: Complete Subjects

REVIEW

Directions: Underline the complete subject in each sentence.

1. The Abenaki people grew much of their own food.
2. One very important crop for their diet was corn.
3. A favorite Abenaki myth tells of the creation of this basic food.
4. A lonely man meets a mysterious woman one day.
5. Her long, flowing hair is remarkably fair and silky.
6. This lovely creature asks the man to follow her instructions carefully.
7. He first sets fire to a field.
8. The obedient man then pulls the woman gently over the ground by her long hair.
9. Her fair, silken hair will then reappear to him each year in the form of corn silks.
10. The gift of golden corn remains with the man and his people forever after.

Directions: Use each word as part of the complete subject in a sentence of your own. Your complete subject should have at least three words.

11. corn

____

____

12. myths

____

____

13. hair

____

____

14. crops

____

____

15. water

____

____

Notes for Home: Your child identified and wrote sentences with complete subjects—the part that tells whom or what the sentence is about. ***Home Activity:*** Look through a newspaper with your child. Identify the complete subjects of some sentences.

Name ________________________________

Grammar: Adjectives

Adjectives modify, or tell more about, nouns or pronouns. Adjectives can tell what kind, which one, how many, or how much.

red sky (what kind) this village (which one) two miles (how many)

Most adjectives come before the nouns they modify. However, **predicate adjectives** follow linking verbs and modify a noun or pronoun in the subject.

Grandmother is very wise. She is also kind.

An adjective formed from a proper noun is called a **proper adjective.** Proper adjectives are capitalized.

European village South African music

Directions: Underline each adjective. Circle the noun it modifies.

1. Toni visited Grandmother's old village.
2. She saw ancient houses and uneven streets.
3. Greek villages seemed pleasant to her.
4. Young and old relatives crowded around her.
5. Toni's American clothes interested them.

Directions: Add adjectives to complete each sentence. Use the clues in ( ) to help. Write each adjective on the matching numbered line to the right.

6. _____ (how many) huge trees hung over the **7.** _____ (what kind) gate. From the gate, a **8.** _____ (what kind) path led to my uncle's **9.** _____ (what kind) garden. The garden had **10.** _____ (how many) different kinds of plants. **11.** _____ (which ones) plants all looked very **12.** _____ (what kind). I noticed that **13.** _____ (how many) plants had grown remarkably tall. Uncle Jim promised to teach me to raise plants as **14.** _____ (what kind) as his. I know I can learn **15.** _____ (which one) skill from my capable uncle.

6. ____________________

7. ____________________

8. ____________________

9. ____________________

10. ____________________

11. ____________________

12. ____________________

13. ____________________

14. ____________________

15. ____________________

Notes for Home: Your child identified and used adjectives, words that describe nouns and pronouns. ***Home Activity:*** Challenge your child to use as many adjectives as he or she can in describing someone or something. See if you can guess whom or what your child is describing.

Grammar: Adjectives

Directions: Underline the adjectives in each sentence. Circle the noun each adjective modifies.

1. The Acoma people occupy an ancient pueblo on a mesa in the Southwest.
2. A mesa is flat at the top.
3. The Acoma still keep the old way of life.
4. They speak the first language of their ancestors.
5. They make beautiful pottery.

Directions: Choose an adjective from the box to complete each sentence. Write the adjective on the line to the left.

steep	young	traditional	hard	full
soft	high	Santa Fe	free	sagebrush

______________ **6.** The _____ children learn how to find clay in nearby canyons.

______________ **7.** They knead the stiff clay, and it becomes _____ enough to shape.

______________ **8.** The painted decorations for the pots are _____ designs that the children learned from their parents.

______________ **9.** Next, the children fire the painted pots, and the clay becomes _____.

______________ **10.** Then the Acoma sell the pots at a _____ market.

Write Instructions

Think about something a family member taught you how to do. You might have learned how to grow a garden, make pottery, or cook a traditional dish. Write a simple set of instructions that a friend could follow to make the same item. Use adjectives in your writing.

Notes for Home: Your child identified and used adjectives, including proper adjectives. ***Home Activity:*** Challenge your child to name something that you describe using proper adjectives: *an American city, an Italian dish,* for example.

Name ___________________________________

Grammar: Adjectives

RETEACHING

Underline each adjective in the sentences.

1. We chose bright material for our new curtains.
2. I didn't want this day to end.
3. Toloma added six kiwis to her basket.
4. Rory the dog is very gentle.
5. We decided to try the Spanish rice.

Adjectives tell more about persons, places, or things that nouns name. Adjectives tell what kind, which one, or how many. Often adjectives appear before the nouns they tell more about. When an adjective appears in the predicate of the sentence, it follows a linking verb and is called a **predicate adjective.** A **proper adjective** is an adjective formed from a proper noun.

Directions: Underline each adjective. Then draw an arrow from each adjective to the noun it tells more about. Hint: There may be more than one adjective modifying the same noun.

1. This mountain had many glaciers.
2. Kim is a brave woman and a skillful climber.
3. She is strong too.
4. In the morning, she put on Norwegian athletic shoes.
5. The sky was pink at the start of the steep climb.
6. The crisp air chilled her.
7. Finally a red sun rose.
8. Kim saw purple flowers and blue dragonflies.
9. These lovely sights refreshed her.
10. Kim climbed over three huge boulders.
11. She rested beside a clear stream.
12. The icy water tasted sweet.

Notes for Home: Your child identified adjectives in sentences and the nouns that they tell about. ***Home Activity:*** Discuss with your child an important event at school. Encourage your child to use adjectives in the discussion.

Name ____

Grammar: Adjectives

Directions: Choose an adjective to sensibly complete each sentence. Write the adjective on the line.

1. ________________ week, my parents decided what our summer project would be.
2. They had been talking about it for ________________ weeks, and my sister and I had been guessing what our parents would choose.
3. Shaunita thought we would have to paint the ________________ garage because the paint was peeling off.
4. Then she mentioned that we might have to wash the ________________ doors in the dining room.
5. I was almost positive we would have to clean out the garage because it hadn't been cleaned in years, and it was ________________.
6. My brother guessed we would have to plant new bushes and shrubs in the ________________ yard.
7. At dinner one night, Mom and Dad announced their ________________ plan.
8. With help, we were going to refinish the ________________ deck behind our house.
9. My brother and sister and I would be in charge of choosing ________________ flowers and paint for the flower boxes and paint for the railings.
10. I chose ______________ flowers and ______________ and ______________ paint.
11. My brother didn't like that idea. He thought ________________ colors wouldn't match the house.
12. We finally agreed on ________________ color for both the flower boxes and the railings.

Directions: Circle each adjective. Underline the noun each adjective tells more about.

13. This summer we began our massive project.
14. My entire family put on their old, dirty clothes.
15. Then we called our helpful neighbors and held a meeting.
16. Mom explained the new project to all seven people.
17. She showed the neighbors the blue paint.
18. Then everyone began this exciting job.
19. We had to let the paint dry on the boxes before we could plant the English flowers.
20. It took us two weeks, but we finished the beautiful deck!

Notes for Home: Your child identified and wrote adjectives in sentences. ***Home Activity:*** Together, listen to a favorite song or instrumental piece. Talk about the music together. Encourage your child to use descriptive adjectives.

Name ______________________________

Word Study: Inflected Endings: *-ed*, *-ing*

Directions: Two endings that are commonly added to verbs are **-ed** and **-ing.** Read the paragraph below. Circle the words with **-ed** and **-ing** endings. Then write the base word for each circled word.

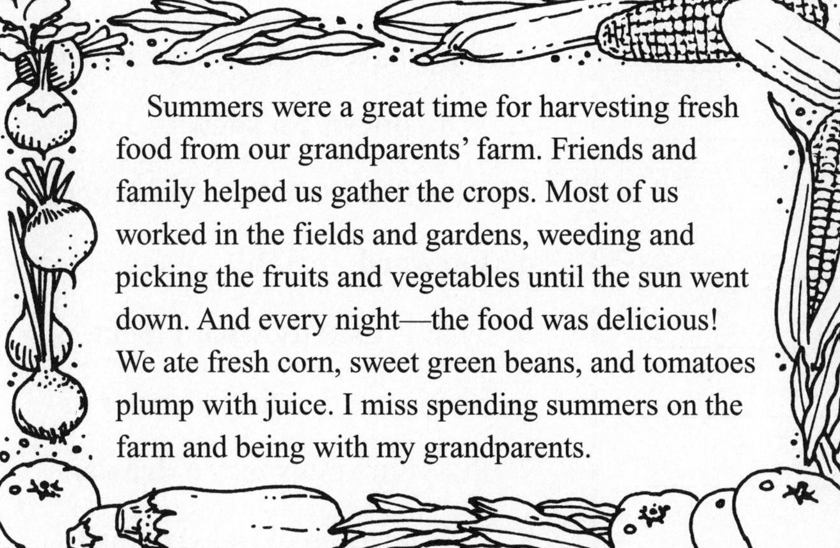

Summers were a great time for harvesting fresh food from our grandparents' farm. Friends and family helped us gather the crops. Most of us worked in the fields and gardens, weeding and picking the fruits and vegetables until the sun went down. And every night—the food was delicious! We ate fresh corn, sweet green beans, and tomatoes plump with juice. I miss spending summers on the farm and being with my grandparents.

1. ______________
2. ______________
3. ______________
4. ______________
5. ______________
6. ______________
7. ______________

Directions: Add **-ed** and **-ing** to each base word. Write the new word on the line.

Base Word	Add -ed	Add -ing
flicker	**8.** ______________	**9.** ______________
follow	**10.** ______________	**11.** ______________
search	**12.** ______________	**13.** ______________
watch	**14.** ______________	**15.** ______________
surround	**16.** ______________	**17.** ______________
return	**18.** ______________	**19.** ______________
invent	**20.** ______________	**21.** ______________
wander	**22.** ______________	**23.** ______________
stroll	**24.** ______________	**25.** ______________

Notes for Home: Your child identified and wrote words ending in *-ed* and *-ing*. ***Home Activity:*** Help your child think of other words with these endings. Make a table with two columns, one for *-ed* words and one for *-ing* words. Have your child write the words in the correct columns.

Name ____________________

Pretest

Spelling: Using Just Enough Letters

Pretest Directions: Fold back the page along the dotted line. On the blanks, write the spelling words as they are dictated. When you have finished the test, unfold the page and check your words.

1. ____________	1. They have **similar** appearances.
2. ____________	2. Why **doesn't** it snow in July?
3. ____________	3. We often learn by **experience**.
4. ____________	4. **Forward**, march!
5. ____________	5. That is **exactly** what I mean.
6. ____________	6. She is my dancing **partner**.
7. ____________	7. Put your socks in the **drawer**.
8. ____________	8. Lobster is an **expensive** dish.
9. ____________	9. Plants **develop** from seeds.
10. ____________	10. His face is **familiar**.
11. ____________	11. A **pigeon** landed on the statue.
12. ____________	12. Dust is **tickling** my nose.
13. ____________	13. Cheaters face a harsh **penalty**.
14. ____________	14. Rain **frustrated** our picnic plans.
15. ____________	15. She is very **athletic**.
16. ____________	16. This calls for a **celebration**.
17. ____________	17. Birds were **circling** overhead.
18. ____________	18. We rode in a **helicopter**.
19. ____________	19. He is **trembling** from the cold.
20. ____________	20. The stars are **sparkling** tonight.

Notes for Home: Your child took a pretest on words with difficult letter combinations. ***Home Activity:*** Help your child learn misspelled words before the final test. Your child should look at the word, say it, spell it aloud, and then spell it with eyes shut.

Name ______________________

Think and Practice

Spelling: Using Just Enough Letters

Word List

similar	exactly	develop	penalty	circling
doesn't	partner	familiar	frustrated	helicopter
experience	drawer	pigeon	athletic	trembling
forward	expensive	tickling	celebration	sparkling

Directions: Choose the words from the box that have three or four syllables. Write each word in the correct column.

Words with Three Syllables

1. ______________________
2. ______________________
3. ______________________
4. ______________________
5. ______________________
6. ______________________
7. ______________________
8. ______________________

Words with Four Syllables

9. ______________________
10. ______________________
11. ______________________

Directions: Choose the word from the box that best matches each clue. Write the word on the line.

______________ **12.** I am the opposite of *backward.*

______________ **13.** I am the feeling you get in your nose when you are surrounded by dusty air or fuzzy sweaters.

______________ **14.** I am a contraction of the words *does* and *not.*

______________ **15.** I am a person you work with or dance with.

______________ **16.** I am a gray, black, and white city bird that coos.

______________ **17.** I am the part of a desk or chest in which you keep things.

______________ **18.** I am similar in meaning to *shaking.*

______________ **19.** I am dazzling and shining in the light.

______________ **20.** I am an action that will cause you to get dizzy if you do it too often or too fast.

Notes for Home: Your child spelled words that are often misspelled by adding too many letters. ***Home Activity:*** Write each spelling word on a card. Show your child a card for ten seconds. Have your child pronounce the word carefully, picture how it looks, and spell it aloud.

Name ______________________________

Spelling: Using Just Enough Letters

Directions: Proofread this description of the Abenaki, a Native American people. Find six spelling mistakes. Use the proofreading marks to correct each mistake.

≡	Make a capital.
/	Make a small letter.
∧	Add something.
℘	Take out something.
⊙	Add a period.
¶	Begin a new paragraph.

The Abenaki lived in the Northeast, in what is now Vermont and Connecticut. Their lives followed a familare seasonal pattern. They stalked game, raised and harvested crops, fished, and hunted waterfowl and pigeon. Close-knit family groups moved often, so they had to devellop movable homes called *wigwams.* While their experientce was gained through hard living, they had fun too. When the Abenaki held a feast or cellebration, the athtletic men played a game called *lacrosse.* In winter the children played in the sparkeling snow.

Spelling Tip

Pronouncing a word correctly and picturing how it looks can help you avoid writing too many letters. Check the description to make sure the words from the box are spelled correctly.

Word List

similar	pigeon
doesn't	tickling
experience	penalty
forward	frustrated
exactly	athletic
partner	celebration
drawer	circling
expensive	helicopter
develop	trembling
familiar	sparkling

Write a Description

On a separate sheet of paper, write a description of your family. Tell about the house you live in, what you do for work and for fun, and what happens when you have a family celebration. Try to use at least five of your spelling words.

Notes for Home: Your child spelled words that are often misspelled by adding too many letters. ***Home Activity:*** Copy the list of spelling words, but misspell some of them by adding extra letters. Give your child the list and have him or her find and correct the misspelled words.

Name ______________________________

Spelling: Using Just Enough Letters

REVIEW

Directions: Choose the word from the box that best fits each definition. Write the word on the line.

Word List	
similar	pigeon
doesn't	tickling
experience	penalty
forward	frustrated
exactly	athletic
partner	celebration
drawer	circling
expensive	helicopter
develop	trembling
familiar	sparkling

______________ **1.** dove-like city bird

______________ **2.** alike

______________ **3.** punishment

______________ **4.** well-known

______________ **5.** small aircraft with a propeller

______________ **6.** shaking; quaking

______________ **7.** ahead

______________ **8.** something you have done or lived through

______________ **9.** going around

______________ **10.** grow and change

Directions: Choose the word from the box that is the correct form of each word in ( ) to complete each sentence. Write the word on the matching numbered line to the right.

"It **11.** (do not) seem to me that they'll want an **12.** (expense) gift," said Mom. "A family treasure would mean a lot more to your grandparents, since this is their fiftieth anniversary **13.** (celebrate)." We were soon **14.** (frustrate) from wondering **15.** (exact) what would be the ideal gift. Then we looked in the attic, sneezing as its dusty air began **16.** (tickle) our noses. In a **17.** (draw) of the big chest, Mom found an old photo of an **18.** (athlete) Gramps and pretty young Grammie with her **19.** (sparkle) smile. The picture showed each **20.** (part) ready to start a fifty-year journey together. It was perfect.

11. ______________

12. ______________

13. ______________

14. ______________

15. ______________

16. ______________

17. ______________

18. ______________

19. ______________

20. ______________

Notes for Home: Your child spelled words that are often misspelled by adding too many letters. ***Home Activity:*** Take turns with your child using each spelling word in a sentence. Then challenge each other to try to use two or more words in each sentence.

Name ______________________________

The *Readers' Guide to Periodical Literature*

The *Readers' Guide to Periodical Literature* is a set of books that alphabetically lists, by author and subject, the articles that are published in periodicals.

Directions: Look at the set of *Readers' Guides.* Then answer the questions that follow.

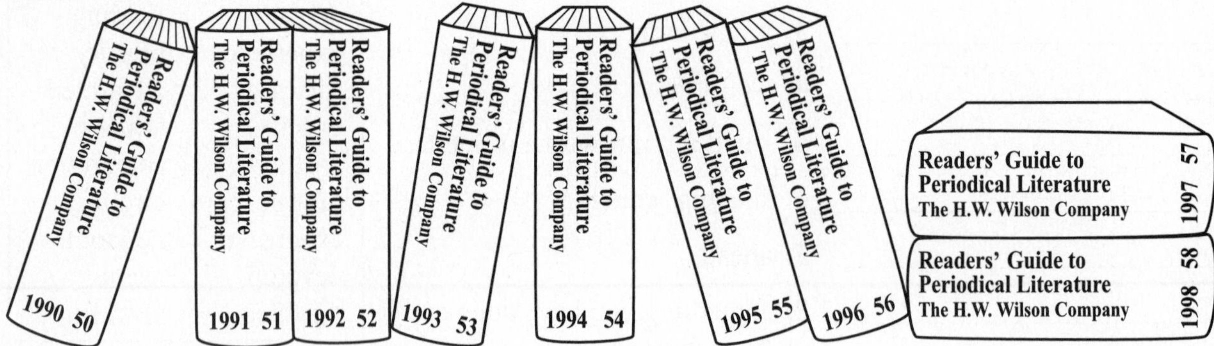

1. How are the guides organized? How can you tell? ______________________________

2. Suppose you wanted to know more about a large Navaho Pow Wow that took place in the summer of 1997. Which volume would you use to see whether any articles had been written about this gathering? Explain.

3. Suppose you are writing about the lives and customs of Native Americans living on reservations today. Would it be more helpful to search recent volumes of the *Readers' Guide* or look in an encyclopedia? Explain.

4. Suppose you are writing about Native American stories by Joseph Bruchac. Why might you have to check several volumes to find an article about or by Joseph Bruchac?

5. Some libraries are now using computer databases to store information about articles published in periodicals. Why might a computer database be easier to use than the *Readers' Guide?* Explain.

Name ______________________________

Entries in the *Readers' Guide to Periodical Literature* are arranged alphabetically by subject or author. Each entry provides the title of the article, author of the article, title of the publication in which the article appears, volume number of the periodical, pages of the article, and other information. Information about abbreviations used in entries can be found at the front of each volume.

Directions: Scan these entries from the *Readers' Guide.* Then answer the questions that follow.

INDIANS OF NORTH AMERICA—

Art

Hidden art treasures of the Indian missions. S. Lowe. il *Arizona Highways* v72 p12-17 D '96

The impact of tradition on Native American art. B. Wright. il *Arizona Highways* v72 p12-19 O '96

Objects of power. A. Wardwell. il Natural History v106 p42-3 Mr '97

Representing Indians [treatment of Indian art in museums] R.White. il *The New Republic* v216 p28-34 Ap 21 '97

Collectors and collecting

Black Hawk's drawing of a vision. G. T. Vincent and J. C. Berlo.il *The Magazine Antiques* v151 p200-1 Ja '97

Exhibitions

American expressions [Native American jewelry and metalwork: contemporary expressions at the Institute of American Indian Arts Museum, Santa Fe] L. Coulter. *American Craft* v57 p72-7 O/N '97

American Indian art [Gifts of the spirit: works by the nineteenth century and contemporary Native American artists at the Peabody Essex Museum] A. E. Ledes. il *The Magazine Antiques* v150 p760 D '96

Nineteenth-century Plains Indian drawings. J. C. Berlo. bibl f il *The Magazine Antiques* v150 p686-95 N '96

Arts and crafts

Buying Indian arts and crafts. B. Wright. il *Arizona Highways* v72 p18-21 N '96

Last of the old-time traders [trading posts in Arizona] S. Negri. il *Arizona Highways* v73 p4-9 Ja '97

The legend of Hubbell Trading Post. L. E. Jacka. il *Arizona Highways* v73 p10-15 Ja '97

6. What main subject and two subtopics are shown? ______________________________

____

7. Name the magazine, volume, page numbers, and year that you could find an article about the impact, or effect, of tradition on Native American art.

____

8. In which article would you find drawings by the Plains Indians of the nineteenth century?

____

9. Which magazine would give you more information about buying Native American arts and crafts? Name the magazine title, volume, month, and year.

____

10. How is using the *Readers' Guide to Periodical Literature* similar to using an index at the back of a textbook or trade book? How is it different?

____

____

____

Notes for Home: Your child answered questions about using the *Readers' Guide to Periodical Literature.* ***Home Activity:*** With your child, look through some magazines. Ask your child to find information such as the volume number, date of publication, and the titles and authors of articles.

Family Times

Name____

Summary

Keeping a Promise

In 1877, the French send the hand and torch of the Statue of Liberty, their gift to the United States, to New York. Geoffrey Gibbon, who has been studying art in Paris, describes the complete statue to his little sister Annie. They promise to meet in the statue's torch in New York once it is completed. On his return to France, Geoffrey is killed in an accident. Annie decides to sell her brother's spyglass and use the money to make a donation to the fund to build the pedestal for the statue. When others find out about Annie's loss and generosity, they also contribute to the fund. Annie is invited to the statue's dedication ceremony. In an emotional moment, she recalls the promise she and her brother made.

Activity

Act It Out. Have your child imagine he or she is Annie at the dedication ceremony. Ask your child to describe the scene from Annie's point of view. What is she thinking and feeling?

Reading Skills

Plot

The **plot** of a story is the series of important events from the story's beginning, middle, and end.

The plot revolves around a central problem, or **conflict**—a struggle between two forces, such as a person against nature. In "A Brother's Promise," the central conflict is whether the Americans will contribute enough money to build a pedestal for the statue.

The **rising action** includes Geoffrey's death and Annie's reaction. The **climax,** or turning point, is the point of highest interest in the story. The climax of the story occurs when Annie keeps her part of the promise by climbing up to the torch. The **resolution,** or outcome of the story, occurs as Annie recognizes that the promise has been kept and she becomes more at peace about her brother's death.

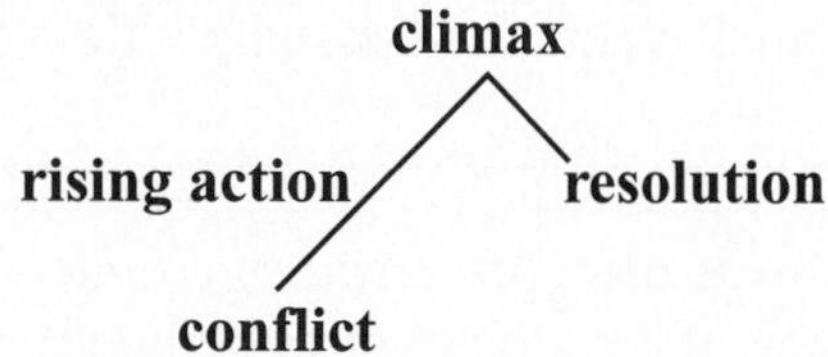

Activity

List Plot Elements. Think about a favorite story or movie. Together, list the elements—the conflict, rising action, climax, and resolution—of the plot. Parts of the plot, such as the rising action, can include several events. Does everyone agree on all the elements? Discuss differences of opinion.

Family Times

Tested Vocabulary

Words to Know

Knowing the meanings of these words is important to reading "A Brother's Promise." Practice using these words to learn their meanings.

contribution donation; gift

fund money set aside for some purpose

gigantic of huge proportions

patriotic demonstrating love and loyal support for one's country

pedestal a base or platform

spyglass a small telescope

symbolizes stands for; represents

Grammar

Comparative and Superlative Adjectives

The **comparative** form of an adjective is used to compare two people, places, and things. It is usually formed by adding the ending **-er** or the word **more.**

The people below looked smaller than mice.
The statue was more beautiful than she thought it would be.

The **superlative** form is used to compare three or more people, places, or things. It is usually formed by adding the ending **-est** or the word **most.**

Annie was the tallest girl there.
It was the most wonderful day of all.

Activity

Make a Chart. Make a chart to show an adjective and its comparative and superlative forms, such as *big, bigger, biggest.* Take turns comparing two or more items using words from your chart.

Tested Spelling Words

______	______	______	______
______	______	______	______
______	______	______	______
______	______	______	______
______	______	______	______

Name ______________________________

Plot

- The **plot** of a story is the series of important events from the story's beginning, middle, and end. The plot revolves around a central problem, or **conflict.**
- In most stories, the conflict is introduced in the beginning. As the story progresses, the conflict leads to other problems. Gradually, the **rising action** builds to a high point, or climax. The **climax** is the highest point of interest in the story. Following the climax, there is **resolution** of the conflict and the action winds down.

Directions: Reread "The Sailor and the Fly." Then complete the plot structure map by identifying each element of the plot. One has been done for you.

Climax (High-Interest Point)

4. ______________________________

____

Rising Action (Other Problems)

2. ______________________________

____

3. ______________________________

____

The fisherman nearly crashes into the sailor.

Resolution (Outcome)

5. ______________________________

____

Conflict (Central Problem)

1. ______________________________

____

____

Notes for Home: Your child identified the elements of plot in a short story. ***Home Activity:*** Use a plot structure map like the one shown to help you and your child make up a short story that features a character with a big problem.

Name ______________________________

Vocabulary

Directions: Choose the word from the box that best completes each sentence. Write the word on the line to the left.

Check the Words You Know
__ contribution
__ fund
__ gigantic
__ patriotic
__ pedestal
__ spyglass
__ symbolizes

________________ **1.** The Statue of Liberty is _____; it is more than 300 feet tall.

________________ **2.** The statue _____ freedom.

________________ **3.** Many _____ people help maintain national monuments.

________________ **4.** The Statue of Liberty stands on a large _____.

________________ **5.** Many people contributed to a _____ that was used to pay for the pedestal.

Directions: Choose the word from the box that best matches each clue. Write the word in the puzzle.

Down

6. a mounting platform

8. demonstrating a love for one's country

Across

7. a small telescope

9. what one gives

10. of huge proportions

Write an Advertisement

On a separate sheet of paper, write an advertisement for a tourist attraction that a patriotic person might wish to visit. For example, you might write about Mount Rushmore or the Statue of Liberty. Use as many vocabulary words as you can.

Notes for Home: Your child identified and used vocabulary words from "A Brother's Promise." ***Home Activity:*** Work with your child to write a paragraph about celebrating a national holiday. Encourage your child to use as many of the listed vocabulary words as possible.

Name ______________________

Plot

- A story's **plot** is the series of important events from the story's beginning, middle, and end.
- A plot revolves around a central problem, or conflict. Other elements of plot include the background, the rising action, the climax, and the resolution, or outcome.

Directions: Reread Joseph Pulitzer's speech about Annie from "A Brother's Promise." Then answer the questions below. Think about which story details are important to the plot.

"You see," he said, turning back to his audience, "she lost her brother last year, a brother who loved the Statue of Liberty. He'd actually seen it in Paris, and Annie sold his special spyglass and sent the money to the Pedestal Fund in his memory. And that led many others to do the same thing."

A few people clapped, and Annie looked down at their faces.

"Annie, I have a surprise for you." He turned around, and someone handed him a long, thin wooden box.

1. List the events that brought Annie and Pulitzer together.

____

____

____

2. How did Annie's sale of the spyglass lead to other story events?

____

3. What does the last line suggest will happen next?

____

4. Why is Pulitzer's surprise important to the story?

____

____

5. On a separate sheet of paper, identify the climax of "A Brother's Promise." Remember, the climax is the "high point" of the story where the story's problem is directly confronted.

Notes for Home: Your child read a passage and identified various parts of its plot. ***Home Activity:*** Encourage your child to draw a diagram that shows the basic plot of an episode of a recent television show.

Name ______________________

Selection Test

Directions: Choose the best answer to each item. Mark the letter for the answer you have chosen.

Part 1: Vocabulary

Find the answer choice that means about the same as the underlined word in each sentence.

1. He placed it on a pedestal.
- A. wide post
- B. table with hinged sides
- C. mound of earth
- D. base on which something stands

2. She looked into the spyglass.
- F. magnifying glass
- G. small telescope
- H. round window
- J. small mirror

3. The statue is gigantic.
- A. huge
- B. strange
- C. expensive
- D. lovely

4. He made a contribution.
- F. statement against something
- G. loud noise or disturbance
- H. description of something
- J. gift of money or help

5. They decided to set up a fund.
- A. work done for the common good
- B. community organization
- C. money set aside for a special purpose
- D. small company

6. We sang patriotic songs.
- F. showing love of one's country
- G. expressing strong emotion
- H. of or about soldiers
- J. originating and handed down among the common people

7. Do you know what the statue symbolizes?
- A. celebrates
- B. attracts
- C. stands for
- D. includes

Part 2: Comprehension

Use what you know about the story to answer each item.

8. Where did Geoffrey see the Statue of Liberty?
- F. Madison Square
- G. Paris
- H. New York Harbor
- J. Philadelphia

9. Why was there a problem in bringing the Statue of Liberty to America?
- A. It was too heavy to move.
- B. The body was not finished.
- C. The statue was a hoax.
- D. There was no base to put it on.

10. After Geoffrey died, Annie's main goal was to—
- F. take Geoffrey's spyglass into the Statue of Liberty.
- G. make sure the Statue of Liberty was placed in New York Harbor.
- H. help others appreciate how wonderful the Statue of Liberty was.
- J. go to France to see where the Statue of Liberty was made.

11. Why did Annie pawn the spyglass?
- A. She hoped someone just like Geoffrey would buy it.
- B. She did not like it.
- C. She wanted to give money to the pedestal fund.
- D. It brought back sad memories.

12. Mr. Pulitzer helped persuade many people to give money for the pedestal by—
- F. buying Geoffrey's spyglass.
- G. printing Annie's letter in the *New York World.*
- H. proving that the statue was real.
- J. giving a speech on Bedloe's Island.

13. The climax of the story occurs when—
- A. Annie writes to Mr. Pulitzer.
- B. Geoffrey and Annie climb up into the torch together.
- C. Geoffrey is killed in an accident.
- D. Annie climbs to the top of the statue with Geoffrey's spyglass.

14. When Annie speaks to Geoffrey from the top of the Statue of Liberty, it—
- F. helps the reader know what Annie sees and feels.
- G. makes the reader wonder whether Geoffrey is really dead.
- H. gives the story the spooky feeling of a ghost story.
- J. ties up loose ends and solves the riddle of the plot.

15. In historical fiction, some parts of the story are based on facts. Which of these statements can you be quite sure is true?
- A. Annie is ten years younger than Geoffrey.
- B. The Statue of Liberty was erected on Bedloe's Island in 1886.
- C. Joseph Pulitzer bought Geoffrey's spyglass from a pawnshop.
- D. Geoffrey was an art student in France.

STOP

Name ____________________

Plot

- A story's **plot** is the series of important events from the story's beginning, middle, and end.
- A plot revolves around a central problem, or conflict. Other elements of plot include the background, the rising action, the climax, and the resolution, or outcome.

Directions: Read the story below.

Uncle Nate walked on crutches and could not climb the cemetery's hills. Leo had promised to take Uncle Nate's place, but the thought of placing flags on graves on Veterans' Day seemed creepy. He'd rather be swimming, hiking, washing dishes—not this.

Leo blocked out his thoughts, grabbed the flags, and hurried to the correct area. As he placed a flag, he stopped to read the gravestone. How interesting! This soldier had served in World War I and had died when he was only a little older than Leo!

Leo felt a lump in his throat. He straightened the flag in its holder. "I will come back every November to honor these young men," he vowed.

Directions: Complete the plot map below. Describe the parts of the plot from the story. The first one has been started for you.

Climax

4. ____________________

____

____

Event/Rising Action

3. ____________________

____

____

Resolution (Outcome)

5. ____________________

____

____

Conflict

2. ____________________

____

Background

1. Uncle Nate is on crutches, so he:

____

____

Notes for Home: Your child identified the important parts of a story's plot. ***Home Activity:*** Have your child describe the plot of a play you both have seen or a story you have both read. Make sure he or she can identify the background, conflict, rising action, climax, and resolution.

Name ______________________________

Visualizing and Theme

REVIEW

Directions: Read the passage. Then read each question about the passage. Choose the best answer to each question. Mark the letter for the answer you have chosen.

A Floating Monument

First the boat dock grew smaller until only a gigantic flag could be seen, waving like an unruly child. Then the traffic jam noises of sirens and horns grew fainter as tugboats guided the *USS Constitution* to the open ocean. Salty winds cooled the excited guests and crew.

Once this old ship had proudly served her country. She was launched in 1797, and took part in many naval battles. During the War of 1812, a sailor gave her the nickname "Old Ironsides." He claimed to have seen British cannonballs bouncing off the sides of the *Constitution!*

By 1830, Old Ironsides' proud career seemed to be over. The navy declared that she was too old and no longer safe to sail. The navy planned to destroy her. But when the poet Oliver Wendell Holmes wrote a farewell poem to the great ship, people remembered her glory and wrote to the navy. They wanted to save Old Ironsides. The navy, surprised, agreed to the people's wishes. In 1833, the *Constitution* was afloat again.

Now, 200 years after her launching, she was about to travel under sail power again. A signal pierced the air. It was time. High above the deck, sailors worked lines and unfurled sails. At first nothing happened. Then sail after sail caught the wind. The ship came alive like a bird carried across the water by huge white wings. As the ship proudly sailed forth, people were once more reminded that the *USS Constitution* symbolizes the courage of a nation.

1. The flag is compared to—
- **A.** a huge white bird.
- **B.** the open ocean.
- **C.** an unruly child.
- **D.** the bravery of a nation.

2. The words traffic jam are used to describe—
- **F.** the confusing jumble of sounds.
- **G.** why the ship sails slowly.
- **H.** decks aboard the ship.
- **J.** crowds of boats in the harbor.

3. The nickname "Ironsides" suggests—
- **A.** age.
- **B.** strength.
- **C.** beauty.
- **D.** grace.

4. As the ship sets sail, it is compared to—
- **F.** a bird.
- **G.** the wind.
- **H.** a flag.
- **J.** a child.

5. One theme the passage expresses is the—
- **A.** courage of sailors.
- **B.** importance of sail power.
- **C.** unusual demands placed on naval vessels.
- **D.** power of patriotic symbols to inspire people.

Notes for Home: Your child identified the descriptive details and the underlying meaning of a passage. ***Home Activity:*** Encourage your child to use a variety of descriptive words that convey the sights, sounds, smells, and mood of a specific place.

Name ___________________________

Writing Across Texts

Directions: Think about "A Brother's Promise" and "Symbols That Make Us Proud." Which selection was your favorite? Complete the following table to contrast the selections and give reasons why one was more appealing to you than the other.

Favorite Selection Title
1.
Reasons I Liked It Better Than the Other Selection
2.
3.
4.
5.

Write a Paragraph that Contrasts

Consider "A Brother's Promise" and "Symbols That Make Us Proud." On a separate sheet of paper, write a paragraph explaining which selection was your favorite to read and why. Be sure to contrast the selections as a way to share your opinions.

Notes for Home: Your child compared two reading selections and chose one as a favorite. ***Home Activity:*** Together, read aloud two magazine or newspaper articles about the same subject. Talk with your child about which article he or she liked more and why.

Name ______________________________

REVIEW

Grammar: Adjectives

Directions: Draw a line under each adjective. Circle the noun it modifies.

1. The enormous copper statue rises over the busy harbor of New York City.
2. The colossal work was a gift to the American people from France.
3. The huge stone pedestal, however, was built with American money.
4. President Cleveland dedicated the beautiful Statue of Liberty in 1886, and it soon became a powerful symbol of freedom.
5. In former years, when new immigrants arrived by ship, the towering statue provided the first sight of America.
6. Anxious newcomers hoping for improved lives in a free country were moved to tears when they saw the mighty lady.
7. In 1924, the famous and familiar statue was declared a national monument.
8. A steep spiral staircase inside the steel framework leads to the crown.
9. From the high crown, numerous visitors have looked out at the breathtaking view.
10. "Miss Liberty" is tall and proud, and she is known to the entire world.

Directions: Complete each sentence with an article or adjective from the box that tells how many or how much. Write the word on the line.

a *or* an	many	two	no	several

______________________ 11. Shana was one of _____ visitors to the Statue of Liberty that crisp fall day.

______________________ 12. She had come with _____ members of her family—her parents, brother, aunt, and uncle.

______________________ 13. They had had _____ food since breakfast, but they were too excited to eat.

______________________ 14. They had moved to America just _____ weeks ago.

______________________ 15. To Shana and her family, the huge statue was _____ amazing sight that they will never forget.

Notes for Home: Your child identified and used adjectives—words that describe nouns and pronouns. ***Home Activity:*** Write some of the adjectives on cards. Then have your child choose a card and use the adjective in a sentence.

Grammar: Comparative and Superlative Adjectives

An adjective describes a person, a place, or a thing.

The **comparative form** of an adjective is used to compare two persons, places, or things. The word **than** sometimes signals this form.

These fireworks are brighter than last year's display.

The **superlative form** of an adjective is used to compare three or more persons, places, or things.

Next year's fireworks will be the brightest of all.

More and **most** are usually used in the comparative or superlative forms of adjectives.

Chili dogs are more delicious than plain hot dogs.
Dad makes the most delicious hot dogs on the grill.

Do not use **more** and **most** with adjectives ending in **-er** or **-est.**
Don't write: Mom's iced lemonade tastes more sweeter than my iced lemonade.
Write: Mom's iced lemonade tastes sweeter than my iced lemonade.

As shown below, the spelling of some adjectives changes in the comparative and superlative forms.

good, better, best	much, more, most
bad, worse, worst	little, less, least

Directions: Circle the correct form of the adjective in ( ) to complete each sentence.

1. To Clara, the Fourth of July was the (better/best) holiday of the year.
2. First, she would twirl her baton and march in the (bigger/biggest) parade in the entire state.
3. The band's uniforms were the (brighter/brightest) red she had ever seen.
4. The notes played by the flute section were (softer/softest) than those played by the trumpet section.
5. The float of the Statue of Liberty was the (larger/largest) of all.
6. Clara's family would always throw one of the (nicer/nicest) parties on the block.
7. Clara would help cook the (tastier/tastiest) hot dogs her friends had ever eaten.
8. In the evening, there would be a fireworks display with the (louder/loudest) noises ever!
9. The red starburst at the end was the (more brilliant/most brilliant) of all the fireworks.
10. Clara couldn't think of anything (better/best) than the Fourth of July.

Notes for Home: Your child identified and used comparative and superlative adjectives to compare people, places, and things. ***Home Activity:*** Challenge your child to think of a sentence with a comparative adjective. You, in turn, supply a sentence with a superlative adjective.

Extra Practice

Grammar: Comparative and Superlative Adjectives

Directions: Use the correct form of the adjective in ( ) to complete each sentence. Write the adjective on the line.

______________ **1.** Thanksgiving is the (great) holiday.

______________ **2.** My family gets together for a feast that's (good) than the one the Pilgrims had.

______________ **3.** Mom is (happy) of all, because my brother comes home from college.

______________ **4.** She always says he looks (tall) than he was when he left.

______________ **5.** We all laugh, but my brother laughs (loud) of all.

______________ **6.** He says he couldn't have grown any (big) than he was three months ago.

______________ **7.** We give thanks for the (good) life we have.

______________ **8.** Then we eat the (delicious) dinner of all—turkey, stuffing, potatoes, and squash.

______________ **9.** Mom's apple pie is (sweet) than her pumpkin pie.

______________ **10.** But I think pumpkin pie is the (good) dessert of all.

______________ **11.** After dinner, we watch the (exciting) football game that we can find on TV.

______________ **12.** My mom is (loyal) to the home team than my brother.

______________ **13.** My brother thinks the team from his college town is (good) than ours.

______________ **14.** When it comes to sports, Mom and my brother have the (lively) discussions of anyone in our family.

______________ **15.** Mom says it's the (enjoyable) debate she has all year long.

Write a Description

Invent a new holiday. On a separate sheet of paper, give the holiday a name and describe what it celebrates. Then explain how people will observe the day. Will they have a parade? Will they prepare a special meal? Use comparative and superlative adjectives in your description.

Notes for Home: Your child wrote the comparative and superlative forms of adjectives. ***Home Activity:*** On small pieces of paper, write a variety of nouns. With your child, take turns choosing a noun and describing it with comparative and superlative forms of adjectives.

RETEACHING

Grammar: Comparative and Superlative Adjectives

The chart below shows some forms of four adjectives. Fill in the missing adjectives in the chart.

	Adjective	Comparative Form	Superlative Form
1.	____________	happier	happiest
2.	expensive	____________	most expensive
3.	good	better	____________
4.	bad	____________	worst

Use the **comparative** form of an adjective to compare two items. Use the **superlative** form to compare three or more items. Most adjectives add **-er, -est, more,** or **most** to form the comparative and superlative forms. Some adjectives have special forms.

Directions: Write the correct adjective form in ( ) to complete each sentence.

1. Some people say the clipper ship was the ____________ ship ever built. (more exciting/most exciting)
2. The vessel of Christopher Columbus's time was a ____________ ship than the galley. (newer/newest)
3. Clipper ships were ____________ than Columbus's ships. (larger/largest)
4. Of all sailing vessels, the clipper was the ____________ ship. (faster/fastest)
5. The ____________ clipper ship ever built was the *Great Republic.* (bigger/biggest)
6. Steamships have been ____________ than sailing ships in recent times. (common/more common)
7. Steamships were ____________ than sailing ships at maintaining a steady pace. (better/best)
8. These ships were the ____________ ships of all time. (more powerful/most powerful)
9. Even today, however, many people find sailboats ____________ than power boats. (enjoyable/more enjoyable)
10. The sailboat is ____________ than the power boat. (most thrilling/more thrilling)

Notes for Home: Your child used comparative and superlative forms of adjectives in sentences. ***Home Activity:*** Take a walk with your child. Talk about what you see by saying sentences with adjectives in comparative and superlative forms.

Name ___________________________

Grammar: Comparative and Superlative Adjectives

Directions: Write the comparative or superlative form of each adjective in ( ).

1. What is the (efficient) of all methods of producing power? ____________
2. Nuclear fusion will produce (clean) power than fission. ____________
3. Some fuels burn for a (long) time than others. ____________
4. Of all types of coal, anthracite burns the (long) time. ____________
5. Anthracite coal is one of the (hard) fuels there is. ____________
6. Bituminous coal is (soft) than anthracite coal. ____________
7. The Donets Basin is one of the (large) of all coal deposits. ____________
8. The United States has the (great) amount of coal of all. ____________
9. The (big) of all anthracite deposits is in Pennsylvania. ____________

Directions: Write the correct form of the adjective in ( ).

10. Which is the (good) region of all for coal? ____________
11. Appalachia is the (large) producer of all. ____________
12. Mining is one of the (dangerous) jobs of all. ____________
13. Liquid fuels are (convenient) than solids. ____________
14. Is oil or gas a (efficient) fuel? ____________
15. Are nuclear fuels (good) than fossil fuels? ____________
16. Someday nuclear fusion may be (common) than fission. ____________
17. Nuclear power is (economical) than coal. ____________
18. Nuclear fuels are (compact) than fossil fuels. ____________

Write a Journal Entry

On a separate sheet of paper, write a journal entry about what a day in your life would be like without electrical power. Be sure to use comparative and superlative forms of adjectives to point out differences.

Notes for Home: Your child identified comparative and superlative forms of adjectives in sentences. ***Home Activity:*** Name an adjective and have your child supply the comparative and superlative forms. Then switch roles.

Name ______________________________

Word Study: Inflected Endings -er, -est

Directions: The ending **-er** is added to words to compare two things. The ending **-est** is added to words to compare two or more things. Add **-er** and **-est** to each base word below. Write the new word on the line.

Base Word	Add -er	Add -est
old	**1.** ______________	**2.** ______________
short	**3.** ______________	**4.** ______________
near	**5.** ______________	**6.** ______________
grand	**7.** ______________	**8.** ______________
small	**9.** ______________	**10.** ______________

Directions: Read each sentence. Add **-er** to the word in ( ). Write the new word on the line.

______________ **11.** It had taken much (long) to finish the building than we thought.

______________ **12.** Now that the building was complete, it reached (high) than ever before.

______________ **13.** The stars never looked (bright) as I stood on the new rooftop.

______________ **14.** Even though I was (young) than the others, I could still appreciate the moment.

______________ **15.** Looking down, the cars below seemed (small) than ants.

Directions: Read each sentence. Add the ending **-est** to the word in ( ). Write the new word on the line.

______________ **16.** The new building was now the (tall) in the city.

______________ **17.** The architect expressed his (deep) gratitude when he was presented with the award.

______________ **18.** The observation tower was the (great) I had ever seen.

______________ **19.** The elevator ride to the top was the (fast) ride I had ever taken.

______________ **20.** After stepping off the elevator, I realized I was looking down from the (high) point of the city.

Notes for Home: Your child formed new words by adding *-er* and *-est* to base words. ***Home Activity:*** Listen to radio advertisements or watch television commercials with your child to find words that end in *-er* and *-est*. Make a list of these words and the products they compare.

Name ______________________________

Pretest

Spelling: Including All the Letters

Pretest Directions: Fold back the page along the dotted line. On the blanks, write the spelling words as they are dictated. When you have finished the test, unfold the page and check your words.

1. ______________	**1.** There is **probably** enough food.
2. ______________	**2.** We keep dishes in the **cabinet**.
3. ______________	**3.** I have a **separate** room.
4. ______________	**4.** I was just **wondering** why.
5. ______________	**5.** It is time to wash the **clothes**.
6. ______________	**6.** What is the **average** test score?
7. ______________	**7.** He went back to the **beginning**.
8. ______________	**8.** She opened a new **restaurant**.
9. ______________	**9.** Do you **promise** to remember?
10. ______________	**10.** Take some **aspirin** for your pain.
11. ______________	**11.** It was a **desperate** battle.
12. ______________	**12.** She was the **twelfth** in line.
13. ______________	**13.** His brother loves to go **skiing**.
14. ______________	**14.** There are many **unwritten** rules.
15. ______________	**15.** It is **roughly** a mile to town.
16. ______________	**16.** The driver kept to his **schedule**.
17. ______________	**17.** My parents might **overrule** me.
18. ______________	**18.** I'm **awfully** sorry for the mistake.
19. ______________	**19.** How much is this **fishhook**?
20. ______________	**20.** The **temperature** is dropping.

Notes for Home: Your child took a pretest on words with difficult letter combinations. ***Home Activity:*** Help your child learn misspelled words before the final test. Your child can underline the word parts that caused the problems and concentrate on those parts.

Name ______________________

Spelling: Including All the Letters

Word List			
probably	temperature	aspirin	skiing
cabinet	average	desperate	unwritten
separate	beginning	awfully	roughly
wondering	restaurant	fishhook	schedule
clothes	promise	twelfth	overrule

Directions: Sort words from the box according to how their endings are spelled. Write each word in the correct column.

Ending in -ing

1. ______________________
2. ______________________
3. ______________________

Ending in -ly

4. ______________________
5. ______________________
6. ______________________

Ending in consonant-vowel-consonant-e

7. ______________________
8. ______________________
9. ______________________
10. ______________________
11. ______________________
12. ______________________
13. ______________________

Directions: Write the word from the box that belongs in each group.

14. cupboard, chest, ______________________
15. shoes, hats, ______________________
16. deli, café, ______________________
17. vitamin, medicine, ______________________
18. unspoken, undone, ______________________
19. tenth, eleventh, ______________________
20. rod, reel, ______________________

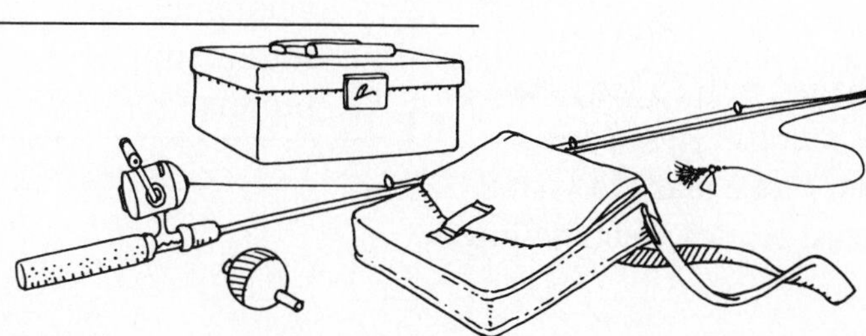

Notes for Home: Your child spelled words with more letters than you might expect. ***Home Activity:*** Help your child spell these words correctly by pronouncing each syllable carefully or by exaggerating the pronunciation of troublesome letters, such as *probably* or *cabinet.*

Spelling: Including All the Letters

Directions: Proofread this letter. Find nine spelling mistakes. Use the proofreading marks to correct each mistake.

≡ Make a capital.
/ Make a small letter.
∧ Add something.
 Take out something.
⊙ Add a period.
¶ Begin a new paragraph.

Dear Sophia,

My trip brings me to New York City at the begining of next month, and I will be there until the twelth. That means we'll probibly have time for a real visit. I know rughly what my schedle will be but should have more details soon. Tell me what clothes to bring, as I don't know what the temprature will be. I'm already wondring what fun things we can do. That reminds me of your promis. This time we really must climb the Statue of Liberty. I've been desprate to see the view from her crown.

Love,

Tom

Spelling Tip

All the spelling words have more letters than you might expect. To spell them, pronounce each syllable carefully or exaggerate the pronunciation of troublesome letters. Check the letter to make sure the words from the box are spelled correctly.

Word List

probably	aspirin
cabinet	desperate
separate	awfully
wondering	fishhook
clothes	twelfth
temperature	skiing
average	unwritten
beginning	roughly
restaurant	schedule
promise	overrule

Write a Letter

On a separate sheet of paper, write a letter to a friend, explaining what interests you about a famous tourist attraction. Make plans to visit it together. Try to use at least five of your spelling words.

Notes for Home: Your child spelled words with more letters than you might expect. ***Home Activity:*** Make up clues or hints about each spelling word, such as *This is something you use to catch a fish.* Challenge your child to guess the word and spell it. *(fishhook)*

Spelling: Including All the Letters

REVIEW

Word List				
probably	clothes	restaurant	awfully	unwritten
cabinet	temperature	promise	fishhook	roughly
separate	average	aspirin	twelfth	schedule
wondering	beginning	desperate	skiing	overrule

Directions: Choose a word from the box that best matches each clue. Write the word in the puzzle.

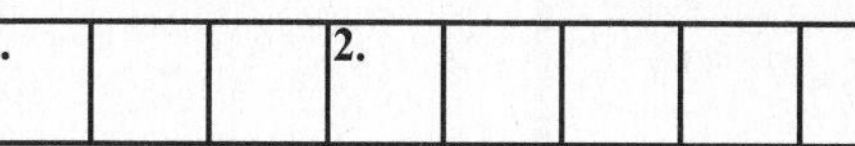

Across

1. very likely
3. ordinary; usual
5. medicine to relieve fever or pain
7. opposite of *gently*

Down

2. opposite of *ending*
4. terribly; horribly
6. a winter sport

Directions: Choose a word from the box that best completes each statement. Write the word on the line to the left.

________________ **8.** Usher: "Your ticket is for the _____ seat in the third row."

________________ **9.** Fisherman: "Bait the _____ carefully."

________________ **10.** Carpenter: "How many shelves go in each _____?"

________________ **11.** Hungry diner: "Let's eat at the new seafood _____ tonight!"

________________ **12.** Weather forecaster: "The _____ is now 90 degrees."

________________ **13.** Boss: "The _____ tells you when you'll be working."

________________ **14.** Teacher: "Write your answers on a _____ sheet of paper."

________________ **15.** Model: "My job is to wear pretty _____ for photographs."

________________ **16.** Judge: "I must uphold the law and _____ the objection."

________________ **17.** Scientists: "We're _____ what life is like on other planets."

________________ **18.** Late children: "We were _____ to get to school on time."

________________ **19.** Mother: "The _____ rule is that there is no running in the house!"

________________ **20.** Witness: "I must keep my _____ to tell the whole truth."

Notes for Home: Your child spelled words with more letters than you might expect. ***Home Activity:*** Work with your child to pronounce each word and count its syllables. Write the words and sort them according to the number of syllables in each word.

Name ____________________

Technology: Encyclopedia

An **encyclopedia** gives general information about many different subjects. If you are using a CD-ROM or online encyclopedia, you can search the entire encyclopedia for your topic. You can usually search by letter or by typing key words. The welcome screen for an on-line encyclopedia might look like this:

Welcome to the Encyclopedia

Choose a letter to browse the encyclopedia.

Or, type the key words to search. Use AND between key words.

A B C D E F G H I J K L M N O P Q R S T U V W X Y Z

Search the Encyclopedia for:

Search for:

- ☐ Articles and Tables
- ☐ Pictures, Flags, Maps, Charts, Sounds
- ☐ Websites
- ☐ All of the Above

If you wanted an encyclopedia article about the Statue of Liberty, you could try clicking on the letter *S.* If that doesn't work, you could try the letter *L.* Then you might get this:

Lewis, Sinclair
Lewis and Clark
Liberal Party
Liberty, Statue of
Liberty Bell
library
lichen
licorice

Try another letter:

A B C D E F G H I J K L M N O P Q R S T U V W X Y Z

Search the Encyclopedia for:

Name ______________________________

When you find an article about your topic, it will probably have links to other articles. The links are often set in all capital letters that are underlined. For example, you might find an article like this about the Statue of Liberty:

Liberty, Statue of

A large statue on Liberty Island in upper New York Bay. It was given to the United States in 1886, by the Franco-American Union to commemorate the AMERICAN REVOLUTION. It was designed by the sculptor F.A. BARTHOLDI. The statue became a national monument in 1924, and was extensively restored in 1986.

Click here to see pictures of the Statue of Liberty.

Directions: Use the sample computer screens to answer these questions.

1. In the first and second computer screens, what happens if you click on a letter?

____

2. Besides clicking on the letters S or L, what is another way to find information about the Statue of Liberty?

____

3. In the second computer screen, what happens if you click on "Liberty Bell"?

____

4. How can you get an article about the person who designed the Statue of Liberty? How can you get pictures of the Statue of Liberty?

____

____

5. How is a CD-ROM or online encyclopedia like and unlike a print encyclopedia?

____

____

____

____

____

Notes for Home: Your child learned how to use a CD-ROM or online encyclopedia. ***Home Activity:*** Ask your child to list possible key words to use to search for articles about other national monuments or interesting sights, such as Mount Rushmore.

Family Times

Name____

Summary

Philip Simmons Is a Blacksmith and an Artist

Philip Simmons began working as a blacksmith when he was just a teenager. He started as an apprentice, learning a craft that has a five-thousand-year-old history. Today, his ornamental wrought iron work decorates gates, fences, and railings in Charleston, South Carolina, and is on display in several museums. When John Vlach sees a snake forged by Philip Simmons that looks almost real, he knows that Philip Simmons is not simply a blacksmith, but a true artist. At John Vlach's invitation, Philip Simmons makes a special gate for the Festival of American Folklife. That gate is now part of the Smithsonian Institution in Washington, D.C.

Reading Skills

Main Idea and Supporting Details

The most important idea about the topic of a paragraph or an article is the **main idea.** In the excerpt from *Catching the Fire,* the main idea is that blacksmithing can be an art form.

To find the main idea of a paragraph or article, first identify the topic. Ask yourself "What is this all about?" Then look for a statement that gives the most important idea about the topic. If a statement is not given, state the main idea in your own words.

To check a main idea, ask yourself "Does this main idea make sense? Does it cover all the important details?"

Activity

Write a Profile. Ask your child about what he or she learned about blacksmiths and Philip Simmons. Then help your child write a profile about Philip Simmons's life and his artwork.

Activity

Draw the Main Idea. Read an article or story. Think about an image that best represents its main idea. Then draw a picture of the main idea and write a caption that states the main idea in your own words.

Family Times

Tested Vocabulary

Words to Know

Knowing the meanings of these words is important to reading the excerpt from *Catching the Fire.* Practice using these words to learn their meanings.

anvil an iron or steel block used to shape metal

businessman person who is in business or runs a business

craftsman person skilled in a craft or trade

horseshoes flat pieces of metal shaped like a U, used to protect horses' hooves

ornamental decorative

workshop shop or building where work is done

Grammar

Comparative and Superlative Adverbs

Adverbs can tell when, where, or how an action takes place.

The **comparative** form is used to compare two actions. It is usually formed by adding the ending **-er** or by placing the word **more** before the adverb: **sooner, faster, more quickly.**

The **superlative** form is used to compare three or more actions. It is usually formed by adding the ending **-est** or by placing the word **most** before the adverb: **soonest, fastest, most quickly.**

Activity

Compare Jobs or Activities. Use comparative and superlative adverbs to compare two or more jobs, hobbies, or sports activities. For example: *Tom ran faster than his opponent in the race.*

Tested Spelling Words

______	______	______	______
______	______	______	______
______	______	______	______
______	______	______	______
______	______	______	______

Main Idea and Supporting Details

- The most important idea about the topic of a paragraph or an article is the **main idea.** Small pieces of information that tell more about the main idea are **supporting details.**
- To find the main idea, first identify the topic. Ask yourself "What is this all about?" Then look for the most important idea about the topic. If it is not stated, put the main idea in your own words.

Directions: Reread "Quilted Memories." Complete the diagram below by writing the topic of the article, its main idea, and several important details that support the main idea.

Topic

1.

Main Idea

2.

Supporting Detail

3.

Supporting Detail

4.

Supporting Detail

5.

Notes for Home: Your child identified the topic and main idea in an article. ***Home Activity:*** Work with your child to identify the topic and main idea of individual paragraphs in a magazine article. Then challenge your child to state the main idea of the entire article.

Name ______________________________

Vocabulary

Directions: Choose the word from the box that matches each definition. Write the word on the line.

Check the Words You Know

__ anvil
__ businessman
__ craftsman
__ horseshoes
__ ornamental
__ workshop

________________ **1.** an iron or steel block on which metals are hammered and shaped

________________ **2.** flat pieces of metal shaped like the letter U used to protect the hooves of horses

________________ **3.** decorative

________________ **4.** a person who is in business or who runs a business

________________ **5.** a shop or building where work is done

Directions: Choose the word from the box that best matches each clue. Write the word on the line.

________________ **6.** They may not be fashionable, but every horse wears four of them.

________________ **7.** You might build or make something here.

________________ **8.** A person who owns a store could be called this.

________________ **9.** The fancy designs on an iron gate might be called this.

________________ **10.** You might see this person at a craft fair selling crafts he has made.

Write a Letter

On a separate sheet of paper, write a letter to a friend in which you describe a visit to a workshop. The letter can be based on an actual workshop that you have visited or one you imagine. Use as many vocabulary words as you can.

Notes for Home: Your child identified and used vocabulary words from *Catching the Fire.* ***Home Activity:*** Read a story with your child and have him or her point out unfamiliar words. Work together to try to figure out the meaning of each word using other words nearby.

Name ____________________________

Main Idea and Supporting Details

- The most important idea about the topic of a paragraph or an article is the **main idea.** Small pieces of information that tell more about the main idea are **supporting details.**
- To find the main idea, first identify the topic. Ask yourself "What is this all about?" Then look for the most important idea about the topic. If it is not stated, put the main idea in your own words.

Directions: Reread this scene from *Catching the Fire* in which John Vlach and Philip Simmons admire the Snake Gate. Then answer the questions below. Think about the main idea of the passage and look for supporting details.

Philip drove John over to East Bay Street to see his Snake Gate. It took him one month to forge that gate. He thought he'd never finish the eye. At first, it stared as if it were dead. Philip "heat and beat, heat and beat, heat and beat," until the snake looked as real as a diamond head rattler. "If it bites you," Philip joked, "you better get to the doctor fast. Blood get up to your heart, you know what happens!"

John Vlach was impressed. These were no ordinary pieces of ornamental ironwork. They were sculpture! Philip Simmons was not just a blacksmith. He was an artist.

1. What does John Vlach think of Philip's work? ____________________________

2. What is the main idea of the passage? ____________________________

3.–4. List two details that support the main idea. ____________________________

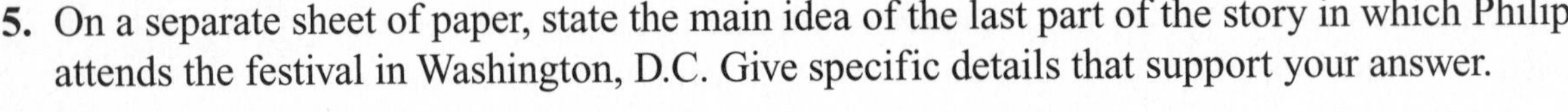

5. On a separate sheet of paper, state the main idea of the last part of the story in which Philip attends the festival in Washington, D.C. Give specific details that support your answer.

Notes for Home: Your child identified the main idea and supporting details of an excerpt from a biography. ***Home Activity:*** Read a magazine article with your child. Work together to identify its main idea and several supporting details.

Name ______________________________

Selection Test

Directions: Choose the best answer to each item. Mark the letter for the answer you have chosen.

Part 1: Vocabulary

Find the answer choice that means about the same as the underlined word in each sentence.

1. Where can I get some horseshoes?
- A. plants with spicy roots
- B. stiff fabrics made from horse hair
- C. riding crops used with horses
- D. u-shaped pieces of metal nailed to horses' hooves

2. He is a wonderful craftsman.
- F. person who loves to hunt
- G. person skilled in a trade
- H. person who likes to compete
- J. person trained to fly airplanes

3. Her workshop is quite small.
- A. strong table used for working
- B. person who is learning a trade
- C. building or room where work is done
- D. room where people exercise

4. Mr. Cole is a wise businessman.
- F. man who interferes in other people's business
- G. man who runs for public office
- H. man who works in a library
- J. man who owns or works in a business

5. She designed an ornamental gate.
- A. for decoration
- B. well-hidden
- C. made of iron
- D. without hinges

6. We bought a new anvil.
- F. iron or steel block on which metals are hammered and shaped
- G. small fireplace where metal is heated
- H. large, heavy hammer, usually swung with both hands
- J. device for producing a strong current of air

Part 2: Comprehension

Use what you know about the selection to answer each item.

7. Philip Simmons's best-known works are—
- A. chandeliers.
- B. plant stands.
- C. gates with animal figures on them.
- D. benches.

8. A master and an apprentice are most like a—
- F. teacher and student.
- G. father and mother.
- H. worker and tool.
- J. brother and sister.

9. The beginning of this selection is mostly about—
- A. a young boy working in his father's blacksmith shop.
- B. how to earn money as a blacksmith's apprentice.
- C. what it was like in Charleston, South Carolina, in 1923.
- D. the ancient tradition of blacksmithing that Philip Simmons followed.

10. You can tell from reading this selection that being a blacksmith like Simmons—
- F. requires little skill.
- G. is a lost art.
- H. combines physical and artistic talent.
- J. is a fairly simple way to make a lot of money.

11. When John Vlach first asked him to go to the festival, Philip—
- A. knew just what he wanted to make.
- B. wasn't sure he wanted to go.
- C. realized it was a great honor.
- D. didn't want to take his apprentices along.

12. Which title best fits the last part of the selection?
- F. "Thanking John Vlach"
- G. "Seeing Washington"
- H. "America in the 1970s"
- J. "Preserving a Lost Art"

13. You can tell from reading this selection that Philip Simmons is not only a blacksmith, he is also—
- A. an accomplished photographer.
- B. a person who knows a lot about history.
- C. a fine artist.
- D. a published author.

14. One of the major reasons that Philip survived as a blacksmith after World War II is that he—
- F. didn't charge much for his work.
- G. was able to buy iron cheaply.
- H. knew how to adapt to changes in the world around him.
- J. always worked in the same neighborhood.

15. The author's main purpose in writing this selection is to—
- A. describe the 1976 Festival of American Folklife.
- B. discuss whether blacksmithing is a dying art.
- C. entertain with an exciting story about life in the 1920s.
- D. give information about Philip Simmons, a talented blacksmith.

STOP

Main Idea and Supporting Details

- The most important idea about the topic of a paragraph or an article is the **main idea.** Small pieces of information that tell more about the main idea are **supporting details.**
- To find the main idea, first identify the topic. Ask yourself "What is this all about?" Then look for the most important idea about the topic. If it is not stated, put the main idea in your own words.

Directions: Read the story below.

Janette has always liked making things. She designs sets and sews costumes for community theater productions. She built a wall of bookshelves for her apartment.

The craft she likes best, though, is glass-blowing. She is a professional glass blower and spends a lot of time experimenting and imagining new things to make. She likes to make paperweights, ornaments, jewelry, and vases.

Janette has made a great success of her work. She recently opened her own studio in Tennessee. Her pieces grace the shelves of many gift shops. Soon, Janette may be able to open a shop of her own.

Directions: Each paragraph in this story has a main idea and supporting details. Complete the table by providing the missing ideas and details.

Paragraph	Main Idea	Supporting Details
1	1.	designs sets and makes costumes 2.
2	3.	4. likes to make paperweights, ornaments, jewelry, and vases
3	Janette is successful.	5. may soon open a shop

Notes for Home: Your child identified the main idea and supporting details of each paragraph in a biography. ***Home Activity:*** Tell your child a story about a real person. Have your child tell you the main idea of the story and some of its supporting details.

Name ______________________________

REVIEW

Author's Purpose

Directions: Read the passage. Then read each question about the passage. Choose the best answer to each question. Mark the letter for the answer you have chosen.

Making Paint

Artists have a variety of paint choices today. Did you know that many materials in current use were also known to paintmakers in ancient times?

The substance that gives paint its color is called *pigment.* It is usually made from clay, lead, chalk, or other natural minerals that are ground into fine powder. In ancient times, people mixed vegetable and earth pigments with water or animal fat. In Colonial America, people used things like coffee, milk, and butter for pigment! Recently the paint industry has developed new chemical pigments.

To hold the color on the picture, pigments must be mixed with a sticky substance, or *binder.* A variety of materials are used, from oils to tree resins, beeswax, and even egg yolks. Recently, acrylic binders made from petroleum have also become popular. Drying time, gloss, and texture are all affected by the binder.

During the Italian Renaissance of the 1500s, painters began inventing new binders and new formulas for mixing pigments and binders. They kept their formulas secret so that other painters could not steal their ideas and profit from them. Most of the time, the new process died with the painter who invented it. Scientific analysis may yet reveal what made Italian paintings from the Renaissance so beautiful, but for now it is a mystery.

1. The topic of this article is—
- **A.** paintmakers of ancient times.
- **B.** how paint is made.
- **C.** finely-ground pigments.
- **D.** minerals and other powders.

2. The main purpose of the article is—
- **F.** to inform.
- **G.** to entertain.
- **H.** to persuade.
- **J.** to express.

3. The article's main idea is that—
- **A.** natural materials make the best paints.
- **B.** Colonial paintmakers used food substances to make pigments.
- **C.** paints are made from different pigments and binders.
- **D.** an artist's style depends upon pigments.

4. Why does the author include the mention of paintmakers of ancient times?
- **F.** to impress readers with his knowledge of history
- **G.** to show that some of their materials are still in use today
- **H.** to show how primitive their materials were
- **J.** to suggest that their materials were better than recent ones

5. The author included the last paragraph to—
- **A.** make the article more entertaining.
- **B.** inform the reader about an interesting period in the history of paintmaking.
- **C.** persuade the reader that the Italian painters of the Renaissance were the best painters.
- **D.** express the beauty of Renaissance paintings.

Notes for Home: Your child read an article and identified the author's purpose. ***Home Activity:*** Together, name some favorite books, TV shows, and movies. Identify the author's purpose or purposes for writing each kind of text.

Name ______________________

Writing Across Texts

Directions: Think about what you learned about fire in the excerpt from *Catching the Fire* and "Fire All Around Us." Use that information to tell how fire is used in each of the processes in the web below.

Uses of Fire

1. How is fire used in travel?

____

____

____

2. How is fire used in working iron?

____

____

____

3. How is fire used to heat homes?

____

____

____

4. How is fire used to make steel?

____

____

____

5. How is fire used in creating electricity?

____

____

____

Write a Paragraph

On another sheet of paper, write a paragraph about how your life would be different without fire. Use the information from the web above as well as your own prior knowledge to write the paragraph.

Notes for Home: Your child wrote a paragraph imagining what his or her life would be like without the use of fire in the world. ***Home Activity:*** With your child, list the ways fire is used in your home.

Name ______________________________________

REVIEW

Grammar: Comparative and Superlative Adjectives

Directions: Fill in the columns below with the comparative and superlative forms of each of the adjectives given.

Adjective	Comparative Form	Superlative Form
extraordinary	**1.** ______________	**2.** ______________
hot	**3.** ______________	**4.** ______________
tame	**5.** ______________	**6.** ______________
steep	**7.** ______________	**8.** ______________
sleepy	**9.** ______________	**10.** ______________

Directions: Complete each sentence with the comparative or superlative form of the adjective in ( ). Write the adjective on the line.

______________ **11.** Mike felt as if he were the (unhappy) person in the world that day in 1935.

______________ **12.** His family's farmland had become (poor) each year, and now nothing would grow on it.

______________ **13.** He and his family were moving to a place with (rich) land—California.

______________ **14.** Mike's family was joining one of the (large) migrations, or movements, in American history.

______________ **15.** In the 1930s, over three million people in the Great Plains moved west to find a (bearable) life.

______________ **16.** Mike had packed his carving tools carefully, for nothing was (precious) to him.

______________ **17.** The figures Mike carved out of wood were some of the (beautiful) people had ever seen.

______________ **18.** In fact, he was (proud) of his carvings than he usually admitted.

______________ **19.** Perhaps in California, Mike could sell his figures and find a (fulfilling) life.

______________ **20.** Mike began to feel (cheerful) as the family's overloaded old car rattled west.

Notes for Home: Your child used the comparative and superlative forms of adjectives to compare people, places, and things. ***Home Activity:*** Have your child make a list of adjectives. Challenge your child to use each adjective in its comparative and superlative forms.

Grammar: Adverbs

An **adverb** is a word that can tell how, where, or when something happens.

Yesterday we walked quietly into the library, read the onscreen instructions for doing a title search, and eventually located a blacksmith's published diary.

Like adjectives, adverbs can be used to make comparisons. Most adverbs have three forms: the adverb itself, the **comparative** form, and the **superlative** form.

Use the comparative form when you talk about two actions. To write the comparative form of most adverbs, add the ending **-er** or the word **more.**

Gram pored over the old diary longer than Mom did.
She studied the diary entries more carefully than Mom did too.

Use the superlative form when you talk about three or more actions. To form the superlative, add the ending **-est** or the word **most.**

Of the three of us, Gram is the one who stays longest in the Rare Books area.
She also is the one who examines those valuable books most carefully.

Most adverbs that end in **-ly** use **more** and **most** to make the comparative and the superlative forms: for example, **rapidly, more rapidly, most rapidly.**

Directions: Complete the table with the comparative and the superlative forms of each adverb.

Adverb	Comparative Form	Superlative Form
warmly	**1.**	**2.**
fast	**3.**	**4.**
quickly	**5.**	**6.**
oddly	**7.**	**8.**
soon	**9.**	**10.**
recently	**11.**	**12.**
late	**13.**	**14.**
hopefully	**15.**	**16.**
early	**17.**	**18.**
easily	**19.**	**20.**

Notes for Home: Your child learned to identify comparative and superlative forms of adverbs. ***Home Activity:*** Challenge your child to describe an activity you do together, using comparative or superlative adverbs.

Grammar: Adverbs

Directions: Write the kind of adverb named in ( ) on the line to the left to complete each sentence.

______________________ **1.** Tanya waited with her classmates _____ the blacksmith's shop that morning. (tell where)

______________________ **2.** _____ she had read a story about blacksmiths and looked forward to seeing them demonstrate their trade. (tell when)

______________________ **3.** She remembered _____ an illustration of a blacksmith working near a hot fire. (tell how)

Directions: Write the correct form of the adverb in ( ) to complete each sentence.

______________________ **4.** "This could not have been the (easy) of all skills to learn," Tanya thought.

______________________ **5.** Blacksmiths have to work (hard) than many other workers today.

______________________ **6.** Blacksmiths also have to work (carefully) to bend and shape the iron than workers do who use machines to do this task.

______________________ **7.** A complicated design means that the blacksmith has to work (skillfully) than usual.

______________________ **8.** Tanya would probably stay (long) than her classmates.

______________________ **9.** She would watch (closely) than the other students too.

______________________ **10.** She wished the shop would open its doors (soon) than 10 A.M.!

Write a Poem

Think about a skill that you admire and a person who does that skill well. On a separate sheet of paper, write a poem about this person. Use comparative and superlative adverbs to compare this skill to another, or to compare the person's ability to another's.

Notes for Home: Your child wrote adverbs, including the comparative and superlative form. ***Home Activity:*** Take turns making up quiz questions, using comparative and superlative adverbs, for example, *What small boat would you have to operate most slowly? (a rowboat)*

Grammar: Adverbs

Underline the adverb in each sentence.

1. I ran quickly through the park.
2. My friend ran quicker than I did.
3. Yesterday she told me she would race me to the school playground.
4. I told her I would race her today.

An **adverb** can tell how, where, or when something happens. When an adverb is used to compare two actions, the **comparative form** is used. Add **-er** or **more** to make the comparative form. When an adverb is used to compare three or more actions, the **superlative form** is used. Add **-est** or **most** to make the superlative form.

Directions: Circle the adverb in each sentence.

1. I have read this book before.
2. The story begins mysteriously.
3. I enjoyed this book more thoroughly than any other mystery book I have read.
4. The dog, Mutt, suddenly disappears.
5. He is gone faster than you can imagine.

Directions: Choose an adverb that best fits each sentence. Write it on the line to the left.

______________________ 6. The heroine, Lila, ________ finds Mutt.

______________________ 7. Lila ________ suspects foul play.

______________________ 8. She ________ discovers a ransom note.

______________________ 9. The kidnappers ________ demand a huge ransom.

______________________ 10. Lila gasps ________.

______________________ 11. She looks ________ for Mutt.

______________________ 12. She approaches the house ________.

______________________ 13. The kidnappers have acted ________.

______________________ 14. They ________ left open a window.

______________________ 15. Mutt arrives home ________.

Notes for Home: Your child identified and used adverbs in sentences. ***Home Activity:*** Watch a television show with your child, but turn off the sound. Have your child use adverbs in sentences to describe what the actors on the show are doing.

Grammar: Adverbs

Directions: Read each sentence. Write the correct form of each adverb in ( ) on the line to the left.

______ **1.** She does her work (carefully) than you.

______ **2.** You write (neatly) of the three.

______ **3.** You write (beautifully) than I ever could.

______ **4.** Print your name (clearly) than you did last time.

______ **5.** Next time erase your mistakes (thoroughly) than this.

______ **6.** This picture is (skillfully) drawn than the first one.

______ **7.** Today our class was dismissed (early) than usual.

______ **8.** I finished (soon) of anyone.

______ **9.** I learned French (easily) than I learned German.

______ **10.** Of the whole class, who works (eagerly)?

Directions: Rewrite each sentence with the correct form of the underlined adverb.

11. Can't you run <u>more faster</u>?

____

12. Of all the bands, this one plays <u>most loudest</u>.

____

13. This building was built <u>latest</u> than that one.

____

14. These books are stacked <u>neatly</u> than those.

____

15. The movie started <u>earliest</u> than we had thought.

____

16. Doesn't Venus shine <u>brightly</u> than Mars?

____

17. This car runs <u>economically</u> of all three.

____

Notes for Home: Your child wrote the correct forms of adverbs in sentences. ***Home Activity:*** Have your child create a five-box comic strip. Challenge him or her to use adverbs in captions for the comic strip.

Name ______________________________

Word Study: Inflected Endings

Directions: If a word ends in a **consonant** and **y,** change the **y** to **i** before adding most endings. For example, **baby** becomes **babies.** You do **not** change **y** to **i** when adding **-ing. Try** becomes **trying.** If a word ends in a single consonant preceded by a single vowel, double the final consonant before adding the ending. For example, **step** becomes **stepped.** Add the given ending to each base word. Write the new word on the line.

1. drop + -ing = ______________
2. strip + -ed = ______________
3. family + -es = ______________
4. big + -er = ______________
5. factory + -es = ______________
6. big + -est = ______________
7. industry + -al = ______________
8. stir + -ed = ______________

Directions: Read each sentence. Write the base word for each underlined word below.

______________ 9. No matter how hard the ironworkers <u>tried</u>, they could not get management to give them a raise.

______________ 10. In order to have their demands met, the laborers were <u>planning</u> to go on strike.

______________ 11. In <u>counties</u> all across the state, there were no other jobs for the workers.

______________ 12. The employees were <u>running</u> out of options for the future.

______________ 13. It would be one of the biggest <u>tragedies</u> of the year if the town's factory were to close its doors.

______________ 14. In order for <u>communities</u> to survive, jobs must be plentiful.

______________ 15. It sometimes takes several <u>industries</u> to make a town a success.

Notes for Home: Your child added endings to base words. ***Home Activity:*** Read a newspaper with your child. Look for words with endings such as *-ing, -ed, -er, -est,* and *-es.* Have your child tell if the base word changed when the ending was added.

Name ______________________________

Pretest

Spelling: Adding *-ed* and *-ing*

Pretest Directions: Fold back the page along the dotted line. On the blanks, write the spelling words as they are dictated. When you have finished the test, unfold the page and check your words.

1. ______________________
2. ______________________
3. ______________________
4. ______________________
5. ______________________
6. ______________________
7. ______________________
8. ______________________
9. ______________________
10. ______________________
11. ______________________
12. ______________________
13. ______________________
14. ______________________
15. ______________________
16. ______________________
17. ______________________
18. ______________________
19. ______________________
20. ______________________

1. No one **answered** the telephone.
2. He spent time **answering** them.
3. She **decided** to take a long trip.
4. I'll wait while you're **deciding**.
5. The award **included** money.
6. We all went, **including** Grandma.
7. The essay **omitted** one detail.
8. I hope you are not **omitting** me.
9. The dog's hunger was **satisfied**.
10. I like **satisfying** endings.
11. The slow train **delayed** us.
12. He kept on **delaying** a decision.
13. My mom **remembered** my lunch.
14. I dislike **remembering** that day.
15. She **exercised** for an hour.
16. I love **exercising**.
17. They have **interfered**.
18. Stop **interfering** and help!
19. A great event just **occurred**.
20. The same thing kept **occurring**.

Notes for Home: Your child took a pretest on words ending in *-ed* and *-ing*. ***Home Activity:*** Help your child learn misspelled words before the final test. Have your child learn to spell the base word and then notice how it changes when *-ed* or *-ing* is added.

Spelling: Adding -ed and -*ing*

Word List

answered	included	satisfied	remembered	interfered
answering	including	satisfying	remembering	interfering
decided	omitted	delayed	exercised	occurred
deciding	omitting	delaying	exercising	occurring

Directions: Choose the words from the box that end in **-ed.** Sort the words according to the way their endings are spelled. Write each word in the correct column.

Just Add -ed

1. ______________________
2. ______________________
3. ______________________

Double the Final Consonant, Then Add -ed

4. ______________________
5. ______________________

Drop the Final e, Then Add -ed

6. ______________________
7. ______________________
8. ______________________
9. ______________________

Directions: Choose the word from the box that best completes each statement. Write the word on the line.

______________________ **10.** *Smiling* is to *grinning* as *happening* is to _____.

______________________ **11.** *Queen* is to *ruling* as *busybody* is to _____.

______________________ **12.** *Love* is to *hating* as *forget* is to _____.

______________________ **13.** *Try* is to *tried* as *satisfy* is to _____.

______________________ **14.** *Drawing* is to *sketching* as *replying* is to _____.

______________________ **15.** *Out* is to *in* as *excluding* is to _____.

______________________ **16.** *Theater* is to *acting* as *gym* is to _____.

______________________ **17.** *Early* is to *late* as *hurrying* is to _____.

______________________ **18.** *On* is to *off* as *enclosing* is to _____.

______________________ **19.** *Pleasure* is to *pleasing* as *satisfaction* is to _____.

______________________ **20.** *Pitcher* is to *throwing* as *umpire* is to _____.

Notes for Home: Your child spelled words ending in *-ed* and *-ing*. ***Home Activity:*** Say the base word for each spelling word, such as *answer* for *answered.* Have your child add *-ed* and *-ing* to each base word and spell the new words he or she has made.

Spelling: Adding *-ed* and *-ing*

Directions: Proofread this paragraph that tells of reactions to a quilting class. Find seven spelling mistakes. Use the proofreading marks to correct each mistake.

≡	Make a capital.
/	Make a small letter.
∧	Add something.
⌇	Take out something.
⊙	Add a period.
¶	Begin a new paragraph.

During the first meeting of my quilting class I had trouble rememberring the many techniques presented by the instructor. In the first week of quilting I made several mistakes because I ommitted important steps in the quilting process. It has occured to me that quilting is a difficult and time consuming skill. I am very satisfyed with the beautiful new quilt that I am making, but the completion of the project has been delaied because I don't have enough time to work on it. In fact, I've spent so much time quilting that it has interferred with my homework and the exerciseing that I must do to get into condition for the upcoming basketball season. Quilting is a very old and beautiful craft. Even though it is a lot of work, I am glad that I decided to take the class.

Spelling Tip

The spelling of some base words changes before adding **-ed** or **-ing.** You may need to drop a final **e** as in **decided,** double the final consonant as in **omitting,** or change a final **y** to **i,** as in **satisfied.**

Write a Paragraph

Find a library book with pictures of quilts and choose one that you like. On a separate sheet of paper, write a paragraph describing the quilt. Try to use at least three of your spelling words.

Word List

answered	delayed
answering	delaying
decided	remembered
deciding	remembering
included	exercised
including	exercising
omitted	interfered
omitting	interfering
satisfied	occurred
satisfying	occurring

Notes for Home: Your child spelled words ending in *-ed* and *-ing. **Home Activity:*** Read the Spelling Tip above. Ask your child to identify the spelling words that fall into the three groups described, as well as the spelling words in which the base word does not change.

Spelling: Adding *-ed* and *-ing*

REVIEW

Word List				
answered	included	satisfied	remembered	interfered
answering	including	satisfying	remembering	interfering
decided	omitted	delayed	exercised	occurred
deciding	omitting	delaying	exercising	occurring

Directions: Choose the word from the box that is the most opposite in meaning to each word below. Write the word on the line.

1. forgot ______________________
2. rushing ______________________
3. dissatisfied ______________________
4. avoiding ______________________
5. including ______________________
6. undecided ______________________
7. not happening ______________________
8. relaxing ______________________
9. questioning ______________________
10. leaving out ______________________

Directions: Choose the word from the box that best replaces the underlined word or words. Write the word on the line.

______________________ 11. The quilting instructor <u>responded to</u> my questions about sewing squares of material together.

______________________ 12. A lot of beautiful details can be <u>enclosed</u> in a single small section of a quilt.

______________________ 13. There is so little room on my four-inch section that some of the fine details were <u>left out</u>.

______________________ 14. The elderly quilters passed the hours <u>recalling</u> and telling old stories.

______________________ 15. Mary and I <u>stretched</u> after quilting for two hours.

______________________ 16. When the instructor demonstrated her skill we all <u>halted</u> our sewing for a while.

______________________ 17. Her many careful instructions <u>meddled</u> with our progress in class.

______________________ 18. <u>Determining</u> that I had an interest in quilting was easy—finishing a quilt is not easy.

______________________ 19. Completing one small portion of the quilt <u>happened</u> very slowly.

______________________ 20. It is <u>pleasing</u> to learn a skill that I can teach to my children someday.

Notes for Home: Your child spelled words ending in *-ed* and *-ing*. ***Home Activity:*** Write all the spelling words that end in *-ed* on separate slips of paper. Take turns drawing words and spelling the words with an *-ing* ending instead of *-ed*.

Name ______________________________

Pictures and Captions

Pictures and captions can provide information about the characters and events in a story or information about the subject in nonfiction writing.

Directions: Use the picture and the caption to answer the questions that follow.

Quilt-making is a popular form of American folk art. Historically, quilting served as a way for women to get together in a "quilting bee." A quilt is generally made from a series of cloth patches sewn together to form a design. Story quilts include images that tell a story.

1. What does the picture show? ______________________________

2. What is a quilting bee? ______________________________

3. How is a quilt generally constructed? ______________________________

4. How are "story quilts" different from other quilts? ______________________________

5. Would this picture and caption be useful for a research essay on American folk art? Explain.

Name ______________________

Directions: Study the picture and caption from a story. Then answer the questions that follow.

John Thomas worked hard into the night. He could picture the snake in his mind and wouldn't rest until he got it right.

6. What do you learn about the character from looking at the picture? ______________________

____

____

7. What do you learn about the character from reading the caption? ______________________

____

____

8. Use what you have learned about the character to write your own caption for the picture.

____

____

____

9. How can you use a picture and a caption to draw conclusions about a character?

____

____

____

10. Why is it important to read captions carefully? ______________________

____

____

Notes for Home: Your child answered questions about pictures and captions. ***Home Activity:*** Look through a magazine or nonfiction book with your child to find pictures with captions. Discuss what you learn from these pictures and captions.

Family Times

Name____

Summary

The Seven Wonders Rediscovered

Who built the Seven Wonders of the Ancient World? Why were they created? What happened to them? *The Seven Wonders of the Ancient World* answers these questions about the Great Pyramid at Giza, the Hanging Gardens of Babylon, Artemis's Temple at Ephesus, the Statue of Zeus at Olympia, the Mausoleum at Halicarnassus, the Colossus of Rhodes, and the Pharos of Alexandria.

Activity

Choose the Most Interesting. Encourage your child to tell you which of the seven wonders of the ancient world is the most interesting and why.

Reading Skills

Text Structure

Text structure refers to the way a piece of writing is organized.

Fiction tells of imaginary people and events. It is usually organized in chronological order, the order in which the events happen.

Nonfiction tells of real people and events or tells information about the real world. It may be organized in chronological order, or by topic, cause and effect, problem and solution, comparison and contrast, or in some other way.

The Seven Wonders of the Ancient World organizes its text according to topic. Each of the seven wonders has its own section. The sections are also ordered chronologically, according to the date each wonder was built.

Local Girl Wins Prize

Town resident takes home literary competion's top prize.

Activity

Describe a Current Event. Imagine you are writing a magazine article about a current event. Would you organize the article chronologically, by topic, or in some other way? Discuss the best organization for your article.

Family Times

Tested Vocabulary

Words to Know

Knowing the meanings of these words is important to reading *The Seven Wonders of the Ancient World.* Practice using these words to learn their meanings.

archaeologists scientists who study the past by unearthing artifacts

classical having to do with ancient Greece and Rome

excavate to unearth; dig up

pharaohs ancient Egyptian kings and queens

structures buildings or constructions

tomb grave, vault, or the like

Grammar

Using Adjectives and Adverbs to Improve Sentences

You can improve your sentences by using **adjectives** and **adverbs.** They can make your sentences more precise and vivid.

Without Adjectives: We saw a statue.

With Adjectives: We saw an enormous statue.

Without Adverbs: The barge sailed up the Nile River.

With Adverbs: The barge sailed slowly up the Nile River.

Activity

Play Best Descriptions. Take turns using adjectives and adverbs to describe a friend or relative and some of the things he or she does. For example, *Uncle Ty speaks quietly.* Challenge each other to give as accurate a description as possible.

Tested Spelling Words

____	____	____	____
____	____	____	____
____	____	____	____
____	____	____	____
____	____	____	____

Name ______________________________

Text Structure

- **Text structure** refers to the way a piece of writing is organized.
- Fiction tells of imaginary people and events. It is usually organized in chronological order, the order in which the events happen.
- Nonfiction tells of real people and events or tells information about the real world. It may be organized in chronological order, or by topic, cause and effect, problem and solution, or some other way.

Directions: Reread "Engineering the Land." Then complete the diagram. Identify the topics and give the main idea of each paragraph related to that topic.

Topic: Terracing

First paragraph: Because much of their land was hard to farm, the Incas had to terrace and dig canals.

1. **Second paragraph:**

2. **Topic:**
3. **Paragraph:**

4. **Topic:**
5. **Paragraph:**

Notes for Home: Your child analyzed the way a nonfiction selection was organized. ***Home Activity:*** Review together the text structure of familiar textbooks. Discuss the ways the different textbook features help readers better understand and remember the information.

Name ______________________________

Vocabulary

Directions: Match each word on the left with its definition on the right. Write the letter of the definition on the line to the left of the word.

______ **1.** pharaohs	**a.** unearth; dig up
______ **2.** classical	**b.** buildings
______ **3.** tomb	**c.** ancient Egyptian kings
______ **4.** structures	**d.** having to do with ancient Greece and Rome
______ **5.** excavate	**e.** scientists who study the past by unearthing artifacts
______ **6.** archaeologists	**f.** grave or vault

Check the Words You Know

__ archaeologists
__ classical
__ excavate
__ pharaohs
__ structures
__ tomb

Directions: Choose the word from the box that best replaces the underlined word or words. Write the word on the line.

______________ **7.** The kings of ancient Egypt had huge pyramids built as a resting place for the dead.

______________ **8.** It took years and thousands of laborers just to build a single burial place.

______________ **9.** Scientists who study these ancient structures are still not completely certain how these pyramids were built.

______________ **10.** They continue to dig near these marvelous structures hoping to learn more about the past.

Write a Journal Entry

On a separate sheet of paper, write a journal entry in which you pretend you are an archaeologist. Describe a dig in which you discover artifacts (objects made by humans) from an ancient civilization. Use as many vocabulary words as you can.

Notes for Home: Your child identified and used vocabulary words from *The Seven Wonders of the Ancient World*. ***Home Activity:*** Work with your child to write an adventure story about an archaeologist, using the vocabulary words listed above.

Name ____________________

Text Structure

- **Text structure** refers to the way a piece of writing is organized.
- Fiction tells stories of imaginary people and events. It is usually organized in chronological order, the order in which the events happened.
- Nonfiction tells of real people and events or tells information about the real world. Some ways to organize nonfiction are chronological order, cause and effect, problem and solution, or comparison and contrast.

Directions: Reread this passage about the Colossus of Rhodes from *The Seven Wonders of the Ancient World.* Then answer the questions below. Think about the way in which the events it describes are organized.

In about 226 B.C., little more than 50 years after it was completed, the Colossus fell. It was toppled by an earthquake and snapped off at the knees. The people of Rhodes were told by an oracle not to rebuild the statue, and so they left it lying where it had fallen. It stayed like this for nearly 900 years, and people would travel to Rhodes just to gaze at the ruins of the fallen sun god.

In A.D. 654 a Syrian prince captured Rhodes and stripped the statue of its bronze plates. People said that he took them back to Syria on the backs of 900 camels. The bronze was sold by merchants and probably turned into coins.

1. What is the topic of the passage?

____

2. About how much time does it take for all the events to happen?

____

3. How are the events in this passage organized?

____

4. Do you think the organization of the passage makes sense? Why or why not?

____

____

5. On a separate sheet of paper, explain how the information in *The Seven Wonders of the Ancient World* is organized. Explain whether you think it was effective and why.

Notes for Home: Your child identified the organization of a text. ***Home Activity:*** Have your child read aloud a passage from a nonfiction book. Have him or her tell how it is organized and why the author might have organized it in that way.

Name ______________________________

Selection Test

Directions: Choose the best answer to each item. Mark the letter for the answer you have chosen.

Part 1: Vocabulary

Find the answer choice that means about the same as the underlined word in each sentence.

1. She wanted to <u>excavate</u> the old fort.
- A. explore
- B. lay out
- C. uncover by digging
- D. bury

2. He discovered an ancient <u>tomb</u>.
- F. fortress
- G. house
- H. earthen jar for storage
- J. grave or vault

3. They found what was left of the <u>structures</u>.
- A. paintings
- B. things that are built
- C. borders
- D. rivers and waterways

4. A team of <u>archaeologists</u> arrived.
- F. scientists who study the surface features of the earth
- G. scientists who study the people and customs of ancient times
- H. scientists who study the earth's climate
- J. scientists who study fossils of animals and plants

5. She was learning about the <u>pharoahs</u>.
- A. kings of ancient Egypt
- B. buildings in ancient Egypt
- C. statues of ancient rulers
- D. priests of an ancient religion

6. He was reading <u>classical</u> literature.
- F. originating in Asia
- G. about music
- H. of ancient Greece and Rome
- J. about school

Part 2: Comprehension

Use what you know about the selection to answer each item.

7. Which of the "Seven Wonders" is still standing today?
- A. the Mausoleum at Halicarnassus
- B. the Statue of Zeus at Olympia
- C. the Temple of Artemis at Ephesus
- D. the Great Pyramid at Giza

8. The "Seven Wonders of the Ancient World" were all located near the—
- F. Mediterranean Sea.
- G. Atlantic Ocean.
- H. Caspian Sea.
- J. Persian Gulf.

9. Why did these particular sites become known as the "Seven Wonders"?
- A. No one knew how they were made.
- B. They were built in seven different countries.
- C. A Greek poet wrote about them.
- D. Scientists today are amazed by them.

10. The main idea of this selection is that the "Seven Wonders" all—
- F. prove that ancient peoples had the same beliefs and values we do today.
- G. honored kings and queens who are no longer important.
- H. were designed and built by people who lived thousands of years ago.
- J. demonstrated the supreme power of nature.

11. The author's main purpose in this selection is to—
- A. entertain.
- B. express feelings.
- C. persuade.
- D. give information.

Name ___________________________________

12. The information in this selection is organized by—
- F. topic.
- G. cause and effect.
- H. problem and solution.
- J. comparison/contrast.

13. For which of these structures is the exact location **not** known?
- A. Great Pyramid at Giza
- B. Hanging Gardens of Babylon
- C. Temple of Artemis at Ephesus
- D. Pharos of Alexandria

14. Which sentence states an opinion?
- F. The Great Pyramid at Giza was built as a tomb.
- G. The main structure of the Temple of Artemis was supported by about 120 marble columns.
- H. The Statue of Zeus at Olympia stood for about 800 years.
- J. The Pharos of Alexandria was the greatest of the Seven Wonders.

15. After reading this selection, you can conclude that what we build today—
- A. is more beautiful than what people built in the past.
- B. may someday be studied by people of the future.
- C. will last much longer than buildings did in the past.
- D. differs very little from what has been built throughout history.

STOP

Name ______________________________

Text Structure

- **Text structure** refers to the way a piece of writing is organized.
- Fiction tells stories of imaginary people and events. It is usually organized in chronological order, the order in which the events happened. Nonfiction tells of real people and events or tells information about the real world. Some ways to organize nonfiction are chronological order, cause and effect, problem and solution, or comparison and contrast.

Directions: Read the passage below.

When it was built in 1910, the Pennsylvania Railroad Station was the pride of New York City. Its huge waiting rooms, great marble walls, and grand staircases made every train journey an event. In 1966, the station was torn down to make room for an office tower and sports arena. The station's owners felt that they could make a lot of money by keeping only the underground train tracks and platforms and selling the space above ground to a builder.

Many New Yorkers were outraged at the fate of the beloved landmark. Laws were passed soon after to protect old buildings like the station. In 1998, Grand Central Station benefited from these laws. It was fully cleaned and restored to the glory it had known on its opening day in 1913.

Directions: Complete the table below. Decide whether each type of text structure listed is used in the passage. Then give an example from the passage or an explanation to support your answer.

Type of Structure	Detail from Passage/Explanation
chronological order	Penn Station is destroyed; laws are passed; Grand Central is saved.
cause/effect	**1.** **2.**
problem/solution	**3.** **4.**
comparison/contrast	Yes **5.**

Notes for Home: Your child identified the different ways information in a passage was organized. ***Home Activity:*** Find other examples of nonfiction, such as a book, a documentary, or a flyer. Discuss how the information is organized.

Name ______________________________

REVIEW

Persuasive Devices

Directions: Read the passage. Then read each question about the passage. Choose the best answer to each question. Mark the letter for the answer you have chosen.

The Eighth Wonder of the World

The next stop on our tour is the Empire State Building. It's no longer the tallest building in New York, but it is still the best-looking. People joke about the World Trade Center being "the box the Chrysler Building came in"—no one would ever mock the Empire State Building like that!

The building is best known for its splendid view from the top of the tower. You can stay up there all day if you want, and take in the surrounding city from every direction. On clear days you can see far beyond the city limits. At night, the view is even better—everything is lit, cars drive along in rows of red and yellow lights, and the city looks magical.

The lobby is just as grand as the view. You've never seen so much marble in one place! It's as lofty as a cathedral. Even the journey to the top can be an adventure. A maze of elevators and hallways are negotiated by visitors before reaching the glorious view from the top of the tower.

No other building in New York has the personality of the Empire State. Hollywood has featured the grand building in many movies. For example, the great ape King Kong once climbed its tower! It is still the greatest tourist attraction in the city, and it deserves to be.

1. The tour guide thinks the Empire State Building is—
- **A.** the tallest building in New York.
- **B.** the smallest building in New York.
- **C.** the best-looking building in New York.
- **D.** the oldest building in New York.

2. Which words persuade the listeners that the view is great?
- **F.** splendid, magical
- **G.** all day, every direction
- **H.** splendid, lit
- **J.** clear days, far beyond

3. Which of the following is an attempt to persuade the listener?
- **A.** The lobby is marble.
- **B.** The view is splendid.
- **C.** King Kong once climbed the tower.
- **D.** The building is tall.

4. Which of the following is a sweeping generalization?
- **F.** No other building has a personality like that of the Empire State.
- **G.** From the tower, you can see a great distance on a clear day
- **H.** The Empire State has a marble lobby.
- **J.** The Empire State is no longer the tallest building in New York.

5. Which of the following is **not** an attempt to persuade the listener?
- **A.** The view is magnificent at night.
- **B.** It is the greatest tourist attraction in the city.
- **C.** No other building has a personality like the Empire State.
- **D.** On a clear day, you can see a lot from the tower.

Notes for Home: Your child identified the persuasive devices in a passage. ***Home Activity:*** Read a newspaper article with your child. Encourage him or her to identify persuasive devices such as generalizations and propaganda, as opposed to facts and information.

Name ______________________________

Writing Across Texts

Directions: Consider what you learned from reading *The Seven Wonders of the Ancient World* and "The Great Pyramids." Think about the reasons ancient civilizations built these structures. Do we build structures for the same reasons today? Compare the information you learned from the selections to what you know about people today. Record your ideas in the following table.

Comparing the Seven Wonders to Today's Structures
Just like the Great Pyramid and the Mausoleum, people still build structures for burial today. Gravestones are one example.
1.
2.
3.
4.
5.

Write an Explanation

On a separate sheet of paper, write an explanation that tells how our reasons for building specific structures today are similar to those in the past. Use ideas from the table above and from *The Seven Wonders of the Ancient World* and "The Great Pyramids."

Notes for Home: Your child wrote about the similarities between the past and today. ***Home Activity:*** Talk with your child about a tradition that your family observes that has been observed by others for centuries, such as weddings.

Name ______________________________

REVIEW

Grammar: Adverbs

Directions: Write the adverb that modifies the underlined verb.

______________ **1.** The world really <u>has</u> more than seven ancient wonders.

______________ **2.** Visitors often <u>climb</u> 7,000 feet to Peru's ancient city of Machu Picchu.

______________ **3.** There they <u>see</u> a temple and a fortress with beautiful stonework.

______________ **4.** Terraced gardens <u>surrounded</u> the city originally.

______________ **5.** Today visitors <u>must imagine</u> the city as it once looked.

Directions: Write an adverb to complete each sentence.

______________ **6.** My cousins will visit the Great Wall of China _____.

______________ **7.** They _____ will take many pictures of that amazing sight.

______________ **8.** Visitors find it hard to believe, but the wall _____ covers 4,000 miles.

______________ **9.** From the ground, one must look _____ thirty feet to see the top of the structure.

______________ **10.** The wall dates _____ to the fourth century B.C.E., but parts were later rebuilt in the fifteenth and sixteenth centuries.

Directions: Complete each sentence with the comparative or superlative form of the adverb in ( ). Write the adverb on the line.

______________ **11.** The British tour buses left London at about the same time, but our bus arrived at Stonehenge (early) of all.

______________ **12.** The question asked (frequently) was why prehistoric people built this group of stones in a circle.

______________ **13.** Certain ideas about Stonehenge are treated (seriously) than others.

______________ **14.** Scholars who claim that Stonehenge was a place of worship seem to argue (convincingly) of all.

______________ **15.** Stonehenge remains a mysterious site that affected me (deeply) than I had imagined.

Notes for Home: Your child used different kinds of adverbs to describe things that happen. ***Home Activity:*** Challenge your child to list as many adverbs as she or he can in one minute. Then have your child make up sentences with the adverbs.

Name ______________________________

Grammar: Using Adjectives and Adverbs to Improve Sentences

To be vivid and precise or to be clear and interesting, a sentence needs descriptive details.

- Add adjectives to describe nouns and pronouns. They can tell which one, how many, how much, or what kind.
- Add adverbs to describe actions. They can tell when, where, and how.

  Without adjectives and adverbs: The tour continued.
  With adjectives and adverbs: The museum tour continued slowly.

Directions: Read each sentence. Underline each adjective and adverb. Draw an arrow to the word it describes.

1. Komiko spoke happily about her interesting trip to Greece.
2. She travels most often to historic places.
3. In Athens, Greece, she admired the magnificent temple of Athena greatly.
4. She writes excitedly about these foreign travels.
5. On another fascinating trip, Komiko saw ancient Egyptian pyramids.

Directions: Add an adjective or adverb to make each sentence more vivid or precise. Then rewrite each sentence on the line.

6. Komiko lectures about her travels.

____

7. People await her talks.

____

8. When she gives a lecture, the hall is full.

____

9. Her slide presentations show the ruins of ancient civilizations.

____

____

10. I love to hear her talk about places.

____

Notes for Home: Your child identified adjectives and adverbs and used them to make sentences more descriptive. ***Home Activity:*** Give your child pairs of similar adjectives and adverbs, such as *quick* and *quickly*. Have him or her use each of the words in a sentence.

Name ______________________________

Grammar: Using Adjectives and Adverbs to Improve Sentences

Directions: Write a different adjective or adverb to replace the one that is underlined.

______________ **1.** The Great Pyramid is an impressive structure.

______________ **2.** When I was there, I listened attentively to the guide.

______________ **3.** I was curious to learn how such a structure could have been built.

______________ **4.** The Great Pyramid is one of the most famous places in Egypt.

______________ **5.** I quickly agreed to a sightseeing trip down the Nile River.

Directions: Add adjectives or adverbs to improve each sentence. Write the new sentence on the line.

6. After every trip, I return home.

____

7. Last year, I took a boat trip on the Aegean Sea.

____

8. We docked at an island called Rhodes.

____

9. I stared out at the sea.

____

10. I thought about the Colossus of Rhodes that used to tower over the harbor.

____

____

Write a Diary Entry

On a separate sheet of paper, write a diary entry about a favorite place. It can be either a place you already know or a place you'd like to visit. Use adjectives and adverbs to describe the place and the types of activities you enjoy there.

Notes for Home: Your child identified and supplied adjectives and adverbs in sentences. ***Home Activity:*** Pick a place you and your child would like to visit. Take turns describing what you want to see and do. Use adjectives and adverbs in your sentences.

Name ______________________

Grammar: Using Adjectives and Adverbs to Improve Sentences

Circle the adjective. Underline the adverb.

1. We spoke quietly to the small child.

Add one adjective and one adverb to improve the sentence.

2. The raft floated.

____

Add **adjectives** and **adverbs** to provide more information about nouns and verbs in sentences, and to make sentences more interesting.

Directions: Add an adjective and/or an adverb to each sentence. Write the new sentence on the line.

1. The movie would begin.

____

2. My friend Janine chewed her popcorn.

____

3. The lights grew dim.

____

4. The actor appeared.

____

5. There was a conversation among the characters.

____

6. Janine laughed at parts.

____

7. People behind us asked her to laugh more quietly.

____

8. When the movie ended, we walked home.

____

Notes for Home: Your child added adjectives and adverbs to sentences to make them more interesting. ***Home Activity:*** Write some simple sentences for your child. Then have him or her add adjectives and adverbs to provide more detail for the reader.

Name ________________________________

Grammar: Using Adjectives and Adverbs to Improve Sentences

Directions: Read each sentence. Underline each adjective and each adverb. Draw an arrow to the word it describes.

1. Fishing can be more exciting than some people think.
2. My grandfather tells some wild stories about frogs that ask questions clearly.
3. Sometimes he says that they generously tell him where to catch the best fish.
4. I'm not sure I believe all of his funny stories, but they make time pass more quickly.
5. Next time I go on a long trip with Grandpa, I'm going to ask him to help me create new stories.

Directions: Add adjectives or adverbs to improve each sentence. Write the new sentence on the line.

6. Boats bob in the water.

____

7. When the sun sets, you can see colors in the sky.

____

8. I like to sit on the end of our dock and watch the clouds change color.

____

____

9. My dog joins me.

____

10. I make up songs about what I see.

____

Write a Song

Write a song about what you might see when the sun goes down. Be creative. Your song may include what animals and plants do when the sun sets. Use at least two adjectives and two adverbs in your song.

Notes for Home: Your child used adjectives and adverbs to improve sentences. ***Home Activity:*** Together, listen to a favorite song. Have your child write down some of the adjectives and adverbs used in the song. Then have your child make up sentences, using those adjectives and adverbs.

Name ___________________________

Word Study: Syllabication; Common Syllable Patterns

- Knowing how to divide words into their syllable parts can help you read and understand them better
- **VCV:** If a word with two syllables has one consonant between two vowels, and the first syllable has a short vowel sound, then the word is divided after the consonant, such as **lev • er.**
- **VCV:** If a word with two syllables has one consonant between two vowels, and the first syllable has a long vowel sound, then the word is divided after the first vowel sound, such as **re • mind.**
- **VCCV:** If a word with two syllables has two consonants between two vowels, then the word is divided between the middle consonants, such as **won • der.**
- **VCCV/VCCCV:** If a word with two syllables has a consonant blend (such as **dr**) or a digraph (such as **th**) between two vowels, then the word is divided after the blend or digraph if the first vowel is short, like **fast • er,** or before the blend or digraph if the vowel is long, such as **re • think.** Follow these same rules, if there are three consonants and two of them are a blend or digraph, such as **hun • dred.**

Directions: Read the words in the box. Sort the words according to the syllable patterns. Write the words to show the syllables like this: **won · der.**

seven	organs	repaint	modern	travel
garden	terrace	chamber	farthest	workmen
destroy	merchants	Romans	worship	smother

Pattern VCV	Pattern VCCV	Pattern VCCCV
1. ________	6. ________	11. ________
2. ________	7. ________	12. ________
3. ________	8. ________	13. ________
4. ________	9. ________	14. ________
5. ________	10. ________	15. ________

Notes for Home: Your child explored vowel-consonant patterns, such as VCV in *lever,* VCCV in *wonder,* and VCCCV in *hundred,* to divide words into syllables. ***Home Activity:*** Together, make a list of words with two or more syllables. Use the rules above to divide each word.

Name ______________________________

Pretest

Spelling: One Consonant or Two?

Pretest Directions: Fold back the page along the dotted line. On the blanks, write the spelling words as they are dictated. When you have finished the test, unfold the page and check your words.

1. ______________________
2. ______________________
3. ______________________
4. ______________________
5. ______________________
6. ______________________
7. ______________________
8. ______________________
9. ______________________
10. ______________________
11. ______________________
12. ______________________
13. ______________________
14. ______________________
15. ______________________
16. ______________________
17. ______________________
18. ______________________
19. ______________________
20. ______________________

1. The flights **connect** in Rome.
2. My dog obeys that **command**.
3. How much does the **mirror** cost?
4. Will they **accomplish** their goal?
5. We proceeded **according** to plan.
6. His **allowance** is one dollar.
7. Sonia's sister went to **college**.
8. Print your **address** clearly.
9. The **Mississippi** River flooded.
10. We have **recess** at noon.
11. Our **committee** will plan the trip.
12. What are your **immediate** plans?
13. A **barricade** surrounds the fort.
14. It is impolite to **interrupt**.
15. Lani ate all of her **broccoli**.
16. They **collect** rare stamps.
17. Can you **afford** the movie ticket?
18. They **possess** a lot of land.
19. They drove through **Tennessee**.
20. Who will **announce** the winner?

Notes for Home: Your child took a pretest on words that have double consonants. ***Home Activity:*** Help your child learn misspelled words before the final test. Have your child divide misspelled words into parts (such as syllables) and concentrate on each part.

Name ______________________________

Spelling: One Consonant or Two?

Word List

connect	according	Mississippi	barricade	afford
command	allowance	recess	interrupt	possess
mirror	college	committee	broccoli	Tennessee
accomplish	address	immediate	collect	announce

Directions: Sort the words from the box according to their double consonants. Write the words in the correct column.

The Double Consonants r or c

1. ____________
2. ____________
3. ____________
4. ____________
5. ____________
6. ____________

Two or More Sets of Double Consonants

7. ____________
8. ____________
9. ____________
10. ____________
11. ____________

Directions: Choose the word from the box that best matches each clue. Write the missing letters of the word in the puzzle.

12. type of school — 12. _ _ l l _ _ _
13. group together — 13. _ _ l l _ _ _
14. right now — 14. _ m m _ _ _ _ _ _
15. sum of money paid regularly — 15. _ l l _ _ _ _ _ _
16. order — 16. _ _ m m _ _ _
17. have the money to buy — 17. _ f f _ _ _
18. school "playtime" — 18. _ _ _ _ s s
19. make a public statement — 19. _ n n _ _ _ _ _
20. join together — 20. _ _ n n _ _ _

Notes for Home: Your child spelled words containing double consonants that stand for only one sound, such as *afford.* ***Home Activity:*** Scramble the letters for each spelling word. Challenge your child to unscramble them so that the words are spelled correctly.

Name ___________________________________

Spelling: One Consonant or Two?

Directions: Proofread this travel brochure. Find five spelling mistakes.Use the proofreading marks to correct each mistake.

- ≡ Make a capital.
- / Make a small letter.
- ∧ Add something.
- ℘ Take out something.
- ⊙ Add a period.
- ¶ Begin a new paragraph.

The Travel Comittee of Community Collidge is proud to announce a new tour offering. We call it the Mayan Quest. We'll conect with our tour guides on our journey through several Mayan city-states. The guides will take you through the ruins of pyramids, palaces, and temples. You will see paintings, carvings, and other relics as you discover what the Mayan culture was able to acommplish. This fifteen-day trip is one you cannot afford to miss. An imediate response to our offer is recommended.

Spelling Tip

All the spelling words have double consonants that stand for only one sound, as in **af<u>f</u>ord.** Try to think of a clue that will help you remember when double consonants are needed. Example: *I can **afford** to have a second **f**.*

Word List

connect	committee
command	immediate
mirror	barricade
accomplish	interrupt
according	broccoli
allowance	collect
college	afford
address	possess
Mississippi	Tennessee
recess	announce

Write a Travel Brochure

On a separate sheet of paper, write a travel brochure to encourage people to visit the ruins of an ancient civilization. What will they see there? Why is it important or noteworthy? You may need to do some research before you write. Try to use at least five of your spelling words.

Notes for Home: Your child spelled words containing double consonants that stand for only one sound, such as *afford.* ***Home Activity:*** Challenge your child to find examples of other words that have two or more sets of double consonants.

Name ___________________________________

Spelling: One Consonant or Two?

REVIEW

Word List				
connect	according	Mississippi	barricade	afford
command	allowance	recess	interrupt	possess
mirror	college	committee	broccoli	Tennessee
accomplish	address	immediate	collect	announce

Directions: Write the word from the box that belongs in each group.

1. asparagus, cauliflower, ____________________
2. order, direct, ____________________
3. Minnesota, Missouri, ____________________
4. school, university, ____________________
5. achieve, finish, ____________________
6. join, unite, ____________________
7. instant, now, ____________________
8. council, group, ____________________
9. barrier, wall, ____________________
10. declare, report, ____________________
11. own, have, ____________________

Directions: Choose the word from the box that best matches each clue. Write the word on the line.

____________________ **12.** I am what you can do when you have enough money.

____________________ **13.** I hang above the sink and show you your face every day.

____________________ **14.** I contain the cities of Nashville and Memphis.

____________________ **15.** I am a break for fun during the school day.

____________________ **16.** I am written on all your mail.

____________________ **17.** I am what many people do with baseball cards or stamps.

____________________ **18.** I mean "to break into someone else's speech or actions."

____________________ **19.** I contain the word *cord.*

____________________ **20.** I am a sum of money given regularly to someone.

Notes for Home: Your child spelled words containing double consonants that stand for only one sound. ***Home Activity:*** List the spelling words, making some double consonants single and some single consonants double. Challenge your child to correct the misspellings.

Name ______________________________

Outlining

Outlining is a good way to organize information found in nonfiction texts. Outlines include main topics, subtopics, and details.

Directions: Read the nonfiction article. Think about the different civilizations described, when they lived, where they lived, and what happened to them. Then follow the directions to write an outline on the next page. Note: You may not need to fill in every line on the outline.

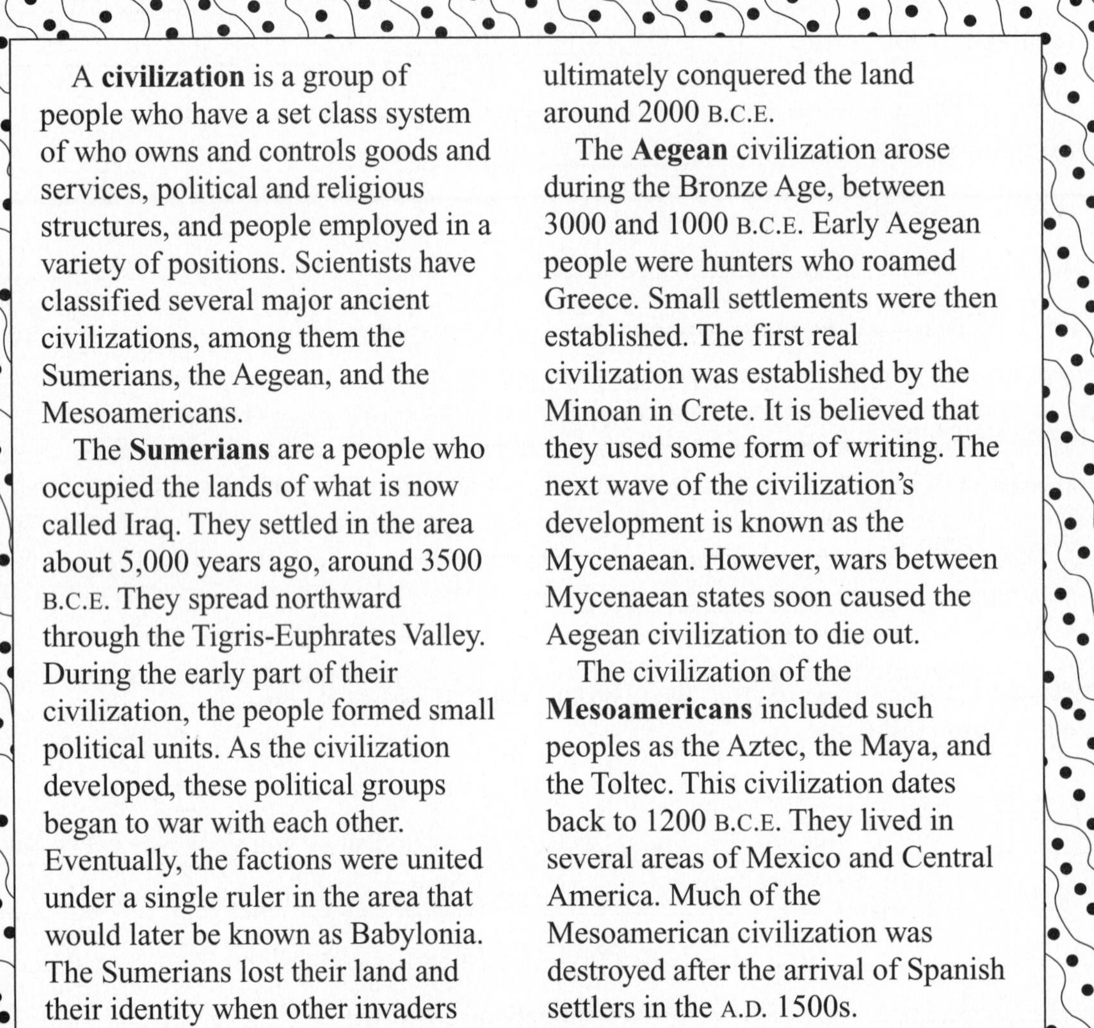

A **civilization** is a group of people who have a set class system of who owns and controls goods and services, political and religious structures, and people employed in a variety of positions. Scientists have classified several major ancient civilizations, among them the Sumerians, the Aegean, and the Mesoamericans.

The **Sumerians** are a people who occupied the lands of what is now called Iraq. They settled in the area about 5,000 years ago, around 3500 B.C.E. They spread northward through the Tigris-Euphrates Valley. During the early part of their civilization, the people formed small political units. As the civilization developed, these political groups began to war with each other. Eventually, the factions were united under a single ruler in the area that would later be known as Babylonia. The Sumerians lost their land and their identity when other invaders ultimately conquered the land around 2000 B.C.E.

The **Aegean** civilization arose during the Bronze Age, between 3000 and 1000 B.C.E. Early Aegean people were hunters who roamed Greece. Small settlements were then established. The first real civilization was established by the Minoan in Crete. It is believed that they used some form of writing. The next wave of the civilization's development is known as the Mycenaean. However, wars between Mycenaean states soon caused the Aegean civilization to die out.

The civilization of the **Mesoamericans** included such peoples as the Aztec, the Maya, and the Toltec. This civilization dates back to 1200 B.C.E. They lived in several areas of Mexico and Central America. Much of the Mesoamerican civilization was destroyed after the arrival of Spanish settlers in the A.D. 1500s.

- What are the three main topics of the article? Write each main topic at I, II, and III.
- What are some subtopics of the main topics I, II, III? Write each at A, B, and C.
- What details support the subtopics A, B, C? Write each at 1 and 2.

Name ______________________________

Title: Three Ancient Civilizations

I. ______________________________

A. ______________________________

1. ______________________________

2. ______________________________

B. ______________________________

1. ______________________________

2. ______________________________

C. ______________________________

1. ______________________________

2. ______________________________

II. ______________________________

A. ______________________________

1. ______________________________

2. ______________________________

B. ______________________________

1. ______________________________

2. ______________________________

C. ______________________________

1. ______________________________

2. ______________________________

III. ______________________________

A. ______________________________

1. ______________________________

2. ______________________________

B. ______________________________

1. ______________________________

2. ______________________________

C. ______________________________

1. ______________________________

2. ______________________________

Notes for Home: Your child organized information in an outline. ***Home Activity:*** Help your child use an outline to help study for an upcoming test. Review material to be tested and organize related information by main topics, subtopics, and details.

Family Times

Name____

Summary

Juan Discovers True Riches

Juan is a thief. He has grown pale and stooped, because he works by night and hides during the day. Juan is searching for a woman he thinks has a lot of gold. As Juan travels, he meets people who can help guide him to the woman. But first he must work with these people so that they will be free to help him. Eventually, Juan learns that work and the company of other people are more valuable than the gold that he seeks.

Reading Skills

Author's Purpose

The **author's purpose** refers to an author's reason or reasons for writing.

Four common purposes for writing are to inform, to persuade, to entertain, and to express. Often an author has more than one purpose for writing. One purpose of *The Gold Coin* is to entertain the reader. But the story also has another purpose: to express an idea. Can you tell what the idea is?

Understanding an author's purpose helps you make judgments about what you read. It also helps to explain the author's choice of words and writing style.

Inform	Persuade	Entertain	Express

Activity

Act It Out. Encourage your child to pretend he or she is Juan. Ask about his travels to Doña Josefa. What happened along the way? What did he discover? Use your child's description to act out a favorite scene from the story.

Activity

Examine Authors' Purposes. Make a list of several titles of books, short stories, articles, and poems you have read. Then make a table like the one shown above that lists four common purposes for writing. List the titles under the appropriate purpose. Some titles may go under more than one purpose.

Family Times

Tested Vocabulary

Words to Know

Knowing the meanings of these words is important to reading *The Gold Coin.* Practice using these words to learn their meanings.

distressed in great pain or sorrow

impatience a lack of patience

insistent continuing to demand

recovery the process of regaining one's health or well-being

stunned shocked

Grammar

Avoiding Misplaced Modifiers

A **modifier** is a word or phrase that changes the meaning of other words. Sometimes a modifier is misplaced. In the following example, the modifier "walking home" seems to refer to the ring, not the girl.

The girl found a shiny ring walking home.

To correct a sentence with a misplaced modifier, place the word or phrase as close as possible to the word or words it modifies.

Walking home, the girl found a shiny ring.

Activity

Put Them in Place. Find the modifiers in the sentences below. Rewrite any sentences with misplaced modifiers.

1. I saw beautiful flowers climbing the hills.
2. Juan dreamed of gold working in the fields.
3. I heard a flock of crows calling to one another.

Tested Spelling Words

____	____	____	____
____	____	____	____
____	____	____	____
____	____	____	____
____	____	____	____

Author's Purpose

- **Author's purpose** refers to an author's reason or reasons for writing.
- Four common purposes for writing are to inform, to persuade, to entertain, and to express. Often an author has more than one purpose for writing.
- Understanding an author's purpose can help you adjust your reading speed and can help explain the author's choice of words and writing style.

Directions: Reread "The Tortoise in the Tree." Then complete the table by writing evidence from the story that supports the purposes given. Then give an example of another folk tale that shares these purposes. Explain your choice.

Author's Purpose	Evidence for Author's Purpose
To entertain	**1.**
	2.
To persuade	**3.**
	4.

Another Folk Tale That Entertains and Persuades
5.

Notes for Home: Your child identified and analyzed an author's purpose for writing a folk tale. ***Home Activity:*** Challenge your child to write a humorous story that explains an animal's behavior or appearance, such as "How the Whale Got Its Tale" or "Why Snakes Hiss."

Name ______________________________

Vocabulary

Directions: Choose the word from the box that best matches each definition. Write the word on the line.

Check the Words You Know
__ distressed
__ impatience
__ insistent
__ recovery
__ stunned

______________ **1.** continuing to demand

______________ **2.** the process of regaining one's health or well-being

______________ **3.** in great pain or sorrow

______________ **4.** shocked

______________ **5.** a lack of patience

Directions: Choose the word from the box that best completes each sentence. Write the word on the line to the left.

______________ **6.** When the factory suddenly closed, Mr. Winters was _____ to find out that he had lost his job.

______________ **7.** He was worried and _____ about his ability to find a new job.

______________ **8.** During his first few weeks at home, Mr. Winters showed great _____; he wanted to settle into a new job as soon as possible.

______________ **9.** Mrs. Winters knew that her husband liked learning new things, so she was _____ that he sign up for a job training class.

______________ **10.** Now Mr. Winters has a job working with computers. His mood and his spirits have made a complete _____.

Write a News Story

On a separate sheet of paper, write a news story about someone who has turned his or her life around. The person can be someone you know or have heard of, or someone that you make up. Use as many vocabulary words as you can.

Notes for Home: Your child identified and used vocabulary words from *The Gold Coin.* ***Home Activity:*** Talk about a time when a family member recovered from an illness. Encourage your child to use the vocabulary words to describe how the person felt.

Name ______________________

Author's Purpose

- The **author's purpose** is the reason or reasons an author has for writing.
- Four common purposes for writing are to inform, to persuade, to entertain, and to express. Often an author has more than one purpose.

Directions: Reread the scene from *The Gold Coin* in which Juan begins to change. Then answer the questions below. Think about why the author is telling this story.

"If you'd like, I'll take you there tomorrow. But first I must gather my squash and beans."

So Juan spent another long day in the fields. Working beneath the summer sun, Juan noticed that his skin had begun to tan. And although he had to stoop down to pick the squash, he found that he could now stretch his body. His back had begun to straighten too.

Later, when the little girl took him by the hand to show him a family of rabbits burrowed under a fallen tree, Juan's face broke into a smile. It had been a long, long time since Juan had smiled.

1. How is Juan changing? ______________________

____

2. What is Juan learning? ______________________

____

____

3. Why does the author include the detail about the little girl and the rabbits?

____

____

4. What is the purpose of this passage? How do you know?

____

____

5. On a separate sheet of paper, explain why you think the author wrote this story. Give specific examples from the story to support your answer.

Notes for Home: Your child read a folk tale and identified the author's purpose. ***Home Activity:*** Encourage your child to read a movie review, a letter to the editor, and a sports article. Have your child tell you each author's purpose and explain his or her answers.

Selection Test

Directions: Choose the best answer to each item. Mark the letter for the answer you have chosen.

Part 1: Vocabulary

Find the answer choice that means about the same as the underlined word in each sentence.

1. Everyone noticed his <u>impatience</u>.
- A. lack of control
- B. unwillingness to put up with delay
- C. lack of manners
- D. shyness

2. Her plea was <u>insistent</u>.
- F. fearless
- G. showing bad judgment
- H. unfriendly; hostile
- J. pressing; urgent

3. We were <u>stunned</u> by the news.
- A. shocked
- B. pleased
- C. excited
- D. angered

4. My uncle made a full <u>recovery</u>.
- F. act of arranging things in a new way
- G. process of repeating or summing up
- H. process of regaining one's health
- J. act of finding something out

5. The old woman looked <u>distressed</u>.
- A. feeling or showing scorn
- B. in high spirits; excited
- C. annoyed or angered
- D. in great pain or sorrow

Part 2: Comprehension

Use what you know about the story to answer each item.

6. Juan looked pale because he—
- F. had been ill.
- G. worked by night.
- H. came from a cold country.
- J. had no friends.

7. Juan heard Doña Josefa say that she must be the—
- A. luckiest person in the world.
- B. hardest-working person in the world.
- C. busiest person in the world.
- D. richest person in the world.

8. As he tried to catch up with Doña Josefa, Juan first had to—
- F. cross a river.
- G. plant crops on a farm.
- H. climb a mountain.
- J. learn to ride a horse.

9. One big change that Juan noticed in himself was that he—
- A. followed Doña Josefa everywhere.
- B. learned to enjoy eating potatoes.
- C. smiled at a little girl.
- D. caught an illness from one of the people he met.

10. Why did Doña Josefa keep moving from house to house?
- F. She had many friends and relations.
- G. She was a house cleaner.
- H. She liked to travel to different places.
- J. She took care of sick people.

11. How is the text of this story organized?
- A. chronological order
- B. cause and effect
- C. problem and solution
- D. comparison and contrast

12. One of the author's main purposes in this story is to—
- F. explain farm work.
- G. compare Juan with Doña Josefa.
- H. teach a lesson.
- J. describe Doña Josefa's work.

13. Why is "The Gold Coin" a good title for this story?

A. The gold coin has Juan's name printed on it.

B. The gold coin is a symbol of Juan's greed and Doña Josefa's generosity.

C. Readers will be attracted to the story because people are attracted to gold.

D. The gold coin represents the hopes and dreams of the people in the story.

14. Which sentence best states a theme of this story?

F. Good things come to those who wait.

G. The key to happiness is giving to others.

H. Wealth comes to those who most deserve it.

J. One gold coin can make many people happy.

15. What is the most important change that has taken place between the first time Juan comes to Doña Josefa's house and the next?

A. Doña Josefa is not quite as willing to help her neighbors as before.

B. A storm is fast approaching.

C. Juan decides to help Doña Josefa rather than simply satisfy his own greed.

D. The house is now in ruins.

Name ________________________________

Author's Purpose

- The **author's purpose** is the reason or reasons an author has for writing.
- Four common purposes for writing are to inform, to persuade, to entertain, and to express. Often an author has more than one purpose.

Directions: Read the story below.

A poor boy named Tom went to sea to seek his fortune with his only friend, a cat named Trapper. One day Trapper gave birth to six kittens. The ship's captain hated cats, so Tom hid them in the hold.

Six months later the captain landed on an island in hopes of trading with the people there. However, the islanders were too upset to think about trading. Swarms of rats were terrorizing their villages. Tom offered his kittens for trade. "Just what we need!" cried the islanders.

For the rest of his life, the captain never sailed without a cat on board.

Directions: Complete the table below. In the first row, list the author's purpose or purposes for writing the story above, and give an explanation for your answer. Then for each purpose listed, give an example of a specific text you've read that fits that purpose. Explain your choices.

Author's Purpose	Title and Explanation
1.	**2.**
to inform	**3.**
to persuade	**4.**
to entertain	**5.**
to express	*Wilma Unlimited,* by Kathleen Krull, expresses Wilma Rudolph's courage and determination to walk again.

Notes for Home: Your child identified an author's purpose for writing. ***Home Activity:*** Talk about different types of books, articles, or movies that you and your child have read or seen. Discuss why a writer would write this material.

Name ___________________________

REVIEW

Drawing Conclusions

Directions: Read the story. Then read each question about the story. Choose the best answer to each question. Mark the letter for the answer you have chosen.

A Frog Fable

Once three frogs lived in a shallow pond. Summer came and with it a severe drought. Their pond shrank to a mud puddle. Two of the frogs decided to search for a new home elsewhere. The third, however, claimed she'd just as soon die in their familiar puddle as some strange lake. She refused to go. Finally, her two friends left her. They promised to return as soon as the drought ended. She watched as they hopped away into the distance.

The two frogs hopped a long way, seeking water. At the end of the first day, they came to an old well. It was so dark by then that they could not see the bottom.

"Surely there is water down below. Let's hop right in!" said the first frog, leaping to the top of the wall.

"Wait, wait!" cried her friend. "We must find out for sure before you leap! What if there is no water down below? What if there is no way to climb out?"

"I know what we'll do!" said the first frog. "You will have to help me, though. We will push this pebble over the edge and listen hard. If we hear a splash, we will know there is water. We can also guess how deep it is and how far we will have to fall before we hit the water. If it is high enough, we can climb out whenever we want."

Working together, the tired frogs shoved the pebble over the side. PLUNK! It hit water almost immediately. Relieved that their suffering was over, they jumped into the well.

Suddenly, there was a booming of thunder! "Rain!" cried the first frog. "The drought is over!"

1. Why did the third frog stay behind?
- **A.** She was afraid of the unknown.
- **B.** She knew it would rain.
- **C.** She was happy in the mud puddle.
- **D.** She hated water.

2. What makes the first two frogs leave the third frog behind?
- **F.** They are thirstier than she is.
- **G.** They are braver than she is.
- **H.** They like to travel.
- **J.** They want to see the world beyond the pond.

3. Why does one frog hesitate at the side of the well?
- **A.** She is afraid of the dark.
- **B.** She is afraid leaping into the well may be dangerous.
- **C.** She has changed her mind and wants to go home.
- **D.** She is angry at the first frog.

4. The frogs know it is safe to jump in the well because—
- **F.** they hear the splash from the pebble right away.
- **G.** they hear nothing after tossing the pebble in the well.
- **H.** it begins to rain.
- **J.** they can see the water when the sun rises.

5. What will the two frogs do now that it's raining?
- **A.** stay in the well
- **B.** return to their home
- **C.** drown in the well
- **D.** push another pebble into the well

Notes for Home: Your child read a story and formed conclusions about its characters. ***Home Activity:*** With your child, think of other well-known folk tales or fables. Discuss why characters act a certain way and what lessons they may have learned.

Name ______________________________

Writing Across Texts

Directions: Although *The Gold Coin* and "Pecos Bill and the Cyclone" are both traditional regional tales, they are very different in style, mood, and theme. Think about the differences between the two stories. How would you contrast these two stories? Write your ideas in the table below.

Differences Between *The Gold Coin* and "Pecos Bill and the Cyclone"
The Gold Coin teaches a lesson. "Pecos Bill and the Cyclone" seems to be written for pure enjoyment.
1.
2.
3.
4.
5.

Write an Explanation

On a separate sheet of paper, write an explanation of how *The Gold Coin* and "Pecos Bill and the Cyclone" are different in style, mood, and theme. Support your opinions with information from each story.

Notes for Home: Your child contrasted two different traditional stories. ***Home Activity:*** Together, read aloud folk tales from two different regions. Help your child list the differences between the style, mood, and theme of the stories.

Name ______________________________

REVIEW

Grammar: Using Adjectives and Adverbs to Improve Sentences

Directions: Add adjectives and/or adverbs to improve the sentences below. Write each new sentence on the line.

1. A frog leaped out of the pond.

____

2. A fly landed on a leaf.

____

3. The two creatures stared at each other.

____

4. "Hello," said the frog.

____

5. "Humm," buzzed the fly.

____

Directions: Cross out any unneeded adjectives or adverbs in the sentences below. Write your new sentence on the line.

6. "Do I actually know you?" asked the friendly young green frog.

____

7. "Humm," loudly buzzed the same old fly again.

____

8. The small young frog looked at the fly thoughtfully and carefully.

____

9. Then soon he stuck out his sticky, gooey tongue, caught the fly, and immediately swallowed it instantly.

____

10. "Yumm," buzzed the happy, smiling frog.

____

Notes for Home: Your child improved sentences by adding needed adjectives and adverbs and removing unneeded ones. ***Home Activity:*** Have your child write some sentences about a person you both know. Then challenge your child to add and/or remove some adjectives and adverbs.

Grammar: Avoiding Misplaced Modifiers

Adjectives and adverbs are called modifiers because they modify, or tell more about, nouns and verbs. In doing so, these modifiers affect the meanings of the nouns and verbs.

Phrases can affect the meaning of nouns and verbs too, as in the following sentence:

With spray paint, vandals seriously damaged the pleasant old city's appearance.

Watch for misplaced modifiers. To avoid confusion, keep modifiers close to the words they modify. Note how the meaning changes when the misplaced modifier in the sentence below is moved closer to the word it is meant to modify.

Misplaced: With nothing better to do, Judge Alvarez said that two strangers had defaced their city's buildings.

Correct: Judge Alvarez said that two strangers with nothing better to do had defaced their city's buildings.

Directions: Read each sentence. If the sentence is correct, write **C** on the line. If it contains a misplaced modifier, write **NC** on the line and circle the misplaced modifier.

__________ **1.** Foolishly, the men thought no one had seen what they had done.

__________ **2.** On the street, people had seen two men running with cans of spray paint.

__________ **3.** These witnesses called the police immediately and appeared in court later.

__________ **4.** Fortunately, the city had laws against graffiti (words and pictures drawn on walls and buildings) and owned a machine for removing them.

__________ **5.** In court, the mayor described the graffiti on one wall with an outraged face.

__________ **6.** He said that the vandals should clean the wall angrily.

__________ **7.** The guilty men faced three possible penalties: detention in jail, heavy fines, or community service.

__________ **8.** As a second chance, the judge sentenced them to community service in the city.

__________ **9.** Carefully, the relieved men agreed to operate the graffiti-removal machine.

__________ **10.** They offered to do other useful work, too, and apologized sincerely for their past behavior on local TV.

Notes for Home: Your child identified misplaced modifiers. ***Home Activity:*** Say *Teri took a picture of a snake with her new camera*. Have your child identify the misplaced modifier and explain why it is misplaced (*with her new camera* seems to refer to the snake instead of to Teri).

Extra Practice

Grammar: Avoiding Misplaced Modifiers

Directions: Read each sentence. If a sentence contains a misplaced modifier, think about the word or words it should describe. Then write the sentence correctly on the line. If a sentence is already correct, write **C** on the line.

1. Mrs. Vu entered a local library full of complaints.

____

2. "The outside looks terrible," she said, "with trash, weedy grass, and no flowers."

____

3. She annoyed everyone with the same kinds of complaints.

____

4. The city needed more money to support the library badly.

____

5. Mrs. Vu suddenly stopped criticizing and started to help.

____

6. She ran fundraising auctions and found donors without much training.

____

7. Thick, green, and healthy, business people donated a new lawn.

____

8. Bright flowers pleased library users in window boxes.

____

9. As a woman of action, everyone praised Mrs. Vu's success.

____

10. Now, the librarians happily watch her daily arrival through the window.

____

Write a Project Profile

On a separate sheet of paper, write a description of a local project you would like to start or be involved with. Make sure there are no misplaced modifiers in your description.

Notes for Home: Your child identified misplaced modifiers. ***Home Activity:*** Write a sentence with a misplaced modifier such as *Sally saw the bear looking through her binoculars*. Have your child rewrite the sentence to correct the misplaced modifier.

Name ______________________________

Grammar: Avoiding Misplaced Modifiers

RETEACHING

Rewrite the sentence so that it makes sense.

I asked a woman if I could borrow her flashlight from down the block.

____

____

Modifiers are words or phrases that tell more about nouns and verbs. Sometimes the placement of a modifier is incorrect, and the sentence doesn't make sense. To avoid confusion, keep modifiers close to the words they modify.

Directions: Read each sentence. If the sentence is correct, write **C** on the short line. If it contains a misplaced modifier, write **NC** on the line and write the sentence correctly.

__________ **1.** A song was playing on the radio about a traveling artist.

____

__________ **2.** That girl asked me a question who was interested in painting.

____

__________ **3.** A boy in my math class offered to help me study for the test.

____

__________ **4.** My neighbor walked his dog who sings in the opera.

____

__________ **5.** The television commercial advertised a new way to brush your teeth.

____

__________ **6.** In great detail, the boy agreed to paint the castle.

____

__________ **7.** In the sky, several people saw a flock of geese flying.

____

Notes for Home: Your child identified misplaced modifiers in sentences and wrote the sentences correctly. ***Home Activity:*** Have your child use some of the sentences on this page to explain to you the importance of keeping modifiers near the words or phrases they modify.

Name ______________________________

Grammar: Avoiding Misplaced Modifiers

Directions: Read each sentence. If the sentence is correct, write **C** on the line. If it contains a misplaced modifier, write **NC** on the line and circle the misplaced modifier.

______________ **1.** Brightly, my family saw the sun shine through the windows.

______________ **2.** My brother thought it looked like a beautiful golden shower.

______________ **3.** My sister needed help climbing up on the chair, who is younger than me.

______________ **4.** Loudly, my grandmother told me about the foghorn that used to sound near her childhood home.

______________ **5.** I whispered softly to the sleeping kitten.

Directions: Read each sentence. If a sentence contains a misplaced modifier, write the sentence correctly on the line. If the sentence is correct, write **correct** on the line.

6. A rabbit ate a carrot with long, floppy ears.

____

7. A girl trains horses in my class.

____

8. A man climbs mountains on my block.

____

9. My sister who dances is going to leave school early today.

____

10. A boy found a dog from my sister's math class.

____

Write a Funny Story

Sentences with misplaced modifiers can be funny. Write a four-sentence story with sentences that have misplaced modifiers. Then rewrite the story so that the sentences make sense. Check your work carefully to make sure you have written modifiers in the correct places.

Notes for Home: Your child identified misplaced modifiers and wrote modifiers correctly in sentences. ***Home Activity:*** Have your child read his or her funny story to you. Add a sentence with a misplaced modifier and have your child write it correctly.

Name ________________________________

Word Study: Word Building

Directions: Read each sentence. Say the underlined word to yourself. Write the letters of the stressed syllable in capital letters and the unstressed syllables in lowercase letters. For example: write **garden** and **garage** as **GAR · den** and **ga · RAGE**.

____________________ **1.** It is sometimes difficult to understand how life used to be long ago.

____________________ **2.** Imagine walking five miles to school every day instead of riding in a comfortable school bus!

____________________ **3.** The past will become more familiar if you compare it to the present.

____________________ **4.** To learn about your family's past, talk to an older relative.

____________________ **5.** Try to keep in touch with family and companions in other parts of the country.

____________________ **6.** My aunt thinks it's wonderful that I keep in touch with my old friends.

____________________ **7.** My impatience to get letters often prompts me to make a telephone call.

____________________ **8.** Sometimes, I travel to the countryside to visit family members.

____________________ **9.** Just remember, traditions will not be forgotten if we work to keep them alive.

Directions: Read the pairs of related words. Say each word to yourself. Circle the stressed syllable in each word.

10. universe **11.** universal

12. accident **13.** accidental

14. history **15.** historical

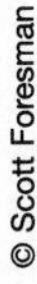

Notes for Home: Your child identified the stressed syllables in words such as *garden* (first syllable) and *garage* (second syllable). ***Home Activity:*** Read a poem or song lyrics with your child. Repeat individual words for your child. Work together to decide which syllable is stressed.

Spelling: Related Words 1

Pretest

Pretest Directions: Fold back the page along the dotted line. On the blanks, write the spelling words as they are dictated. When you have finished the test, unfold the page and check your words.

1. ______________________
2. ______________________
3. ______________________
4. ______________________
5. ______________________
6. ______________________
7. ______________________
8. ______________________
9. ______________________
10. ______________________
11. ______________________
12. ______________________
13. ______________________
14. ______________________
15. ______________________
16. ______________________
17. ______________________
18. ______________________
19. ______________________
20. ______________________

1. Language is a **human** trait.
2. Treat animals in a **humane** way.
3. Please **clean** your room.
4. The rain will **cleanse** the street.
5. He loved to be out in **nature**.
6. She eats only **natural** foods.
7. His college **major** was English.
8. A **majority** voted for her.
9. What is your favorite **poem**?
10. Her speech was quite **poetic**.
11. We all have **equal** rights.
12. Please solve this **equation**.
13. **Unite** for the common good.
14. Understanding promotes **unity**.
15. They diffused the **bomb** in time.
16. He'll **bombard** us with questions.
17. Exercise builds **muscle**.
18. The athlete was very **muscular**.
19. As of next week, I hereby **resign**.
20. Please hand in your **resignation**.

Notes for Home: Your child took a pretest on related words that have parts spelled the same but pronounced differently. ***Home Activity:*** Help your child learn misspelled words before the final test by underlining the parts that are different in each pair and concentrating on those.

Name ____________________

Think and Practice

Spelling: Related Words 1

Word List

human	nature	poem	unite	muscle
humane	natural	poetic	unity	muscular
clean	major	equal	bomb	resign
cleanse	majority	equation	bombard	resignation

Directions: Listen carefully as you read each word from the box aloud. Find the five pairs of related words in which the stressed syllable changes. For example, listen to the difference in stress between **office** and **official.** Write the words on the lines.

Changes in Stressed Syllables

1. ____________________
2. ____________________
3. ____________________
4. ____________________
5. ____________________
6. ____________________
7. ____________________
8. ____________________
9. ____________________
10. ____________________

Directions: Choose the word from the box that best matches each clue. Write the word on the line.

____________________ **11.** I am what a shirt is after you wash it.

____________________ **12.** I am written in verses that may or may not rhyme.

____________________ **13.** I am a weapon that explodes.

____________________ **14.** I rhyme with *bends.*

____________________ **15.** I am how you might describe a strong athlete.

____________________ **16.** I am what makes you able to clench your fist.

____________________ **17.** I include all things not made by humans, like forests and oceans.

____________________ **18.** I am how you might describe a nicely phrased sentence.

____________________ **19.** I am what children might do to each other with snowballs.

____________________ **20.** I am the opposite of *artificial.*

Notes for Home: Your child spelled related words that have parts with similar spellings but different pronunciations, such as *human* and *humane. **Home Activity:*** Work with your child to use several spelling words to make a crossword puzzle.

Name ____________________

Spelling: Related Words 1

Directions: Proofread this "Help Wanted" ad for new storybook characters. Find six spelling mistakes. Use the proofreading marks to correct each mistake.

≡	Make a capital.
/	Make a small letter.
∧	Add something.
⟆	Take out something.
⊙	Add a period.
¶	Begin a new paragraph.

Help Wanted

Due to the resignasion of several characters, new folk tale heroes, villains, and comic sidekicks are needed. Applicants must be able to act in a mature manner. Villains should resign themselves to losing. Heroes must be able to treat all creatures in a humain fashion. A musculler shape is not necessary, but a clean face is required. The ability to use poetac language is a definite plus, especially for princes and knights! Equell opportunities will be given to all applicants, animal or humen. Come join our team!

Spelling Tip

Related words like *resign* and *resignation* have parts that are spelled the same but pronounced differently. Pronounce each word carefully to spell it correctly. Note that the **g** in **resign** is not silent when a suffix is added to form **resignation.**

Word List

human	equal
humane	equation
clean	unite
cleanse	unity
nature	bomb
natural	bombard
major	muscle
majority	muscular
poem	resign
poetic	resignation

Write an Advertisement

On a separate sheet of paper, write an advertisement to find a replacement for a favorite book or movie character. Describe the qualities the applicant needs in order to fill the position. Try to use at least five of your spelling words.

Notes for Home: Your child spelled related words that have parts with similar spellings but different pronunciations, such as *human* and *humane.* ***Home Activity:*** Play a board game. Make the new rule that before moving, a player must spell a word from the box correctly.

Name ________________________________

Spelling: Related Words 1

REVIEW

Word List				
human	nature	poem	unite	muscle
humane	natural	poetic	unity	muscular
clean	major	equal	bomb	resign
cleanse	majority	equation	bombard	resignation

Directions: Choose the word from the box that best completes each statement. Write the word on the line to the left.

________________ **1.** *Breathe* is to *lung* as *move* is to _____.

________________ **2.** *Fake* is to *real* as *artificial* is to _____.

________________ **3.** *Blast* is to *dynamite* as *explosion* is to _____.

________________ **4.** *Weak* is to *flabby* as *powerful* is to _____.

________________ **5.** *Cruel* is to *kind* as *merciless* is to _____.

________________ **6.** *Messy* is to *dirty* as *neat* is to _____.

________________ **7.** *Separate* is to *join* as *divide* is to _____.

________________ **8.** *Stanza* is to *song* as *verse* is to _____.

________________ **9.** *English* is to *sentence* as *mathematics* is to _____.

________________ **10.** *Mechanic* is to *car* as *doctor* is to _____.

________________ **11.** *Small* is to *large* as *minor* is to _____.

Directions: Choose the word from the box that best replaces the underlined words. Write the word on the line.

________________ **12.** Glenda told the Villains' Committee that she would quit.

________________ **13.** She gave them her written notice of quitting.

________________ **14.** She made a speech laced with vivid, flowing language.

________________ **15.** Glenda was tired of struggling against all the forces at work in the world.

________________ **16.** People would heavily attack her for her wicked deeds.

________________ **17.** Glenda wanted to make clean herself of all evil.

________________ **18.** She wanted to give the same time to doing good.

________________ **19.** The largest part of the Committee agreed to let her go.

________________ **20.** In a rare show of togetherness, the Committee agreed on a replacement.

Notes for Home: Your child spelled related words that have parts with similar spellings but different pronunciations. ***Home Activity:*** Challenge your child to find and spell a third word that relates to each pair of words on the list, such as *humane, human, humanity.*

Name ____________________

Recipe

A **recipe** is a set of directions for preparing something to eat. It gives step-by-step instructions and may include pictures. Using recipes will strengthen your skills in following directions and understanding pictures or diagrams.

Directions: Read the recipe. Then answer the questions that follow.

Baked Chinese Egg Rolls

Ingredients:

1 cup all-purpose flour

2 cups water

2 eggs

$\frac{1}{2}$ teaspoon salt

3 tablespoons vegetable oil

$\frac{1}{2}$ cup chopped celery

$\frac{3}{4}$ cup chopped cabbage

4 scallions, chopped

$\frac{1}{2}$ cup diced shrimp

$\frac{1}{2}$ cup diced pork, cooked

$\frac{1}{2}$ cup chopped water chestnuts

$\frac{1}{2}$ cup bean sprouts

1 clove garlic, chopped

$\frac{1}{4}$ cup soy sauce

$\frac{1}{2}$ teaspoon sugar

Steps:

1. Sift flour into bowl.
2. Stir in water.
3. Beat in eggs and salt to make a smooth batter.
4. Grease a skillet with some cooking oil, butter, or margarine, and set the skillet on low heat.
5. Pour 1 tablespoon of batter into the pan to form a thin pancake. Flip so it cooks on the opposite side. Remove and set on a plate. Repeat Step 5 to make more thin pancakes. These are the outside of the egg rolls.
6. In another skillet, heat the vegetable oil.
7. Then add the celery, cabbage, and scallions. When they are nicely fried, stir in the shrimp and pork. Cook for about 3 minutes.
8. Then add the water chestnuts, bean sprouts, garlic, soy sauce, and sugar. Cook for another 5 minutes. This is the filling for the egg rolls.
9. Spoon about 4 tablespoons of filling onto each pancake.
10. Roll the pancake around the filling and fold up the ends.
11. Place on a tray in a 425°F oven for 15 minutes.
12. Serve with sweet-and-sour sauce, Chinese mustard, or soy sauce.

Makes about 12 egg rolls.

1. Before starting this recipe, which cooking tools would you need to get together?

2. How is the list of ingredients organized?

3. In which way are most of the vegetables prepared?

4. What do you have to do to the pork before you can add it in Step 7? How do you know?

5. What part of the Baked Chinese Egg Rolls is made first?

6. Do you think you would be able to cook the pancakes and the vegetables at the same time? Why or why not?

7. If you had two dozen people to serve, what would you need to do to this recipe? Why?

8. Why do you think the ingredients are listed separate from the steps of the recipe?

9. Do the pictures help you understand the recipe? Explain.

10. Why do you think using recipes will help you strengthen your skills in following directions and understanding pictures and diagrams?

Notes for Home Your child read a recipe, and answered questions about its organization and contents. ***Home Activity:*** Help your child write a recipe for a favorite dish by listing the ingredients and steps to follow. Work together, using the recipe to make the dish.

Name ______________________________

How-To Chart

Directions: Fill in the how-to chart with information about your project.

Explain task ______________________________

____

Materials ______________________________

____

____

Introduction ______________________________

____

____

Steps ______________________________

____

____

____

Conclusion ______________________________

____

Notes for Home: Your child has been preparing to write a how-to report. ***Home Activity:*** Think of a simple task such as setting the table, making popcorn, or playing a game. Ask your child to outline the steps in the process. Try it out. Are there any steps missing?

Name ____

Elaboration

Sense Words

- One way to elaborate is by adding **sense words** that help readers picture things clearly.
- You can provide vivid images by telling how things look, sound, feel, taste, and smell.

Directions: Add words from the box to make the sentences below more interesting. Write the new sentences using the words you picked.

autumn	crisp	fascinating	pine	smooth
bright	delicate	fragrant	sandy	unique
colorful	disposable	natural	small	

1. You can make crafts from objects.

____

2. Search beaches for seashells.

____

3. Hunt for leaves one day.

____

4. Check the forest for cones.

____

5. Be on the lookout for stones.

____

6. Flowers can be pressed or ironed.

____

7. Dye fruit seeds in containers.

____

8. Make cards, mobiles, boxes, and frames.

____

Notes for Home: Your child expanded sentences by adding sense words. ***Home Activity:*** Ask your child to describe something he or she has made, using sense words. For example: *I can make warm, tasty cocoa with a fluffy marshmallow on top.*

Name ______________________________

Self-Evaluation Guide

How-to Report

Directions: Think about the final draft of your how-to report. Then answer each question below.

	Yes	No	Not sure
1. Did I include all the steps in the right order?			
2. Did I provide enough information to accomplish the task?			
3. Did I indicate the steps with words like *first* and *next?*			
4. Did I use clear sentences to guide my audience?			
5. Did I proofread and edit carefully to avoid errors?			

6. What did I learn from this report?

____

____

____

____

____

7. Write one thing that you could change to make this how-to report even better.

____

____

____

____

____

Notes for Home: Your child recently wrote a how-to report. ***Home Activity:*** Encourage your child to give you an oral explanation of the steps. You might also ask for a demonstration of the how-to report.

Family Times

Name____________________

Summary

Danger and Trials Greet Arctic Explorers

In "To the Pole," an explorer records the highlights of a trip to the North Pole. From the explorer's log, we learn about the challenges of traveling in the Arctic. The ice is covered with two feet of snow, but that's just the beginning! The travelers must cross "leads"—rivers or lakes of water created where the ice splits apart. Sometimes the dogs help the explorers out of trouble. The log also describes the purpose of the trip, which is to draw attention to the environmental problems of the Arctic.

Activity

Prepare for an Arctic Trip. Pretend you are going on a trip to the North Pole. Make a list of items you will need. Discuss the various difficulties you may encounter on the journey.

Reading Skills

Fact and Opinion

A **statement of fact** can be proven true or false by reading, observing, asking an expert, or checking it in some way. "To the Pole" lists temperatures and other Arctic data. These data are facts because they can be checked.

A **statement of opinion** tells someone's belief, judgment, or way of thinking about something. It cannot be proven true or false, but it can be supported or explained. For example, the author of "To the Pole" says that mounds of ice covered by snowdrifts are easy for the dogs to climb over. This is an opinion because it cannot be proven true or false. The author supports this opinion by saying that the drifts are like ramps.

Activity

Stating Facts and Opinions. Make statements about a subject, such as your town or school. Challenge others to tell whether your statements are statements of fact or opinion. Discuss how the facts could be proven and how the opinions could be supported.

Family Times

Tested Vocabulary

Words to Know

Knowing the meanings of these words is important to reading "To the Pole." Practice using these words to learn their meanings.

Arctic the north polar region

collide to crash into something

expeditions journeys for exploration or scientific study

latitude distance north or south of the equator

longitude distance east or west of the prime meridian

satellite an artificial object launched by rocket into an orbit around Earth

strenuous tiring; exhausting

terrain land that is thought to have particular natural features

Grammar

Possessive Pronouns

Pronouns that show ownership are called **possessive pronouns.** Possessive pronouns do not use apostrophes. They may be used with nouns, or they may stand alone.

Used with Nouns	Used Alone
This is my sled.	This sled is mine.
This is your sled.	This sled is yours.
This is his sled.	This sled is his.
This is her sled.	This sled is hers.
This is its sled.	
This is our sled.	This sled is ours.
This is their sled.	This sled is theirs.

Activity

Perform a Survival Play. Make up a play about characters caught in an Arctic storm. Talk to each other about survival techniques and what you will do to continue. Use possessive pronouns.

Tested Spelling Words

____	____	____	____
____	____	____	____
____	____	____	____
____	____	____	____
____	____	____	____

Name ______________________________

Fact and Opinion

- A **statement of fact** can be proven true or false. You can prove it true or false by reading, observing, asking an expert, or checking it in some way.
- A **statement of opinion** tells someone's belief, judgment, or way of thinking about something. It cannot be proven true or false, but it can be supported or explained.
- Some sentences contain both facts and opinions.

Directions: Reread "Mount Everest: The Ultimate Challenge." Then complete the table. Write **X** in the proper column to show whether each statement contains a fact or an opinion.

Statement	Fact	Opinion
1. The peak of Mount Everest used to be a tough place to reach.		
2. The mountain is on the border of Nepal and China.		
3. Many climbers have come away with an incredible experience.		
4. Climbers have contributed $90 million to Nepal's economy.		
5. Modern technology makes it easier for climbers to communicate with faraway people.		
6. Too many inexperienced climbers attempt to scale Everest's treacherous terrain.		
7. About one in every thirty Everest climbers dies in the attempt.		
8. Eight climbers died in May 1996.		
9. Climbers leave behind oxygen cylinders, food remains, and other garbage.		
10. The May disaster will make climbers rethink their attitudes about climbing Mount Everest.		

Notes for Home: Your child read an article and decided whether statements were statements of fact or opinion. ***Home Activity:*** Have your child describe his or her school day, giving at least three statements of fact and three statements of opinion.

Vocabulary

Directions: Choose the word from the box that best completes each sentence. Write the word on the line to the left.

Check the Words You Know
__ Arctic
__ collide
__ expeditions
__ latitude
__ longitude
__ satellite
__ strenuous
__ terrain

____________________ **1.** I own many books about _____ to faraway places.

____________________ **2.** I've always wanted to go to the _____ and reach the North Pole.

____________________ **3.** I'm sure that hiking through a place like that would be _____.

____________________ **4.** The icy _____ creates challenges for even the most experienced explorers.

____________________ **5.** The weather conditions at that latitude and _____ can be quite severe.

Directions: Choose the word from the box that best matches each clue. Write the word in the puzzle.

Down

6. distance north or south of the equator

8. natural features of a region

9. crash into something

Across

7. an artificial object that orbits around a planet

10. journeys to uncharted areas

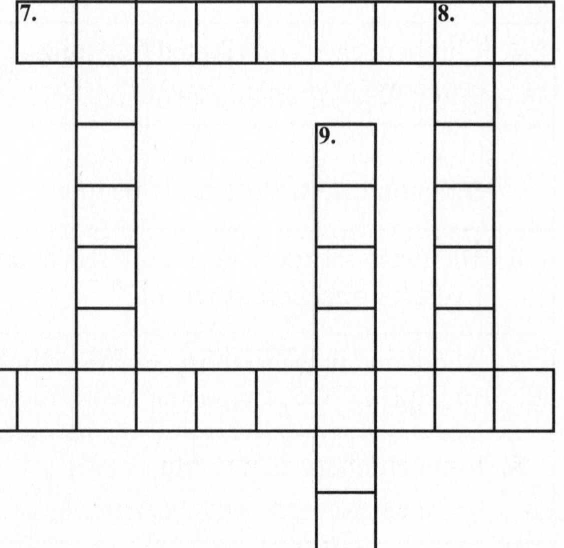

Write a Story

On a separate sheet of paper, write a story about exploring an unfamiliar place. Use as many vocabulary words as you can.

Notes for Home: Your child identified and used vocabulary words from "To the Pole." ***Home Activity:*** Read a story about exploration with your child. Encourage your child to try to find synonyms—words with similar meanings—to the vocabulary words listed above.

Name ____

Fact and Opinion

- A **statement of fact** can be proven true or false. You can prove it true or false by reading, observing, asking an expert, or checking it in some way.
- A **statement of opinion** tells someone's belief, judgment, or way of thinking about something. It cannot be proven true or false, but it can be supported or explained.
- Some sentences contain both facts and opinions.

Directions: Reread the part of "To the Pole" in which Will Steger describes sharing a tent with Victor. Then answer the questions below. Think about whether statements can be proven true or false.

Victor and I are sharing a tent. In our travels across Antarctica and Greenland we have tented together many nights before. He is good company—we know each other's habits well, and his optimism is always a boost to me.

We're like a little family of two, living inside a space the size of a car. Our arrangement is that I prepare dinner and he makes breakfast. In the morning, while I'm still in my sleeping bag, I know exactly what time it is by the breakfast sounds Victor is making. When I hear him stirring dried fruit and hot chocolate powder into a steaming bowl of leftover rice—my favorite on-the-ice breakfast—I know it is 6:40. Ten minutes later he will pour hot water for our tea.

1. What is Will's opinion of Victor? How do you know?

____

2. What facts are given about how chores will be done in the tent?

____

3. Will writes, "We are like a little family . . ." Is this a statement of fact or opinion? Explain.

____

4. Is Will's statement "I know it is 6:40" a statement of fact or opinion? Explain.

____

5. How might the facts and opinions found in "To the Pole" be useful to another expedition? Explain your thinking on a separate sheet of paper.

Notes for Home: Your child identified statements of fact and opinion in a nonfiction text. ***Home Activity:*** Read the promotional material from a book or video cover with your child. Have him or her identify the statements of fact and the statements of opinion.

Selection Test

Directions: Choose the best answer to each item. Mark the letter for the answer you have chosen.

Part 1: Vocabulary

Find the answer choice that means about the same as the underlined word in each sentence.

1. They struggled over the rough terrain.
- A. the surface of the ocean
- B. a ridge of high mountains
- C. violent, rushing stream of water
- D. the natural features of a region

2. He wanted to know the latitude.
- F. distance north or south of the equator
- G. height above the earth's surface
- H. space in between two points
- J. distance east or west on the earth's surface

3. We hoped the wagons wouldn't collide.
- A. break apart
- B. crash into each other
- C. topple over
- D. cave in

4. They traveled to the Arctic.
- F. south polar region
- G. high mountains in Asia
- H. north polar region
- J. desert in Africa

5. She had been on several expeditions.
- A. journeys for a special purpose, such as exploration or study
- B. long periods in outer space
- C. visits to a zoo or museum
- D. cruise ships

6. The journey was strenuous.
- F. exciting; full of adventure
- G. causing worry or fuss
- H. dull and uninteresting
- J. requiring much energy

7. The camps were at the same longitude.
- A. height above the earth's surface
- B. distance east or west on the earth's surface
- C. space in between two points
- D. distance north or south of the equator

8. They communicated via satellite.
- F. a system of telephones connected by wires
- G. an artificial object launched into orbit around the earth
- H. a machine with an engine and wheels
- J. an unidentified flying object

Part 2: Comprehension

Use what you know about the selection to answer each item.

9. Which condition presented the biggest challenge for Will Steger and his companions?
- A. big mounds of ice
- B. snowdrifts
- C. open water
- D. pressure ridges

10. The job of the "point person" is to—
- F. ski out ahead to find a safe path.
- G. steer the lead sled.
- H. use the Global Positioning System.
- J. set up the campsite.

GO ON

11. Which sentence states an opinion?
- A. "We have reached the North Pole exactly as planned, on Earth Day."
- B. "Our friends have brought supplies with them—including letters and small gifts."
- C. "But I got the best present—an apple pie baked by my mother."
- D. "Victor is the first Russian to reach both the North and South poles by skis."

12. Which of the following sentences states a fact?
- F. "But then, just before we got here, it began to look like heaven."
- G. "We passed 89 degrees north latitude, which means we are less than 60 miles from the pole!"
- H. "So far, the most surprising aspect of the whole trip is all the snow."
- J. "When we left the North Pole, it seemed like a perfect day."

13. Most of the information in this selection is organized by—
- A. comparison/contrast.
- B. cause and effect.
- C. problem and solution.
- D. chronological order.

14. Which generalization seems to be based on the author's personal opinion?
- F. In most years, the Arctic has little precipitation.
- G. On most days, the ice they crossed was more than three years old.
- H. Female sled dogs are often very bright.
- J. The peoples of the Arctic have adapted to the environment.

15. Which part of this selection best supports the author's goal of showing "how all parts of the world are interconnected"?
- A. the section on pollution in the Arctic
- B. the part describing animals of the Arctic
- C. the entry for April 22, when the team reached the North Pole
- D. the section called "Facts from the Trip"

STOP

Fact and Opinion

- A **statement of fact** can be proven true or false. You can prove it true or false by reading, observing, asking an expert, or checking it in some way.
- A **statement of opinion** tells someone's belief, judgment, or way of thinking about something. It cannot be proven true or false, but it can be supported or explained.
- Some sentences contain both facts and opinions.

Directions: Read the passage below.

In 1804, President Thomas Jefferson asked his secretary Meriwether Lewis to lead an expedition to explore America's West and Northwest. Mr. Lewis, a naturalist and ex-army officer, chose William Clark to act as his co-leader. Mr. Clark was Mr. Lewis's friend from their army days together. The two men had the ideal qualities for leading such an expedition: they were brave, intelligent, and resourceful.

President Jefferson instructed the two men to take detailed notes of everything they saw: peoples, animals, plants, and geographical features. Mr. Lewis and Mr. Clark returned from their journey with careful and extensive records of everything they had seen. Because of their expedition, many Americans became eager to see the West for themselves.

Directions: Tell whether each statement is a fact or opinion. Two have been done for you.

Fact or Opinion?	Statement
Fact	President Jefferson asked Meriwether Lewis to explore the West and Northwest.
Fact	Meriwether Lewis chose William Clark as his co-leader.
1.	Mr. Lewis and Mr. Clark had known one another during their army days.
2.	Mr. Lewis and Mr. Clark were brave and resourceful.
3.	President Jefferson asked Mr. Lewis and Mr. Clark to take detailed notes about everything they saw.
4.	Mr. Lewis and Mr. Clark kept extensive records of their journey.
5.	Because of their expedition, many Americans became eager to see the West for themselves.

Notes for Home: Your child read a passage and identified statements of fact and opinion. ***Home Activity:*** Read an advertisement with your child. Challenge him or her to identify statements that can be proved true or false (facts) and those that cannot (opinions).

Summarizing and Text Structure

REVIEW

Directions: Read the passage. Then read each question about the passage. Choose the best answer to each question. Mark the letter for the answer you have chosen.

Travels of the Past

The explorer and anthropologist Thor Heyerdahl went on many adventures in order to test his ideas. He believed ancient peoples regularly traveled great distances, and that this is why we find similar objects in places that are very far apart. He tested his ideas by crossing oceans in small handmade boats like those used in ancient times.

One of Thor Heyerdahl's ideas was that the native peoples of Peru were able to sail to Polynesia in the distant past. He thought that even though they did not know latitude and longitude, they were able to follow ocean currents and the stars in the sky. He tried out his idea by building a balsa raft like the ones Peruvians made long ago. His movie about this successful trip won an Academy Award in 1951. With his small crew, he led several other successful expeditions from South America to the East Pacific, to show that such long journeys would have been possible for Native American people.

Thor Heyerdahl also was able to cross the Atlantic from North Africa in a boat modeled after ancient Egyptian papyrus boats. He believed that ancient Egyptians actually did travel to South America this way and that the Egyptians are the ancestors of the Aztec and Inca people.

Thor Heyerdahl also believed that the Sumerians, who lived between the Tigris and Euphrates Rivers 5,000 years ago in what is now Iraq, traveled from their homeland to the Indian Ocean. However, war in the region kept him from testing his idea and the model reed boat he had built.

1. A summary of this article should **not** include the information about—
- **A.** travel from South America to Polynesia.
- **B.** journeys by Egyptians to America.
- **C.** the movie about the trip to Polynesia.
- **D.** Sumerian travel to the Indian Ocean.

2. A main idea of this article is that ancient peoples—
- **F.** followed currents and stars.
- **G.** were smart.
- **H.** did not know latitude and longitude.
- **J.** traveled far in simple crafts.

3. A summary of this article should include information about Thor Heyerdahl's —
- **A.** ways of testing his ideas about ancient travel.
- **B.** balsa raft.
- **C.** crew.
- **D.** education.

4. Thor Heyerdahl believes that journeys made in ancient times explain why—
- **F.** his film won an Academy Award.
- **G.** Egyptians used boats made of papyrus.
- **H.** similar objects are found in places great distances apart.
- **J.** the native peoples of Peru built such excellent boats.

5. Which text structure best describes the organization of this article?
- **A.** chronological order
- **B.** comparison-contrast
- **C.** problem-solution
- **D.** cause-effect

Notes for Home: Your child read a passage and identified its main ideas and text structure. ***Home Activity:*** Read a nonfiction article from a magazine with your child. Have your child identify its main ideas and then summarize it.

Name ___________________________________

Writing Across Texts

Directions: In "To the Pole!" and "Antarctica Melts" you read about opposite ends of the Earth. These two areas of the world differ in some ways, but they have many things in common. Read the following sentences and decide if they are true about the Arctic, Antarctica, or both. Then add them to the correct place on the chart.

1. The average temperature is below zero.

2. The Inuit live there.

3. There are problems with pollution.

4. This area is at the north end of the Earth.

5. The average temperatures are rising.

6. The area has many icebergs.

7. This area is at the south end of the Earth.

8. Will Steger has visited there.

9. Ice island B-10A broke from there.

10. This area is reached by going north through Canada.

The Arctic	Antarctica	Both

Write a Comparison/Contrast Paragraph

Write a paragraph comparing and contrasting the Arctic with Antarctica. Use information from the chart above and from both selections. Use a separate sheet of paper for your paragraph.

Notes for Home: You child wrote a paragraph comparing the Arctic with the continent of Antarctica. ***Home Activity:*** Discuss with your child journeys you have taken. Share things you experienced for the first time as your child takes notes.

REVIEW

Grammar: Possessive Nouns

Directions: Decide whether the underlined possessive noun is singular or plural. Write **S** on the line if it is singular. Write **P** if it is plural.

__________ **1.** What was the class's choice for the next field trip?

__________ **2.** The students' decision was to visit the Museum of Science.

__________ **3.** They especially wanted to see the museum's new exhibit on the Arctic.

__________ **4.** Everyone applauded as the bus's doors closed, and the class was on its way.

__________ **5.** At the museum, the students watched a short film about polar bears' habits.

__________ **6.** Animals' lives are hard in the Arctic.

__________ **7.** A seal's life is often in great danger for it is a polar bear's favorite food.

__________ **8.** People's safety cannot be guaranteed around these powerful animals either.

__________ **9.** The flapping of snowy owls' wings can be heard in parts of the Arctic.

__________ **10.** This harsh environment is also the Arctic fox's home.

Directions: Correct each underlined word by adding an apostrophe to make it possessive. Write the possessive noun on the line.

____________________ **11.** Isn't the Arctic Ocean the worlds smallest ocean?

____________________ **12.** Besss question was addressed to the museum guide.

____________________ **13.** The groups guide replied that the answer was yes.

____________________ **14.** You will not find reptiles footprints in the Arctic because these creatures cannot survive the cold.

____________________ **15.** Geeses honks can be heard, however, especially in Greenland.

____________________ **16.** Wolves howls are not unusual in the Arctic.

____________________ **17.** Parts of Canada, Russia, Iceland, and other nations are included in the Arctic, but a countrys borders are hard to find.

____________________ **18.** To the listeners surprise, the guide told the group that the Arctic Circle is not an actual place.

____________________ **19.** Rather, it is a mapmakers aid, marking the area that has at least one 24-hour day and one 24-hour night each year.

____________________ **20.** At the museum exit, childrens voices mixed with those of other visitors, who chatted about all they had learned.

Notes for Home: Your child used an apostrophe to form singular and plural possessive nouns—nouns that show ownership. ***Home Activity:*** With your child, look through a newspaper for possessive nouns. Decide which ones are singular and which ones are plural.

Practice

Grammar: Pronouns

Pronouns are words that can take the place of nouns or noun phrases. Like nouns, pronouns have singular and plural forms. A singular pronoun replaces a singular noun. A plural pronoun replaces a plural noun.

Singular pronouns: I, me, you, he, she, him, her, it
Plural pronouns: we, us, you, they, them

Pronouns that show ownership are **possessive pronouns.** There are two kinds of possessive pronouns. One kind is used before nouns. The second kind stands alone without a noun following it.

Used before nouns: my, your, his, her, its, our, their
Used alone: mine, yours, his, hers, ours, theirs

Possessive pronouns, unlike possessive nouns, do not use apostrophes.

Allen has given <u>his</u> dog sled <u>its</u> first coat of yellow paint.

Directions: Choose a pronoun in ( ) to replace the underlined words in each sentence. Write the pronoun on the line.

______________ **1.** <u>Norah, Joan, and I</u> went on a hiking trip. (We/She)

______________ **2.** These trails were new to <u>Joan and Norah</u>. (her/them)

______________ **3.** <u>Joan and Norah</u> felt like explorers. (We/They)

______________ **4.** I pointed out an enormous tree to <u>Joan</u>. (it/her)

______________ **5.** <u>The tree</u> looked as if it were hundreds of feet tall. (It/You)

Directions: Circle the correct possessive pronoun in ( ) to complete each sentence.

6. That backpack is (my/mine).

7. (My/mine) compass is in the front pocket.

8. (Their/Theirs) tent is larger than this one.

9. This tent is (our/ours).

10. (Your/Yours) sense of direction is better than mine.

Notes for Home: Your child used pronouns, such as *he, you,* and *they,* and possessive pronouns, such as *his, your,* and *theirs,* in sentences. ***Home Activity:*** Challenge your child to describe something that happened in school today, using pronouns and possessive pronouns.

Grammar: Pronouns

Directions: Choose a pronoun in ( ) to replace the underlined words in each sentence. Write the pronoun on the line.

______________ **1.** The explorer talked to my friends and me. (us/them)

______________ **2.** Mr. Johnson had been to the Arctic three times. (We/He)

______________ **3.** The explorer and his colleagues are famous. (We/They)

______________ **4.** I enjoyed listening to Mr. Johnson. (him/them)

______________ **5.** My friends and I had a number of questions for Mr. Johnson. (We/They)

Directions: Choose a possessive pronoun in ( ) to complete each sentence correctly. Write the possessive pronoun on the line.

______________ **6.** The Smith family and (our/their) family have lived in Smithtown for 300 years.

______________ **7.** The Smiths' ancestors bought so much land that most of Smithtown once was (his/theirs).

______________ **8.** My great-great-grandfather claimed that 100 acres of the Smiths' land was really (mine/his).

______________ **9.** With (his/their) approval, I explored and made a list of the contents of my grandparents' attic.

______________ **10.** I told Liddy Smith that one of my family's oldest books must have belonged first to (her/my) family, not to ours.

Write a Log

Imagine that you keep a log as you travel to some faraway place, such as a polar region. On a separate sheet of paper, write several entries in your log. Describe the journey and your experiences. Tell about the people who travel with you. Use singular and plural pronouns and possessive pronouns.

Notes for Home: Your child used singular and plural pronouns, such as *he, you,* and *they,* and possessive pronouns, such as *his, your,* and *theirs*. ***Home Activity:*** With your child, describe items in your home and in your neighborhood using possessive pronouns.

Name ______________________________ **To the Pole**

Grammar: Pronouns

RETEACHING

Singular Pronouns			
I	me	my	mine
he	you	your	yours
her	she	it	him
	his	hers	its

Plural Pronouns			
we	us	our	ours
you	your	yours	
they	them	their	theirs

Complete the sentences. Write pronouns from the boxes.

1. Maria likes basketball.
   ____________ likes basketball.

2. Maria plays with some friends.
   Maria plays with ____________.

A **pronoun** takes the place of a noun or nouns. Pronouns may be singular or plural. **Possessive pronouns** show ownership.

Directions: Write the pronoun from each sentence.

1. They played basketball at Maria's house. ____________
2. Maria's parents gave her a new basketball. ____________
3. Maria thanked them before breakfast. ____________
4. Maria is very happy with their gift. ____________
5. Rachel and Tomas like it too. ____________
6. Other friends will join their game. ____________
7. Neighbors such as us will watch. ____________
8. We should have an exciting afternoon. ____________

Directions: Write a pronoun to replace the underlined word or words.

9. Maria wanted a party for her birthday. ____________
10. Mr. and Mrs. Santos agreed to Maria's request. ____________
11. Mr. and Mrs. Santos arranged for a surprise. ____________
12. The surprise was a visit from a basketball star. ____________
13. He signed a basketball for Maria and her family. ____________

Notes for Home: Your child used singular and plural pronouns and possessive pronouns. ***Home Activity:*** Have your child observe a family member and take notes. Then have your child write sentences from his or her notes, using pronouns.

Name ______________________

Grammar: Pronouns

Directions: Circle each pronoun.

1. He built a boat and sailed it around the world.
2. She made him a flag to fly on it.
3. We sailed in my boat last week.
4. I think that her boat is bigger than ours.
5. Can you tell the difference between mine and hers?
6. Where do they store their sails?
7. Gina keeps her sails where we keep our oars.
8. Peter folds his sails and puts them aboard the boat.
9. Do you think we should take a water safety course?
10. My aunt and uncle took theirs from the Coast Guard.

Directions: Write each sentence, completing it with a pronoun that makes sense.

11. Since boating is fun, many people enjoy (pronoun) as a pastime.

____

12. Some people paddle (pronoun) own canoes.

____

13. My brother likes to fish from (pronoun) rowboat.

____

14. People with boats sail (pronoun) on breezy days.

____

15. My aunt would never sell (pronoun) motorboat.

____

16. Aunt Sal likes riding in (pronoun) so much.

____

17. (pronoun) family often rides with her.

____

Notes for Home: Your child identified pronouns in sentences and wrote sentences with pronouns. ***Home Activity:*** Together, look for pronouns in a favorite story. Have your child identify whether they are singular or plural, and whether they are possessive.

Name ______________________________

Word Study: Prefixes

Directions: A letter or group of letters added to the beginning of a word is a **prefix.** A prefix can change the meaning of a word. Add a prefix to each word below to make a new word. Write each new word on the line.

1. re + heat = ____________

2. in + active = ____________

3. un + wrap = ____________

4. in + complete = ____________

5. re + place = ____________

6. un + lock = ____________

7. in + audible = ____________

8. re + play = ____________

Directions: Read the newspaper story below. Look for the words with the prefixes **un-, re-,** or **in-.** Circle these words. Then write the prefix and the rest of the word on the line, connected by a + sign. For example, for **undone,** you would write **un + done.**

★★★★★★★★★★★★★★★★★★★★★★

AMAZING JOURNEY!

An unlikely group has reached the North Pole. Students from a local college have journeyed with their teachers over unstable ice floes and uneven terrain to reach territory not many have seen. This unusual accomplishment was funded by a major corporation, who met the group at critical points along the way to restock their food supply and check on their health. The group made it by the end of the summer, just before the ice floes reformed and froze solid. It was an incredible show of courage and fortitude!

9. ____________

10. ____________

11. ____________

12. ____________

13. ____________

14. ____________

15. ____________

Notes for Home: Your child formed new words by adding the prefixes *un-, re-,* and *in-* to base words. ***Home Activity:*** Read a newspaper story with your child. Help your child find words that have these prefixes. Have your child write each word and circle its prefix.

Name ____________________

Spelling: Negative Prefixes

Pretest Directions: Fold back the page along the dotted line. On the blanks, write the spelling words as they are dictated. When you have finished the test, unfold the page and check your words.

1. ____________________
2. ____________________
3. ____________________
4. ____________________
5. ____________________
6. ____________________
7. ____________________
8. ____________________
9. ____________________
10. ____________________
11. ____________________
12. ____________________
13. ____________________
14. ____________________
15. ____________________
16. ____________________
17. ____________________
18. ____________________
19. ____________________
20. ____________________

1. I've never done anything **illegal**.
2. Your conclusion is **illogical**.
3. Ink stains left my note **illegible**.
4. The watch is very **inexpensive**.
5. Rumors are often **inaccurate**.
6. He gave an **indirect** answer.
7. It was an **informal** gathering.
8. Don't pretend to be **incapable**.
9. A tornado's power is **incredible**.
10. It is **impolite** to stare at people.
11. That was an **improper** remark.
12. A crack made the cup **imperfect**.
13. I'm **impatient** with my little sister.
14. I have an **imbalance** in my diet.
15. His tantrum was quite **immature**.
16. His actions were **irresponsible**.
17. He has an **irregular** heartbeat.
18. His **irrational** thinking worries me.
19. The puppy is simply **irresistible**.
20. An heirloom is **irreplaceable**.

Notes for Home: Your child took a pretest on words with the negative prefixes *il-*, *in-*, *im-*, and *ir-*. ***Home Activity:*** Help your child learn misspelled words. Your child should look at the word, notice its prefix, say it, spell it aloud, and then spell it with eyes shut.

Name ______________________________

Spelling: Negative Prefixes

Word List

illegal	inaccurate	incredible	impatient	irregular
illogical	indirect	impolite	imbalance	irrational
illegible	informal	improper	immature	irresistible
inexpensive	incapable	imperfect	irresponsible	irreplaceable

Directions: Choose the word from the box that is formed by adding **il-** or **in-** to each word. Write the word on the line.

1. formal ______________

2. logical ______________

3. accurate ______________

4. direct ______________

5. legible ______________

6. expensive ______________

7. capable ______________

8. legal ______________

9. credible ______________

Directions: Choose the word from the box that best matches each clue. Use each word only once. Write the word on the line.

______________ **10.** I am how you feel when you are in a hurry and have to wait.

______________ **11.** I am something hard to resist.

______________ **12.** I am the kind of behavior that is considered not proper.

______________ **13.** I am the kind of spelling word that doesn't follow a rule.

______________ **14.** I am the kind of person who does not act like an adult.

______________ **15.** I am the kind of person who you do not trust to do an important task.

______________ **16.** I am the result when one side is heavier than the other.

______________ **17.** I am how you behave when you aren't thinking clearly.

______________ **18.** I am not ideal; I have flaws.

______________ **19.** I am something or someone that is unique.

______________ **20.** I am how you describe a person who has bad manners.

Notes for Home: Your child spelled words with the negative prefixes *il-*, *in-*, *im-*, and *ir-*. ***Home Activity:*** Have your child add the prefix *in-* to *effective* and *frequent* and use each word in a sentence. Discuss how adding this prefix changes the meaning of words.

Name ______________________

Spelling: Negative Prefixes

Directions: Proofread this letter from an Arctic expedition. Find seven spelling mistakes. Use the proofreading marks to correct each mistake.

≡	Make a capital.
/	Make a small letter.
∧	Add something.
℘	Take out something.
⊙	Add a period.
¶	Begin a new paragraph.

Dear Dad,

If this letter ever reaches you, it will be by a very undirect route, but the temptation to try is iresistible. We're stuck in a settlement that has iregular contact with the outside world, so any prediction of when my letter can go is bound to be innaccurate.

The Arctic is incredible—I'm imcapable of finding words for it! I feel an unlogical impulse to speak in a whisper—I'm almost afraid to break the vast silence of the landscape. Maybe twenty-four hours of daylight has made me irrational.

If my writing is illegible, it's Ben's fault—he is inpatient to go exploring. We are both well and eager to see you and Mom soon.

Love,

Marianne

Spelling Tip

When negative prefixes are added to base words, the spelling of the base word does not change. Check the letter to make sure the beginnings of words are spelled correctly.

Word List

illegal	improper
illogical	imperfect
illegible	impatient
inexpensive	imbalance
inaccurate	immature
indirect	irresponsible
informal	irregular
incapable	irrational
incredible	irresistible
impolite	irreplaceable

Write a Letter

On a separate sheet of paper, write a letter to Marianne from her father. Try to use at least three spelling words.

Notes for Home: Your child spelled words with the negative prefixes *il-*, *in-*, *im-*, and *ir-*. ***Home Activity:*** Give your child the base word for each spelling word. Have him or her add one of the negative prefixes to each base word to form a spelling word *(il + legal = illegal)*.

Spelling: Negative Prefixes

REVIEW

Word List				
illegal	inaccurate	incredible	impatient	irregular
illogical	indirect	impolite	imbalance	irrational
illegible	informal	improper	immature	irresistible
inexpensive	incapable	imperfect	irresponsible	irreplaceable

Directions: Choose the word from the box that is the negative form of the word in parentheses and that makes sense in the sentence. Write the word on the line.

______________ **1.** I am (patient) to begin the trip north to the Arctic.

______________ **2.** Arctic travel is (logical) without careful planning.

______________ **3.** You can freeze to death if you wear (proper) clothing.

______________ **4.** Going alone would be (regular); groups are safer.

______________ **5.** (Responsible) people could endanger the whole group.

______________ **6.** That means we can't take Celia; she is too (mature).

______________ **7.** Celia can't overcome her (rational) fear of snow.

______________ **8.** An (direct) route will take longer, but we will see more.

______________ **9.** The (balance) of the load on the sled will make it tip over.

______________ **10.** We all enjoy our (formal) dinners around the campfire.

Directions: Choose the word from the box that best matches each definition. Write the word on the line.

______________ **11.** unique; impossible to replace

______________ **12.** flawed or defective

______________ **13.** ill-mannered; rude

______________ **14.** cheap; easily affordable

______________ **15.** against the law

______________ **16.** overwhelming; strongly tempting

______________ **17.** without ability

______________ **18.** difficult or impossible to read

______________ **19.** containing mistakes; not exact

______________ **20.** hard to believe; extraordinary

Notes for Home: Your child spelled words with the negative prefixes *il-*, *in-*, *im-*, and *ir-*. ***Home Activity:*** Write the four negative prefixes on separate sheets of paper. Say each spelling word aloud and have your child write the word on the correct sheet.

Name ______________________________

Schedule

A **schedule** is a specialized chart that lists events and when they take place, side by side.

Directions: Read the schedule for cruise ships. Note the names of the cruise ships, their departure dates, routes, and arrival dates. Then answer the questions that follow.

Cruise Ship	Departure/ Anchorage, Alaska	Arrive at Prudhoe Bay (3-day stay)	Sail Through Queen Elizabeth Islands	Final Destination/ Frobisher Bay, Canada
Alaskan Princess	June 1	June 5	June 8–10	June 15
Arctic Mist	June 11	June 15	June 18–20	June 25
Northern Explorer	June 26	June 30	July 3–5	July 10
Polar Princess	July 4	July 8	July 11–13	July 18
Vancouver Vacation	July 16	July 20	July 23–25	July 30
Queen Elizabeth's Quest	July 23	July 27	July 30–August 1	August 6
Alaskan Princess	July 31	August 4	August 7–9	August 14
Arctic Mist	August 8	August 12	August 15–17	August 22
Northern Explorer	August 19	August 23	August 26–28	September 2
Polar Princess	August 30	September 3	September 6–8	September 13
Vancouver Vacation	September 11	September 15	September 18–20	September 25
Queen Elizabeth's Quest	September 21	September 25	September 28–30	October 5

1. How many days is each cruise? How can you tell? ______________________________

____

2. How many ships travel this route? How can you tell? ______________________________

____

3. If you traveled on the first sailing of the *Arctic Mist,* during which days would you cruise through the Queen Elizabeth Islands?

____

4. What happens at Prudhoe Bay? How can you tell? ______________________________

____

5. If you wanted to sail on the *Polar Princess,* for which dates could you schedule a trip?

____

Name ______________________________

Directions: Use the schedule of shipboard events to answer the questions that follow.

Schedule of Activities for June 10							
Activity	7 A.M. to 9 A.M.	9 A.M. to 11 A.M.	11 A.M. to 1 P.M.	1 P.M. to 3 P.M.	3 P.M. to 5 P.M.	5 P.M. to 7 P.M.	7 P.M. to 9 P.M.
Bird Watching	✓	✓	✓				
Ship Walk	✓	✓	✓	✓	✓	✓	
Whale Watching	✓	✓	✓	✓	✓		
Shuffleboard			✓	✓	✓		
Midday Movie Feature			✓				
Iceberg Viewing	✓	✓	✓	✓	✓	✓	
Ping-Pong Tournament					✓	✓	✓
Line Dancing Instruction					✓		✓
First Dinner Seating						✓	
Talent Show							✓
Photography Class		✓		✓			✓
✓ = Activity is available.							

6. What do the checkmarks on the schedule represent? How do you know?

____

____

7. Between which hours might you be able to watch for whales? ______________

8. Which activities occur at the same time as the talent show? ______________

____

9. If you watched the Midday Movie Feature, which activities would you be missing?

____

____

10. How does the schedule assist passengers in planning their day? ______________

____

Notes for Home: Your child answered questions about schedules. ***Home Activity:*** Obtain a schedule for a bus or train route. Plan a trip with your child. Choose a destination and a departure time, and then figure out your arrival time and how long the trip would take.

Family Times

Name______________________________

Summary

El Güero's Family Forced to Journey North

One day, El Güero is called out of class. His father, a judge, has been ordered to a distant part of Mexico. El Güero and his family must move, immediately. For El Güero, the trip is an adventure, filled with new foods, sights, and sounds. But he soon realizes there are many dangers on such a long trip as well.

Activity

Pretend to be El Güero. Have your child pretend he or she is El Güero and is telling a friend about the trip. Encourage your child to describe what was most difficult or exciting about the journey.

Reading Skills

Context Clues

Context clues are words that come before or after an unfamiliar word and help you figure out what it means.

A context clue may be a **synonym,** a word with nearly the same meaning as an unknown word, or it may be an **antonym,** a word with an opposite meaning.

Everyone calls me El Güero, or the Blond One.
The word *or* shows you that *El Güero* and the *Blond One* are synonyms with nearly the same meaning.

A context clue may also be a definition or explanation of the unknown word, or a series of examples.

We traveled on a freighter, a ship that carries goods.

"A ship that carries goods" defines *freighter.*

Activity

Challenge with Context Clues. Make a list of unfamiliar words. Use a dictionary if necessary. Each person should then make up sentences, leaving a blank space for the unfamiliar words. Include context clues explaining the words' meanings. Read each sentence aloud, and challenge others to decide which word goes in the blank.

Family Times

Tested Vocabulary

Words to Know

Knowing the meanings of these words is important to reading the excerpt from *El Güero.* Practice using these words to learn their meanings.

bandits outlaws

caravans groups traveling together for safety

conserve to keep from being used up

embark to set out

exiled banished from an area

merciful showing or feeling unusual kindness

Grammar

Subject/Object Pronouns

A **subject pronoun** is a personal pronoun used as the subject of a sentence. *I, you, he, she, it, we,* and *they* can be used as subject pronouns. The subject pronoun and the verb of a sentence must agree.

He travels to a new town.

They protect his caravan.

A personal pronoun used as an object after the verb in a sentence is called an **object pronoun.** *Me, you, him, her, it, us, you,* and *them* are object pronouns.

I thanked them.

Marc gave the map to us.

Activity

Play the Pronoun Game. Choose sides for the Pronoun Game. The Subject Pronoun team challenges the Object Pronoun team with a sentence containing a subject pronoun. The Object Pronoun team has to use the matching object pronoun correctly in a sentence of its own. (*I* and *me* would be matching pronouns.) Teams trade roles and repeat the challenge.

Tested Spelling Words

______	______	______	______
______	______	______	______
______	______	______	______
______	______	______	______
______	______	______	______

Context Clues

- **Context clues** are words that come before or after an unfamiliar word and help you figure out what it means.
- A context clue may be a synonym, a word with nearly the same meaning as the unknown word, or an antonym, a word with an opposite meaning.
- A context clue may also be a definition or explanation of the unknown word, or a series of examples.

Directions: Reread "For the First Time." Then complete the table. Use context clues to determine the meaning of each word or group of words from the story.

Words	Meaning
gallina rellena	**1.**
frijoles machacados	**2.**
guacamole salad	**3.**
bollitos	**4.**
tortillas	**5.**

Notes for Home: Your child read a story and used context clues to figure out the meaning of five words from the story. ***Home Activity:*** Read a story with your child. Prompt your child to point out unfamiliar words. Help him or her use context clues to figure out the meaning of these words.

Name ______________________________

Vocabulary

Directions: Choose the word from the box that best answers each question. Write the word on the line.

Check the Words You Know

__ bandits
__ caravans
__ conserve
__ embark
__ exiled
__ merciful

__________ **1.** Which word describes people who break the law?

__________ **2.** Which word describes someone who does not like to see other people suffer?

__________ **3.** Which word has a similar meaning to the word *begin?*

__________ **4.** Which word means to save something, such as energy or resources?

__________ **5.** Which word describes groups of people who are traveling?

Directions: Choose the word from the box that best replaces the underlined word or words. Write the word on the line to the left.

__________ **6.** Shefki was <u>banished</u> from his country because of his political beliefs.

__________ **7.** If it were not for a <u>kind, sympathetic</u> judge, he might have been imprisoned for life.

__________ **8.** Not knowing where to go, he decided to <u>set out</u> on a journey across the desert.

__________ **9.** He joined one of the <u>groups of travelers</u> that were going to Asia to trade for silks and spices.

__________ **10.** The groups traveled together for protection against <u>outlaws</u> who might rob them.

Write a Poem

On a separate sheet of paper, write a poem that tells a story of someone who must leave his or her homeland and travel to a strange unknown place. Use as many vocabulary words as you can in your poem.

Notes for Home: Your child identified and used vocabulary words from *El Güero.* ***Home Activity:*** Act out an adventure story with your child using the listed vocabulary words.

Name ______________________________

Context Clues

- **Context clues** are words that come before or after an unfamiliar word and help you figure out what it means.
- Specific types of context clues include a synonym, a word with the same or nearly the same meaning as the unfamiliar word; an antonym, a word that means the opposite of the unfamiliar word; a definition or explanation that appears before or after the unfamiliar word; or an example to explain the unfamiliar word.

Directions: Reread the passage from *El Güero* in which the characters are introduced. Then use context clues and refer to the list of types of context clues to answer the questions below.

My name is Porfirio, but nobody ever calls me by my name. It is because most people in this country have dark eyes and dark hair, while my eyes are green and my hair is yellow. It is for this reason that everyone calls me El Güero, or the Blond One. My little sister, María, is called Maruca. I call my Aunt Victoria Tía Vicky, and my mother Mamacita. Everyone in Mexico has a nickname, or a short, affectionate form of his name. Only my father, the Judge, who is so dignified and taciturn, is called by his name, Cayetano, and then only by Mamacita and Tía Vicky. I have been told to call him Papá, though the other children I know call their fathers Papacito, dear little father.

1. What context clues are used to explain the meaning of *El Güero* in the passage?

____

2. Which type of context clue helps you understand the meaning of *nickname?*

____

3. Which context clues can be used to understand what *taciturn* means? How might you check if your understanding is correct?

____

____

4. What does *Papacito* mean? How do you know?

____

5. On a separate sheet of paper, list three other unfamiliar words from *El Güero* that you defined with the help of context clues. Write the meaning of each word.

Notes for Home: Your child used context clues to figure out the meaning of unfamiliar words. ***Home Activity:*** Read a brief magazine article with your child. Help him or her to use context clues to determine the meaning of any unfamiliar words.

Selection Test

Directions: Choose the best answer to each item. Mark the letter for the answer you have chosen.

Part 1: Vocabulary

Find the answer choice that means about the same as the underlined word in each sentence.

1. The former president was <u>exiled</u>.
- A. held back
- B. assigned to a different job
- C. imprisoned
- D. forced to leave one's country or home

2. The family was ready to <u>embark</u>.
- F. set out; start
- G. make a decision
- H. make their own way
- J. take a rest

3. The merchants traveled in <u>caravans</u>.
- A. small, fast sailing ships
- B. groups of people traveling together for safety
- C. trails marked in the woods
- D. wagons with covers that can be taken off

4. A group of <u>bandits</u> approached.
- F. pilgrims; travelers
- G. soldiers
- H. robbers; outlaws
- J. peasants

5. Mr. Alexander was <u>merciful</u>.
- A. showing mercy or kindness
- B. having a stern expression
- C. honest and truthful
- D. tending to be cruel

6. We learned to <u>conserve</u> water.
- F. be thankful for
- G. find many uses for
- H. make clean; purify
- J. keep from wasting or using up

Part 2: Comprehension

Use what you know about the story to answer each item.

7. The narrator of the story is called "El Güero" because—
- A. he is strong.
- B. it is his name.
- C. he is small.
- D. his hair is yellow.

8. *Cayetano* is—
- F. the nickname El Güero's mother uses
- G. El Güero's father's name
- H. a word meaning "dear little father"
- J. the Spanish word for "judge"

9. Why was El Güero's family upset at the beginning of the story?
- A. The President had offered El Güero's father a new job.
- B. They were being forced to leave their home.
- C. They had decided to move to a different country.
- D. A war had begun, and they had to escape.

10. Why did the bandit leader decide to protect the judge and his family?
- F. He hoped for a reward.
- G. He was grateful for how the judge had treated him.
- H. He was afraid of the judge.
- J. He liked the judge's family.

11. El Güero explains, "There he had written poetry and had <u>declaimed</u> it before large audiences." <u>Declaimed</u> means—
- A. took something back.
- B. burned.
- C. recited in public.
- D. copied.

12. El Güero's father buys quinine from a pharmacist. You can figure out the meaning of the word <u>pharmacist</u> from the clue that—
    F. quinine is made from a tree in Peru.
    G. the pharmacist lives in Acapulco.
    H. quinine is a medicine.
    J. the family is staying in a hotel.

13. From the family's experiences on their journey, you can conclude that—
    A. physical health is the first thing to suffer in such situations.
    B. people tend to become very selfish when resources are limited.
    C. difficult situations can strengthen people and relationships.
    D. people who are in a faraway place really get on each other's nerves.

14. Which clue helps you understand that this story takes place in the past?
    F. The ship burns coal to power its steam engine.
    G. The judge has to pay the captain of the ship for passage.
    H. The food on the ship is heavy and salty.
    J. Tía Vicky carries scissors, thread, and cloth in her baggage.

15. At Cabo San Lucas, who seems to give up the most to help the family?
    A. El Güero
    B. Maruca
    C. Tía Vicky
    D. Mamacita

STOP

Name ______________________________

Context Clues

- **Context clues** are words that come before or after an unfamiliar word and help you figure out what it means.
- Specific types of context clues include a synonym, a word with the same or nearly the same meaning as the unfamiliar word; an antonym, a word that means the opposite of the unfamiliar word; a definition or explanation that appears before or after the unfamiliar word; or an example to explain the unfamiliar word.

Directions: Read the story below. Use context clues to think about the meaning of the underlined words.

About dawn of April 18, 1906, I was roused from a sound sleep by large pieces of my plaster ceiling falling about me. The whole house was shaking. It was an earthquake! I jumped up, dressed quickly, and ran outside. People were milling about. No one seemed to have any idea where to go.

The tremors soon ended, but fires broke out and threatened to destroy the entire city. Stunned by the shock of events, we could only watch our beloved San Francisco disintegrate into ruins.

The presence of the army kept people from looting any goods from houses or stores. The Red Cross dispensed free meals during the emergency. The people recovered sooner than anyone thought possible. Before the fires were out, we were determined to rebuild our city.

Directions: Use context clues to write a definition for each word in the table. One has been done for you.

Words	Definitions
roused	woken up
tremors	**1.**
milling	**2.**
disintegrate	**3.**
looting	**4.**
dispensed	**5.**

Notes for Home: Your child used context clues to determine the meaning of unfamiliar words. ***Home Activity:*** Read a story with your child. Encourage your child to use context clues to figure out the meaning of unfamiliar words. Then check definitions in a dictionary.

Name ______________________________

REVIEW

Setting

Directions: Read the story. Then read each question about the story. Choose the best answer to each question. Mark the letter for the answer you have chosen.

The Endless Count

Jonelle and her friends gathered at their wooden table under the oak, each carrying a breakfast tray. None of the other people around the girls seemed aware of the awful situation they were in. The others talked excitedly about the day's activities, but Jonelle's friends did not need to talk.

No words, just numbers. Each of them was silently counting the days left until they could return to civilization. How could their parents have sent them off into the heat, the flies, the bugs, the pollen, the dust, the unfamiliar sheets, the shared bathrooms, the tiny cabins?

Jonelle's parents had been sure she would enjoy a month of camping. In spite of her protests that she would rather stay at home, they made the arrangements and bundled Jonelle into the car. "It's for your own good, honey" and "You'll thank us by the time you come home" were two sentences that stuck in Jonelle's mind. During the drive to camp, her mother told stories about her childhood summers in the hot city and her longing for a country vacation. Her father told stories about the great times he had had at camp when he was a boy. But Jonelle knew better. She would hate it!

The camp leaders had promised another day of walking through woods, looking at birds and plants. This was not life as Jonelle knew and liked it. No friends' houses, no lazy afternoons by the pool, no shopping malls, not even school. Jonelle was shocked. Could she actually be eager for the new school year to start?

1. Jonelle and her friends eat breakfast—
- **A.** cold.
- **B.** outside.
- **C.** in a hall.
- **D.** in a cabin.

2. Jonelle and the others are staying in—
- **F.** a school.
- **G.** a prison.
- **H.** a friend's home.
- **J.** a camp.

3. Which of the following is **not** part of the setting?
- **A.** a swimming pool
- **B.** an oak tree
- **C.** tiny cabins
- **D.** a wooden table

4. What effect does the setting have on Jonelle?
- **F.** She hates being away from "civilization."
- **G.** She misses her parents.
- **H.** She wants to go on a nature walk.
- **J.** She doesn't want to return to school.

5. The time of year is most likely—
- **A.** spring.
- **B.** summer.
- **C.** fall.
- **D.** winter.

Notes for Home: Your child read a story and answered questions about its setting. ***Home Activity:*** After watching a movie together, encourage your child to discuss its setting. Talk about how the setting affected the characters and their actions.

Name ______________________________

Writing Across Texts

Directions: Think about what you learned from the excerpt from *El Güero* and from "The California Rancheros." Use that information to answer the questions below about the history of the area.

Of what three countries has California been a part since the 1770's?
1.
What happened in Mexico that made it necessary for the judge and his family to flee?
2.
To what area of Mexico was the Treviño family headed?
3.
What happened in 1821, and how did it change things in Mexico?
4.
What is the difference between a rancho and a hacienda?
5.

Write a Comparison/Contrast Paragraph

Use the information you gathered to write a paragraph on the history of northern Mexico and southern California. Write your paragraph on a separate sheet of paper.

Notes for Home: Your child used information from two sources to write a paragraph. ***Home Activity:*** Read aloud a story set in the past. With your child, discuss how things are alike or different today.

Name ______________________________

REVIEW

Grammar: Pronouns

Directions: Underline the pronoun in each sentence. Hint: Some pronouns are possessive pronouns.

1. Juan had mixed feelings about his new life in the United States.
2. The earthquake at home had caused great damage, and he and his family decided to move to America.
3. Life was good in America, but it was also strange and unfamiliar.
4. The social worker had been kind, and her advice was helpful.
5. Still, newcomers in a new land have their own particular problems.

Directions: Rewrite each pronoun and verb as a contraction.

6. we have ______________
7. he will ______________
8. she had ______________
9. they are ______________
10. it is ______________
11. I am ______________
12. we are ______________
13. you have ______________
14. they will ______________
15. you are ______________
16. we will ______________
17. he would ______________
18. she is ______________
19. I have ______________
20. he is ______________
21. it will ______________
22. you will ______________
23. she has ______________
24. he had ______________
25. they have ______________

Directions: Choose the pronoun in ( ) that completes each sentence. Write the pronoun on the line.

__________ **26.** Juan and his family were moving into (their/they're) new apartment.

__________ **27.** None of the furniture was really (their's/theirs), for they had had to leave everything behind.

__________ **28.** They thought longingly of their real home, with (it's/its) open, airy rooms.

__________ **29.** "Welcome to (your/you're) new home," said the woman who was helping them get settled.

__________ **30.** "My country is now (your's/yours)," she said.

Notes for Home: Your child identified and used pronouns—words that take the place of nouns. ***Home Activity:*** Point to different things in your home and ask questions such as "Whose is that?" Have your child respond, using a pronoun in the answer.

Practice

Grammar: Subject/Object Pronouns and Agreement

A pronoun takes the place of one or more nouns or noun phrases. When a pronoun is used as the subject of a sentence, it is called a **subject pronoun.**

My family moved to a new town. We moved to a new town.

Subject Pronouns: I, you, he, she, it, we, they

A pronoun used as an object in a sentence is called an **object pronoun.** An object pronoun used as a direct object follows an action verb and tells who or what receives the action.

My dog explored the new house. My dog explored it.

Object Pronouns: me, you, him, her, it, us, them

The **referent** is the noun or nouns to which the pronoun refers. A pronoun and its referent must agree. A singular pronoun agrees with a singular referent. A plural pronoun agrees with one or more plural referents. A pronoun and its referent can appear in separate sentences or in the same sentence.

My parents looked for a long time. They wanted to find a good place to live.

My mother and father were sure they had made the right choice.

Directions: Write a pronoun that best replaces the underlined words in each sentence. Then write **S** if it is a subject pronoun. Write **O** if it is an object pronoun.

________________ **1.** Last April, my family moved to Acapulco, Mexico.

________________ **2.** The move surprised my brother and me.

________________ **3.** My parents said that the move would be a good experience.

________________ **4.** Later, my brother and I agreed with our parents.

________________ **5.** My brother and I enjoyed learning Spanish and living by the sea.

Directions: Underline the pronoun in each sentence. Then circle its referent.

6. When Mary first moved to Hawaii, she had a hard time making new friends.

7. Friends from home kept in touch. They called and wrote letters.

8. After a week, Mary made her first new friend.

9. Steven showed Mary the big island. He knew about many interesting places.

10. Steven and Mary biked to the top of a mountain. They could see the whole island below.

Notes for Home: Your child wrote subject pronouns and object pronouns, and identified pronouns and their referents. ***Home Activity:*** Use pronouns in sentences. Have your child tell you if each pronoun is a subject pronoun or an object pronoun.

Grammar: Subject/Object Pronouns and Agreement

Directions: Write a pronoun that best replaces the underlined words. Then write **S** if it is a subject pronoun. Write **O** if it is an object pronoun.

______________ **1.** Last September, Renata arrived in town.

______________ **2.** Renata and her family came from Veracruz, Mexico.

______________ **3.** Renata taught my friends and me about Mexico and its culture.

______________ **4.** My friends and I were guests at Renata's house for a holiday called *Cinco de Mayo.*

______________ **5.** We all thanked Renata for including us in the holiday.

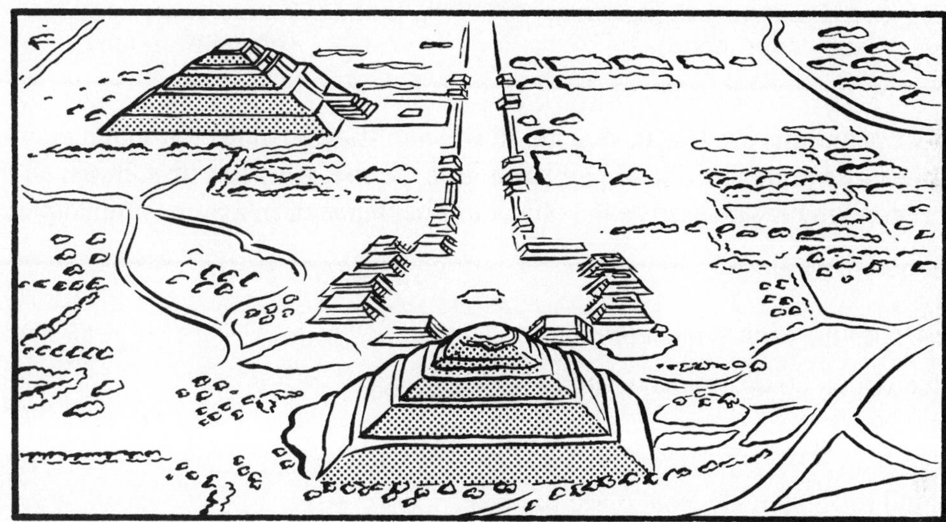

Directions: Underline the pronoun in each sentence. Then circle its referent.

6. Ellen's family took a trip to Mexico. They saw many amazing things.

7. Ellen was interested in the Mayan ruins. She had read about the pyramids and temples.

8. Ellen first saw the Pyramid of the Sun. It was over 200 feet high.

9. When she reached the top of the pyramid, Ellen stared down at the rest of the city.

10. A guide who was with Ellen pointed out the important sites to her.

Write a Newspaper Story

On a separate sheet of paper, write a story about a current event in your town or school. Include subject and object pronouns in your composition, and make sure they agree with their referents. When you are finished, underline each pronoun and circle its referent.

Notes for Home: Your child wrote subject pronouns, object pronouns, and identified pronouns and their referents. ***Home Activity:*** With your child, read a few paragraphs from a story. Have your child identify each pronoun and its referent.

Name ______________________________

RETEACHING

Grammar: Subject/Object Pronouns and Agreement

Subject Pronouns	Object Pronouns
I, you, she, he, it, we, they	me, you, her, him, it, us, them

Complete each sentence. Use a pronoun from the boxes. The clues in ( ) will help you.

1. Once ____________ (subject pronoun) wrote a message to ____________ (object pronoun).
2. ____________ (subject pronoun) looked at ____________ (object pronoun).

The **subject pronouns** are **I, you, she, he, it, we,** and **they.** A subject pronoun may be used as the subject of a sentence. The **object pronouns** are **me, you, her, him, it, us,** and **them.** An object pronoun may be used as the object in a sentence or in a prepositional phrase.

Directions: Underline each subject pronoun.

1. She knows some interesting facts about the telegraph.
2. It was the first way to send messages with electricity.
3. They could travel quickly from place to place.
4. "I want to be remembered as an inventor," Morse said.
5. "We will teach others to send messages," telegraph operators said.

Directions: Underline each object pronoun.

6. The operators taught me the code.
7. Morse's invention brought them to the world's attention.
8. People compared him to the great inventors of the past.
9. Does the telegraph affect us today?
10. The telephone, radio, and television have largely replaced it.

Notes for Home: Your child identified subject and object pronouns in sentences. ***Home Activity:*** Have your child use some of the pronouns from this page in other sentences. Ask him or her to tell you if they are subject or object pronouns.

Grammar: Subject/Object Pronouns and Agreement

Directions: Write the subject pronoun from each sentence.

1. I am studying the dragonfly for science class. ____________
2. You should hear the facts about the insect. ____________
3. It has four large delicate wings. ____________
4. They look like fine netting. ____________

Directions: Write the object pronoun from each sentence.

5. The wings move them rapidly through the air. ____________
6. The speed of the insect surprised her. ____________
7. People can spot it near water in summer. ____________
8. A dragonfly's unique appearance pleases me. ____________

Directions: Write a pronoun to replace the underlined word or words in each sentence.

9. Ms. Wasp assigned a report about <u>dragonflies</u>. ____________
10. <u>The report</u> will require some research. ____________
11. <u>Pat and Toni</u> worked on theirs at the library. ____________
12. The instructor praised <u>Pam and me</u> today. ____________
13. <u>Beth</u> discovered dragonflies lay eggs in water. ____________
14. That did not surprise <u>Rafael</u> very much. ____________
15. <u>Patrick</u> said, "The adults live only a few weeks." ____________
16. <u>Kim and I</u> observed live dragonflies for hours. ____________
17. We saw <u>a dragonfly</u> eat many kinds of insects. ____________

Write an Observation Journal Entry

On a separate sheet of paper, write an observation journal entry about an insect you have seen. Use subject and object pronouns to help you explain how it looked, where it was, and what it was doing.

Notes for Home: Your child identified subject and object pronouns in sentences. ***Home Activity:*** Have your child read his or her Observation Journal Entry to you. Ask your child to underline subject pronouns and circle object pronouns.

Name ________________________________

Word Study: Suffixes

Directions: A letter or group of letters added to the end of a word is called a **suffix.** A suffix can change the meaning of the base word. Add a suffix to each word below to make a new word. Write each new word on the line.

1. right + ful = ____________
2. flex + ible = ____________
3. final + ly = ____________
4. mercy + ful = ____________
5. care + ful + ly = ____________
6. fortune + ate + ly = ____________

Directions: Read the sentences below. Look and listen for words with the suffixes **-ly, -ful,** or **-ible.** Circle these words. Then write the base word and the suffix on the line, connected by a + sign. For example, for **doubtful,** you would write **doubt + ful.**

____________ 7. Sadly, the family packed their belongings and left their home behind.

____________ 8. Being sensible, they took the first ship they could find traveling out of the country.

____________ 9. The new travelers tried to make themselves useful on board.

____________ 10. They helped prepare meals and entertained the crew willingly.

____________ 11. Once, a fog drifted in, and the ship's captain realized that the ship was slightly off course.

____________ 12. He instantly took action to correct the direction.

____________ 13. When the ship docked, the family gazed with joy at the beautiful city that would be their new home.

____________ 14. How wonderful it felt to stand on solid ground again!

____________ 15. As they made a new life for themselves, they tried to forget the painful memories of leaving their old home.

Notes for Home: Your child formed new words by adding the suffixes *-ly, -ful,* and *-ible* to base words. ***Home Activity:*** Read a magazine article with your child. Help your child notice words with these suffixes. Have your child group words with the same suffix together and write them in a list.

Spelling: Suffixes *-ation, -tion, -ion*

Pretest Directions: Fold back the page along the dotted line. On the blanks, write the spelling words as they are dictated. When you have finished the test, unfold the page and check your words.

Pretest

1. ____________	1. **Relaxation** lessens tension.
2. ____________	2. Space **exploration** continues.
3. ____________	3. What is your **occupation**?
4. ____________	4. The train reached its **destination**.
5. ____________	5. New students attend **orientation**.
6. ____________	6. He made the **recommendation**.
7. ____________	7. **Determination** helps success.
8. ____________	8. My cut has a minor **infection**.
9. ____________	9. The **collection** was for the sick.
10. ____________	10. His **reaction** was one of surprise.
11. ____________	11. It was a difficult **situation**.
12. ____________	12. Please turn off the **television**.
13. ____________	13. Ours is a hopeful **generation**.
14. ____________	14. On **reflection**, I'll try it.
15. ____________	15. The forest faces **destruction**.
16. ____________	16. Pay **attention** to the lesson.
17. ____________	17. Use **deduction** to solve it.
18. ____________	18. We held the wedding **reception**.
19. ____________	19. We need a **solution** quickly.
20. ____________	20. The **convention** was at the hotel.

Notes for Home: Your child took a pretest on words that have the suffixes *-ation*, *-tion*, and *-ion*. ***Home Activity:*** Help your child learn misspelled words before the final test. Your child can underline the word parts that caused the problems and concentrate on those parts.

Think and Practice

Spelling: Suffixes *-ation, -tion, -ion*

Word List

relaxation	recommendation	situation	attention
exploration	determination	television	deduction
occupation	infection	generation	reception
destination	collection	reflection	solution
orientation	reaction	destruction	convention

Directions: Add a suffix to each base word below to form a word from the box. Write the word on the line.

1. determine ____________________
2. convene ____________________
3. situate ____________________
4. generate ____________________
5. solve ____________________
6. televise ____________________
7. attend ____________________
8. occupy ____________________
9. deduce ____________________
10. explore ____________________
11. receive ____________________
12. destiny ____________________

Directions: Choose the word from the box that best completes each equation. Write the word on the line.

13. re + commence – ce + dation = ____________________
14. destroy – oy + uction = ____________________
15. re + lax + a + tion = ____________________
16. reach – h + tion = ____________________
17. in + fect – t + tion = ____________________
18. color – or + lec + tion = ____________________
19. orient + ate – te + tion = ____________________
20. reflexes – xes + c + tion = ____________________

Notes for Home: Your child spelled words with the suffixes *-ation, -tion,* and *-ion.* ***Home Activity:*** Challenge your child to add the suffix *-ion* to each of these words and use the new words in sentences: *elect, act, construct.*

Name ______________________________

Spelling: Suffixes *-ation, -tion, -ion*

Directions: Proofread this humorous account of a canine exile's thoughts. Find six spelling mistakes. Use the proofreading marks to correct each mistake.

≡	Make a capital.
/	Make a small letter.
∧	Add something.
⌇	Take out something.
⊙	Add a period.
¶	Begin a new paragraph.

How can I get back in? Is my life of relaxashon in front of the telavision over? I miss the attention and affection of the people inside.

I didn't mean any harm. I was wandering about without a specific destination and decided a little exploreation under the shed would be fun. Who knew a spray in the face would be my recepsion? And now, though I've barked my reccomendation to be allowed in, I'm banned from the house until the skunk smell wears off. I never expected this reaction to my situasion.

Spelling Tip

When adding the suffixes **-ation, -tion,** or **-ion,** some base words do not change: **relaxation.** Other base words may drop a final **e** or **y: exploration, occupation.** Some base words have other changes: **receive + -tion = reception**

Word List

relaxation	situation
exploration	television
occupation	generation
destination	reflection
orientation	destruction
recommendation	attention
determination	deduction
infection	reception
collection	solution
reaction	convention

Write a Narrative

On a separate sheet of paper, write a narrative that describes thoughts that might occupy an exile's mind. It can be humorous, like the dog's tale above, or serious. What does an exile feel? What might an exile do? Try to use at least five spelling words in your narrative.

Notes for Home: Your child spelled words with suffixes *-ation, -tion, -ion.* ***Home Activity:*** Challenge your child to identify the base word in each word from the box and to tell whether the spelling of the base word changed when the suffix was added.

Spelling: Suffixes *-ation, -tion, -ion* REVIEW

Word List			
relaxation	recommendation	situation	attention
exploration	determination	television	deduction
occupation	infection	generation	reception
destination	collection	reflection	solution
orientation	reaction	destruction	convention

Directions: Choose the word from the box that best completes each sentence. Write the word on the line to the left.

________________ **1.** Before school started in the fall, her _____ was being a lifeguard at the local beach.

________________ **2.** The train took her straight to her _____: Lowwood School.

________________ **3.** Her _____ by the older students was warm and friendly.

________________ **4.** They had taken up a _____ to buy party refreshments to make the "new girl in town" feel more at home.

________________ **5.** She found a _____ to her isolation in new friendships.

________________ **6.** She paid _____ in class, wanting to do well in her studies.

________________ **7.** Dinner was a welcome form of _____ after each busy day.

________________ **8.** She rarely found time to watch _____ after dinner.

________________ **9.** Her _____ to make a better life for herself in this country was admired by many.

________________ **10.** Each _____ in her family had always had at least one person eager to try new adventures.

Directions: Choose the word from the box that has the same or nearly the same meaning as each word or words below. Write the word on the line.

11. response ________________

12. search ________________

13. adjustment ________________

14. mirror image ________________

15. subtraction ________________

16. suggestion ________________

17. disease ________________

18. conference ________________

19. circumstances ________________

20. ruin ________________

Notes for Home: Your child reviewed words with suffixes *-ation, -ion, -tion.* ***Home Activity:*** Write the base word of each spelling word on index cards. Have your child pick a card and add a suffix to form a spelling word *(occupy + -tion = occupation).*

Evaluate Reference Sources

In order to decide whether a source is reliable and valid, you need to **evaluate reference sources.** You need to decide whether the information in the source is complete, unbiased, factual, and up-to-date, and ask yourself whether the source provides the kind of information you need for your research purposes.

Directions: Study the different reference sources. Then answer the questions that follow.

TRAVELING THE WORLD

Table of Contents

Getting from Here to There: A History of Travel

Contents

The World Almanac 1998, Index

World Travel

Vol. 232 Issue 9 February 1999

Features

Photo Essay

Interview

1. Read the chapter titles for *Traveling the World.* What is this book mostly about?

____

2. Read the chapter titles for *Getting from Here to There.* What is this book mostly about?

____

3. Suppose you are writing a paper about exciting, yet difficult, journeys. Which of these two books would be the most helpful? Why?

____

4. Suppose you wanted historical information about ships from long ago. Which of the resources shown would be most useful? Explain.

____

____

5. Would an almanac be a good place to find out the population of Jamaica? Explain.

____

6. Suppose you wanted to read about someone's real-life travel experiences. Would the magazine *World Travel* be helpful? Explain.

____

____

7. Suppose you were writing a report on the invention of the airplane and you discovered that the book *Getting from Here to There* was published in 1995. Would this book still be a useful reference source? Explain.

____

____

8. When evaluating books, why is it important to check the copyright page?

____

____

9. How can an index or a table of contents help you evaluate a reference source?

____

____

10. Why is it important to set a purpose for your research before evaluating reference sources?

____

____

Notes for Home: Your child evaluated reference sources for specific research purposes. ***Home Activity:*** With your child, think of a topic and write questions about what you would like to know. Discuss what kinds of reference sources would be the most helpful.

Family Times

Name________________________________

Summary

Life on Mars

You are on a mission to search for evidence of life on Mars and to set up a base for future colonization. You learn that earlier probes of Mars found no evidence of life forms. Scientists believe no life exists there because no liquid water is available. One of your tasks will be to explore the possibility of heating the atmosphere of Mars enough to melt the ice.

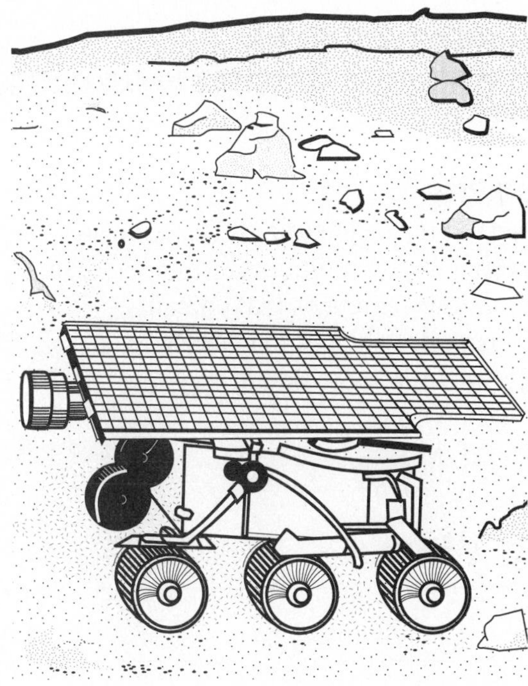

Activity

Record Log Entries. Imagine you are the captain or crew member on a mission to Mars. Record log entries that describe your mission and tell what you see and do on Mars.

Reading Skills

Steps in a Process

The actions you perform in order to make something or to reach a goal are the **steps in a process.**

Sometimes the steps in a process will have numbers. Other clues to the order of the steps are words like *first, begin, next, then,* and *last.*

If there are no clue words or numbers to help you keep the steps in order, use your common sense. Think about what you already know about the process and how it is done.

The selection explains how scientists hope to warm up Mars enough to melt the water in the polar caps. The words *first* and *begin* identify the first steps in the process. The remaining steps are explained in order, so you know what to do should you ever need to warm up a planet.

Activity

Follow Directions. Read the steps for an interesting recipe or simple craft project. Then follow them in order to make something new, tasty, or useful.

Family Times

Tested Vocabulary

Words to Know

Knowing the meanings of these words is important to reading "Destination: Mars." Practice using these words to learn their meanings.

commander person in charge

concepts ideas; notions

detected discovered; found

organism a living thing

radiation radioactivity

Grammar

Prepositions and Prepositional Phrases

A **preposition** is a word that shows certain relationships between other words. Prepositions include words such as *from, with, in,* and *by.*
A **prepositional phrase** is a group of words that begins with a preposition and usually ends with a noun or pronoun.

The rover <u>from the lander</u> probed the soil.

You can use prepositional phrases to elaborate ideas and create more interesting sentences.

The soil covered the ice.
The soil <u>beneath the rover's wheels</u> covered the ice.

Activity

Describe an Experiment. Describe an experiment you might perform on another planet. Use sentences that contain prepositional phrases to describe your experiment in more detail.

Tested Spelling Words

______	______	______	______
______	______	______	______
______	______	______	______
______	______	______	______
______	______	______	______

Steps in a Process

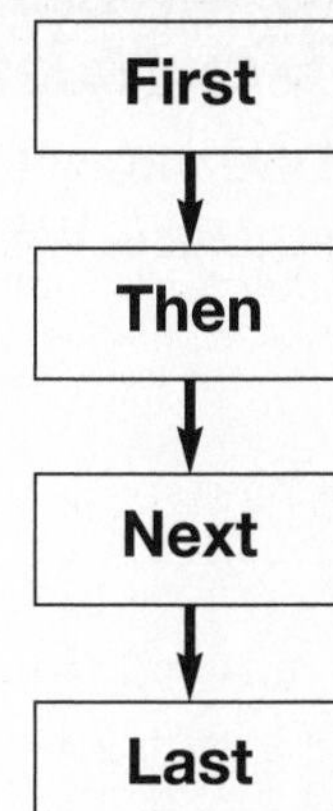

- The actions you perform in order to make something or to reach a goal are the **steps in a process.**
- Sometimes the steps in a process will have numbers. Other clues to the order of the steps are words like *first, begin, next, then,* and *last.* If there are no clue words or numbers to help you keep the steps in order, use your common sense.
- Sometimes the steps in a process refer to a process in nature, such as the growth of a plant.

Directions: Reread "Living in Space." Then complete the flow chart to describe the process by which oxygen, water, and carbon dioxide are constantly recycled in a bottle garden. Write the steps in the flow chart in the order in which they occur. Some steps have been started for you.

1. Plants collect

2. Plants convert

3. The leaves also produce

4.

5.

Notes for Home: Your child read about a process and listed the steps in the process in the order in which they occur. ***Home Activity:*** Encourage your child to list the steps in an everyday process, such as making breakfast or playing a compact disc.

Name ______________________________

Vocabulary

Directions: Choose the word from the box that best completes each sentence. Write the word on the line to the left.

Check the Words You Know

__ commander
__ concepts
__ detected
__organism
__ radiation

____________ **1.** The _____ had led many dangerous missions.

____________ **2.** This mission was created because scientists thought they had _____ life on another planet.

____________ **3.** The commander and his crew were to determine whether there was a living _____ on the planet.

____________ **4.** The scientists were eager to find out if their _____ about alien life forms were valid.

____________ **5.** However, when the ship got near the planet, it was surrounded by dangerous levels of _____. The mission could not be completed successfully.

Directions: Choose the word from the box that best matches each clue. Write the word in the puzzle.

Down

6. ideas; notions

7. discovered; found

8. a living thing

Across

9. person in charge

10. radioactivity

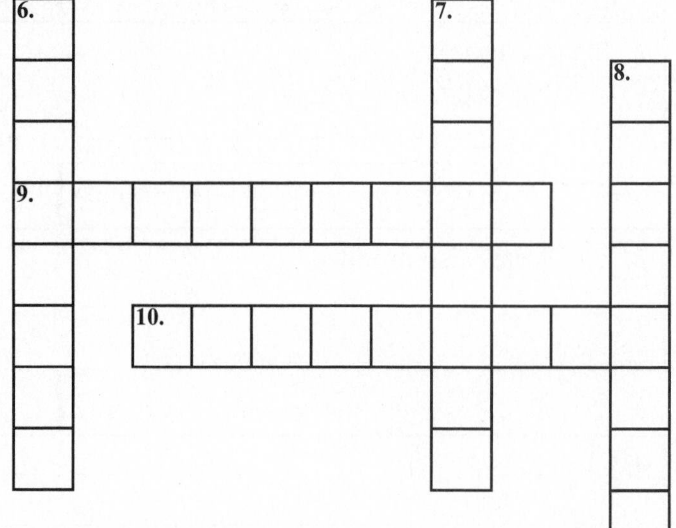

Write a Brochure

A brochure is a small pamphlet that tells detailed information about a place or a product. Use separate sheets of paper to write a brochure advertising a tourist trip to another planet. Include as many vocabulary words as you can.

Notes for Home: Your child identified and used vocabulary words from "Destination: Mars." ***Home Activity:*** With your child, act out a space adventure. Try to use as many vocabulary words as you can.

Name ________________________________

Steps in a Process

- The actions you perform in order to make something or to reach a goal are the **steps in a process.**
- Sometimes the steps in a process will have numbers. Other clues to the order of the steps are words like *first, begin, next, then,* and *last.*

Directions: Reread the part of "Destination: Mars" that tells what will be done after landing on Mars. Then answer the questions below. Think about the order of steps to take in establishing life on Mars.

Soon after landing, your crew will cover your habitat with sandbags to protect it against ultraviolet radiation and solar flares. You will set up experimental greenhouses, to see what plants can be grown without soil, *hydroponically*. You will determine what needs to be done to the Martian soil so that it can support plant life. Perhaps you will set up pools for fish, as a future source of protein. You will study the Martian weather and geology. You will investigate the possibilities of terraforming.

1. Which step will be done first and why?

____

____

2. Before trying to grow plants in Martian soil, which step should be done?

____

____

3. Which step will have to be done to provide a source of protein on Mars?

____

____

4. What are the final steps mentioned in this passage?

____

____

5. On a separate sheet of paper, explain why the steps described in the passage above are being taken. Reread that part of the selection to help you explain.

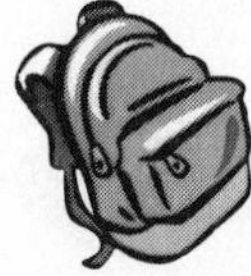

Notes for Home: Your child read a passage from a selection and identified the steps in a process. ***Home Activity:*** Read an instruction guide for using a simple household machine with your child. Encourage her or him to retell the steps for use in the correct order.

Selection Test

Directions: Choose the best answer to each item. Mark the letter for the answer you have chosen.

Part 1: Vocabulary

Find the answer choice that means about the same as the underlined word in each sentence.

1. He was studying the effects of radiation.
- A. the process of changing from a liquid to a gas
- B. rays of light
- C. particles or waves produced by nuclear decay
- D. electronic signals received by radio

2. We detected some salt in the water.
- F. discovered
- G. placed
- H. wished for
- J. required

3. Dr. Graham found an organism in the bay.
- A. sunken ship
- B. disease that spreads from one person to another
- C. type of musical instrument
- D. animal, plant, or other living thing

4. We waited to hear from the commander.
- F. person who takes part in combat
- G. self-piloted space vehicle
- H. person in charge
- J. person who makes things

5. Janice does not understand the concepts of law.
- A. documents
- B. ideas; general notions
- C. decisions
- D. problems; puzzles

Part 2: Comprehension

Use what you know about the selection to answer each item.

6. The atmosphere of Mars is mainly—
- F. oxygen.
- G. carbon dioxide.
- H. water vapor.
- J. hydrogen.

7. How long will it take a spacecraft to make the trip from Earth to Mars?
- A. 6 months
- B. 12 months
- C. 18 months
- D. 30 months

8. In space there is no "down" because there is no—
- F. floor.
- G. returning to Earth.
- H. air.
- J. gravity.

9. The first step in becoming a member of the Mars mission is—
- A. training in Antarctica.
- B. passing the psychological testing.
- C. participating in role playing.
- D. going through countless interviews.

GO ON

10. You are on a mission to Mars, and the spaceship is now in orbit around Earth. What is the next step?
F. You wait for the next "launch window" before heading toward Mars.
G. The ship slides toward Mars in a Hohman transfer.
H. The commander fires the rockets to fling the ship away from Earth's gravity.
J. An unmanned rocket is sent to Mars, carrying cargo you will need when you get there.

11. Why do a person's muscles become weak in outer space?
A. They no longer need to fight gravity.
B. There are few opportunities for exercise.
C. The food is not healthful.
D. The cabin of the spacecraft is small and cramped.

12. What is the same about solar flares and galactic rays?
F. They give about an hour's warning.
G. They are hot and bright.
H. They are harmful to humans.
J. They constantly bombard the spaceship.

13. People from Earth have to remain on Mars for eighteen months because—
A. they need that long for exploring and doing experiments.
B. they need time to readjust to living with gravity.
C. it takes that long to make enough fuel for the return trip.
D. it would not be possible for them to reach Earth if they tried to leave earlier.

14. Which statement is an opinion?
F. "Thousands of people applied to join the first Mars mission."
G. "It is one of the richest areas for finding dinosaur fossils in the world."
H. "Most of this loss occurs in your spine and hips."
J. "There are no magic pills for gravity yet."

15. Which is the greatest obstacle to human survival on Mars?
A. lack of air and water
B. lack of gravity
C. distance from Earth
D. lack of a native civilization

STOP

Name ______________________________

Steps in a Process

- The actions you perform in order to make something or to reach a goal are the **steps in a process.**
- Sometimes the steps in a process will have numbers. Other clues to the order of the steps are words like *first, begin, next, then,* and *last.*

Directions: Read the story below.

There is a lot to do to get the spaceship ready for our trip to the asteroid belt. First we have to unload all the stuff left behind by the last crew. Once the ship is empty, we have to clean it. Then all the controls have to be checked. We need to be sure everything is working properly before we take off. After that, we have to load the supplies: food, extra clothing, tape recorders, writing materials, and emergency gear. Then we need to have the fuel tanks filled. The last step is to make sure everyone is on board and ready to go.

Directions: The steps for preparing the spaceship are out of order in the box on the left. Reread the passage to put the steps in the right order in the flow chart. The last step has been done for you.

Out of Order
board the ship
load the supplies
unload the ship
clean the ship
fill the fuel tanks
check the controls

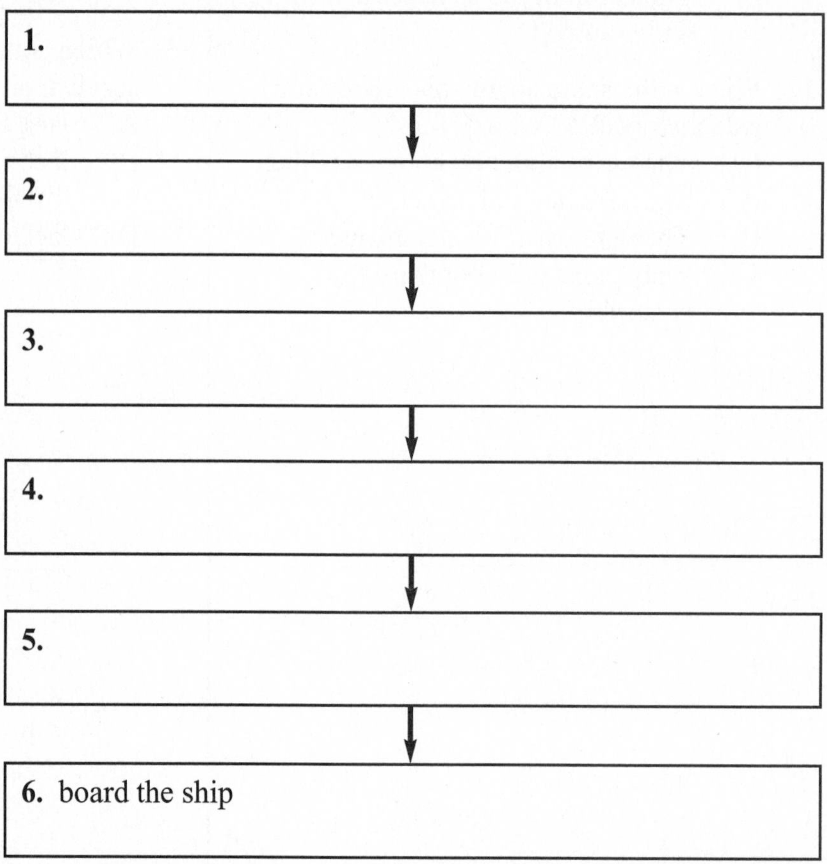

Notes for Home: Your child read a passage and wrote the steps of the process described in order. ***Home Activity:*** Together, read the directions on a food package for preparing a simple dish. Challenge your child to repeat the steps for preparation in their correct order.

REVIEW

Paraphrasing

Directions: Read the passage. Then read each question about the passage. Choose the best answer to each question. Mark the letter for the answer you have chosen.

The Time Machine

For centuries, people have been fascinated by the idea of time travel. Many stories from past centuries are about this concept.

Before people thought about traveling in space, they used the idea of an enchanted sleep as a way to get a person from one time period to another. In the French fairy tale "Sleeping Beauty," princess Briar Rose pricks her finger on a spindle and falls asleep. Generations pass. The prince who finally awakens her was born over a century after Briar Rose—and yet they seem to be about the same age!

A Connecticut Yankee in King Arthur's Court is a funny 19th century story of time travel by Mark Twain. In this story, an ordinary young man is knocked unconscious in a fight and awakens in Camelot in the year 528. His knowledge of everyday modern objects like forks and bicycles cause Arthur's knights and ladies to marvel.

More recent time-travel stories have involved complicated machines that literally transport people through time. In the popular film *Back to the Future,* a high school student suddenly finds himself going to class with his own mother and father. In the film, the time travel machine uses radioactive materials, lightning, and garbage as sources of fuel.

1. Which of the following is a paraphrase of the article's main idea?
   A. Time travel has been a popular subject of stories for centuries.
   B. Some time machines need lightning to travel.
   C. An enchanted sleep is one way of traveling through time.
   D. A Yankee once traveled to Camelot.

2. Which of the following best paraphrases the main idea of the second paragraph?
   F. Briar Rose pricks her finger and falls asleep.
   G. Many young men want to wake her up.
   H. The prince is 100 years younger than Briar Rose.
   J. In old stories, people travel through time by sleeping through it.

3. Which of the following best paraphrases the main idea of the third paragraph?
   A. The Yankee tells Arthur about forks.
   B. Mark Twain wrote a funny story about time travel.
   C. In the year 528, Arthur was king of Great Britain.
   D. Everyone in Camelot learns how to ride a bicycle.

4. Which of the following best paraphrases the main idea of the last paragraph?
   F. Recent time-travel stories use complicated machines to transport people through time.
   G. Characters no longer sleep through time anymore.
   H. *Back To The Future* was a popular film about time travel.
   J. Time machines can let you meet your parents as teenagers.

5. Which of the following is **not** a paraphrase of something in the article?
   A. Time-travel stories are popular.
   B. One day, a young American wakes up in King Arthur's court.
   C. Rip Van Winkle sleeps for many years.
   D. Briar Rose falls asleep when she pricks her finger.

Notes for Home: Your child read a passage and identified paraphrases of statements in the passage. ***Home Activity:*** Tell your child a story about time travel. Have your child retell the story in his or her own words.

Name ______________________________

Writing Across Texts

Directions: Think about what you learned about a space mission to Mars from "Destination: Mars" and "Exploring Mars." Complete the first column of the table by listing what you learned about a trip to Mars from "Destination: Mars." In the second column, make a list of facts from "Exploring Mars."

"Destination: Mars"	"Exploring Mars"
It would take 30 months to travel to Mars and back.	Viking landers made the trip there in a year.
1.	**6.**
2.	**7.**
3.	**8.**
4.	**9.**
5.	**10.**

Write a Research Report

Use the library or the Internet to find updated information about missions to Mars. Write a research report detailing the successes and failures of the last few years.

Notes for Home: Your child wrote a research report about recent missions to Mars. ***Home Activity:*** Read a news article with your child. Write questions you each have about the topic. Identify and paraphrase a topic sentence in the article that tells what the article is about.

Name ________________________________

REVIEW

Grammar: Pronouns and Their Referents

Directions: In each sentence, underline the pronoun and draw a circle around its referent. Hint: Some pronouns are possessive pronouns.

1. Wanda, would you like to travel through space?
2. Spaceships were just a dream years ago, but today they are becoming a reality.
3. Imagine how Neil Armstrong must have felt when he first stepped onto the moon in 1969.
4. Wanda would like to be the first person to step onto Mars, and perhaps she will be.
5. Many people throughout history have had their dreams about space travel.
6. This generation is the first that may see its dreams come true.
7. Astronauts in space have looked down at Earth, with its mountains and oceans.
8. Travel in outer space is exciting, but it can also be very dangerous.
9. Nevertheless, Wanda has made up her mind.
10. Look for Wanda and others someday as they zoom far out into space.

Directions: Replace the underlined word or words in each sentence with a pronoun. Write your new sentences on the lines.

11. With young people like Wanda, humans may actually visit other planets someday.

____

____

12. One day a spaceship may take off with Wanda and other young people inside it.

____

13. Years later, these astronauts will reach their destination planet.

____

14. When Wanda sends her first message back to Earth, what will Wanda say?

____

____

15. She is probably working on that first message of Wanda's already!

____

Notes for Home: Your child matched pronouns with their referents and rewrote sentences with pronouns. ***Home Activity:*** Work with your child to write a short dramatic scene about landing on a new planet. Have your child underline all the pronouns in the script.

Practice

Grammar: Prepositions and Prepositional Phrases

A **prepositional phrase** begins with a **preposition** and ends with a noun or pronoun that is called the **object of the preposition.**

Have you seen any photos of lunar eclipses?

In the sentence above, *eclipses* is the object of the preposition *of.* Notice that the object of the preposition may have a modifier, such as *lunar.*

Common Prepositions:
about, above, across, after, along, among, around, at, before, behind, below, beside, between, by, down, for, from, in, inside, into, near, of, off, on, onto, out, outside, over, through, to, toward, under, until, up, with

Directions: Underline the prepositional phrase or phrases in each sentence. Draw a second line under the preposition. Circle the object of the preposition.

1. Astronauts in orbit have traveled around our planet.
2. In 1969, two American astronauts landed on the moon.
3. Will human visitors ever step onto the surface of Mars?
4. Our family watched TV news coverage of John Glenn's 1998 mission in space.
5. By that time, "a de-orbit burn" was part of the English language.
6. I often think about a trip across the galaxy!
7. With a telescope, I can look through the atmosphere and see into space.
8. I have read about Saturn, and it seems interesting to me.
9. The *Cassini* will reach out and study Saturn by 2004.
10. Data from *Cassini* will tell us more about Saturn's atmosphere.

Directions: Choose a preposition that makes sense in each sentence. Write the preposition on the line to the left.

________________ **11.** In Roman myths, Saturn was the god _____ harvests.

________________ **12.** Saturn is the sixth planet _____ the Sun, and Jupiter is the fifth planet.

________________ **13.** Each of these planets travels in orbit _____ the Sun and has its own moons.

________________ **14.** Saturn or Jupiter would make a good subject _____ a painting.

________________ **15.** Look _____ Jupiter, huge and silvery, near an autumn moon, and dream of going there!

Notes for Home: Your child identified prepositional phrases, such as *across the galaxy.* ***Home Activity:*** Make up some short sentences. Have your child use the list of prepositions above to add prepositional phrases to each one.

Name ______________________________

Grammar: Prepositions and Prepositional Phrases

Directions: Write a prepositional phrase, using the preposition in ( ). Add the phrase to the word group to form a complete sentence. Write the sentence on the line.

1. Sometimes, I imagine living (on) ______.

____

2. I would be far away (from) ______.

____

3. I would be part of a colony (of) ______.

____

4. Lighted tunnels would run (through) ______.

____

5. Fruits and vegetables would grow (inside) ______.

____

6. There might be fish (in) ______.

____

7. We would have an observatory (in) ______.

____

8. We would look at Earth (through) ______.

____

9. Fields and forests would lie (beyond) ______.

____

10. We could hide our rockets (under) ______.

____

Write a Journal Entry

Imagine that you are an astronaut. On a separate sheet of paper, write a journal entry in which you describe a day in your life on a trip to Mars. Include several sentences that use prepositions, such as *beside, into,* and *toward,* and prepositional phrases, such as *on the way* and *upon arrival.*

Notes for Home: Your child wrote prepositional phrases. ***Home Activity:*** Talk together about a trip you have taken. Have your child identify each prepositional phrase he or she uses, for example: *We traveled to the beach.*

Name ______________________________

Grammar: Prepositions and Prepositional Phrases

RETEACHING

Underline the prepositional phrase in each sentence.

1. Emily thinks about the colors.
2. She chooses the color of daffodils.
3. Her room looks wonderful with yellow paint.

A **preposition** relates a noun or pronoun to another word in the sentence. The noun or pronoun that follows a preposition is the **object of the preposition.** A preposition, its object, and any words that describe the object make up a **prepositional phrase.**

Directions: Underline each prepositional phrase in the sentences below.

1. Paintings called frescos are on wet plaster.
2. You can mix dry colors with egg yolks.
3. Tempera is the result of the mixture.
4. Painters once used tempera on linen surfaces.
5. Cave pictures were the earliest type of paintings.
6. Egyptians painted the walls of pharaohs' tombs.
7. Artists painted books in medieval times.
8. Small pictures appeared near letters.
9. Artists painted words and pictures by hand.
10. No printing presses existed at that time.
11. The paper consisted of long-lasting parchment.
12. We have many books made by medieval monks.

Directions: Write the prepositional phrases from the sentences above. Circle the object of each preposition.

13. ______________________ 19. ______________________

14. ______________________ 20. ______________________

15. ______________________ 21. ______________________

16. ______________________ 22 ______________________

17. ______________________ 23. ______________________

18. ______________________ 24. ______________________

Notes for Home: Your child identified prepositions in prepositional phrases. ***Home Activity:*** Name an animal. Have your child describe something the animal can do and use a prepositional phrase in the description. Switch roles.

Name ______________________________

Grammar: Prepositions and Prepositional Phrases

Directions: Underline the prepositional phrase in each sentence. Circle each preposition.

1. We use paper in books.
2. We also use it for homework and other tasks.
3. People write letters on paper.
4. Have you ever wrapped a present in paper?
5. Some factories make paper from fibers.
6. Most paper is made with wood fibers.
7. Fibers from cloth are important too.
8. A chipping machine cuts a log into tiny chips.
9. Machines mix the chips and rags in water.
10. The mixture is treated with chemicals.
11. The watery pulp hardens between thin molds.
12. Through many machines the sheets are processed.
13. The machines press them into long paper strips.

Directions: Complete each sentence. Write prepositional phrases.

14. I use paper ______________________________.
15. I write on paper ______________________________.
16. ______________________________ I learned handwriting.
17. You can find paper ______________________________.
18. Wrapping paper is printed ______________________________.
19. Paper ______________________________ is often dull and colorless.
20. Paper comes ______________________________.
21. Many products ______________________________ are made from wood.
22. The man spoke ______________________________ at the paper factory.

Write a Description

On a separate sheet of paper, describe something you can make from paper. Use prepositional phrases in your sentences.

Notes for Home: Your child wrote prepositional phrases to complete sentences. ***Home Activity:*** Write complete subjects of sentences on slips of paper *(The baseball team)* and have your child add words including a prepositional phrase to finish the sentence. *(The baseball team cheered for each other.)*

Word Study: Singular Possessives

Directions: Words that show ownership, or possession, are called **possessives.** Add an **apostrophe (')** and **s** to form possessives of singular nouns: **Mom's.** Read the phrases below. Change each phrase to form possessive nouns. Write the new phrase on the line.

the brightness of the star — the star's brightness

1. the orders of the commander ______________
2. the surface of Earth ______________
3. the canyons of Mars ______________
4. the months of a year ______________
5. the rays of the Sun ______________

Directions: Read the paragraph below. Look for ten words with apostrophes ('). Five words are possessives. The other five words are contractions. Write each word in the correct column to show which type of word it is.

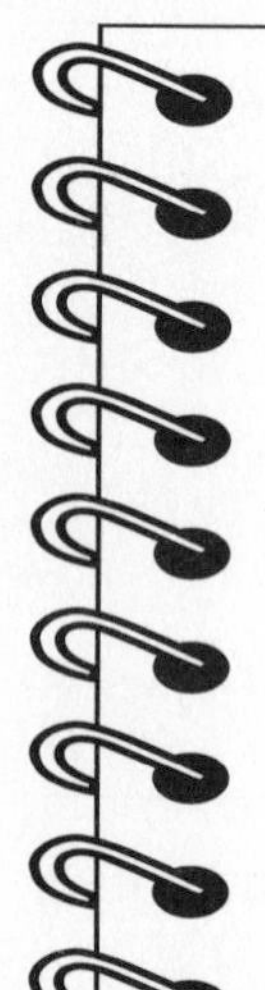

Dr. McKay's Notes
July 2000

It's with a child's wonder and a scientist's concern that I gaze toward the stars and speculate about the ship we've sent into space. As a child, I'd always wanted to venture to that great beyond and view another planet's splendor and colors, especially Saturn's rings. But the ship doesn't carry any crew or passengers. We'll track it by computer and download the pictures of space.

Possessives	**Contractions**
6. ______________	11. ______________
7. ______________	12. ______________
8. ______________	13. ______________
9. ______________	14. ______________
10. ______________	15. ______________

Notes for Home: Your child wrote possessives and sorted contractions and possessives. ***Home Activity:*** With your child, write ten contractions and ten possessives on separate index cards. Take turns choosing two cards to try to get two possessives or two contractions.

Name ______________________

Pretest

Spelling: Opposite Prefixes

Pretest Directions: Fold back the page along the dotted line. On the blanks, write the spelling words as they are dictated. When you have finished the test, unfold the page and check your words.

1. ______________________
2. ______________________
3. ______________________
4. ______________________
5. ______________________
6. ______________________
7. ______________________
8. ______________________
9. ______________________
10. ______________________
11. ______________________
12. ______________________
13. ______________________
14. ______________________
15. ______________________
16. ______________________
17. ______________________
18. ______________________
19. ______________________
20. ______________________

1. The **pretrial** hearing was short.
2. We will **prearrange** the vacation.
3. The crime was not **premeditated**.
4. She found a **prehistoric** fossil.
5. Proper **precaution** is wise.
6. The houses **postdate** the farm.
7. **Postwar** Europe prospered.
8. The **postponement** is temporary.
9. She did **postgraduate** studies.
10. Do not **overcook** the rice.
11. The cliffs **overlook** the sea.
12. The pot began to **overflow**.
13. The zoo was **overpopulated**.
14. Stay **undercover** until it is safe.
15. The bear looked **undernourished**.
16. The luggage was **underweight**.
17. Does the meal **include** a salad?
18. I like to **inhale** baking smells.
19. Do not **exclude** your friends.
20. They **exhale** audibly.

Notes for Home: Your child took a pretest on words with the prefixes *pre-, post-, over-, under-, in-,* and *ex-*. ***Home Activity:*** Help your child learn misspelled words before the final test. Dictate the word and have your child spell the word aloud for you or write it on paper.

Name ______________________

Spelling: Opposite Prefixes

Word List				
pretrial	precaution	postgraduate	overpopulated	include
prearrange	postdate	overcook	undercover	inhale
premeditated	postwar	overlook	undernourished	exclude
prehistoric	postponement	overflow	underweight	exhale

Directions: Choose the words from the box that have the prefixes **pre-, post-, in-** or **ex-**. Write each word in the correct column.

Prefix pre-

1. ______________________
2. ______________________
3. ______________________
4. ______________________
5. ______________________

Prefix post-

8. ______________________
9. ______________________
10. ______________________
11. ______________________

Prefix in-

6. ______________________
7. ______________________

Prefix ex-

12. ______________________
13. ______________________

Directions: Choose the word from the box that matches each definition. Write the word on the line.

______________________ **14.** cook too much

______________________ **15.** not heavy enough

______________________ **16.** not eating a healthful diet

______________________ **17.** go over or beyond the limits; flood

______________________ **18.** not to see something

______________________ **19.** in secret

______________________ **20.** crowded with people

Notes for Home: Your child spelled words with the prefixes *pre-, post-, over-, under-, in-,* and *ex-*. ***Home Activity:*** Have your child name two words not on the list that can be formed by adding the prefix *under-* and two words that can be formed by adding the prefix *over-*.

Proofread and Write

Spelling: Opposite Prefixes

Directions: Proofread this space log. Find seven spelling mistakes. Use the proofreading marks to correct each mistake.

≡	Make a capital.
/	Make a small letter.
∧	Add something.
℘	Take out something.
⊙	Add a period.
¶	Begin a new paragraph.

Today we made our first poswar visit to Elkan. After 40 years of isolation, conditions on the planet are, by our standards, perhistoric. Going without is a way of life for this population, which appears undrnourished and underweight.

The purposes of our prarranged meeting included locating a suitable site for pertrial hearings and discussing the charges of premeditated war crimes. I discovered that the former leaders charged with these crimes have taken the preccaution of filing for a trial posponement. I fear this mission will be a long one.

Spelling Tip

When adding the prefixes **pre-, post-, over-, under-, in-,** and **ex-,** do not make any changes in the base word.

Write a Space Log Entry

On a separate sheet of paper, write an entry in a space log. What did you do in space today? Were there any problems? Try to use at least five spelling words.

Word List

pretrial	overlook
prearrange	overflow
premeditated	overpopulated
prehistoric	undercover
precaution	undernourished
postdate	underweight
postwar	include
postponement	inhale
postgraduate	exclude
overcook	exhale

Notes for Home: Your child spelled words with the prefixes *pre-, post-, over-, under-, in-,* and *ex-*. ***Home Activity:*** Help your child separate the prefixes from the base words in the spelling list *(pretrial = pre + trial)*. Discuss how prefixes change the meaning of base words.

Name ________________________________

Spelling: Opposite Prefixes

REVIEW

Word List

pretrial	precaution	postgraduate	overpopulated	include
prearrange	postdate	overcook	undercover	inhale
premeditated	postwar	overlook	undernourished	exclude
prehistoric	postponement	overflow	underweight	exhale

Directions: Find two words in each sentence that can be combined to form a word from the box. Write the word from the box on the line.

____________ **1.** Put the papers under the brass weight.

____________ **2.** I went over to his house to look for him.

____________ **3.** That post was destroyed in the war.

____________ **4.** If you come over for dinner, I will cook spaghetti.

____________ **5.** The post office stamps the date on each letter.

____________ **6.** Let's go over to the bridge and watch the river flow.

____________ **7.** He left his military post just as his son was about to graduate.

____________ **8.** I found a book under the couch; look at the dust on its cover!

____________ **9.** We traveled over stretches of country populated by cattle.

____________ **10.** Clams live under the water; they are nourished by the sea.

Directions: Choose the word from the box that best answers each riddle. Write the word on the line.

____________ **11.** I am what you do when you take in a breath.

____________ **12.** I am what you do when you release your breath.

____________ **13.** I am from the time before written history.

____________ **14.** I am what you ask for if you want to put something off until later.

____________ **15.** I am what you do when you make an arrangement in advance.

____________ **16.** I am what you do when you make someone part of a group.

____________ **17.** I am what you take beforehand to ensure your safety.

____________ **18.** I am a meeting before a trial.

____________ **19.** I am what you do when you shut something or someone out.

____________ **20.** I am a type of action that has been thought out in advance.

Notes for Home: Your child reviewed words with the prefixes *pre-, post-, over-, under-, in-,* and *ex-*. ***Home Activity:*** Write the spelling words on separate index cards. Take turns with your child choosing a card from the stack, spelling the word, and using it in a sentence.

Technology: Electronic Media

There are two types of **electronic media**—computer and non-computer. Computer sources include computer software, CD-ROMs, and the Internet. Non-computer sources include audiotapes, videotapes, films, film strips, television, and radio.

To find information on the Internet, use a search engine and type in your key words. Be specific. It's a good idea to use two or more key words, typing AND between key words. For example, if you typed "Mars AND photographs," you might get a list of web pages like the one below. To get to a web page, click on the underlined link.

Directions: Use the Internet search results to answer the questions that follow.

You Searched For: Mars AND Photographs

Top 5 of 38 matches.

1 Ruins on Mars Striking color photographs of what may be ancient ruins on the surface of Mars are now available.

2 Mars Home Page All about Mars—missions to Mars, images of Mars, and plans for Mars exploration and settlement in the future.

3 Mars: Past Missions Past missions include 1962: The first attempt to fly to Mars ended when a Russian probe was lost after traveling 66 million miles. 1964: A U.S. flyby returns 21 images of Mars to Earth. 1971–1972: America's *Mariner IX* and Russia's *Mars 3* orbit the planet, providing data and photographs.

4 Spacelink - Mars Global Surveyor Mars Global Surveyor is a polar-orbiting spacecraft designed to provide global maps of surface topography, distribution of minerals, and monitoring of global weather.

5 Mars Pathfinder On July 4, 1997, the Mars *Pathfinder* spacecraft arrived on the Red Planet. *Pathfinder* sent out a small rover called *Sojourner* to explore the Martian landscape. Learn more intriguing information here.

Click here to continue → ☐

Name ______________________________

1. How do you get to a specific web page? ______________________

2. What information will web page 5 have? ______________________

____

3. Which web page has information about the Mars Global Surveyor? ____________

4. What key words could you use to find web pages about the history of exploration on Mars?

____

5. Why is it important to choose your key words carefully when searching the Internet?

____

____

6. What are some of the advantages of using the Internet as a source of information for research?

____

____

7. How might you use a documentary videotape on Mars for a research report?

____

____

8. How might you use an audiotape of conversations between astronauts on a space mission and the mission command center?

____

____

____

9. Name some ways television could be used as a research source.

____

____

____

10. Is electronic media always the best choice as a research source? Explain why or why not.

____

____

____

Notes for Home: Your child answered questions about the results of a web page search on the Internet and other forms of electronic media. ***Home Activity:*** Make a list of the different forms of electronic media. Discuss how each form could be used for research or study.

Family Times

Name____

Summary

Not What He Expected!

Milo, who has nothing to do, finds a toy tollbooth at home one day. He drives his electric car through it and is suddenly speeding along a country road in the land of Expectations. He takes a wrong turn while daydreaming. The scenery grows dull and the car slows, finally stopping altogether. Several small creatures who take on the color of their surroundings explain that he is now in the Doldrums, where nothing happens and nothing changes. Milo is rescued by a ticking watchdog named Tock.

Activity

Draw a Map. Ask your child to draw a map of Expectations. Have him or her include Milo's route and various features of the regions he visits.

Reading Skills

Summarizing

Summarizing means giving a brief statement of the main idea of an article or the most important events in a story.

When you summarize a story, include only the main actions of the characters and the outcomes of those actions. If a character performs several related actions, try to think of one action that includes them all. For example, in "The Land of Expectations," Milo meets characters whose daily routine calls for them to daydream, loaf, nap, dawdle, delay, and linger. Your summary of these events might be: *Milo meets lazy characters.*

Activity

Shorten a Tale. Challenge your child to summarize a favorite tale or story in as few sentences as possible.

Family Times

Tested Vocabulary

Words to Know

Knowing the meanings of these words is important to reading "The Land of Expectations." Practice using these words to learn their meanings.

assembled put together

destination place to which you are traveling

encounter to find by chance; meet with; come upon

expectations good reasons for thinking that something will happen

regulations rules; laws

tollbooth booth or gate at which tolls are collected from travelers

Grammar

Conjunctions

A **conjunction** is a word that joins words, phrases, or entire sentences. *And, but,* and *or* are conjunctions.

- Use *and* to add information or join related ideas.
  Milo looked around and admired the view.
- Use *or* to show a choice.
  Did Milo lose his way or stay on the main road?
- Use *but* to show a difference or join different ideas.
  Milo was lost, but he was beginning to enjoy himself.

Activity

Outrageous Statements. Take turns making outrageous statements and then combining them using conjunctions. Keep a list of favorite combined statements.

Tested Spelling Words

Name ______________________________

Summarizing

- To **summarize** means to give a brief statement of the main idea of an article or the most important events in a story.
- When you summarize a story, include only the main actions of the characters and the outcomes of those actions.

Directions: Reread "To Surprise the Children." Then summarize the story by choosing the five sentences from the box that best describe the most important actions or events. Write the sentences in the flow chart in the correct order.

The main character asked a bricklayer what would happen if the brick fell on somebody.
The main character went somewhere and looked up.
The bricklayers supported the brick by building a whole house around it.
The main character asked what would happen if the brick fell on somebody.
Some people, including the main character, moved into the house.
The main character looked up and saw a brick sitting in the air.
Everyone was looking at the brick.
The bricklayer called for other bricklayers to come.
Some people moved into the house.

Event 1:

↓

Event 2:

↓

Event 3:

↓

Event 4:

↓

Event 5:

Notes for Home: Your child summarized a story. ***Home Activity:*** Work with your child to summarize a story or movie. Be sure to include only the most important events.

Name ______________________________

Vocabulary

Directions: Choose the word from the box that best matches each definition. Write the word on the line.

Check the Words You Know
__ assembled
__ destination
__ encounter
__ expectations
__ regulations
__ tollbooth

__________________ **1.** place to which you are traveling

__________________ **2.** a gate at which money is collected before or after driving on a road

__________________ **3.** to find by chance

__________________ **4.** rules

__________________ **5.** good reasons for thinking that something will happen

__________________ **6.** put together

Directions: Read the diary entry. Choose the word from the box that best completes each sentence. Write the word on the matching numbered line below.

I dreamed I was in a country with strange laws. There were **7.** _____ that stated how many minutes you could talk each day. If you wanted to take a trip, a court had to approve your final **8.** _____. At every **9.** _____ on the highway, you had to answer math word problems. Finally, I gathered the parts I needed to build a spaceship. I **10.** _____ the ship and quickly escaped.

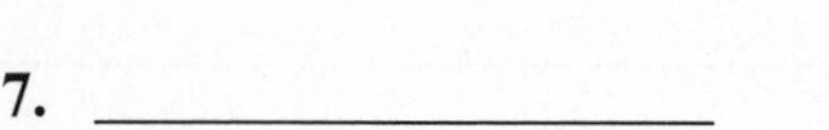

7. __________________ **9.** __________________

8. __________________ **10.** __________________

Write a Dialogue

Imagine being in a strange place and not knowing your way or the rules of the road! On a separate sheet of paper, write a dialogue between a space traveler and a toll booth attendant. Use as many vocabulary words as you can.

Notes for Home: Your child identified and used vocabulary words from the story "The Land of Expectations." ***Home Activity:*** Talk about a fantasy trip to outer space or some strange place in another time. Encourage your child to use vocabulary words during your discussion.

Name ______________________

Summarizing

- **Summarizing** means giving a brief statement of the main idea of an article or the most important events in a story.

Directions: Reread the passage below in which the author introduces Milo. Then follow the instructions below. Think about which information belongs in your summary.

There was once a boy named Milo who didn't know what to do with himself—not just sometimes, but always.

When he was in school he longed to be out, and when he was out he longed to be in. On the way he thought about coming home, and coming home he thought about going. Wherever he was he wished he were somewhere else, and when he got there he wondered why he'd bothered. Nothing really interested him—least of all the things that should have.

"It seems to me that almost everything is a waste of time," he remarked one day as he walked dejectedly home from school. "I can't see the point in learning to solve useless problems, or subtracting turnips from turnips, or knowing where Ethiopia is or how to spell February." And, since no one bothered to explain otherwise, he regarded the process of seeking knowledge as the greatest waste of time of all.

1. Write a summary of the first paragraph.

____

2. Write a summary of the second paragraph.

____

3. Write a summary of the third paragraph.

____

4. Give an example of something you left out of your summary of the third paragraph. Why did you leave this information out?

____

____

5. Summarize the story and how Milo changes by the end. Explain your ideas on a separate sheet of paper.

Notes for Home: Your child read a story and summarized what happened in it in a few sentences. ***Home Activity:*** After watching a movie together with your child, challenge him or her to write a brief summary of it. Discuss which events were included and why.

Name ______________________________

Selection Test

Directions: Choose the best answer to each item. Mark the letter for the answer you have chosen.

Part 1: Vocabulary

Find the answer choice that means about the same as the underlined word in each sentence.

1. Dad stopped at the <u>tollbooth</u>.
- A. place where people sit to watch a game or contest
- B. vehicle for traveling
- C. booth or gate at which money is collected from travelers
- D. place for selling maps

2. Diana had few <u>expectations</u>.
- F. things that are looked forward to
- G. reasons to remember something
- H. things that are decided beforehand
- J. observations

3. The team <u>assembled</u> it quickly.
- A. performed
- B. put together
- C. opened
- D. broke apart

4. Our <u>destination</u> was near.
- F. source of ideas
- G. place where someone lives
- H. fortune; luck
- J. place to which someone or something is going

5. We read the <u>regulations</u>.
- A. rules
- B. tools
- C. letters
- D. guides

6. Did you <u>encounter</u> anyone on the hike?
- F. go along with
- G. meet unexpectedly
- H. watch closely
- J. lose track of

Part 2: Comprehension

Use what you know about the story to answer each item.

7. Why was Milo hurrying to get home from school?
- A. He always liked to get places as quickly as possible.
- B. He never seemed to have enough time to do all the things he wanted to.
- C. He was eager to find out what was waiting for him at home.
- D. He felt nervous and afraid of what he might run into on the way home.

8. What was odd about the map Milo found in the surprise package?
- F. Milo had to unfold it to see what it looked like.
- G. It showed roads, rivers, and seas.
- H. Milo had never heard of any of the places on the map.
- J. The places on the map were beautiful and historic.

9. Milo got into the Doldrums by—
- A. following the map.
- B. making a foolish choice.
- C. listening to the Whether Man.
- D. not thinking.

10. Which sentence best summarizes what happens to Milo?
- F. He meets a dog with a clock for a body.
- G. He takes an unexpected trip to a very unusual place.
- H. He talks with the Whether Man.
- J. He finds a package in his room.

GO ON

11. Which of these events would be important to include in a summary of this story?
- A. The Whether Man released a dozen balloons that sailed off into the sky.
- B. The Lethargarians described their busy schedule to Milo.
- C. Tock the watchdog helped Milo get out of the Doldrums.
- D. Tock explained that it is traditional for watchdogs to be ferocious.

12. What can you tell about the Whether Man?
- F. He enjoys life to the fullest.
- G. He does not know where he is.
- H. He doesn't like to make up his mind.
- J. He is Milo's best friend.

13. Where will Milo probably go next?
- A. back to the Doldrums
- B. to Dictionopolis
- C. back to his apartment
- D. to Tock's home

14. In Tock's view, the most valuable thing in the world is—
- F. time.
- G. diamonds.
- H. sleep.
- J. weather.

15. One thing that Tock likes to do is—
- A. chase after cars.
- B. kill time.
- C. socialize with the Lethargarians.
- D. tell long stories about his family.

STOP

Name ____________________

Summarizing

- **Summarizing** means giving a brief statement of the main idea of an article or the most important events in a story.

Directions: Read the story below.

Lu had always thought he could fly. Sure enough, there he was one night, soaring above Earth. He tried some fancy moves to test his skill. It was better than floating on the lake in summertime.

A little later, Lu joined a flock of geese on their way south for the winter. They didn't seem to mind his company as long as he kept up with them. All Lu had to do was follow the leader. He dipped, turned right or left, or sped up when the leader did.

At that moment, the sky grew dark. It began to rain heavily. Lu lost sight of the geese! "Help!" he shouted. Suddenly he realized he was sitting bolt upright in his own warm bed. He sighed in relief, but also in regret. Flying was wonderful, even in a dream.

Directions: Complete the table. Write a summary for the two details given in each row. One has been done for you.

Detail	Detail	Summary
Lu thought he could fly.	Lu soars above Earth.	Lu can fly.
Lu tries fancy moves.	It's better than floating.	**1.**
Lu keeps up with the geese.	Lu follows the leader.	**2.**
The sky grows dark.	Rain falls heavily.	**3.**
Lu sits up in bed.	Lu sighs in relief.	**4.**

Directions: Summarize the story. Use the completed table to help you.

5. ____________________

____

____

Notes for Home: Your child read a story and summarized it. ***Home Activity:*** Read a story with your child. After reviewing the main events and ideas together, challenge him or her to summarize the story in no more than three sentences.

REVIEW

Cause and Effect

Directions: Read the story. Then read each question about the story. Choose the best answer to each question. Mark the letter for the answer you have chosen.

The Monster, the Maze, and the Fall

King Minos of Crete asked the architect Daedalus to build a maze. The maze was to be a prison for the Minotaur, a fierce monster who was half human and half bull. Minos wanted a maze from which the monster would never be able to escape. Daedalus created a maze, so full of twists and turns that the Minotaur could never find his way out.

Minos' daughter Ariadne had fallen in love with the hero Theseus. When Minos threatened to feed Theseus to the Minotaur, Ariadne thought of a way to save his life. She told Theseus to fasten a thread to the maze's entrance. If he kept hold of the thread's other end, he would be able to find his way out. Theseus killed the Minotaur and escaped from the maze.

King Minos was so angry about Theseus's escape that he imprisoned Daedalus and his son Icarus in a tower. Daedalus made wings of wood, wax, and feathers for himself and his son so that they could fly away from their prison. Daedalus warned Icarus not to fly too close to the sun. If the wax melted, the feathers would fall from the frames.

Icarus enjoyed flying so much that he forgot his father's warning. He flew too close to the sun. The wax on his wings melted, and he fell into the sea. Grief-stricken, Daedalus recovered his son's body and buried it on a nearby island.

1. The Minotaur cannot escape because—
- **A.** the maze is too complicated.
- **B.** it is part animal.
- **C.** it will be killed if it escapes.
- **D.** Ariadne refuses to help it.

2. Because Daedalus is an excellent architect—
- **F.** he is put in prison.
- **G.** he traps King Minos.
- **H.** he is asked by the King to build a flying machine.
- **J.** he is asked by the King to build an escape-proof maze.

3. Thanks to the help of Ariadne—
- **A.** Icarus escapes.
- **B.** Daedalus escapes.
- **C.** Theseus escapes.
- **D.** King Minos kills Theseus.

4. Daedalus makes wings in order to—
- **F.** escape the tower.
- **G.** teach his son to fly.
- **H.** kill the monster.
- **J.** challenge the king.

5. Icarus is killed because—
- **A.** he flies into the sea.
- **B.** he forgets his father's warning.
- **C.** the wings don't work very well.
- **D.** the king is angry with him.

Notes for Home: Your child read a story and identified the causes and effects of its events. ***Home Activity:*** Read a myth or folk tale with your child. Encourage him or her to tell what happens in the story (effects) and why these events happen (causes).

Name ___________________________________

Writing Across Texts

Directions: Think about what you have read about journeys to other lands in "To the Pole," the excerpt from *El Güero,* and "Destination: Mars." Complete the Venn diagram by choosing the journey in one of these selections and comparing and contrasting it to the journey in "The Land of Expectations."

The Land of Expectations | **Both Journeys** | **Title:** ____________

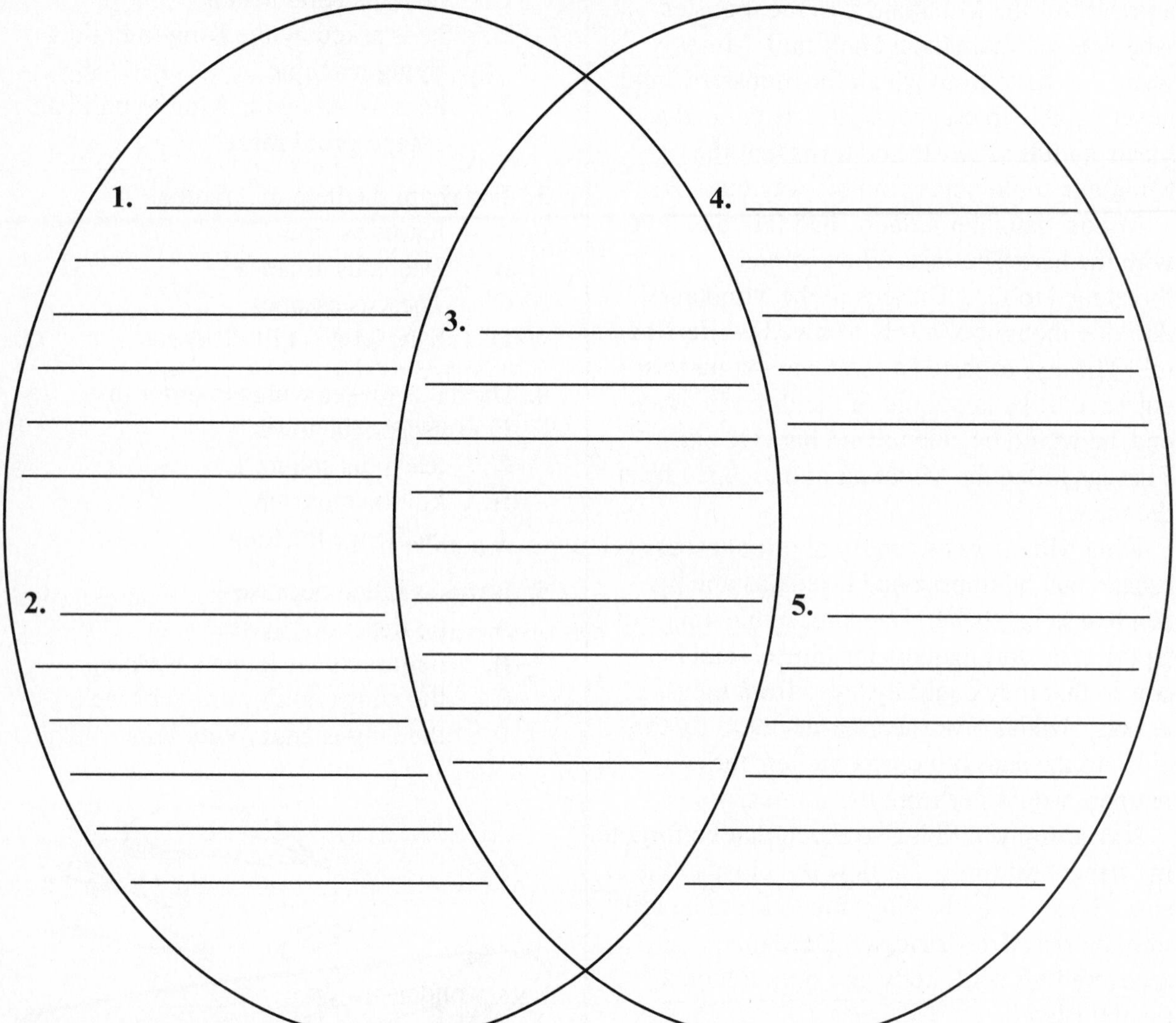

1. ____________

2. ____________

3. ____________

4. ____________

5. ____________

Write an Opinion

Based on your diagram, write a paragraph or two giving your opinion about which experience would be more exciting. Support your opinion with information from the selections.

Notes for Home: Your child compared and contrasted two selections to form an opinion. ***Home Activity:*** Read a story with your child, and then compare and contrast it with other stories on the same topic. Ask your child to voice opinions about the stories and topics.

Name ___________________________

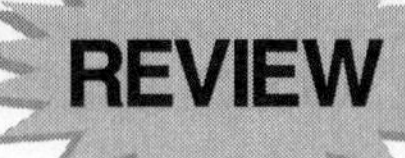

Grammar: Compound and Complex Sentences

Directions: Write **compound** or **complex** on the line to describe each sentence.

_______________ **1.** After I saw the movie *The Wizard of Oz,* I read the book.

_______________ **2.** I enjoyed the movie, but I enjoyed the book even more.

_______________ **3.** Who could forget Dorothy and her dog as they are blown by a tornado to the Land of Oz?

_______________ **4.** Will Dorothy find her way back to Kansas, or will she have to stay in Oz?

_______________ **5.** Dorothy meets a scarecrow, a tin man, and a cowardly lion, and they set off to find the Wizard of Oz.

_______________ **6.** The wizard is described as all-powerful, and he may be able to grant their wishes.

_______________ **7.** Scarecrow wants a brain, the tin man wants a heart, the lion wants courage, and Dorothy just wants to go home.

_______________ **8.** Although the wizard turns out to be an impostor, the group's wishes all do come true.

_______________ **9.** If you enjoyed *The Wizard of Oz,* you may also enjoy the many other books about Oz.

_______________ **10.** L. Frank Baum must have enjoyed his own visits to the Land of Oz because he wrote more than a dozen books about it.

Directions: Use a joining word to combine each pair of sentences. Create a new sentence of the kind shown in ( ). Write your new sentence on the line.

11. You could go anywhere in the world. Where would you go? (complex)

____

12. I might want to climb Mt. Everest. I might prefer to dive deep below the ocean. (compound)

____

13. Fantastic journeys are exciting. Simpler ones can be wonderful too. (complex)

____

14. Imagine yourself on a lovely ocean beach. You will understand my point. (compound)

____

15. You travel all around the world. You will still enjoy coming home. (complex)

____

Notes for Home: Your child identified and wrote compound and complex sentences. ***Home Activity:*** Work with your child to write simple sentences about a family trip. Then use joining words to make pairs of related sentences compound or complex.

Name ______________________________

Grammar: Conjunctions

Conjunctions can be used to join words, phrases, or entire sentences. Conjunctions are used to write compound subjects, compound predicates, and compound sentences. The three most commonly used conjunctions are *and, but,* and *or. And* joins related ideas. *But* joins contrasting ideas. *Or* suggests a choice between ideas.

Compound Subject: Our hearts and minds long for adventures.
Compound Predicate: We may live quietly but imagine taking trips to see marvelous things.
Compound Sentence: We may climb high mountains, or we may explore the depths of the sea.

Directions: Circle the conjunction in each sentence. Underline the two words or groups of words that the conjunction connects.

1. I went to the stage and faced my audience.
2. The men and women in the room were quiet.
3. I liked the audience but felt nervous at first.
4. I told a story about an imaginary world, and they seemed pleased.
5. Everyone in the story lived under the sea or had an island home.
6. Some people lived in hollow coral reefs, but others lived in caves beneath the sea.
7. Fish or other sea creatures were the sea dwellers' food.
8. Only a few islands and houses stood above the water.
9. The people and animals on the islands were called surface dwellers.
10. The surface dwellers never entered the sea, but no one knew why.

Directions: Use *and, but,* or *or* to complete each sentence. The words in ( ) tell what the conjunction should do. Write the conjunction on the line to the left.

______________ 11. Four-legged animals lived on the islands, _____ birds were living there too. (join related ideas)

______________ 12. Many of the birds ate berries, _____ the larger birds caught fish. (show a difference)

______________ 13. The fisher birds ate some of the fish _____ carried the rest to the people. (add information)

______________ 14. Sea dwellers dived _____ hid among the reefs. (show a choice)

______________ 15. The sea dwellers _____ the surface dwellers remained separate societies. (add information)

Notes for Home: Your child used the conjunctions *and, but,* and *or* to complete sentences. ***Home Activity:*** Give your child two sentences with the same subject, such as *I washed the plates. I scrubbed the pots.* Have him or her use the conjunction *and* to combine the two sentences.

Grammar: Conjunctions

Directions: Choose the conjunction that best completes each sentence. Write the conjunction on the line.

______________ **1.** Explorers have made long, hopeful journeys in search of treasure (but/or) a perfect society.

______________ **2.** Legends (but/and) fables have prompted some of the searches.

______________ **3.** The Spanish explorers De Niza (and/but) Coronado searched for the Seven Cities of Cibola in North America.

______________ **4.** In South America, seekers of jewels (or/but) precious metals looked for El Dorado.

______________ **5.** Even today, some groups hope to find Atlantis, an island of peace (and/but) happiness.

Directions: Use *and, or,* or *but* to combine each pair of sentences. Write the new sentence on the line.

6. Would you like to explore a whole new world? Would you rather go in search of treasure?

____

____

7. Divers can enter the underwater world. Divers can discover treasure there.

____

8. Old pirate ships lie on the ocean floor. Their chests full of coins have remained intact.

____

____

9. Cannons hundreds of years old are on those ships. Cannonballs hundreds of years old are on those ships.

____

10. Other kinds of ships also sank centuries ago. Divers are still discovering interesting objects on these old ships.

____

____

Write a Postcard

On a separate sheet of paper, write a postcard to a friend that tells about a trip to an imaginary land. Underline the conjunctions **and, but,** and **or** in your postcard message.

Notes for Home: Your child used conjunctions, such as *and, but,* and *or,* to connect ideas and form interesting sentences. ***Home Activity:*** Pick a topic and say two simple sentences related to that topic. Challenge your child to join the sentences with a conjunction.

Grammar: Conjunctions

RETEACHING

A conjunction connects words, phrases, or sentences. Underline the words the conjunctions **and, or,** and **but** connect.

1. Is that insect a butterfly or a moth?
2. They have pretty but delicate wings.
3. They both lay and hatch eggs.
4. Wing markings hide them easily and well.

A **conjunction** joins words or groups of words. A conjunction may join nouns, pronouns, verbs, adjectives, or adverbs.

Directions: Circle each conjunction in the sentences below.

1. Butterflies and moths are very similar.
2. Butterflies flutter and fly from plant to plant.
3. A female butterfly lays tiny but numerous eggs.
4. Larvae can see and chew.
5. They quickly grow and shed their skin often.
6. An adult life span may be only a few days or weeks.
7. Moths have feathery or smooth antennae.
8. Some species have beautiful but poisonous wings.
9. Kim and Alan gave a report about butterflies.
10. These beautiful insects fascinated them and me.

Directions: Read each sentence. Choose a conjunction that makes the most sense from those in ( ) and write it on the line.

11. Many insects (and/but) spiders spin silk threads. ______________
12. The silkworm spins the finest (and/or) strongest threads. ______________
13. Farmers handle the silkworms carefully (or/and) patiently. ______________
14. China produces more silk than Japan (or/but) South Korea. ______________
15. Show this silk scarf to her (but/and) him. ______________

Notes for Home: Your child used conjunctions in sentences. ***Home Activity:*** Say two simple sentences about something your family has done recently. Have your child use a conjunction to combine the sentences to form a compound sentence.

Grammar: Conjunctions

Directions: Circle the conjunction in each sentence. Underline the words or groups of words that the conjunction connects.

1. Andrew Jackson was a lawyer and a military leader.
2. He was orphaned and was reared by an uncle.
3. He grew to be a determined but thoughtful leader.
4. He was feared or was respected by others.
5. He brilliantly but unexpectedly won a battle.
6. You and I might enjoy a visit to his home, the Hermitage.
7. Friends and admirers supported him.
8. He campaigned hard but won easily.
9. Jackson was a courageous and clever president.
10. He supported democracy and the union of the states.

Directions: Write **and, but,** or **or** to complete each sentence below.

11. Jackson could have won ______________ lost the election.
12. He became an effective ______________ popular president.
13. Sometimes his official cabinet ______________ an unofficial "kitchen cabinet" gave him advice.
14. This group met ______________ chatted in the White House kitchen.
15. President Jackson could sign ______________ veto bills.
16. Jackson could agree ______________ disagree with a group.
17. He was a strong ______________ kindly man.
18. Young America grew ______________ prospered under his leadership.

Write a Paragraph

On a separate sheet of paper, write a paragraph about the special qualities of someone you admire. Use the conjunctions **and, but,** and **or.**

Notes for Home: Your child identified and wrote conjunctions in sentences. ***Home Activity:*** Talk with your child about the role of each conjunction in a sentence.

Name ____________________

Word Study: Suffixes

Directions: A letter or group of letters added to the end of a word is called a **suffix.** A suffix can change the meaning of the base word. The words below have been formed by adding suffixes. Read each word pair. Write the suffix on the line.

1. useless, endless ________
2. traditional, logical ________
3. silvery, rusty ________
4. historic, apologetic ________
5. festive, massive ________
6. magical, natural ________
7. meaningless, clueless ________
8. classy, showy ________
9. hypnotic, idiotic ________
10. preventive, inventive ________

Directions: Read the letter below. Look and listen for words that have the suffixes **-less, -al, -y, -ic,** and **-ive.** Circle these words. Then write the base word and the suffix on the line, connected by a + sign. For example, for **restless,** you would write **rest + less.**

Dear Marisa,

You'll never believe what happened to me! I went on a magical journey. It was quite dreamy and fantastic. You see, I haven't been very active these days. So when my uncle suggested that I join him on his traditional yearly trip, I said sure. But where he went and what I saw made me speechless! He took me up in a hot-air balloon. Wish you had been there. I could see for endless miles. My head was spinning. Even my uncle got emotional. It felt like a historic moment in my life. I'm so lucky.

Your friend,

Dianne

11. ________
12. ________
13. ________
14. ________
15. ________
16. ________
17. ________
18. ________
19. ________
20. ________

Notes for Home: Your child identified and wrote words with the suffixes *-less, -al, -y, -ic,* and *-ive.* ***Home Activity:*** Read a short story with your child. Encourage your child to find words with these suffixes. Have your child write down the words and underline the suffixes.

Name ______________________________

Spelling: Suffixes *-ate, -ive, -ship*

Pretest

Pretest Directions: Fold back the page along the dotted line. On the blanks, write the spelling words as they are dictated. When you have finished the test, unfold the page and check your words.

1. ______________	**1.** Let's **originate** a new recipe.
2. ______________	**2.** I'm **fortunate** to have friends.
3. ______________	**3.** Please **activate** my account.
4. ______________	**4.** Her cat is very **affectionate**.
5. ______________	**5.** He is kind and **considerate**.
6. ______________	**6.** Your duties **obligate** you to try.
7. ______________	**7.** We had a **productive** lesson.
8. ______________	**8.** This toy is **defective**.
9. ______________	**9.** Her ideas were **constructive**.
10. ______________	**10.** He has an **attractive** apartment.
11. ______________	**11.** She is an **inventive** writer.
12. ______________	**12.** The insult had a **negative** effect.
13. ______________	**13.** He is a **creative** painter.
14. ______________	**14.** I claim **ownership** of this book.
15. ______________	**15.** The club **membership** is free.
16. ______________	**16.** Poverty is a terrible **hardship**.
17. ______________	**17.** What is your **relationship**?
18. ______________	**18.** We have a solid **friendship**.
19. ______________	**19.** We will win the **championship**.
20. ______________	**20.** She has natural **leadership**.

Notes for Home: Your child took a pretest on words that have the suffixes *-ate*, *-ive*, and *-ship*. ***Home Activity:*** Help your child learn misspelled words before the final test. Have your child divide misspelled words into parts (such as syllables) and concentrate on each part.

Name ______________________________

Spelling: Suffixes *-ate, -ive, -ship*

Word List			
originate	obligate	inventive	hardship
fortunate	productive	negative	relationship
activate	defective	creative	friendship
affectionate	constructive	ownership	championship
considerate	attractive	membership	leadership

Directions: Choose the words from the box that have the suffixes **-ate** and **-ive.** Write each word in the correct column.

Suffix -ive	**Suffix -ate**
1. ________________	**8.** ________________
2. ________________	**9.** ________________
3. ________________	**10.** ________________
4. ________________	**11.** ________________
5. ________________	**12.** ________________
6. ________________	**13.** ________________
7. ________________	

Directions: Choose the word from the box that best answers each riddle. Write the word on the line.

________________ **14.** I am a victory in the World Series or the Super Bowl.

________________ **15.** I am a synonym of the word *possession.*

________________ **16.** I am poverty, sorrow, difficulty, or hunger.

________________ **17.** I am the link between any two people who know each other.

________________ **18.** I am the link between two people who are friends.

________________ **19.** I am a quality generals, presidents, and kings should have.

________________ **20.** I am what you apply for if you want to join a club or group.

Notes for Home: Your child spelled words with suffixes *-ate, -ive,* and *-ship.* ***Home Activity:*** Help your child identify the base word of each spelling word. Then discuss whether the spelling of the base word changed when the suffix was added.

Name ______________________________

Proofread and Write

Spelling: Suffixes -ate, -ive, -ship

Directions: Proofread this transcript of a sports broadcast. Find five spelling mistakes. Use the proofreading marks to correct each mistake.

- ≡ Make a capital.
- / Make a small letter.
- ∧ Add something.
- ℘ Take out something.
- ⊙ Add a period.
- ¶ Begin a new paragraph.

After five days of long, wet, dark hardship, Jennifer Dizeck can almost see the finish line of the Center of the Earth Championnship. Owneship of the prized cup seems almost certain. But what's this? She is taking on water! Will a defective canoe obligate Jennifer to pull out of the race?

Jennifer seems to be back in control. It is fortunite she is so resourceful. She was inventave enough to plug the hole with her waterproof jacket. That's good, creative thinking on Jennifer's part! She's regained her leadershap position in the last mile of the race. Jennifer Dizeck wins by a few feet!

Spelling Tip

For base words that end in **e,** drop the **e** before adding the suffixes **-ate, -ive,** or **-ship: obligate, creative.**

Word List

originate	inventive
fortunate	negative
activate	creative
affectionate	ownership
considerate	membership
obligate	hardship
productive	relationship
defective	friendship
constructive	championship
attractive	leadership

Write a Sports Broadcast

On a separate sheet of paper, write a sports broadcast about an imaginary new sporting event. Remember that a broadcaster reports the action as he or she watches it happen. Try to use at least three spelling words.

Notes for Home: Your child spelled words with the suffixes *-ate, -ive,* and *-ship*. ***Home Activity:*** Have your child scan a magazine article to find other words that contain the suffixes *-ate, -ive,* and *-ship*. Encourage him or her to tell you the base word of each of the words.

Name ______________________________

Spelling: Suffixes *-ate, -ive, -ship*

REVIEW

Word List				
originate	considerate	constructive	creative	relationship
fortunate	obligate	attractive	ownership	friendship
activate	productive	inventive	membership	championship
affectionate	defective	negative	hardship	leadership

Directions: Write the word from the box that belongs in each group.

1. fellowship, companionship, ________________
2. faulty, imperfect, ________________
3. disapproving, pessimistic, ________________
4. authority, guidance, ________________
5. fertile, fruitful, ________________
6. begin, start, ________________
7. burden, misfortune, ________________
8. affiliation, association, ________________
9. possession, title, ________________
10. loving, cuddly, ________________

Directions: Choose the word from the box that best replaces the underlined word or words. Write the word on the line.

________________ 11. My <u>association</u> with time travel began long ago.

________________ 12. In an <u>imaginative</u> mood, I built my own time machine.

________________ 13. My best friend Josh offered <u>helpful</u> criticism.

________________ 14. Josh was <u>ingenious</u> enough to fix the flaws in the machine.

________________ 15. I was very <u>lucky</u> to have a sympathetic friend like him.

________________ 16. Together we had won the <u>victory</u> medal in the science fair.

________________ 17. My voyage will <u>begin</u> here in Kansas City; my destination is Paris in 1899.

________________ 18. The trip sounded <u>appealing</u> to Josh, but he couldn't come.

________________ 19. He did <u>require</u> me to promise that he could go on the next trip.

________________ 20. It was very <u>thoughtful</u> of Josh to see me off.

Notes for Home: Your child reviewed words with the suffixes *-ate, -ive,* and *-ship.* ***Home Activity:*** Challenge your child to spell *inventive* and *creative,* use each word in a sentence, and explain the similarities and differences between the meanings of the two words.

Name ______________________________

Manual

A **manual** is usually in the form of a booklet or book. It contains a written set of directions that help the reader understand, use, or build something.

Directions: Study the table of contents and diagram from a manual for a VCR (video cassette recorder). Then answer the questions that follow.

Table of Contents for Your VCR

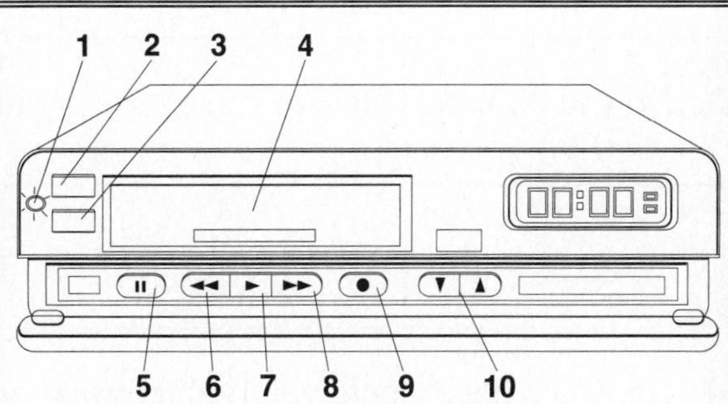

Front Panel Features

1. Power Indicator Light—A red light appears when the VCR is on.
2. Power Button—Use to turn the VCR on and off.
3. Stop/Eject Button—Press to stop videotape. Then press again to eject tape.
4. Tape Compartment—Insert videotape here.
5. Pause Button—Use to view single frame or picture while playing a videotape.
6. Rewind Button—Press to rewind tape after pressing stop. If pressed during playback, video may be viewed in rapid reverse.
7. Play Button—Press to play videotape.
8. Fast Forward Button—Press to advance the tape. If pressed during playback, video may be viewed in rapid forward.
9. Record Button—Use for recording.
10. Channel Up/Channel Down Buttons—Use to select TV channels on VCR.

Name ______________________________

1. What is the purpose of this manual? ______________________________

2. When might you use this manual? Give an example. ______________________________

3. Do you think this table of contents is organized well? How might it help you use the manual?

4. On which page would you find information about setting the clock? ______________

5. Suppose you wanted to record a TV program about space travel. Which page would you turn to in the manual to see how to do this? Which front panel features would you most likely use?

6. Which front panel feature confirms that the VCR is actually on? ______________

7. What does the rewind button do? ______________________________

8. If you were unable to make the VCR work properly, on what page would you find a phone number to get help?

9. Why do you think a diagram was included in this manual? ______________

10. Why is it important to be able to follow directions carefully and correctly when using a manual?

Notes for Home: Your child studied a sample page from an instruction manual and answered questions about it. ***Home Activity:*** With your child, look at an instruction manual. Discuss the information in it, such as the table of contents, diagrams, and instructions.

Family Times

Name________________________________

Summary

Brave Young Cowboy Rescues Horses

In "The Trail Drive" a young escaped slave, Midnight, is put in charge of the horses on Joe B's cattle drive across Texas. Midnight quickly settles into the hard daily routine, full of dust and danger. Crossing the Red River is a fearful experience, but Midnight brings the horses across safely. One night, he sees a cougar stalking the horses. Midnight wrestles the cat and gets badly clawed, but he scares it off and saves the horses.

Activity

Retell the Story. Ask you child to retell the part of the story where Midnight crosses the Red River. Encourage him or her to explain why this is a fearful experience.

Reading Skills

Character

Characters are the people or animals who take part in the events of a short story, novel, play, or other form of fiction.

You can learn about characters by noticing what they think, say, and do. You can also learn about characters by paying attention to the way other characters treat them or speak about them.

The lasting qualities of a character's personality are called character traits. *Brave, stubborn,* and *honest* are examples of character traits. Midnight fights the cat because he has certain character traits: he's *resourceful* and *brave.*

Activity

Describe Characters. Discuss the character traits of favorite characters from television shows or movies. Make a list of the things they think, say, and do. Then summarize their actions with the names of different traits.

Family Times

Tested Vocabulary

Words to Know

Knowing the meanings of these words is important to reading "The Trail Drive." Practice using these words to learn their meanings.

drive the act of moving cattle overland

mustang a small, wild horse

pounce attack suddenly and unexpectedly

scorching very hot; burning

weariness exhaustion

Grammar

Interjections

Interjections are words that express feelings. When an interjection expresses a strong feeling, the interjection is followed by an exclamation mark. When the feeling is less strong, the interjection is separated from the rest of the sentence by a comma.

Yikes! The cattle are stampeding!

Oh, that saddle needs to be repaired.

Interjections are rarely used in formal writing. They are most often used in conversations, friendly letters, and other informal materials.

Activity

Draw a Comic Strip. Draw a comic strip that shows a trail drive. Use interjections in the characters' speeches where appropriate.

Tested Spelling Words

Name ______________________________

Character

- **Characters** are the people or animals who take part in the events of a short story, novel, play, or other form of fiction.
- You can learn about characters by noticing what they think, say, and do. You can also learn about characters by paying attention to how other characters treat them and what others say about them.
- The lasting qualities of a character's personality are called character traits. *Brave, stubborn,* and *honest* are examples of character traits.

Directions: Reread "The Pleasantest Days." Complete the web by writing about what Sam likes. Then write a sentence describing Sam.

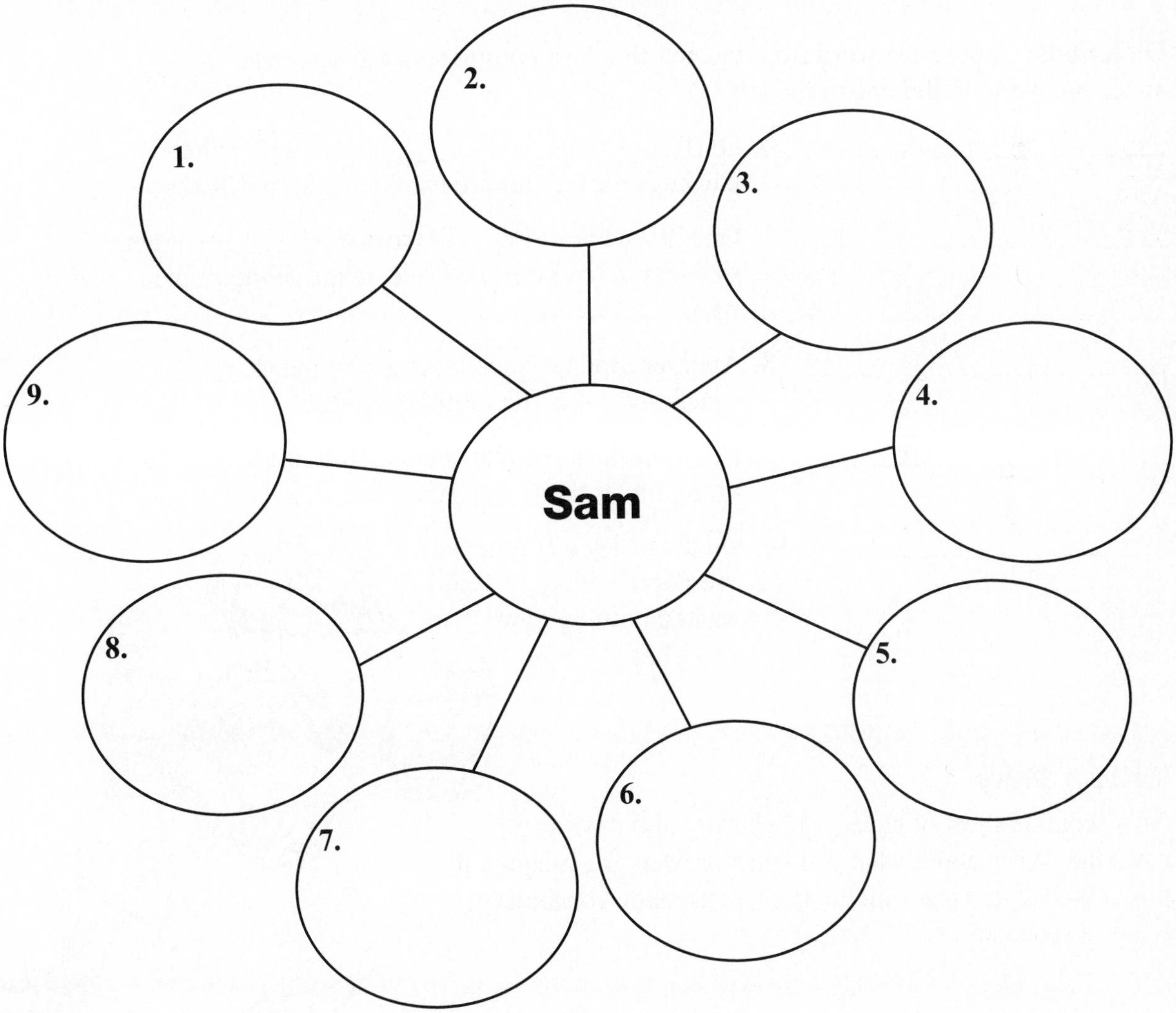

Sam

1.

2.

3.

4.

5.

6.

7.

8.

9.

10. Sam is ______________________________.

Notes for Home: Your child described a story character. ***Home Activity:*** Encourage your child to make a list of character traits for different characters in stories, movies, and TV programs. Work together to draw a picture and write a caption that describes each character.

Name ______________________________

Vocabulary

Directions: Choose the word from the box that best matches each definition. Write the word on the line.

Check the Words You Know
__ drive
__ mustang
__ pounce
__ scorching
__ weariness

_______________ **1.** a small, wild horse

_______________ **2.** to attack suddenly, usually from above

_______________ **3.** exhaustion

_______________ **4.** the act of moving cattle overland to a shipping point

_______________ **5.** very hot

Directions: Choose the word from the box that best completes each sentence. Write the word on the line to the left.

_______________ **6.** On Tyrone's first cattle _____, he and the other cowboys moved hundreds of cattle across Texas.

_______________ **7.** One day while riding, Tyrone saw a _____ galloping free across the prairie with its mane flying in the wind.

_______________ **8.** Another time he spied a cougar trying to _____ on a jackrabbit, but the rabbit got away.

_______________ **9.** But most days, Tyrone spent long hours riding under the _____ sun.

_______________ **10.** On those days, Tyrone was overcome with _____ and wanted nothing more than a soft bed.

Write a Story

On a separate sheet of paper, write a story about being a cowhand. Write about what you know or what you imagine it might be like to work with horses. Use as many vocabulary words as you can.

Notes for Home: Your child identified and used vocabulary words from "The Trail Drive." ***Home Activity:*** Act out a conversation between two cowhands. Try to use as many listed vocabulary words as you can.

Name ______________________________

Character

- **Characters** are the people or animals who take part in the events of a short story, novel, play, or other form of fiction.
- You can learn about characters by noticing what they think, say, and do.
- You can also learn about characters by paying attention to how other characters in the story treat them and what these other characters say about them.

Directions: Reread the part of "The Trail Drive" about Midnight's first day on the drive. Then answer the questions below. Think about what the passage tells you about the characters.

One by one Midnight tethered six ponies to the picket line. He worked on, not paying attention to anyone or anything else. Sweat rolled down his temples. He licked the salty taste off his lips and kept going. Six more. At last he tied Dahomey to the line and stood to wipe his forehead. Midnight looked back at the work he'd done. The horses hadn't really given him any trouble. His first day on the drive was over, and he was satisfied.

"Good job for your first time." Joe B. strolled up and tugged on the last rope line Midnight had stretched. It was so tight that the rope bounced against Joe's hand. He nodded and looked at Midnight.

1. What action tells you that Midnight feels that working hard is more important than socializing or watching the others?

____

2. How does Midnight feel about his first day on the drive?

____

3. What do Joe B.'s words tell you about how he feels about Midnight's work?

____

____

4. What action by Joe B. suggests that he feels Midnight did a good job tying the ropes?

____

5. On a separate sheet of paper, describe what you learn about the character of Midnight from reading the story. Give examples from the story to support your answer.

Notes for Home: Your child read a story and analyzed its characters. ***Home Activity:*** Read a short story with your child. Encourage your child to describe what he or she learns about its characters.

Selection Test

Directions: Choose the best answer to each item. Mark the letter for the answer you have chosen.

Part 1: Vocabulary

Find the answer choice that means about the same as the underlined word in each sentence.

1. Those cowboys saw the <u>drive</u>.
- A. a public sale of animals
- B. act of moving cattle overland
- C. a rodeo show
- D. fenced-in area for cattle

2. <u>Weariness</u> overtook them.
- F. state of being confused
- G. nervousness; fear
- H. state of being alert
- J. deep tiredness

3. It was <u>scorching</u> weather.
- A. very hot
- B. unpredictable
- C. very wet
- D. unpleasant

4. He kept his eye on the <u>mustang</u>.
- F. leader in a group of horses
- G. group of spare horses
- H. small wild stray horse
- J. horse used for carrying loads

5. The cat was about to <u>pounce</u>.
- A. begin eating
- B. hunch down with eyes alert
- C. turn over on its back
- D. leap suddenly and seize something

Part 2: Comprehension

Use what you know about the story to answer each item.

6. This story begins with—
- F. Midnight's first day on a long trip.
- G. a river crossing.
- H. the last day of a long trip.
- J. a terrible storm.

7. What is Midnight's job in the evenings?
- A. watching the edges of the herd
- B. helping to make dinner
- C. taking care of the spare horses
- D. finding water for the herd

8. What is Slim's job on the drive?
- F. boss
- G. cook
- H. scout
- J. guard

9. Why did Midnight tie Rusty to the picket line before the other horses?
- A. He noticed that other horses seemed to follow her.
- B. She was the horse he rode on the drive.
- C. He could tell she was hungry.
- D. He thought she was the one most likely to give him trouble.

10. You can tell that Slim was a little worried about—
- F. the horses.
- G. whether there was enough food.
- H. the weather.
- J. how things were going for Midnight.

11. Midnight showed he was brave and determined when he—
- A. set up a picket line for the first time.
- B. took the horses across the Red River.
- C. avoided talking to Lou Boy about Curly.
- D. fell asleep on the bare ground.

12. Nighttime reminded Midnight of—
- F. the first time he saw a horse.
- G. his escape from slavery.
- H. crossing large bodies of water.
- J. his arrival in Mexico.

GO ON

13. What feeling deep inside Midnight was the main cause of his fight with the cougar?
- A. fear that he would lose his job if he wasn't brave enough
- B. love for the horses in his care
- C. anger over things that happened in the past
- D. hatred of wild cats

14. In some parts of the story, the author uses *italic* type to call attention to—
- F. Midnight's thoughts.
- G. important ideas.
- H. events from the past.
- J. make-believe events.

15. Slim cautions Midnight not to—
- A. risk his life for a horse.
- B. leave camp without a partner.
- C. get too friendly with the other cowboys.
- D. let bad memories control him.

STOP

Character

- **Characters** are the people or animals who take part in the events of a short story, novel, play, or other form of fiction.
- You can learn about characters by noticing what they think, say, and do.
- You can also learn about characters by paying attention to how other characters in the story treat them and what these other characters say about them.

Directions: Read the journal entry below.

March 31, 1895

I am sailing with my husband to India. What an adventure it will be! I have always wanted to travel, but until now I've never left Ireland. I have become friends with the captain—everyone else seems to be seasick! "We may be in for storms before long, Mrs. Clancy," he warned me. "Yet I see that you take the rough weather in stride."

One day, the sails suddenly started to flap, and the boat began to toss and weave. I dashed to the deck. Huge waves crashed over the deck. Fierce winds tossed the ship. The captain's calm but strong commands set her back on course as the wind died down. The captain suddenly saw me at the railing. "Mrs. Clancy," he called, bowing, "I wish all my crew were as brave as you!"

Directions: Complete the web below. Use details from the journal entry to tell about Mrs. Clancy. Below the web, describe Mrs. Clancy in your own words.

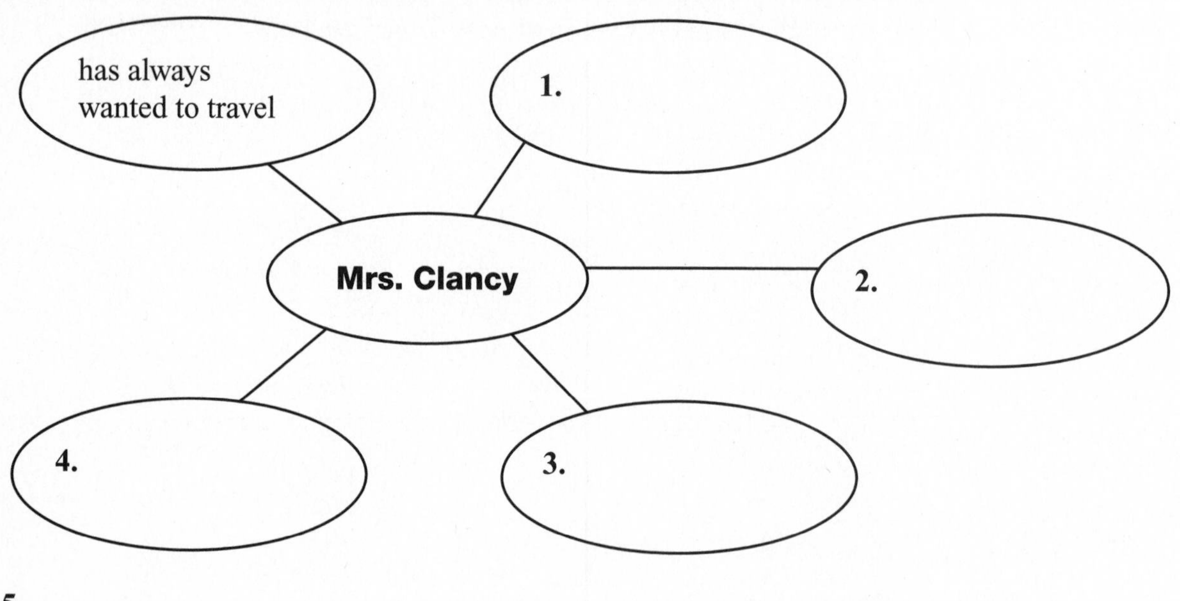

5. ____

____

Notes for Home: Your child read a story and listed details about its main character. ***Home Activity:*** Read a story with your child. Encourage your child to write a sentence describing each character. Discuss how he or she decided what to write about each character.

Generalizing

REVIEW

Directions: Read the passage. Then read each question about the passage. Choose the best answer to each question. Mark the letter for the answer you have chosen.

Explosive Earth

Most volcanoes are made out of lava flows, or streams of melted rock, and other materials. The lava shoots upward in the eruption and falls back again. It lands as cinders or ashes and is shot into the air again. This rise and fall happens many times and forms the cone shape common to most volcanoes. Mount Vesuvius in Italy is a famous volcano of this kind.

A number of volcanoes have deep basins, called calderas, which become filled with water over a long period of time. Crater Lake in Oregon is an example. Forceful explosions that destroy the volcano itself form some calderas.

Many volcanoes are born underwater on the sea floor. Mount Etna and Mount Vesuvius began as underwater volcanoes. So did the huge cones found in the Hawaiian Islands.

Some volcanoes are much more active than others. A number of constantly active volcanoes are found in a belt called the Ring of Fire that encircles the Pacific Ocean. Other volcanoes become inactive, or dormant, for months or years. The eruption that follows a long dormant period is usually violent. This was true in the state of Washington when Mount Saint Helens erupted violently after a 123-year period of quiet.

One reason scientists study volcanoes is that they can be dangerous to life forms. In addition to the dangers of lava and ash, the eruptions can melt ice and snow and cause deadly mud flows. Harmful gases can pour out of volcanoes long after they have erupted.

1. Which of the following statements is **not** a generalization?
- **A.** Most volcanoes are made out of lava flows and other materials.
- **B.** Mount Vesuvius is a famous volcano in Italy.
- **C.** A number of volcanoes have deep basins.
- **D.** Most volcanoes have a cone shape.

2. Underwater volcanoes are born—
- **F.** only in Italy.
- **G.** inactive.
- **H.** on the sea floor.
- **J.** only in the Ring of Fire.

3. Many active volcanoes are found—
- **A.** only on the sea floor.
- **B.** in Oregon.
- **C.** in a rim around the Pacific.
- **D.** everywhere on Earth.

4. An eruption after a period of inactivity usually—
- **F.** occurs in the Ring of Fire.
- **G.** is violent.
- **H.** creates a cone-shaped volcano.
- **J.** forms a caldera.

5. Which statement below is a valid generalization?
- **A.** All volcanoes become active again after a quiet time.
- **B.** Few volcanic eruptions are dangerous.
- **C.** Danger from volcanoes ends with the eruptions.
- **D.** Some volcanoes are more active than others.

Notes for Home: Your child identified generalizations—broad statements about several things or people—in a passage. ***Home Activity:*** Read a brief magazine article with your child. Challenge him or her to write one or two generalizations that are supported by the facts in the article.

Name ______________________________

Writing Across Texts

Directions: Consider what you know about cowboys and what you learned from "The Trail Drive" and "A Cowboy's Job." Add more examples to the table below to tell why a cowboy's life would be fun and why it would be difficult.

Why a Cowboy's Life Would Be Fun	Why a Cowboy's Life Would Be Difficult
Cowboys learn how to do rope tricks.	Cowboys work long hours.
1.	**6.**
2.	**7.**
3.	**8.**
4.	**9.**
5.	**10.**

Write a Persuasive Paragraph

Would a cowboy's life be fun or difficult? Write a persuasive paragraph that convinces readers of your opinion. Support your opinion with information from "The Trail Drive" and "A Cowboy's Job."

Notes for Home: Your child used information from more than one source to support an opinion. ***Home Activity:*** As you read stories or articles with your child, discuss how the ideas connect with other material read. Encourage your child to make comparisons.

Name ______________________

REVIEW

Grammar: Exclamations

Directions: Decide whether each group of words is a complete exclamatory sentence. Write **S** on the line if it is a sentence. Write **N** if it is not.

_______ **1.** He really used to be a cowboy!

_______ **2.** Wow!

_______ **3.** What a piece of luck!

_______ **4.** Watch out for that horse!

_______ **5.** Be careful of those hooves!

_______ **6.** How absolutely terrifying!

_______ **7.** Just a minute, please!

_______ **8.** Whew, what a relief!

_______ **9.** I cannot imagine that!

_______ **10.** What a gorgeous horse that is!

Directions: Read each sentence. Then write an exclamation to respond to each sentence.

11. That horse just lost its shoe.

____

12. Do you think cowboys led exciting lives?

____

13. Real cowboys often had to manage thousands of cows.

____

14. Cara does not look comfortable on that horse.

____

15. What did you think of that old cowboy movie?

____

Notes for Home: Your child recognized and wrote exclamations—statements that show strong feeling and that end with exclamation marks. ***Home Activity:*** Together write a short skit for a TV show you both know. Use some exclamations.

Name ______________________________

Grammar: Interjections

Interjections are used to express strong feeling. When the feeling is especially strong, the interjection is followed by an exclamation mark. When the feeling is less strong, the interjection is followed by a comma.

Wow! That horse is wild.
Hey, get back here.

Directions: Circle the interjection in each sentence.

1. Hey! There's a cowboy movie on TV.
2. Wow! Being on a cattle drive looks like fun.
3. Ugh! It's probably harder than it seems.
4. Ouch! Falling from a horse can't feel good.
5. Hooray! They finally found that poor runaway cow.
6. Whew, that's a relief.
7. Oops, they forgot to tie up that horse.
8. Yikes! The horse is running away!
9. Oh my! He's never going to catch that horse.
10. Say, that movie was pretty good.

Directions: Choose an appropriate interjection and punctuation mark to add to the beginning of each sentence. Write the interjection on the line.

11. ______________________ Do you really own a pony of your own?
12. ______________________ I've had this pony for six months.
13. ______________________ This horse is really big.
14. ______________________ I don't know how to stop this horse!
15. ______________________ Thanks for getting him to stop.

Notes for Home: Your child identified interjections, words that express strong feeling, such as *Wow, Oh my,* and *Hey*. ***Home Activity:*** Together, write a letter or brief note to a relative. Choose a place to insert one interjection.

Extra Practice

Grammar: Interjections

Directions: Write the interjection in each sentence on the line.

______ **1.** My, I'd like to climb a mountain like Mount Everest.

______ **2.** Oh! Being at the top must be incredible.

______ **3.** Say, have you ever seen films of mountain climbers?

______ **4.** Wow! It looks like quite an adventure.

______ **5.** Well, I think it would be very hard to do.

______ **6.** Hey! Don't get discouraged.

______ **7.** My goodness, they looked determined.

______ **8.** Oh no! That cable broke.

______ **9.** Ouch! He fell a few feet.

______ **10.** Whew, the climber didn't get hurt.

Directions: On each line, write a sentence expressing the feeling that the interjection suggests.

11. Oh no! ______

12. Good grief, ______

13. Hah! ______

14. What! ______

15. Great! ______

16. Yes, ______

17. Yuck! ______

18. Hey! ______

19. Oops, ______

20. Wow, ______

Write an Advertisement

On a separate sheet of paper, write an advertisement for an adventure trip such as rafting, mountain climbing, or going on safari. Use interjections in some of your sentences. Underline each one that you use.

Notes for Home: Your child identified interjections, words that express strong feeling, such as *Wow, Oh my,* and *Hey,* and wrote sentences using interjections. ***Home Activity:*** Challenge your child to describe something enjoyable, using interjections to show his or her feelings.

Name ______________________________

Grammar: Interjections

RETEACHING

Underline each interjection.

1. Whoa! We're going so fast!
2. Eek! It's really dark in here!

An interjection is used to express strong feeling. Often an interjection is followed by an exclamation mark. If the feeling is less strong, the interjection is followed by a comma.

Directions: Circle the interjection in each sentence.

1. Aha! I've found the answer!
2. Oops, I missed that word.
3. Oh, I guess I'll go.
4. Ow! That's my sore hand.
5. Wow! I won first prize!
6. Ugh! That tastes awful.
7. Well, you finally got here.
8. Right, I understand.
9. Yikes! That scared me!
10. Whee! I love fast rides!

Directions: Write an interjection that makes sense in each sentence.

11. ____________________ We are so far away!
12. ____________________ I'm afraid of that dog.
13. ____________________ that boat is huge!
14. ____________________ I made a mistake.
15. ____________________ I guess I'd better go home.
16. ____________________ What a mess that is!

Notes for Home: Your child identified and wrote interjections in sentences. ***Home Activity:*** Together, look through old photographs. Have your child write captions for them, using interjections.

Name ______________________________

Grammar: Interjections

Directions: On each line, write a sentence expressing the feeling that that interjection suggests.

1. Ugh! ______________________________
2. My, ______________________________
3. Well, ______________________________
4. Ouch! ______________________________
5. Yikes! ______________________________
6. Oh my! ______________________________
7. Say, ______________________________
8. Yes! ______________________________
9. Uh, oh! ______________________________
10. Man! ______________________________

Directions: Write on the line the interjection from each sentence.

______________ **11.** Oh no! I forgot my homework!

______________ **12.** Yuck! That milk is spoiled.

______________ **13.** Whew! That was close!

______________ **14.** Well, I guess you're right.

______________ **15.** No way! I'm not climbing that fence!

______________ **16.** Wow! I've never seen that kind of car before.

______________ **17.** Whoops, I slipped on that patch of ice.

______________ **18.** Gee! That completely slipped my mind!

______________ **19.** My, that was a long speech.

______________ **20.** All right! We won the game!

Write a Scary Story

On a separate sheet of paper, write a story about people in an imaginary scary place. Think about how characters in your story might react to different situations. Include dialogue in your story. Use interjections in some of your sentences.

Notes for Home: Your child used interjections in sentences. ***Home Activity:*** Write interjections (For example: *Wow! Oh, no! My goodness!*) on cards. Hold up a card and have your child use that interjection in a sentence.

Name ______________________________

Word Study: Plural Possessives

Directions: Add an apostrophe (') to form the possessive of plural nouns that end in **s: sisters'.** For plural nouns that do not end in **s,** add an **apostrophe (')** and **s** to form the possessive: **oxen's.** Read the phrases below. Change each phrase to form a possessive noun. Write each new phrase on the line.

the scales of the fish — the fish's scales

1. the chores of the men ______________
2. the toys of the boys ______________
3. the experiences of the women ______________
4. the squeaks of the mice ______________
5. the heavy loads of the trucks ______________

Directions: Read each sentence. Use the possessive form of the noun in ( ) to complete each sentence. Write the possessive noun on the line.

______________ 6. Before they fell asleep, the (girls) last thoughts were of the next day's trail drive.

______________ 7. The next morning, the (horses) whinnies sounded clearly across the field.

______________ 8. The (children) excitement was infectious as they gathered around the horses.

______________ 9. The (parents) concerns had been that their children might get hurt.

______________ 10. But the (families) worries were laid to rest when they saw how gentle the horses were.

______________ 11. The (trails) rocky terrain made the ride a little rough for those not used to traveling on horseback.

______________ 12. Even the (men) warnings of dangers along the trail could not dampen the group's enthusiasm.

______________ 13. Everyone kept a sharp eye out looking for the (moose) tracks.

______________ 14. They saw marks on the ground where the (elk) hooves had dug in the dirt.

______________ 15. The guide pointed to scratches where the (deer) antlers had rubbed against the tree bark.

Notes for Home: Your child formed plural possessives, such as *sisters'* and *oxen's*. ***Home Activity:*** Read a biography with your child about a person she or he finds interesting. Look for possessive nouns. Have your child write the words and notice how they were formed.

Name ____________________

Spelling: Using Apostrophes

Pretest

Pretest Directions: Fold back the page along the dotted line. On the blanks, write the spelling words as they are dictated. When you have finished the test, unfold the page and check your words.

1. ____________________
2. ____________________
3. ____________________
4. ____________________
5. ____________________
6. ____________________
7. ____________________
8. ____________________
9. ____________________
10. ____________________
11. ____________________
12. ____________________
13. ____________________
14. ____________________
15. ____________________
16. ____________________
17. ____________________
18. ____________________
19. ____________________
20. ____________________

1. **It's** not time to go already, is it?
2. **Let's** go bowling.
3. I think **that's** a great idea.
4. **We'd** rather go to the zoo.
5. They **don't** know who called.
6. **There's** a pie for dessert.
7. The **coach's** hat fell off.
8. The **coaches'** whistles are loud.
9. That **man's** pants are plaid.
10. Those **men's** jobs are all done.
11. **You're** just the person I need.
12. **She'd** tell us if she knew.
13. You **mustn't** stay out too late.
14. It is after ten **o'clock**.
15. Our **guide's** walking stick broke.
16. The **guides'** station is over there.
17. She sat in the **director's** desk.
18. The **directors'** offices are locked.
19. This **city's** mayor is Mr. Jones.
20. Those **cities'** names are alike.

Notes for Home: Your child took a pretest on contractions and possessives with apostrophes. ***Home Activity:*** Help your child learn misspelled words before the final test by concentrating on which two words are shortened to one or on whether one person or more than one person owns something.

Name ______________________________

Think and Practice

Spelling: Using Apostrophes

Word List

it's	don't	man's	mustn't	director's
let's	there's	men's	o'clock	directors'
that's	coach's	you're	guide's	city's
we'd	coaches'	she'd	guides'	cities'

Directions: Choose the words from the box that are possessive nouns. Write each word in the correct column.

Singular Possessive Nouns	**Plural Possessive Nouns**
1. ______________	6. ______________
2. ______________	7. ______________
3. ______________	8. ______________
4. ______________	9. ______________
5. ______________	10. ______________

Directions: Choose the word from the box that best replaces each underlined word or words. Write the word on the line.

______________ 11. "<u>It is</u> morning! Time to get up!" called Aunt Carmela.

______________ 12. "Seven <u>A.M.</u> is too early to get up," grumbled Alice.

______________ 13. "On a farm, <u>that is</u> very late," her aunt explained.

______________ 14. "<u>We would</u> never get our work done if we slept that late."

______________ 15. "After you've eaten," said Uncle Tony, "<u>let us</u> go to the barn."

______________ 16. "<u>You are</u> going to learn how to milk, Alice," he explained.

______________ 17. "I <u>do not</u> think I can," objected Alice. "Cows scare me."

______________ 18. "You <u>must not</u> be scared, Alice. They are very gentle."

______________ 19. "Look, Uncle Tony!" cried Alice later. "<u>There is</u> the full pail of milk!"

______________ 20. After this success, Alice knew <u>she would</u> like living on the farm.

Notes for Home: Your child used apostrophes to spell contractions and possessives. ***Home Activity:*** Challenge your child to tell you the two words each contraction represents. Note that some can stand for different combinations: *she'd* = *she had, she did,* or *she would.*

Name ______________________________

Spelling: Using Apostrophes

Directions: Proofread this cowboy song. Find five spelling mistakes. Use the proofreading marks to correct each mistake.

≡	Make a capital.
/	Make a small letter.
∧	Add something.
℘	Take out something.
⊙	Add a period.
¶	Begin a new paragraph.

A citys' lights do'nt mean a thing to me.

That's not where this mans' heart will ever be.

Its the Chisholm Trail that calls.

Let's ride the range, we will see it all.

Theres' joy and laughter when you're riding free.

Word List

it's	there's	you're	guides'
let's	coach's	she'd	director's
that's	coaches'	mustn't	directors'
we'd	man's	o'clock	city's
don't	men's	guide's	cities'

Spelling Tip

man's men's cities'

To form the possessive of a singular noun or a plural noun that does not end in **s,** add an **apostrophe** and an **s: man's, men's.** For plural nouns that end in **s,** just add an apostrophe to form the possessive: **cities'.** Check the cowboy song to be sure the plurals are formed correctly.

Write a Song

On a separate sheet of paper, write your own cowboy song. Think about experiences that a cowhand on a ranch might have. Try to use at least five spelling words.

Notes for Home: Your child used apostrophes to spell contractions and possessives. ***Home Activity:*** Have your child use the spelling words in sentences. Check for the correct use of singular and plural possessives.

Spelling: Using Apostrophes

REVIEW

Word List

it's	don't	man's	mustn't	director's
let's	there's	men's	o'clock	directors'
that's	coach's	you're	guide's	city's
we'd	coaches'	she'd	guides'	cities'

Directions: Each underlined word is missing its apostrophe. Write each word correctly on the line, inserting the apostrophe in its proper place.

______________ **1.** Jud: Theres a fair this Saturday. Would you like to go?

______________ **2.** Laurey: I dont know. Where is it going to be held?

______________ **3.** Jud: Its near the Simpson ranch.

______________ **4.** Laurey: Oh, thats not far. I would like to go!

______________ **5.** Jud: It starts at 8 oclock.

______________ **6.** Laurey: Well, lets not be late.

______________ **7.** Jud: Wed better invite your sister to come along.

______________ **8.** Laurey: Shed probably like that.

______________ **9.** Jud: We mustnt forget to ask her.

______________ **10.** Laurey: Youre coming to dinner tonight. We'll ask her then.

Directions: Complete each phrase with the correct possessive word in ( ). Write the word on the line.

______________ **11.** Singular: (director's/directors') chair

______________ **12.** Plural: (coach's/coaches') offices

______________ **13.** Plural: (guide's/guides') presentations

______________ **14.** Singular: (city's/cities') art museum

______________ **15.** Plural: (director's/directors') awards

______________ **16.** Singular: (coach's/coaches') whistle

______________ **17.** Singular: (man's/men's) hat

______________ **18.** Singular: (guide's/guides') tour

______________ **19.** Plural: (city's/cities') skyscrapers

______________ **20.** Plural: (man's/men's) choirs

Notes for Home: Your child used apostrophes to spell contractions and possessives. ***Home Activity:*** Help your child write sentences that contain both a contraction and a possessive from the word list.

Name ______________________________

Interpret Information/ Draw Conclusions

To interpret information and draw conclusions about it, you need to decide what the information means and whether it suits your research purposes.

Directions: Read the passage. Next, complete the web by telling what you learned from reading the passage. Then answer the questions that follow the web.

The True Life of the Cowboy

Imagine working up to 20 hours a day in grueling weather with unpredictable animals. Now imagine you only got paid about $25 to $40 a month! Even back then, this wasn't a lot of money. This was what a cowboy's life was really like.

Cowboys have become almost legendary in American history as bold, heroic figures who led glamorous lives in the Old West. However, the cowboy's life was anything but glamorous. Besides being poorly paid, the work they did was very strenuous and very difficult, not to mention dirty and dangerous. A cowboy's job was to take a herd of cattle from one place to another, usually from Texas into either Kansas, Nebraska, or Wyoming. Each minute of every hour of every day cowboys needed to stay constantly alert in order to avoid disaster. They had to guard the cattle from predators—both animal and human. They also had to prevent, if possible, cattle stampedes. They had to round up any stray cattle, as well as take care of the ones already in their possession.

The era of the cowboy spanned about 25 years from 1865–1890. With the expansion of the railroad, these underpaid workers were no longer needed to do long cattle drives. However, "cowboys" continue to live on through the many western stories written about them and the TV shows and movies made about them.

Name ______________________________

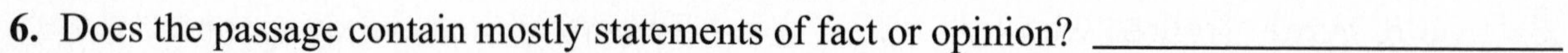

6. Does the passage contain mostly statements of fact or opinion? ______________________________

7. What is the main idea of the passage? ______________________________

8. Why were cowboys not needed for cattle drives after the expansion of the railroad?

9. Would the information in this passage be useful for a research report on the work that cowboys did? Explain.

10. Would the information in this passage help you answer the question: "What is life like for cowboys on ranches today?" Explain.

Notes for Home Your child read a nonfiction passage, interpreted information in it, and drew conclusions about it. ***Home Activity:*** Challenge your child to read a newspaper article and tell you the main idea of the article.

Name ______________________________

K-W-L Chart

Directions: Write your topic (the place you will research) on the topic line. In the chart, write what you know about your topic and what you want to know about it. Then write information sources you can use. As you research, write information you learn that you can use in your report.

Topic: ______________________________

K What I Know	W What I Want to Know	L What I Learn (Information to Use in My Report)
	What kinds of books and other sources can help me?	

Notes for Home: Your child has learned about finding information for a research report. ***Home Activity:*** Think of a topic, such as a person in history or an event. Ask your child what kinds of books or other sources may offer valuable information about the topic.

Name ____________________

Elaboration

Explanatory Phrases

- One way to elaborate is by adding an **explanatory phrase.**
- Often, you can supply information by adding a comma and a phrase that explains a word.

Directions: Complete each sentence by picking a phrase that tells more about a word. The line in the sentence tells where the phrase goes. Be sure to use a comma before and after each phrase. Write the new sentence on the long line. Use each phrase only once.

Explanatory Phrases
with only twelve letters
which joined the Union in 1959
a British naval officer
over 1,523 miles long
a graceful dance
many of Polynesian descent
wreaths of flowers
the Aloha State

1. Captain James Cook ________ reached Hawaii in 1778.

____

2. Hawaii ______ is the youngest state.

____

3. Hawaii's people _______ welcome tourists.

____

4. Leis ________ are given to newcomers.

____

5. Do the hula ________ and attend a pig roast.

____

6. The Hawaiian alphabet ________ is unusual.

____

7. Hawaii's nickname ________ means "love."

____

8. These islands ________ are beautiful.

____

Notes for Home: Your child has added information to sentences by using explanatory phrases. ***Home Activity:*** Ask your child to describe a place such as Hawaii, using at least one explanatory phrase to give information about a word.

Name ______________________________

Self-Evaluation

Research Report

Directions: Think about the final draft of your research report. Then answer each question below.

	Yes	No	Not sure
1. Did I present information clearly?			
2. Did I write a good introduction and conclusion?			
3. Did I keep my purpose and audience in mind?			
4. Did I use my sources of information well?			
5. Did I proofread and edit carefully to avoid errors?			

6. What is the best part of my research report?

____

____

____

____

7. Write one thing that you would change about this research report if you had the chance to research or write it again.

____

____

____

____

Notes for Home: Your child has answered questions about preparing and writing a research report. ***Home Activity:*** Ask your child what kinds of books or other sources gave the most useful information. Ask whether the place he or she chose was a good topic to research.

Family Times

Name ____

Summary

Boy Prevents Wedding Disaster

When Noah's mother tells him to write his grandparents a thank-you note, he argues that since his quick thinking saved the day, they should be thanking him instead! When Allen, the groom's nephew, trips over a toy wagon, topples the wedding cake, and wrenches his ankle, Noah has to take Allen's place as best man. But Noah also remembers his new friends, his writing lesson, and the gifts he has received. He realizes he should also be thankful for the great experiences he had and the things he learned.

Activity

Write an Invitation. Ask your child to invite Noah to visit him or her during vacation. Have your child suggest activities and places to visit that might interest Noah.

Reading Skills

Generalizing

A broad statement about what several people or things have in common is a **generalization.** Some generalizations contain clue words, such as *most, many, all, sometimes, generally, always,* or *never.*

<u>Most</u> children do not like to write thank-you notes.

A generalization that is supported by facts and agrees with what you already know is valid. If it is not supported by facts, it is faulty. Noah tells about a faulty generalization when he says his friend thinks the ballpoint pen led to the decline of western civilization.

Activity

Check the Ads. Find generalizations in the advertisements for products you use. Then discuss how valid they are in relation to what you already know.

Family Times

Tested Vocabulary

Words to Know

Knowing the meanings of these words is important to reading "Noah Writes a B & B Letter." Practice using these words to learn their meanings.

calligraphy a fancy style of handwriting

circumstances conditions

committee a group of people organized for a special purpose

generation people born at about the same time

handwriting writing done by hand

stationery writing materials

Grammar

Capitalization of Titles

Capitalize the first word, the last word, and every important word in the titles of books, movies, songs, newspapers, magazines, plays, stories, poems, and articles. *A, and, the, but,* and short prepositions such as *to* and *from* are examples of unimportant words.

Century Village Journal (newspaper)
The Wedding from Another Planet (movie)
Noah's Writing Crisis (play)
"The Gift of the Pen" (short story)
"Allen Sitting on a Cake" (song)
"Plan for Your Dream Trip" (article)

Activity

Make Up Titles. Read the made-up titles above. Then make up and write several titles of your own for books, movies, and songs about weddings and Noah's adventures. Check your work to be sure you have capitalized all important words.

Tested Spelling Words

____________	____________	____________	____________
____________	____________	____________	____________
____________	____________	____________	____________
____________	____________	____________	____________
____________	____________	____________	____________

Name ______________________________

Generalizing

- A broad statement about what several people or things have in common is a **generalization.**
- Some generalizations contain clue words such as *most, many, all, sometimes, generally, always,* or *never.*
- A valid generalization is supported by facts and agrees with what you already know. A faulty generalization is not supported by facts.

Directions: Reread "Almost Ready for School." Then complete the table. Circle **Yes** if the statement is a generalization. Circle **No** if it is not. Explain your answer. Identify any clue words that signal a generalization.

Statement	Generalization?	Explanation
Sixth-graders were always chosen to help out in the office or in the halls.	**1.** Yes No	**2.**
Dad made an appointment for me with a new dentist.	**3.** Yes No	**4.**
Dentists always slip into the room so quietly you don't even know they're there.	**5.** Yes No	**6.**
I immediately opened my mouth.	**7.** Yes No	**8.**
People grind their teeth when they're tense.	**9.** Yes No	**10.**

Notes for Home: Your child read a story and identified generalizations. ***Home Activity:*** Take turns using *always, sometimes,* and *never* to make generalizations. Discuss whether each generalization is valid or faulty.

Name ____

Vocabulary

Directions: Draw a line to connect each word on the left with its definition on the right.

Check the Words You Know

__ calligraphy
__ circumstances
__ committee
__ generation
__ handwriting
__ stationery

1. handwriting	a group of people who plan something
2. generation	writing materials, such as paper and envelopes
3. stationery	writing by hand
4. calligraphy	people born about the same time
5. committee	a style of handwriting

Directions: Choose the word from the box that best completes each sentence. Write the word on the line.

____________________ **6.** Before there were typewriters or computers, well-educated people learned an elegant style of writing called __________ to make their letters beautiful.

____________________ **7.** Since their __________ was too expensive to waste, they wrote carefully.

____________________ **8.** This older __________ who wrote so carefully may criticize the way young people write now.

____________________ **9.** They might like to set up a __________ to suggest changes, but it probably would not do much good.

____________________ **10.** The __________ of modern life have changed, and most people type or e-mail their letters today.

Write a Comparison

On a separate sheet of paper, write a paragraph that compares e-mail messages to conventional letters. Think about the benefits of both forms of communication. Do you think the advantages of one type of writing outweighs the other type? Use as many vocabulary words as you can in your comparison.

Notes for Home: Your child identified and used vocabulary words from the story. "Noah Writes a B & B Letter." ***Home Activity:*** Discuss which is more important: improving one's handwriting or typing skills.

Name ______________________________

Generalizing

- A broad statement about what several people or things have in common is a **generalization.**
- Some generalizations contain clue words such as *most, many, all, sometimes, generally, always,* or *never.*
- A valid generalization is supported by facts and agrees with what you already know. A faulty generalization is not supported by facts.

Directions: Reread what happens in "Noah Writes a B & B Letter" when Noah begins to write a letter to his grandparents. Then answer the questions below. Think about how generalizations sum up the story details.

I took a box of notepaper out of my desk drawer. The notes were bigger than postage stamps, but not by much. I took out a ballpoint pen and started pressing it against a piece of scrap paper, making dents in the paper but not making a mark. Ballpoint pens sometimes take a while to get started. When I was down in Florida, Tillie Nachman had said, "The ballpoint pen has been the biggest single factor in the decline of Western Civilization. It makes the written word cheap, fast, and totally without character." My mother and Tillie should get together. Between them, they have come up with the two major reasons why Western Civilization is about to collapse.

1. What is Noah's first generalization?

____

2. What clue word did you use to identify this generalization? ____________

3. Does Noah support his generalization? Explain.

____

____

4. If Noah had said, "ballpoint pens always get started easily," would this be a valid or faulty generalization? Explain.

____

____

5. On a separate sheet of paper, write a valid generalization about the people of Century Village. Give evidence from the story to support your generalization.

Notes for Home: Your child identified generalizations and decided if they were valid or faulty. ***Home Activity:*** Take turns using *most, all, always,* and *never* to make generalizations about your neighborhood. Discuss whether each generalization is valid or faulty.

Name ______________________________

Selection Test

Directions: Choose the best answer to each item. Mark the letter for the answer you have chosen.

Part 1: Vocabulary

Find the answer choice that means about the same as the underlined word in each sentence.

1. Emma practiced her <u>handwriting</u>.
- A. a method of painting on paper with fingers instead of brushes
- B. using hand and finger movements to spell out words in the air
- C. making letters or words with a pen, pencil, or other writing tool
- D. any means of communicating that involves the hands

2. Martin used a <u>calligraphy</u> pen.
- F. expressing meaning without words
- G. writing in code
- H. of or related to black
- J. beautiful handwriting

3. Dad checked his <u>stationery</u> supplies.
- A. writing materials, such as paper, cards, and envelopes
- B. staying in one place
- C. furniture, such as desks, chairs, and file cabinets
- D. related to weather

4. Considering the <u>circumstances</u>, she was doing well.
- F. difficulties
- G. conditions for an act or event
- H. goals
- J. time left to complete something

5. My dad just doesn't understand our <u>generation</u>.
- A. method of getting something done
- B. the people on one side of a family
- C. standards of taste or style
- D. all the people born at about the same time

6. They formed a <u>committee</u>.
- F. group of persons elected to make laws
- G. business
- H. group of persons appointed or elected to do a certain task
- J. large circle

Part 2: Comprehension

Use what you know about the story to answer each item.

7. What is a "B & B letter"?
- A. an invitation
- B. a thank-you letter
- C. a business letter
- D. a story in letter form

8. Why did Noah go to Florida to stay with his grandparents?
- F. His parents were away on a cruise.
- G. His grandparents needed his help.
- H. He wanted to meet his grandparents' friends.
- J. He wanted to visit a theme park in Florida.

9. What kind of place is Century Village?
- A. a small town
- B. a nursing home
- C. a vacation resort
- D. a retirement community

10. What generalization can you make about the residents of Century Village based on the information in the story?
- F. Most came to Florida from Epiphany, New York.
- G. Many have grandchildren living with them.
- H. Most like to grow flowers.
- J. Many get involved in community events.

11. Which sentence from the story is a valid generalization?
   A. "The ball-point pen has been the biggest single factor in the decline of Western Civilization."
   B. "Almost everyone who lives there is retired."
   C. "I looked totally presentable in my tuxedo T-shirt, which was a real work of art."
   D. "Fortunately, Grandpa Nate took its picture right after she finished it."

12. What did everyone at Century Village believe about Tillie Nachman?
   F. She was a great artist.
   G. She should become a professional calligrapher.
   H. She did not make mistakes.
   J. She was unhappy living in Florida.

13. During the preparations for the wedding, Noah seems to think that almost everything is—
   A. educational.
   B. unnecessary.
   C. extremely annoying.
   D. going wrong in some way.

14. The author's purpose in writing this story was to—
   F. describe life in southern Florida.
   G. tell an amusing story.
   H. help the reader distinguish between facts and opinions.
   J. show that young people are not good judges of adults.

15. Noah's mother thinks the decline of Western Civilization will come about because—
   A. young people don't do things the way they used to be done.
   B. boys wear T-shirts instead of tuxedos.
   C. young people do not learn calligraphy.
   D. children let computers think for them.

STOP

Name ______________________________

Generalizing

- A broad statement about what several people or things have in common is a **generalization.**
- Some generalizations contain clue words such as *most, many, all, sometimes, generally, always,* or *never.*
- A valid generalization is supported by facts and agrees with what you already know. A faulty generalization is not supported by facts.

Directions: Read the story below.

Jill, Vani, and I are best friends even though we're very different. Vani is the smart one with all the good ideas, Jill is the strong and athletic one, and I tell the best stories. We think maybe we have such good times together because of being different, not in spite of it!

Look at what happened on the camping trip last fall. Jill was able to blow up the air mattresses when the hand pump broke. Then Vani figured out the complicated directions for setting up the tent—just before the rain began falling! I kept them entertained all evening with scary stories. If all three of us had had the same talents, that trip would never have been so much fun!

Directions: Complete the table. Decide if each generalization is valid or faulty. Give an explanation to support your decision.

Generalization	Valid or Faulty?	Explanation
The girls are all different.	**1.**	The narrator says that Vani is the smart one, Jill is the athlete, and she is the storyteller.
The girls are resourceful.	**2.**	**3.**
The girls would have more fun together if they were more alike.	**4.**	**5.**

Notes for Home: Your child evaluated generalizations to see if they were valid or faulty. ***Home Activity:*** Name related facts about school, and ask your child to sum up the ideas by making generalizations, such as *School always ends at 3:00 P.M.*

Character and Visualizing

REVIEW

Directions: Read the story. Then read each question about the story. Choose the best answer to each question. Mark the letter for the answer you have chosen.

A Hoop, a Game Show, and a Good Idea

"I know you'll find a way to help me out, Desirée," said Desi's mother as she turned back to the work on her desk. When Mom spoke in that tone of voice, Desi knew she meant what she said. Her mother, she knew, had a deadline to meet with her publisher, and she couldn't stop working until their relatives actually arrived in an hour. But how was Desi to entertain her four little cousins on a rainy day?

Desi surveyed her cluttered room. A huge, striped hoop, five dusty sneakers, and colorful scarves sat in one corner. Wads of crumpled paper crowded her wastebasket, like so much popcorn, and her closet and shelves overflowed with toys and books. Old prizes from parties—cheap plastic rings, whistles, and so on—looked like crickets escaping from the tipped box nearby. An old box of cards with trivia questions and answers had spilled like a waterfall onto the carpet. Only her compact discs were carefully arranged on her desk by the CD player, like soldiers lined up for inspection. It was the one corner of the room Desi always kept neat, dusted, and organized.

"Maybe I can make an obstacle course in the basement," thought Desi. "The hoop, scarves, and shoes will be handy for that. The plastic prizes will be useful too, but I'll also need a timer." Surely Desi could find one in an old game box! Now, how could she use those worn-out trivia cards? "Hmmm. I'll set up my room as a TV game show. The kids can answer trivia questions and win play money. Perfect, but I'd better get busy! They'll be here in an hour!"

1. Desi's thoughts show that she is—
   - **A.** puzzled by her mother's request.
   - **B.** good at solving problems.
   - **C.** easily upset by a change of plans.
   - **D.** a constant complainer.

2. Desi's CDs are neatly arranged because—
   - **F.** she likes to keep her room neat.
   - **G.** she likes loud music.
   - **H.** the CDs are important to her.
   - **J.** her mother likes to see things neat and orderly.

3. The word *crickets* is used to describe how—
   - **A.** bugs could be heard outside.
   - **B.** the plastic prizes were all one color.
   - **C.** the prizes jumped around the room.
   - **D.** the prizes were scattered about.

4. The CDs were compared to soldiers to show—
   - **F.** how much Desi likes toy soldiers.
   - **G.** how neat and orderly they were.
   - **H.** the kinds of music recorded on them.
   - **J.** the similarity of their cover designs.

5. In the next hour, Desi will probably—
   - **A.** set up games for her cousins.
   - **B.** make lunch for her cousins.
   - **C.** reorganize her CD collection.
   - **D.** help her mom with her work.

Notes for Home: Your child identified a character's traits and visualized the setting based on images from a passage. ***Home Activity:*** Take turns describing the bedrooms or favorite rooms of family members. Discuss how each room reveals something about that person.

Name ______________________________________

Writing Across Texts

Directions: Read the steps in the box below that outline the process of doing calligraphy as described in "Noah Writes a B & B Letter" and "Learn Calligraphy." Then, place the steps in the correct order in the table below.

Dip nib into ink.	Obtain lined paper.
Hold pen at 45-degree angle.	Practice writing "X" thicker in one direction.
Do not twist marker.	Turn pen plunger counterclockwise.
Turn plunger clockwise to fill pen.	Wipe nib.
Practice all 26 letters of the alphabet.	Place paper at an angle.

Noah Writes a B & B Letter	Learn Calligraphy
Buy calligraphy pen and ink.	Obtain chisel-tip felt marker.
1.	**6.**
2.	**7.**
3.	**8.**
4.	**9.**
5.	**10.**
Begin to address invitations.	Practice patterns of numbers and letters in model.

Write a "How-To" Paragraph

Write two or three how-to paragraphs about one of the skills discussed in the reading selections. You may use information from both selections and the table to write about the steps involved in doing calligraphy, or you may write about other skills—how to write a B & B letter, decorate a wedding cake, fill an ink pen, paint a T-shirt, call 911 in an emergency, and so on. Write your paragraph on a separate sheet of paper.

Notes for Home: Your child has combined and used information from more than one selection. ***Home Activity:*** When reading stories or articles, have your child point out steps in a process, whenever possible.

Name ____________________

Grammar: Proper Nouns and Proper Adjectives

REVIEW

Directions: Rewrite each sentence. Capitalize each proper noun and proper adjective.

1. My brother arnold and I call our grandmother by her first name, rachel.

2. My grandfather's name is edward benedict miller, but we call him ted.

3. They live in twin falls, idaho, not too far from the snake river.

4. Recently they moved from a house on weston dr. to an apartment on ridgewood ave.

5. Rachel came to the united states from china, and ted came from great britain.

6. My family, including our irish setter, nellie, visits them every january and june.

7. Having a chinese grandmother and a british grandfather can be very interesting.

8. rachel and ted have a siamese cat and a south american parrot.

9. In their apartment building, a vietnamese neighbor lives on one side of them and an iranian family lives on the other.

10. They are really just american grandparents who live in idaho, but visiting them is like taking a trip around the world.

Notes for Home: Your child capitalized proper nouns and proper adjectives. ***Home Activity:*** Help your child write a thank-you letter, thanking someone who has helped him or her. Have your child check that all proper nouns and adjectives are capitalized.

Practice

Grammar: Capitalization

Directions: When you write a letter to a friend or family member, remember to follow these rules for capitalizing words.

- Capitalize the first word of the greeting: Dear Aunt Sarah,
- Capitalize the first letter of every sentence: My grandparents came to visit.
- Capitalize the pronoun *I:* Uncle Joe and I had a lot of fun.
- Capitalize the first word of the closing: Your nephew,
- Capitalize proper nouns and proper adjectives. Remember that proper nouns name particular persons, places, and things: Jana Collins, Hackensack River, American Riverboats, January 24, 2001
- Capitalize the personal titles of people: Dr. Sandra P. Weintraub

Directions: Read the following parts of a letter. Rewrite the words on the line using the correct capital letters.

1. dear Uncle joe, ______________________
2. your friend, ______________________
3. dear martin, ______________________
4. sincerely yours, ______________________
5. april 6, 2001 ______________________

Directions: Rewrite each sentence. Use capital letters where they are needed.

6. I wanted to visit my grandparents, jacques and sophie marceau.

____

7. they used to live in amarillo, texas, but they just moved to memphis, tennessee.

____

8. Their favorite thing about Memphis is that it's next to the mississippi river.

____

9. i think their new address is 748 bishop court, but i'm not sure about that!

____

10. Their neighbors are captain dennis healy and his wife, mrs. jennifer healy.

____

Notes for Home: Your child used rules of capitalization to write different parts of a letter and to correct capitalization errors in sentences. ***Home Activity:*** Have your child write your home address using capital letters for your name, street, city, and state abbreviation.

Name ______________________________

Extra Practice

Grammar: Capitalization

Directions: Underline each word in the letter that needs to begin with a capital letter. Then rewrite the words correctly on the lines to the right.

dear Grandpa morris,

Thank you for having me at your house last week. As i told my mom, it was one of the best visits ever. It was great fun meeting your famous neighbor, dr. Hugo p. Science. I still remember how surprised he was when we predicted that storm. If he had looked behind him at hurley's river, he would have understood. Those black clouds above the river looked liked they covered all of edwards county!

your grandson,

Scott

1. ______________
2. ______________
3. ______________
4. ______________
5. ______________
6. ______________
7. ______________
8. ______________
9. ______________
10. ______________

Write a Thank-You Letter

On a separate sheet of paper, write a thank-you letter to a friend or relative. Remember to capitalize words when necessary.

Notes for Home: Your child identified and corrected capitalization errors in a letter. ***Home Activity:*** With your child, read over a letter from a friend or family member. Have your child explain why different parts of the letter are capitalized.

Grammar: Capitalization

RETEACHING

Capitalize the following groups of words correctly.

1. dear grandma, ______________
2. answer the phone. ______________
3. chicago tribune ______________
4. north carolina ______________
5. february 21, 2001 ______________
6. mason champlin ______________
7. 1426 wellsley dr. ______________
8. *great expectations* ______________

Capitalize all important words in a proper noun and in a title. Capitalize the first word of a greeting and a closing in a letter. Also capitalize the first word in a sentence.

Directions: Read the letter. Underline each word or group of words with a capitalization error. Write the words correctly on the lines.

2520 central st.

evanston, illinois 60201

august 13, 2001

dear uncle chris,

how are you feeling? I'm sorry you broke your leg at jones pond. I bought you a book called fun things to do while stuck indoors. it was written by amy sargeant. She also wrote a song called "sunny days will come again." I will sing it for you on thanksgiving. Write back soon if you feel up to it.

yours truly,

charlie

1. ______________
2. ______________
3. ______________
4. ______________
5. ______________
6. ______________
7. ______________
8. ______________
9. ______________
10. ______________
11. ______________
12. ______________
13. ______________

Notes for Home: Your child identified and corrected capitalization errors in a letter. ***Home Activity:*** Write a short letter to your child, but include some mistakes in capitalization. Have your child read the letter carefully and rewrite it correctly.

Name ________________________________

Grammar: Capitalization

Directions: Answer each question with a complete sentence. Use capital letters correctly.

1. What is the name of the month in which you were born?

____

2. What is the name of your town and street?

____

3. What is the name of your favorite book, and who wrote it?

____

4. What is the name of your favorite song, and who sings it?

____

5. How would you begin a letter to a relative or close friend?

____

6. What is the name of a newspaper you have seen?

____

7. What day is it today?

____

8. What is the name of a lake or river near your town?

____

Directions: Rewrite each sentence. Use capital letters where they are needed.

9. gene has a dentist appointment with dr. grey at 8775 north bentley ave.

____

____

10. mr. fenton said the party was on saturday, june 14, 2001.

____

____

11. please buy the book *seven days in the jungle* by steven stafford.

____

____

Notes for Home: Your child used capital letters correctly in sentences. ***Home Activity:*** Have your child write a letter to a friend or relative. Help him or her check for capitalization mistakes.

Name ______________________________

Phonics: Vowel Digraphs

Directions: Read the words in the box. Each word contains the vowel combination **oo.** Say each word to yourself. Listen for those words with the same vowel sound as **choose** and those words with the same vowel sound as **stood.** Write each word in the correct column.

bedroom	fishhook	look
books	fooling	moon
cook	good	pooled
cookie	groom	stool

Vowel sound in *choose*	**Vowel sound in *stood***
1. ____________	**7.** ____________
2. ____________	**8.** ____________
3. ____________	**9.** ____________
4. ____________	**10.** ____________
5. ____________	**11.** ____________
6. ____________	**12.** ____________

Directions: Read the words below. Each word contains the vowel combination **ow.** Circle the words that have the same vowel sound as **grow.**

13. row now slowly however brown sowing cowboy

14. down grown gown towns tow mowing lowly

15. owed flowers stow show know Howard below

Directions: For each word below, give three more words that have the same vowel sound and spelling.

16. throat ____________ ____________ ____________

17. weight ____________ ____________ ____________

18. flow ____________ ____________ ____________

19. room ____________ ____________ ____________

20. good ____________ ____________ ____________

Notes for Home: Your child distinguished vowel digraphs, such as *oo* in *room, ow* in *owe, oa* in *toast,* and *ei* in *weight. **Home Activity:*** With your child, read a letter or card you have received from family or friends. Look for these vowel sounds and spellings.

Name ______________________________

Pretest

Spelling: Easily Confused Words

Pretest Directions: Fold back the page along the dotted line. On the blanks, write the spelling words as they are dictated. When you have finished the test, unfold the page and check your words.

1. ______________________
2. ______________________
3. ______________________
4. ______________________
5. ______________________
6. ______________________
7. ______________________
8. ______________________
9. ______________________
10. ______________________
11. ______________________
12. ______________________
13. ______________________
14. ______________________
15. ______________________
16. ______________________
17. ______________________
18. ______________________
19. ______________________
20. ______________________

1. It has been raining **since** noon.
2. That movie made no **sense**.
3. You must **choose** only one.
4. He **chose** a vanilla milkshake.
5. The bus **finally** arrived.
6. The watch is **finely** engraved.
7. Everybody went **except** Todd.
8. We **accept** your apology.
9. A tree stands **beside** the barn.
10. I like all fruit **besides** pears.
11. The Internet is a **recent** invention.
12. I **resent** your rude comments.
13. She needs **access** to those files.
14. I have an **excess** of comic books.
15. We will meet at home **later**.
16. I like the **latter** parts of the play.
17. The gate was made of **metal**.
18. The soldier earned a **medal**.
19. It is a **personal** matter.
20. He is in charge of **personnel**.

Notes for Home: Your child took a pretest on words that are easily confused because of similar pronunciations and spellings. ***Home Activity:*** Help your child learn misspelled words before the final test. Your child should look at the word, say it, spell it aloud, and then spell it with eyes shut.

Spelling: Easily Confused Words

Word List				
since	finally	beside	access	metal
sense	finely	besides	excess	medal
choose	except	recent	later	personal
chose	accept	resent	latter	personnel

Directions: Choose the word from the box that best matches each definition. Write the word on the line.

__________ **1.** too much; overflow

__________ **2.** right to enter or use

__________ **3.** feel injured and angry

__________ **4.** not long ago

__________ **5.** select

__________ **6.** selected

__________ **7.** in the end

__________ **8.** delicately

__________ **9.** next to

__________ **10.** other than, in addition to

__________ **11.** award; decoration

__________ **12.** a substance such as iron, steel, silver, or gold

Directions: Choose the word in ( ) that best completes each sentence. Write the word on the line.

____________________ **13.** The couple will gladly (except/accept) any wedding presents.

____________________ **14.** Ever (since/sense) yesterday, guests have been arriving for the wedding.

____________________ **15.** The (later/latter) of the two flower girls in the procession was taller.

____________________ **16.** (Except/Accept) for Jill, the bridesmaids were all blonde.

____________________ **17.** The (personal/personnel) from the church were glad to help.

____________________ **18.** The groom had the (since/sense) that the bride was nervous.

____________________ **19.** He knew that (later/latter) in the day she would feel better.

____________________ **20.** In my (personal/personnel) opinion, it was a lovely wedding.

Notes for Home: Your child spelled words that are easily confused because of similar pronunciations and spellings. ***Home Activity:*** Write a definition of each spelling word on an index card. Have your child choose a card, spell the word defined, and use it in a sentence.

Name ____________________

Spelling: Easily Confused Words

≡	Make a capital.
/	Make a small letter.
∧	Add something.
⤳	Take out something.
⊙	Add a period.
¶	Begin a new paragraph.

Directions: Proofread the signs Lynn saw in her grandparents' store. Find six spelling mistakes. Use the proofreading marks to correct each mistake.

All personall are to separate plastic bottles from metal cans and containers.

It's getting latter by the minute, so get busy!

Do not except checks without two forms of identification.

Do not block access to this door.

Due to resent weather problems, vegetable prices have risen!

Please dispose of eksess boxes properly.

The new uniforms you chose last month have finely arrived!!!

Spelling Tip

Some words are easily confused because they have similar pronunciations and spellings. Check the signs to make sure that the words from the box are spelled correctly.

Word List

since	recent
sense	resent
choose	access
chose	excess
finally	later
finely	latter
except	metal
accept	medal
beside	personal
besides	personnel

Write Signs

On a separate piece of paper, create several signs that give helpful tips for employees, friends, family, or students. Try to use at least five of your spelling words.

Notes for Home: Your child spelled words that are easily confused because they have similar pronunciations and spellings. ***Home Activity:*** Work with your child to design and decorate a poster that presents warnings or rules. Use some of the spelling words in your poster.

Name ______________________________

Spelling: Easily Confused Words

REVIEW

Word List			
since	finely	recent	latter
sense	except	resent	metal
choose	accept	access	medal
chose	beside	excess	personal
finally	besides	later	personnel

Directions: Choose the word from the box that contains each word below. Write the word on the line.

1. ate ______________________
2. fine ______________________
3. sent ______________________
4. hose ______________________
5. cent ______________________
6. met ______________________
7. sides ______________________
8. sin ______________________

Directions: Choose a word from the box that best replaces the underlined words in each book title. Write the word on the line.

______________________ 9. *At Last, We Were Champions!*

______________________ 10. *Food Over Fashion: Who Cares About the Second of the Two?*

______________________ 11. *Nothing Left to Say but Goodbye*

______________________ 12. *A Private Memoir of My Life in Kenya*

______________________ 13. *Too Much Is Never Enough for Some People*

______________________ 14. *Ten Easy Steps to Popularity with Your Employees*

______________________ 15. *Gold Award Champions of the Winter Olympics*

______________________ 16. *How to Keep Your Pet Next to You When You Walk*

______________________ 17. *Why No One Gets Admittance Without Proper I.D.*

______________________ 18. *How To Select the Right Tile for Your Bathroom*

______________________ 19. *Just Desserts: Sweets to Please Any Awareness of Taste*

______________________ 20. *How to Receive a Compliment and What to Say Back*

Notes for Home: Your child spelled words that are easily confused because they have similar pronunciations and spellings. ***Home Activity:*** Deliberately misuse some of the spelling words in sentences (for instance, use *sense* instead of *since*). Have your child correct the mistakes.

Dictionary

A **dictionary** is a book of words, listed in alphabetical order, and their meanings. Guide words appear at the top of each page that tell the first and last words that appear on the page. Each entry shows a word's spelling, syllable parts, pronunciation, definitions, and parts of speech. Some entries will also include illustrative, or sample, phrases or sentences, and an etymology that tells how the word came into the English language from other languages.

Directions: Use the dictionary entries to answer the questions that follow.

re • la • tion • ship (ri lā ´ shən ship), **1** a connection: *What is the relationship of clouds to rain?* **2** the condition of belonging to the same family. **3** the state that exists between people or groups that deal with each other: *I have good relationships with all of my teachers this year. noun.*

rel • a • tive (rel ´ ə tiv), **1** a person who belongs to the same family as another, such as a father, brother, aunt, nephew, or cousin. **2** compared to each other: *We discussed the relative advantages of city and country life.* **3** depending for meaning on a relation to something else: *East is a relative term; for example, Chicago is east of California but west of New York.* 1 *noun*, 2, 3 *adjective.* **relative to, 1** about; concerning: *The teacher asked me some questions relative to my plans for the summer.* **2** in comparison with; in proportion to; for: *He is strong relative to his size.*

rel • a • tive • ly (rel ´ ə tiv lē), in relation to something else; comparatively: *You are relatively tall for your age. adverb.*

re • lax (ri laks´), **1** to loosen up; make or become less stiff or firm: *Relax your muscles to rest them. Relax when you dance.* **2** to make or become less strict or severe; lessen in force: *Discipline is relaxed on the last day of school.* **3** to relieve or be relieved from work, effort, or worry: *We relaxed during the holidays. Relax! Everything will be all right. verb.*

re • lax • a • tion (rē ´ lak sā ´ shən), **1** a loosening: *the relaxation of the muscles.* **2** a lessening of strictness, severity, or force: *the relaxation of discipline over the holidays.* **3** recreation; amusement: *Walking and reading are relaxations. noun.*

re • lay (rē ´ lā *for 1;* rē ´ lā ´ *or* ri lā ´ *for 2*), **1** a fresh supply: *New relays of firefighters were sent in.* **2** to take and carry farther: *Please relay this message to your parents.* 1 *noun,* 2 *verb,* **re • lays, re • layed, re • lay • ing.**

re • lay race (rē ´ lā rās ´), a race in which each member of a team runs or swims only a certain part of the distance.

Name ______________________________

1. Does the *e* in *relationship* sound like the first *e* in *relative* or the *e* in *relax?* Explain.

____

____

2. Find the word that can be used as both a noun and a verb. Write two sentences using the word, one for each part of speech.

____

____

3. How many syllables does *relative* have? ______________________________

4. Which meaning of the word *relax* best refers to rules or enforcers of rules?

____

5. If the guide words *reign* and *relay race* were shown above the entries, list three words that might appear on this page before the word *relationship*.

____

6. Which meaning of *relationship* is being used in the following sentence?
The relationship between the two old friends was as strong today as it was twenty years ago.

____

7. Are the spellings of the underlined words in the following sentence correct? If not, identify and correct any misspelled words.
My relatives were relativly relaxed given that the groom was rather late.

____

8. Why are guide words helpful when you are searching for a specific entry?

____

____

____

9. Do you think the illustrative phrases are helpful? Explain. ______________________________

____

10. How might you use a dictionary to help you as you read and write?

____

____

____

Notes for Home: Your child answered questions about several dictionary entries. ***Home Activity:*** Play a dictionary game in which one person picks a word from a dictionary and uses it in an illustrative sentence. The other players write down what they think the word means.

Family Times

Name____

Summary

Opening the World of Books

A childhood accident leaves Louis Braille blind at age five but still eager to learn. At ten, Louis Braille attends the National Institute for Blind Youth in Paris, where he hears Charles Barbier explain "Night Writing," his new invention. This system inspires Louis Braille to invent an even simpler system for blind readers, using raised dots to stand for letters. Louis Braille's system gains many supporters, but for years French authorities refuse to recognize its usefulness. Louis Braille dies six months before the Institute finally adopts his system. Slowly, other schools in Europe and the U.S. adopt the Braille system, and it continues to be used throughout the world today.

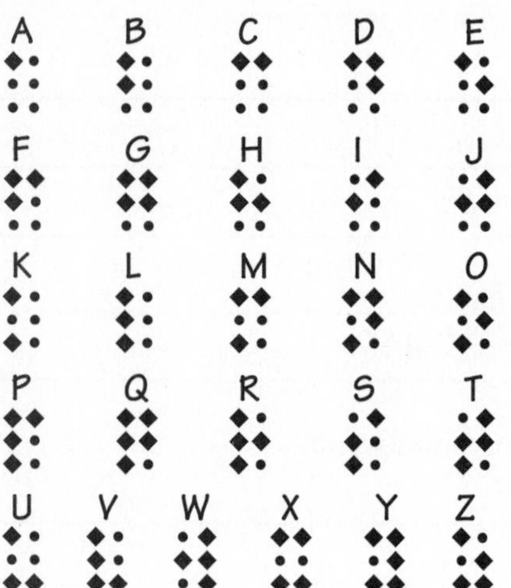

Activity

Invent a System. Encourage your child to explain how the Braille system works. Have him or her compare it to other systems people have tried.

Reading Skills

Author's Viewpoint/Bias

Author's viewpoint is the way an author thinks about the subject of his or her writing. You can identify an author's viewpoint by looking at the words an author uses. Some authors use loaded words such as *terrible* or *wonderful* to express a strong preference, or bias.

Balanced writing presents both sides of an issue. Biased writing shows strong feeling for or against someone or something and presents only one side of an issue.

The author of *Louis Braille* admires Louis Braille's work. However, his writing is balanced because he presents other systems in use at the time.

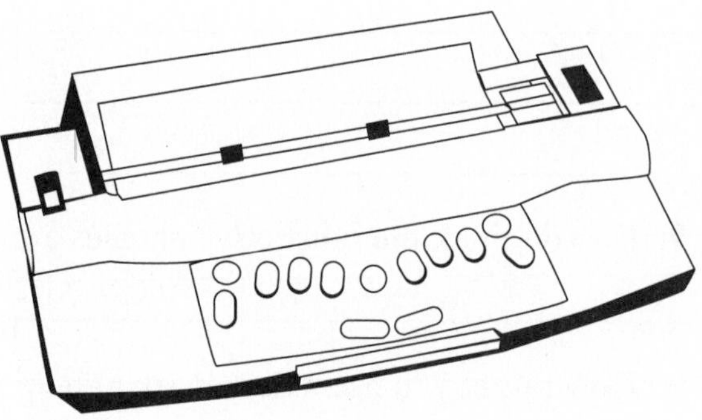

Activity

Learn About Inventions. Use library resources or the Internet to find out about other inventions that assist people without sight or with visual impairments.

Family Times

Tested Vocabulary

Words to Know

Knowing the meanings of these words is important to reading *Louis Braille*. Practice using these words to learn their meanings.

advantages benefits

ambitions things strongly desired

blindness inability to see

complicated hard to understand

merit worth or value

recognition favorable notice; acceptance

visual of, for, or by sight

Grammar

Commas That Set Off Words

A **comma** is a punctuation mark that is used to set off one word or group of words from another.

❖ Use commas to separate names directly addressed from the rest of the sentence. Examples:

Please, Monique, come visit us.

Gabriel, you are my best friend!

❖ Use a comma after the greeting and after the closing in a friendly letter.

My dearest Mama,
Dear Dr. Pignier,

Sincerely,
Very truly yours,

Activity

Write a Letter. Write a letter to a friend explaining what you like best about being your particular age. Check for the correct use of commas.

Tested Spelling Words

______	______	______	______
______	______	______	______
______	______	______	______
______	______	______	______
______	______	______	______

Name ____________________

Author's Viewpoint/Bias

- **Author's viewpoint** is the way an author thinks about the subject of his or her writing.
- You can identify an author's viewpoint by looking at the words an author uses. Some authors use loaded words, such as *terrible* or *wonderful,* to express a strong preference, or bias.
- *Balanced writing* presents both sides of an issue. *Biased writing* shows strong feeling for or against someone or something and presents only one side of an issue. You should read biased writing critically.

Directions: Reread "Normal." Then complete the table. Write whether you think the author would agree or disagree with each statement below. Explain your thinking with evidence from the article.

Statement	Agree or Disagree? Explain.
Normal is different for each individual.	**1.**
Students cannot learn anything from a person in a wheelchair.	**2.**
A person can learn to overcome any problem.	**3.**
When something is *normal* to a person, that person does not think about it.	**4.**
Normal is what is average or what the majority accepts.	**5.**

Notes for Home: Your child read an article and analyzed the author's viewpoint. ***Home Activity:*** Have a family debate. Write topics on slips of paper. Take turns choosing one and expressing a viewpoint on the topic. Later, discuss whether any speaker used loaded words.

Name ______________________

Vocabulary

Directions: Choose the word from the box that best matches each definition. Write the word on the line.

Check the Words You Know

__ advantages
__ ambitions
__ blindness
__ complicated
__ merit
__ recognition
__ visual

______________ **1.** of, for, or by sight

______________ **2.** worth or value; quality

______________ **3.** favorable notice

______________ **4.** benefits

______________ **5.** things strongly desired

______________ **6.** condition of being without sight

Directions: Read the diary entry of an inventor. Choose the word from the box that best completes each sentence. Write the word on the matching numbered lines below.

Tomorrow I will show off my new invention. I hope everyone will see the **7.** _____ of making a device that makes it easier for people to open cans and jars. For this invention to be a success, it can't be too **8.** _____, or people won't want to use it. If tomorrow's test goes well, my ideas will soon get the **9.** _____ they deserve. My friends tell me that my **10.** _____ are too high, but I know that this invention could change people's lives for the better. I'm sure of it!

7. ______________ **9.** ______________

8. ______________ **10.** ______________

Write a Commercial

On a separate sheet of paper, write a television or radio commercial for a new invention. Your commercial should briefly tell what your invention can do and convince people of its merit. Use as many vocabulary words as you can.

Notes for Home: Your child identified and used vocabulary words from *Louis Braille*. ***Home Activity:*** Talk to your child about an invention that has changed the lives of those who use it. Make a two-column list that shows the advantages and drawbacks of the invention.

Name ______________________________

Author's Viewpoint/Bias

- **Author's viewpoint** is the way an author thinks about the subject of his or her writing. You can identify an author's viewpoint by looking at the words an author uses. Some authors use loaded words, such as *terrible* or *wonderful,* to express a strong preference, or bias.
- *Balanced writing* presents both sides of an issue. *Biased writing* shows strong feeling for or against someone or something and presents only one side of an issue. You should read biased writing critically.

Directions: Reread the passage from *Louis Braille* which describes the governor's reaction to the Braille system. Then answer the questions below. Think about the words the author uses to support his viewpoint.

Although Braille's system was brilliant, and although it was supported by all the pupils and many of the teachers at the National Institute for Blind Youth, it was disliked by the Institute's governors. They supported other systems of reading and writing, such as Haüy's raised wooden letters, which they knew how to read themselves but which was far too cumbersome to be efficient when used by the blind.

Because the governors of the Institute were not blind themselves, they couldn't understand the tremendous advantages of Braille. They did not realize its simplicity and the fact that it allowed blind people to write as well as to read. They distrusted a new system that they were unable to use without first having to learn Braille's language of dots.

1. What word or words indicate the author's view of Louis Braille's system?

____

2. What word or words indicate the author's view of Haüy's system?

____

3. Why does the author think the governors favor Haüy's system?

____

____

4. Which system of reading does the author favor?

____

5. On a separate sheet of paper, explain the author's viewpoint of Louis Braille and his invention. Is the author biased? Explain.

Notes for Home: Your child analyzed the way an author presented his viewpoint. ***Home Activity:*** Discuss the viewpoint presented in a newspaper editorial. Think about the bias of the writer and how convincing and valid the evidence is.

Name ______________________

Selection Test

Directions: Choose the best answer to each item. Mark the letter for the answer you have chosen.

Part 1: Vocabulary

Find the answer choice that means about the same as the underlined word in each sentence.

1. Her <u>blindness</u> was caused by a childhood illness.
- A. condition of being slow to learn
- B. condition of being unable to see
- C. condition of having weak muscles
- D. condition of being unable to hear

2. John spoke of his <u>ambitions</u>.
- F. plans for a building
- G. ideas about education
- H. things that are strongly desired
- J. places where students are taught

3. Dr. Casey gained <u>recognition</u> for his ideas.
- A. favorable notice; acceptance
- B. award of money
- C. distrust; lack of faith
- D. permission to change

4. Candace got a raise based on <u>merit</u>.
- F. time spent on a job
- G. ability to plan ahead
- H. condition of being older than others
- J. something that deserves praise or reward

5. Maureen has great <u>visual</u> skills.
- A. used for teaching; educational
- B. related to sight
- C. from a certain time in history
- D. related to machines

6. These instructions are <u>complicated</u>.
- F. freely offered
- G. hard to understand
- H. providing correct information
- J. well organized

7. Her plan had some <u>advantages</u>.
- A. unfavorable conditions
- B. supporters
- C. causes of cancellation or delay
- D. benefits

Part 2: Comprehension

Use what you know about the selection to answer each item.

8. The school in Paris that Louis Braille attended in 1819 was—
- F. the first school for boys and girls with special needs.
- G. a school for children who were gifted.
- H. the only school for blind children in France.
- J. a school for music students.

9. At the National Institute for Blind Youth, students learned mainly by—
- A. listening and remembering.
- B. reading books published in "Night Writing."
- C. going on field trips.
- D. making things and doing experiments.

10. The writing system developed by Charles Barbier was easier to read than embossed books because—
- F. it was first developed for sighted people to use at night.
- G. dots and dashes are easier to recognize by touch than the shapes of letters.
- H. it was based on sounds rather than spelling.
- J. each letter could be quickly recognized by a single touch of the finger.

Name ______________________________

11. In his efforts to improve Charles Barbier's system, Louis Braille's major breakthrough came when he—
- A. dropped all dashes from the system.
- B. learned to write with a stylus.
- C. invented a system of only six dots to represent letters.
- D. talked to Dr. Pignier, the school principal, about his experiments.

12. The author of this selection seems to think that—
- F. Louis Braille was a truly remarkable person.
- G. schools in the past gave students more opportunities to be creative than those of today.
- H. Louis Braille has been given too much credit for something another man invented.
- J. Louis Braille's success was based largely on luck.

13. Which words do you think the author would use to describe school principal Dr. Pignier?
- A. creative and fun
- B. mean-spirited
- C. thoughtful and open-minded
- D. stubbornly proud

14. Which of these statements would be impossible to verify as a fact?
- F. Gabriel Gauthier went to school with Louis Braille.
- G. Boys who broke the rules were kept after school and made to write punishment papers.
- H. Charles Barbier had invented a secret military code based on dots and dashes.
- J. Louis's face lit up with excitement when he realized what a great opportunity he had.

15. In writing this selection, the author has combined known facts with—
- A. fictional characters and events.
- B. exaggerated statements and humor.
- C. what he imagines the characters may have thought and felt.
- D. poetic language and rhythms.

STOP

Author's Viewpoint/Bias

- **Author's viewpoint** is the way an author thinks about the subject of his or her writing. You can identify an author's viewpoint by looking at the words an author uses. Some authors use loaded words, such as *terrible* or *wonderful,* to express a strong preference, or bias.
- *Balanced writing* presents both sides of an issue. *Biased writing* shows strong feeling for or against someone or something and presents only one side of an issue. You should read biased writing critically.

Directions: Read the story below.

American history books highlight men's inventions, but they often overlook women's efforts or credit them to men. Among the first to agree would be Martha Coston (1826–1906). She spent almost ten years struggling to develop, improve, and market special chemical flares used to signal seagoing ships at night. Her signal system proved very successful and saved many sailors during the Civil War. Martha Coston held two patents on her system. Many years after it had been in use, Lieutenant E. Very improved the hand-held cartridge from which the flares were fired. The device was named the "Very pistol" in his honor. As always, American history denies women the credit for what they do.

Directions: Complete the table. Think about the author's beliefs and the facts used to support them.

Summary of Main Idea	1.
Author's Viewpoint on the Subject	2.
Facts Supporting Author's Views	3.
Loaded Words Used	4.
Author's Unstated Belief	5.

Notes for Home: Your child identified an author's viewpoint/bias. ***Home Activity:*** Challenge your child to find examples of balanced and biased writing in a newspaper. Discuss how your child decided whether it was balanced or biased writing.

Persuasive Devices

REVIEW

Directions: Read the passage. Then read each question about the passage. Choose the best answer to each question. Mark the letter for the answer you have chosen.

Simply Speaking

Hands off that keyboard! Make editing and spell-checking things of the past. Join the revolution that has everyone talking—and all the computers listening!!

From stressed typists to keyboard klutzes, every computer-user can find a use for this advanced technology. Known in the industry as *continuous-speech recognition,* these programs can turn natural speech into typed pages almost instantly. (This means that you speak and your words appear automatically on the screen. Over 90 percent of the time, they appear correctly spelled and punctuated.) Many of these high-powered programs also come with simple voice commands that make formatting, editing, and moving through files a breeze. When combined with other programs, some products can sort through records, search for data, even send messages and read them aloud, simply based on voice commands. As a result, all office workers can increase their speed and output, as can students, researchers, and anyone else who talks!

The sharpest minds in the business are already switching to speech recognition programs, so don't be left out of the conversation. Speak up and install your own right away!

1. The author believes that the product is best suited for—
- **A.** people who are poor spellers.
- **B.** everyone needing to search for data.
- **C.** those who write exactly the way they speak.
- **D.** anyone who owns a computer and can talk.

2. Which of the following claims is an attempt to persuade you?
- **F.** The programs can turn natural speech into typed pages.
- **G.** The smartest people are using it already.
- **H.** Some programs can even send messages and read them aloud.
- **J.** Some products can sort through records.

3. Loaded words used to influence the reader include—
- **A.** keyboard and voice commands.
- **B.** commands and technology.
- **C.** revolution and high-powered.
- **D.** recognition and punctuated.

4. Which of the following is a sweeping generalization?
- **F.** As a result, all office workers can increase their speed and output.
- **G.** Some products can sort through records.
- **H.** Continuous-speech recognition programs turn natural speech into typed pages.
- **J.** Continuous-speech recognition programs come with simple voice commands.

5. The purpose of this passage is to persuade readers to—
- **A.** quit using computers.
- **B.** install continuous-speech recognition programming.
- **C.** spell-check more often.
- **D.** increase their speed and output.

Notes for Home: Your child analyzed various persuasive techniques in an advertisement. ***Home Activity:*** Have your child find examples of persuasive language in magazine advertisements and identify what evidence, if any, is given to support the claims made.

Name ______________________________

Writing Across Texts

Directions: Refer to *Louis Braille* and the selection you read in Unit 3, "Elizabeth Blackwell: Medical Pioneer." Complete the left-hand side of the diagram to tell about Louis Braille's problem, the steps he took to solve it, and his solution. Then complete the right-hand side of the diagram for Elizabeth Blackwell.

Louis Braille	Elizabeth Blackwell
Problem Louis Braille wanted to find an easier way to teach the blind to read and write.	**Problem** 6.
Attempts to Solve the Problem 1. 2. 3. 4.	**Attempts to Solve the Problem** 7. 8. 9.
Solution 5.	**Solution** 10.

Write a Comparison/Contrast Essay

Refer to the reading selections about Louis Braille and Elizabeth Blackwell and the diagram. Write an essay to compare and contrast the problems faced by the two pioneers, the steps they took to solve their problems, and their solutions.

Notes for Home: Your child combined information from two sources. ***Home Activity:*** As you read selections about historical characters, have your child make problem and solution charts about them similiar to the diagram above.

Name ______________________________

Grammar: Compound Subjects and Objects

REVIEW

Directions: Combine each set of sentences to form a new sentence with a compound subject or a compound object. Write the new sentence on the lines. Remember to make verbs agree with their subjects and pronouns agree with their referents. (You may need to make other changes as well.)

1. Sightless people have reason to be grateful to Louis Braille. People with poor vision do too.

____

____

____

2. Louis Braille developed a printing system for the blind. In addition, he developed a writing system for the blind.

____

____

3. With this system of six raised dots in different combinations, people can handle reading. They can use it for writing too. They can even produce musical notation.

____

____

____

4. Braillewriters use keys to form letters. So do typewriters.

____

____

5. *Braille* is a type of word called *eponym*—a word based on someone's name. *Braillewriter* is also an eponym.

____

____

____

Notes for Home: Your child combined sentences to form new sentences with compound subjects and compound objects. ***Home Activity:*** Together, look through books to find sentences with compound subjects and objects. Try to break each one down into two or more sentences.

Grammar: Commas

A **comma** is a punctuation mark that is used to set off a word or a group of words from other words. In a friendly letter, use a comma after the greeting and the closing.

Dear Louis,   Sincerely,   Your friend,

In a date, use a comma between the day of the week and the month, and between the day of the month and the year. In an address, use a comma between the city and the state or country.

Saturday, April 2   March 12, 1895   Gotham City, ID 06007

Commas are also used to separate three or more nouns or phrases in a series.

The five senses are sight, hearing, smell, taste, and touch.
Some people can't see, some have no hearing, and some are unable to speak.

When you speak to, or address, a person by name or title, you are using direct address. Commas are used to set off the name when it apppears at the beginning, in the middle, or at the end of a sentence. When the name is in the middle of a sentence, two commas are used.

Thomas, is your cousin a professional dancer?
He is, Mark, and he is also deaf.
That's amazing, Thomas.

Directions: Read the following letter. Add commas where they are needed.

Dear Otto

I am reading an interesting book about people who are deaf. Did you know that some people are born deaf some become deaf from injury and others become deaf from disease? There are actors athletes and even dancers who are deaf. Dancers keep the beat by feeling the vibrations from the music.

This book has inspired me to learn sign language Otto. I'm going to write to a school for the deaf in Rochester New York. They offer to send books tapes and a videotape to help people learn sign language.

Your brother
Phillip

Notes for Home: Your child inserted commas in a letter. ***Home Activity:*** Help your child write a letter to a friend or relative. Talk about the places where commas are needed.

Name ____________________

Extra Practice

Grammar: Commas

Directions: Read the following parts of a letter. Add commas where they are needed.

1. Your friend
2. Dear Myra
3. With love
4. November 11 1911
5. Monday February 20
6. Oakdale CA

Directions: Rewrite each sentence on the line, adding commas where they are needed.

7. Ellen did I tell you about my new invention?

____

8. It will warn me when a dog a cat or another animal enters the yard.

____

9. It works whether the animal walks runs or crawls into the yard.

____

10. The new alarm uses packing paper strings and bells.

____

11. I think you are wrong Mom when you say this system is impractical.

____

12. It will appeal to homeowners renters and landlords.

____

13. I won't charge a lot for my alarm Mom.

____

14. I'm thinking about charging two dollars three dollars or four dollars.

____

15. Did you say Mom that you would trade the alarm for a pizza tonight?

____

Write a Letter

Write a letter to someone who shares a hobby of yours, such as coin collecting, drawing, or a playing a particular computer game. Remember to use commas where necessary.

Notes for Home: Your child inserted commas in parts of a letter, in dates, in addresses, to set off a person's name, and to separate words or phrases in a series of three or more. ***Home Activity:*** Invite your child to write entries in an address book, using commas correctly.

Name ______________________________

Grammar: Commas

RETEACHING

Insert commas where they are needed in each phrase or sentence.

1. Dear Jack
2. Bring me the scissors the stapler and the tape.
3. I wanted to go see the new exhibit at the art museum but I didn't have time.
4. Although she looked nervous Kathy made a wonderful presentation.
5. Amanda don't you think you should be more careful with that vase?
6. We are moving to Maryland on Wednesday April 27 2001.
7. I will miss you Kari.

A **comma** is used to set off a word or a group of words from other words. In a friendly letter, use a comma after the greeting and the closing. In a date, use a comma between the day of the week and the month, and between the date and the year (*Monday, June 22* or *June 22, 2004*). In an address, use a comma between the city and the state. Use commas to separate three or more nouns or phrases in a series. Also use a comma to set off a name used in direct address.

Directions: Insert commas where they are needed in each sentence. Draw an **X** through commas that do not belong.

1. Remember, to feed the cat water the flowers and do your homework.
2. I can't do all that, in fifteen minutes Sandra!
3. I need someone to do it or I'll get in big trouble.
4. Ask Tanya. She lives at 421 Amber Road Merriwether Wisconsin.
5. I hope she is home although often she is out, on Tuesday afternoons.
6. Dina maybe you should call her, before you go.
7. I'll call her pack my things and walk there.
8. Don't forget the festival on Sunday March, 8.
9. I tried, to open the door but it was locked.
10. You need, to ring the doorbell knock on the door or try the back door.

Notes for Home: Your child inserted commas where they belong in sentences and marked commas that do not belong. ***Home Activity:*** Have your child use this page to explain to you where commas are often used.

Name ____

Grammar: Commas

Directions: Each sentence is missing one or more commas. Rewrite each sentence, inserting commas where they belong.

1. Yes John the correct date is October 8 1822.

____

2. I live at 42 Main Street Columbus Ohio Mrs. Gordon.

____

3. We went to London England a week later Sally.

____

4. Lee is the correct address 650 Olive Avenue Bangor Maine 04401?

____

5. By the way Heather just where is Hannibal Missouri?

____

6. Have we run out of bags or are there more back there?

____

7. This is hard work but it's for a good cause.

____

8. Doreen is a skier a pilot and a dancer.

____

9. Her patients will see Dr. Rodriguez or they will make appointments for another day.

____

____

10. Don't you think that I look terrific Louisa?

____

11. I know of a spot near 14 Olivera Street Pamplona Spain that's just like it.

____

____

12. I caught a big trout there on June 12 1998 at noon.

____

Notes for Home: Your child correctly used commas in sentences. ***Home Activity:*** Write some sentences without commas, and have your child insert commas where they belong. Help your child check his or her work.

Name ______________________________

Phonics: Diphthongs and Digraphs

Directions: Read the word pairs below. Each word contains the vowel combination **ou.** For each pair, circle the word that has the same vowel sound as **out.**

1.	house	tough	**4.** announcements	thorough
2.	through	trousers	**5.** bought	bound
3.	though	mountains	**6.** astound	thought

Directions: Read each sentence below. Each sentence has two words with the letters **ou,** but only one of the words has the same vowel sound as **out.** Circle that word and write it on the line.

______________ **7.** The group of science students was experimenting with the principles of sound.

______________ **8.** They wanted to learn about how music travels through water.

______________ **9.** They brought a stereo speaker up to the outside of an aquarium tank filled with water.

______________ **10.** Then they turned up the stereo, loud enough to feel the vibrations on the speaker.

______________ **11.** By noticing the vibrations in the water, the students proudly concluded that music could travel underwater.

Directions: Read the paragraph below. Look and listen for words that have the letters **au** with the same vowel sound as in **sauce;** the letters **ew** with the same vowel sound as in **threw;** or the letters **oi** with the same vowel sound as in **moist.** Circle the words and write them on the lines.

> The students did not want to be disappointed again. They'd been extra cautious this time, adjusting a few dials and pointing out any possible problems. They'd trusted the voices inside their heads, as well as the science lessons their teacher had taught them. Now they were ready. Because they'd followed each step to the letter, their anticipation grew. Their hopes had been renewed that this time their invention would be a success.

au as in *sauce*	**ew as in *threw***	**oi as in *moist***
12. ______________	**15.** ______________	**18.** ______________
13. ______________	**16.** ______________	**19.** ______________
14. ______________	**17.** ______________	**20.** ______________

Notes for Home: Your child sorted words with the vowel sounds heard in *sauce, threw, moist,* and *out.* ***Home Activity:*** Together, write other words with *au, ew, oi,* and *ou.* Take turns using these words in sentences.

Pretest

Spelling: Vowel Sounds /oi/, /ou/, /ȯ/

Pretest Directions: Fold back the page along the dotted line. On the blanks, write the spelling words as they are dictated. When you have finished the test, unfold the page and check your words.

1. ____________________
2. ____________________
3. ____________________
4. ____________________
5. ____________________
6. ____________________
7. ____________________
8. ____________________
9. ____________________
10. ____________________
11. ____________________
12. ____________________
13. ____________________
14. ____________________
15. ____________________
16. ____________________
17. ____________________
18. ____________________
19. ____________________
20. ____________________

1. He will **outlast** his opponent.
2. She opened a bank **account**.
3. The show will **astound** you.
4. A fence is an unnatural **boundary**.
5. The bird flew **southeast**.
6. Set the box on the **counter**.
7. The **sunflower** bloomed today.
8. We have to get there **somehow**.
9. I do not like this clam **chowder**.
10. That bully is really a **coward**.
11. The movie left us **disappointed**.
12. Their **voices** blended together.
13. They publish a weekly **tabloid**.
14. She is the **employee** of the year.
15. They gave a **joyful** shout.
16. The guests **applaud** the speaker.
17. Turn off that dripping **faucet**.
18. Proceed with **caution**.
19. She's my favorite **author**.
20. He was treated for mental **trauma**.

Notes for Home: Your child took a pretest on words that have the vowel sounds /oi/, /ou/, and /ȯ/. ***Home Activity:*** Help your child learn misspelled words before the final test. Your child can underline the word parts that caused the problems and concentrate on those parts.

Spelling: Vowel Sounds /oi/, /ou/, /ȯ /

Word List

outlast	counter	disappointed	applaud
account	sunflower	voices	faucet
astound	somehow	tabloid	caution
boundary	chowder	employee	author
southeast	coward	joyful	trauma

Directions: Choose the words from the box with the vowel sound /ou/. Write each word in the correct column.

Words with /ou/ spelled ou

1. ______________________
2. ______________________
3. ______________________
4. ______________________
5. ______________________
6. ______________________

Words with /ou/ spelled ow

7. ______________________
8. ______________________
9. ______________________
10. ______________________

Directions: Choose the word from the box that best matches each clue. Write the word on the line.

______________ **11.** I am a newspaper with huge headlines and lots of photos.

______________ **12.** I work for another person.

______________ **13.** I am how you feel when you don't achieve a goal.

______________ **14.** I am a severe injury, wound, or shock.

______________ **15.** We are what the singers in the choir use to make music.

______________ **16.** I write books, plays, stories, and scripts.

______________ **17.** I show concern for safety.

______________ **18.** I am what you do when you clap your hands.

______________ **19.** I am delighted and happy.

______________ **20.** I am a fixture for drawing liquid from a pipe.

Notes for Home: Your child spelled words with the vowel sounds /oi/, /ou/, and /ȯ/. ***Home Activity:*** Challenge your child to spell words from the list in which *oy* spells the vowel sound in *boy* and *au* spells the vowel sound in *fault.*

Proofread and Write

Spelling: Vowel Sounds /oi/, /ou/, /ȯ /

Directions: Proofread this biography. Find seven spelling mistakes. Use the proofreading marks to correct each mistake.

- ≡ Make a capital.
- / Make a small letter.
- ∧ Add something.
- ⅋ Take out something.
- ⊙ Add a period.
- ¶ Begin a new paragraph.

Louis Braille lost his sight from a childhood trama, but he never felt limited by his blindness or any bowndry set by other people's thinking. More than one accownt of his life says that Braille got his idea for his system when he was only twelve. That is a fact sure to astouned anyone.

Braille worked for years to improve his idea until somehouw he invented the simple raised-dot system still in use today. Braille was disappoynted that his writing system was not officially recognized in his lifetime, but he would be joyful to learn that Braille writing is widely used now. It has managed to owtlast many other systems.

Spelling Tip

The vowel sound /ou/ is spelled **ou** and **ow: outlast, somehow.** The vowel sound /oi/ is spelled **oi** and **oy: voices, joyful.** The vowel sound /ȯ/ is often spelled **au: author.**

Word List

outlast	disappointed
account	voices
astound	tabloid
boundary	employee
southeast	joyful
counter	applaud
sunflower	faucet
somehow	caution
chowder	author
coward	trauma

Write a Biography

Whom do you admire for his or her invention? On a separate sheet of paper, write a brief biography of the inventor of your choice. Explain why you feel his or her work is important. Try to use at least three spelling words.

Notes for Home: Your child spelled words with the vowel sounds /oi/ spelled *oi* and *oy,* /ou/ spelled *ou* and *ow,* and /ȯ/ spelled *au.* ***Home Activity:*** Write the spelling words in a list. Include several misspellings. Invite your child to proofread and correct the list.

Name ______________________________

Spelling: Vowel Sounds /oi/, /ou/, /ȯ/

REVIEW

Word List

outlast	southeast	chowder	tabloid	faucet
account	counter	coward	employee	caution
astound	sunflower	disappointed	joyful	author
boundary	somehow	voices	applaud	trauma

Directions: Write the word from the box that belongs in each group.

1. worker, staff, ______________
2. barrier, border, ______________
3. someday, somewhere, ______________
4. northeast, northwest, ______________
5. happy, delighted, ______________
6. care, wariness, ______________
7. writer, journalist, ______________

Directions: Choose the word from the box that best completes each sentence about a person's activity. Write the word on the line to the left.

______________ 8. The cook made _____ for the entire seafood restaurant.

______________ 9. The store clerk stood behind the _____ as he served the customers.

______________ 10. The magician was able to _____ the audience with his tricks.

______________ 11. The long-distance runner managed to _____ all her opponents in order to win.

______________ 12. The nurse monitored the patients in the _____ ward.

______________ 13. The audience stood to _____ the actor's fine performance.

______________ 14. The plumber tightened the bolt to fix the dripping _____.

______________ 15. The gardener was proud that his tall, yellow _____ won the contest.

______________ 16. The banker needed to fix the problems with an _____.

______________ 17. The _____ cringed with fear.

______________ 18. The reporter for the weekly _____ called in the story.

______________ 19. The singers' _____ sounded full, clear, and triumphant.

______________ 20. The manager was _____when the shortstop made an error.

Notes for Home: Your child spelled words with the vowel sounds /oi/ spelled *oi* and *oy,* /ou/ spelled *ou* and *ow,* and /ȯ/ spelled *au.* ***Home Activity:*** Read a newspaper or magazine with your child. Make a list of other words that have these vowel sounds and spellings.

Name ______________________________

Chart/Table/Time Line

A **chart** organizes information visually, such as in a list, table, or diagram.
A **table** is a special kind of chart that shows information in rows and columns.
A **time line** is a bar divided into periods of time that shows a sequence of events.

Directions: Use the time line to complete the table on the next page. List in the table's second column the different types of transportation shown on the time line. Then answer the questions that follow.

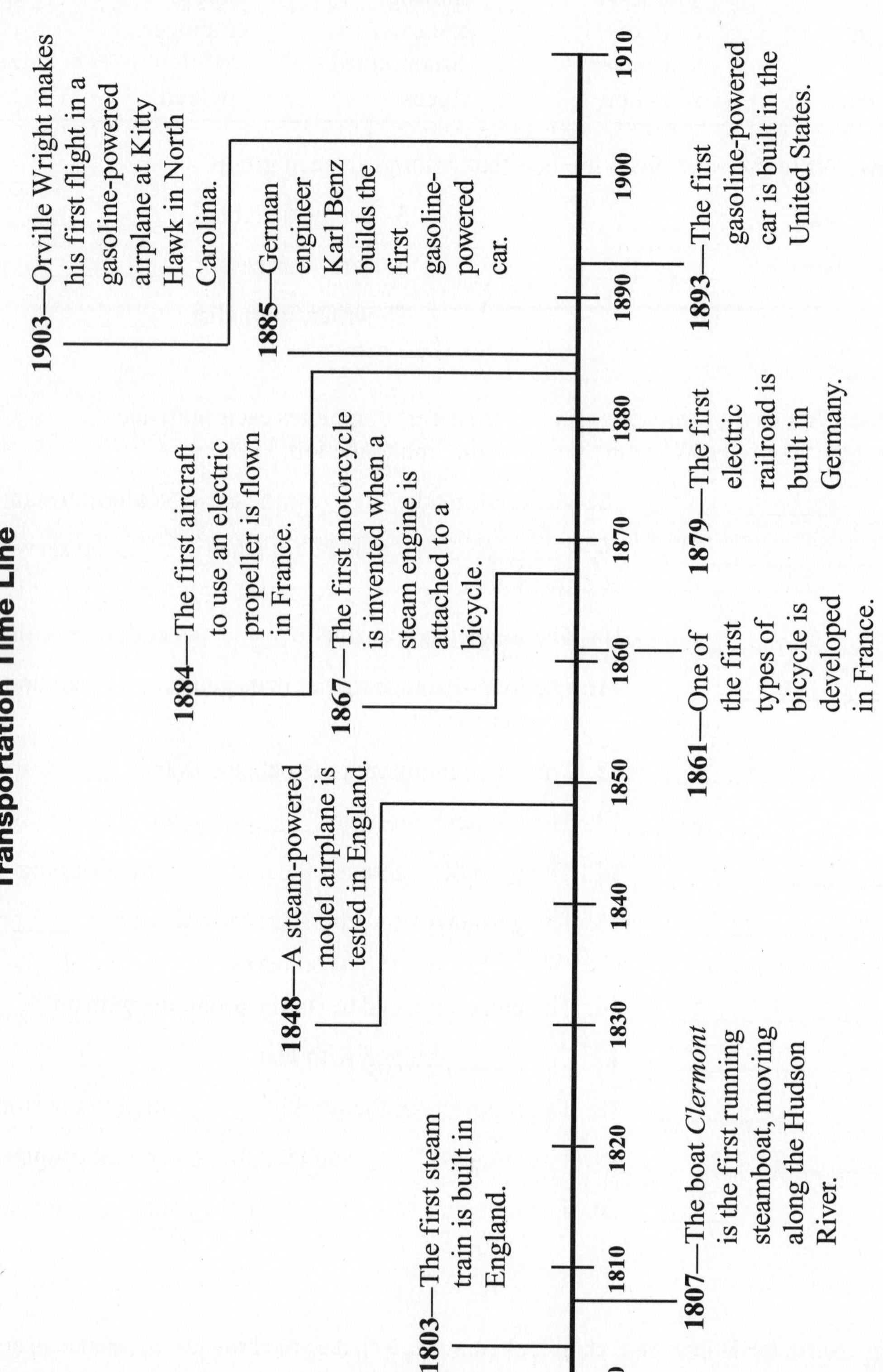

Name ______________________

Travel by . . .	Transportation Invention
Land	**1.**
Sea	**2.**
Air	**3.**

4. How many years does the time line cover? Into what periods of time is the line divided?

____

____

5. What information does this time line show? Is a time line a good way to organize this information? Explain.

____

____

____

6. How many years before Orville Wright flew at Kitty Hawk did the first successful plane flight take place in France?

____

7. How many years after the first gasoline-powered car in Germany was invented was a gasoline-powered car built in the United States?

____

8. If you were living in France in 1861, what might you have seen that no one else had?

____

9. For what research topic would this time line be useful? ______________________

____

10. How might you use a chart, table, or time line as you research information for a report?

____

____

Notes for Home: Your child read a time line, used it to complete a table, and answered questions about it. ***Home Activity:*** Set up a time line with your child for activities you do during an evening. Write the hours along a line; then write the activities beside each hour.

Family Times

Name____________________

Summary

A Question of Circumference

Over 2,000 years ago in Alexandria, Egypt, the scholar Eratosthenes decided to use geometry to figure out Earth's circumference. Using various measures and calculations, he gave the circumference of Earth to be about 24,660 miles, which is only about 200 miles different from the number in use today.

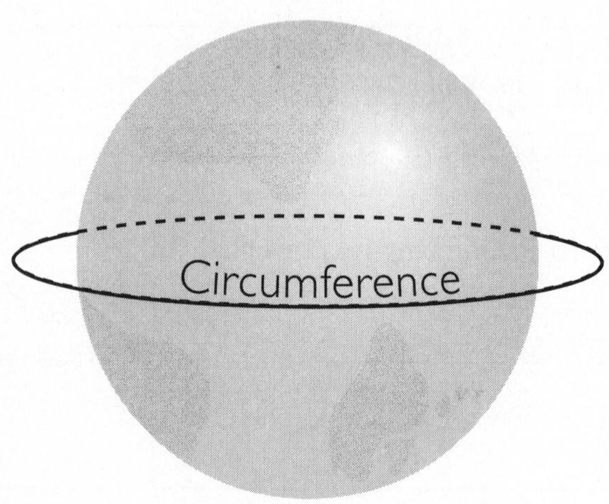

Activity

Demonstrate the Steps. Ask your child to demonstrate the different steps Eratosthenes had to complete in order to measure the circumference of Earth. Have your child use a baseball, orange, or grapefruit to demonstrate the steps as clearly as possible.

Reading Skills

Graphic Sources

A **graphic source** of information is something that shows information visually. Some common graphic sources are pictures, charts, maps, graphs, and diagrams.

A graphic source of information may present new information in the text differently, or it may show more information.

Before you read, preview a story or article to see if there are graphic sources that give you an idea of what the text is about. As you read, compare information in graphic sources to information in the text. In *The Librarian Who Measured the Earth,* the illustration of the library at Alexandria helps you understand what papyrus scrolls were by showing what they looked like and how they were tagged and stored on the library shelves.

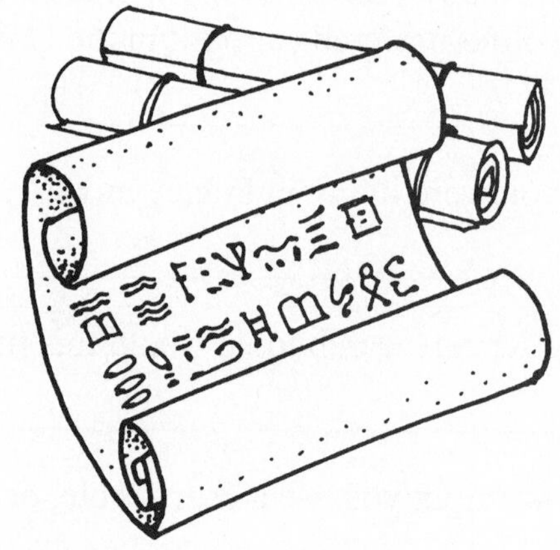

Activity

Make a Map. Draw a map to show how to get from your school's front door to the library. Label different rooms and objects such as *Lockers, Principal's Office,* and *Library.*

Family Times

Tested Vocabulary

Words to Know

Knowing the meanings of these words is important to reading *The Librarian Who Measured the Earth*. Practice using these words to learn their meanings.

accurate precise; exact

angle space between two lines that meet

arc any part of a circle's circumference

calculate compute information

estimate make a judgment or guess based on available facts

formula combination of mathematical symbols

scholar a person of learning

sphere a globe

Grammar

Direct Quotations

A person's exact words are a **direct quotation.** Show a direct quotation by:

❖ Enclosing it in quotation marks.
❖ Using commas to set off introductory words coming before or after the direct quotation.
❖ Beginning the direct quotation with a capital letter. End it with end punctuation or a comma placed inside the quotation marks.

The Greek asked himself, "What is the earth's circumference?"

❖ Setting off any interruptions to the quotation with commas, and starting the quotation again with a small letter.

"I'll do my best," he thought, "to find the answer I need."

Activity

Quote the Speakers. Choose two of your favorite characters from a book or a TV show. Write a make-believe conversation between them, using direct quotations.

Tested Spelling Words

______	______	______	______
______	______	______	______
______	______	______	______
______	______	______	______
______	______	______	______

Name ______________________________

Graphic Sources

- A **graphic** or **graphic source** of information is something that shows information visually.
- Some common graphic sources of information are pictures, charts, maps, graphs, and diagrams.
- A graphic source can present new information in the text differently or show more information.

Directions: Reread "Ptolemy—An Early Map Maker," and review the maps. Then follow the directions below to mark the map to show areas Ptolemy did and did not know about. You may need to refer to another map to complete the last two directions.

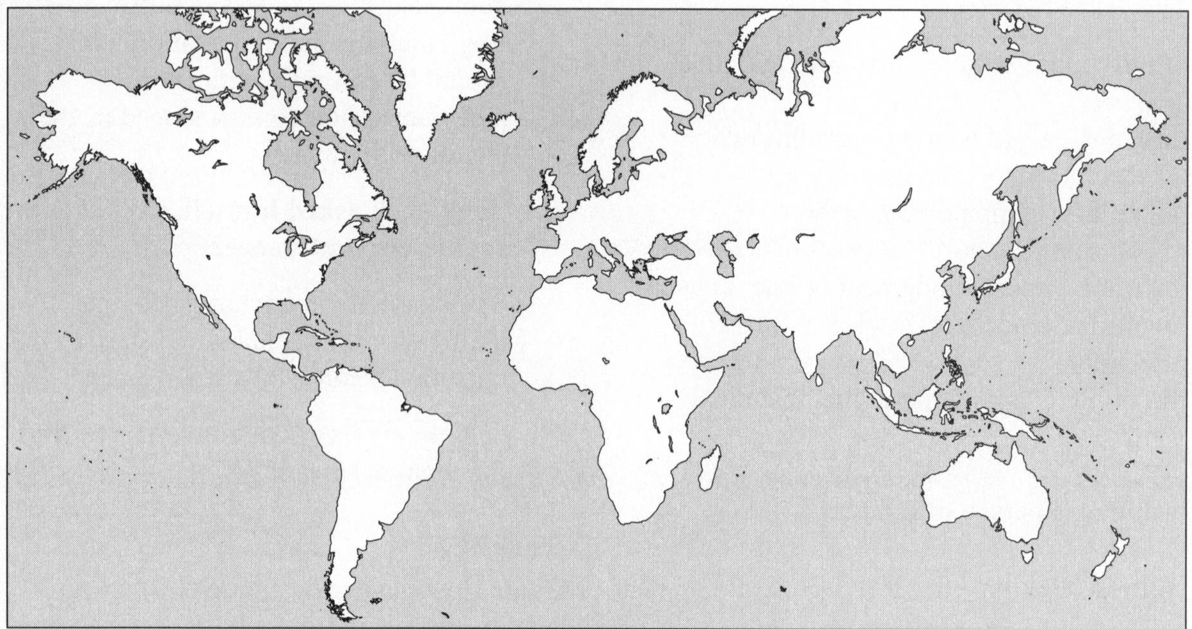

1. Label the city where Ptolemy was from.
2. Shade the land areas that Ptolemy knew about.
3. Use a different color to shade the areas of water that Ptolemy knew about.
4. Label the two continents that Ptolemy did not know about.
5. Label the ocean that Ptolemy did not know about.

Notes for Home: Your child marked a map to show his or her understanding of the material. ***Home Activity:*** With your child, find a newspaper or magazine article that includes a picture, map, or graph. Discuss how the graphic source of information relates to the article.

Name ______________________________

Vocabulary

Directions: Choose the word from the box that best completes each sentence. Write the word on the line to the left.

Check the Words You Know
__ accurate
__ angle
__ arc
__ calculate
__ estimate
__ formula
__ scholar
__ sphere

______________ **1.** Scientists can make _____ predictions about a satellite's path.

______________ **2.** They can make an _____ based on what they know about space flight.

______________ **3.** Sometimes, scientists _____ an exact answer.

______________ **4.** They use a _____ in which symbols stand for different pieces of data.

______________ **5.** Sometimes, a _____ who studies mathematics or science will discover a new formula.

Directions: Choose the word from the box that best matches each clue. Write the word in the puzzle.

Down

6. a person of learning

7. to compute information

Across

8. any part of a circumference

9. space between two lines that meet

10. a round solid object

Write an E-mail Message

On a separate sheet of paper, write an e-mail message. Imagine you are a scientist who has made a new discovery and that you are describing your discovery to another scientist. Use as many vocabulary words as you can.

Notes for Home: Your child identified and used vocabulary words from *The Librarian Who Measured the Earth.* ***Home Activity:*** Talk with your child about math in everyday life. Encourage him or her to use vocabulary words during the discussion.

Name ___________________________________

Graphic Sources

- A **graphic** or **graphic source** of information is something that shows information visually.
- Some common graphic sources of information are pictures, charts, maps, graphs, and diagrams.
- A graphic source can present new information in the text differently or show more information.

Directions: Reread the passage from *The Librarian Who Measured the Earth* in which the author explains how to find Earth's circumference. Then follow the instructions below.

Perhaps [Eratosthenes] imagined the earth as a grapefruit. If [a grapefruit] is sliced in half, you can see its sections. In order to measure the distance all the way around the edge of the grapefruit (the circumference), you would need to know only the distance along the edge of one section (the arc) and how many of these same-size sections it would take to make up the whole grapefruit.

1. Use the description in the passage and the picture of the grapefruit to trace the circumference of the grapefruit. Label the circumference you traced.
2. Draw and label an arc on the picture of the grapefruit.
3. Shade in one section.
4. How does the image of the grapefruit help you better understand the main idea of the passage?

____

____

____

5. Reread the story. Are there other places in the story where a picture helps you better understand the text? Explain your thinking on a separate sheet of paper.

Notes for Home: Your child used a graphic source of information to help him or her understand the passage's main idea. ***Home Activity:*** Look at some newspaper graphics. Ask each other questions that can be answered using the graphic source.

Name ______________________________

Selection Test

Directions: Choose the best answer to each item. Mark the letter for the answer you have chosen.

Part 1: Vocabulary

Find the answer choice that means about the same as the underlined word in each sentence.

1. We asked him to <u>estimate</u> the cost.
- A. agree to pay on a fixed schedule
- B. make a judgment or guess based on available facts
- C. pay no attention to
- D. say that something is larger or greater than it is

2. I knew that the news story was not <u>accurate</u>.
- F. interesting
- G. well written
- H. recent
- J. correct; exact

3. I need to <u>calculate</u> the distance.
- A. make shorter and narrower
- B. increase
- C. find by using numbers
- D. imagine

4. She found the <u>formula</u> she needed.
- F. combination of symbols used in mathematics to state a rule or principle
- G. list of ingredients and procedures for preparing food
- H. a formal written or oral discussion of a topic
- J. an explanation based on observation only

5. The moon is a <u>sphere</u>.
- A. figure shaped like an oval
- B. a round solid object; globe
- C. object that revolves around a planet
- D. solid block

6. He needed to know the distance along the <u>arc</u>.
- F. one side of a triangle
- G. a curved structure capable of carrying weight
- H. a type of boat
- J. any part of a circle's circumference

7. She measured the <u>angle</u>.
- A. space between two lines or surfaces that meet
- B. distance along the curve of a circle
- C. point where two lines meet
- D. side of a square or rectangle

8. His mother is a famous <u>scholar</u>.
- F. person who writes plays
- G. person who has much knowledge
- H. woman who sings with a high voice
- J. person who practices magic

Part 2: Comprehension

Use what you know about the selection to answer each item.

9. When did Eratosthenes live?
- A. less than 900 years ago
- B. about 1,000 years ago
- C. more than 2,000 years ago
- D. about 4,000 years ago

10. At the gymnasium, Eratosthenes wrote with—
- F. charcoal on slate tablets.
- G. pen and ink on paper.
- H. sharp sticks on wax tablets.
- J. brushes and ink on papyrus.

GO ON

Name ______________________________

11. Why was Eratosthenes glad to go to Alexandria to tutor the king's son?
- A. Life in Cyrene offered few challenges for him.
- B. It was near the place where he had grown up as a boy.
- C. It was a great honor to teach the son of the king.
- D. Alexandria was the best place in the world to study and learn.

12. In this selection, the pictures of a circle and a grapefruit help to show—
- F. why the sun's rays strike only one section of the earth at a time.
- G. how applying geometry to everyday objects could help Eratosthenes figure out the size of the earth.
- H. why circles are measured in degrees.
- J. how Eratosthenes measured the distance from Alexandria to Syene.

13. The picture of Eratosthenes measuring the shadow of a pole helps to show how he—
- A. measured the angle of the sun's rays.
- B. organized books in the library.
- C. traveled to Syene.
- D. demonstrated to others that his numbers were correct.

14. Which statement would be most difficult to verify as a fact?
- F. "He would crawl across the kitchen floor to follow the path of ants."
- G. "He also made a list of all the winners of the Olympic Games."
- H. "At the museum there were laboratories and libraries, dining halls and private studios."
- J. "Eratosthenes dedicated the solution to the king."

15. In order to write this selection, the author most likely spent a lot of time—
- A. visiting Athens, Alexandria, and other cities named in the selection.
- B. solving geometry problems.
- C. talking with people who knew Eratosthenes.
- D. doing historical research.

Name ________________________________

Graphic Sources

- A **graphic** or **graphic source** of information is something that shows information visually.
- Some common graphic sources of information are pictures, charts, maps, graphs, and diagrams.
- A graphic source can present new information in the text differently or show more information.

Directions: Read the steps and look at the pictures.

Try this triangle experiment. Take one sheet of construction paper. Then cut a large triangle from the paper and measure its three angles. Add the three angle measures together.

Tear off the three angles, making sure the pieces are fairly big. Lay the three pieces down so that the angles all touch at one point. Look at the figure that is formed. Repeat two more times and you'll discover that the sum of the angles of any triangle is 180°—the same as a straight line.

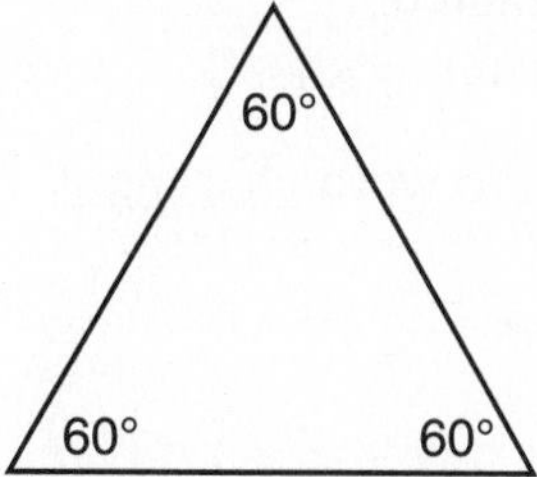

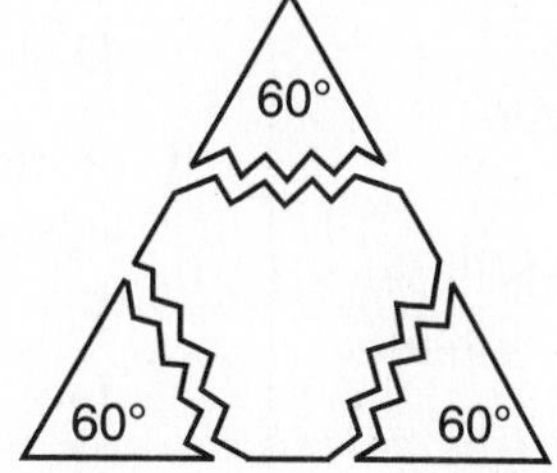

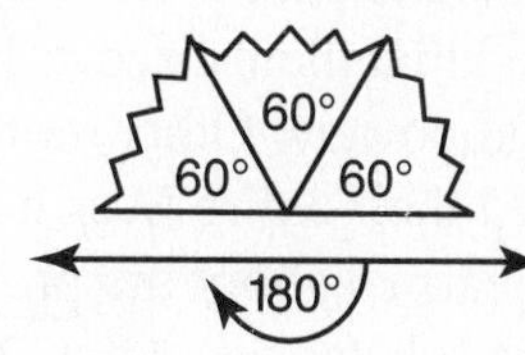

Directions: Answer the questions below. Think about how the diagram helps you figure out the answers.

1. What are the measures of the three angles of the triangle shown? ________________
2. What is the sum of the three angles? ________________
3. What figure do you see when the three pieces of the triangle are laid out touching at their X marks?

____

4. What do you think will happen if you repeat the experiment with a different sized triangle?

____

5. How does looking at the pictures and reading the steps help you understand a rule about the angles of a triangle?

____

____

____

Notes for Home: Your child read steps for an experiment and looked at pictures to understand a mathematical rule. ***Home Activity:*** Look at some newspaper and magazine graphics with your child. Discuss what each visual shows and how it helps you understand the text.

Name ______________________________________

Context Clues

REVIEW

Directions: Read the passage. Then read each question about the passage. Choose the best answer to each question. Mark the letter for the answer you have chosen.

Before Chemistry

Over 800 years ago, some European scholars practiced alchemy, an early form of chemistry. These alchemists had three main goals. They wanted to discover the secret of transmutation, a process in which base metals such as iron or lead could be turned into costly silver or gold. They also hoped to discover the philosopher's stone, an unusual substance that would make transmutation easier. Additionally, many alchemists aspired to discover the proper chemical mix for a potion to cure all diseases and prolong lives by hundreds of years.

Some alchemists were charlatans who claimed that their discoveries gave them magical powers. Other more honest scholars devoted their entire lives to their experiments. They learned about the properties of various substances. After all, knowing the characteristics of a chemical —its hardness and melting point, and the ways it reacts with other substances—might one day be the key to a success. As a result, alchemists added new information to the pool of knowledge about chemicals. New kinds of tools and equipment were needed to aid them in their work, so they invented special scales, tools to melt metals, and other equipment. Alchemy may seem foolish by today's standards, but alchemists' research helped lay the foundations of modern chemistry.

1. Transmutation is a process that alchemists believed could—
- **A.** remove the metal found in rocks.
- **B.** help them live longer.
- **C.** change lead into gold.
- **D.** change gold into base metals.

2. In this passage, base metals are those that are—
- **F.** low in weight.
- **G.** the supporting layers for other metals.
- **H.** the most important ingredients in the philosopher's stone.
- **J.** low in cost or value.

3. In this passage, the word aspired means—
- **A.** hoped to achieve a goal.
- **B.** expressed a thought clearly.
- **C.** took for granted.
- **D.** worried or annoyed.

4. In this passage, the word charlatans means—
- **F.** street actors.
- **G.** frauds.
- **H.** scientists.
- **J.** cure-alls.

5. In this passage, the word properties means—
- **A.** rightful owners.
- **B.** magic powers.
- **C.** characteristics of chemical substances.
- **D.** owned pieces of land.

Notes for Home: Your child figured out the meaning of unfamiliar words by using context clues. ***Home Activity:*** Encourage your child to use context clues to figure out the meanings of unfamiliar words in stories he or she reads. Together, use a dictionary to check these words.

Name ______________________

Writing Across Texts

Directions: Consider what you know about the two selections, *The Librarian Who Measured the Earth* and "A Revolution." Use the table below to list ways that mapmaking has changed since Eratosthenes.

How Mapmaking has changed
Both discuss how to measure.
1.
2.
3.
4.
5.

Write a Paragraph

The Librarian Who Measured the Earth and "A Revolution" are about mapmaking. How are these selections alike? How are they different? On a separate sheet of paper, write a paragraph comparing and contrasting these two selections.

Notes for Home: Your child used information from two different sources to write a comparison/contrast paragraph. ***Home Activity:*** As you read a story or article with your child, discuss how its ideas connect to other reading your child has done.

Name ___________________________________

Grammar: Commas

Directions: Add a comma where needed to correct each sentence.

1. Was Euclid an ancient Greek mathematician or was he an ancient Roman?
2. Euclid lived in Greece in ancient times but we still rely on his work today.
3. Geometry students may not know Euclid's name but they learn his principles.
4. Start at one point and you can always draw a straight line to another point.
5. Measure one right angle and you will know the measurement of every other right angle.
6. Points, lines, and angles are the subject of geometry but triangles are the subject of trigonometry.
7. Trigonometry is used to study light and electricity and it is crucial in surveying, navigation, and astronomy.
8. Euclidean geometry is basic but there are other kinds of geometry.
9. Mathematicians might work on analytic geometry or they might prefer descriptive geometry.
10. Much has been learned since Euclid's day but his work remains the starting point.

Directions: Add a comma where needed to correct each sentence. If no comma is needed, write **N** on the line.

__________ **11.** If you could meet someone from the past would you like to meet Euclid?

__________ **12.** Although he was a brilliant mathematican, he may not have been fun to talk to one-on-one.

__________ **13.** While you are meeting mathematicians, you might want to talk to Descartes.

__________ **14.** Descartes worked on geometry after Euclid had been dead for centuries.

__________ **15.** Although Euclid lived so long ago his principles are still used and tested hundreds of years later.

__________ **16.** Amazingly, Euclid's principles are still recalled by mathematicians whenever they use geometry.

__________ **17.** "If you want to find the area of a rectangle" explained Mr. Sams, "multiply the length of the base by the height."

__________ **18.** If you do not multiply the base by the height and divide by 2 you will not find the area of a triangle.

__________ **19.** After you use such calculations a few times you will find them less difficult.

__________ **20.** "When you study geometry" Mr. Sams said, "remember to think of Euclid and thank him."

Notes for Home: Your child added commas where needed to punctuate compound and complex sentences correctly. ***Home Activity:*** Read aloud an interesting written passage for your child to write down. Then help your child check that commas were used correctly.

Name ______________________________________

Practice

Grammar: Quotation Marks and Paragraph Indentation

A **direct quotation** is made up of the exact words a speaker says. When you write a direct quotation, enclose it in quotation marks (“ ”), and capitalize the first word. Begin a new paragraph each time the speaker changes.

Use commas to set off words that introduce a direct quotation. Place the comma that ends the quotation inside the quotation marks. If the quotation is a question or exclamation, place the question or exclamation mark inside the quotation marks.

Ms. Fisher said, “Today, you will do an experiment.”
“What will we do today?” Jolene asked.

In interrupted quotations, a comma is used when the second part of the quotation does not begin a new sentence. If the second part begins a new sentence, a capital letter and proper end mark are used in this second part.

“What,” asked Robert, “will the experiment be about?”
The class waited in silence.
“We will observe acceleration,” Ms. Fisher said. “You will use marbles of different sizes, a ramp, and a stopwatch.”

Directions: Use quotation marks to enclose the direct quotation in each sentence.

1. I want to see what it’s like to live without clocks, Ken said.
2. Sarah said, What do you mean?
3. What I mean, Ken said, is that I want to test my sense of time.
4. If I take a walk, Ken said, will I be able to guess how long I have been walking?
5. Or will you be able to tell about what time of the day it is? Sarah said.
6. Right, now you understand, Ken said.
7. I’d like to know whether I would do things faster or more slowly, if I wasn’t looking at a clock, said Jenny.
8. That’s a good idea, Sarah said. Let’s try it.
9. I’ll carry a watch, Lori said, but none of you will look at it.
10. I’ll list the times, Lori continued, at which we start and finish things.

Notes for Home: Your child inserted quotation marks before and after direct quotations. ***Home Activity:*** With your child, write a few sentences of a conversation. Have your child insert quotation marks before and after the exact words each person says.

Name ______________________________

Extra Practice

Grammar: Quotation Marks and Paragraph Indentation

Directions: Add quotation marks, commas, end marks, and capital letters to form complete sentences. Write the sentences on the lines.

1. please do your geometry homework now Mom said

____

2. what makes you think that I'm not going to do it I asked

____

3. I know you like to put off your homework Mom replied.

____

4. Then she added but geometry is very important

____

5. what do you mean by that I asked

____

6. without geometry Mom answered life itself would be impossible

____

7. mom I answered i think that's a little extreme

____

8. she replied maybe I am speaking a little too strongly

____

9. I know why I said

____

10. you can't help it I added you're my geometry teacher

____

Write a Conversation

On a separate sheet of paper, write a few lines of a conversation between two characters. Have them work out a complicated math problem. Remember to use quotation marks and punctuate each sentence correctly. Start a new paragraph each time the speaker changes.

Notes for Home: Your child used quotation marks and other punctuation marks to set off direct quotations. ***Home Activity:*** With your child, listen to a conversation on a television show. Have your child "insert quotation marks" before and after each person's words, using hand gestures.

Name ______________________________

Grammar: Quotation Marks and Paragraph Indentation

Study the following quotations. Then insert quotation marks, commas, periods, question marks, and exclamation marks where they belong.

I have a question he said

She replied Go ahead

Why does an elephant have wrinkles he asked

It's hard to iron an elephant she answered

That he sighed is not very funny

You're wrong she laughed It's hilarious

Use **quotation marks** to show the exact works of a speaker.

Directions: Write each quotation using capital letters and punctuation correctly.

1. I threw the clock so I could see time fly said Dotty.

____

2. Meet me at the corner said the wall to the ceiling

____

3. The elevator sighed life has its ups and downs

____

4. How do you know it is raining cats and dogs asked Fern

____

5. Because I just stepped in a poodle exclaimed LaVerne.

____

6. Which hand do you write with Willy inquired

____

7. I do not write with my hand said Nilly I write with a pencil

____

Notes for Home: Your child punctuated quotations. ***Home Activity:*** Let your child listen to a conversation between you and another family member. Have your child write part of the conversation, using quotation marks to signal a speaker's exact words.

Name ____

Grammar: Quotation Marks and Paragraph Indentation

Directions: Add all necessary punctuation to the sentences below.

1. Pyramids are interesting structures said Marie
2. Philip asked Who built them
3. Egyptians built many of them replied Marie
4. In the Americas added Mrs. Conti the Mayans built pyramids
5. Egyptian pyramids are very old remarked Marie
6. You are right noted Mrs. Conti They were built from about 2700 B.C. to about 1000 B.C., thousands of years ago
7. Why were they built asked Philip
8. Marie explained Egyptian pyramids were used as tombs for royalty

Directions: Rewrite the conversation below. Use correct punctuation and capitalization. Begin a new paragraph each time the speaker changes.

9.–16.

the largest pyramid in Egypt Marie remarked is the Great Pyramid. I read about it in the encyclopedia said Jeff it is amazing. it is one of the Seven Wonders of the World explained Mrs. Conti. how big is it asked Philip. It is nearly five hundred feet tall said Jeff. each side measures over seven hundred fifty feet added Marie. wow exclaimed Philip it must have contained some treasure. you can see it continued Marie if you travel to Egypt.

____

____

____

____

____

____

____

____

____

Notes for Home: Your child correctly wrote and punctuated a conversation. ***Home Activity:*** Have your child write an imaginary conversation between two made-up characters. Help him or her add quotation marks to signal a speaker's exact words.

Name 

Phonics: *r*-Controlled Vowels

Directions: Read the diary entry below. Look and listen for words with **ar** that sound like **garden.** Circle the words and write them on the lines.

January 9

As I gaze at the stars, I am bombarded with all sorts of questions. How did these outer-space lights find their place in the sky? Could they be as random as marbles thrown across a playing field? Or is there a pattern, something no one has yet discovered? Several look closer together while others seem far from each other. You need to be sharp to study the universe. I wonder if I am smart enough to figure out such cosmic mysteries?

1. ____________________
2. ____________________
3. ____________________
4. ____________________
5. ____________________
6. ____________________

Directions: Read the word pairs below. Each word contains the letters **or.** For each pair, circle the word that has the same vowel sound as **for.**

7. born working

8. word morning

9. worthless formula

10. transport worm

Directions: Read each sentence below. Listen for a word that has the same vowel sound as **shirt.** Hint: This vowel sound can be spelled different ways. Circle the word and write it on the line.

____________________ **11.** Thousands of years ago, it seemed impossible to find out exactly how big our world was.

____________________ **12.** Only those with the desire and skill could calculate Earth's size.

____________________ **13.** Thanks to the research of one ancient scholar, this was solved long ago.

____________________ **14.** Who knows who else might have been the first to find out some of the very basic things?

____________________ **15.** Much of the work of scholars in ancient times has not been recorded in history.

Notes for Home: Your child identified words with *r*-controlled vowels, such as *garden, for,* and *shirt. **Home Activity:*** Read a nonfiction book with your child. Help your child find words with these sounds. Make a chart to record the words you find.

Name ____________________

Pretest

Spelling: Words from Greek and Latin

Pretest Directions: Fold back the page along the dotted line. On the blanks, write the spelling words as they are dictated. When you have finished the test, unfold the page and check your words.

1. ____________________
2. ____________________
3. ____________________
4. ____________________
5. ____________________
6. ____________________
7. ____________________
8. ____________________
9. ____________________
10. ____________________
11. ____________________
12. ____________________
13. ____________________
14. ____________________
15. ____________________
16. ____________________
17. ____________________
18. ____________________
19. ____________________
20. ____________________

1. Who invented the **automobile**?
2. He got the star's **autograph**.
3. The car has **automatic** windows.
4. She wrote her **autobiography**.
5. The plane was on **autopilot**.
6. This **telescope** is very powerful.
7. The speech will be **telecast** now.
8. He received an urgent **telegram**.
9. The **telegraph** wires fell down.
10. Is that the **telephone** ringing?
11. Her computer is **portable**.
12. We **import** toys into the country.
13. Cotton is an important **export**.
14. Trucks are used for **transport**.
15. He went to apply for a **passport**.
16. This is a sensitive **microphone**.
17. Please take off your **headphones**.
18. I play in a **symphony** orchestra.
19. He bought a new **saxophone**.
20. He sang into the **megaphone**.

Notes for Home: Your child took a pretest on words with Greek and Latin word parts. ***Home Activity:*** Help your child learn misspelled words before the final test. Dictate the word and have your child spell the word aloud for you or write it on paper.

Name ______________________________

Spelling: Words from Greek and Latin

Word List			
automobile	telescope	portable	microphone
autograph	telecast	import	headphones
automatic	telegram	export	symphony
autobiography	telegraph	transport	saxophone
autopilot	telephone	passport	megaphone

Directions: Choose the words from the box that have the Greek word part **auto-** and the Latin word part **phon.** Write each word in the correct column.

Words with auto-

1. ______________________
2. ______________________
3. ______________________
4. ______________________
5. ______________________

Words with phon

6. ______________________
7. ______________________
8. ______________________
9. ______________________
10. ______________________
11. ______________________

Directions: Use **port** or **tele-** to form a word from the box that completes each equation. Write the word on the line.

12. exact – act + ? = ______________________
13. microscope – micro + ? = ______________________
14. password – word + ? = ______________________
15. cablegram – cable + ? = ______________________
16. transform – form + ? = ______________________
17. phonograph – phono + ? = ______________________
18. remarkable – remark + ? = ______________________
19. forecast – fore + ? = ______________________
20. improve – prove + ? = ______________________

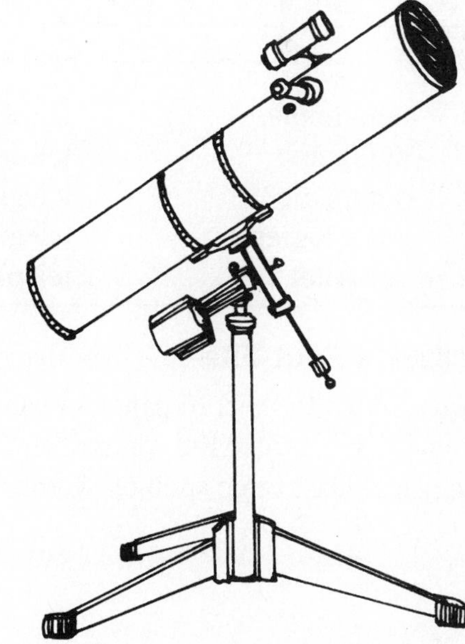

Notes for Home: Your child spelled words with Greek *(auto-, tele-)* and Latin *(port, phon)* word parts. ***Home Activity:*** Use the spelling words to create a set of word cards. Take turns choosing two cards to try to match words with the same Greek or Latin word parts.

Name ______________________________

Spelling: Words from Greek and Latin

Directions: Proofread this fact file. Find five spelling mistakes. Use the proofreading marks to correct each mistake.

≡	Make a capital.
/	Make a small letter.
∧	Add something.
ɣ	Take out something.
⊙	Add a period.
¶	Begin a new paragraph.

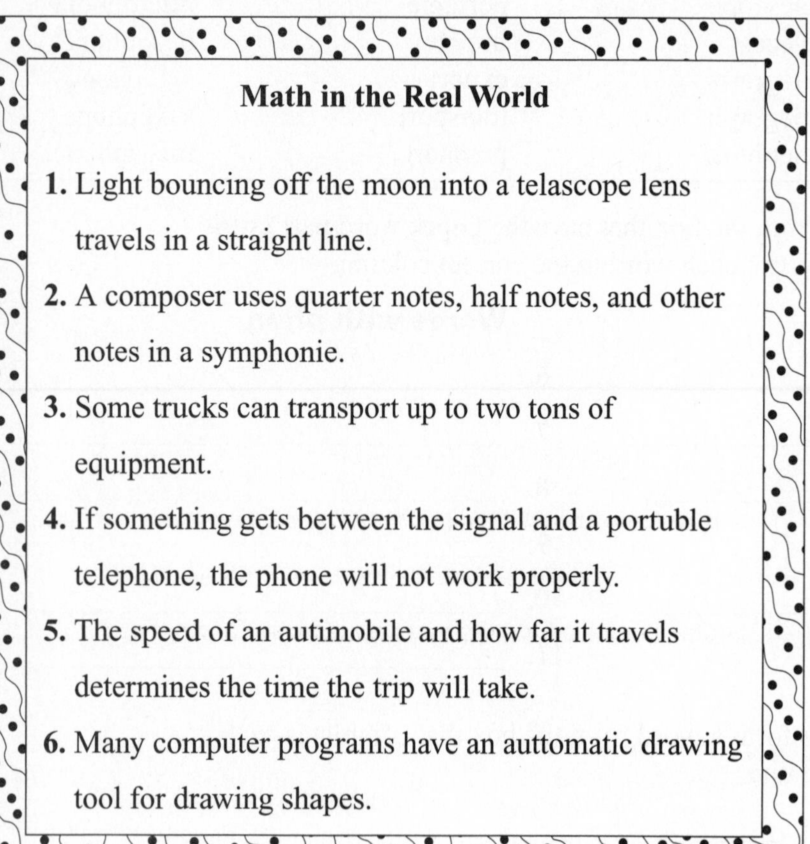

Math in the Real World

1. Light bouncing off the moon into a telascope lens travels in a straight line.
2. A composer uses quarter notes, half notes, and other notes in a symphonie.
3. Some trucks can transport up to two tons of equipment.
4. If something gets between the signal and a portuble telephone, the phone will not work properly.
5. The speed of an autimobile and how far it travels determines the time the trip will take.
6. Many computer programs have an auttomatic drawing tool for drawing shapes.

Spelling Tip

The Greek word part **tele-** means "far off." Be sure to keep the second **e** when spelling words with this word part. Remember, the word part has an **e** for each syllable: **t<u>e</u>l<u>e</u>phone.**

Word List

automobile	telescope	portable	microphone
autograph	telecast	import	headphones
automatic	telegram	export	symphony
autobiography	telegraph	transport	saxophone
autopilot	telephone	passport	megaphone

Write a Fact File

On a separate sheet of paper, create a fact file of your own. Give examples that show how mathematics or another school subject relates to everyday living. Try to use at least three spelling words.

Notes for Home: Your child spelled words with Greek *(auto-, tele-)* and Latin *(port, phon)* word parts. ***Home Activity:*** Give a clue that helps define each spelling word. Challenge your child to guess the word and spell it.

Name ______________________________

REVIEW

Spelling: Words from Greek and Latin

Word List				
automobile	autopilot	telegraph	export	headphones
autograph	telescope	telephone	transport	symphony
automatic	telecast	portable	passport	saxophone
autobiography	telegram	import	microphone	megaphone

Directions: Write the word from the box that belongs in each group.

1. oboe, clarinet, ____________
2. binoculars, spyglass, ____________
3. sonata, concerto, ____________
4. vehicle, car, ____________
5. memoir, life story, ____________
6. move, carry, ____________
7. message, wire, ____________
8. pay phone, cell phone, ____________
9. signature, name, ____________
10. reflex, spontaneous, ____________

Directions: Choose the word from the box that best completes each statement. Write the word on the line.

____________ 11. Retailer: "We should _____ more sweaters from Peru."

____________ 12. Director: "If I yell through the _____, they will all hear."

____________ 13. Pilot: "Let me adjust my _____ so I can hear the control tower."

____________ 14. Traveler: "My _____ shows that I am a Mexican citizen."

____________ 15. Producer: "The _____ of the World Series will air at 8:00."

____________ 16. Manufacturer: "We plan to _____ our products to China."

____________ 17. Astronaut: "If I set the shuttle's computer on _____, I can get some sleep."

____________ 18. Actor: "By using a _____, the back row will hear me, even if I'm speaking quietly."

____________ 19. Camper: "That small _____ stove is nice to have on a long hike."

____________ 20. Office Employee: "We used to _____ urgent messages."

Notes for Home: Your child spelled words with Greek *(auto-, tele-)* and Latin *(port, phon)* word parts. ***Home Activity:*** Work with your child to identify other words that have these same word parts.

Name ____________________________

Diagram

A **diagram** is a special drawing with labels. A diagram usually shows how something is made or how it works.

Directions: Study the diagram of a tree house. Then use it to answer the questions that follow.

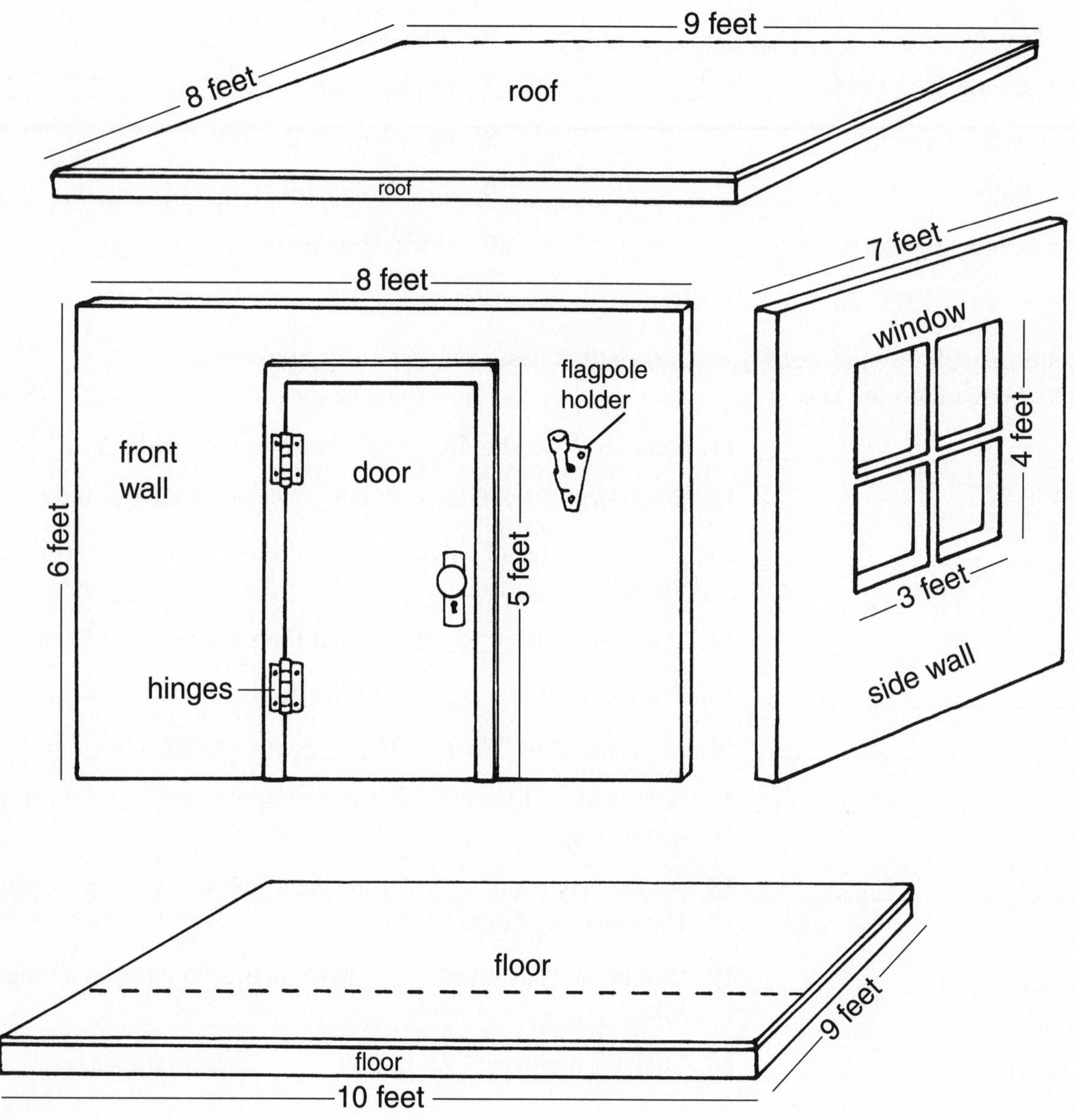

Name ____

1. What is the purpose of this diagram? ______________________________

2. What else besides this diagram will you need to build a tree house? ______________________________

3. What do the numbers on the diagram tell you? ______________________________

4. Why would you want to study this diagram carefully before purchasing building materials?

5. What is the widest measurement for this tree house? How do you know? ______________________________

6. About how tall is the tree house? How can you tell? ______________________________

7. What would happen if you made the measurements of the roof $1\frac{1}{2}$ feet shorter than shown in the diagram?

8. Why do you think the left side wall and the back wall of the tree house are not shown?

9. Would you be more likely to find this diagram in a manual, a dictionary, an encyclopedia, or a fiction story? Explain.

10. Describe a situation when you might draw a diagram. ______________________________

Notes for Home: Your child examined a diagram that showed how to put something together. ***Home Activity:*** Find a diagram that shows how to make something or how something works. Take turns asking one another questions about what the diagram shows.

Family Times

Name______________________________

Summary

Two United by Music

The human colonists and the native Argans on the planet Harmony do not trust each other. But when the Argan Amadeus meets the human boy Tyree, he teaches Tyree to play Argan tunes on his flute. Tyree's skills slowly improve. Eventually, while playing for an Argan audience, Tyree discovers how to express feelings through his music. In that moment, Tyree and Amadeus find their common ground.

Activity

Finish the Story. Ask your child to write a new story ending in which Tyree's love of music helps humans and Argans get along better.

Reading Skills

Paraphrasing

To **paraphrase** is to explain something in your own words.

To paraphrase a piece of writing, first ask yourself what the author is trying to say. Then restate the ideas or description in your own words, without changing the meaning or adding opinions of your own. A paraphrase describing Argan music might be:

Unlike human music, an Argan song uses a musical theme to tell a simple story. The musician adds other themes to create new and original variations each time the song is played.

To check your paraphrasing, ask yourself: "Did I use my own words? Did I keep the author's meaning?"

Activity

Paraphrase the Paraphrase. Have one person paraphrase a passage from a story, poem, or article. Have the next person then paraphrase that person's version. Keep going until you run out of ways to paraphrase.

Family Times

Tested Vocabulary

Words to Know

Knowing the meanings of these words is important to reading "Tyree's Song." Practice using these words to learn their meanings.

abandoned deserted

alien an imaginary creature from space

anxiety uneasy or worried feelings

improvise compose on the spur of the moment

themes the principal melodies in pieces of music

variations altered or varied forms of something

Grammar

Confusing Contractions

A **contraction** can be formed by combining a pronoun and a verb. An apostrophe replaces the letter or letters that have been taken out.

It's almost time for the concert.
I think you're about to be surprised.
When they're not playing, they listen.

When you write, take care not to confuse contractions with other words that look and sound similar.

Contraction/Meaning	Similar Words/ Meanings
it's = it is	its = belonging to it
you're = you are	your = belonging to you
they're = they are	their = belonging to them; there = opposite of *here*

Activity

Build Sentences. Take turns writing sentences that contain contractions and words that sound the same (it's and its; you're and your; they're, there, and their).

Tested Spelling Words

Name ____________________

Paraphrasing

- To **paraphrase** is to explain something in your own words.
- To paraphrase a piece of writing, first ask yourself what the author is trying to say. Then restate the ideas or description in your own words, without changing the meaning or adding opinions of your own.

Directions: Reread "A Lesson from the Master." Complete the table by paraphrasing portions of the story. Then answer the question below.

Passage	Paraphrase
Graybeard got to his feet. He lifted his thin arms over his head and stretched. Then he looked down at the boy. "Now it is time to begin," he said.	**1.**
The old man stopped him immediately, shaking his head briskly. "That is wrong. I have told you, always make your first sketch in charcoal. Black is better. And start with an outline of the body and the head."	**2.**
As he followed Graybeard's instructions Tao found he was drawing easier, faster. He smiled with a quick feeling of satisfaction. Just a few words from the master made a big difference.	**3.**
Graybeard nodded. "You are learning, my friend. It takes time, but you are learning."	**4.**

5. Why is it important not to add your own opinions when parapharasing a piece of writing?

____

____

Notes for Home: Your child read a story and used his or her own words to restate what happened in various parts of the story. ***Home Activity:*** With your child, read a paragraph from a story or article. Help your child use his or her own words to restate the ideas in the paragraph.

Name ____

Vocabulary

Directions: Choose the word from the box that best fits each definition. Write the word on the line.

Check the Words You Know

__ abandoned
__ alien
__ anxiety
__ improvise
__ themes
__ variations

______________________ 1. altered or varied forms of something

______________________ 2. deserted

______________________ 3. compose music on the spur of the moment

______________________ 4. uneasy thoughts or fears about what may happen

______________________ 5. an imaginary creature from space

______________________ 6. the principal melodies in pieces of music

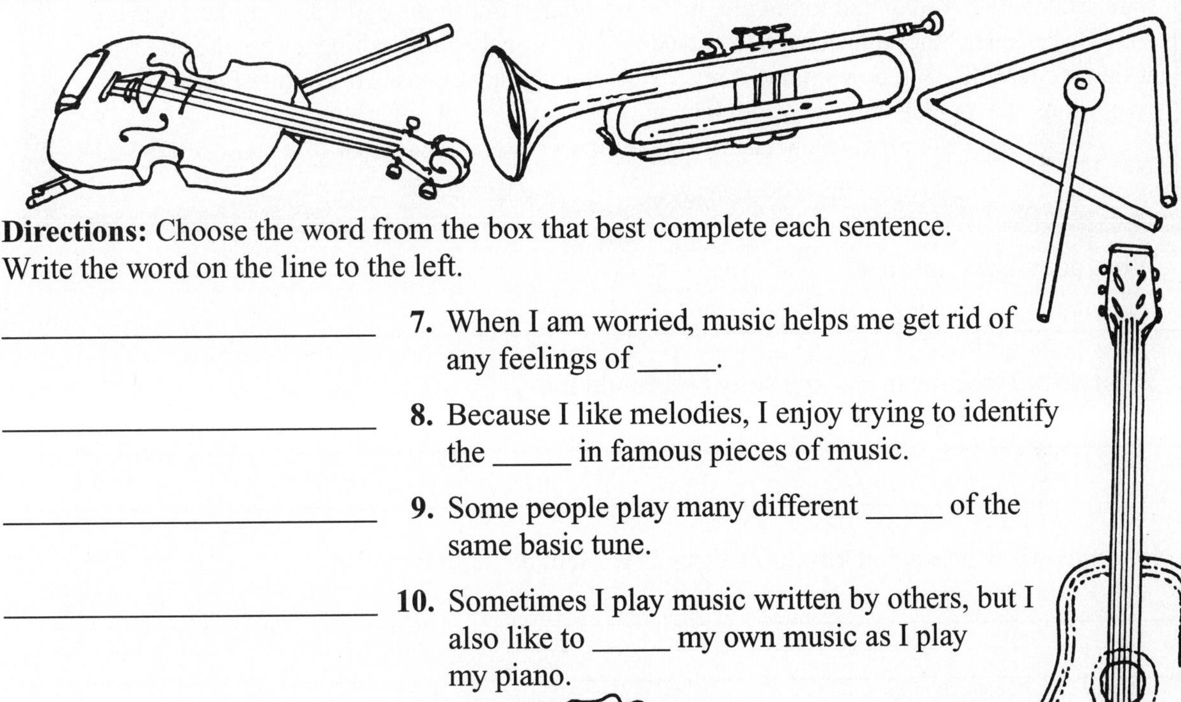

Directions: Choose the word from the box that best complete each sentence. Write the word on the line to the left.

______________________ 7. When I am worried, music helps me get rid of any feelings of _____.

______________________ 8. Because I like melodies, I enjoy trying to identify the _____ in famous pieces of music.

______________________ 9. Some people play many different _____ of the same basic tune.

______________________ 10. Sometimes I play music written by others, but I also like to _____ my own music as I play my piano.

Write a Descriptive Paragraph

On a separate sheet of paper, write a paragraph about a strange new instrument that an alien taught you to play. Describe the instrument and the kinds of music you can play with it. Use as many vocabulary words as you can.

Notes for Home: Your child identified and used vocabulary words from "Tyree's Song." ***Home Activity:*** Play some music that you and your child like. Use vocabulary words to discuss why people enjoy music.

Name ______________________________

Paraphrasing

- To **paraphrase** is to explain something in your own words.
- To paraphrase a piece of writing, first ask yourself what the author is trying to say. Then restate the ideas or description in your own words, without changing the meaning or adding opinions of your own.

Directions: Reread the scene from "Tyree's Song" in which Tyree plays for the Argans. Then answer the questions below. Think about how you would paraphrase each sentence.

I shut my eyes against all the furry faces and the star-clustered eyes and I tilted my head up toward the night sky, toward the real stars. Suddenly my song had found me. It was "Sweetwater," the song Jubal had played at that winter fête—but now I made it my own. I took the melody and I played it like an Argan, modeling my song after an Argan song about a lost child looking for its mother. All the months of frustration and loneliness poured out of me and I played like *I* was the lost, lonely child calling across the empty light-years of space to Mother Earth.

1. What does Tyree do first?

____

2. What does Tyree mean by "my song had found me"?

____

____

3. In your own words, what emotions does Tyree feel as he plays?

____

____

4. Paraphrase the entire passage in two or three sentences.

____

____

____

5. On a separate sheet of paper, paraphrase what happens on Tyree's first trip to Sheol.

Notes for Home: Your child restated events from story passages in his or her own words. ***Home Activity:*** Challenge your child to restate paragraphs from a favorite book in simpler form. Be sure your child includes the author's original ideas and opinions.

Selection Test

Directions: Choose the best answer to each item. Mark the letter for the answer you have chosen.

Part 1: Vocabulary

Find the answer choice that means about the same as the underlined word in each sentence.

1. Darla thinks she saw an <u>alien</u>.
- A. a creature that is part animal and part human
- B. a person who makes others laugh
- C. a visitor from another country
- D. a creature from outer space

2. Ronnie was filled with <u>anxiety</u>.
- F. feeling of terror
- G. uneasy thoughts or fears about what might happen
- H. feeling of sadness or gloominess
- J. act of sharing someone else's sorrow or hardship

3. The performers began to <u>improvise</u>.
- A. make up music, poetry, or drama on the spur of the moment
- B. move together at the same rate
- C. take turns performing alone
- D. practice for a public performance

4. He used the same <u>themes</u> over and over.
- F. words repeated in a song
- G. ordered scales of notes
- H. combinations of musical instruments
- J. principal melodies in pieces of music

5. They played several <u>variations</u>.
- A. unusual musical instruments
- B. slight changes in tunes
- C. slow, sad songs
- D. humorous imitations of serious music

6. The town had been <u>abandoned</u>.
- F. deserted
- G. buried
- H. completed
- J. displayed for sale

Part 2: Comprehension

Use what you know about the story to answer each item.

7. This story takes place on—
- A. Earth.
- B. the moon.
- C. the planet Harmony.
- D. a space station.

8. Why did the Silkie colonists leave Sheol?
- F. They wished to return to Earth.
- G. They were angry with the Argans.
- H. Their homes were flooded.
- J. Argans drove them out.

9. When they first met, the Argan musician gripped Tyree with his—
- A. claws.
- B. magnetic force.
- C. jaws.
- D. suction pads.

10. In this episode, you can tell that the Argans and the Silkies—
- F. are alike in most ways.
- G. do not trust each other.
- H. all came from Earth.
- J. depend on each other.

11. "I moored my skiff to one of the pillars of the portico and splashed up the steps." Which is the best paraphrase of this sentence?
- A. I left my skiff near a pillar of the portico and went up the steps.
- B. I tied my boat to the porch and walked up the steps.
- C. I docked my skiff in front of the elegant mansion and went up the staircase.
- D. I steered my boat to a pillar and made my lonely way up the stairs.

12. "I had to trade twenty feet of my best nylon fishing line to Red Genteel, but he agreed to do my chores in the garden for that day while I napped." Which is the best paraphrase of this sentence?

F. Red Genteel needed twenty yards of fishing line for the garden. He used it while I napped.

G. Lucky for me, Red Genteel was willing to do my chores that day so long as I gave him a bit of fishing line.

H. Red Genteel and I traded days for fishing, doing chores in the garden, and napping.

J. In exchange for some fishing line, Red Genteel agreed to do my chores so that I could take a nap.

13. Which is a major theme in this story?

A. True friendship can be found in unexpected places.

B. Humans will live on faraway planets in the future.

C. If you mistreat people, they will not go out of their way to help you.

D. Music is the same everywhere.

14. When Tyree plays "Sweetwater" for the Argans, his song suggests that he—

F. wants the Argans to like him.

G. feels lonely.

H. would prefer to be an Argan.

J. is very nervous about performing.

15. What is the most important thing that Amadeus does for Tyree in this story?

A. teaches him that he must let the music find him

B. makes him feel that he is a very special person

C. gets other Argans to accept him

D. helps him understand the differences between Argan and human styles of music

STOP

Name ______________________________

Paraphrasing

- To **paraphrase** is to explain something in your own words.
- To paraphrase a piece of writing, first ask yourself what the author is trying to say. Then restate the ideas or description in your own words, without changing the meaning or adding opinions of your own.

Directions: Read the story in the first column below. After you finish reading, reread each paragraph and briefly retell it in your own words.

Paragraphs	Paraphrases
In the year 2331, robots commonly performed the routine jobs they had done for the last 250 years. Robot designers had also created "smarter" models that proved to be excellent pilots, sports stars, and yes, even nannies! The nanny 2-Bane was one such model, built to guard, guide, and raise children.	**1.**
Quite efficient, 2-Bane had earned ninety merit stars in her sixty years of service. Her hard drives overflowed with the data she had collected over those years. This background was what made 2-Bane so perfect for a new experiment. She had been reprogrammed to be an artist.	**2.**
2-Bane painted nonstop for three days. Her new programs calculated the painting colors, shapes, and sizes perfectly. Her technique, of course, was flawless, and she turned out photo-like portraits in record time.	**3.**
The programmers' reactions, though, told 2-Bane she had failed. Their human faces registered surprise and disappointment. Their experiment had failed. To humans, her paintings had no feelings. They were just paint on a board.	**4.**
"Perhaps," said 2-Bane politely, "I disappoint because I am asked to paint human subject matter. I can only express a robot's viewpoint. Ask me to show the joy of computing numbers or the pain of virus damage. Those experiences are what I can show in my art."	**5.**

Notes for Home: Your child restated paragraph details in his or her own words. ***Home Activity:*** Give your child a set of directions to perform a simple task, and encourage him or her to restate them more simply.

Author's Purpose and Theme

REVIEW

Directions: Read the passage. Then read each question that follows the passage. Choose the best answer to each question. Mark the letter for the answer you have chosen.

At the Movies

Movies are made up of pictures and sound. Actors speak their lines, but there is another important sound happening—background music. This music is known as a film's *score.* The score is as important as any other part of a movie because it helps provide the mood for a scene.

The score can add the extra "punch" to make a movie a success. Does the script call for feelings of awe or mystery? Sorrow or anger? Tension or joy? Filmmakers can provide a real sense of excitement or nervousness by adding music that has a quick rhythm. By emphasizing the mood, music can express the same emotions caught by the camera lens.

Music can also show changes in location. You can change from a quiet forest scene to a noisy city street with the help of different styles of music. Sometimes music can even replace the actors' dialogue!

Some film scores are written especially for movies. Many composers spend their whole careers writing scores for films. Other film scores are made up of popular songs or dance music that suits the characters and events in the film. This kind of score can be just as effective as one that was written for a movie.

Although it will never replace the camera as the filmmaker's favorite tool, music serves an important purpose in movie making. If the pictures are what make the meal, it is the music that provides the spice to flavor it.

1. The author wrote this passage to—
- **A.** provide an entertaining story.
- **B.** inform readers about careers in filmmaking.
- **C.** express an opinion about music in movies.
- **D.** persuade readers to watch more movies.

2. The main theme of the passage is that—
- **F.** movies have pictures and sound.
- **G.** music can replace dialogue in films.
- **H.** music can describe a location.
- **J.** music plays an important role in movies.

3. The author compared music to spice in a meal in order to—
- **A.** show the relationship between a film's music and its pictures.
- **B.** tell what kind of music is best.
- **C.** emphasize a need for music with quick rhythms.
- **D.** suggest that music appeals to an audience's sense of taste.

4. The author assumes that the reader—
- **F.** has heard music in movies.
- **G.** likes to go to action movies.
- **H.** likes movies set in big cities.
- **J.** believes that movies should be more exciting.

5. The author supports his or her opinions by—
- **A.** giving examples.
- **B.** quoting experts.
- **C.** making vague generalizations.
- **D.** explaining how music is recorded for movies.

Notes for Home: Your child identified the theme of a passage and the author's purpose in writing it. ***Home Activity:*** Challenge your child to find examples of materials written for different purposes, such as editorials, advertisements, clothing care labels, and so on.

Writing Across Texts

Directions: The story and illustrations in "Tyree's Song" and "Noah Writes a B & B Letter" give details about different creative activities. Consider what you learned about the ways that people express themselves creatively. Complete the web by listing things people do to create works of art or express themselves. You may use examples from the selections or list your own examples.

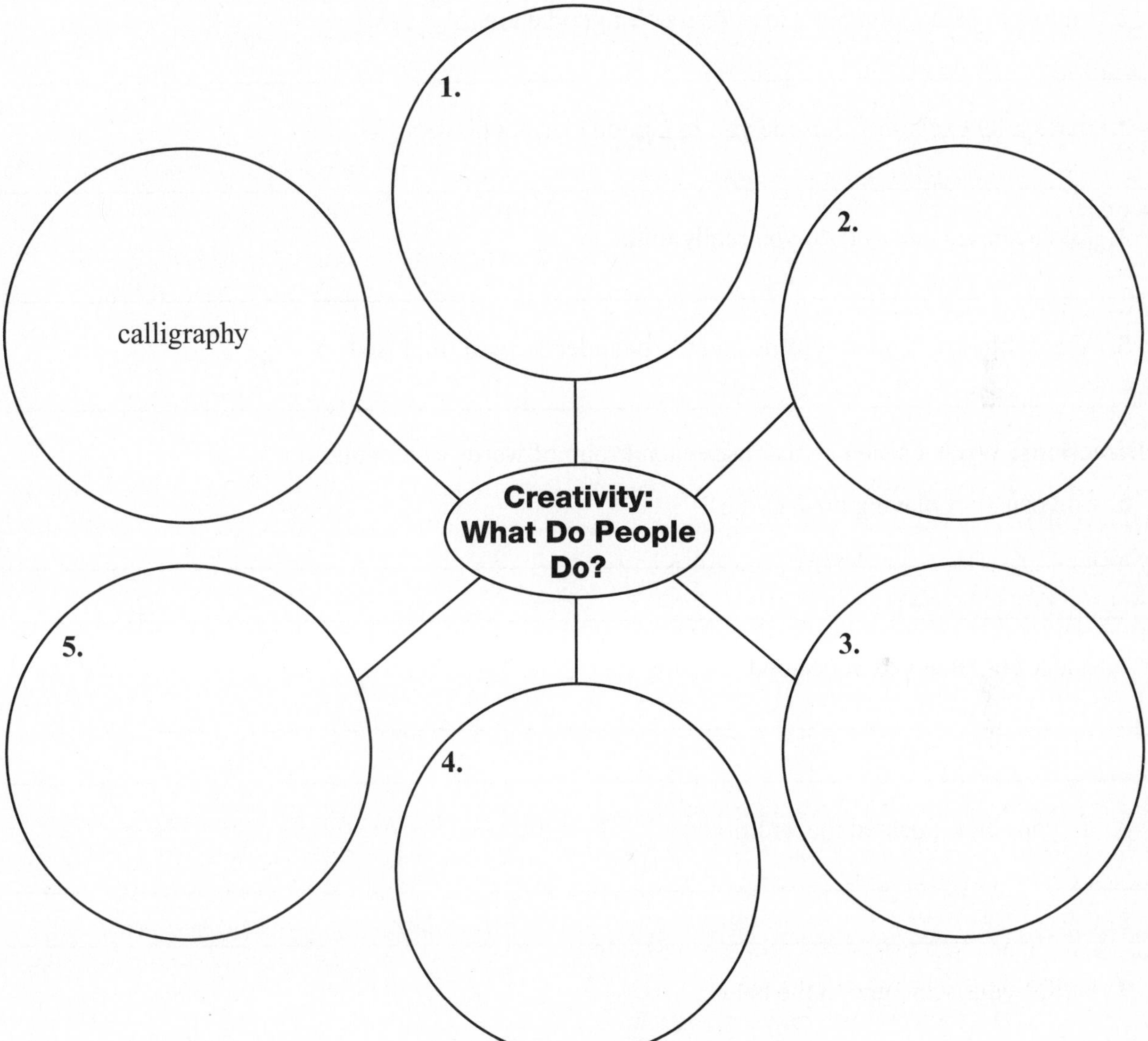

Creativity: What Do People Do?

calligraphy

1.

2.

3.

4.

5.

Write an Essay

Which creative activity would you most like to pursue? Write a short essay that describes more about the activity and why it would appeal to you. Write your essay on a separate sheet of paper.

Notes for Home: Your child listed details about creative activities from two different selections. ***Home Activity:*** Discuss ways members of your family have to express their creativity. Work together to make a web similar to the one above.

Grammar: Quotation Marks

REVIEW

Directions: Rewrite the sentences, adding quotation marks, commas, periods, question marks, and exclamation marks as needed.

1. are you trying out for the band asked Jerome

____

2. i'd like to said Lydia but I'm not sure I'm good enough

____

3. that's silly exclaimed Jerome you're a good clarinet player

____

4. Lydia smiled and said do you really think so

____

5. Yes, I think so replied Jerome and the band leader will think so too

____

Directions: Write a sentence that uses each group of words as a quotation.

6. you can start playing now, Lydia

____

____

7. thank you. that was very good

____

____

8. do you think I passed the audition

____

____

9. well, Lydia, welcome to the band

____

____

10. great I did it

____

____

Notes for Home: Your child corrected and wrote sentences that included quotations. ***Home Activity:*** Have a conversation with your child about a favorite song or musical group. Then challenge your child to write the conversation as if it were part of a story.

Name ______________________________

Grammar: Contractions

A **contraction** can be formed by combining a pronoun and a verb. An apostrophe replaces the letter or letters that are left out. Here are some common contractions:

Pronoun + Verb	Contraction	Pronoun + Verb	Contraction
I am	I'm	I will	I'll
she is	she's	he has	he's
it is	it's	it has	it's
you are	you're	we have	we've
they are	they're	I would	I'd

Contractions can also be formed by combining a verb and *not*. Since *not* is a negative word, these contractions are called **negative contractions.** Here are some common negative contractions.

Verb + *not*	Negative Contraction	Verb + *not*	Negative Contraction
are not	aren't	do not	don't
is not	isn't	does not	doesn't
were not	weren't	did not	didn't
was not	wasn't	has not	hasn't
would not	wouldn't	have not	haven't

Use only one negative to make a sentence mean "no" or "not."
Don't write: Don't never do that again.
Write: Don't do that again.
Or: Never do that again.

Directions: Combine each pair of words to form a contraction. Write the contraction on the line.

1. he will ______________
2. would not ______________
3. she has ______________
4. does not ______________
5. they are ______________
6. I have ______________

Directions: Combine each pair of words in ( ) to form a contraction that completes each sentence. Write the contraction on the line.

______________ 7. (I would) like to learn how to play the guitar.

______________ 8. (It is) an instrument that you can play alone.

______________ 9. (You have) listened to guitar players, haven't you?

______________ 10. I (have not) heard any sound quite as beautiful.

Notes for Home: Your child practiced writing contractions. ***Home Activity:*** Play a matching game. Write words such as *I am, he has,* and *are not* on index cards. Then write the contraction for each on another set of cards. Place them face down and try to pick a matching pair.

Name ______________________________

Grammar: Contractions

Directions: Match each word in the column to the left with its contraction in the column to the right. Write the letter of the matching contraction on the line.

______	**1.** they have	**a.** he's
______	**2.** is not	**b.** you're
______	**3.** he has	**c.** I'd
______	**4.** we will	**d.** we'll
______	**5.** you are	**e.** isn't
______	**6.** were not	**f.** doesn't
______	**7.** it is	**g.** it's
______	**8.** I had	**h.** they've
______	**9.** you have	**i.** you've
______	**10.** does not	**j.** weren't

Directions: Choose a contraction from the box to complete each sentence. Write the contraction on the line to the left.

she's	we'd	aren't	she'd	isn't

______________ **11.** For Kelly, there _____ anything more fun than painting.

______________ **12.** _____ do it every day if she had time.

______________ **13.** Kelly says that there _____ enough hours in the day to do everything she wants to do.

______________ **14.** I think Kelly is a great musician, but _____ not so sure of herself.

______________ **15.** My friends and I told her that _____ all come to her concert.

Write a Journal Entry

On a separate sheet of paper, write a journal entry about a song that you really like. Tell what the song means to you. Include some contractions.

Notes for Home: Your child practiced writing contractions, such as *aren't* for *are not*. ***Home Activity:*** Say some sentences, using a few of the contractions on this page. Encourage your child to tell you the two words that form each contraction.

Name ______________________________

Grammar: Contractions

RETEACHING

Write the contraction for each pair of words.

1. I have ________ **2.** she has ________ **3.** they will ________

4. you are ________ **5.** is not ________ **6.** would not ________

A **contraction** is a short way to write two words. It is formed by taking out one or more letters and replacing them with an **apostrophe (')**. A contraction can be formed by combining a pronoun and a verb or by combining a verb and the word *not.*

Directions: Circle the correctly spelled contraction for each pair of words at the left.

1. will not	willn't	won't	will'not
2. cannot	can't	cant	cann't
3. she had	shed'	shed	she'd
4. should not	shouldnt	shouldn't	should'nt
5. have not	haven't	have'nt	havent
6. we are	were	we're	wer'e
7. she will	she'll	shell	shel'l
8. do not	don't	do'nt	dont
9. you had	youd	yo'ud	you'd
10. he is	hes	he's	h'es
11. were not	were'nt	weren't	werent'
12. I will	Ill	I'wll	I'll
13. had not	had'not	hadt'n	hadn't
14. there is	there's	theres	ther'is
15. was not	was'not	wasn't	wa'nt

Notes for Home: Your child identified contractions that were spelled and punctuated correctly. ***Home Activity:*** Have your child use some of the contractions on this page in sentences. Ask your child to form contractions of other word pairs, such as *might have* or *you have.*

Name ______________________________

Grammar: Contractions

Directions: Form twenty contractions by choosing one word from each box and writing the contraction on the line.

I	can	might
she	have	were
he	has	was
we	did	you
they	do	

am	not
are	will
was	have
were	has
is	had

1. ____________ **2.** ____________

3. ____________ **4.** ____________

5. ____________ **6.** ____________

7. ____________ **8.** ____________

9. ____________ **10.** ____________

11. ____________ **12.** ____________

13. ____________ **14.** ____________

15. ____________ **16.** ____________

17. ____________ **18.** ____________

19. ____________ **20.** ____________

Directions: Choose a contraction from the box that best completes each sentence. Write the contraction on the line to the left.

you've	don't	haven't	hasn't	shouldn't

______________ **21.** I ________ been able to read for pleasure since we moved far away from the library.

______________ **22.** As long as ________ got a library card, you will always have something to read.

______________ **23.** Please ________ walk on the flowers.

______________ **24.** I know it is important to you, but you ________ leave school to go to the concert.

______________ **25.** She ________ visited Grandma in three months.

Write a Poem

On a separate sheet of paper, write a poem about what you can do and what you would like to be able to do better. Use contractions in your poem.

Notes for Home: Your child formed contractions and used contractions in sentences. ***Home Activity:*** Together, watch ten minutes of a television program. Have your child write as many contractions as possible that were used in the program.

Name ________________________________

Phonics: Complex Spelling Patterns

Directions: Some words have letters that don't match the sounds we hear. Read the words in the box. Listen carefully to each sound. Then read the clues. Match the clues with the words. Write each word on the line.

privilege	miniature	acoustics	creature
ballet	ancient	mediocre	maneuver

_______________ **1.** This word has the letter *c*, but the *c* stands for a sound like *shut*.

_______________ **2.** This word has the long *u* sound, but the letters that represent the sound start with the letter *e*.

_______________ **3.** This word has the letter *a*, but you hear it as a schwa sound.

_______________ **4.** This word ends with the letters *-et*, but you say it with a long *a* sound.

_______________ **5.** This word has the letters *eat*, but it rhymes with the word *teacher*.

_______________ **6.** This word has the letter *g*, but the word sounds like it should be spelled with *dg*.

_______________ **7.** This word has the same ending sound as *father*, but it's spelled *re*.

_______________ **8.** This word has the long *u* sound, but the letters that represent the sound start with the letter *o*.

Directions: Read the words in the box. Then read each related word below. Write the word from the box next to its related word. Then circle the part of the word that is spelled differently from the related word.

creature	variation	decision	musician	competition	gratitude

9. music _______________ **12.** create _______________

10. vary _______________ **13.** decide _______________

11. grateful _______________ **14.** compete _______________

Directions: Choose one of the word pairs above. Use both words in one sentence.

15. ____

Notes for Home: Your child explored words in which the spelling did not match the sound. ***Home Activity:*** Read a short story with your child. Challenge your child to find words that have unusual spellings. Write them down to review after you read.

Name ______________________________

Spelling: Words with *ci* and *ti*

Pretest Directions: Fold back the page along the dotted line. On the blanks, write the spelling words as they are dictated. When you have finished the test, unfold the page and check your words.

1. ______________________________
2. ______________________________
3. ______________________________
4. ______________________________
5. ______________________________
6. ______________________________
7. ______________________________
8. ______________________________
9. ______________________________
10. ______________________________
11. ______________________________
12. ______________________________
13. ______________________________
14. ______________________________
15. ______________________________
16. ______________________________
17. ______________________________
18. ______________________________
19. ______________________________
20. ______________________________

1. Dogs are **social** creatures.
2. A diamond is a **precious** stone.
3. I never liked this **commercial**.
4. He is **especially** fond of berries.
5. The soda has **artificial** coloring.
6. Her aunt is a **financial** analyst.
7. Please thank our **gracious** hosts.
8. A **glacier** once covered the land.
9. What is our **national** bird?
10. Look it up in the **dictionary**.
11. The gears went into **motion**.
12. Which **position** do you play?
13. The **population** keeps growing.
14. Be **cautious** of strangers.
15. That is a very personal **question**.
16. I will consider your **suggestion**.
17. I forgot to **mention** my name.
18. He ate a **fraction** of the pie.
19. She collapsed from **exhaustion**.
20. Drinking liquids aids **digestion**.

Notes for Home: Your child took a pretest on words with the sound /sh/ spelled *ci* and *ti*. ***Home Activity:*** Help your child learn misspelled words. Have your child divide misspelled words into parts (such as syllables), concentrate on each part, and notice how the sound /sh/ is spelled.

Think and Practice

Spelling: Words with *ci* and *ti*

Word List

social	financial	motion	suggestion
precious	gracious	position	mention
commercial	glacier	population	fraction
especially	national	cautious	exhaustion
artificial	dictionary	question	digestion

Directions: Choose the words from the box that have the sound **/sh/** spelled **ci** or **ti.** Write each word in the correct column. Hint: **ti** can also represent the sound **/ch/**.

/sh/ spelled ci	/sh/ spelled ti
1. ______________	9. ______________
2. ______________	10. ______________
3. ______________	11. ______________
4. ______________	12. ______________
5. ______________	13. ______________
6. ______________	14. ______________
7. ______________	15. ______________
8. ______________	16. ______________

Directions: Choose the word from the box that best matches each clue.

______________ **17.** I am what you ask when you want to know the answer.

______________ **18.** I am a condition of being extremely tired and worn out.

______________ **19.** I am the process in your body that breaks down the food you eat.

______________ **20.** I am what you offer when you have an opinion or recommendation.

Notes for Home: Your child spelled words with the sound /sh/ spelled *ci* and *ti* as in *especially* and *dictionary,* and the sound /ch/ spelled *ti* as in *question.* ***Home Activity:*** Help your child write humorous tongue-twister sentences that include several spelling words.

Spelling: Words with *ci* and *ti*

Directions: Proofread these song lyrics. Find six spelling mistakes. Use the proofreading marks to correct each mistake.

≡	Make a capital.
/	Make a small letter.
∧	Add something.
℘	Take out something.
⊙	Add a period.
¶	Begin a new paragraph.

The Martian Dilemma

Where has all the water gone—preshous water?

Is it in a glatier or an artifficial pool?

What can a population do with no water?

Be careful, don't be a fool!

Being cawtious is the rule.

Where will all the water go—that's the quesion.

Should we share our reservoirs, a nashional debate?

Let us learn new ways to find

Cool, clean water.

Spelling Tip

The sound /sh/ can be spelled *ci* or *ti:* **artificial, national.** Check the song lyrics to make sure that words with this sound are spelled correctly.

Word List

social	motion
precious	position
commercial	population
especially	cautious
artificial	question
financial	suggestion
gracious	mention
glacier	fraction
national	exhaustion
dictionary	digestion

Write a Song

On a separate sheet of paper, write your own song lyrics. In your song, persuade others that your ideas about an issue are important. Try to use at least four spelling words.

Notes for Home: Your child spelled words with the sound /sh/ spelled *ci* and *ti* as in *especially* and *dictionary,* and the sound /ch/ spelled *ti* as in *question.* ***Home Activity:*** Say each spelling word twice. Have your child visualize each word and then spell it aloud.

Name ______________________________

Spelling: Words with *ci* and *ti*

REVIEW

	Word List		
social	financial	motion	suggestion
precious	gracious	position	mention
commercial	glacier	population	fraction
especially	national	cautious	exhaustion
artificial	dictionary	question	digestion

Directions: Choose the word from the box that is the most opposite in meaning for each word below. Write the word on the line.

1. energy ______________________

2. whole ______________________

3. reckless ______________________

4. generally ______________________

5. answer ______________________

6. stillness ______________________

7. local ______________________

8. rude ______________________

9. natural ______________________

10. worthless ______________________

Directions: Choose a word from the box that best matches each definition. Write the word on the line.

______________________ **11.** a place or way of being placed

______________________ **12.** a hint, proposal, or recommendation

______________________ **13.** the process of breaking down food once eaten

______________________ **14.** an advertisement on television or on the radio

______________________ **15.** having to do with money

______________________ **16.** having to do with human beings and their relationships

______________________ **17.** a casual reference to something

______________________ **18.** the total number of people in a given area

______________________ **19.** a huge mass of ice

______________________ **20.** a book of words, origins, pronunciations, and definitions

Notes for Home: Your child spelled words with the sound /sh/ spelled *ci* and *ti* as in *especially* and *dictionary,* and the sound /ch/ spelled *ti* as in *question. **Home Activity:*** Scramble the letters of each spelling word. Challenge your child to unscramble them.

Take Notes/Highlight

Taking notes about or **highlighting** key information in a text can help you understand and remember the text better. It can also help you organize information to study for a test or to include in a research report. There is no one right way to take notes. You might make a list, an outline, a story map, a word web, a table, or write a summary. When you highlight, you can circle, underline, or mark with special pens the important details in what you have read.

Directions: Read the passage and then read the questions that follow. Highlight details in the passage that will help you answer the questions, and then answer the questions.

Music has been around for thousands of years—perhaps as long as 30,000 years. Archaeologists—scientists who research and study objects from long ago—have found musical instruments that date back this long. In fact, it is possible that making music may even have developed before people learned to talk. It is believed that early music was used for religious purposes, as well as for entertainment, dance, and telling stories. Most cultures have developed musical instruments and specific musical traditions and styles.

In Europe, the first songs were really simple chants. Dots were written down, above or below a line, to remind the singer if the next note was higher or lower. It was not until the 1700s that the tradition of writing music notes on lined paper was developed.

In China, writings have been found dating back over 2500 years that refer to musical performances. In fact, much of the music in some cultures is the same today as it was centuries ago. The Japanese *gagaku* of the 8th century is a style of music that still exists today. The Chinese *guenzhen* of the 16th century is another style that can still be heard today in its original form. In fact, much of the music that we listen to today has components picked up from classical pieces of centuries before.

The many cultures of Africa also have a rich musical history. Traditionally, African music has been associated with drums, but it has also included a variety of instruments, such as bells, rattles, gongs, and even xylophones. A guitar-like instrument, called the *lamellaphone,* or "thumb piano" is made up of metal or bamboo strips strung across a board or box. The strips are plucked with the fingers. These rhythmic instruments give African music a sound of its own.

1. Which specific continents or countries are discussed in the article? ______________________

2. How long ago were some of the earliest musical instruments made?

3. For what purposes has music been used? ______________________

4. Which facts would be useful in a report about written music? ______________________

5. What are two styles of Asian music that can still be heard today? ______________________

6. What are the names of the instruments that are used in African music?

7. How is this article organized? ______________________

8. Suppose you wanted to make a table to organize the information in this passage. Describe what your table might look like. What heads might your table have?

9. When you take notes, why is it important to write the names of the sources you have read?

10. Why is it important to think about your questions of inquiry before you begin taking notes?

Notes for Home: Your child read a nonfiction passage and highlighted key details to help him or her answer questions about it. ***Home Activity:*** Read a magazine or newspaper article with your child. Ask your child to highlight or take notes about important details in the article.

Family Times

Name____

Summary

Stone, Toil, and Talent Build a Cathedral

Begun in 1892, the Cathedral of St. John the Divine in New York City rises stone by stone, a result of the efforts and talents of many people. Workers in Indiana quarries blast, drill, and cut huge limestone blocks, which are then shipped to the building site. There masons, cut, shape, and polish the stone blocks to fit into the walls, towers, and arches. Meanwhile, carvers sculpt other pieces of stone into the intricate statues and decorations.

Activity

Discuss the Jobs. Ask your child to describe the jobs of the cathedral cutters and carvers. Then discuss the skills and training that are needed to do the jobs well.

Reading Skills

Fact and Opinion

A **statement of fact** can be proven true or false by reading, observing, asking an expert, or checking it in some other way.

A **statement of opinion** tells someone's belief, judgment, or way of thinking about something. It cannot be proven true or false, but it can be supported or explained. A statement of opinion that has support is valid; one that does not is faulty.

In *Cutters, Carvers, and the Cathedral,* a master carver states that his tools are a hammer and chisel, a fact that can be checked. He also says that his work is less important than the mason's job. This is a valid statement of opinion since he is an expert in his field.

Activity

Check the Statements. Discuss how to check the statements of fact in a movie review or sports commentary. Discuss the validity of the statements of opinion.

Family Times

Tested Vocabulary

Words to Know

Knowing the meanings of these words is important to reading *Cutters, Carvers, and the Cathedral*. Practice using these words to learn their meanings.

apprentices people learning a trade

architecture art of designing buildings

carver sculptor

cathedral a large or important church

intricate complicated; detailed

masons people who build with stone, bricks, and so on

quarry place for cutting stone from the earth

Grammar

Colons

To introduce something such as a list, quotation, example, or explanation, you may need to use a **colon.**

When the words *as follows* or *the following* are used in an introductory statement, use a colon to separate the list from the introduction.
The tools to be ordered are as follows: hammers, chisels, and saws.

In a play, use a colon after each new speaker's name. Then write the speaker's exact words.
MASON: **When can I start cutting blocks?**
BOSS: **Why, begin right now!**

Use a colon, not a comma, after the greeting in a business letter.
To Whom It May Concern:

Activity

Scavenger Hunt. Collect different examples of colons in printed material. See who can find the most uses in one passage, the most incorrect uses, and so on.

Tested Spelling Words

________	________	________	________
________	________	________	________
________	________	________	________
________	________	________	________
________	________	________	________

Name ___________________________

Fact and Opinion

- A **statement of fact** can be proven true or false by reading, observing, asking an expert, or checking it in some way.
- A **statement of opinion** tells someone's belief, judgment, or way of thinking about something. It cannot be proven true or false, but it can be supported or explained.
- A valid statement of opinion is supported by facts or by the authority of an expert. A faulty statement of opinion is not.

Directions: Reread "Three Wondrous Buildings." Then complete the table. For each building, write one statement of fact and one statement of opinion from the article. One fact has been done for you.

The Taj Mahal	The Parthenon	Our Lady of Chartres
Fact: The Taj Mahal is in a small city in northern India.	**2. Fact:**	**4. Fact:**
1. Opinion:	**3. Opinion:**	**5. Opinion:**

Notes for Home: Your child read an article and identified statements of fact and opinion. ***Home Activity:*** With your child, watch a news program. Help your child identify statements of fact, as well as valid and faulty statements of opinion.

Name ______________________________

Vocabulary

Directions: Match each word on the left with its definition on the right. Write the letter of the definition on the line to the left of the word.

______ **1.** quarry
______ **2.** architecture
______ **3.** apprentices
______ **4.** carver
______ **5.** intricate
______ **6.** masons

a. people who build with stones, bricks, and so on
b. sculptor
c. complicated; detailed
d. place for cutting stone from the earth
e. people learning a trade
f. art of designing buildings

Check the Words You Know

__ apprentices
__ architecture
__ carver
__ cathedral
__ intricate
__ masons
__ quarry

Directions: Read the newspaper article. Choose the word from the box that best completes each sentence. Write the word on the matching numbered line.

New Student Learns to Sculpt

Kelly was one of the **7.** _____ who was learning to sculpt stone. She was studying under a master **8.** _____ who was very well respected. She wanted to learn how to make beautiful, **9.** _____ designs. Someday, Kelly hoped to carve stones to be used in a **10.** _____ or church.

7. ______________________ **9.** ______________________

8. ______________________ **10.** ______________________

Write a Persuasive Argument

On a separate sheet of paper, write a persuasive argument telling why it is important to learn an art or a craft, such as drawing or woodworking . Use as many vocabulary words as you can.

Notes for Home: Your child identified and used vocabulary words from *Cutters, Carvers, and the Cathedral*. ***Home Activity:*** With your child, look at local architecture and talk about its special features, using the listed vocabulary words.

Name ____________________

Fact and Opinion

- A **statement of fact** can be proven true or false by reading, observing, asking an expert, or checking it in some way.
- A **statement of opinion** tells someone's belief, judgment, or way of thinking about something. It cannot be proven true or false, but it can be supported or explained.
- A valid statement of opinion is supported by facts or by the authority of an expert. A faulty statement of opinion is not.

Directions: Reread this description of a mason's job from *Cutters, Carvers, and the Cathedral.* Then answer the questions below. Think about how the statements of fact and statements of opinion are different.

Deep below the cathedral floor, "Jeep" Kincannon, the chief masonry draftsman, works in the architecture office. "To be a good mason, you must have a good sense of geometry," he says. "With the computer, I can produce the templates for the blocks that go into the cathedral. The masons use these templates, or patterns, to shape each block of stone." All the blocks are cut to fit into their specific places, and they rise one above the other into columns, arches, walls, and steeples.

1. What statement of opinion does Jeep Kincannon offer?

____

____

2. Is his statement valid or faulty? How do you know?

____

3. What is a statement of fact about templates?

____

____

4. How might you prove this statement of fact true or false?

____

5. On a separate sheet of paper, tell which of the jobs described in *Cutters, Carvers, and the Cathedral* seems the most difficult to you. Support your statement of opinion with facts or expert opinions from the selection.

Notes for Home: Your child distinguished between statements of fact and statements of opinion. ***Home Activity:*** Work together to identify facts and opinions in a newspaper article. Discuss how well the author's opinions are supported by the facts presented.

Name ______________________

Selection Test

Directions: Choose the best answer to each item. Mark the letter for the answer you have chosen.

Part 1: Vocabulary

Find the answer choice that means about the same as the underlined word in each sentence.

1. He worked in a <u>quarry</u>.
- A. place where stone is dug or cut from the earth
- B. temporary structure for holding workers and materials
- C. place where stone or brick is stored for use in construction
- D. a large factory for building houses

2. Her father was a <u>carver</u>.
- F. person who designs buildings
- G. person who builds with bricks
- H. person who sculpts by cutting stone or wood
- J. person who transports stone blocks

3. The <u>cathedral</u> was in the capital city.
- A. an immense building
- B. a large room with a high ceiling
- C. a large or important church
- D. a place where people work with stone

4. The artist had several <u>apprentices</u>.
- F. people learning a trade or art
- G. areas set aside for keeping materials while working
- H. people who give aid or help
- J. styles or methods of working

5. My brother wants to study <u>architecture</u>.
- A. rocks of a particular area
- B. the art of making figures by carving, modeling, or casting
- C. the science of the forms of life represented by fossils
- D. the art of designing buildings

6. She was fascinated by the <u>intricate</u> designs.
- F. unusual
- G. complicated and detailed
- H. bold
- J. delicate and difficult to see

7. The <u>masons</u> had gone home for the day.
- A. people who draw diagrams
- B. people who build with stone or brick
- C. people who pound wedges into stone to separate ledge from seam
- D. people who operate saws

Part 2: Comprehension

Use what you know about the selection to answer each item.

8. Where does the stone for the Cathedral of Saint John the Divine come from?
- F. Indiana
- G. England
- H. New York
- J. Pennsylvania

9. What is dynamite used for in a limestone quarry?
- A. separating the ledge from the seam
- B. causing a section of ledge to crash to the ground
- C. uncovering a new section of the limestone seam
- D. finding fossils in the limestone

10. In the process of removing limestone from the earth, which step comes first?
- F. Small blocks are cut from the ledge.
- G. Drill runners drive holes into the base of the ledge.
- H. Rubber bags are inflated by hoses to push the ledge out.
- J. Saw runners cut blocks called ledges into the stone.

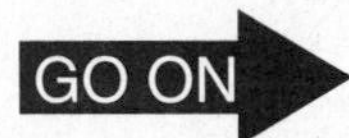

11. Which item states a fact?

A. "To be a carver, you have to have a passion for it, to love it with all your heart."

B. "The following Sunday, the Second World War broke out."

C. "The breaker has to have a good 'lick' to hit those wedges just right."

D. "But it is less important than the masons'. . . ."

12. In which of these sentences does the author state an opinion?

F. "Construction on the cathedral has stopped for lack of funding."

G. "Some of the figures portray leaders in the struggle for social justice, such as Nelson Mandela."

H. "If the limestone took three hundred million years to form, a hundred years to build a monument to faith doesn't seem so very long."

J. "Yet, services are held, concerts are performed, and festivals are celebrated."

13. The author uses quotations from actual workers in this selection to—

A. give the reader a more vivid picture of what the work is really like.

B. add humor to the selection.

C. avoid having to restate what he has learned from them.

D. make it seem as if the construction was completed long ago.

14. If you are very good at geometry, which of these jobs is most likely to suit you best?

F. breaker

G. stone carver

H. drill runner

J. masonry draftsman

15. Which of these workers uses the same tools he or she would have used 100 years ago?

A. limestone quarrier

B. stone mason

C. masonry draftsman

D. master carver

Name ______________________________

Fact and Opinion

- A **statement of fact** can be proven true or false by reading, observing, asking an expert, or checking it in some way.
- A **statement of opinion** tells someone's belief, judgment, or way of thinking about something. It cannot be proven true or false, but it can be supported or explained.
- A valid statement of opinion is supported by facts or by the authority of an expert. A faulty statement of opinion is not.

Directions: Read the passage below.

When the final blasting and carving are finished, this huge granite mountain will become an impressive memorial to Lakota warrior-chief Crazy Horse. The statue, designed and begun by Korczak Ziolkowski, shows Crazy Horse mounted on a pony, pointing toward the lands of his people.

Mr. Ziolkowski was invited to come to the Black Hills of South Dakota in 1947. There he began the huge statue, using jackhammers, blowtorches, and dynamite to fashion features from the rough granite. He died in 1982, but many of his children and grandchildren continue his project. Already the nine-story face and portions of the arm have been carved. When finished, the 563-foot-high statue is certain to inspire awe in all who see it.

Directions: Complete the table below. Decide if each statement is a fact or an opinion. If it is a fact, tell how it might be proved true or false. If it's an opinion, tell whether it is valid or faulty and why you think so.

Statements	Fact or Opinion	If fact, how can it be proved true or false? If opinion, is it valid or faulty?
The monument to Crazy Horse will be impressive.	opinion	Valid; its great size and height are characteristics that often impress many people.
Mr. Ziolkowski was invited to come to the Black Hills of South Dakota in 1947.	**1.**	**2.**
When finished, the statue of Crazy Horse will point toward the lands of the Lakota.	fact	**3.**
Mr. Ziolkowski's children and grandchildren don't care about the project.	**4.**	**5.**

Notes for Home: Your child identified statements of fact and opinion. ***Home Activity:*** Together, discuss statements of opinion made on television news reports. In particular, talk about how well the opinions are supported by factual evidence.

Name ______________________

REVIEW

Graphic Sources and Steps in a Process

Directions: Read the passage and look at the picture. Then read each question about the passage and picture. Choose the best answer to each question. Mark the letter for the answer you have chosen.

Building a Flower

Imagine a "Metallic Flower" rising into the sky in a field of old factories. Such a flower has grown into a reality in the form of Frank Gehry's Guggenheim Museum in Bilbao, Spain. The building's most striking feature is an immense roof constructed of curving, twisting metal that reminds people of a flower.

This building is a result of a process that began with an international competition. The competition invited leading architects to design a building that would blend with the Bilbao skyline and be different from all other buildings in the world. While Frank Gehry's winning design reminds some people of the unusual shape of New York City's Guggenheim Museum, it has elements all its own.

The roof's unusual sculpted curving shape required careful planning. First, Mr. Gehry built a wood and paper model of the museum. Next, he entered mathematical data about the curves of the model's walls and roof into a computer. Mr. Gehry said afterwards that the computer was essential to turning his designs into reality.

Roof of Guggenheim Museum in Bilbao, Spain

1. The first step in building the museum was to—
- **A.** invite Frank Gehry to design it.
- **B.** build the roof.
- **C.** use a computer to begin the design.
- **D.** hold an international competition.

2. The picture helps you understand—
- **F.** the shape of the roof.
- **G.** the location of the museum.
- **H.** how the computer software works.
- **J.** how Gehry's design was different from other designs.

3. Which picture would be of further help in understanding the article?
- **A.** a portrait of Frank Gehry
- **B.** a portrait of Solomon R. Guggenheim
- **C.** a picture of the Guggenheim Museum in New York City
- **D.** a picture of the city of Bilbao

4. What was the first step in moving from the design on paper to the actual building?
- **F.** looking at the Guggenheim Museum in New York
- **G.** assigning the job to Frank Gehry
- **H.** entering mathematical data about the curves of the walls and roof
- **J.** building a model of the design

5. Before Mr. Gehry was able to use the computer for help, he had to—
- **A.** win the competition.
- **B.** enter mathematical data about the curve of the roof and walls into the computer.
- **C.** invent a new computer program.
- **D.** name the roof "Metallic Flower."

Notes for Home: Your child analyzed a passage and a picture and identified the steps in a process. ***Home Activity:*** Describe a house or a room to your child. Encourage him or her to draw a picture of the house or room, based on your description.

Name ____________________

Writing Across Texts

Directions: Consider what you learned about building design and function from *Cutters, Carvers, and the Cathedral* and "How Does the Use of a Building Affect What It Ends Up Looking Like?" In the chart below, compare the cathedral from *Cutters, Carvers, and the Cathedral* and one building from the selection by Caroline Grimshaw. How does each compare in terms of its function, size, building material(s), shape, and how its design fits its function?

Criteria	The Cathedral	Comparison Building
Function	1.	2.
Size	3.	4.
Building Materials	5.	6.
Shape	7.	8.
How the Design Fits the Function	9.	10.

Write a Comparison/Contrast Paragraph

On another sheet of paper, write a paragraph comparing and contrasting the two buildings from the chart above. Use information from *Cutters, Carvers, and the Cathedral* and "How Does the Use of a Building Affect What It Ends Up Looking Like?"

Notes for Home: Your child compared two buildings in terms of function, size, building materials, shape, and how well the design of the building fits its function. ***Home Activity:*** Talk with your child about how the design of your residence fits its function.

Name ______________________________

Grammar: Conjunctions

REVIEW

Directions: Use the conjunctions *and, but,* or *or* to complete the sentences. Write the conjunction on the line to the left.

__________ **1.** You may think you want to be an architect, _____ you should consider these questions first.

__________ **2.** Do engineering _____ art both appeal to you?

__________ **3.** When you travel, would you rather look at buildings _____ go to the beach?

__________ **4.** Architects may enjoy the beach, _____ buildings come first.

__________ **5.** If you enjoy building things _____ drawing pictures, perhaps architecture is the career for you.

Directions: Combine each pair of sentences with the conjunctions *and, but,* or *or.*

6. *Form* refers to the appearance of a building. *Function* refers to its purpose.

____

____

7. Does form depend on function? Does function depend on form?

____

____

8. Architects are always asking this question. No one has found the final answer.

____

____

9. Is beauty more important? Is comfort more important?

____

____

10. Architects may not agree on the answer. They still manage to design wonderful buildings.

____

____

Notes for Home: Your child used the conjunctions *and, but,* and *or* to complete and combine sentences. ***Home Activity:*** Make a card for each of the three conjunctions. Then make word cards. Take turns choosing two word cards and a conjunction card to use in forming a sentence.

Grammar: Semicolons, Colons, and Hyphens

Semicolons (;)

- Use a semicolon to join two closely related, short sentences:
  Friends and neighbors worked hard; the barn was built in a day.

Colons (:)

- Use a colon to separate the hour from the minute: 8:45 P.M.
- Use a colon to punctuate the greeting in a business letter: Dear Senator Young:
- Use a colon to introduce a list that comes after words like *following* or *these:*
  These are some of the creative arts: painting, sculpture, and architecture.
- Use a colon to set off the name of a speaker in a play:
  MOLLY: *(Quietly)* I've never told anyone this, but I want to be an architect someday.

Hyphens (-)

- Use a hyphen to join words that are thought of as one:
  Michelangelo was a well-known sculptor, painter, and architect.
- Use a hyphen to write the numbers twenty-one to ninety-nine.

Directions: Join each pair of sentences with a semicolon. Write the new sentence on the line.

1. I like to stand and stare at buildings. Someday I think I'll try to design one.

____

____

2. Some architects specialize in skyscrapers. Other architects specialize in bridges or tunnels.

____

____

Directions: Add a colon or a hyphen to each sentence.

3. The reasons I want to design buildings are these they last a long time, they're useful and necessary, and they can be very beautiful.
4. I may be soft spoken, but I work very hard to get what I want.
5. My first architecture class begins at 9 30 A.M.

Notes for Home: Your child used semicolons (;), colons (:), and hyphens (-). ***Home Activity:*** Have your child explain four different ways to use colons.

Extra Practice

Name ____________________

Grammar: Semicolons, Colons, and Hyphens

Directions: Use a semicolon to join a sentence in the first column to a sentence in the second column. Write the new sentences on the matching numbered line.

1. I want to travel.

2. I especially love modern skyscrapers.

3. I want to see the Leaning Tower of Pisa.

4. I also want to go to Egypt to see the pyramids.

a. Every year it tilts a little bit more.

b. My favorite is the Sears Tower in Chicago.

c. They were built five thousand years ago.

d. That way, I can see the great buildings of the world.

1. ____________________
2. ____________________
3. ____________________
4. ____________________

Directions: Add a colon and a series of items to complete each sentence.

5. To build these bird houses, we need the following materials ____________________

6. These are the birds we want to attract ____________________

7. Good teamwork requires the following skills ____________________

Directions: Use a hyphen to combine the two words given. Write the new word on the line.

8. well, liked ____________________

9. eighty, nine ____________________

10. vice, president ____________________

Write a Description

On a separate sheet of paper, write a description of the most beautiful building you've ever seen. Tell what you know about the building's history, including when it was built and how it's been used. Include colons, semicolons, and hyphens as needed in your description.

Notes for Home: Your child used semicolons (;), colons (:), and hyphens (-). ***Home Activity:*** Write two sentences that can be combined with a semicolon, such as *I like plays. However, I like movies better*. Have your child use a semicolon to combine the two sentences.

Name ______________________________

RETEACHING

Grammar: Semicolons, Colons, and Hyphens

Insert a semicolon to join the pair of sentences. Write the new sentence.

1. My brother and I love reading. However, we haven't had time to go to the library this week.
2. ______________________________

____

Insert colons where they belong.

3. Please bring the following shoes, socks, and a bucket.
4. I arrived at 4 30.
5. Dear Governor Smith
6. GENE Look out!

Insert hyphens where they belong.

7. She had a worn out hat.
8. Read page fifty eight.

Semicolons are used to join two short sentences that are closely related. **Colons** are used to separate the hour from the minute when giving the time. Colons are also used to punctuate the greeting in a business letter, to set off the name of a speaker in a play, and to introduce a list. **Hyphens** are used to join words that are thought of as one word and to write the numbers twenty-one to ninety-nine.

Directions: In each sentence, add a colon or a hyphen where it belongs.

1. She had these three ideas for a project making a collage, building a model, and painting a portrait.
2. Mr. Nevins looks young, but he is sixty two.
3. BARBARA I wonder where they are.
4. Dear Doctor Fields

Directions: Join the pair of sentences with a semicolon. Write the new sentence on the line.

5. Our friends were avid skiers. Colorado was their home away from home.

____

____

Notes for Home: Your child used colons, semicolons, and hyphens to correctly punctuate sentences. ***Home Activity:*** Have your child find in a newspaper or magazine examples where colons, semicolons, and hyphens are used. Ask your child to explain the punctuation in one example.

Grammar: Semicolons, Colons, and Hyphens

Directions: Insert colons, semicolons, and hyphens where they belong.

THE TRICKY BEAR

These are the characters Lucy, Bud, and a Bear. The play starts at 5 00 in the afternoon.

BUD We're lost. What do we do now?

LUCY Bud, don't be so negative. This is a very pleasant grove of trees.

BUD Hey, what's that?

LUCY Looks like a falcon. *(rubbing her hands together)* Just look at those gleaming talons.

BUD It's quite obvious you're trying to scare me however, it won't work. *(A fierce growl is heard offstage.)* Yikes! It's a bear!

LUCY Don't be silly. It's probably one of the other kids trying to trick us.

BUD A lot you know. I'm getting out of here. *(He hesitates.)* Wait. What if I run right into it?

LUCY Climb that tree. But there aren't any bears within eighty nine miles of here.

BUD That's no good—bears can climb trees. *(The growling sound is very loud now.)* I'm getting out of here!

(Bud runs off just as the bear runs in, and they collide. As they fall, the Bear's head comes off and we see that it is Kevin, a friend of theirs.)

Write an Ending

On the lines, write an ending to the script you corrected. Think about what the characters might say to each other, and how they might act. Use colons where they belong. Also use at least one semicolon and one hyphen.

BUD ___________________________

____

KEVIN ___________________________

____

LUCY ___________________________

____

Notes for Home: Your child correctly used colons, semicolons, and hyphens to punctuate a script for a play. ***Home Activity:*** Together, write a short script of a conversation during a family meal. Help your child punctuate the script correctly.

Name ______________________________

Word Study: Word Building

Directions: Read the word pairs below. Listen to how each word in a pair is different from the other. Underline the stressed syllable in each word, for example: **rectangle** and **rectangular.** Use a dictionary to check your work.

1. electric electricians
2. history prehistoric
3. specify specific
4. restore restorations
5. certify certification

Directions: Read the letter below. It contains five related word pairs—a base word and a new word formed by adding a prefix or a suffix, for example: **electric** and **electricians.** Find each pair. Write each word in the correct column.

Dear Miguel,

I am having a great time helping to restore the old church in town. The restoration process is slow and tedious, but the people I work with dedicate as much time as necessary to the work. You'd be amazed at the decorations we've brushed off and cleaned. You know I've always been inspired by history. Well, some of the carvings we've found look almost prehistoric! We have to separate the very old workmanship from the new additions. This separation is very time-consuming. However, our dedication is paying off! Every day we marvel at how the carvers and cutters of long ago chose to decorate this amazing church. I wish you could see it!

Your friend,

Amelia

Base Word	New Word
6. ________	11. ________
7. ________	12. ________
8. ________	13. ________
9. ________	14. ________
10. ________	15. ________

Notes for Home: Your child compared the sounds of words with suffixes and prefixes to their base words. ***Home Activity:*** Read a magazine article with your child. Look for words that have been built from other words. Figure out the base word. Say the words to hear the sound changes.

Name ______________________________

Pretest

Spelling: Related Words 2

Pretest Directions: Fold back the page along the dotted line. On the blanks, write the spelling words as they are dictated. When you have finished the test, unfold the page and check your words.

1. ____________	1. The road to my house is **direct**.
2. ____________	2. I went in the wrong **direction**.
3. ____________	3. He studied American **history**.
4. ____________	4. This is a **historical** site.
5. ____________	5. The **fact** is I am tired.
6. ____________	6. She gave a **factual** account.
7. ____________	7. He is a film **critic** on TV.
8. ____________	8. Don't **criticize** if you don't know.
9. ____________	9. The factories **produce** radios.
10. ____________	10. I help with the play's **production**.
11. ____________	11. He learned to do **magic** tricks.
12. ____________	12. The **magician** lost his wand.
13. ____________	13. He saw an **electric** eel.
14. ____________	14. The **electrician** fixed the lamp.
15. ____________	15. Their voices **distract** me.
16. ____________	16. That noise is a **distraction**.
17. ____________	17. What is a good cough **remedy**?
18. ____________	18. Her sister took **remedial** math.
19. ____________	19. Where is the **origin** of the stream?
20. ____________	20. This is an **original** story.

Notes for Home: Your child took a pretest on related words that have parts spelled similarly but pronounced differently. ***Home Activity:*** Help your child learn misspelled words before the final test by underlining the parts that are different in each pair and concentrating on those.

Name ______________________________

Spelling: Related Words 2

Word List

direct	fact	produce	electric	remedy
direction	factual	production	electrician	remedial
history	critic	magic	distract	origin
historical	criticize	magician	distraction	original

Directions: Choose the pair of related words from the box that contain the same letter pronounced differently. Write the words in the correct group.

Word Pairs in Which the Sound of c is Different

1. ______________ **2.** ______________

3. ______________ **4.** ______________

5. ______________ **6.** ______________

7. ______________ **8.** ______________

Word Pairs in Which the Sound of t is Different

9. ______________ **10.** ______________

11. ______________ **12.** ______________

13. ______________ **14.** ______________

Directions: Choose the word in ( ) that best completes each sentence. Write the word on the line.

______________ **15.** This arch is a (history/historical) monument that honors the war dead.

______________ **16.** The monument has a long and colorful (history/historical).

______________ **17.** The sculptor's (origin/original) idea had been for a statue, not an arch.

______________ **18.** The marble used in the arch is of Italian (origin/original).

______________ **19.** He needed a quick (remedy/remedial) when funding was cut back.

______________ **20.** Fortunately, a millionaire gave some money as a (remedy/remedial) measure until further funds could be raised.

Notes for Home: Your child spelled related words that have parts with similar spellings but different pronunciations. ***Home Activity:*** Say each pair of related words aloud. Have your child spell each word and use it in a sentence.

Name ______________________________

Proofread and Write

Spelling: Related Words 2

Directions: Proofread this passage from a gardening encyclopedia. Find five spelling mistakes. Use the proofreading marks to correct each mistake.

≡	Make a capital.
/	Make a small letter.
∧	Add something.
⅃	Take out something.
⊙	Add a period.
¶	Begin a new paragraph.

Landscape architects design parks and landscapes for the grounds around buildings. They are asked to produse pleasing and useful outdoor areas. Electric lights strung through tree branches look madgical when lit up at night. Highly originel and effective designs can remedee urban locations that are ugly and barren. Some gardens are designed strictly to focus attention on a beautiful view or the historrical features of a building. Whatever the project, landscape architects work magic with a combination of trees, shrubs, and flowers.

Spelling Tip

Related words often have parts that are spelled the same but that sound different: **direct, direction.** Check the passage to make sure that related words are spelled correctly.

Word List

direct	fact	produce	electric	remedy
direction	factual	production	electrician	remedial
history	critic	magic	distract	origin
historical	criticize	magician	distraction	original

Write an Article

Imagine that you are a writer of encyclopedias. On a separate sheet of paper, write an encyclopedia entry on some aspect of building, architecture, or construction. Describe the skills and training that are needed. Try to use at least three spelling words.

Notes for Home: Your child spelled related words that have parts with similar spellings but different pronunciations. ***Home Activity:*** Help your child write sentences that use pairs of related words. For example: *The historical society has a great interest in history.*

Name ______________________________

Spelling: Related Words 2

REVIEW

Word List

direct	fact	produce	electric	remedy
direction	factual	production	electrician	remedial
history	critic	magic	distract	origin
historical	criticize	magician	distraction	original

Directions: Choose the word from the box that best matches each clue. Write the word on the line.

__________________ **1.** any point on the compass

__________________ **2.** a record of past events

__________________ **3.** a type of light that uses electricity

__________________ **4.** curing; relieving

__________________ **5.** source; starting point

__________________ **6.** statement that can be proven true or false

__________________ **7.** a person who makes judgments

__________________ **8.** concerned with history

__________________ **9.** the act or result of producing

__________________ **10.** something that makes it hard to concentrate

__________________ **11.** a type of trick, like pulling a rabbit out of a hat

__________________ **12.** to draw one's attention away from a task

__________________ **13.** a cure

Directions: Write the word from the box that belongs in each group.

14. authentic, unique, __________________

15. clown, acrobat, __________________

16. judge, analyze, __________________

17. truthful, realistic, __________________

18. plumber, engineer, __________________

19. create, make, __________________

20. order, command, __________________

Notes for Home: Your child spelled related words that have parts with similar spellings but different pronunciations. ***Home Activity:*** Work with your child to create dictionary entries. For each spelling word, write a definition and an example sentence.

Name ______________________________

Technology: Order Form/Following Directions

An **order form** is a special chart with spaces to be filled in. It can be used to purchase merchandise or obtain other materials. Since order forms are often complex, it is important to **follow directions** carefully.

Suppose you wanted to order a book from an online bookstore. You might begin searching to see if the bookstore has the book you want to purchase. The computer screen could look like the one below. You type words in the boxes and click on the round buttons beneath the boxes. Then click "Search Now."

Welcome to Our Bookstore!

You can search by author, title, or subject.

Author [ ]

○ Exact Name ○ Last Name ○ Start of Last Name

Title [ ]

○ Exact Title ○ Key Words ○ Start of Title

Subject [ ]

○ Exact Subject ○ Key Words ○ Start of Subject

[**Search Now**] [**Start Over**]

Directions: Use the computer screen above to answer these questions.

1. How would you find a book about architecture? ______________________________

2. How would you find a book written by the architect Frank Lloyd Wright? ______________________________

3. How would you find the book called *Understanding Architecture?* ______________________________

Name ______________________________

Once you have found the book you want, you might get an order form like the one below. To purchase a book, you would need to complete the order form and then click "Order Now." Never use a person's credit card without that person's permission. Never give information about a credit card unless you are sure that this information will be confidential.

Place Your Order Now

You have chosen the book:

Understanding Architecture: Its Elements, History, and Meaning

by Leland M. Roth

List Price: $28.00 Our Price: $22.40 You Save: $5.60 (20%)

Name [ ]

Address [ ]

City [ ] **State** [ ] **Zip Code** [ ]

Telephone Number [ ] **E-mail Address** [ ]

Method of Payment ○ Credit Card ○ Bill Me

Credit Card Type [ ]

Credit Card Number [ ]

Order Now **Start Over**

Directions: Use the computer screen above to answer these questions.

4. What would you do if you realized you had made a mistake typing in information or the book selected was not the one you wanted?

____

____

5. Why is it important to follow all directions carefully when filling out order forms?

____

____

Notes for Home: Your child learned about filling out an order form to order a book. ***Home Activity:*** Show your child different types of order forms and discuss how to fill them out. Help your child complete an order form to make an imaginary purchase.

Name ______________________________

Persuasive Argument Organizer

Directions: Complete the entire organizer. In each box, write a reason that supports the arguing statement. Next to each box, write three sentences that explain the reason.

Title: ______________________________

Arguing Statement: ______________________________

____

Concluding Statement: ______________________________

____

Notes for Home: Your child recently completed a persuasive argument organizer. ***Home Activity:*** Ask your child if this organizer made it easier to plan the essay. Have your child explain.

Name ____________________

Elaboration

Using a Thesaurus

- When you write a persuasive argument, you can elaborate by **using a thesaurus** to find vivid words to replace ordinary words.
- This will make your essay sound more interesting and convincing.

Thesaurus

alive: awake, exhilarated, vivacious	**laugh:** howl, giggle, guffaw
carry: lug, move, haul	**tired:** fatigued, weary, faint
cry: howl, whimper, whine	**well:** wisely, excellently, favorably
dull: dreary, pale, boring	

Directions: Elaborate each sentence by replacing the boldfaced word with a word from the Thesaurus box. Rewrite the sentence with the new word, as this example shows.

I felt **tired** after I ran the marathon.
I felt **faint** after I ran the marathon.

1. My dog **cries** when he wants to come inside.

____

2. Washing the car makes me feel **tired.**

____

3. We had to **carry** all the groceries upstairs.

____

4. Spend your money **well.**

____

5. Exercising makes you feel **alive.**

____

6. Paint that **dull** looking wall a better color.

____

7. The baby **laughed.**

____

Notes for Home: Your child elaborated sentences by adding vivid words. ***Home Activity:*** Take a walk with your child. Give your child sentences that use ordinary words to tell about what you see. Ask your child to change the sentences by replacing the ordinary words with vivid words.

Name ______________________________

Self-Evaluation Guide

Persuasive Argument

Directions: Think about the final draft of your persuasive argument. Then answer each question below.

	Yes	No	Not sure
1. Did I use the correct form for a five-paragraph essay?			
2. Did I express good reasons that will persuade my reader?			
3. Did I choose vivid words?			
4. Did I use transition words such as *first, next,* and *finally?*			
5. Did I use persuasive words such as *certainly?*			

6. In what ways has your writing improved this year?

____

____

____

____

____

7. Write one mistake you made this time that you will avoid the next time.

____

____

____

____

____

Notes for Home: Your child wrote and evaluated a five-paragraph persuasive argument. ***Home Activity:*** Ask your child to tell you what he or she likes best about the persuasive argument.

Directions: Use the tables below to find the percentage score for the total number correct out of the total number of items. The last entry in each table shows the total number of items.

Number Correct	1	2	3	4	5
Percentage Score	20%	40%	60%	80%	100%

Number Correct	1	2	3	4	5	6	7	8	9	10
Percentage Score	10%	20%	30%	40%	50%	60%	70%	80%	90%	100%

Number Correct	1	2	3	4	5	6	7	8	9	10	11	12	13	14	15
Percentage Score	7%	13%	20%	27%	33%	40%	47%	53%	60%	67%	73%	80%	87%	93%	100%

Number Correct	1	2	3	4	5	6	7	8	9	10
Percentage Score	5%	10%	15%	20%	25%	30%	35%	40%	45%	50%
Number Correct	11	12	13	14	15	16	17	18	19	20
Percentage Score	55%	60%	65%	70%	75%	80%	85%	90%	95%	100%

Number Correct	1	2	3	4	5	6	7	8	9	10	11	12	13
Percentage Score	4%	8%	12%	16%	20%	24%	28%	32%	36%	40%	44%	48%	52%

Number Correct	14	15	16	17	18	19	20	21	22	23	24	25
Percentage Score	56%	60%	64%	68%	72%	76%	80%	84%	88%	92%	96%	100%

Number Correct	1	2	3	4	5	6	7	8	9	10	11	12	13	14	15
Percentage Score	3%	7%	10%	13%	17%	20%	23%	27%	30%	33%	37%	40%	43%	47%	50%
Number Correct	16	17	18	19	20	21	22	23	24	25	26	27	28	29	30
Percentage Score	53%	57%	60%	63%	67%	70%	73%	77%	80%	83%	87%	90%	93%	97%	100%

Name______________________________

1.	Ⓐ	Ⓑ	Ⓒ	Ⓓ
2.	Ⓕ	Ⓖ	Ⓗ	Ⓙ
3.	Ⓐ	Ⓑ	Ⓒ	Ⓓ
4.	Ⓕ	Ⓖ	Ⓗ	Ⓙ
5.	Ⓐ	Ⓑ	Ⓒ	Ⓓ
6.	Ⓕ	Ⓖ	Ⓗ	Ⓙ
7.	Ⓐ	Ⓑ	Ⓒ	Ⓓ
8.	Ⓕ	Ⓖ	Ⓗ	Ⓙ
9.	Ⓐ	Ⓑ	Ⓒ	Ⓓ
10.	Ⓕ	Ⓖ	Ⓗ	Ⓙ
11.	Ⓐ	Ⓑ	Ⓒ	Ⓓ
12.	Ⓕ	Ⓖ	Ⓗ	Ⓙ
13.	Ⓐ	Ⓑ	Ⓒ	Ⓓ
14.	Ⓕ	Ⓖ	Ⓗ	Ⓙ
15.	Ⓐ	Ⓑ	Ⓒ	Ⓓ

Practice Book 6.1, p. 1

Name ______________________ Tony and the Snark

Sequence

- **Sequence** refers to the order of events in both fiction and nonfiction. Sequence can also refer to steps in a process.
- Clue words such as *when, first, then,* and *next* will help you follow the order in which events happen. Dates and times of day are other clues to the order of events.

First → Next → Last

Directions: Reread "Jerry Takes Off." Then complete the flow chart. Write the story events from the box in the flow chart in order.

Story Events

Tanya and Tony churned up water as Jerry demonstrated his backstroke.
After Jerry perfected his flip turn, he learned how to dive properly.
When Jerry touched the opposite edge of the pool, Wayne Cabot shouted down to the three of them.
When Tony arrived at the shallow end, Coach Fulton described the way he wanted Jerry to practice his turns.
Then Jerry demonstrated how well he learned to start off in a backstroke race.
During the next week, Jerry managed to work in some extra coaching.

1. **When Tony arrived at the shallow end, Coach Fulton described the way he wanted Jerry to practice his turns.**

During the next week, Jerry managed to work in some extra coaching.

2. **After Jerry perfected his flip turn, he learned how to dive properly.**
3. **Then Jerry demonstrated how well he learned to start off in a backstroke race.**
4. **Tanya and Tony churned up water as Jerry demonstrated his backstroke.**
5. **When Jerry touched the opposite edge of the pool, Wayne Cabot shouted down to the three of them.**

Notes for Home: Your child read a story and listed events from the story in the order in which they happened. ***Home Activity:*** Have your child describe five things that he or she did today in the order in which they happened.

Practice Book 6.1, p. 2

Name ______________________ Tony and the Snark

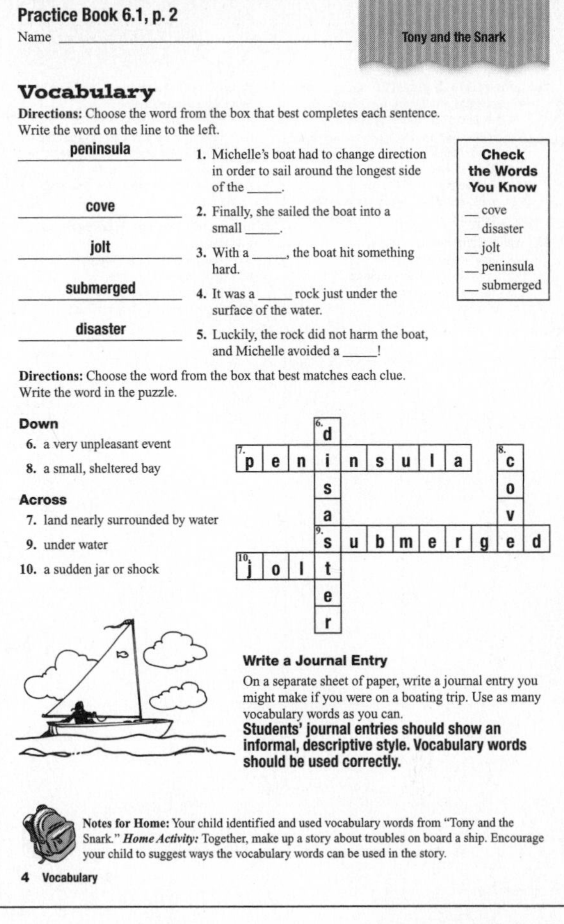

Vocabulary

Directions: Choose the word from the box that best completes each sentence. Write the word on the line to the left.

Check the Words You Know
__ cove
__ disaster
__ jolt
__ peninsula
__ submerged

peninsula 1. Michelle's boat had to change direction in order to sail around the longest side of the _____.

cove 2. Finally, she sailed the boat into a small _____.

jolt 3. With a _____, the boat hit something hard.

submerged 4. It was a _____ rock just under the surface of the water.

disaster 5. Luckily, the rock did not harm the boat, and Michelle avoided a _____!

Directions: Choose the word from the box that best matches each clue. Write the word in the puzzle.

Down
6. a very unpleasant event
8. a small, sheltered bay

Across
7. land nearly surrounded by water
9. under water
10. a sudden jar or shock

6. d i s a s t e r
7. p e n i n s u l a
8. c o v e
9. s u b m e r g e d
10. j o l t

Write a Journal Entry

On a separate sheet of paper, write a journal entry you might make if you were on a boating trip. Use as many vocabulary words as you can.

Students' journal entries should show an informal, descriptive style. Vocabulary words should be used correctly.

Notes for Home: Your child identified and used vocabulary words from "Tony and the Snark." ***Home Activity:*** Together, make up a story about troubles on board a ship. Encourage your child to suggest ways the vocabulary words can be used in the story.

Practice Book 6.1, p. 3

Name ______________________ Tony and the Snark

Sequence

- **Sequence** is the order in which things happen or characters perform actions.
- **Sequence** can also refer to the steps in a process.
- Sometimes events happen at the same time. Clue words like *while, as,* and *during* signal two events happening at the same time.

Directions: Reread what happens in "Tony and the Snark" when the boat capsizes. Then answer the questions below. Notice that some story events happen at the same time.

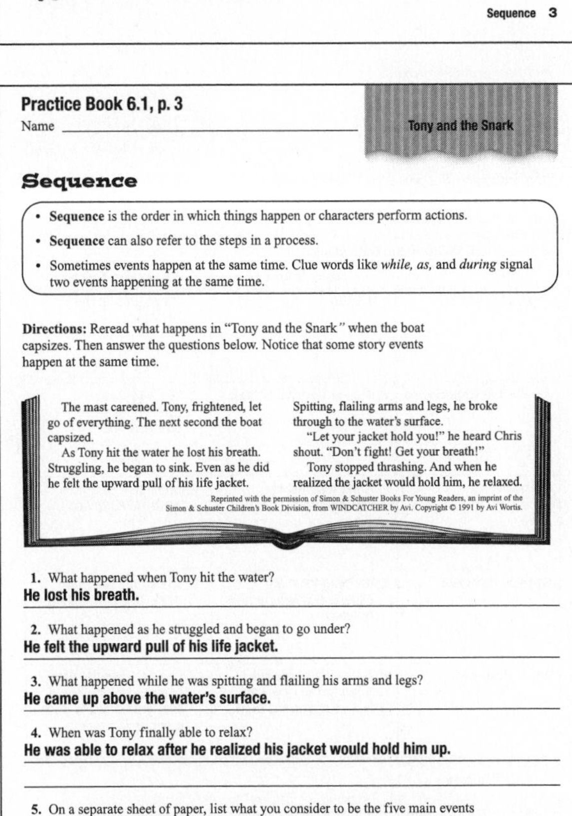

The mast careened. Tony, frightened, let go of everything. The next second the boat capsized.

As Tony hit the water he lost his breath. Struggling, he began to sink. Even as he did he felt the upward pull of his life jacket.

Spitting, flailing arms and legs, he broke through to the water's surface.

"Let your jacket hold you!" he heard Chris shout. "Don't fight! Get your breath!"

Tony stopped thrashing. And when he realized the jacket would hold him, he relaxed.

Reprinted with the permission of Simon & Schuster Books For Young Readers, an imprint of the Simon & Schuster Children's Book Division, from WINDCATCHER by Avi. Copyright © 1991 by Avi Wortis.

1. What happened when Tony hit the water?
He lost his breath.

2. What happened as he struggled and began to go under?
He felt the upward pull of his life jacket.

3. What happened while he was spitting and flailing his arms and legs?
He came up above the water's surface.

4. When was Tony finally able to relax?
He was able to relax after he realized his jacket would hold him up.

5. On a separate sheet of paper, list what you consider to be the five main events of "Tony and the Snark." Check to be sure that your events are in the right sequence. **Answers may vary. Possible sequence: Tony sees the boat. Tony buys the boat. They go to Grandma Souza's house. They sail and capsize. Tony finds the book on sailing.**

Notes for Home: Your child read a story and used details to understand sequence—the order of events in the story. ***Home Activity:*** Encourage your child to make a schedule of his or her evening activities on a typical school night. Help your child list the events in sequential order.

Practice Book 6.1, p. 5

Name ______________________ Tony and the Snark

Selection Test

Directions: Choose the best answer to each item. Mark the letter for the answer you have chosen.

Part 1: Vocabulary

Find the answer choice that means about the same as the underlined word in each sentence.

1. Homes on that peninsula are very expensive.
   A. steep hill
   B. cleared land in a forest
   C. low, grassy land near a stream
   (D) land almost surrounded by water

2. Diane practiced sailing in the cove.
   (F) a small, sheltered bay
   G. a small pond
   H. a lake
   J. a slow-moving river

3. Watch out for the submerged rocks!
   (A) under the surface of the water
   B. floating on the water
   C. falling
   D. overhead

4. Sam thought his first date was a disaster.
   F. a surprise
   (G) an event that causes much suffering
   H. a sad moment
   J. a joyous event

5. The car stopped with a jolt.
   A. loud noise
   B. gradual slowing
   (C) jerk or sudden jarring movement
   D. smell of something burning

Part 2: Comprehension

Use what you know about the story to answer each item.

6. Before Tony's parents said he could buy the *Snark,* they—
   F. went to the Mart to see it.
   G. bought a life jacket.
   (H) discussed it with his grandmother.
   J. made him clean and wax the car.

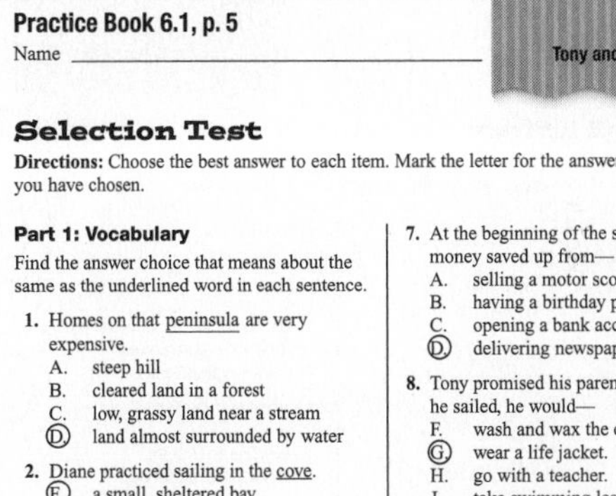

7. At the beginning of the story, Tony had money saved up from—
   A. selling a motor scooter.
   B. having a birthday party.
   C. opening a bank account.
   (D) delivering newspapers.

8. Tony promised his parents that whenever he sailed, he would—
   F. wash and wax the car.
   (G) wear a life jacket.
   H. go with a teacher.
   J. take swimming lessons.

9. Where does most of this story take place?
   A. at Tony's house
   B. at the Mart
   (C) on the Connecticut shore
   D. in Jamal's driveway

10. Why did Tony's face get hot after he capsized the *Snark?*
   F. He scraped his face on a rock.
   G. His face felt hot compared to the cold water.
   (H) He was embarrassed.
   J. He was scared.

11. What happened after Tony and Chris got all the water out of the *Snark?*
   (A) Tony sailed it back to the harbor.
   B. Tony's father drove them to the harbor.
   C. They waded back to the harbor.
   D. Chris and Tony went swimming.

GO ON

Practice Book 6.1, p. 6

Name ______________________ **Tony and the Snark**

12. Chris most likely started the sailing lesson by explaining words like "port" and "dagger board" so that Tony would—
    - F. sound like a sailor when he talked to other people.
    - G. lose his confidence and listen to her.
    - H. realize that sailing is not easy.
    - (J.) understand her directions when she told him what to do.

13. Which words best describe Chris?
    - A. loud and bossy
    - (B.) confident and encouraging
    - C. daring and pushy
    - D. shy and unsure

14. When Tony first arrived at Carluci's Fish Store, he assumed that—
    - (F.) Chris was a boy.
    - G. sailboats were faster than speedboats.
    - H. Chris knew where treasure was buried.
    - J. he could learn to sail in one afternoon.

15. You can tell that Chris thinks Swallows Bay Harbor is—
    - A. too dangerous for sailing.
    - B. a boring place to live.
    - C. too crowded with people.
    - (D.) a good place to learn sailing.

Selection Test 7

Name ______________________ **Tony and the Snark**

Sequence

- **Sequence** is the order in which things happen or characters perform actions.
- **Sequence** can also refer to the steps in a process.
- Sometimes events happen at the same time. Clue words such as *while, as,* and *during* signal that two events happen at the same time.

Directions: Read the story below.

Tarik felt the fear hit him while he waited for the curtain to go up. When he saw the audience in front of him, he grew even more scared. "What if I forget my lines? What if I trip on my costume?"

However, when it was his turn to speak, all nervous thoughts flew away. He felt the story take over as he spoke, moved, and acted. He went through the scene perfectly.

When the curtain came down, Tarik felt proud of himself. He boasted to his classmates, "We did it! We were a hit!" while they waited together to take a bow.

Directions: Use the flow chart below to place the listed story events in correct order. Events that happen at the same time can be listed side by side. Some have been done for you. **Possible answers given.**

Story Events

Tarik felt proud of himself.
They waited to take a bow.
Tarik saw the audience in front of him.
It was Tarik's turn to speak.
Tarik felt a jolt of fear.
Tarik forgot his fear.
The curtain came down.
Tarik boasted to his classmates.

Tarik felt a jolt of fear.
↓
1. **Tarik saw the audience in front of him.**
↓
2. **It was Tarik's turn to speak.** ↔ 3. **Tarik forgot his fear.**
↓
The curtain came down. ↔ 4. **Tarik felt proud of himself.**
↓
5. **Tarik boasted to his classmates.** ↔ They waited to take a bow.

Notes for Home: Your child read a story and used its details to understand the sequence of events, including events that happen at the same time. ***Home Activity:*** With your child, discuss the order of the steps for making and serving breakfast.

8 Sequence

Practice Book 6.1, p. 7

Name ______________________ **Tony and the Snark**

Cause and Effect

REVIEW

Directions: Read the story. Then read each question about the story. Choose the best answer to each question. Mark the letter for the answer you have chosen.

The Dark Day

Mira woke with a jolt. Dad was shaking her by the shoulder, saying, "Mira, wake up! You overslept."

"Oh, no," groaned Mira. "I'm going to be late for school. I'll miss math review. This day is a disaster already!"

Her father looked concerned. "I'm sorry, honey. How quickly can you get ready? I'll drive you to school. I'm sure I can get you there in time."

Mira jumped into her blue jeans and raced to the kitchen, buttoning her shirt as she ran. She put two frozen waffles—her favorite breakfast treats—into the toaster. She flipped the light switch as she gulped down her juice, but nothing happened. "Everything's going wrong today. Now the light has burned out too."

Mira popped up her waffles, planning to eat them on the way to school. They were as cold and pale as before. "Hey, wait a minute!" She dashed to the window. No lights shone from other houses. The cars were still, buried under mounds of snow.

Then she saw her father shaking his head and smiling.

Mira could see tomorrow's headlines now:

MAJOR SNOWSTORM CAUSES
POWER FAILURE!!
LINES DOWN,
TRAFFIC HALTED!

1. Mira is going to be late for school because—
    - (A.) she overslept.
    - B. she made waffles for breakfast.
    - C. she'll miss math review.
    - D. it was a dark morning.

2. Mira's waffles are pale and cold because—
    - F. she's late for school.
    - G. she likes them that way.
    - H. she can't see their color in the darkened kitchen.
    - (J.) there's no electric power.

3. The kitchen light doesn't work because—
    - A. it burned out.
    - B. she didn't turn it on.
    - (C.) the snowstorm caused a power failure.
    - D. everything's going wrong that day.

4. What was the first cause that set off the chain of effects in this story?
    - (F.) a snowstorm
    - G. no electricity
    - H. Mira oversleeping
    - J. Mira's father oversleeping

5. What was the storm's most serious effect?
    - A. The morning was gray, and Mira overslept.
    - B. Mira's waffles were cold.
    - (C.) There was no electricity, and people couldn't travel.
    - D. People needed shovels and boots.

Notes for Home: Your child read a story and noted the causes and effects of events in the story. ***Home Activity:*** Watch a television news program with your child. Ask her or him to explain what happened and why. See if your child can identify more than one cause or effect.

Cause and Effect 9

Name ______________________ **Tony and the Snark**

Writing Across Texts

Directions: Consider what you learned from the fiction selection, "Tony and the Snark" and the nonfiction article, "Swimming for the Gold." Complete the table with information about story events and the characters Tony Souza and Amy Van Dyken. **Possible answers given.**

	Tony Souza	Amy Van Dyken
Type of Activity	1. **sailing**	6. **swimming in the Olympics**
Amount of Experience	2. **This is Tony's first day.**	7. **She has been swimming since she was six.**
Preparation	3. **Chris teaches him sailing terms.**	8. **She has a five-hour workout each day.**
Keys to Success	4. **learning from an expert, and willingness to learn**	9. **determination, hard work, and propulsion**
What Happens	5. **Tony gets confused, turns the wrong way, and capsizes the boat.**	10. **She became the first woman to take home four gold medals from a single Olympics.**

Write a Paragraph

Both "Tony and the Snark" and "Swimming for the Gold" tell about learning experiences. Write a paragraph that compares and contrasts the experiences the two young people had. Use the information you recorded in the table above. Write your paragraph on a separate sheet of paper. **Paragraphs will vary. Students should note that one selection is fiction, the other nonfiction. Both tell about learning experiences. Check that details come from the stories.**

Notes for Home: Your child used information from different sources to write a comparison-contrast paragraph. ***Home Activity:*** As you read stories and articles with your child, discuss ways the ideas connect to other literature, informational articles, and television shows.

10 Writing Across Texts

Grammar Practice Book 6.1, p. 1

Name ______________________ **Tony and the Snark**

Grammar: Sentences

REVIEW

Directions: Read each group of words. Write **S** if it is a sentence. Write **NS** if it is not a sentence.

S	**1.** During my summer vacation, I visited the United Nations for the first time.
NS	**2.** Located in New York City.
S	**3.** It began with 50 member countries.
NS	**4.** Now has a total of 185 member countries.
S	**5.** The UN has its own flag and stamps!
NS	**6.** Even a web site of its own!
S	**7.** I was very impressed by the building.
NS	**8.** All the flags from all the nations.
NS	**9.** People from many countries, many in colorful native clothing.
S	**10.** I really enjoy learning new things.

Directions: Add a word or group of words to complete each sentence. Write the complete sentence on the line. Remember to start each sentence with a capital letter. **Possible answers given.**

11. For the first time, I _____.
For the first time, I went sailing on Lake Superior.

12. _____ was very exciting!
Steering the ship by myself was very exciting!

13. I could hardly wait to _____.
I could hardly wait to tell my friends about my adventures.

14. _____ was the best experience of all!
Racing against the other sailboats was the best experience of all!

15. I recommend _____.
I recommend sailing to anyone who loves being on the water.

Notes for Home: Your child identified and wrote complete sentences. *Home Activity:* Together, write a letter or postcard to a family member or friend. Use complete sentences.

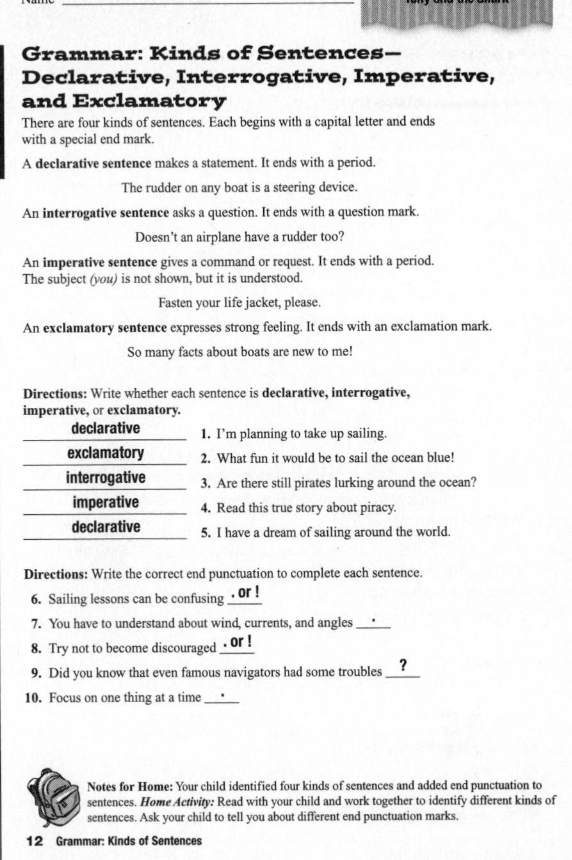

Grammar Practice Book 6.1, p. 2

Name ______________________ **Tony and the Snark**

Grammar: Kinds of Sentences—Declarative, Interrogative, Imperative, and Exclamatory

There are four kinds of sentences. Each begins with a capital letter and ends with a special end mark.

A **declarative sentence** makes a statement. It ends with a period.

The rudder on any boat is a steering device.

An **interrogative sentence** asks a question. It ends with a question mark.

Doesn't an airplane have a rudder too?

An **imperative sentence** gives a command or request. It ends with a period. The subject *(you)* is not shown, but it is understood.

Fasten your life jacket, please.

An **exclamatory sentence** expresses strong feeling. It ends with an exclamation mark.

So many facts about boats are new to me!

Directions: Write whether each sentence is **declarative, interrogative, imperative,** or **exclamatory.**

declarative	**1.** I'm planning to take up sailing.
exclamatory	**2.** What fun it would be to sail the ocean blue!
interrogative	**3.** Are there still pirates lurking around the ocean?
imperative	**4.** Read this true story about piracy.
declarative	**5.** I have a dream of sailing around the world.

Directions: Write the correct end punctuation to complete each sentence.

6. Sailing lessons can be confusing **. or !**

7. You have to understand about wind, currents, and angles **.**

8. Try not to become discouraged **. or !**

9. Did you know that even famous navigators had some troubles **?**

10. Focus on one thing at a time **.**

Notes for Home: Your child identified four kinds of sentences and added end punctuation to sentences. *Home Activity:* Read with your child and work together to identify different kinds of sentences. Ask your child to tell you about different end punctuation marks.

Grammar Practice Book 6.1, p. 3

Name ______________________ **Tony and the Snark**

Grammar: Kinds of Sentences—Declarative, Interrogative, Imperative, and Exclamatory

Directions: Add the correct end punctuation to each sentence.

1. Tami was sure she was braver than anyone else **.**

2. Isn't she afraid of anything **?**

3. She should be careful around strange animals **.**

4. What a narrow escape I had yesterday **!**

5. I mistakenly thought a wild animal was tame **.**

6. Climb the cliff with us **.**

7. Don't forget the mountain climbers' rules **.**

8. I was absolutely terrified **!**

9. Some people are afraid of heights **.**

10. Aren't you ever afraid **?**

Directions: Read each sentence and decide which kind of sentence it is. Then change it to the kind of sentence named in ( ). Write the new sentence on the line, using correct end punctuation. **Possible answers given.**

11. Do we believe in using common sense? (declarative)
We believe in using common sense.

12. You can ask the Appalachian Mountain Club for advice. (imperative)
Ask the Appalachian Mountain Club for advice.

13. Think about climbing Mount Everest. (interrogative)
Do you ever think about climbing Mount Everest?

14. Would that be a wonderful adventure? (exclamatory)
That would be a wonderful adventure!

15. You haven't ever climbed Mount Washington. (interrogative)
Haven't you ever climbed Mount Washington?

Write a Paragraph **Check for different kinds of sentences.**

On a separate sheet of paper, write a paragraph about an event you remember. Use at least one of each of the four kinds of sentences in your paragraph.

Notes for Home: Your child identified and wrote different kinds of sentences. *Home Activity:* Say different kinds of sentences aloud. Have your child use hand signs to show the end punctuation for each one. For example, point a forefinger for a period.

Grammar Practice Book 6.1, p. 4

Name ______________________ **Tony and the Snark**

Grammar: Kinds of Sentences—Declarative, Interrogative, Imperative, and Exclamatory

RETEACHING

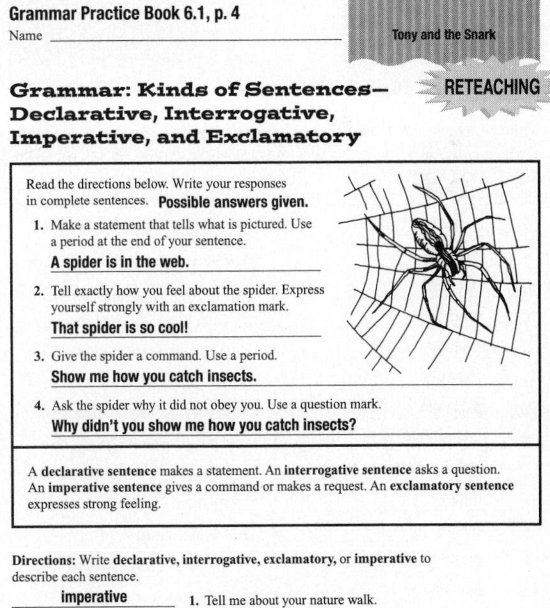

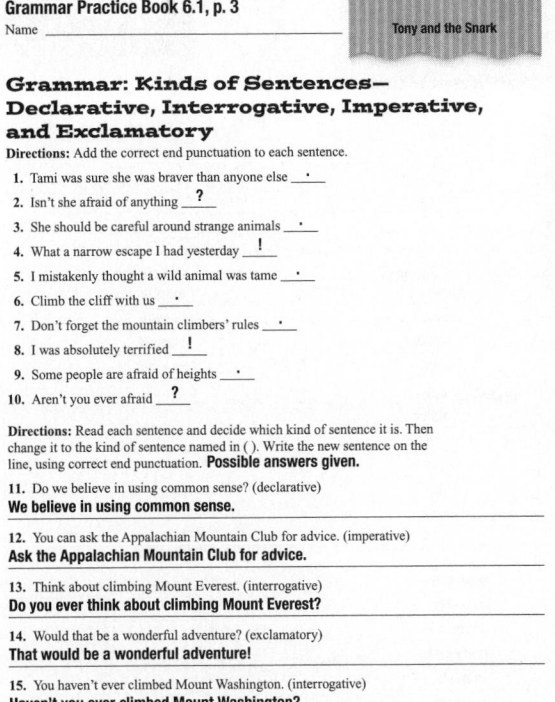

Read the directions below. Write your responses in complete sentences. **Possible answers given.**

1. Make a statement that tells what is pictured. Use a period at the end of your sentence.
A spider is in the web.

2. Tell exactly how you feel about the spider. Express yourself strongly with an exclamation mark.
That spider is so cool!

3. Give the spider a command. Use a period.
Show me how you catch insects.

4. Ask the spider why it did not obey you. Use a question mark.
Why didn't you show me how you catch insects?

A **declarative sentence** makes a statement. An **interrogative sentence** asks a question. An **imperative sentence** gives a command or makes a request. An **exclamatory sentence** expresses strong feeling.

Directions: Write **declarative, interrogative, exclamatory,** or **imperative** to describe each sentence.

imperative	**1.** Tell me about your nature walk.
interrogative	**2.** Did you see the bright orange salamander?
exclamatory	**3.** What a beautiful beetle that is!
interrogative	**4.** Are earthworms good for the soil?
declarative	**5.** Ants are very strong for their size.
imperative	**6.** Listen for the crickets on summer evenings.
exclamatory	**7.** How slowly those snails move!
declarative	**8.** Lightning bugs glow in the dark.

Notes for Home: Your child identified declarative, interrogative, imperative, and exclamatory sentences. *Home Activity:* Have your child look at advertisements in newspapers and magazines and identify each type of sentence he or she finds.

Grammar Practice Book 6.1, p. 5

Name ______________________ Tony and the Snark

Grammar: Kinds of Sentences—Declarative, Interrogative, Imperative, and Exclamatory

Directions: Add end punctuation. Circle any letters that need capitalization.

1. (h)ow interesting the solar system is **!**
2. (v)enus is covered with thick clouds **.**
3. Jupiter, the largest planet, has the shortest day **.**
4. (w)hich planet would you visit first **?**
5. Look through a telescope at the craters on the moon **.**
6. Did you know that Mercury is closest to the sun **?**
7. (w)hat a great distance Pluto is from the sun **!**
8. Watch for meteor showers in June, August, and December **.**
9. (t)he polar caps on Mars change with the seasons **.**
10. What are the lines on the surface of Mars **?**
11. How vast the Milky Way is **!**
12. (i)t has more than 100 billion stars **. or !**

Directions: Use the sentence below to write new sentences about Saturn. Write the kind of sentence asked for in ( ). **Possible answers given.**

Saturn is a bright planet with beautiful rings.

13. **What does Saturn look like?** (interrogative)
14. **How bright Saturn is!** (exclamatory)
15. **Look at Saturn's rings.** (imperative)
16. **Saturn has beautiful rings.** (declarative)
17. **Compare Saturn to another planet.** (imperative)

Write a Letter

On a separate sheet of paper, write a letter to the President. Tell why you should be one of the first students chosen to take a trip to the moon. Explain your motivations, and ask questions about space. Add variety to your writing by using different kinds of sentences. **Letters will vary. Check that students use a variety of sentence types.**

Notes for Home: Your child punctuated and wrote four types of sentences. ***Home Activity:*** Write a declarative sentence. (For example: *We walked out the door.*) Together, change the sentence into an imperative sentence, an interrogative sentence, and an exclamatory sentence.

Practice Book 6.1, p. 8

Name ______________________ Tony and the Snark

Phonics: Common Word Patterns

Directions: Read each word below. Some words have a word pattern **consonant-vowel-consonant-e (CVCe)** as in **gave.** Most CVCe words have a **long vowel** sound. Other words have a word pattern **vowel-consonant-consonant-vowel (VCCV)** as in **pocket.** Often, the first vowel in VCCV words has a **short vowel** sound. Sort the words according to their word patterns. Write each word in the correct column.

listen	drove	bladelike	fifteen	home
smile	history	windows	life	jacket

CVCe gave	VCCV pocket
1. **smile**	6. **listen**
2. **drove**	7. **history**
3. **bladelike**	8. **windows**
4. **life**	9. **fifteen**
5. **home**	10. **jacket**

Directions: You can use word patterns to help you pronounce words. Read each sentence. Say the underlined word to yourself. Which pattern do you see and hear? Circle the correct pattern in ( ). Some words might have both.

11. Learning a new skill makes us feel confident inside. ((CVCe)(VCCV))
12. It is not always easy to avoid disaster when trying something new. (CVCe(VCCV))
13. Even though the boat capsized, the sailing student did not give up. ((CVCe)(VCCV))
14. It is probably best not to be alone when trying something new for the first time. ((CVCe)VCCV)
15. History shows us that only those who take a chance come out a winner. (CVCe(VCCV))

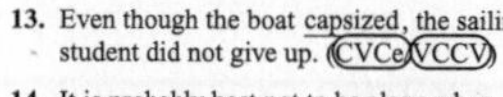
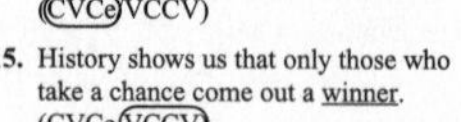

Notes for Home: Your child sorted and wrote words based on letter patterns such as *gave (CVCe)* and *pocket (VCCV).* ***Home Activity:*** Write *gave* and *pocket.* Take turns changing one letter of each word to make a new word without changing the *CVCe* or *VCCV* patterns.

Spelling Workbook 6.1, p. 1

Name ______________________ Tony and the Snark

Spelling: Short Vowels

Pretest Directions: Fold back the page along the dotted line. On the blanks, write the spelling words as they are dictated. When you have finished the test, unfold the page and check your words.

1. **admire**	1. We **admire** beautiful sunsets.
2. **canyon**	2. The **canyon** was very deep.
3. **magnify**	3. Use a microscope to **magnify** it.
4. **cannon**	4. The old ship has a **cannon**.
5. **lemonade**	5. Offer him a glass of **lemonade**.
6. **method**	6. What new **method** did you use?
7. **decorate**	7. The bakers **decorate** the cake.
8. **distance**	8. She ran the longest **distance**.
9. **swimming**	9. Let's go **swimming** tomorrow.
10. **strict**	10. His parents are not very **strict**.
11. **injury**	11. Her **injury** was not too serious.
12. **tissue**	12. I need a **tissue**.
13. **modern**	13. My sister studies **modern** dance.
14. **comedy**	14. This movie is a **comedy**.
15. **honesty**	15. He is known for his **honesty**.
16. **property**	16. This land is private **property**.
17. **husband**	17. Her **husband** gave her a ring.
18. **clumsy**	18. I get **clumsy** when I am tired.
19. **hundredth**	19. The **hundredth** customer wins.
20. **dungeon**	20. The castle has an old **dungeon**.

Notes for Home: Your child took a pretest on words that have short vowel sounds. ***Home Activity:*** Help your child learn misspelled words before the final test. Your child should look at the word, say it, spell it aloud, and then spell it with eyes shut.

Spelling Workbook 6.1, p. 2

Name ______________________ Tony and the Snark

Spelling: Short Vowels

Word List

admire	method	injury	property
canyon	decorate	tissue	husband
magnify	distance	modern	clumsy
cannon	swimming	comedy	hundredth
lemonade	strict	honesty	dungeon

Directions: Choose the words from the box that have a short **u, a,** or **i** vowel sound. Write each word in the correct column. **Order may vary.**

Short u as in under

1. **husband**
2. **clumsy**
3. **hundredth**
4. **dungeon**

Short a as in land

5. **admire**
6. **canyon**
7. **magnify**
8. **cannon**

Short i as in fit

9. **distance**
10. **swimming**
11. **strict**
12. **injury**
13. **tissue**

Directions: Choose the word from the box that contains each word below. Write the word on the line.

- **decorate** 14. rate
- **property** 15. prop
- **modern** 16. mode
- **lemonade** 17. lemon
- **honesty** 18. one
- **method** 19. met
- **comedy** 20. come

Notes for Home: Your child spelled words with short vowel sounds: *a* as in *apple, e* as in *leg, i* as in *tin, o* as in *concert, u* as in *hunt.* ***Home Activity:*** Write each word on a slip of paper. Take turns choosing a word and using it in a sentence.

Spelling Workbook 6.1, p. 3

Name ____________________ **Tony and the Snark**

Spelling: Short Vowels

Directions: Proofread this diary entry. Find five spelling mistakes. Use the proofreading marks to correct each mistake.

- ≡ Make a capital.
- / Make a small letter.
- ∧ Add something.
- Take out something.
- ⊙ Add a period.
- ¶ Begin a new paragraph.

August 19th

This is my first time sailing at night. The dark seems to magn(i)fy each sound. I can hear the surf in the dist(a)nce booming like a ca(n)non. I think I like sailing at night because I can lie on deck and admire the stars, which dec(o)rate the sky like so many tiny lights.

I'd better get some sleep. Tomorrow we are sailing to our friend's beach property to go swim(m)ing at her house.

Spelling Tip

swimming

Remember to double the final consonant of one-syllable words that end with **consonant-vowel-consonant.**

Word List

admire	method	injury	property
canyon	decorate	tissue	husband
magnify	distance	modern	clumsy
cannon	swimming	comedy	hundredth
lemonade	strict	honesty	dungeon

Write a Diary Entry

Imagine you are the captain of a large ship. On a separate sheet of paper, write a diary entry from the captain's personal log. Try to use at least five of your spelling words. **Answers will vary, but each diary entry should include at least five spelling words.**

Notes for Home: Your child spelled words with short vowel sounds: *a* as in *apple*, *e* as in *leg*, *i* as in *tin*, *o* as in *concert*, *u* as in *hunt*. ***Home Activity:*** Have your child demonstrate the difference between a short *e* sound and a long *e* sound, using a variety of words.

Spelling Workbook 6.1, p. 4

Name ____________________ **Tony and the Snark**

Spelling: Short Vowels

REVIEW

Word List

admire	lemonade	swimming	modern	husband
canyon	method	strict	comedy	clumsy
magnify	decorate	injury	honesty	hundredth
cannon	distance	tissue	property	dungeon

Directions: Choose the word from the box that best completes each sentence. Write the word on the line to the left.

lemonade 1. My favorite drink on a hot day is ____.

husband 2. My brother-in-law is my sister's ____.

injury 3. A bicycle helmet may protect you from an ____.

cannon 4. Every Fourth of July, a ball is fired from the old ____.

swimming 5. Wendy and I are on our way to the lake to go ____.

dungeon 6. The jail in a castle is called a ____.

comedy 7. We laughed and laughed at a television ____.

tissue 8. I am going to sneeze; please hand me a ____.

canyon 9. I called it a valley, but Sue said it is a ____.

hundredth 10. One out of one hundred is one ____.

Directions: Choose the word from the box that has the same or nearly the same meaning as each word below. Write the word on the line.

11. possession **property**
12. truthfulness **honesty**
13. rigid **strict**
14. adorn **decorate**
15. respect **admire**
16. enlarge **magnify**
17. way **method**
18. length **distance**
19. current **modern**
20. awkward **clumsy**

Notes for Home: Your child spelled words with short vowel sounds: *a* as in *apple*, *e* as in *leg*, *i* as in *tin*, *o* as in *concert*, *u* as in *hunt*. ***Home Activity:*** Scramble the letters of each spelling word. Have your child unscramble each word.

Practice Book 6.1, p. 9

Name ____________________ **Tony and the Snark**

Map/Atlas

A **map** is a drawing of a place. A **map key** shows what the symbols used on a map mean. A **compass** shows the directions north, south, east, and west. The **scale** shows distances. An **atlas** is a book of maps.

Directions: The map below shows the route taken by the explorers Meriwether Lewis and William Clark from 1804 to 1806. President Thomas Jefferson believed it was possible to sail across North America from the Mississippi River to the Pacific Ocean, and he sent Lewis and Clark to look for this water route. Use the map to answer the questions on the next page.

Lewis and Clark Exploration of the Northwest, 1804–1806

Key: ← Trip West; ---→ Trip East; ---- Borders of Present-Day State; R. River; 0 100 200 Miles; 0 100 200 Kilometers

Practice Book 6.1, p. 10

Name ____________________ **Tony and the Snark**

1. How does the map key help you understand the map? **Possible answer: The key explains the different symbols used on the map.**
2. What do the dashed lines with arrows represent? What do the solid lines with arrows represent? **The dashed lines with arrows represent the route traveling east. The solid lines with arrows represent the route traveling west.**
3. Why do you think only some sites along Lewis and Clark's trips are labeled? **Possible answer: The labeled sites are probably the most important ones.**
4. Which river did they follow from St. Louis to Montana? **Missouri River**
5. Would the map be more useful if it showed the entire United States? Explain. **Possible answer: No; readers do not need it to see Lewis and Clark's travels.**
6. How many miles does one inch on the map represent? **200 miles**
7. About how many miles did Lewis and Clark travel through Missouri as they went west? **approximately 225 miles**
8. Through which present-day state did they travel east separately? **Montana**
9. In which present-day state was Fort Mandan located? **North Dakota**
10. In which present-day state did they have a confrontation with the Teton Sioux? **South Dakota**
11. In which present-day western state is the Lolo Trail? **Idaho**
12. Why do you think the map key uses the term "present-day states"? Hint: Think about when Lewis and Clark made their explorations. **Possible answer: The key uses the term "present-day states" because not all of the territories were states during the time of Lewis and Clark's exploration.**
13. What is the name of the fort where they turned to begin their trip back east? **Fort Clatsop**
14. Were Lewis and Clark able to sail directly from the Mississippi River to the Pacific Ocean? **Possible answer: No; no one river connects the Mississippi River to the Pacific Ocean. They "sailed" to the Pacific Ocean using many different rivers.**
15. How does the map help you understand Lewis and Clark's travels? **Possible answer: It shows the length of their travels, some important sites, the fact that they made it to the Pacific, and the failure to find a direct sailing route.**

Notes for Home: Your child read a historical map and answered questions about it. ***Home Activity:*** Show your child a weather map from the newspaper. Take turns asking one another questions about it, such as: *Where is it going to rain? What does this symbol represent?*

Practice Book 6.1, p. 11

Name ______________________ Teammates

Author's Viewpoint

- An **author's viewpoint** is the way an author looks at the subject he or she is writing about.
- An author's viewpoint may be one of anger, admiration, pity, or some other feeling.
- You can identify an author's viewpoint by thinking about the words an author uses to describe a subject.

Directions: Reread "Play Ball!" Complete the table by providing phrases from the story that reveal the author's viewpoint about the main character. Then identify the author's viewpoint about the story's subject using details given in the story.

Character or Subject	Phrases that Describe Character/Subject	Author's Viewpoint
Kenny	Kenny hops up.	The author admires Kenny. He thinks that Kenny is quick, alert, and responsible.
	1. **He then dashes... and runs back into the dugout.**	
	2. **Kenny is all concentration.**	
	3. **He must stay with the action.**	
	4. **His swift darting in and out keeps the rhythm of the game flowing.**	
Baseball	The team's three doctors are also in the dugout, watching how the players' bodies are working during the game.	5. **The author takes the game of baseball seriously.**
	. . . that sacred moment. . . .	
	. . . a tense batter throws his helmet and bat. . . .	

Notes for Home: Your child read a story and used words from the story to identify the author's viewpoint. ***Home Activity:*** Describe a person, place, or thing. Then ask your child to describe how you feel about that person, place, or thing, based on your description.

Practice Book 6.1, p. 12

Name ______________________ Teammates

Vocabulary

Directions: Choose the word from the box that best matches each definition. Write the word on the line.

Check the Words You Know
- __ abuse
- __ dedication
- __ hateful
- __ hostility
- __ prejudice
- __ racial
- __ tremendous

hateful 1. showing or causing hate

abuse 2. rough or cruel treatment

tremendous 3. very great; enormous

dedication 4. devotion to a purpose

prejudice 5. unfounded dislike

Directions: Choose a word from the box that best matches each clue. Write the word on the line to the left.

racial 6. During the Civil Rights movement of the 1950s and 1960s, many men and women were working and fighting for _____ equality for all Americans.

hostility 7. These Civil Rights workers often had to face the _____ of angry crowds.

dedication 8. Despite these obstacles, the _____ of the workers paid off as unfair laws were overturned.

tremendous 9. Since the 1950s, there have been some _____ changes in the way people of different races relate to one another.

prejudice 10. Although _____ against others still exists, the Civil Rights movement was successful in getting laws passed to protect against unfair treatment of others based on their race.

Write an Opinion

Think about a time you felt others had treated you unfairly because you were "different" from them. How did this make you feel? On a separate sheet of paper, write an opinion on how prejudice affects the way people treat one another. Use as many vocabulary words as you can.

Vocabulary words should be used appropriately in students' opinions.

Notes for Home: Your child identified and used vocabulary words from the story *Teammates.* ***Home Activity:*** Select five words from a story you and your child read together. Take turns telling each other what the word means and using it in a sentence.

Practice Book 6.1, p. 13

Name ______________________ Teammates

Author's Viewpoint

- **Author's viewpoint** is the way an author thinks about the subject of his or her writing.
- An author's viewpoint may be one of fear, admiration, pity, amusement, or other feeling.
- You can identify an author's viewpoint by thinking about the words an author uses to describe a subject.

Directions: Reread the part of *Teammates* in which Pee Wee Reese takes a stand. Then answer the questions below. Think about how the author shows his viewpoint.

> With his head high, Pee Wee walked directly from his shortstop position to where Jackie was playing first base. The taunts and shouting of the fans were ringing in Pee Wee's ears. It saddened him, because he knew it could have been his friends and neighbors. Pee Wee's legs felt heavy, but he knew what he had to do.
>
> As he walked toward Jackie wearing the gray Dodger uniform, he looked into his teammate's bold, pained eyes. The first baseman had done nothing to provoke the hostility except that he sought to be treated as an equal. Jackie was grim with anger. Pee Wee smiled broadly as he reached Jackie. Jackie smiled back.
>
> Stepping beside Jackie, Pee Wee put his arm around Jackie's shoulders.
>
> Excerpt from TEAMMATES by Peter Golenbock, copyright © 1990 by Golenbock Communications, reprinted by permission of Harcourt Brace and Company.

Possible answers given.

1. How does the author signal that Pee Wee is going to do something important?
He describes Pee Wee holding his head high.

2. Why is it difficult for Pee Wee to listen to the taunts of the crowd?
He knows that some of them may be his friends and neighbors.

3. How does the author show his opinion of the crowd?
He thinks the crowd is mean and unfair. He says that Jackie did nothing to provoke the hostility.

4. What is the author's opinion of Jackie Robinson?
He admires Jackie for fighting for his right to be treated as an equal and for accepting Pee Wee's gesture of friendship.

5. What does the author think of Pee Wee Reese? Explain your thinking on a separate sheet of paper. Give examples from the selection to support your answer.
The author admires Pee Wee Reese for taking a stand and doing what is right. He thinks Pee Wee was brave to let everyone know that he will stand by Jackie Robinson. Author describes the two men as "great athletes."

Notes for Home: Your child read a selection and used its details to identify the author's viewpoint. ***Home Activity:*** Read a newspaper or magazine letter to the editor with your child. Ask your child to tell you the writer's viewpoint.

Practice Book 6.1, p. 15

Name ______________________

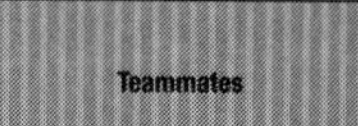

Teammates

Selection Test

Directions: Choose the best answer to each item. Mark the letter for the answer you have chosen.

Part 1: Vocabulary

Find the answer choice that means about the same as the underlined word in each sentence.

1. The hostility between them is obvious.
   - A. cooperation
   - (B) dislike; unfriendliness
   - C. respect
   - D. strong affection
2. Jack wished he could take back his hateful comments.
   - (F) showing strong dislike
   - G. clever
   - H. not correct
   - J. silly
3. Marty has the dedication needed to win the award.
   - A. lack of interest
   - B. ill will
   - (C) determination to reach a goal
   - D. talent
4. That law has put a stop to the abuse of animals.
   - F. movement
   - (G) cruel treatment
   - H. housing
   - J. daily care
5. The truck carried a tremendous load.
   - A. important
   - B. very old
   - (C) huge
   - D. valuable
6. Margo talked about her racial background.
   - F. of or about jobs
   - G. related to history
   - H. of or about art
   - (J) of or about a race of people
7. I'll never understand Daisy's prejudice.
   - A. way of expressing oneself
   - B. interest in something
   - (C) dislike without a reason
   - D. attraction to something

Part 2: Comprehension

Use what you know about the selection to answer each item.

8. Before Jackie Robinson tried out for the Dodgers, he—
   - F. became friends with Pee Wee Reese.
   - (G) played in the Negro Leagues.
   - H. played against the Cincinnati Reds.
   - J. played in the Major Leagues.
9. African Americans gathered in crowds to watch Jackie Robinson at his first tryout with the Dodgers because they—
   - (A) hoped he would become the first African American player in the Major Leagues.
   - B. thought he should play in the Negro Leagues.
   - C. did not know if he was a very good player.
   - D. wanted to protect him from people who threatened him.
10. The author most likely wrote this selection to—
    - F. persuade readers to learn more about baseball.
    - G. describe the people of the 1940s.
    - (H) inform readers about a hero.
    - J. compare Jackie Robinson and Pee Wee Reese.

GO ON

Practice Book 6.1, p. 16

Name ______________________ **Teammates**

11. Branch Rickey and Pee Wee Reese both thought that Jackie Robinson—
    A. could end segregation in America.
    B. should not play for the Dodgers.
    C. might take their jobs.
    Ⓓ could help the Dodgers win games.
12. What is the main idea of this selection?
    F. There were many extraordinary baseball players in the Negro Leagues.
    G. Branch Rickey was not afraid of change.
    H. Pee Wee Reese and Jackie Robinson played on the same team.
    Ⓙ Jackie Robinson overcame prejudice to become the first African American player in Major League baseball.
13. Which sentence states a generalization that is valid?
    A. Everyone in the Major Leagues supported racial segregation.
    Ⓑ Many players in the Negro Leagues were good baseball players.
    C. Everyone hoped Jackie Robinson would become a star player for the Dodgers.
    D. Most players in the Negro Leagues became famous.
14. The author of this selection believes that all baseball players should be—
    Ⓕ treated equally, regardless of race.
    G. paid exactly the same salary.
    H. made famous throughout the world.
    J. yelled at by fans.
15. The author of this selection would most likely agree that—
    A. people should not be concerned about racial problems.
    B. Jackie Robinson's skills were more important to Branch Rickey than his self-control.
    Ⓒ Branch Rickey was a smart and courageous man.
    D. Pee Wee Reese was just like the rest of Robinson's teammates.

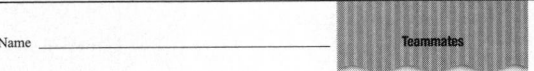

Name ______________________ **Teammates**

Author's Viewpoint

- **Author's viewpoint** is the way an author thinks about the subject of his or her writing.
- An author's viewpoint may be one of fear, admiration, pity, amusement, or other feeling.
- You can identify an author's viewpoint by thinking about the words an author uses to describe a subject.

Directions: Read the passage below.

When it comes to pets, leave the dogs in their kennels! Give me a lizard any time.

Dogs, whose moist eyes and wide grins appear to show affection for their owners, fool people. They know what their easily tricked owners want to see.

Dogs need their owners to amuse them and keep them company. So they make huge efforts to warm their masters' hearts. They fetch and roll over to get what they want—an extra doggie treat or a cozy spot in the bedroom.

Lizards have no need to hide who they are. "Love me or leave me," they say. They let you know right away, "We can be friends if you see that we're equals. But don't expect me to perform for you or put on a happy face just because you're around. I've got my own life."

They're not being hateful, only honest and independent. Who can resist a lizard?

Directions: The table below shows evidence of the author's viewpoint about lizards. Fill in the other half of the table with evidence of the author's viewpoint about dogs. Below the table, state your conclusions about the author's viewpoint about both animals. **Possible answers given.**

Lizards	Dogs
Lizards don't hide who they are.	1. **Dogs "appear to show affection."**
Lizards think they are their owners' equals.	2. **Dogs trick their owners easily.**
Lizards have their own lives.	3. **Dogs need owners to amuse them.**
Lizards are honest and independent.	4. **Dogs perform to get what they want.**

5. **Author's viewpoint is in favor of lizards and against dogs. Author says nice things about lizards, but suggests that dogs only pretend to love their owners in exchange for food, petting, and a soft place to sleep.**

Notes for Home: Your child read a selection and used its details to identify the author's viewpoint. ***Home Activity:*** Read a news article with your child. Have him or her circle words and phrases that reveal an author's thoughts or feelings about a subject.

Practice Book 6.1, p. 17

Name ______________________ **Teammates**

Main Idea and Supporting Details

REVIEW

Directions: Read the passage. Then read each question about the passage. Choose the best answer to each question. Mark the letter for the answer you have chosen.

A Sport Unlike Any Other

Baseball is a sport unlike any other. It is a team sport that depends largely on individual effort. The pitcher must make his pitch and get it in the spot he wants to hit—until he releases the ball, his teammates can do nothing to help him. Teammates back one another up on all plays, but each fielder has to catch the balls within his reach and make accurate throws to get runners out. Each player is responsible for covering his own territory.

In no other sport does the defense hold the ball. The idea of basketball, football, and hockey is to take the ball (or puck) away from the opponent; the two teams fight for possession of the ball throughout the game. In baseball, the point is to cross home plate more often than the other team.

When the first batter comes up in a game, he is his team's only active player, against the nine active players in the field for the other team. In no other sport are the sides designed to be uneven at all times. The greatest number of active players on the offensive team is four—if the bases are loaded and a man is up to bat.

Professional baseball teams play a 162-game season—more than twice as many games as basketball teams, and more than ten times as many as football. The season lasts for six months, with a game almost every day.

1. What is the main idea of the passage?
   A. Baseball is the best sport.
   B. Baseball is just like any other sport.
   Ⓒ Baseball is unlike any other sport.
   D. Baseball is duller than any other sport.
2. The main idea of the first paragraph is that—
   F. the pitcher's teammates cannot help him until he throws the ball.
   Ⓖ baseball depends on individual effort.
   H. outfielders cover a lot of territory.
   J. fielders have to make accurate throws.
3. The main idea of the second paragraph is—
   A. that football is similar to basketball.
   Ⓑ that baseball is not a battle for possession of the ball.
   C. that hockey is played with a puck.
   D. that a football has a shape all its own.
4. The main idea of the third paragraph is—
   F. that there are never more than four offensive players at one time.
   G. that there can never be more than three runners on base.
   H. that the first batter faces nine opponents.
   Ⓙ that in baseball, the sides are never even.
5. Which of the following is **not** a supporting detail of the last paragraph?
   Ⓐ Baseball is the most popular sport.
   B. Professional basketball has fewer games in a season than baseball.
   C. Teams play every day for six months.
   D. Professional baseball has a 162-game season.

Notes for Home: Your child has identified the main ideas of a passage and the details that support those ideas. ***Home Activity:*** Review a magazine advertisement with your child. Challenge him or her to identify the main idea and supporting details.

Name ______________________ **Teammates**

Writing Across Texts

Directions: Think about what you learned about the "Negro Leagues" from the story *Teammates* and the selection "Legends." Then fill out the chart below with information from the selections about the players in those leagues. **Possible answers given.**

Player	Team(s) He Played On	One Fact About Him
Josh Gibson	1. **Pittsburgh Crawfords**	6. **unofficially hit more than 900 home runs, batting average .350**
Leroy "Satchel" Paige	2. **the Indians**	7. **a pitcher with an enthusiastic personality**
James "Cool Papa" Bell	3. **the Monarchs, the Grays, and the Crawfords**	8. **fast runner, great batting stroke**
Jackie Robinson	4. **the Monarchs and the Dodgers**	9. **first black major league baseball player**
Oscar Charleston	5. **the Homestead Grays**	10. **is in the Baseball Hall of Fame**

Write an Essay

Our relationships with others help us learn more about ourselves. In *Teammates,* you read about the first African American to play in the Major Leagues, Jackie Robinson. Write an essay about what you think Jackie Robinson may have learned through his experiences with baseball fans, teammates, and friends, before and after he joined the Major Leagues. Write your essay on a separate sheet of paper.

Essays will vary, but might make the point that despite the trials he endured as the first African American ballplayer in the Major Leagues, Robinson probably had his self-esteem renewed by the acceptance of men such as Branch Rickey and Pee Wee Reese. He probably hoped that this would be the beginning of a change in attitude that would improve the chances for African Americans to succeed in the Major Leagues.

Notes for Home: Your child compared a selection with the unit theme, "Myself and Others." ***Home Activity:*** As you read stories and articles with your child, discuss ways the ideas connect to what your child knows about himself or herself and others.

Grammar Practice Book 6.1, p. 6

Name ______________________ **Teammates**

Grammar: Four Kinds of Sentences — REVIEW

Directions: Add the correct punctuation mark to the end of each sentence. Then tell whether the sentence is **declarative, interrogative, imperative,** or **exclamatory.**

declarative	1. Intolerance usually results from a lack of information **.**
interrogative	2. Do you feel uncomfortable, for example, around a person with a disability **?**
imperative	3. Don't let this feeling make you ignore the person **.**
exclamatory	4. A good friend may be right in front of you **!**
imperative	5. Make the effort to find out more about this person **.**

Directions: Write five sentences about someone who has experienced prejudice from others. It can be a real person or an imaginary character. Write the kind of sentence shown in ( ). Remember to start each sentence with a capital letter and end each one with the correct end punctuation. **Possible answers given.**

6. (declarative)
A friend of mine is hearing impaired.

7. (interrogative)
Do you know any hearing impaired people?

8. (declarative)
My friend communicates by making hand signs in American Sign Language.

9. (imperative)
Watch how fast she can sign.

10. (exclamatory)
I think my friend is amazing!

Notes for Home: Your child identified and wrote the four different kinds of sentences and added the correct punctuation mark at the end of each of them. ***Home Activity:*** Challenge your child to use the same word—such as *dog* or *school*—in each of the four kinds of sentences.

Grammar Practice Book 6.1, p. 7

Name ______________________ **Teammates**

Grammar: Subjects and Predicates

The **subject** is the word or group of words about which something is said in the sentence. All the words in the subject are called the **complete subject.** The most important word in the complete subject is called the **simple subject.** It is usually a noun or a pronoun. Some simple subjects, such as *Jackie Robinson,* are more than one word.

All citizens can enjoy one another's talents and ideas.

The **predicate** is the word or group of words that tells something about the subject. All the words in the predicate make up the **complete predicate.** The most important word in the complete predicate is the verb. It is called the **simple predicate.** Some simple predicates can have more than one word.

People from other countries may bring us new music and foods.

A sentence fragment is a group of words that looks like a sentence but does not express a complete thought. Correct sentence fragments by adding words to make a complete sentence or by joining the fragment to a related sentence.

Sentence fragment: The names of immigrants' music and foods.

Sentence: The names of immigrants' music and foods add words to American English.

Directions: Decide if the underlined group of words is the complete subject, the complete predicate, or a sentence fragment. Circle **CS, CP,** or **SF** to show your answer.

1. The five girls enjoyed the overnight trip.	CP
2. The clear blue lake was beautiful.	CS
3. Set up their tents at night.	SF
4. Millions of stars sparkled overhead.	CS
5. Each girl had brought some homemade food.	CP
6. Alanna O'Brian offered Irish bread.	CS
7. The happy girls ate Denise's Greek baklava for dessert.	CP
8. The girls in the group.	SF
9. They packed up their tents.	CS
10. Climbed into their van again.	SF

Notes for Home: Your child has learned to identify complete subjects, complete predicates, and sentence fragments. ***Home Activity:*** Play a game in which you or your child gives a complete subject and the other person adds a complete predicate to form a complete sentence.

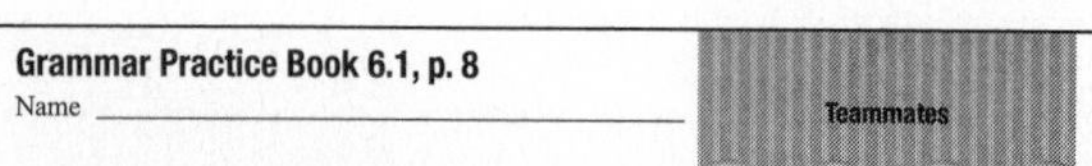

Grammar Practice Book 6.1, p. 8

Name ______________________ **Teammates**

Grammar: Subjects and Predicates

Directions: For each sentence, underline the complete subject once. Underline the complete predicate twice. Then, circle the simple subject and simple predicate.

1. Banneker Middle School had a fine glee club.
2. It was holding auditions last week.
3. Dominic wanted to join that musical group.
4. Mr. Dixon, the glee club director, gave him a voice test.
5. The boy was singing way off key.
6. Some students in the glee club were snickering.
7. Their unkind behavior displeased the director.
8. However, Dominic simply shrugged his shoulders.
9. He said something to Mr. Dixon.
10. The surprised director waved a hand toward the piano.

Directions: Correct each sentence fragment by adding words to make it a complete sentence. Write the new sentence on the line.

11. Some sheet music.
Some sheet music was on the piano.

12. Could read the music and was playing it!
Dominic could read the music and was playing it!

13. The singers in the glee club.
The singers in the glee club were surprised.

14. Asked Dominic to be the glee club pianist.
Mr. Dixon asked Dominic to be the glee club pianist.

15. At glee club practice after that.
Dominic played the piano at the glee club practice after that.

Write an Invitation

On a separate sheet of paper, write an invitation to a friend to go to a concert with you. Use complete sentences. Identify the simple subject and predicate in each.
Check that students have correctly identified the simple subjects and predicates.

Notes for Home: Your child identified simple and complete subjects and predicates in sentences and corrected sentence fragments. ***Home Activity:*** Ask your child to explain these terms, using the exercises above as examples.

Grammar Practice Book 6.1, p. 9

Name ______________________ **Teammates**

Grammar: Subjects and Predicates — RETEACHING

In each of the complete sentences, underline the complete subject once and the complete predicate twice. Circle the simple subject and the simple predicate. Draw a line through the sentence fragment.

1. Six members of the team looked for a good place to watch the animals.
2. ~~Plenty of sunlight to see the lions.~~
3. We all worked together to reach our common goal.

The **subject** is the word or group of words about which something is said in a sentence. The most important part of the subject is called the **simple subject.** It is usually a noun or a pronoun. All the words in the subject make up the **complete subject.** The **predicate** is the word or group of words that tells something about the subject. The most important part of the predicate is the verb. It is called the **simple predicate.** All the words in the predicate make up the **complete predicate.** A **sentence fragment** is an incomplete sentence.

Directions: Draw a line through each sentence fragment. In each complete sentence, underline the complete subject once. Circle the simple subject. Then underline the complete predicate twice and circle the simple predicate.

1. Some lions live in the wild.
2. Most male lions are larger than female lions.
3. Cubs are young lions.
4. ~~Live together in a group called a pride.~~
5. A group of lions may include over ten animals.
6. The diet of lions is mostly meat.
7. ~~Sleep many more hours per day than humans do.~~
8. All wild lions hunt other animals.
9. ~~Children of many countries.~~
10. Special people train lions for the circus.
11. The fascinated crowds admire the beauty and strength of lions.
12. Some wild animals live freely in Africa and Asia.
13. The powerful lion is known as "the king of beasts."
14. ~~Of a lion in a zoo is twenty to twenty-five years.~~

Notes for Home: Your child identified sentence fragments and simple subjects and predicates. ***Home Activity:*** Together, read a movie review. Then read the subject of one sentence. Have your child write a new predicate. Read a predicate and have your child write a subject.

Grammar Practice Book 6.1, p. 10

Name ______________________ Teammates

Grammar: Subjects and Predicates

Directions: Draw a line between the complete subject and the complete predicate in each sentence. Circle each simple subject and simple predicate.

1. Several cities | served as the capital before 1800.
2. The national government | moved away from Philadelphia.
3. Washington, D.C., | has been the capital since then.
4. George Washington | chose a location in 1791.
5. His choice | included land in both Maryland and Virginia.
6. Those states | gave their land to the government.
7. Congress | located the capital near a river.
8. The capital | was built on ten square miles of government land.
9. Pierre L'Enfant | was the designer of the project.
10. This famous engineer | planned the city.

Directions: Circle the simple subject in each sentence. Then complete the puzzle with those words. (Hint: Each word can fit correctly in only one place.)

11. Many tourists visit Washington, D.C., every year.
12. This city with its famous buildings has many attractions.
13. The President's home is called the White House.
14. Visitors tour its many public rooms.
15. The first President in the White House was John Adams.

			V					c
			i					i
P	r	e	s	i	d	e	n	t
			i					y
			t					
	h		o					
t	o	u	r	i	s	t	s	
	m		s					
	e							

Notes for Home: Your child identified subjects and predicates in sentences and added information to form complete sentences from sentence fragments. ***Home Activity:*** Say some sentence fragments to your child. *(Answered a question.)* Have him or her add information to form complete sentences.

Practice Book 6.1, p. 18

Name ______________________ Teammates

Phonics: Vowel Digraphs

Directions: The **long e** sound heard in **feet** can be spelled: **ea, ee, ei,** or **ie.** The **long a** sound heard in **wait** can be spelled **ai.** Read the newspaper story below. Say the underlined words to yourself. Match each underlined word with a word to the right that rhymes. Write the word on the correct line.

SPORTS

Yesterday was an amazing day in sports. Athletes from all over the world took the field. If the athletes were afraid of the competitions that were about to begin, it never showed. They received thunderous applause from the fans who had come to see them compete. Indeed, everyone who attended the games believed they were about to witness performances by the world's greatest athletes. They couldn't wait for the sports series to begin.

1. wearies **series**
2. heaved **received**
3. be **see**
4. relieved **believed**
5. pealed **field**
6. stayed **afraid**
7. bead **Indeed**

Directions: Read each sentence. Say each underlined word to yourself. Listen for the word with the **long e** sound as in **feet,** or the **long a** sound as in **wait.** Write the word with the long vowel sound on the line.

team 8. When playing a team sport, everybody is responsible for a win or a loss.

pain 9. The pain of losing is bearable if you have the thrill of winning too.

season 10. A dedicated athlete could, if she or he wished, play a sport during each season.

leagues 11. Often communities have local sports leagues for amateur athletes.

unbelievable 12. It is an unbelievable feeling when all players work together on a team.

aim 13. Often athletes aim to be number one in their sport.

feel 14. Most athletes love the challenge they feel from competing against others.

field 15. Many consider playing sports to be their field of dreams.

Notes for Home: Your child worked with words with long *e* (*see, sea, field, receive*) and long *a* (*wait*) vowel sounds. ***Home Activity:*** Read a sports story with your child. Try to find other words with these vowel sounds and spelling patterns.

Spelling Workbook 6.1, p. 5

Name ______________________ Teammates

Spelling: Words with *ei* and *ie*

Pretest Directions: Fold back the page along the dotted line. On the blanks, write the spelling words as they are dictated. When you have finished the test, unfold the page and check your words.

1. **ceiling** — 1. There is a cobweb on the **ceiling**.
2. **receipt** — 2. The cashier gave him a **receipt**.
3. **deceive** — 3. I did not mean to **deceive** you.
4. **neither** — 4. **Neither** John nor Jamila will go.
5. **leisure** — 5. You may do it at your **leisure**.
6. **protein** — 6. Many foods provide **protein**.
7. **receiver** — 7. He is the team's wide **receiver**.
8. **seize** — 8. **Seize** the opportunity.
9. **conceited** — 9. He is very **conceited**.
10. **field** — 10. The cows graze in the **field**.
11. **achieve** — 11. You can **achieve** your dreams.
12. **belief** — 12. That is a farfetched **belief**.
13. **brief** — 13. Let's keep this talk **brief**.
14. **relief** — 14. The rain was a welcome **relief**.
15. **apiece** — 15. We made four dollars **apiece**.
16. **shield** — 16. The knight picks up his **shield**.
17. **niece** — 17. I am my aunt's only **niece**.
18. **diesel** — 18. The truck runs on **diesel** fuel.
19. **grief** — 19. Accidents can cause **grief**.
20. **yield** — 20. Cars must **yield** to pedestrians.

Notes for Home: Your child took a pretest on words with the letters *ei* and *ie*. ***Home Activity:*** Help your child learn misspelled words before the final test. Your child can underline the word parts that caused the problems and concentrate on those parts.

Spelling Workbook 6.1, p. 6

Name ______________________ Teammates

Spelling: Words with *ei* and *ie*

Word List

ceiling	leisure	conceited	brief	niece
receipt	protein	field	relief	diesel
deceive	receiver	achieve	apiece	grief
neither	seize	belief	shield	yield

Directions: Choose the words from the box that rhyme with each word below. Write the words on the lines. **Order may vary.**

wield
1. **field**
2. **shield**
3. **yield**

piece
4. **apiece**
5. **niece**

either
6. **neither**

thief
7. **belief**
8. **brief**
9. **relief**
10. **grief**

believe
11. **deceive**
12. **achieve**

Directions: Choose the word from the box that best completes each sentence. Write the word on the line to the left.

conceited 13. Luis's pride in his home runs made him seem _____ to some people.

leisure 14. However, Luis worked hard, practicing even during _____ time on days off.

receipt 15. The _____ from Mighty Mike's Batting Cages showed the number of hours Luis spent practicing.

seize 16. Luis had to _____ the moment before they lost the game.

ceiling 17. It was a good thing they played in an outdoor stadium, because the ball Luis hit would have broken any _____ overhead.

diesel 18. Luis ran around the bases as if on _____ fuel.

receiver 19. Luis was the proud _____ of his teammates' congratulations.

protein 20. "It was the _____ in the hot dogs that did it!" Luis joked.

Notes for Home: Your child spelled words with *ei* and *ie*. ***Home Activity:*** Have your child name two words, one with *ei* and one with *ie,* that have the long *e* sound as in *believe.* Make sure your child can spell each word correctly.

Spelling Workbook 6.1, p. 7

Name ______________________ Teammates

Spelling: Words with *ei* and *ie*

Directions: Proofread this poem. Find five spelling mistakes. Use the proofreading marks to correct each mistake.

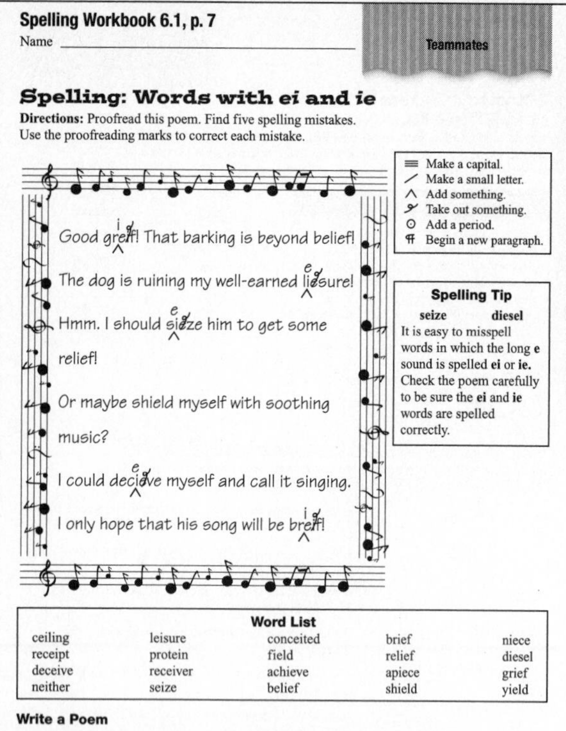

- ≡ Make a capital.
- / Make a small letter.
- ∧ Add something.
- Take out something.
- ⊙ Add a period.
- ¶ Begin a new paragraph.

Spelling Tip

seize **diesel**

It is easy to misspell words in which the long **e** sound is spelled **ei** or **ie.** Check the poem carefully to be sure the **ei** and **ie** words are spelled correctly.

Word List

ceiling	leisure	conceited	brief	niece
receipt	protein	field	relief	diesel
deceive	receiver	achieve	apiece	grief
neither	seize	belief	shield	yield

Write a Poem

On a separate sheet of paper, write a poem in which you describe how your tolerance was tested. How did you handle the situation? What did it teach you about being tolerant? Try to use at least three of your spelling words. **Answers will vary, but each poem should include at least three spelling words.**

Notes for Home: Your child spelled words with *ei* and *ie*. *Home Activity:* Take turns saying and spelling each word from the box. Continue adding and practicing other hard-to-spell *ei* and *ie* words.

Spelling Workbook 6.1, p. 8

Name ______________________ Teammates

Spelling: Words with *ei* and *ie* — REVIEW

Word List

ceiling	protein	achieve	shield
receipt	receiver	belief	niece
deceive	seize	brief	diesel
neither	conceited	relief	grief
leisure	field	apiece	yield

Directions: Choose the word from the box that has the same or nearly the same meaning as each word below. Write the word on the line.

1. sales slip **receipt**
2. gain **achieve**
3. comfort **relief**
4. lie **deceive**
5. relaxation **leisure**
6. grab **seize**
7. give way **yield**
8. thought **belief**
9. vain **conceited**
10. fuel **diesel**
11. each **apiece**
12. sorrow **grief**

Directions: Choose the word from the box that best completes each statement. Think about the relationship of the pairs of words being compared. Write the word on the line to the left. See the example below.

Woman is to *man* as *lioness* is to *lion.*

niece 13. *Uncle* is to *aunt* as *nephew* is to _____.

ceiling 14. *Earth* is to *sky* as *floor* is to _____.

shield 15. *Catcher* is to *mask* as *knight* is to _____.

receiver 16. *Pitcher* is to *catcher* as *sender* is to _____.

field 17. *Fish* is to *stream* as *sheep* is to _____.

neither 18. *All* is to *none* as *both* is to _____.

protein 19. *Spinach* is to *iron* as *meat* is to _____.

brief 20. *Tall* is to *short* as *lasting* is to _____.

Notes for Home: Your child spelled words with *ei* and *ie*. *Home Activity:* Point out that if you can spell *belief,* you can spell *believe.* Then have your child name other words you can spell if you can spell *receipt, deceive,* and *relief* correctly.

Practice Book 6.1, p. 19

Name ______________________ Teammates

Technology: Newspaper

You can find current **newspapers** and **news magazines** online using a computer and the Internet. When you connect to the Internet, you may see a welcome screen with choices such as "news" or "newsstand." If you click on this kind of button, you might get a screen like the one below. The underlined words at the bottom of the screen are links to other web pages. If you click on a link, you'll get a new web page.

Directions: Use the computer screen to answer the questions that follow.

Newsstand
Check the box you want, then click Go!
Go!
Atlantic Weekly
Business News
Chicago Gazette
Entertainment Today
The New York News
Home
Search All Publications
More Choices
Help

1. Explain how you can get to the web page for *The New York News.* **You check the box for *The New York News* and then click Go!**
2. How might you be able to get to other newspapers not listed on this screen? **You could click on the link More Choices.**
3. What should you do if you need help? **You can click on the link Help.**
4. How is an online "newsstand" similar to a real newsstand? How is it different? **Possible answer: You can find newspapers and news magazines at both an online newsstand and a real newsstand. You have to buy a newspaper or magazine to get information from a newsstand. You may have to pay a monthly fee for Internet access to an online newsstand.**

Practice Book 6.1, p. 20

Name ______________________ Teammates

After you get to an online newspaper or magazine, you may be able to search by a specific section of the newspaper, such as sports. There will probably also be a search box in which you can type key words. Use "AND" between each key word.

Directions: Use the computer screen to answer the questions that follow.

5. In which section would you search for information about a museum exhibit? **Arts**
6. In which section would you search for information about current news about Europe? **International**
7. In which section would you search for information about the people running for mayor? **Politics or Editorials**
8. In which section would you search for information about decorating your living room? **Home/Living**
9. Give two ways to find a list of upcoming baseball games. **Click on the link Sports, or type key words such as "baseball AND schedule" in the search box.**
10. If you wanted to find an article that had been printed in the newspaper a few months ago, would you search an online newspaper or go to the library to look for a print newspaper or a microfilm of a newspaper? Explain. **Possible answer: You would go to the library because the Internet only shows current newspapers.**

Notes for Home: Your child answered questions about finding infomation in a newspaper or magazine on the Internet. *Home Activity:* Look through your local newspaper with your child or search for one on the Internet. Discuss the different sections of the paper.

Practice Book 6.1, p. 21

Name ______________________ April's Mud

Cause and Effect

- An **effect** is something that happens. A **cause** is why something happens.
- To find an effect, ask yourself, "What happened?" To find a cause, ask yourself "Why did it happen?"
- An effect may have more than one cause, and a cause may have more than one effect.
- Sometimes an author does not state a cause, and you need to draw your own conclusions about why something happens.

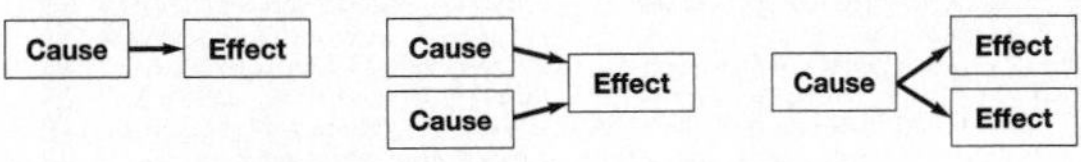

Directions: Reread "Leaving Home." Then complete the table. Provide each missing cause or effect. **Possible answers given.**

Cause (Why did it happen?)	Effect (What happened?)
1. **Pa liked to be in open spaces.**	Pa felt it was too crowded where they lived.
2. **Land was available out West.**	Pa decided to move the family out West.
They would have to leave family and friends behind.	3. **Mama was filled with sadness.**
4. **The family was leaving on their journey.**	Mama's friends gathered to say farewell.
Mama was sad to leave.	5. **Mama cried.**

Notes for Home: Your child identified causes and effects in a story. ***Home Activity:*** Ask your child to relate the events of the day. Discuss the events together, encouraging your child to identify any cause-effect relationships among the day's events.

Practice Book 6.1, p. 22

Name ______________________ April's Mud

Vocabulary

Directions: Choose the word from the box that has the same or nearly the same meaning as each word or words below. Write the word on the line.

Check the Words You Know
- __ adobe
- __ authentic
- __ concrete
- __ converted
- __ heritage
- __ normal

concrete 1. building mixture of crushed stone, sand, cement, and water

authentic 2. real

converted 3. changed

normal 4. usual

heritage 5. traditions

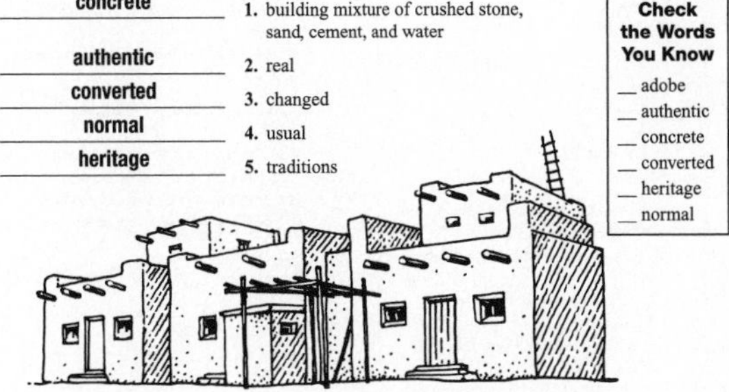

Directions: Choose the word from the box that best completes each sentence. Write the word on the line to the left.

converted 6. With hard work, the Pueblo people _____ clay, straw, and water into a place to live.

adobe 7. They made _____ bricks to build the walls.

normal 8. It was _____ for them to use these natural materials for building their homes.

heritage 9. It was part of the _____ passed down from their elders.

authentic 10. There are still people today who would much rather live in an _____ adobe home than in one built with newer materials.

Write a Description

On a separate sheet of paper, write a description of something a family member taught you to do or make. It could be a skill like woodcarving, playing an instrument, or cooking a special meal. Use as many vocabulary words as you can in your description.
Vocabulary words should be used appropriately to describe a skill passed down through one or more generations.

Notes for Home: Your child identified and used vocabulary words from "April's Mud." ***Home Activity:*** Challenge your child to make up a story about building a place to live, using the vocabulary words listed above.

Practice Book 6.1, p. 23

Name ______________________ April's Mud

Cause and Effect

- An **effect** is something that happens. A **cause** is why something happens.
- An effect may have more than one cause, and a cause may have more than one effect.
- Sometimes you need to draw your own conclusions about what happens and why.

Directions: Reread the passage of "April's Mud" that describes what happens when the Ellises try to make adobe bricks. Then answer the questions below. Look for effects that have more than one cause.

> At the end of the day they were all so sore and tired they could hardly move. But they forgot to cover the finished adobes, and when a rainstorm came up suddenly during the night, the adobes melted right back to mud again. Then, because the clay was so dense and Tom hadn't mixed in enough straw, their next batch cracked.
>
> "April's Mud" from RIO GRANDE STORIES, copyright © 1994 by Carolyn Meyer, reprinted by permission of Harcourt Brace and Company.

Possible answers given.

1. Why are the Ellises hardly able to move?
They are very sore and tired from making bricks all day.

2. Name two causes of the adobes melting back into mud.
The Ellises forgot to cover the adobes. The rainstorm caused the uncovered adobes to melt.

3. Name two causes of the adobes cracking.
The clay was too dense. Tom didn't mix enough straw with the clay.

4. What might the family do next time to save the adobe bricks from melting?
They will remember to cover the bricks in case of rain.

5. On a separate sheet of paper, list the causes and effects of Tom's decision to build an adobe house. Remember that the author may not always state causes and effects directly. **Causes: Tom always does things himself rather than hiring people. Tom has a book that says building an adobe house is easy. Tom wants to build the house like the early settlers did. Effects: They will move out of the bus. April's grandparents are shocked.**

Notes for Home: Your child read part of a story and used its details to identify causes and effects. ***Home Activity:*** Read a story or watch a TV drama or comedy with your child. Take turns challenging each other to identify what happens (effects) and why (causes).

Practice Book 6.1, p. 25

Name ______________________ April's Mud

Selection Test

Directions: Choose the best answer to each item. Mark the letter for the answer you have chosen.

Part 1: Vocabulary

Find the answer choice that means about the same as the underlined word in each sentence.

1. Luke does not lead a normal life.
   - A. healthful
   - B. special
   - (C) usual; like most other people's
   - D. exciting; filled with interesting events

2. The bed was a converted sofa.
   - (F) changed into another form
   - G. expensive
   - H. decorated with bright colors
   - J. repainted

3. Dad has an authentic 1956 race car.
   - A. one of a kind
   - B. fake; copied
   - C. in the latest style
   - (D) real; genuine

4. It was cool inside the adobe house.
   - F. made of wood
   - (G) building material made of baked clay
   - H. new
   - J. shaded

5. Mr. Alvarez made concrete stairs.
   - (A) mixture of sand, cement, and water
   - B. wood
   - C. plaster that sets in a hard coat
   - D. dried mud

6. Sam wanted to learn about his heritage.
   - F. neighborhood
   - G. friends from school
   - H. childhood
   - (J) beliefs and traditions handed down from earlier generations

Part 2: Comprehension

Use what you know about the story to answer each item.

7. The first adobes that April's family made were ruined because they—
   - A. dried out too fast.
   - (B) were washed away by rain.
   - C. baked in the sun.
   - D. did not have enough straw.

8. In this story, April learns that—
   - F. her parents are hippies.
   - G. she is going to attend a new school.
   - (H) her classmates think her father is interesting.
   - J. she has classmates who live in old buses.

9. Which event from the story happened before April saw the floor plan?
   - A. April's father taught her class to build a *horno*.
   - (B) April's family made adobe bricks.
   - C. April's father visited her class at school.
   - D. April decided to invite her class-mates to visit her home.

10. In his plans for the house, Tom seems to feel that it is most important to—
    - F. make sure April and Susan have their own rooms.
    - G. make the house bigger than Mr. Flores's house.
    - (H) make the house very much like houses of the old days.
    - J. make the house as modern as possible.

Practice Book 6.1, p. 26

Name ______________________ **April's Mud**

11. Compared to the beginning of the story, at the end April is more—
    A. embarrassed.
    B. shy.
    C. lonely.
    Ⓓ confident.

12. The finished shape of the *horno* is like the shape of—
    Ⓕ an igloo.
    G. a bus.
    H. an adobe house.
    J. a teepee.

13. Why did April feel better about the school project by the end of the story?
    A. She always enjoyed working with her father.
    B. Her classmates did not know she lived in a bus.
    C. Her friends already knew how to work with adobe mud.
    Ⓓ Her classmates enjoyed making the *horno*.

14. The author's main purpose in this selection is to—
    Ⓕ tell an entertaining story about April.
    G. explain how to make adobe bricks.
    H. persuade people not to build adobe houses.
    J. compare adobe houses with wooden houses.

15. When their adobe house is built, April will most likely—
    A. decide to build a room for herself.
    Ⓑ feel proud of her family's work.
    C. be embarrassed by the dirt floor.
    D. try to keep people from seeing it.

Name ______________________ **April's Mud**

Cause and Effect

- An **effect** is something that happens. A **cause** is why something happens.
- An effect may have more than one cause, and a cause may have more than one effect.
- Sometimes you need to draw your own conclusions about what happens and why.

Directions: Read the story below.

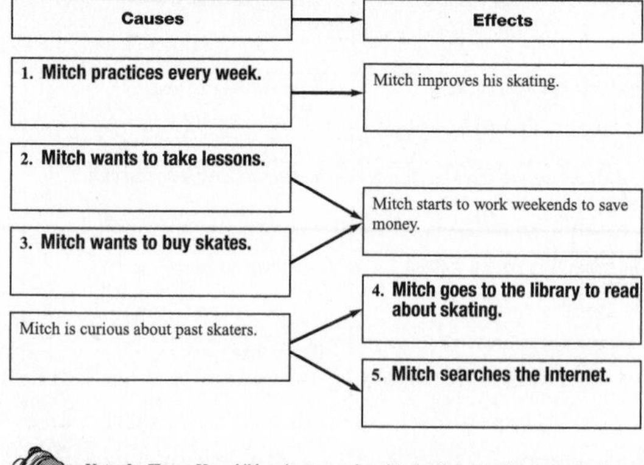

Mitch had no idea that ice skating would change his life. At first, he practiced at the rink a couple of times a week.

The more he practiced, the better he got at skating. Mitch decided he wanted to take figure skating lessons and buy new skates, so he worked on weekends to save the money.

His parents noticed Mitch's growing dedication and took him to see a championship performance. The exciting shows made Mitch curious about past skaters. He began combing the library shelves to learn something about the history of skating. He also searched the Internet for information. It didn't take long for him to get connected with other figure skaters, including some champions!

Directions: Write causes and effects in the boxes to complete the table.

Causes	Effects
1. **Mitch practices every week.**	Mitch improves his skating.
2. **Mitch wants to take lessons.**	Mitch starts to work weekends to save money.
3. **Mitch wants to buy skates.**	Mitch starts to work weekends to save money.
Mitch is curious about past skaters.	4. **Mitch goes to the library to read about skating.**
Mitch is curious about past skaters.	5. **Mitch searches the Internet.**

Notes for Home: Your child read a story and used its details to identify causes and effects. ***Home Activity:*** Talk with your child about events that happened at school or at home. For each event, discuss why it happened. Consider whether there is more than one cause for each effect.

Practice Book 6.1, p. 27

Name ______________________ **April's Mud**

Making Judgments and Plot

REVIEW

Directions: Read the story. Then read each question about the story. Choose the best answer to the question. Mark the letter for the answer you have chosen.

Undercover Artist

No one paid much attention to the new kid, Max. Who would? He didn't talk much. At lunch, Max just about disappeared. Some of his new classmates thought he was homesick. Others just thought he was boring.

One morning a cartoon of Mr. Foley's sixth grade class appeared on the chalkboard. You could easily identify people in it. The artist had caught the personalities of everyone in the class. It showed Joey gazing out the window. Kathy was waving her hand to answer a question. Keisha was shown taking lots of notes. It captured Mr. Foley perfectly with his glasses on top of his head and chalk marks all over his suit.

Almost everybody laughed and praised the drawing. Mr. Foley didn't erase it. Max said nothing. He didn't seem very interested.

By lunch time, the class was dying to discover who the mystery artist was. No one in the sixth grade had such talent.

Then Rosa remembered that Max always doodled while the rest of the class talked and joked. She went to look over Max's shoulder. Sure enough, he was deep into a funny drawing of their last baseball game.

"I guess the cat's out of the bag now," said Max.

"It sure is," said Lou, "and we're glad. We need you on the class newspaper!"

1. The rising action of this story begins when—
   A. we first read about Max.
   Ⓑ the cartoon appears on the board.
   C. the class is at lunch.
   D. the newspaper comes out.

2. The climax of the story occurs when—
   F. Lou says, "We need you on the class newspaper!"
   G. Max just about disappears at lunch.
   H. the class sees the drawing on the chalkboard.
   Ⓙ the class realizes that Max is the artist.

3. At first, the class assumed Max was
   A. very talented.
   B. an athlete.
   C. very involved in schoolwork.
   Ⓓ uninteresting or homesick.

4. By the story's end, the class
   F. thinks Rosa is very smart.
   G. wants to frame a picture by Max.
   H. wants to print the next issue of the newspaper.
   Ⓙ has new ideas about Max.

5. Max was quiet because—
   A. he didn't like his classmates.
   Ⓑ he was always busy drawing.
   C. he didn't know the answers.
   D. he was doing his homework.

Notes for Home: Your child read a story and used its details to identify important characters and events and to make judgments about them. ***Home Activity:*** Ask your child to outline the main events of a story you both know. Talk together about your judgments of the main characters.

Name ______________________ **April's Mud**

Writing Across Texts

Directions: Consider what you learned about working with adobe in "April's Mud" and "El Horno." Complete the table below by recording facts that you learned about adobe. **Possible answers given.**

Adobe
Adobe is a mixture of mud, straw, and water.
1. **Adobe can be used to make ovens and houses.**
2. **Adobe is energy-efficient.**
3. **Adobe bricks are made in wooden forms.**
4. **Adobe bricks come out more easily from forms that were wet when the adobe mixture was put in the forms than from dry forms.**
5. **Adobe mix with stabilizers can be bought at a store.**
6. **Adobe made with too little straw will crack.**
7. **If adobe is set directly on the ground, it will soak up ground water.**
8. **To make an adobe oven, you have to use bricks, rocks, and adobe mud and mud plaster.**
9. **The finished house or oven must be completely dry before you can use it.**
10. **Traditionally, it is the woman's job to plaster the finished adobe.**

Write an Encyclopedia Article

Pretend you work for a book publisher. Your job is to write an encyclopedia article about adobe. Use details from "April's Mud" and "El Horno" to help you create the article. Use a separate piece of paper for your writing. **Articles will vary. Check that students have used information from both selections to write their articles.**

Notes for Home: Your child listed details from a fiction story and a nonfiction selection to write an encyclopedia article. ***Home Activity:*** As you read stories and nonfiction selections with your child, ask your child how the reading connects to other texts he or she has read.

Grammar Practice Book 6.1, p. 11

Name ____________

April's Mud

Grammar: Subjects and Predicates

REVIEW

Directions: In each sentence below, underline the complete subject once and the complete predicate twice.

1. Some people think that what you wear says a lot about who you are.
2. Students in my school seem to believe these ideas about clothes.
3. They think the latest styles identify a "cool" person.
4. The fads are sometimes expensive and uncomfortable.
5. Many people wear them anyway.
6. I don't think clothes are all that important.
7. I believe that clothing tells only about the outside of a person.
8. Some schools have dress codes that tell what students can wear.
9. Students in other schools wear uniforms that all look alike.
10. Students in those schools may focus more on what's inside the people they meet.

Directions: Write sentences that include the following simple subjects and predicates. Remember to begin each sentence with a capital letter and end each one with a punctuation mark. **Possible answers given.**

11. style is
One of the top styles at our school is designer sneakers.

12. people spend
Some people spend all of their money on clothes.

13. rules would be
Having rules about clothes would be annoying.

14. friends dress
My friends all dress differently.

15. I would like
I would like it if clothes weren't so important.

Notes for Home: Your child identified simple and complete subjects and predicates and wrote sentences using simple subjects and predicates. ***Home Activity:*** Challenge your child to complete a sentence that is missing a subject or a predicate.

Grammar Practice Book 6.1, p. 12

Name ____________

April's Mud

Grammar: Independent and Dependent Clauses

A sentence part that has a subject and a predicate and makes sense by itself is called an **independent clause.**

Hal likes to dive, and he is also a good swimmer.
independent clause — independent clause

A **dependent clause** also has a subject and a predicate, but it does not make sense by itself. It cannot stand alone as a sentence.

Before he dives in an unfamiliar spot, he checks it for depth and for other safety factors.
dependent clause

Directions: Write **I** if the underlined words are an independent clause. Write **D** if the underlined words are a dependent clause.

I 1. Carlos bought new shoes, but he didn't really like them.
D 2. Since the shoes had high backs, they were just like other kids' shoes.
D 3. Because they were so high, the backs of the shoes hurt Carlos's feet.
I 4. The other kids would laugh at him if he didn't wear shoes like theirs.
D 5. Blisters develop when your shoes rub the wrong place.
D 6. Try on a lot of shoes before you buy a pair.
I 7. Choose carefully, and don't buy anything uncomfortable.
I 8. Think for yourself, or you'll wish you did!
D 9. If you don't think for yourself, you're acting like a sheep.
D 10. A sheep will follow another sheep, even if it walks into danger.

Notes for Home: Your child identified independent clauses, which make complete sentences by themselves, and dependent clauses, which must be part of a longer sentence. ***Home Activity:*** Have your child mark and identify clauses in a newspaper article.

Grammar Practice Book 6.1, p. 13

Name ____________

April's Mud

Grammar: Independent and Dependent Clauses

Directions: Write **I** if the underlined words are an independent clause. Write **D** if the underlined words are a dependent clause.

I 1. Lily made a wish that her casts would come off soon.
D 2. Lily would practice before autumn came.
I 3. After school started, she could play again.
I 4. Lily watched the game, but she was feeling sad.
I 5. Before she was injured, she had been a very active girl.

Directions: Add an independent clause to complete each sentence. Write the new sentence on the line. **Possible answers given.**

6. If Lily looks eager to talk,
If Lily looks eager to talk, people come over to her.

7. She could coach other players now, or
She could coach other players now, or she could play chess with a friend.

8. Lily can move around on crutches, and
Lily can move around on crutches, and she feels good about that.

9. When she calls friends on the phone,
When she calls friends on the phone, she enjoys their news.

10. Because she likes mystery films,
Because she likes mystery films, she rents them often.

Write a Description

On a separate sheet of paper, write a description of a good friend. Use at least three sentences that contain independent clauses.
Students' descriptions should include three sentences that each contain an independent clause correctly used.

Notes for Home: Your child identified independent clauses, which can be sentences by themselves, and dependent clauses, which must be part of a longer sentence. ***Home Activity:*** Write some simple sentences. Have your child add a dependent clause to each one.

Grammar Practice Book 6.1, p. 14

Name ____________

April's Mud

Grammar: Independent and Dependent Clauses

RETEACHING

Underline each independent clause once. Underline each dependent clause twice.

1. Although our house might seem strange, my family lives a happy life.
2. We grow our own food, and we read lots of books.
3. I've thought about moving back into an apartment, but I would miss being outside.

An **independent clause** is a sentence part that has a subject and a predicate. It can make sense as a complete sentence. A **dependent clause** is a sentence part that has a subject and a predicate, but it cannot make sense as a complete sentence.

Directions: Write **I** if the underlined group of words is an independent clause. Write **D** if the underlined group of words is a dependent clause.

I 1. It was my first day at the new school, and I wasn't sure how other kids would react to my name.
D 2. When I sat down at my new desk, I looked around at my classmates' faces.
I 3. Everyone looked pretty nice, but no one had spoken to me.
D 4. Because I was a little shy, I hoped someone would introduce herself or himself to me.
I 5. My teacher started taking attendance, and I listened to her.

Directions: Add an independent clause to complete each sentence. Write each new sentence on the line. **Possible answers given.**

6. When the teacher said, "Sunshine Bluebird McGuire,"
When the teacher said, "Sunshine Bluebird McGuire," I blushed and my face felt hot.

7. Although I was nervous about what my new classmates might say,
Although I was nervous about what my new classmates might say, I said, "Call me Sunny."

Notes for Home: Your child used independent clauses, which make complete sentences by themselves, and dependent clauses, which must be parts of longer sentences. ***Home Activity:*** Together, listen to a news report on the radio. Have your child identify independent and dependent clauses.

Grammar Practice Book 6.1, p. 15

Name ______________________ **April's Mud**

Grammar: Independent and Dependent Clauses

Directions: Add an independent clause to complete each sentence. Write each new sentence on the lines. **Possible answers given.**

1. As soon as I was old enough,
As soon as I was old enough, I learned how to write my name.

2. When I have my next birthday,
When I have my next birthday, I will turn twelve.

3. Although I would rather be with my friends,
Although I would rather be with my friends, I do my homework right after school.

4. Because I like to do my best in school,
Because I like to do my best in school, I study every day.

Directions: Add a dependent clause to complete each sentence. Write each new sentence on the lines. **Possible answers given.**

5. ______________________, I will probably go on to college.
After I graduate from high school, I will probably go on to college.

6. ______________________, I like to spend time thinking about my day.
When I go to bed, I like to spend time thinking about my day.

7. ______________________, we travel or spend time doing work around the house.
After school lets out for the summer, we travel or spend time doing work around the house.

8. ______________________, my sister and I have become very good at sharing.
Because we sleep in the same bedroom, my sister and I have become very good at sharing.

Notes for Home: Your child wrote independent and dependent clauses in sentences. ***Home Activity:*** Together, look at "April's Mud." Have your child identify independent and dependent clauses in sentences in the story.

Grammar: Independent and Dependent Clauses **59**

Practice Book 6.1, p. 28

Name ______________________ **April's Mud**

Phonics: Diphthongs and Digraphs

Directions: Each sentence contains an underlined word with the letter combination **au, aw, ew,** or **ou.** Say the underlined word to yourself. Listen to the sounds that the letters **au, aw, ew,** and **ou** represent. Circle the word in ( ) that has the same vowel sound as the underlined word.

1. The class knew that building the playhouse would be a lot of hard work. (knee/**new**)
2. It takes many people to build a house. (**hound**/hoot)
3. They paused to inspect the land on which the house would be built. (pace/**paw**)
4. The builders showed the plans they had drawn to their supervisor. (**author**/away)
5. The carpenter tried to figure out about how much wood she would need. (soup/**round**)
6. Then she made a list of other raw materials she needed to get. (say/**sauce**)

Directions: Read the sentences below. Each sentence contains a word with a vowel sound heard in **saw, new,** or **loud.** Underline this word and write it on the line.

authentic 7. Today, some people still live in authentic adobe homes.
ground 8. It is best to build an adobe home on level ground.
outdoors 9. Examine your space outdoors to see where a home can be built.
draw 10. Before building, most people draw a plan of their home so they have an idea of what it will look like.
outline 11. A basic plan for constructing the home is usually an outline that shows where each room will be and how big it will be.
few 12. The adobe will be made with a few simple materials.
straw 13. One of the ingredients in an adobe brick is straw.
about 14. An adobe brick measures about half a foot long.
cause 15. The completion of an adobe home is often cause for celebration.

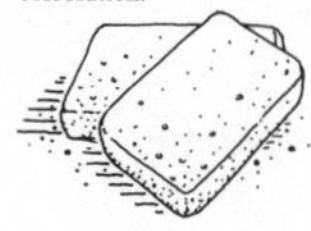

Notes for Home: Your child identified the vowel sounds of words with *au (sauce), aw (saw), ew (few),* and *ou (out).* ***Home Activity:*** Read a story with your child. Try to find other words with these vowel sounds and spelling patterns. Make a list of these words together.

60 Phonics: Diphthongs and Digraphs

Spelling Workbook 6.1, p. 9

Name ______________________ **April's Mud**

Spelling: Vowel Sounds in *rule* and *view*

Pretest Directions: Fold back the page along the dotted line. On the blanks, write the spelling words as they are dictated. When you have finished the test, unfold the page and check your words.

1. **reduce**	1. The store must **reduce** its staff.
2. **attitude**	2. She has a casual **attitude**.
3. **costume**	3. It will be a **costume** party.
4. **absolutely**	4. The night was **absolutely** dark.
5. **assume**	5. I **assume** you know each other?
6. **sewer**	6. The **sewer** flooded in the storm.
7. **New York**	7. They moved to **New York** City.
8. **renew**	8. I must **renew** my membership.
9. **review**	9. Let us **review** today's lesson.
10. **viewpoint**	10. He has a detached **viewpoint**.
11. **interview**	11. The reporters **interview** the star.
12. **preview**	12. We went to a **preview** of the film.
13. **value**	13. Which cereal is the better **value**?
14. **continue**	14. **Continue** with your game.
15. **rescue**	15. The **rescue** team arrived in time.
16. **humid**	16. It's **humid** by the seashore.
17. **universe**	17. The **universe** must be vast.
18. **uniform**	18. The soldier put on his **uniform**.
19. **reunion**	19. She went to her class **reunion**.
20. **United States**	20. The **United States** is a country.

Notes for Home: Your child took a pretest on words with vowel sounds such as those in *rule* and *view*. ***Home Activity:*** Help your child learn misspelled words before the final test. Dictate the word and have your child spell the word aloud for you or write it on paper.

Spelling: Vowel Sounds in *rule* and *view* **61**

Spelling Workbook 6.1, p. 10

Name ______________________ **April's Mud**

Spelling: Vowel Sounds in *rule* and *view*

Word List

reduce	assume	review	value	United States
attitude	sewer	viewpoint	continue	universe
costume	New York	interview	rescue	uniform
absolutely	renew	preview	humid	reunion

Directions: Choose the words from the box that have the same vowel sound as **rule.** Write each word in the correct column. **Order may vary.**

Spelled u-consonant-e	Spelled ew
1. **reduce**	6. **sewer**
2. **attitude**	7. **New York**
3. **costume**	8. **renew**
4. **absolutely**	
5. **assume**	

Directions: Choose the words from the box that have the same vowel sound as **view** spelled **iew.** Write the words on the lines. **Order may vary.**

9. **review** 11. **interview**
10. **viewpoint** 12. **preview**

Directions: Find eight words from the box in the puzzle. They may be printed across or down. Circle the words in the puzzle. Then write them on the lines. Hint: Each word has the same vowel sound as **view** spelled **ue** or **u.** **Order may vary.**

13. **value**
14. **continue**
15. **rescue**
16. **humid**
17. **United States**
18. **universe**
19. **uniform**
20. **reunion**

U	N	I	T	E	D	S	T	A	T	E	S
N	Y	E	X	T	A	R	W	U	R	R	O
I	A	W	H	U	M	I	D	N	E	E	L
V	A	L	U	E	O	R	E	S	C	U	E
E	C	O	N	T	I	N	U	E	U	N	P
R	C	A	S	E	B	M	E	O	C	I	Z
S	H	P	M	D	D	W	S	R	E	O	I
E	V	U	N	I	F	O	R	M	T	N	L

Notes for Home: Your child spelled words with the vowel sounds in *rule* (spelled *u-consonant-e* and *ew*) and *view* (spelled *iew, ue,* and *u*). ***Home Activity:*** Ask your child to name some words that rhyme with *view.* Discuss how each rhyming word is spelled.

62 Spelling: Vowel Sounds in *rule* and *view*

Spelling Workbook 6.1, p. 11

Name ______________________ April's Mud

Spelling: Vowel Sounds in *rule* and *view*

Directions: Proofread this advertisement. Find five spelling mistakes. Use the proofreading marks to correct each mistake.

Proofreading marks
≡ Make a capital.
/ Make a small letter.
∧ Add something.
Take out something.
⊙ Add a period.
¶ Begin a new paragraph.

Build Your Own Home!

Why live in a unifrom house like everyone else's?

Redeuce the expense of hiring builders!

Build it yourself!

A place you have built yourself will have far greater valew than a place made for other people!

It's fun! It's easy! Read all about it!

Prevue, interview, and consultation absoluetly free!

Spelling Tip

New York **United States**

Remember to capitalize both words in place names such as **New York** and **United States.**

Word List

reduce	interview
attitude	preview
costume	value
absolutely	continue
assume	rescue
sewer	humid
New York	United States
renew	universe
review	uniform
viewpoint	reunion

Write an Advertisement

On a separate sheet of paper, write an advertisement to sell a product of your choice. Try to use at least three of your spelling words. **Answers will vary, but each advertisement should include at least three spelling words.**

Notes for Home: Your child spelled words with the vowel sounds in *rule* (spelled *u-consonant-e* and *ew*) and *view* (spelled *iew, ue,* and *u*). ***Home Activity:*** Write each spelling word, deliberately misspelling some words. Have your child check and correct the words.

Spelling Workbook 6.1, p. 12

Name ______________________ April's Mud

Spelling: Vowel Sounds in *rule* and *view*

REVIEW

Word List

reduce	sewer	interview	humid
attitude	New York	preview	United States
costume	renew	value	universe
absolutely	review	continue	uniform
assume	viewpoint	rescue	reunion

Directions: Choose the word from the box that best completes each sentence. Write the word on the line to the left.

United States 1. "The _____ is as much fun as Italy!" exclaimed Tony.

uniform 2. Here he did not have to wear a _____ to school.

viewpoint 3. From Tony's _____, his temporary new home looked good.

New York 4. Tony visited the famous city of _____ in the fall.

costume 5. He wore a fancy _____ to march in the San Genaro parade.

universe 6. It was so crowded that it seemed as if everyone in the _____ must be there.

humid 7. The _____ weather made Tony so warm he almost fainted.

rescue 8. Another marcher had to _____ Tony from being trampled.

reduce 9. Tony decided to _____ his layers of clothing to stay cooler.

review 10. Later, he sent his little sister a newspaper _____ of the parade.

Directions: Choose the word from the box that best matches each definition. Write the word on the line.

11. positively; certainly **absolutely**
12. talk with; question **interview**
13. a gathering after separation **reunion**
14. a pipe for carrying waste **sewer**
15. manner **attitude**
16. make like new; restore **renew**
17. view or show in advance **preview**
18. take for granted **assume**
19. keep on; not stop **continue**
20. worth or importance **value**

Notes for Home: Your child spelled words with the vowel sounds in *rule* (spelled *u-consonant-e* and *ew*) and *view* (spelled *iew, ue,* and *u*). ***Home Activity:*** Help your child use the spelling words in sentences.

Practice Book 6.1, p. 29

Name ______________________ April's Mud

Research Process

The **research process** involves locating information and organizing findings from that information. First, choose a research topic. Then list questions about the topic that you want to answer through your research. Next, locate and collect information from different sources. Take careful notes as you read the information you've collected. Use your notes to interpret, summarize, and organize information for your audience, revising your questions and answers as you proceed in the research process.

Directions: Use the description of the research process above and the resources pictured below to answer the questions that follow.

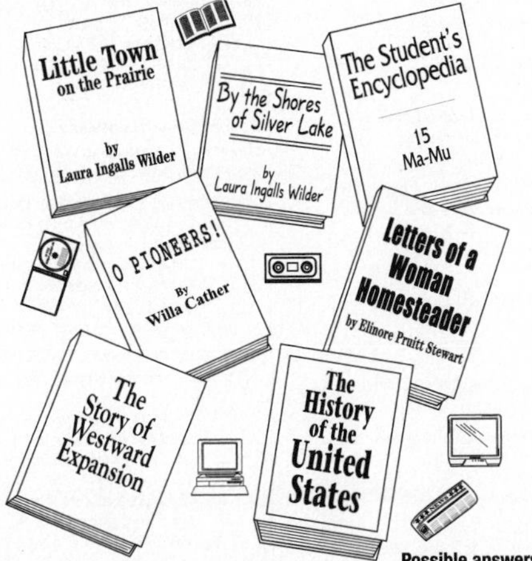

Possible answers given.

1. Why is it important to choose your topic as the first step in the research process?
It helps you decide what kinds of information you will need.

2. How can forming questions about your topic help you begin your research?
Forming questions can help guide your research and help you evaluate and interpret the information you collect.

Practice Book 6.1, p. 30

Name ______________________ April's Mud

3. Name several print and electronic media resources you might use to do research for a report.
Print: books, newspapers, magazines, encyclopedias, atlases, photographs; Electronic media: computers (CD-ROMs, Internet, computer software), TV, videotapes, audiotapes, films, film strips, and microfilm.

4. You can use outlines, time lines, tables, diagrams, and graphs to organize information. Choose one of these and explain why it is helpful for organizing information.
Answers will vary. Students' explanations should demonstrate an understanding of the value of the type of graphic organizer chosen.

5. Why is it important to think about who your audience will be as you decide how to present your research?
Your audience affects how you present your information. For example, you would present information differently to a younger audience.

6. Which of the resources shown would give a detailed history of the movement of settlers to the West?
The Story of Westward Expansion

7. When they were children, both Laura Ingalls Wilder and Willa Cather moved west with their families and later wrote about the struggles of pioneers. What value might Laura Ingalls Wilder's and Willa Cather's novels have for a report about pioneers?
These novels may give realistic descriptions and details about what life was like for pioneers.

8. Why might old letters by a female pioneer be a useful resource for a report on pioneers?
People can be an important resource. Letters can give personal details about what pioneer life was like for one woman.

9. Use the book titles shown to help you write a research question about pioneers.
Why did people choose to move West?

10. In "April's Mud," April and her family move to the Southwest and learn many new things. Choose a topic related to life in the Southwest and write a research question about it.
Topic: Adobe homes; Question: How are adobe homes today like or unlike adobe homes of long ago?

Notes for Home: Your child learned about the research process. ***Home Activity:*** Together with your child, brainstorm a list of research topics. Discuss questions you could ask about each topic and possible sources of information for each topic.

Practice Book 6.1, p. 31

Name ______________________ **Hot Dogs and Bamboo Shoots**

Generalizing

- **A generalization** is a broad statement about what several people or things have in common.
- Clue words such as *most, many, all, sometimes, generally, always,* and *never* can help you identify generalizations in what you read

Directions: Reread "The Key." Then complete the table. Tell whether each of the statements is a generalization. Explain your answers.

Statement	Generalization?	How do you know?
Lek was a collector.	1. Yes (No)	2. **It doesn't say what people have in common.**
Many children in rural Thailand are collectors.	3. (Yes) No	4. **It says what several people have in common.**
Collecting made sense to Nong.	5. Yes (No)	6. **It doesn't say what people have in common.**
Collectors sometimes collect items of great value.	7. (Yes) No	8. **It says what several people have in common.**
Nong kept hunting for things to collect.	9. Yes (No)	10. **It doesn't say what people have in common.**

Notes for Home: Your child identified generalizations—statements that tell what several people or things have in common *Home Activity:* Ask your child to look around a room in your house and make a generalization about it, such as *All the walls are painted white.*

Practice Book 6.1, p. 32

Name ______________________ **Hot Dogs and Bamboo Shoots**

Vocabulary

Directions: Draw a line to connect each word on the left with its definition on the right.

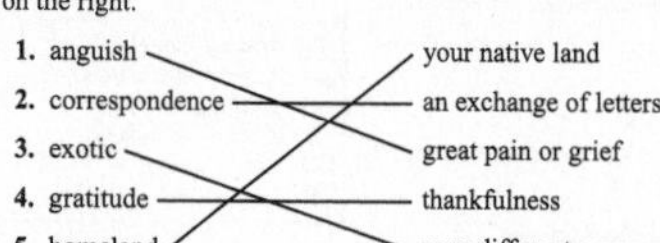

1. anguish — your native land
2. correspondence — an exchange of letters
3. exotic — great pain or grief
4. gratitude — thankfulness
5. homeland — very different or unusual

Check the Words You Know

- __ anguish
- __ correspondence
- __ exotic
- __ foreigner
- __ gratitude
- __ homeland
- __ traditional
- __ uprooted

Directions: Choose the word from the box that best completes each sentence. Write the word on the matching numbered line to the right.

The twins' first day at school was difficult. The other children thought the twins' clothes looked **6.** _____, although these were **7.** _____ clothes worn by many young girls in their culture. They felt **8.** _____ from their friends, and they missed their **9.** _____very much. Each of the girls felt strange knowing that others saw her as a **10.** _____ living in a new country and culture.

6. **exotic**
7. **traditional**
8. **uprooted**
9. **homeland**
10. **foreigner**

Write an E-mail Message

On a separate sheet of paper, write an e-mail message to a friend. Imagine you are traveling in some distant or exotic place. How does it feel to be a stranger in a new land? What new things might you see and do? Use as many vocabulary words as you can to describe what you see or how you feel.
Messages should be in a friendly, casual style. Look for appropriate use of vocabulary words.

Notes for Home: Your child identified and used vocabulary words from "Hot Dogs and Bamboo Shoots." *Home Activity:* Challenge your child to name objects that are ordinary to him or her but that might be exotic to someone from another place or culture.

Practice Book 6.1, p. 33

Name ______________________ **Hot Dogs and Bamboo Shoots**

Generalizing

- A broad statement about what several people or things have in common is a **generalization.**
- Clue words such as *most, many, all, sometimes, generally, always,* and *never* can help you identify generalizations in what you read.
- Valid generalizations are supported by facts and agree with what you already know. Faulty generalizations are not.

Directions: Reread the part of "Hot Dogs and Bamboo Shoots" that tells about Obah San. Then answer the questions below. Look for generalizations that show actions that happen many times the same way.

> We all went to the Japanese Union Church on Sundays, and Obah San was always the first one ready. Dressed in her best clothes, wearing her hat and gloves, she would sit on the sofa, patiently waiting for the rest of us to get ready.
>
> She did the same thing if we invited her to go with us to see a movie. Obah San loved going out, and was always ready to have a good time with her grandchildren.
>
> Because she'd never had much in life, she was always frugal and careful. She never let any food go to waste, and any fruit that was beginning to spoil had to be eaten before we could touch the good fruit.
>
>

1. Is "We all went to the Japanese Union Church on Sundays" a generalization?
Yes; It tells what several people have in common—going to church on Sundays.

2. What generalization can you make about Obah San and her grandchildren?
She and her grandchildren have good times together.

3. How is this generalization supported?
The text says she is always ready to have a good time with them.

4. List all the clue words you can find in the passage that signal generalizations.
all, always, never

5. What generalization can you make about the importance of family among the Uchidas? Explain your thinking on a separate sheet of paper. **Generalization: Family is very important to the Uchidas. Evidence: Relatives spend a lot of time together. They all attend movies and church together. Uchidas travel all the way to Japan to visit mother's family. Japanese relatives give a warm welcome to American relatives.**

Notes for Home: Your child used story details to recognize and form generalizations. *Home Activity:* Challenge your child to state a generalization that shows what several people have in common. Encourage him or her to use clue words such as *always* or *most.*

Practice Book 6.1, p. 35

Name ______________________ **Hot Dogs and Bamboo Shoots**

Selection Test

Directions: Choose the best answer to each item. Mark the letter for the answer you have chosen.

Part 1: Vocabulary

Find the answer choice that means about the same as the underlined word in each sentence.

1. Lester felt like a person who was uprooted.
   - A. old and slow
   - (B.) removed from a place
   - C. smart and clever
   - D. hard-working
2. Her neighbors thought of Liz as a foreigner.
   - F. baby
   - G. one who leads a group
   - (H.) person from another country
   - J. troublemaker
3. I would like to try those exotic foods.
   - (A.) strange and unusual
   - B. hot and spicy
   - C. expensive
   - D. tasty
4. Dad and Granddad keep up their correspondence.
   - F. bitter disagreement
   - G. garden or small farm
   - H. contest against each other
   - (J.) exchange of letters
5. Mom expressed her gratitude.
   - (A.) thankfulness
   - B. hopes
   - C. plans
   - D. beliefs
6. Alana wore a traditional dress.
   - F. reddish blue
   - G. long and white with lace
   - H. very expensive; costly
   - (J.) reflecting old beliefs or customs
7. Mr. Pearson planned a visit to his homeland.
   - A. any gift of property
   - B. place where people share a language
   - C. subdivision
   - (D.) original or native land
8. The old man cried in anguish.
   - F. surprise
   - (G.) great pain or grief
   - H. joy or gladness
   - J. excitement

Part 2: Comprehension

Use what you know about the selection to answer each item.

9. At the time of this selection, most young Japanese Americans did not know their grandparents because—
   - A. their families were separated by war.
   - B. their grandparents had died.
   - (C.) their grandparents lived in Japan.
   - D. they could not speak Japanese.
10. The first time Yoshiko Uchida understood that her mother was also a daughter was when—
    - (F.) her mother saw Grandmother Umegaki on the pier in Japan.
    - G. her family's ship left San Francisco.
    - H. she saw her uncle and cousins in Union Station.
    - J. her family gathered for the New Year's feast.

Practice Book 6.1, p. 36

Name ______________________ **Hot Dogs and Bamboo Shoots**

11. Why was Yoshiko Uchida in such awe of her cousins?
- A. She had never been to Los Angeles before.
- Ⓑ They were more sophisticated and worldly.
- C. She had never been to the movies before.
- D. They traveled more than she did.

12. Which generalization based on this selection is most likely valid?
- F. Children cannot have fun during a Japanese New Year's feast.
- G. Everyone likes all the dishes served at a Japanese New Year's feast.
- H. The Japanese New Year's feast is a very serious and quiet time.
- Ⓙ It usually takes several days to prepare a Japanese New Year's feast.

13. From the information in the selection, you can tell that most people in Japan—
- Ⓐ greet one another by bowing.
- B. forget about family who have moved away.
- C. have American names.
- D. cannot read Japanese.

14. Why did the author feel like an outsider when she was in Japan?
- F. She blended in with the other people in Japan.
- G. She did not like to eat the Japanese foods.
- Ⓗ She looked Japanese but did not know the language and culture.
- J. She did not like wearing Japanese clothes.

15. Yoshiko Uchida concludes that she is both American and Japanese because she—
- A. reads and writes both Japanese and English.
- B. wears Japanese clothes in America.
- C. speaks English in Japan.
- Ⓓ grew up in America, but with many Japanese customs.

Name ______________________ **Hot Dogs and Bamboo Shoots**

Generalizing

- A broad statement about what several people or things have in common is a **generalization.**
- Clue words such as *most, many, all, sometimes, generally, always,* and *never* can help you identify generalizations in what you read.
- Valid generalizations are supported by facts and agree with what you already know. Faulty generalizations are not.

Directions: Read the story below.

"The samovar is ready. Have some tea, Sasha," called Baba. My great-grandparents didn't speak Russian often, but *samovar,* the urn for tea, was a familiar word. When they were growing up in Russia, just about every home had a samovar. They brought the urn with them from their homeland. Like many other people, my great-grandparents liked to keep ties to their past.

They hardly ever made their tea in the samovar anymore. In America, they found teabags quicker and easier to use. But even then they drank their tea as they always had. Baba put a sugar cube between her teeth, sweetening her drink as she sipped. Dada stirred jam into his tea glass. "That's the way people in my village always drank their tea," he explained.

Baba said, "We like to keep some of the old ways in our life here."

Directions: Complete the table by deciding whether the generalization is valid or faulty. Use evidence from the passage to explain why it is valid or not.

Generalization	Valid or Faulty?	Evidence from Text
In the past, samovars were found in most Russian homes.	1. **Valid**	2. **In Russia, just about every home had a samovar.**
Sasha's great-grandparents never brew tea anymore.	3. **Faulty**	4. **It says they *hardly ever* brew tea.**
Great-grandparents never try new things.	5. **Faulty**	6. **Sasha's great-grandparents began using teabags.**
Some Russians sweeten their tea with jam.	7. **Valid**	8. **Dada says that in his village people sweeten their tea with jam.**
Some people enjoy holding onto things from the past.	9. **Valid**	10. **Both Baba and Dada continue to observe several Russian traditions.**

Notes for Home: Your child used details from a story to decide if certain generalizations were valid. ***Home Activity:*** Read a news article with your child. Look for generalizations that use clue words such as *sometimes, always, many, most,* or *never.*

Practice Book 6.1, p. 37

Name ______________________ **Hot Dogs and Bamboo Shoots**

Sequence

REVIEW

Directions: Read the story. Then read each question about the story. Choose the best answer to each question. Mark the letter for the answer you have chosen.

A Day-Long Celebration

Connie and Joe arrived at the annual Fourth of July parade as the flag bearer and the drummers came into view. Then came the high school marching band. The musicians looked handsome in their navy uniforms and tall plumed hats.

The parade's highlight was next. The mayor, dressed in colonial costume, read the Declaration of Independence aloud. Afterwards, a boy rang a model of the Liberty Bell. People waved small American flags. Everyone cheered and clapped when a large, colorful float came into view.

After the parade, Connie and Joe went to a picnic. While everyone was eating, the Glee Club sang.

Later that evening, the mayor made a speech about America, giving thanks for the freedoms Americans enjoy. After dark, the day's celebration ended with a thrilling fireworks display. Connie and Joe went home, tired but excited and happy.

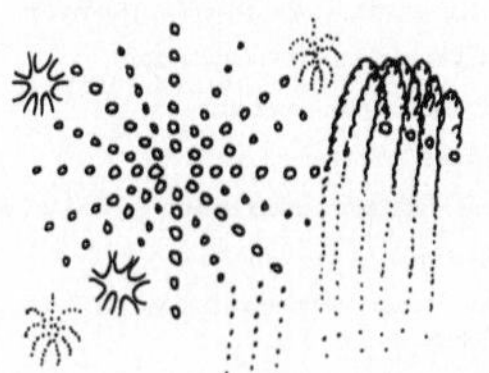

1. Directly after the flag bearer and drummers marched by, Connie and Joe saw—
- **A.** the Liberty Bell float.
- **B.** the mayor.
- **C.** the Glee Club.
- Ⓓ the marching band.

2. When a large, colorful float passed by—
- Ⓕ people cheered.
- **G.** the Glee Club sang.
- **H.** fireworks went off.
- **J.** the mayor gave a speech.

3. While people picnicked, they—
- **A.** heard speeches.
- **B.** watched fireworks.
- Ⓒ heard the Glee Club.
- **D.** listened to the mayor.

4. The mayor gave a speech—
- **F.** to start the day's celebration.
- **G.** just before the band came by.
- Ⓗ before the fireworks.
- **J.** while striking the model Liberty Bell.

5. The final event of the day's celebration was—
- **A.** a picnic.
- **B.** the mayor's speech.
- Ⓒ a fireworks display.
- **D.** the Glee Club performance.

Notes for Home: Your child recalled the order of events in a short story. ***Home Activity:*** Talk with your child about the events of a family tradition or preparations for the start of the school year. Challenge your child to list the events in order.

Name ______________________ **Hot Dogs and Bamboo Shoots**

Writing Across Texts

Directions: Reread "Society and Culture" to find the definitions of the characteristics of a culture that are listed in the first column of the table below. Find examples of these characteristics of culture in "Hot Dogs and Bamboo Shoots" to explain how Yoshiko Uchida was influenced by both American and Japanese cultures. The first one is done for you. **Possible answers given.**

	American Culture	Japanese Culture
Work and Rewards	Father worked for the railroad; he got passes for his family to travel.	1. **Uncle Yukio was a silversmith. Minoru was a college professor. Seizo was a priest.**
Organized Groups	2. **Yoshiko Uchida lived with her parents and sister and visited her cousins and grandmother in Los Angeles.**	3. **Yoshiko Uchida visited her uncles and grandmother in Japan.**
Norms and Customs	4. **Yoshiko Uchida went with American cousins to movies and learned to dance.**	5. **Yoshiko Uchida went to communal baths, slept on the floor on tatami mats, and bowed when greeting others in Japan.**

Write a Paragraph

Reread "Society and Culture" to find the characteristics of a culture. Apply these definitions to "Hot Dogs and Bamboo Shoots." On a separate sheet of paper, write a paragraph or two that explains how Yoshiko Uchida was part of two different cultures. Use the information you recorded in the table above.

Ideas will vary. Students should note that the author felt partly, but never completely, at home in either culture, and that she enjoyed family and traditions from both cultures.

Notes for Home: Your child used information from different sources to write an explanatory paragraph. ***Home Activity:*** As you read stories and articles with your child, talk about how different characteristics of a culture are reflected in the writing.

Grammar Practice Book 6.1, p. 16

Name ____________________ Hot Dogs and Bamboo Shoots

Grammar: Independent and Dependent Clauses

REVIEW

Directions: Read each sentence. Underline all the independent clauses once. Underline all the dependent clauses twice.

1. If you like learning about different cultures, museums are a great place to start.
2. Some museums show the culture and history of one group of people, but others show many different groups.
3. When you visit California, stop by the California African American Museum in Los Angeles.
4. You can learn about African American culture at this museum, because it has many exhibits by and about African Americans.
5. After you visit there, you could also go to the Museum of African American History in Detroit, Michigan.
6. This museum includes a large model of a slave ship, but it also has modern displays.

Directions: Add an independent clause to each dependent clause below. **Possible answers given.**

7. If you are interested in cultural history, **you might enjoy the Museum of Natural History.**
8. Whenever I visit there, **I always find something new and interesting to see.**
9. Because I'm interested in American Indian history, **I look first for the American Indian exhibit.**
10. As I learn more about different cultures, **I see that differences are what make people so interesting.**

Notes for Home: Your child identified dependent and independent clauses and wrote independent clauses. ***Home Activity:*** Ask your child to write sentences about a favorite tradition, and then identify the dependent and independent clauses in the sentences.

Grammar Practice Book 6.1, p. 17

Name ____________________ Hot Dogs and Bamboo Shoots

Grammar: Compound and Complex Sentences

Compound sentences and **complex sentences** help make writing more interesting.

A **compound sentence** contains two independent clauses joined with a comma and a word such as *or, and,* or *but.*

A woman wove rugs, and her husband made drums.
(independent clause) (independent clause)

A **complex sentence** contains one independent clause and one or more dependent clauses. The independent and dependent clauses are joined with words such as *if, because,* or *when.*

Because she dyes her own yarn, she weaves brightly colored rugs.
(dependent clause) (independent clause)

Directions: Write whether each sentence is **compound** or **complex.**

compound 1. Kit likes to cook, and she likes to travel.
complex 2. Wherever she goes, she collects recipes.
compound 3. Her collection is huge, but the recipes are all different.
complex 4. After Kit comes home, her friends love to visit.
complex 5. Since Kit loves company, she cooks her own favorite foods, which are very tasty.
compound 6. Kit buys spices from around the world, and she brings them home.
compound 7. She likes spicy food, but her friends don't care for it.
complex 8. If she cooks for herself, Kit uses many spices.
complex 9. Whenever she travels, she eats spicy food.
complex 10. While she's here at home, Kit will write a cookbook.

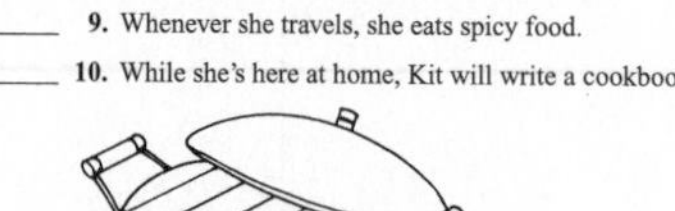

Notes for Home: Your child identified compound and complex sentences. ***Home Activity:*** Give your child a simple sentence, and challenge him or her to change it into a compound sentence or a complex sentence.

Grammar Practice Book 6.1, p. 18

Name ____________________ Hot Dogs and Bamboo Shoots

Grammar: Compound and Complex Sentences

Directions: Write whether each sentence is **compound** or **complex.**

compound 1. Anthropologists are scientists, and human beings are their field of study.
complex 2. Since each culture is different, a scientist may explore just one.
compound 3. Some cultures are known for their music, but no culture is known for music alone.
complex 4. When I see a piece of art, I think about who made it.
complex 5. You can learn about a culture, if you look at its food, music, and art.

Directions: Choose the group of words in ( ) that will complete each sentence. Write the complete sentence on the line, adding a comma if necessary.

6. Try Vietnamese beef stew ____.
(and enjoy its spicy flavor/although I don't have a recipe)
Try Vietnamese beef stew, and enjoy its spicy flavor.

7. If a feast is held, ____.
(and at certain other times/a culture may have a special dance)
If a feast is held, a culture may have a special dance.

8. Cultures new to you are interesting, ____.
(because someone invites you/and learning about them is fun)
Cultures new to you are interesting, and learning about them is fun.

9. When we study another culture, ____.
(and its people study us, in turn/we also learn about ourselves)
When we study another culture, we also learn about ourselves.

10. When you try another culture's specialties, ____.
(some dishes may seem different/but never do this in a hurry)
When you try another culture's specialties, some dishes may seem different.

Write an E-mail Message

Write an e-mail message to tell a friend about a culture you find interesting. Include both compound and complex sentences.
Messages should include correctly written compound and complex sentences.

Notes for Home: Your child identified compound sentences and complex sentences. ***Home Activity:*** Ask your child to point out compound and complex sentences in newspaper or magazine articles.

Grammar Practice Book 6.1, p. 19

Name ____________________ Hot Dogs and Bamboo Shoots

Grammar: Compound and Complex Sentences

RETEACHING

Underline each independent clause.

1. Jonathan wants to travel to Milan, but he is too busy this month.

Underline the dependent clause once and the independent clause twice.

2. Although I felt nervous, I took the test anyway.

A **compound sentence** contains two independent clauses joined with a comma and a word such as *and, or,* or *but.* A **complex sentence** contains one dependent clause and one independent clause joined by a word such as *if, because,* or *although.*

Directions: Write whether each sentence is **compound** or **complex.**

compound 1. The sign goes here, and the banner goes there.
complex 2. While you direct traffic, John can do his job.
compound 3. Sue is in charge of books, but she's not here yet.
complex 4. If you cover for her, I'll give you a hand.
compound 5. This is a big event, and nothing must go wrong.
compound 6. I'm weary too, but we don't have time to rest.
compound 7. Did Mrs. Ellis donate the hat, or was it Mr. West?
complex 8. Because we are doing so well, we may be able to close early.
compound 9. The shoes are selling fast, but no one's buying ties.
compound 10. This suit cost ten dollars, but it's worth more.
compound 11. That red hat looks good, but that one looks better.
complex 12. You should go home if you aren't going to help.
compound 13. May I help you, or are you just browsing?
complex 14. Although we haven't marked the price on that one, we'll sell it to you for five dollars.
compound 15. We have done very well, but let's stay open for another half an hour.

Notes for Home: Your child identified compound and complex sentences. ***Home Activity:*** Have your child use this page to explain to you the differences between compound and complex sentences.

Grammar Practice Book 6.1, p. 20

Name ______

Hot Dogs and Bamboo Shoots

Grammar: Compound and Complex Sentences

Directions: Write whether each sentence is **compound** or **complex.**

compound 1. Math is my favorite subject, but my grades are often low.

complex 2. My teacher helps and encourages me when I come to her with questions.

complex 3. If I spend a little extra time on my math homework each night, I will understand more of the discussion in class the next day.

compound 4. Memorizing is hard for me, and I forget important rules.

compound 5. I must study hard, or my grades will not improve.

complex 6. Because I am a hard worker, I know I will get better in time.

Directions: Add a word such as *and, or,* or *but* and more information to complete each compound sentence.

7. It is important to do your work carefully **, and you should do it well.**

8. I like to write stories **, but I don't show them to anyone.**

9. My teacher is very patient **, and she listens to what we have to say.**

Directions: Add a dependent clause to complete each complex sentence. Write the new sentence on the lines.

10. ______, we can skip doing homework one night.
If we do well on the test, we can skip doing homework one night.

11. ______, my friends went to the movie without me.
Because I was sick, my friends went to the movie without me.

12. ______, I will be very happy.
When I am better, I will be very happy.

Notes for Home: Your child identified and completed compound and complex sentences. ***Home Activity:*** Have your child read a newspaper or magazine article and mark two compound sentences and two complex sentences. Then have him or her make up another one of each.

Practice Book 6.1, p. 38

Name ______

Hot Dogs and Bamboo Shoots

Phonics: *r*-Controlled Vowels

Directions: The letters **or** can have two different sounds. The **or** in **work** sounds different than the **or** in **for.** Read the words in the box. Say the words to yourself. Listen to the different sounds that the letters **or** represent. Sort the words by their sounds. Write each word in the correct column.

according	worry	boring	worse	world
porthole	sorts	worthy	morning	worship

Order may vary.

work		for	
1.	worry	6.	according
2.	worthy	7.	porthole
3.	worse	8.	sorts
4.	world	9.	boring
5.	worship	10.	morning

Directions: Read each sentence. Read the words in ( ). Both words fit the sentence, but only one has the vowel sound you hear in **work.** Circle the word that has the vowel sound you hear in **work.** Write the word on the matching numbered line. Underline the letters that represent the **r-controlled vowel** sound.

Some people feel an **11.** (urgent/immediate) need to travel. Their curiosity about the world is **12.** (bubbling/bursting) within them. They are so excited, they never know what to look at **13.** (first/fully). A ruined castle? An old fortress? A famous **14.** (cathedral/church)? Someone should tell them there is no need to be in such **15.** (distress/turmoil). These buildings aren't going anywhere!

11. urgent
12. bursting
13. first
14. church
15. turmoil

Notes for Home: Your child sorted and wrote words with *r*-controlled vowels, such as *for, world, first,* and *church.* ***Home Activity:*** Read a story with your child. As you find words spelled with *or, ir,* and *ur,* cover the words. Have your child tell you the correct spelling.

Spelling Workbook 6.1, p. 13

Name ______

Hot Dogs and Bamboo Shoots

Spelling: Vowel Sounds with *r*

Pretest Directions: Fold back the page along the dotted line. On the blanks, write the spelling words as they are dictated. When you have finished the test, unfold the page and check your words.

1. report	1. She finished the book **report.**
2. order	2. The soldiers obeyed his **order.**
3. sword	3. I need a **sword** for my costume.
4. forty	4. They do **forty** laps in the pool.
5. enormous	5. This is an **enormous** sandwich.
6. explore	6. Let's **explore** the forest.
7. ignore	7. It was hard to **ignore** the sound.
8. therefore	8. I get hungry; **therefore** I eat.
9. expert	9. She is an **expert** skier.
10. service	10. The **service** station was closed.
11. determine	11. Skill will **determine** the winner.
12. permanent	12. This is a **permanent** marker.
13. research	13. This project requires **research.**
14. earning	14. I am **earning** enough money.
15. worth	15. That book is **worth** reading.
16. worst	16. The **worst** part is over.
17. thorough	17. Your research is very **thorough.**
18. attorney	18. Shania's mother is an **attorney.**
19. disturb	19. Do not **disturb** the residents.
20. purchase	20. Are you ready to **purchase** it?

Notes for Home: Your child took a pretest on words that have vowel sounds with the letter *r.* ***Home Activity:*** Help your child learn misspelled words before the final test. Have your child divide misspelled words into parts (such as syllables) and concentrate on each part.

Spelling Workbook 6.1, p. 14

Name ______

Hot Dogs and Bamboo Shoots

Spelling: Vowel Sounds with *r*

Word List

report	enormous	expert	research	thorough
order	explore	service	earning	attorney
sword	ignore	determine	worth	disturb
forty	therefore	permanent	worst	purchase

Directions: Choose the words from the box that have the same vowel sound as **fort.** Write each word in the correct column. **Order may vary.**

Spelled or		Spelled ore	
1.	report	6.	explore
2.	order	7.	ignore
3.	sword	8.	therefore
4.	forty		
5.	enormous		

Directions: Choose the words from the box that have the same vowel sound as **work.** Write each word in the correct column. **Order may vary.**

Spelled or		Spelled ur	
9.	worth	13.	disturb
10.	worst	14.	purchase
11.	thorough		
12.	attorney		

Directions: Choose the word from the box that best completes each sentence. Write the word on the line to the left.

expert 15. My friend Yanni is an _____ who knows everything about gardens.

research 16. His first book took years of study and _____.

permanent 17. Some garden designs are _____; others change every year.

service 18. Books provide an important _____ for home gardeners.

earning 19. Yanni has the chance of _____ a great prize if his book is selected by the judges.

determine 20. To _____ who will win, judges have to read all the books.

Notes for Home: Your child spelled words with the vowel sound heard in *report* and *explore,* and the vowel sound heard in *expert, research,* and *disturb.* ***Home Activity:*** Challenge your child to find other words with these two vowel sounds. Discuss how these words are spelled.

Spelling Workbook 6.1, p. 15

Name ____________________

Hot Dogs and Bamboo Shoots

Spelling: Vowel Sounds with *r*

Directions: Proofread these two Japanese *haiku* (short poems about simple images). Find five spelling mistakes. Use the proofreading marks to correct each mistake.

- ≡ Make a capital.
- / Make a small letter.
- ∧ Add something.
- Take out something.
- ⊙ Add a period.
- ¶ Begin a new paragraph.

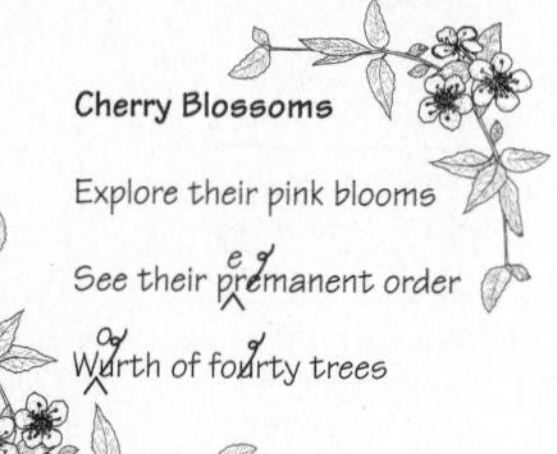

Cherry Blossoms

Explore their pink blooms
See their premanent order
Wurth of fourty trees

Battle

Enormus power
The dragonfly kills the bee
With a golden sord

Spelling Tip

report worth

Watch for letter pairs that represent different vowel sounds. The letters **or** can represent two different vowel sounds, as heard in **report** and **worth.**

Word List

report	determine
order	permanent
sword	research
forty	earning
enormous	worth
explore	worst
ignore	thorough
therefore	attorney
expert	disturb
service	purchase

Write a Haiku

Answers will vary, but each haiku should include the correct verse form and at least three spelling words.

On a separate sheet of paper, write a haiku of your own. A haiku always has three lines. The first and third lines have five syllables each. The second line has seven syllables. A haiku usually focuses on a single, simple image. Try to use at least three of your spelling words.

Notes for Home: Your child spelled words with the vowel sound heard in *report* and *explore,* and the vowel sound heard in *expert, research,* and *disturb. Home Activity:* Encourage your child to describe the haiku he or she has written. Discuss the image in the haiku.

Spelling Workbook 6.1, p. 16

Name ____________________

Hot Dogs and Bamboo Shoots

Spelling: Vowel Sounds with *r* REVIEW

Word List

report	enormous	expert	research	thorough
order	explore	service	earning	attorney
sword	ignore	determine	worth	disturb
forty	therefore	permanent	worst	purchase

Directions: Write the word from the box that belongs in each group.

1. article, story, **report**
2. blade, knife, **sword**
3. value, importance, **worth**
4. overlook, disregard, **ignore**
5. consequently, thus, **therefore**
6. help, aid, **service**
7. twenty, thirty, **forty**
8. decide, conclude, **determine**

Directions: Choose the word from the box that is the most opposite in meaning for each word below. Write the word on the line.

9. sell **purchase**
10. best **worst**
11. spending **earning**
12. beginner **expert**
13. temporary **permanent**
14. tiny **enormous**

Directions: Choose the word from the box that best replaces the underlined word. Write the word on the line.

order 15. Arrange the coins by value.
research 16. The biologist's study may help find a cure for a disease.
thorough 17. I am taking my cat in for a complete health check.
disturb 18. Ben is sleeping; please do not bother him.
attorney 19. Connie has an appointment with her lawyer.
explore 20. I want to investigate where the mouse could have gone.

Notes for Home: Your child spelled words with the vowel sound heard in *report* and *explore,* and the vowel sound heard in *expert, research,* and *disturb. Home Activity:* Have your child choose a spelling word and find another word with the same vowel sound spelled the same way.

Practice Book 6.1, p. 39

Name ____________________

Hot Dogs and Bamboo Shoots

Parts of a Book

The main **parts of a book** include its cover, title page, copyright page, table of contents, chapter titles, section heads, captions, footnotes, index, bibliography, and appendix.

Directions: Use the table of contents from a book of folk tales to answer the questions below and on the next page.

Folk Tales from Japan, China, and India

1. How are the folk tales organized in this book? How do you know?
The folk tales are organized by the country from which they came. The section heads in the table of contents show this information.
2. From what country is the folk tale *The Five Sparrows?* **Japan**
3. On which page does the first of the Indian folk tales begin? **page 57**

Practice Book 6.1, p. 40

Name ____________________

Hot Dogs and Bamboo Shoots

4. Name two folk tales that are from India. **Students should name any two of the tales listed under "Stories from India."**
5. Which part of the book would you look at to find information about other folk tales to read?
bibliography
6. Suppose you wanted to compare the fairy tale *Cinderella* with a similar folk tale from another country. Would this book be helpful? Explain.
Possible answer: Yes, the book includes the Chinese folk tale *Yeh-Shen: A Cinderella Story from China,* which could be used to compare to the fairy tale *Cinderella.*
7. Suppose you wanted to see if any of these folk tales included a story about a tiger. Which section of the book would help you figure this out? Explain.
Possible answer: The index would tell what subjects are covered in the book. You can use the index to see if the book includes something about tigers.
8. Suppose you were writing a research report on jackals to tell facts about this animal. Would *The Blue Jackal* on page 66 be useful for your report? Explain.
Possible answer: No, a folk tale about a jackal would not be a good resource because it would probably not contain reliable, factual information about jackals.
9. Can you judge a book by its cover? What information will you find on a book cover?
Possible answer: Yes, you can look at a book cover to get information that will help you figure out what it is about. The book cover will show the title of the book and its author and maybe its illustrators. Illustrations may also help show what the book is about.
10. A copyright page tells when a book was published. Why might this information be important when you are doing research?
Possible answer: Knowing when a book was published helps you evaluate how up-to-date its information is.

Notes for Home: Your child answered questions about different parts of a book. *Home Activity:* Examine some fiction and nonfiction books with your child. Have your child point out different parts of each book and explain what information it shows.

Practice Book 6.1, p. 41

Name ______________________ The Telephone Call

Character

- **Characters** are the people or animals who take part in the events of a short story, novel, play, or other form of fiction.
- You can learn about characters from their thoughts, words, and actions.
- You can also learn about characters by paying attention to how other characters in the story treat them and what other characters say about them.

Directions: Reread "Granny's Chair." Then complete the table. Provide the missing phrases or sentences to tell what Rachel is like, how she is feeling, and how you know.

Possible answers given.

What is Rachel like? How is she feeling?	How do you know?
Rachel feels uncertain.	1. **She stands awkwardly; she has to be asked to sit down; she sits gingerly.**
Rachel's thoughts are wandering.	2. **She doesn't realize she has thrown the core into the tub. She thinks about the games outdoors.**
3. **Rachel has a good memory. Rachel misses her grandmother.**	She remembers Granny's hands in detail.
4. **Rachel wants to be like the grownups.**	She stays inside with the grownups. She smiles at her uncle. She doesn't complain, and she tries to imitate the rhythm of their hands.
Rachel feels left out.	5. **Rachel sighs when she thinks about playing outside.**

Notes for Home: Your child used details from a story to describe a character. ***Home Activity:*** Choose a character from a book or television show. Have your child describe what the character is like and provide details to support his or her description.

Practice Book 6.1, p. 42

Name ______________________ The Telephone Call

Vocabulary

Directions: Choose the word from the box that best replaces the underlined word or words. Write the word on the line.

Check the Words You Know
- __ bewilderment
- __ cope
- __ objective
- __ orphan
- __ tactful

cope 1. Sandy can handle difficult situations well.

objective 2. She takes an open, unprejudiced approach when conflicts arise.

tactful 3. When people get angry, Sandy is polite, saying and doing just the right thing.

bewilderment 4. When she is in a state of confusion, she looks for facts that will help her solve the problem.

orphan 5. Her common sense and kindness were just what the parentless child needed.

Directions: Choose the word from the box that best matches each clue. Write the letters of the word on the blanks. The boxed letters spell a synonym for *crisis.*

6. not influenced by emotion
7. great confusion
8. a child who has no living parents
9. deal or struggle with
10. able to say and do the right thing

6. **o b j** [e] **c t i v e**
[m]
7. **b e w i l d** [e] **r m e n t**
8. **o** [r] **p h a n**
[g]
9. **c o p** [e]
[n]
10. **t a** [c] **t f u l**
[y]

A synonym for *crisis:* **emergency**

Write a Narrative

On a separate sheet of paper, write about an event or time in your life that was funny, sad, exciting, or interesting. Describe what happened in the order that it happened. Make sure your narrative has a beginning, middle and end. Use as many vocabulary words as you can.

Check that the vocabulary words are used correctly in students' narratives of memorable events.

Notes for Home: Your child identified and used vocabulary words from "The Telephone Call." ***Home Activity:*** With your child, explore different ways to describe feelings, using as many of the listed vocabulary words as you can.

Practice Book 6.1, p. 43

Name ______________________ The Telephone Call

Character

- **Characters** are the people or animals who take part in the events of a short story, novel, play, or other form of fiction.
- You can learn about characters through their thoughts, words, and actions.
- You can also learn about characters by paying attention to how other characters in the story treat them and what others say about them.

Directions: Reread what happens in "The Telephone Call" when Uncle Douglas explains empathy. Then answer the questions below. Use the information in the passage to tell about the characters.

"But why does John know what to say, and how to say it, and all I can do is act stupid, as though it didn't matter?"

"Just because it matters too much. Have you ever heard of *empathy?*"

I shook my head.

"John can show Aunt Elena how sorry he is because he has a scientific mind and he can see what has happened from the outside. All good scientists have to be observers. He can be deeply upset about Uncle Hal and deeply sorry for Aunt Elena, but he can be objective about it. You can't."

"Why?"

"Because you have an artistic temperament, Vicky, and I've never seen you be objective about anything yet. When you think about Aunt Elena and how she must be feeling right now, it is for the moment as though you *were* Aunt Elena; you get right inside her suffering, and it becomes your suffering, too. That's empathy. . . ."

Possible answers given.

1. How does Vicky think she handles the situation?
Vicky thinks she is stupid.

2. What does Uncle Douglas think of Vicky?
Uncle Douglas thinks Vicky is artistic and able to share Aunt Elena's suffering.

3. What does Uncle Douglas think of John?
Uncle Douglas thinks John is observant and objective.

4. Based on what he has said, what do you think of Uncle Douglas?
Uncle Douglas seems kind and understanding.

5. Later in the story, Mother takes John and Vicky to watch the night sky. What does this action tell you about Mother? Explain your thinking on a separate sheet of paper. **Mother is sensitive and understanding because she comforts John and Vicky and helps them put their feelings into words.**

Notes for Home: Your child read a short story and learned about the characters. ***Home Activity:*** Read a story together or watch a TV program together. Then encourage your child to explain what he or she has learned about each character.

Practice Book 6.1, p. 45

Name ______________________ The Telephone Call

Selection Test

Directions: Choose the best answer to each item. Mark the letter for the answer you have chosen.

Part 1: Vocabulary

Find the answer choice that means about the same as the underlined word in each sentence.

1. Grandma tries to cope with her illness.
   - A. heal
   - B. rest
   - (C) deal with
   - D. fight against
2. Aunt Margaret is the most tactful person I have ever known.
   - F. warm and loving
   - (G) skilled at saying the right thing in difficult situations
   - H. graceful and beautiful
   - J. direct and to the point
3. Elsie tried to write an objective letter.
   - A. long and detailed
   - B. clear and easy to understand
   - C. personal or friendly
   - (D) not affected by personal feelings
4. Alexa looked at us in bewilderment.
   - (F) great confusion
   - G. fear
   - H. eager excitement
   - J. wonder
5. Marie is an orphan.
   - (A) a child whose parents are dead
   - B. an infant
   - C. a person who is married
   - D. a woman

Part 2: Comprehension

Use what you know about the story to answer each item.

6. What made the Saturday evening at the beginning of the story unusual?
   - F. Suzy was playing doctor with her dolls.
   - G. The house was filled with noise.
   - (H) Aunt Elena called about an accident.
   - J. Daddy had to see a sick patient.
7. Maggy came to live with the Austins because she—
   - (A) no longer had a family of her own.
   - B. was Suzy's best friend.
   - C. wanted to spend more time with other children.
   - D. did not like Aunt Elena.
8. How did Vicky feel when she first learned that Maggy would be staying with them?
   - F. excited about having a new friend
   - G. upset because she did not like Maggy
   - (H) confused about how the changes would affect her
   - J. sorry that she could not help Maggy feel better

GO ON

Practice Book 6.1, p. 46

Name ______________________ **The Telephone Call**

9. What happened just after Vicky found Aunt Elena trying to make coffee in the kitchen?
Ⓐ John came in and hugged Aunt Elena.
B. Uncle Douglas drove up to the house.
C. Suzy and Maggy set the table.
D. The telephone rang.

10. You can tell from the story that Vicky preferred people around her to be—
F. misleading.
G. secretive.
H. loud.
Ⓙ calm.

11. Compared with John, Vicky had a harder time trying to—
A. feel sorry for other people.
B. understand how Aunt Elena felt.
C. feel her mother's pain.
Ⓓ say the right things to people.

12. What was one way Aunt Elena dealt with losing Uncle Hal?
F. She prayed that Hal would come back to her.
G. She cried hard and felt no hope.
Ⓗ She remembered the good times they had together.
J. She kept busy so she could forget him.

13. The author's main purpose in this selection is to—
A. describe how to make other people feel better.
Ⓑ tell a story about how a family deals with a crisis.
C. persuade people not to fly planes.
D. explain why change is necessary.

14. Why did Vicky feel more sympathy for Aunt Elena than for Maggy?
F. Vicky had known Maggy longer.
Ⓖ Vicky liked and understood Aunt Elena.
H. Vicky did not feel sorry for Aunt Elena.
J. Vicky was closer to Maggy in age.

15. Why was Mother more patient with Maggy when she knocked over chairs than she would have been with her own children or their friends?
Ⓐ Maggy was having a hard time and did not yet know what was expected of her.
B. Maggy was too young to know any better.
C. Maggy was always so well behaved that Mother assumed it was an accident.
D. Maggy could not control the movements of her body.

Name ______________________ **The Telephone Call**

Character

- **Characters** are the people or animals who take part in the events of a short story, novel, play, or other form of fiction.
- You can learn about characters through their thoughts, words, and actions.
- You can also learn about characters by paying attention to how other characters in the story treat them and what others say about them.

Directions: Read the story below.

Anita's mother had been rushed to the hospital last night. Anita felt lost without her.

Her father didn't know how he was going to manage. He worked long hours, and he wanted to be at the hospital. He needed someone else to take care of Anita. He asked Aunt Martine, Uncle Sid, and Aunt Fran.

"I'd love to have you, but my expensive glass collection is in the only extra room," said Aunt Martine. "I'm not used to having children around."

"I'm always willing to do my duty," Uncle Sid said with tight lips. "Of course I'll take the child if it's necessary."

Aunt Fran smiled warmly and put her arm around Anita. "Anita, I could use some company in the house. What do you think?" Anita smiled back.

Directions: Write words or phrases to describe Anita's relatives in the four blank boxes below. The box for Anita has been done for you. **Possible answers given.**

Anita	Dad	Aunt Martine
lost frightened	1. **worried, hard-working, needs help**	2. **worried about her glass collection, not used to children, cares more about objects than people**

Uncle Sid	Aunt Fran
3. **dutiful, disapproving, cold, insincere**	4. **warm, kind, caring, welcoming, likes company**

5. Which relative should Anita stay with? Explain your choice.
Anita should stay with Aunt Fran because Aunt Fran is kind and will make her welcome.

Notes for Home: Your child used story details to describe different characters. ***Home Activity:*** Take turns describing the traits of family members or close friends. Challenge your child to sum up each character description with a few key words.

Practice Book 6.1, p. 47

Name ______________________ **The Telephone Call**

Cause and Effect

REVIEW

Directions: Read the story. Then read each question about the story. Choose the best answer to each question. Mark the letter for the answer you have chosen.

The Lucky Return

Steve couldn't wait to grow old enough to take care of his cousin's dog! Steve's cousin Sandy had a beautiful dog named Rex. Steve often visited Sandy because he enjoyed caring for and playing with her dog.

Imagine Steve's joy when Sandy asked him to care for Rex for an entire weekend. The first day that Steve was caring for Rex it was raining lightly, but Steve decided to take Rex outside to play.

Steve walked several blocks to a nearby park. Suddenly, the rain shower turned into a heavy rain and the wind began to blow.

As Steve was leaving the park with Rex, another dog ran in front of them. Rex surprised Steve by lunging after the large dog. Steve's hand was so wet from the rain that he couldn't hold the leash. Rex bolted after the other dog and the two animals ran swiftly through the park. Steve ran as fast as he could, but the dogs got farther and farther away.

When he realized that he couldn't catch Rex, Steve sat down, right in a puddle of rain, and began to cry. He was afraid that he had lost Sandy's beautiful dog forever.

As he was crying, Steve heard a familiar bark and looked up to see Rex running toward him. Steve gave Rex a big hug as Rex licked his face. "Please forgive me, Rex. I'll never take you out in bad weather again."

As the rain began to stop, Steve started to walk Rex home. This time he held the leash firmly with both hands.

1. Steve often visited Sandy because—
A. she is his cousin.
B. his parents were away a lot.
C. he enjoyed caring for her cat.
Ⓓ he enjoyed playing with her dog.

2. Steve was unable to hold the leash because—
F. the wind was blowing.
G. he was scared.
Ⓗ his hand was wet and slippery.
J. he couldn't see in the rain.

3. Steve begins to cry because—
A. he didn't want to care for Rex.
B. he sat in a rain puddle.
Ⓒ he was afraid that he had lost Rex for good.
D. he was afraid of the other dog.

4. Which of the following is **not** an effect of losing Rex?
F. Steve promises not to take Rex out in bad weather again.
Ⓖ The rainstorm makes it difficult for Steve to hold the leash.
H. Steve cries.
J. Steve sits in a rain puddle.

5. Steve might not have lost Rex if—
Ⓐ the weather had been nice.
B. the park wasn't so far away.
C. he had not sat in the puddle.
D. he had not cried.

Notes for Home: Your child used details to identify causes and effects in a story. ***Home Activity:*** Help your child identify some of the things she or he does to get good results, such as practicing for sports, setting aside enough time for homework, or studying for a test.

Name ______________________ **The Telephone Call**

Writing Across Texts

Directions: Consider how the experiences of Vicky from "The Telephone Call" and Yoshiko Uchida, author of "Hot Dogs and Bamboo Shoots," are alike and different. Complete the table below to compare and contrast these selections. **Possible answers given.**

	The Telephone Call	Hot Dogs and Bamboo Shoots
Characters	Vicky	Yoshiko Uchida
Setting	Rural America today	3. **California and Japan before World War II.**
Events	Uncle Hal dies. 1. **Maggie moves in with them. Vicky doesn't know how to tell her Aunt Elena how sorry she is about Uncle Hal.**	4. **Yoshiko Uchida and her family travel to Japan to visit her grandmother and other relatives. She enjoys Japan and all the Japanese traditions, and likes looking the same as the rest of the people.**
Ending	2. **Mom, John, and Vicky go to the top of a hill at night to discuss the events and their feelings.**	5. **Yoshiko Uchida realizes that part of her belongs in both worlds, and part of her belongs in neither world.**

Write a Letter

"The Telephone Call" and "Hot Dogs and Bamboo Shoots" are two selections about young girls who experience changes in their lives. How are their experiences alike? How are they different? Write a friendly letter from one of the characters to the other discussing the changes that have occurred and how the character feels about them. Use a separate sheet of paper for your letter.
Letters will vary. Check that students' letters reflect the voice and thoughts of either Vicky or Yoshiko Uchida.

Notes for Home: Your child compared and contrasted information from two selections. ***Home Activity:*** As you read stories with your child, discuss the changes that the characters face and how those changes may be similar to or different from changes your child has experienced.

Grammar Practice Book 6.1, p. 21

Name ______________________

The Telephone Call

Grammar: Compound and Complex Sentences

REVIEW

Directions: Write whether each sentence is compound or complex.

complex	1. While a customer is eating, he suddenly cannot breathe.
compound	2. He turns blue, and his finger points to his throat.
compound	3. The Heimlich maneuver could save his life, and fortunately the waitress knows how to perform the maneuver.
complex	4. As she stands behind the customer, she wraps her arms around his waist.
complex	5. When she presses quickly on his stomach, the stuck piece of food finally comes out.

Directions: Add an independent clause to the first two sentences to make them compound sentences. Add independent clauses to the last three sentences to make them complex sentences. Write the complete sentences on the lines. **Possible answers given.**

6. (compound sentence) Life is full of emergencies, and _____.
Life is full of emergencies, and it is wise to be prepared for them.

7. (compound sentence) You should learn CPR and the Heimlich maneuver, but _____.
You should learn CPR and the Heimlich maneuver, but you may never use them.

8. (complex) _____, if you couldn't help someone in need.
It would be terrible, if you couldn't help someone in need.

9. (complex) If you can swim, _____.
If you can swim, you may save a person's life some day.

10. (complex) When there is an emergency, _____.
When there is an emergency, you can always call 911.

Notes for Home: Your child identified and wrote compound and complex sentences. ***Home Activity:*** Give your child two simple sentences and challenge him or her to combine them into a compound sentence.

Grammar: Compound and Complex Sentences 99

Grammar Practice Book 6.1, p. 22

Name ______________________

The Telephone Call

Grammar: Combining Sentences

If two sentences have different subjects but the same predicate, you can combine the subjects to form a **compound subject** by using the word *and.*

Simple sentences: Jason gazed at the stars above. His sister gazed at the stars above.

Compound subject: Jason and his sister gazed at the stars above.

If two sentences have the same subject and different predicates, you can combine the predicates to form a **compound predicate** by using the word *and.*

Simple sentences: Marika waited for the bus. Marika watched the darkening sky.

Compound predicate: Marika waited for the bus and watched the darkening sky.

If two sentences have related ideas, you can combine the sentences to form a **compound sentence** by using a comma and words like *or, but,* or *and.*

Simple sentences: I was nervous. My knees were knocking.

Compound sentence: I was nervous, and my knees were knocking.

Directions: Combine each pair of sentences to form a compound subject, a compound predicate, or a compound sentence. Use the joining word *and.*

1. Sook and Lin Yu were frightened. Sook and Lin Yu wanted to go home.
Sook and Lin Yu were frightened and wanted to go home.

2. They were in the woods. They saw how dark it was.
They were in the woods and saw how dark it was.

3. Sook saw a mysterious shape. Lin Yu saw a mysterious shape too.
Sook and Lin Yu saw a mysterious shape.

4. The shape came forward. It was huge.
The shape came forward, and it was huge.

5. Sook shivered. Lin Yu shook.
Sook shivered, and Lin Yu shook.

Notes for Home: Your child has learned to combine sentences. ***Home Activity:*** Using a favorite book, ask your child to show you how to combine sentences.

100 Grammar: Combining Sentences

Grammar Practice Book 6.1, p. 23

Name ______________________

The Telephone Call

Grammar: Combining Sentences

Directions: Combine each pair of sentences to form a compound subject, a compound predicate, or a compound sentence. Use the joining words *or, and,* or *but.*

1. Tara smiled happily. Tara hummed a little song.
Tara smiled happily and hummed a little song.

2. Tara planned to have fun. Her friends planned to have fun.
Tara and her friends planned to have fun.

3. They would swim. They would dive.
They would swim and dive.

4. The parking lot was empty. The beach was empty.
The parking lot and the beach were empty.

5. Huge waves came in. Huge waves broke on the sand.
Huge waves came in and broke on the sand.

6. Tara felt nervous. Her friends yelled happily.
Tara felt nervous, but her friends yelled happily.

7. The waves were big. Tara stepped backward.
The waves were big, and Tara stepped backward.

8. Tara sat down on the sand. Her friends went wading.
Tara sat down on the sand, but her friends went wading.

9. A wave crashed down. Angie disappeared.
A wave crashed down, and Angie disappeared.

10. The water grew calmer. Angie stood up.
The water grew calmer, and Angie stood up.

Write a Paragraph

Write a paragraph to finish the story of Tara and her friends. Then look for sentences you can combine to make your writing more interesting.
Check that students have included sentences with compound subjects and predicates, as well as compound sentences.

Notes for Home: Your child combined short sentences to form longer, more interesting sentences. ***Home Activity:*** Ask your child to explain various ways of combining sentences. Then, together, examine newspaper ads, looking for sentences that can be combined.

Grammar: Combining Sentences 101

Grammar Practice Book 6.1, p. 24

Name ______________________

The Telephone Call

Grammar: Combining Sentences

RETEACHING

Combine each pair of sentences. Write each new sentence.

1. Margaret walked home. Peter walked home.
Margaret and Peter walked home.

2. Margaret went to the library. Margaret stopped by the store.
Margaret went to the library and stopped by the store.

3. They left for the airport early. They got stuck in traffic.
They left for the airport early, but they got stuck in traffic.

Form a **compound subject** by combining two sentences with the same predicate but different subjects. Form a **compound predicate** by combining two sentences that have the same subject but different predicates. Form a **compound sentence** by combining two simple sentences that have related ideas.

Directions: Combine each pair of sentences to form a sentence with a compound subject or a compound predicate, or to form a compound sentence. Use the joining word *or, and,* or *but.* Write each new sentence on the line. **Possible answers given.**

1. Jane Wilkinson is new at Kennedy School this year. Ray Wilkinson is new at Kennedy School this year.
Jane and Ray Wilkinson are new at Kennedy School this year.

2. Jane and Ray don't know anyone at school. They would like to make new friends.
Jane and Ray don't know anyone at school, but they would like to make new friends.

3. My brother invites Ray to club meetings. My brother's friends invite Ray to club meetings.
My brother and his friends invite Ray to club meetings.

4. Carole opened the newspaper. Carole read about Taylor and Ushma.
Carole opened the newspaper and read about Taylor and Ushma.

5. They had entered a literary contest. They had tied for first prize.
They had entered a literary contest and tied for first prize.

Notes for Home: Your child wrote compound sentences and sentences with compound subjects and compound predicates. ***Home Activity:*** Write simple sentences about your family. Have your child combine them to form compound sentences or sentences with compound subjects or predicates.

102 Grammar: Combining Sentences

Grammar Practice Book 6.1, p. 25

Name ______________________ The Telephone Call

Grammar: Combining Sentences

Directions: Combine each pair of sentences to form a sentence with a compound subject or a compound predicate, or to form a compound sentence. Use the joining word *and, but,* or *or.* Write each new sentence. **Possible answers given.**

1. I am the oldest child in my family. I am not the tallest.
I am the oldest child in my family, but I am not the tallest.

2. My younger brother Josh is taller than I am. My younger brother Sam is taller than I am.
My younger brothers Josh and Sam are taller than I am.

3. I have more responsibilities than my brothers and sister. I do more chores than my brothers and sister.
I have more responsibilities and do more chores than my brothers and sister.

4. My mother expects me to make snacks for my siblings after school. I have to make sure they start their homework right away.
My mother expects me to make snacks for my siblings after school, and I have to make sure they start their homework right away.

5. I return our library books on my way home from school. I buy fresh bread for dinner.
I return our library books on my way home from school, and I buy fresh bread for dinner.

6. My dad broke his leg last year. He wasn't able to do many of the things around the house that he normally does.
My dad broke his leg last year, and he wasn't able to do many of things around the house that he normally does.

7. The doctor said he had to stay in bed. He could sit in a chair with his leg elevated and watch TV.
The doctor said he had to stay in bed, or he could sit in a chair with his leg elevated and watch TV.

8. My brothers wanted to be helpful to our dad. They weren't sure how.
My brothers wanted to be helpful to our dad, but they weren't sure how.

9. We had a big celebration for my dad the day his cast was taken off. We made a cake for my dad the day his cast was taken off.
We had a big celebration and made a cake for my dad the day his cast was taken off.

Notes for Home: Your child wrote compound sentences and sentences with compound subjects and predicates. ***Home Activity:*** Have your child look at a story that he or she enjoyed as a young child. Have your child combine simple sentences from the story to form compound sentences.

Grammar: Combining Sentences 103

Practice Book 6.1, p. 48

Name ______________________ The Telephone Call

Phonics: Complex Spelling Patterns

Directions: Read the words in the box. They may look alike, but they have very different vowel sounds. Read the words to the left. Match each word to the left with a word from the box that has the same vowel sound. Write the word on the line.

through	thought	though

1. taught **thought**
2. throw **though**
3. threw **through**

Directions: Read the words in the box. Match them with the words below that have the same vowel sound. Write the words on the lines.

bought	dough	sought	soup	soul	coupon

4. thought **bought** **sought**
5. though **dough** **soul**
6. through **soup** **coupon**

Directions: Read each sentence. Say the underlined word to yourself. Circle the word in ( ) that has the same vowel sound as the underlined word.

7. Although it was getting late, they didn't want to leave Marcie alone. (bought/**boulder**)
8. She thought everyone was kind for trying to make her feel better. (**caught**/count)
9. After the death of her uncle, her emotions went through many changes. (though/**rule**)
10. No one thought she was insensitive for not being able to express her feelings. (foul/**fought**)
11. Everyone tried to be a little cheerful, even though the occasion was a somber one. (**bowl**/brought)
12. It helps to have friends around to get you through the good times and the bad times. (know/**knew**)

Possible answers given.

Directions: Write a sentence for each of these words: **through, thought, though.**

13. **It helps to think through what you want to say before you say it.**
14. **Everyone thought the newcomer was a special person.**
15. **Even though the party was over, everyone was still at the house.**

Notes for Home: Your child identified the different vowel sounds for words with *ough,* such as *through, thought,* and *though.* ***Home Activity:*** Write several *ough* words on separate slips of paper. Have your child read each word and use it in a sentence.

104 Phonics: Complex Spelling Patterns

Spelling Workbook 6.1, p. 17

Name ______________________ The Telephone Call

Spelling: Getting Letters in Correct Order

Pretest Directions: Fold back the page along the dotted line. On the blanks, write the spelling words as they are dictated. When you have finished the test, unfold the page and check your words.

1. **poetry**	1. Her **poetry** is wonderful.
2. **beautiful**	2. I smelled a **beautiful** flower.
3. **thirteen**	3. His sister is **thirteen** years old.
4. **tongue**	4. The cat has a scratchy **tongue**.
5. **pieces**	5. Some **pieces** of candy were left.
6. **thousand**	6. I've saved two **thousand** dollars.
7. **through**	7. We walked **through** the park.
8. **unusual**	8. What an **unusual** story!
9. **building**	9. The **building** was torn down.
10. **license**	10. Mrs. Patel got a fishing **license**.
11. **remodel**	11. They will **remodel** the house.
12. **grateful**	12. She was **grateful** for the help.
13. **enemy**	13. I'm your friend, not your **enemy**.
14. **instrument**	14. What **instrument** do you play?
15. **perform**	15. A jazz band will **perform**.
16. **prefer**	16. Do you **prefer** milk or juice?
17. **judged**	17. My mother **judged** the dog show.
18. **adjusted**	18. He **adjusted** the recliner.
19. **soldier**	19. The **soldier** laid down his gun.
20. **neighborhood**	20. My **neighborhood** is nearby.

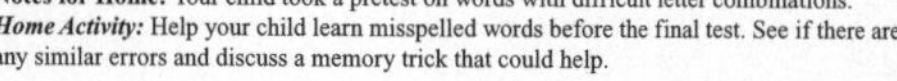

Notes for Home: Your child took a pretest on words with difficult letter combinations. ***Home Activity:*** Help your child learn misspelled words before the final test. See if there are any similar errors and discuss a memory trick that could help.

Spelling: Getting Letters in Correct Order 105

Spelling Workbook 6.1, p. 18

Name ______________________ The Telephone Call

Spelling: Getting Letters in Correct Order

Word List

poetry	neighborhood	license	perform
beautiful	thousand	remodel	prefer
thirteen	through	grateful	judged
tongue	unusual	enemy	adjusted
pieces	building	instrument	soldier

Directions: Choose the word from the box that is the base word of each word below. Write the word on the line.

1. preferably **prefer**
2. gratefulness **grateful**
3. licensed **license**
4. performance **perform**
5. instrumental **instrument**
6. beautifully **beautiful**
7. remodeling **remodel**
8. thirteenth **thirteen**

Directions: Choose the word from the box that completes each equation. Write the word on the line.

9. thought – ght + sand = **thousand**
10. un + use – e + ual = **unusual**
11. poem – m + try = **poetry**
12. ad + justify – ify + ed = **adjusted**
13. pie + crust – rust + es = **pieces**
14. judgment – ment + ed = **judged**
15. neigh + boring – ing + hood = **neighborhood**
16. sole – e + diet – t + r = **soldier**
17. tongs – s + ue = **tongue**
18. the – e + rough = **through**
19. energy – rgy + my = **enemy**
20. built – t + ding = **building**

Notes for Home: Your child spelled words with letter combinations that are hard to keep in order. ***Home Activity:*** Have your child spell each spelling word aloud. If your child mixes up some letters, give a spelling hint that will help him or her remember the correct spelling.

106 Spelling: Getting Letters in Correct Order

Spelling Workbook 6.1, p. 19

Name ______________________

The Telephone Call

Spelling: Getting Letters in Correct Order

Directions: Proofread this letter about a family crisis. Find seven spelling mistakes. Use the proofreading marks to correct each mistake.

- ≡ Make a capital.
- / Make a small letter.
- ∧ Add something.
- Take out something.
- ⊙ Add a period.
- ¶ Begin a new paragraph.

Dear Jane,

You won't believe what happened. My father decided to remodal the bedroom himself. "You don't need a lisence to put in a couple of windows," he said.

I perfer not to think about it. I can still hear the unuzual sound he made as he fell. The sound echoed right thrugh our building. We are graetful to the people in the nieghborhood who came running. The window had broken into a thousand pieces. Luckily, the only thing seriously hurt was Dad's pride.

Write soon,

Rafael

Spelling Tip

through prefer

Your spelling words contain letters that are hard to keep in order. Study the Word List carefully before proofreading the letter.

Word List

poetry, beautiful, thirteen, tongue, pieces, neighborhood, thousand, through, unusual, building, license, remodel, grateful, enemy, instrument, perform, prefer, judged, adjusted, soldier

Write a Letter

Imagine you are Jane. On a separate sheet of paper, write a letter to Rafael describing a family crisis and how it was solved. Try to use at least five of your spelling words. **Answers will vary, but each letter should include at least five spelling words.**

Notes for Home: Your child spelled words with letter combinations that are hard to keep in order. ***Home Activity:*** Help your child to make up sentences that contain the words *perform* and *pieces*. Have your child check his or her sentences to see that all words are correctly spelled.

Spelling Workbook 6.1, p. 20

Name ______________________

The Telephone Call

Spelling: Getting Letters in Correct Order

REVIEW

Word List				
poetry	pieces	unusual	grateful	prefer
beautiful	neighborhood	building	enemy	judged
thirteen	thousand	license	instrument	adjusted
tongue	through	remodel	perform	soldier

Directions: Choose the word from the box that best matches each clue. Write the word on the line.

pieces 1. I am what the parts of a jigsaw puzzle are called.
thousand 2. I am ten hundreds.
soldier 3. I am a person who serves in the army.
thirteen 4. I am always between twelve and fourteen.
tongue 5. I am needed for speech.
enemy 6. I am something or someone who tries to harm.
license 7. I am a permit that allows a person to drive.
poetry 8. I am a group of words that sometimes rhyme.
building 9. I am both a place to live and a game played with blocks.
instrument 10. I am something with which you can make music.

Directions: Choose the word from the box that best matches each definition. Write the word on the line.

neighborhood 11. community or area
unusual 12. strange
judged 13. decided or concluded from evidence
prefer 14. like better
grateful 15. thankful
beautiful 16. lovely
remodel 17. make over
perform 18. act or carry out
through 19. in one side and out the other
adjusted 20. changed or fixed slightly

Notes for Home: Your child spelled words with combinations of letters that are hard to keep in order. ***Home Activity:*** Encourage your child to find as many shorter words within the words in the list as possible. For example, *instrument* contains *in* and *strum*.

Practice Book 6.1, p. 49

Name ______________________

The Telephone Call

Telephone Directory

A **telephone directory** is a book with entries listed alphabetically by last name of a person or by the name of a business. The **white pages** lists telephone numbers and addresses of individuals and businesses. The **yellow pages** lists phone numbers, addresses, and advertisements of businesses. It is arranged alphabetically by category of business.

Directions: Use the following section of the yellow pages to answer the questions on the next page.

145 Movers—Newspapers

Movers

Great Bear Moving and Storage
30 Morocco St 555-5645
Jack and Jill Movers
315 3rd St 555-9080
Moonstone Movers Inc
82 College Ave 555-1309
Two Guys Movers
200 4th St 555-9008
Where or When Movers Inc
3 College Ave 555-5536

Music Instruction

Arbor Music School
321 7th St 555-6710

Music—Sheet

Napoleon's Guitars
67 7th St 555-8971
Phantom Music Inc
333 7th St 555-4439
Scores and More
352 2nd St 555-1130

Musical Instruments—Repairs

Napoleon's Guitars
67 7th St 555-7322
Poliuto's Pianos
69 7th St 555-1083

Musical Instruments—Sales

Napoleon's Guitars
67 7th St 555-4445
Poliuto's Pianos
69 7th St 555-0102

We've Got Rhythm

No one has a larger selection of rhythm and percussion instruments than we do!
Monday–Friday, 10 A.M. to 6 P.M.
Saturday, 1:00 P.M. to 8 P.M.
Free drum lesson, Saturdays at 1 P.M.
208 Garfield Place
(near Westwood Mall)
555-1782

Newspapers

The Daily Yell
74 College Avenue 555-6543
The Mirror
85 College Avenue 555-3548
Advertisements 555-0762
Arts Desk 555-9398
City Desk 555-8285
Copy Chief 555-5301
Sports Desk 555-5324
The Tribune
99 College Avenue 555-9021

Practice Book 6.1, p. 50

Name ______________________

The Telephone Call

1. What business categories are listed?
Movers, Musical Instruction, Music—Sheet, Musical Instruments—Repairs, Musical Instruments—Sales, Newspapers

2. Are these entries near the beginning, middle, or end of the yellow pages? Explain.
in the middle because M is halfway through the alphabet

3. Which of the newspapers listed is probably the largest? Why do you think so?
The Mirror; It has several phone numbers listed.

4. Would you turn ahead or back in the directory to find a plumber? Why?
Look ahead; P for "plumber" comes after M in the alphabet.

5. Can you purchase a guitar and have one repaired at the same shop? Explain.
Yes; Napoleon's Guitars sells and repairs guitars.

6. Which business uses an advertisement? What information does the advertisement give that the other listings do not give?
We've Got Rhythm uses an advertisement. The advertisement tells something about its selection of instruments, the hours the store is open, when the free drum lessons are available, and tells that its location is near the Westwood Mall.

7. Would Vicky Austin's phone number be in the white pages or the yellow pages? Explain.
Vicky Austin is a "person," so a listing for her family would be in the white pages.

8. Would you look in the white pages or the yellow pages if you needed the phone number for a locksmith? Explain.
Since you don't have a specific name of a locksmith, you would look in the yellow pages under the category "locksmiths" to find the information.

9. If you lived on Third Street, where would you go to buy sheet music? Why?
Possible answer: Scores and More is on 2nd Street, so it is the closest music store.

10. Many directories will list emergency numbers at the front of the directory in a separate section. Why do you think this information is listed this way?
Possible answer: In an emergency, you would want to be able to find a phone number quickly. Putting it in the front of the directory makes it easier to find.

Notes for Home: Your child answered questions about a telephone directory. ***Home Activity:*** Take turns saying a person's name or a name or type of business. Use the white pages or yellow pages to find each listing.

Name ______________________________

Story Organizer

Directions: Fill in the graphic organizer with information about the event or experience that you plan to write about. **The Story Organizer should be filled out completely.**

Possible title: ______________________________

Event: ______________________________

When? ______________________________

Where? ______________________________

Details

1. ______________________________

2. ______________________________

3. ______________________________

4. ______________________________

How did it end? ______________________________

Notes for Home: Your child planned a personal narrative. *Home Activity:* Have your child tell you about the experience he or she is writing about. Ask for details and explore the range of emotions.

Name ______________________________

Elaboration

Add Details

- When you write, you can elaborate by **adding vivid and specific details** that help readers picture your subject more clearly.
- You can provide precise details by telling how things look, sound, feel, taste, and smell.

Directions: Read the sentences about a basketball game. Then use vivid, precise words to add details to each sentence. Use the phrases from the box for ideas for your sentences. Write the new sentences on the lines.

grabbed	charged	ticks of the clock
roared with excitement	three-point shot	sky high
like a glove	swished	jump shot

Responses will vary. Reasonable answers are given.

1. There were only six seconds left.
There were only six ticks of the clock left.

2. Kathy jumped for the ball.
Kathy jumped sky high for the ball.

3. I caught the rebound.
I grabbed the rebound.

4. On defense, she covered me closely.
On defense, she covered me like a glove.

5. She ran right into me.
She charged right into me.

6. She made a long shot at the buzzer.
She made a long three-point shot at the buzzer.

7. The ball went through the net.
The ball swished through the net.

8. The crowd cheered.
The crowd roared with excitement.

Notes for Home: Your child used vivid, precise words to add details to sentences. *Home Activity:* Invite your child to give you an oral description of the end of this game, pretending he or she is a sports announcer.

Name ______________________________

Self-Evaluation Guide

Personal Narrative Checklist

Directions: Think about the final draft of your personal narrative. Then answer each question below. **Students' responses should show that they have given careful thought to the content of their personal narratives.**

	Yes	No	Not sure
1. Does my narrative flow smoothly from beginning to middle to end?			
2. Did I use enough details to let my audience know how I feel about the event?			
3. Did I keep my audience and purpose in mind?			
4. Did I use vivid words to express myself?			
5. Did I proofread and edit carefully to avoid errors?			

6. Which sentence of your personal narrative uses the most precise, vivid words? Copy it here.

7. If you were asked to write a sequel, or continuation, of your personal narrative, what would you write about?

Notes for Home: Your child has just completed a self-evaluation of a personal narrative. *Home Activity:* Discuss with your child what he or she would do differently if he or she could rewrite this personal narrative.

Practice Book 6.2, p. 51

Name ______________________________ A Trouble-Making Crow

Making Judgments

- **Making a judgment** means forming an opinion about someone or something.
- When you make a judgment, you think about your own experiences and beliefs, as well as the information the author provides.
- When an author expresses a judgment about someone or something, test the author's judgment by looking for evidence to support it.

Directions: Reread "The Truth About Wolves." Then complete the table. Tell what judgments the author expresses about lions and wolves and the evidence he provides to support each judgment. Then answer the question below. **Possible answers given.**

The Author's Judgment About . . .	Supporting Evidence
Dogs: Dogs are humans' best friends.	Dogs are friendly, loyal, intelligent, and playful.
Lions: 1. **Lions are marvelous hunters.**	2. **Lions work together to hunt their prey.**
Wolves: 3. **Wolves are misunderstood.**	4. **Wolves are loyal, playful, and intelligent, just like dogs.**

5. Do you agree with the author's judgment about wolves? Does the author support his judgment well?
Possible answer: I agree with the author that wolves have many appealing qualities, just like dogs. The author supports his opinion well by giving examples and making comparisons.

Notes for Home: Your child identified judgments made by an author, and then made his or her own judgments about the author's ideas. *Home Activity:* Help your child identify the judgments expressed in a newspaper editorial. Check whether the judgments are supported.

Practice Book 6.2, p. 52

Name ______________________ A Trouble-Making Crow

Vocabulary

Directions: Choose the word from the box that best matches each definition. Write the word on the line.

Check the Words You Know
__ aggressive
__ attributes
__ outwit
__ persisted
__ secretive
__ tolerated
__ vengeance

persisted 1. refused to stop

aggressive 2. very active; not passive

vengeance 3. revenge

attributes 4. qualities or characteristics

secretive 5. not open; having secrets

Directions: Choose the word from the box that best completes each sentence. Write the word on the line to the left. Then find and circle the words in the puzzle below. Words may appear across, down, or diagonally.

attributes 6. Tom Cat knew that the package on the counter contained fish. An experienced cat burgular like himself knew well the delicious _____ of fresh fish.

secretive 7. He did not want Teeter, the kitten, in on the heist, so he was very _____.

outwit 8. Tom planned to _____ the kitten and get the fish all for himself.

vengeance 9. He wasn't afraid of Teeter's _____.

tolerated 10. He was patient and _____ Teeter, but he didn't think the kitten was very smart.

```
Q U J A L F P F S R E A B B M
A T T R I B U T E S V Z T J U
I D E B T V F I C A T I O N W
L U I A X Y J E R R O I L H N
P Z H I Q J T C E G V I E B Z
B K E O U T W I T F L A R X E
I W H J D T U I I X S S A H K
N Y I R B E A L V H Z E T T O
T I J Z V E N G E A N C E E Q
A J U W I M L Y Z G F D D L D
```

Write a Story

On a separate sheet of paper, write a story about a character (an animal or imaginary person) who wants something so badly that he or she is willing to trick others to get it. Use as many vocabulary words as you can. **Students' stories may have characteristics of a folk tale. Check that any included vocabulary is used correctly.**

Notes for Home: Your child identified and used vocabulary words from "A Trouble-Making Crow." ***Home Activity:*** Think of fictional characters from a book or a movie that you or your child can describe using the vocabulary words.

Practice Book 6.2, p. 53

Name ______________________ A Trouble-Making Crow

Making Judgments

- **Making a judgment** means forming an opinion about someone or something.
- When you make a judgment, you think about your own experiences and beliefs, as well as the information the author provides.
- As you read, look for evidence to support your judgments or the author's judgments.

Directions: Reread what happens in "A Trouble-Making Crow" after Craig's mother tells him that the crow New York has to go. Then answer the questions below. Think about what happens in the story to help you make judgments.

> "People come first," I said. "How would you feel if Hilde was blinded by our crow?"
> His eyes widened as he understood the seriousness of New York's vengeance.
> "I don't want to kill him," I said. "I want to take him far away and let him go—far from Hilde."
> "Will he dive at anyone else's eyes?"
> "No. Hilde must have kicked him or hurt him somehow, and he's taking it out on her. He won't forget. Crows are like that."
> Craig ran into the yard to find New York, and I went to the cellar for an animal carrying case.

1. Do you think it would make sense to kill New York? Explain your answer.
No. The problem can be solved by taking the crow far away.

2. Do you think that the mother's decision to let New York go free is fair? Explain.
The solution is fair, because it protects Hilde without killing the crow.

3. Do you think Craig's mother understands animal behavior? Why?
Yes. She is able to explain why New York attacked Hilde.

4. Does Craig understand his mother's decision? How do you know?
Even though Craig is unhappy about losing New York, he goes to find and catch him so his mother can take him away.

5. Think about the story of Dr. Kalmbach's crow at the end of "A Trouble-Making Crow." On a separate sheet of paper, explain how the story affected your opinion of what Craig's mother did about New York. **Dr. Kalmbach's story showed that it is not easy for humans to discipline crows, so the decision to relocate New York was probably a good one.**

Notes for Home: Your child used story details to make judgments about characters and actions. ***Home Activity:*** With your child, make judgments about characters or actions in a movie you've seen or a book you've read together.

Practice Book 6.2, p. 55

Name ______________________ A Trouble-Making Crow

Selection Test

Directions: Choose the best answer to each item. Mark the letter for the answer you have chosen.

Part 1: Vocabulary

Find the answer choice that means about the same as the underlined word in each sentence.

1. The old dog tolerated the puppy.
   A. chased after
   B. looked for
   C. played with
   (D) put up with

2. Sharon persisted for five days.
   F. got better
   (G) refused to stop
   H. went away
   J. studied hard

3. Margo has many good attributes.
   A. faults
   B. feelings or emotions
   (C) qualities or characteristics
   D. ways to help others

4. Sam cannot outwit his brother.
   (F) be more clever than
   G. act friendly toward
   H. catch by surprise
   J. run faster than

5. Members of the club are very secretive.
   A. talking for a long time
   B. special in a certain way
   (C) not open; keeping things hidden from others
   D. proud of themselves

6. The dog seemed to want vengeance.
   (F) revenge
   G. comfort
   H. warmth
   J. safety

7. The tennis player made an aggressive move toward his opponent.
   A. friendly
   (B) ready to attack
   C. brief
   D. quiet or shy

Part 2: Comprehension

Use what you know about the selection to answer each item.

8. New York got into trouble because he—
   F. stole some food.
   G. took money from children.
   H. tore cabbage leaves.
   (J) dived at a child's eyes.

9. According to this selection, crows know how to—
   A. sing songs with words.
   B. polish shoes.
   (C) avoid danger.
   D. give directions.

10. The George family began to teach Crowbar to talk just after—
    F. Crowbar said hello at a picnic.
    (G) they read about how crows are like parrots.
    H. the man delivering milk heard him say hello.
    J. a police officer tried to scare him away.

11. Who is Hilde?
    A. a pet crow
    B. one of the author's children
    C. one of the author's pet salamanders
    (D) a girl who lives in the neighborhood

GO ON

Practice Book 6.2, p. 56

Name ______________________ A Trouble-Making Crow

12. Which example offers the best proof that crows are intelligent?
    F. A crow that caws three times is identifying itself.
    G. Crowbar ate a piece of cold cheeseburger.
    H. New York flew into Baird Park and did not return.
    (J) Crowbar used a lid to slide with the children.

13. Crows do not make good pets because they—
    (A) seek revenge against those who hurt them.
    B. can pick out one person in a crowd.
    C. can learn to talk.
    D. are able to count.

14. Most of the time, the author describes and reacts to the pets in her house as if they were—
    F. wild animals.
    (G) friends.
    H. scientific experiments.
    J. celebrities.

15. At the end of the story, the author feels sad because she—
    A. is afraid of the large flock of crows.
    B. is happy that Crowbar will not bother her anymore.
    (C) will miss Crowbar.
    D. worries that the wild crows will hurt Crowbar.

STOP

Name ______________________ A Trouble-Making Crow

Making Judgments

- **Making a judgment** means forming an opinion about someone or something.
- When you make a judgment, you think about your own experiences and beliefs, as well as the information the author provides.
- As you read, look for evidence to support your judgments or the author's judgments.

Directions: Read the story below.

Like most dogs, Myra is gentle and quiet. But recently she developed a problem. Every once in a while, she would start to bark and run around the living room as if something were driving her crazy.

Grandpa worried that Myra might hurt the baby. He thought we should keep Myra in a separate room. But Mom, Dad, and I didn't think there was danger.

I watched Myra carefully. I noticed that every time she acted strangely, Grandpa was in the house listening to his favorite CD of loud marching bands. It was the music that was upsetting Myra! So we asked Grandpa not to play that CD when Myra was in the house. Grandpa cheerfully agreed.

Directions: Complete the table by finishing the judgments made or by giving reasons to support a judgment.

Judgment	Reason for Judgment
I think the narrator of the story is intelligent and observant.	1. **The narrator watches Myra and figures out what makes her act strangely.**
2. I think Grandpa's idea about keeping Myra out was: **a good idea, but unfair.**	Myra only barked when the music was on.
3. I think the solution of not playing the music when Myra is in the house is: **fair and intelligent.**	4. **The problem is solved without punishing Myra.**
I think that Grandpa is reasonable.	5. **Grandpa cheerfully agrees to the solution.**

Notes for Home: Your child used story details to make judgments about characters and actions. ***Home Activity:*** Have your child choose a favorite story. Together, decide whether a character's actions and ideas are fair or good.

Practice Book 6.2, p. 57

Name ______________________ A Trouble-Making Crow

Paraphrasing

REVIEW

Directions: Read the passage. Then read each question about the passage. Choose the best answer to each question. Mark the letter for the answer you have chosen.

The Crow Family

The crow family is a group of large black birds. Crows, jays, jackdaws, magpies, ravens, and rooks are all members of this family.

The common crow has glossy black feathers and a strong bill with a sharp point. Crows have strong feet that are good for walking. Male and female crows look very much alike, but the female is a little bit smaller.

Crows are highly intelligent. A crow can be a good pet if the owner obtains the crow when the crow is young. Most people recognize a crow's harsh cry, *"Caw! Caw!"* The crow can make many other noises. Sometimes people can teach crows to speak a few words.

Crows are attracted by shiny objects. They pick up stray coins, lost earrings, and any other small shiny things they find. Crows will keep these small treasures forever. They always have places where they hide their growing collections. They are famous for their habit of hoarding things.

Crows are found all over the world, except in New Zealand. The common crow is seen in many parts of North America. In recent years, crows have even become more common in big cities like New York City.

1. Which of the following statements accurately paraphrases information in the passage?
   - **A.** There is only one kind of crow.
   - **B.** Magpies, ravens, rooks are the only kinds of crows.
   - **(C)** There are many kinds of crows.
   - **D.** No crows make good pets.
2. Which of the following statements accurately paraphrases information in the passage?
   - **F.** Crows can't walk.
   - **G.** Male and female crows are the same size.
   - **(H)** The common crow has black feathers.
   - **J.** The crow's bill isn't pointed.
3. A crow—
   - **A.** can't be a good pet.
   - **B.** can make a good pet if disciplined.
   - **C.** can be trained to be a pet at any age.
   - **(D)** can be a good pet if you get it when it is young.
4. A crow—
   - **F.** can sometimes have a large vocabulary.
   - **(G)** can sometimes learn to say a few words.
   - **H.** cannot imitate sounds.
   - **J.** makes one noise.
5. The common crow—
   - **(A)** lives everywhere but New Zealand.
   - **B.** lives everywhere but North America.
   - **C.** lives only in New Zealand.
   - **D.** lives only in North America.

Notes for Home: Your child chose statements that paraphrased information in a nonfiction article. ***Home Activity:*** With your child, read a few paragraphs of a newspaper or magazine article. Have your child restate each paragraph in his or her own words.

Name ______________________ A Trouble-Making Crow

Writing Across Texts

Directions: Consider what you learned about crows in the two selections "A Trouble-Making Crow" and "The Crow and the Pitcher." What are some of the characteristics of a crow? Add five examples to the web below. **Possible answers given.**

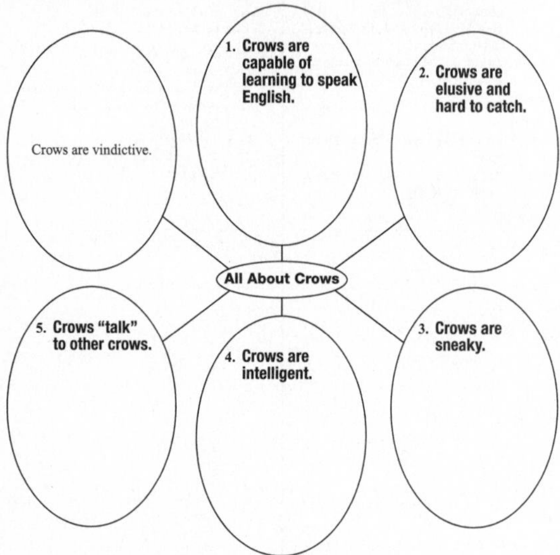

Crows are vindictive.
1. Crows are capable of learning to speak English.
2. Crows are elusive and hard to catch.
All About Crows
5. Crows "talk" to other crows.
4. Crows are intelligent.
3. Crows are sneaky.

Write an Encyclopedia Article

Use the completed web and the selections "A Trouble-Making Crow" and "The Crow and the Pitcher" to write an encyclopedia article about the characteristics of crows. Write your article on a separate sheet of paper. **Students' encyclopedia articles will vary. Check to see that they have used specific details from both selections in their articles.**

Notes for Home: Your child has used two different sources to complete a web and write an encyclopedia article. ***Home Activity:*** Read other stories or articles about animals. Encourage your child to create a similar web and use it to name the characteristics of other animals.

Grammar Practice Book 6.2, p. 26

Name ______________________ A Trouble-Making Crow

Grammar: Subjects

REVIEW

Directions: Underline the complete subject in each sentence. Then circle the simple subject. (There may be more than one simple subject in a sentence.)

1. All (crows) have feathers of a glossy black color.
2. The hooded (crow) has touches of gray as well.
3. (North America) and (Eurasia) are home to the most common kinds of crows.
4. (Eurasia) includes both Europe and Asia.
5. The crow's (name) comes from its "caw" or "craw" sound.
6. (Grains), (berries), (insects), dead (animals), and other birds' (eggs) are its favorite food.
7. Fifteen to twenty (years) is not an unusual life span for a crow in captivity.
8. This big, noisy, sociable (bird) is extremely smart.
9. Some (owners) of pet crows have taught their birds to "speak" on command.
10. Other (crows) in laboratories have been taught to count up to three or four.

Directions: Use each of the following subjects in a sentence of your own. Write the sentence on the line. Then circle the simple subject. **Possible answers given.**

11. A group of big black birds
    A (group) of big black birds gathered in the tree.
12. A nest full of robin's eggs
    A (nest) full of robin's eggs sat on a branch below.
13. One of the hungry birds
    (One) of the hungry birds swooped down and stole some eggs.
14. A second black bird
    A second black (bird) stole an egg too.
15. A female robin and then the male
    A female (robin) and then the (male) came back to an empty nest.

Notes for Home: Your child recognized simple and complete subjects and used them in sentences. ***Home Activity:*** Look through a newspaper, magazine, or book with your child. Encourage your child to find the simple and complete subjects of sentences.

Grammar Practice Book 6.2, p. 27

Name ______________________ A Trouble-Making Crow

Grammar: Proper Nouns and Common Nouns

A noun names one or more persons, places, or things (Things include ideas.). A **proper noun** is the name of a *particular* person, place, or thing: *Anne D. Gray, Texas, Tuesday,* and *Dr. Fiorenza* are proper nouns.

A proper noun, such as *Martin Luther King Jr. School,* may consist of more than one word. Begin each important word in a proper noun with a capital letter.

Nouns that are not proper nouns are called **common nouns.** A common noun does not name any particular person, place, or thing. The words *sister, state,* and *day,* are common nouns. Common nouns are not capitalized.

Directions: Underline the nouns in each sentence. If a noun is a proper noun, underline it twice.

1. A flock of crows lives near the open meadow.
2. Each morning joggers can hear these birds all over Central Park.
3. When Mrs. Wall is walking her terrier nearby, the crows sound an alarm.
4. "Mr. Jet" is my name for the crow with the harshest voice.
5. His nest is high in the tallest evergreen near Turtle Pond.
6. Students from Barnard College check their guides to local birds.
7. Roger Tory Peterson wrote five guides for birdwatchers.
8. Do ravens really live at the Tower of London?
9. In Manhattan, falcons lay their eggs on the ledges of skyscrapers.
10. Gyrfalcons are found at the Arctic Circle, not in New York City.

Directions: Write **C** if the noun is a common noun. Write **P** if the noun is a proper noun. If it is a proper noun, rewrite it correctly on the line.

11. field **C**
12. hoyt park **P; Hoyt Park**
13. labor day **P; Labor Day**
14. binoculars **C**
15. mr. a. p. finney **P; Mr. A. P. Finney**

Notes for Home: Your child identified proper nouns and common nouns. ***Home Activity:*** Just for fun, challenge your child to try to speak for five minutes without using *any* nouns.

Grammar Practice Book 6.2, p. 28

Name ______________________ A Trouble-Making Crow

Grammar: Proper Nouns and Common Nouns

Directions: Underline the nouns in each sentence. If a noun is a proper noun, underline it twice.

1. Our family visited Maine this summer.
2. The trip began with a drive up the coast to a town called Camden.
3. Kennebunkport and Bangor are full of shops and restaurants.
4. The next stop was at Acadia National Park.
5. Outstanding features of the trip were Thunder Hole and Cadillac Mountain.

Directions: Rewrite each sentence on the lines below. Capitalize all proper nouns.

6. The ocean was spectacular that day, and acadia park was beautiful.
The ocean was spectacular that day, and Acadia Park was beautiful.

7. Dad drove through washington county to nova scotia.
Dad drove through Washington County to Nova Scotia.

8. The bay of fundy is an unusual body of water.
The Bay of Fundy is an unusual body of water.

9. Because of the shape of this bay, which is in canada, the tide comes in suddenly.
Because of the shape of this bay, which is in Canada, the tide comes in suddenly.

10. A 42-foot wall of water rushes in from the atlantic ocean in just minutes!
A 42-foot wall of water rushes in from the Atlantic Ocean in just minutes!

Write About a Place

Write a paragraph or two describing the town or city where you live. Name a few points of interest, such as parks or buildings, and explain why they are important. Use at least three common nouns and three proper nouns.
Check whether proper nouns are capitalized correctly.

Notes for Home: Your child identified proper nouns and common nouns and capitalized proper nouns. ***Home Activity:*** Together, write a variety of common and proper nouns on slips of paper. Take turns with your child drawing slips and using the noun in a sentence.

Grammar Practice Book 6.2, p. 29

Name ______________________ A Trouble-Making Crow

Grammar: Proper Nouns and Common Nouns

RETEACHING

Draw a line to join each common noun on the left with a proper noun on the right.

Common Noun	Proper Noun
inventor	New Jersey
month	Thomas Alva Edison
state	February

A **common noun** names any of a kind of person, place, or thing. A **proper noun** names a particular person, place, or thing. Proper nouns always begin with capital letters.

Directions: Write **common noun** or **proper noun** to describe the underlined word.

1. Thomas Edison invented the lightbulb. **proper noun**
2. Thomas Alva Edison was born in Ohio in 1847. **proper noun**
3. He was educated at home by his mother. **common noun**
4. At age twelve he was a newsboy. **common noun**
5. Edison later worked on a train in Michigan. **proper noun**

Directions: Underline the common nouns and proper nouns in each sentence.

6. Edison patented over a thousand inventions.
7. Where did the busy inventor work in America?
8. The laboratory was in New Jersey.
9. His phonograph was famous in Europe.
10. Thomas Edison helped to invent movies.

Directions: Copy the nouns you underlined in items 6–10. Write each one in the correct column.

Common Nouns	Proper Nouns
11. **inventions**	12. **Edison**
13. **inventor**	14. **America**
15. **laboratory**	16. **New Jersey**
17. **phonograph**	18. **Europe**
19. **movies**	20. **Thomas Edison**

Notes for Home: Your child identified and categorized common nouns and proper nouns. ***Home Activity:*** Together, write a list of nouns that name persons, places, and things in your home. Have your child capitalize proper nouns correctly.

Grammar Practice Book 6.2, p. 30

Name ______________________ A Trouble-Making Crow

Grammar: Proper Nouns and Common Nouns

Directions: Read the paragraph. Write each underlined noun in the correct column.

Do you know about the huge statues of heads on Easter Island? Easter Island is located in the South Pacific west of Chile. Scientists do not know much about the background of the statues. There are more than 600 of these giant heads with long ears. Jacob Roggeven first saw the carved giants in 1722. The heads weigh fifty tons and do not look like the Polynesians on this Pacific island.

Common Nouns	Proper Nouns
1. **statues**	2. **Easter Island**
3. **heads**	4. **South Pacific**
5. **scientists or Scientists**	6. **Chile**
7. **ears**	8. **Jacob Roggeven**
9. **giants**	10. **Polynesians**

Directions: Underline each common noun once and each proper noun twice.

11. The statues on Easter Island are made of red stone.
12. Some statues are over 40 feet and weigh 90 tons.
13. Islanders carved the statues from the rock of extinct volcanoes.
14. The builders of these figures are still unknown to the experts.
15. Thor Heyerdahl sailed to Easter Island on a raft.
16. This explorer from Norway studied the currents of the Pacific Ocean.
17. Heyerdahl wrote an interesting book about the monuments.
18. This book contains ideas about the mystery of the lonely island in the Pacific.
19. Today its population includes many Chileans.
20. The librarian will find the book for the class.

Write an Announcement

On a separate sheet of paper, write an announcement about a discovery you made, such as an unusual stone or a special place. Before you begin writing, think about what you were doing right before you made the discovery. Then start to write. Tell what you discovered and where you found it. Use common and proper nouns. **Make sure that students have capitalized proper nouns correctly.**

Notes for Home: Your child has identified common nouns and proper nouns and capitalized proper nouns correctly. ***Home Activity:*** Have your child read his or her announcement. Then have him or her underline common nouns and circle proper nouns.

Practice Book 6.2, p. 58

Name ______________ A Trouble-Making Crow

Phonics: Consonant Sounds for *c* and *g*

Directions: Read the sentences below. Two words in each sentence have the letter **c.** Circle the word with the **hard-c** sound as in **cold.** Underline the word with the **soft-c** sound as in **place.**

1. We were certain the (country) would be a great spot for our day off.
2. We saw a large bird sitting on the fence while we had our (picnic).
3. Seeing a wild (crow) was a new experience for our family.
4. The bird eventually (escaped) our stares by flying to a nearby spruce tree.
5. No matter how we (coaxed) the bird would not leave its place up high.

Directions: Read the sentences below. Two words in each sentence have the letter **g.** One has a **hard-g** sound as in **go.** The other word has a **soft-g** sound as in **gentle.** Circle the words with the **hard-g** sound. Underline the words with the **soft-g** sound.

6. Sometimes several crows would hide in the (garden) among the cabbages.
7. The crows (gathered) around looking for food like scavengers.
8. The birds seemed to (beg) urgently with their loud squawks.
9. It appeared as if the huge crow was the leader of the (group).
10. Large crows can be very (aggressive) sometimes.

Directions: Read the sentences below. Each underlined word has both a **c** and a **g.** Circle the two words in each group that have the same consonant sounds as the **c** and **g** in the underlined word.

11. I did not recognize the calls of the little crow when I first heard it.
    (cat) trance (goat) giant
12. The baby bird had fallen between the cabbage leaves and was calling for help.
    fence (frantic) good (giant)
13. We encouraged the crow to fly off on its own.
    cellar (complex) forgive (page)
14. It took a few hops, then it gracefully flew to a tree branch.
    (gate) gem corn (stance)
15. Although some people may not like crows, it's hard to imagine that the gentle bird we saw would ever seek vengeance.
    frog (stage) (certain) picnic

Notes for Home: Your child identified the sounds that the letters *c* and *g* can represent, such as *go, cabbage* (hard *g*, soft *g*), *crow, fence* (hard *c*, soft *c*). ***Home Activity:*** Read a book about animals with your child. Find words with these letters and have your child say them aloud.

Spelling Workbook 6.2, p. 21

Name ______________ A Trouble-Making Crow

Spelling: Words from Many Cultures

Pretest Directions: Fold back the page along the dotted line. On the blanks, write the spelling words as they are dictated. When you have finished the test, unfold the page and check your words.

1. moose — The **moose** has huge antlers.
2. cobra — We saw a **cobra** at the zoo.
3. alligator — The **alligator** lives in a swamp.
4. vanilla — I want **vanilla** ice cream.
5. banana — He has never eaten a **banana.**
6. tomato — **Tomato** sauce can stain clothing.
7. mustard — Please use a lot of **mustard.**
8. hula — Her parents learned the **hula.**
9. picnic — What's in your **picnic** basket?
10. barbecue — Let's have a **barbecue.**
11. crocodile — It isn't wise to pet a **crocodile.**
12. coyote — The **coyote** barked at the birds.
13. koala — A **koala** lives in this big tree.
14. macaroni — She likes **macaroni** and cheese.
15. catsup — Please pass me the **catsup.**
16. polka — They danced the **polka** all night.
17. ballet — We are going to the **ballet.**
18. waltz — My parents like to **waltz.**
19. banquet — We ate at a **banquet** hall.
20. buffet — I made two trips to the **buffet.**

Notes for Home: Your child took a pretest on words that come from other languages. ***Home Activity:*** Help your child learn misspelled words before the final test. Your child should look at the word, say it, spell it aloud, and then spell it with eyes shut.

Spelling Workbook 6.2, p. 22

Name ______________ A Trouble-Making Crow

Spelling: Words from Many Cultures

Word List				
moose	banana	picnic	koala	ballet
cobra	tomato	barbecue	macaroni	waltz
alligator	mustard	crocodile	catsup	banquet
vanilla	hula	coyote	polka	buffet

Directions: Write the words from the box that belong in each group. **Order may vary.**

Animals	Things to Eat	Dances
1. moose	7. vanilla	13. hula
2. cobra	8. banana	14. polka
3. alligator	9. tomato	15. ballet
4. crocodile	10. mustard	16. waltz
5. coyote	11. macaroni	
6. koala	12. catsup	

Directions: Choose the word from the box that best matches each clue. Write the word on the line.

17. barbecue — It is both an open grill and meat cooked in a spicy sauce.
18. picnic — It is a meal eaten outdoors. Hint: Ants love them.
19. buffet — It is a meal at which people serve themselves from a sideboard or counter.
20. banquet — It is a feast or large meal with many courses.

Notes for Home: Your child spelled words that come from other languages. ***Home Activity:*** Challenge your child to use the spelling words to write several sentences. Have him or her check the sentences to be sure all the words are spelled correctly.

Spelling Workbook 6.2, p. 23

Name ______________ A Trouble-Making Crow

Spelling: Words from Many Cultures

Directions: Proofread these minutes from a meeting. Find seven spelling mistakes. Use the proofreading marks to correct each mistake.

≡ Make a capital.
/ Make a small letter.
∧ Add something.
Take out something.
⊙ Add a period.
¶ Begin a new paragraph.

Minutes from August Meeting

- This summer's picnick was great. We'll plan to have another one next June. [k taken out]
- We ran short of catsup, musterd, relish, macaronie salad, and meat. We'll need more food, more barbaque grills, and extra cooks. [musterd → mustard; macaronie → macaroni; barbaque → barbecue]
- The vanila ice cream melted. Let's try strawberry shortcake next time. [add l: vanilla]
- Next year we should set up the food on a buffett table. [t taken out]
- The guests really enjoyed dancing, especially the waltz and poka. Let's include those dances and add others. [add l: polka]

Word List
moose, cobra, alligator, vanilla, banana, tomato, mustard, hula, picnic, barbecue, crocodile, coyote, koala, macaroni, catsup, polka, ballet, waltz, banquet, buffet

Spelling Tip

ballet buffet

Many English words come from other languages and may have unexpected spellings. **Ballet** and **buffet** are French words, so they follow the French rule that **-et** sounds like the English long **a.**

Write Minutes from a Meeting

Imagine that you are the head caretaker of a wild animal park. You hold a meeting to discuss ways to keep the animals healthy and happy. On a separate piece of paper, make a list of plans for the park. Use at least five spelling words.

Answers will vary, but each set of minutes should include at least five spelling words.

Notes for Home: Your child spelled words that come from other languages. ***Home Activity:*** Work with your child to create a crossword puzzle using several of the spelling words.

Spelling Workbook 6.2, p. 24

Name ______________ A Trouble-Making Crow

Spelling: Words from Many Cultures REVIEW

Word List				
moose	banana	picnic	koala	ballet
cobra	tomato	barbecue	macaroni	waltz
alligator	mustard	crocodile	catsup	banquet
vanilla	hula	coyote	polka	buffet

Directions: Choose the word from the box that best matches each definition. Write the word on the line.

crocodile 1. a lizard-like reptile with a narrow head (Greek)
alligator 2. a large reptile with a short, flat head (Spanish)
ballet 3. a theatrical dance (French, from Italian)
tomato 4. a red or yellow juicy fruit (Nahuatl [Aztec])
macaroni 5. a tube-shaped type of pasta (Italian)
buffet 6. a meal at which people serve themselves (French)
moose 7. a large mammal with broad antlers (Algonquin)
waltz 8. a smooth, gliding dance in triple time (German)
banana 9. a curved yellow or red tropical fruit (Spanish)
mustard 10. a yellow seasoning (French)
catsup 11. a spicy sauce made from tomatoes (Malay)
polka 12. a lively folk dance (Polish)

Directions: Choose the word from the box that best completes each command. Write the word on the line to the left.

barbecue 13. Roast the meat on the outdoor _____.
coyote 14. Hear the howling of the wild _____.
banquet 15. Plan to eat several courses at the ceremonial _____.
vanilla 16. Stir the cake batter and then add the _____.
cobra 17. Please avoid stepping on that poisonous _____!
koala 18. Look at the furry Australian _____ in the tree.
picnic 19. Put the _____ basket on that blanket under the tree.
hula 20. Dance the graceful Hawaiian _____.

Notes for Home: Your child spelled words that come from other languages. ***Home Activity:*** With your child, write tongue twisters for the spelling words, such as *Minnie the Moose munched many mangoes.*

Practice Book 6.2, p. 59

Name ______________ A Trouble-Making Crow

Questions for Inquiry

Formulating and revising **questions for inquiry** about a topic can help you set a purpose for your reading and help you focus your research. Before you begin your research, think about the questions you want answered about the topic. As you read, you may need to revise your questions to focus more specifically on the topic.

Directions: Before you read the encyclopedia entry below, answer the first two questions on the next page. Then read the entry and use it to answer the rest of the questions.

Common Crow

Family: *Corvidae* (includes jays, ravens, magpies, rooks, and jackdaws)

Scientific name: *Corvus brachyrhynchos*

Size: 17–21 inches long (43 to 53 centimeters)

Color: black

Diet: corn, wheat, insects, spiders, small birds, eggs, rodents, dead flesh

Common crow, also called the American crow, or *corvus brachyrhynchos,* is probably, with the robin and the pigeon, one of the three most easily-recognized birds in the United States. Crows are medium-sized, coal-black birds, much larger than robins and other songbirds, but much smaller than eagles, gulls, or hawks. This bird can be found in many parts of the world, although there are no crows in New Zealand, the Antarctic, or South America.

Crows use more than 23 different calls to communicate with one another. They cooperate with one another much more than other birds do. Both parents look after the nestling crows, and crows in the same flock will take turns keeping watch for enemies, gathering food, and attacking intruders. Flocks of crows can number in the thousands.

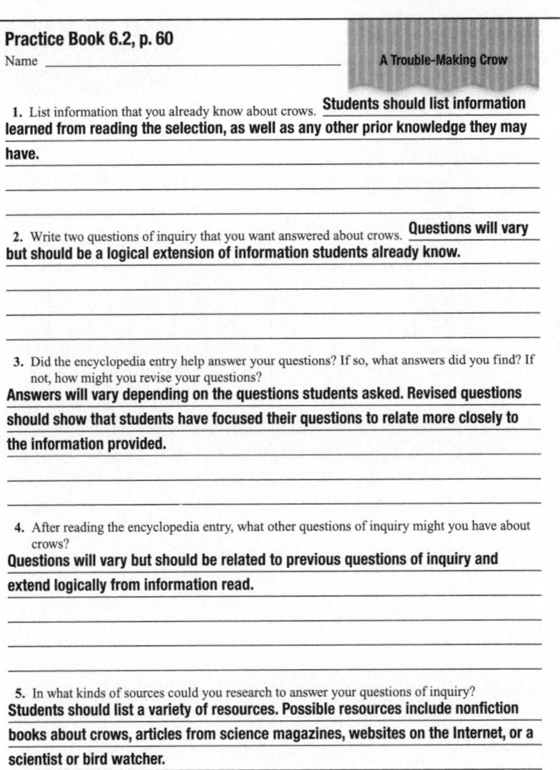

Practice Book 6.2, p. 60

Name ______________ A Trouble-Making Crow

1. List information that you already know about crows. **Students should list information learned from reading the selection, as well as any other prior knowledge they may have.**

2. Write two questions of inquiry that you want answered about crows. **Questions will vary but should be a logical extension of information students already know.**

3. Did the encyclopedia entry help answer your questions? If so, what answers did you find? If not, how might you revise your questions?
Answers will vary depending on the questions students asked. Revised questions should show that students have focused their questions to relate more closely to the information provided.

4. After reading the encyclopedia entry, what other questions of inquiry might you have about crows?
Questions will vary but should be related to previous questions of inquiry and extend logically from information read.

5. In what kinds of sources could you research to answer your questions of inquiry?
Students should list a variety of resources. Possible resources include nonfiction books about crows, articles from science magazines, websites on the Internet, or a scientist or bird watcher.

Notes for Home: Your child formulated questions for inquiry about crows. ***Home Activity:*** Have your child write a list of questions about an interesting animal. Work together to answer these questions using a nature program, an encyclopedia, a nonfiction book, or the Internet.

Practice Book 6.2, p. 61

Name ______________ From a Spark

Predicting

- To **predict** means to state what might happen next in a story or article. To make a prediction, think about what you know and what has already happened.
- After making a prediction, continue reading to check its accuracy. Revise your prediction if it does not agree with new information.

Directions: Reread "At the Water's Edge." Then complete each box. Read each question and tell what logical prediction can be made based on what you have read up to that point in the story. Give a reason for each prediction.

Question: What do you predict Alec might see from the high rock?
1. **Prediction:** **He may see some edible shellfish.**
2. **Reason:** **He is specifically looking for shellfish.**

Question: What do you predict Alec might do after he first tastes the moss?
3. **Prediction:** **He will gather and eat as much as he can.**
4. **Reason:** **He is very hungry.**

Question: What might Alec do next? Why do you think so?
5. **Prediction:** **He will explore the island, looking for more food or for shelter.**
6. **Reason:** **Eating will cheer him up and make him feel strong enough to explore.**

Notes for Home: Your child read a story and made predictions about what would happen next. ***Home Activity:*** Tell your child a story about a real-life experience. Pause throughout the story to have your child make and/or revise predictions about what will happen next.

Practice Book 6.2, p. 62

Name ____________________ **From a Spark**

Vocabulary

Directions: Choose the word from the box that best completes each sentence. Write the word on the line to the left.

Check the Words You Know
__ hatchet
__ ignite
__ painstaking
__ smoldered
__ survival

survival 1. In winter, a person's _____ depends on having a source of heat.

hatchet 2. A _____ is a handy tool to cut small pieces of dry wood for the fire.

ignite 3. Dry matches are needed to _____ a campfire.

painstaking 4. Without matches, it is a _____ job to get a fire started.

smoldered 5. Safety rules are very important with fires. Many forest fires have begun from an untended campfire that _____ and then burst into flames.

Directions: Choose the word from the box that best matches each clue. Write the word in the puzzle.

Down

6. small ax with a short handle
8. to set on fire

Across

7. requiring careful effort or attention
9. the act of staying alive
10. burned and smoked without flames

6. hatchet
7. painstaking
8. igniter
9. survival
10. smoldered

Write an Essay

On a separate sheet of paper, write one or two paragraphs explaining the uses of fire in everyday life. Do you think fire is as imporant to our lives today as to people in the past? Explain your thinking using as many vocabulary words as you can.

Students' explanations of fire's importance should make correct use of vocabulary words.

Notes for Home: Your child identified and used vocabulary words from "From a Spark." ***Home Activity:*** With your child, make up a story of having to survive in the woods. Use as many of the vocabulary words as you can.

Practice Book 6.2, p. 63

Name ____________________ **From a Spark**

Predicting

- To **predict** means to state what you think might happen next in a story or article.
- To make a prediction, think about what you already know and what has already happened.
- Check and change your prediction as you encounter new information.

Directions: Reread what happens in "From a Spark" after Brian wakes up from the dream about his father and Terry. Then answer the questions below. Think about the predictions you made as you were reading the story.

Fire. The hatchet was the key to it all. When he threw the hatchet at the porcupine in the cave and missed and hit the stone wall it had showered sparks, a golden shower of sparks in the dark, as golden with fire as the sun was now.

The hatchet was the answer. That's what his father and Terry had been trying to tell him. Somehow he could get fire from the hatchet. The sparks would make fire.

Brian went back into the shelter and studied the wall. . . . It only took him a moment to find where the hatchet had struck. The steel had nicked into the edge of one of the darker stone pieces.

Possible answers given.

1. What do you think Brian will do with the hatchet?
Brian will hit the hatchet against a rock so that it makes fire.

2. Which clues helped you make this prediction?
The story mentions that the hatchet made sparks when it hit the stone wall and that "somehow he could get fire from the hatchet."

3. How will Brian use the wall to help him make fire?
Brian will strike a dark stone with the hatchet.

4. Which clues helped you make this prediction?
When the hatchet hit the dark stone, it made sparks.

5. Do you think Brian will survive? Explain your thinking on a separate sheet of paper.
Yes. Brian built a fire, did not give up until he succeeded, and used his intelligence to help himself.

Notes for Home: Your child used story details to predict what would happen next in a story. ***Home Activity:*** With your child, read the first paragraph of an article or a story. Work together to predict what will happen next or what the article or story will be about.

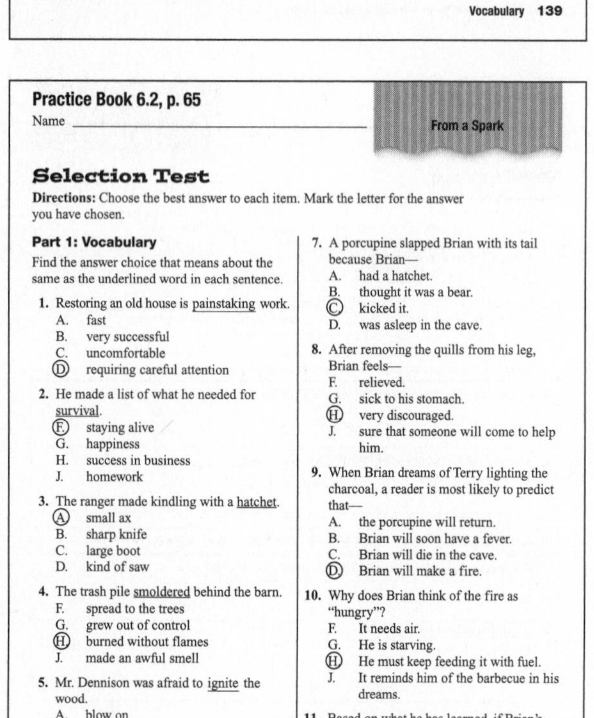

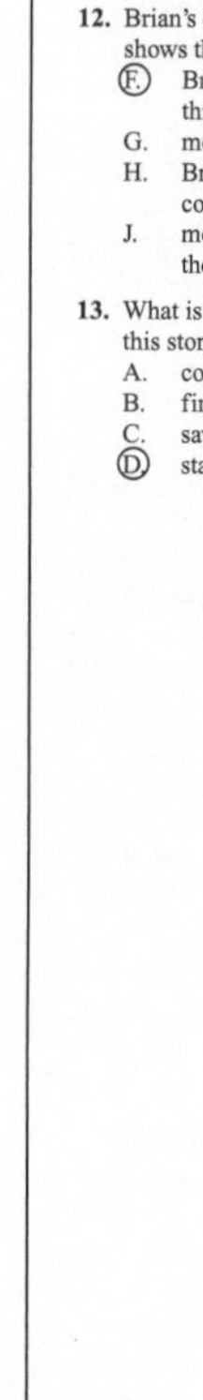

Practice Book 6.2, p. 65

Name ____________________ **From a Spark**

Selection Test

Directions: Choose the best answer to each item. Mark the letter for the answer you have chosen.

Part 1: Vocabulary

Find the answer choice that means about the same as the underlined word in each sentence.

1. Restoring an old house is painstaking work.
   - A. fast
   - B. very successful
   - C. uncomfortable
   - (D) requiring careful attention
2. He made a list of what he needed for survival.
   - (F) staying alive
   - G. happiness
   - H. success in business
   - J. homework
3. The ranger made kindling with a hatchet.
   - (A) small ax
   - B. sharp knife
   - C. large boot
   - D. kind of saw
4. The trash pile smoldered behind the barn.
   - F. spread to the trees
   - G. grew out of control
   - (H) burned without flames
   - J. made an awful smell
5. Mr. Dennison was afraid to ignite the wood.
   - A. blow on
   - (B) set on fire
   - C. break up
   - D. cut into pieces

Part 2: Comprehension

Use what you know about the story to answer each item.

6. At the beginning of the story, Brian wakes up to the smell of—
   - F. pine trees.
   - (G) an animal.
   - H. smoke.
   - J. raspberries.
7. A porcupine slapped Brian with its tail because Brian—
   - A. had a hatchet.
   - B. thought it was a bear.
   - (C) kicked it.
   - D. was asleep in the cave.
8. After removing the quills from his leg, Brian feels—
   - F. relieved.
   - G. sick to his stomach.
   - (H) very discouraged.
   - J. sure that someone will come to help him.
9. When Brian dreams of Terry lighting the charcoal, a reader is most likely to predict that—
   - A. the porcupine will return.
   - B. Brian will soon have a fever.
   - C. Brian will die in the cave.
   - (D) Brian will make a fire.
10. Why does Brian think of the fire as "hungry"?
    - F. It needs air.
    - G. He is starving.
    - (H) He must keep feeding it with fuel.
    - J. It reminds him of the barbecue in his dreams.
11. Based on what he has learned, if Brian's fire goes out he is most likely to—
    - A. give up on having a fire.
    - (B) make a new fire.
    - C. look for matches.
    - D. cry in self-pity.

GO ON

Practice Book 6.2, p. 66

Name ____________________ **From a Spark**

12. Brian's experience in getting the fire going shows that—
    - (F) Brian is able to remember and use things he has learned.
    - G. most fires don't need oxygen.
    - H. Brian should have taken a survival course.
    - J. most animals will approach a fire if they need to get warm.
13. What is Brian most concerned about in this story?
    - A. controlling the fire
    - B. finding Terry
    - C. saving his money
    - (D) staying alive
14. Brian threw the hatchet because he thought that—
    - F. a porcupine would be scared by a shower of sparks.
    - (G) he had to protect himself from a large animal.
    - H. a snake would not be moving around at night.
    - J. a bad dream was coming true.
15. Which statement best describes Brian?
    - (A) He has not had much experience living outdoors.
    - B. He does not like his family.
    - C. He does not have much patience.
    - D. He cannot think clearly because of his injury.

Name ______________________ From a Spark

Predicting

- To **predict** means to state what you think might happen next in a story or article.
- To make a prediction, think about what you already know and what has already happened.
- Check and change your prediction as you encounter new information.

Directions: Read the story below.

Shocked, Matt looked at the footprints in the snow. They were his footprints! He had been wandering in circles. Matt began to panic. He would never find his way back to camp! He would freeze out in the wild!

Matt took a deep breath. He knew he had to stay calm. He thought of other times when he had been scared. He never got scared when his father was there. When his father wasn't there, it helped Matt just to think about him.

Ahead of Matt, there were many rocks and hollows in the hill. Matt suddenly remembered that if you could get inside a little cave or hollow, you could build a wall of snow by the entrance to keep warm.

Directions: Complete the table by answering the questions below. **Possible answers given.**

Question	Prediction	Story Clues Used to Make Prediction
What will Matt do to calm himself?	1. **Matt will think about his father.**	2. **In the past, thinking about his father has helped Matt.**
How will Matt keep warm?	3. **Matt will find a cave or hollow and wall himself in with snow.**	4. **Matt sees hollows on the hill.**
		5. **He remembers that you can wall yourself into a cave or hollow to stay warm.**

Notes for Home: Your child used story details to make predictions about what could happen next. ***Home Activity:*** With your child, observe characters in television shows or movies. Make predictions together about what they will do next.

Name ______________________ From a Spark

Setting and Steps in a Process

REVIEW

Directions: Read the passage. Then read each question about the passage. Choose the best answer to each question. Mark the letter for the answer you have chosen.

A Cold Journey

Roald Amundsen left Norway secretly. He wanted to beat the British explorer Robert Scott to the South Pole. No explorer had traveled so far.

Amundsen and his team reached the edge of Antarctica in January. They took a few trips inland to set up supplies of food and fuel. Then they waited for spring to arrive so they could travel.

In October, spring arrived. Amundsen's team began its trip through Antarctica to the South Pole. The trip was painstaking. They ran out of the food they had brought. In order to survive, they had to kill and eat the weaker sled dogs. But on December 14, 1911, Amundsen and his team became the first people to reach the South Pole. Soon Amundsen was famous throughout the world.

1. Most of this story is set—
   A. in Norway.
   B. in Britain.
   Ⓒ in Antarctica.
   D. all over the world.

2. How would this story be different if Robert Scott had already reached the South Pole?
   Ⓕ Amundsen would not have left secretly.
   G. Amundsen could have traveled in January.
   H. Amundsen could have gotten food from Scott.
   J. Amundsen would have been as famous as Scott.

3. What did Amundsen do first?
   A. He set up camp at the edge of Antarctica.
   Ⓑ He left Norway secretly.
   C. He set up supplies.
   D. He began his trip through the Antarctic.

4. Before Amundsen left the edge of the Antarctic, he—
   F. killed weaker sled dogs.
   Ⓖ set up supplies of food and fuel.
   H. met with Robert Scott.
   J. traveled to the South Pole.

5. How does the Antarctic setting affect Amundsen's actions?
   Ⓐ Dogs have to be killed and eaten when food runs out.
   B. He has to get more dogs to keep traveling.
   C. He has to send far away for help.
   D. He has to travel alone.

Notes for Home: Your child identified the time and place in which a story takes place, and the order in which story events happened. ***Home Activity:*** Have your child choose a favorite story. With your child, identify the time and place in which the story takes place.

Name ______________________ From a Spark

Writing Across Texts

Directions: Consider the selections "A Trouble-Making Crow" and "From a Spark." Complete the table by listing the problems the characters experienced. **Possible answers given.**

From a Spark	A Trouble-Making Crow
Brian is alone in the Canadian wilderness.	New York, their pet crow, started diving at Hilde Black's eyes.
1. **He could not see in the dark.**	6. **The mother had to catch the crow and take him away.**
2. **He was starving.**	7. **They could not get Crowbar to talk.**
3. **He was hurt by the quills of a porcupine.**	8. **Crowbar would eat the neighbors' picnic food.**
4. **He could not remember how to start a fire.**	9. **Crowbar would take children's coins.**
5. **His fire kept going out.**	10. **Crowbar was stealing toys from the sandbox.**

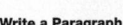

Write a Paragraph

Use the information from the table above to write a paragraph that compares and contrasts the problems that Brian has with the problems of the family in "A Trouble-Making Crow." Write your paragraph on a separate sheet of paper.
Paragraphs will vary. Check that students use details from both selections to make their comparisons.

Notes for Home: Your child used details from two different selections to write a comparison/contrast paragraph. ***Home Activity:*** As you read other stories or articles, encourage your child to point out their likenesses and differences.

Name ______________________ From a Spark

Grammar: Nouns

REVIEW

Directions: Underline each noun in the sentences that follow. Underline proper nouns twice.

1. My Aunt Fay and her children, Alana and Nathan, were taking a bus from New Hampshire to Cape Cod.
2. From the bus, Nathan pointed out Boston and Plymouth.
3. Of course, Plymouth and Plymouth Rock are famous as the landing place of the Pilgrims in the seventeenth century.
4. The passengers felt a sudden jolt, and the bus went into a skid along Route 95.
5. Fortunately, Officer Eileen Regan and Officer Jamal Davis were on the scene quickly, and no one suffered serious injury.

Directions: Write each sentence correctly. Remember to capitalize all proper nouns.

6. The famous mt. everest lies in the himalayan mountains in asia.
   The famous Mt. Everest lies in the Himalayan mountains in Asia.
7. In 1953, edmund hillary and tenzing norgay became the first climbers to reach the soaring peak.
   In 1953, Edmund Hillary and Tenzing Norgay became the first climbers to reach the soaring peak.
8. Thousands have climbed mt. mcKinley in north america and mt. kilimanjaro in africa.
   Thousands have climbed Mt. McKinley in North America and Mt. Kilimanjaro in Africa.
9. Hundreds of climbers from europe, the americas, japan, and other parts of the world have died in these attempts.
   Hundreds of climbers from Europe, the Americas, Japan, and other parts of the world have died in these attempts.
10. A chilling book by jon krakauer tells of the twelve climbers who died climbing mt. everest in may 1996.
    A chilling book by Jon Krakauer tells of the twelve climbers who died climbing Mt. Everest in May 1996.

Notes for Home: Your child identified and used common and proper nouns in sentences. ***Home Activity:*** Take a walk with your child. Encourage your child to list the people, places, and things you see, using common and proper nouns.

Grammar Practice Book 6.2, p. 32

Name ______________________ **From a Spark**

Grammar: Plural Nouns

A noun that names more than one person, place, thing, or idea is a **plural noun.**

Regular Nouns

- Add **-s** or **-es** to most nouns to make them plural: fork, forks.
- Add **-es** to nouns ending in **ch, sh, x, z, s** or **ss:** match, matches; wish, wishes; box, boxes; buzz, buzzes; bus, buses; success, successes.
- If a noun ends in a **vowel** followed by **y,** add **-s.** If a noun ends in a **consonant** and **y,** change the **y** to **i** and add **-es:** journey, journeys; lady, ladies.

Irregular Nouns

- Some nouns have the same singular and plural form: elk/elk; deer/deer.
- Some nouns change the spelling of the word to form the plural: child, children; ox, oxen.
- You can form the plurals of some nouns ending in **f** or **fe** by changing **f** or **fe** to **v** and adding **-es:** wolf, wolves; knife, knives.
- Add **-s** to certain nouns that end in **f:** roof, roofs; chief, chiefs.
- Add **-s** to nearly all nouns that end in **ff:** sheriff, sheriffs.
- Add **-s** to nouns ending in a **vowel** and **o:** patio, patios; stereo, stereos.
- Check the dictionary for plurals of nouns ending in a consonant followed by **o:** photo, photos; piano, pianos; hero, heroes; tomato, tomatoes.

Directions: Write the plural form of each underlined noun or nouns. Use a dictionary if you need help.

thieves; sheriffs 1. Kelly saw a <u>thief</u>, but not the kind a <u>sheriff</u> would arrest.
foxes; mice 2. The <u>fox</u> was holding a large <u>mouse</u> in its jaw.
bandits; latches 3. The <u>bandit</u> couldn't unlock the <u>latch</u> of the gate.
fences 4. It managed to slip under the <u>fence</u>.
gardens 5. It ran across the vegetable <u>garden</u>.
babies 6. The fox would feed its <u>baby</u> before eating.
sheep 7. The <u>sheep</u> in the field was alarmed.
hoofs or hooves 8. It stamped its <u>hoof</u> in fear.
heroes 9. It wished a <u>hero</u> would come to the rescue!
roofs; ospreys 10. High above the <u>roof</u>, an <u>osprey</u> wished it had caught the mouse.

Notes for Home: Your child wrote plural nouns. ***Home Activity:*** Look through a catalog or an illustrated encyclopedia with your child. Ask your child to tell you how to form plurals of the names of objects pictured.

Grammar Practice Book 6.2, p. 33

Name ______________________ **From a Spark**

Grammar: Plural Nouns

Directions: Write the plural form of each noun in ( ). Use a dictionary if you need help.

cliffs 1. The (cliff) towered above the two climbers.
Patches 2. (Patch) of blue could be seen between the rocky slopes.
elk 3. Were those (elk) scrambling over the rocks?
children 4. Even as (child), the climbers had dreamed about this mountain!
stories 5. They also had heard many (story) about its dangers.
heroes 6. They were not (hero), just two people trying to reach its peak.
axes 7. Therefore, they were well equipped with (ax) and other tools.
surprises 8. Some unpleasant (surprise) awaited them, however.
lives 9. Soon their (life) would be in great danger.
skies 10. Would they reach camp before the (sky) turned dark?

Directions: Write five sentences. Use the plural form of each noun in the box in each sentence. **Possible answers given.**

journey	foot	challenge	spy	knife

11. **Journeys into the rain forest were always dangerous.**
12. **The climbers were only a hundred feet from the mountain top.**
13. **They had faced such challenges many times.**
14. **Were the two climbers really dangerous spies?**
15. **They used the knives to cut the ropes and escape.**

Write a TV News Report

Think of a real or fictional person who was caught in a dangerous situation and survived. On a separate sheet of paper, write a short report for the TV evening news. Include at least three plural nouns in your report.

Students' reports should include the correct form of at least three plural nouns.

Notes for Home: Your child wrote the plural form of various nouns. ***Home Activity:*** Ask your child to use a book or a magazine to find plural nouns and tell you the singular form of each one.

Grammar Practice Book 6.2, p. 34

Name ______________________ **From a Spark**

Grammar: Plural Nouns

RETEACHING

Draw a line to connect each noun pair in each box.

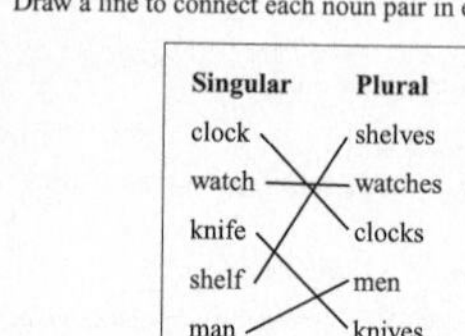

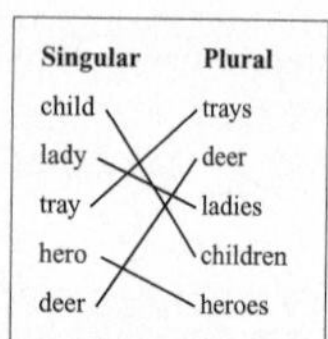

A **plural noun** names more than one person, place, thing, or idea. Most nouns add **-s** to make the plural form. Some nouns change their spellings in the plural forms. A few have the same singular and plural spellings.

Directions: Write the plural form of each noun.

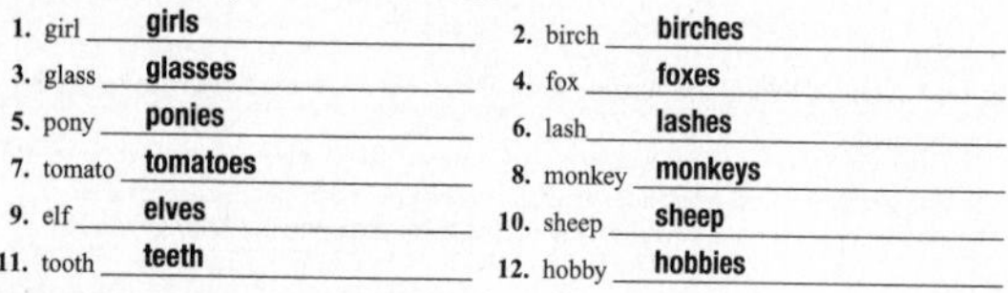

1. girl **girls**
2. birch **birches**
3. glass **glasses**
4. fox **foxes**
5. pony **ponies**
6. lash **lashes**
7. tomato **tomatoes**
8. monkey **monkeys**
9. elf **elves**
10. sheep **sheep**
11. tooth **teeth**
12. hobby **hobbies**

Directions: Write each sentence. Use the plural form of the noun in ( ).

13. (Clock) and (watch) are timepieces.
Clocks and watches are timepieces.
14. Many (person) observed their (shadow).
Many persons/people observed their shadows.
15. (Century) ago Egyptian (child) used shadow clocks.
Centuries ago Egyptian children used shadow clocks.

Notes for Home: Your child used plural forms of nouns in sentences. ***Home Activity:*** Have your child cut out pictures from magazines and make a collage that represents himself or herself. Your child should label pictures with plural and singular nouns.

Grammar Practice Book 6.2, p. 35

Name ______________________ **From a Spark**

Grammar: Plural Nouns

Directions: Write the plural form of each word in ( ).

1. six **mice** (mouse)
2. a few **tomatoes** (tomato)
3. two **men** (man)
4. several **shelves** (shelf)
5. many **monkeys** (monkey)
6. young **children** (child)
7. several **batches** (batch)
8. three **thieves** (thief)
9. red **balloons** (balloon)
10. big **cities** (city)
11. four **plates** (plate)
12. eight **elves** (elf)
13. five **fish/fishes** (fish)
14. some **matches** (match)

Directions: Write each sentence. Use the plural form of each noun in ( ).

15. Our school gave all the (child) (pass) to the state fair.
Our school gave all the children passes to the state fair.
16. We saw (booth) with (display) of prize-winning vegetables.
We saw booths with displays of prize-winning vegetables.
17. Two (tomato) and four (squash) won ribbons.
Two tomatoes and four squash/squashes won ribbons.
18. We tasted several (variety) of delicious (pie).
We tasted several varieties of delicious pies.
19. (Box) of homemade jams and (jelly) lined the (shelf).
Boxes of homemade jams and jellies lined the shelves.
20. We visited the 4-H Club exhibit of (calf) and (sheep).
We visited the 4-H Club exhibit of calves and sheep.
21. Have you ever seen (cowboy) ride (pony) in (rodeo)?
Have you ever seen cowboys ride ponies in rodeos?

Write a Paragraph

On a separate sheet of paper, write a paragraph about what you would like to see at a state fair. Try to use as many plural nouns as possible in your sentences.

Make sure students have spelled plural nouns correctly.

Notes for Home: Your child identified plural forms of nouns and used them in sentences. ***Home Activity:*** Have your child make a list of items needed to do a particular task. Then have him or her write the plural forms of the names of those items.

Practice Book 6.2, p. 68

Name ______________________ From a Spark

Phonics: Silent Consonants

Directions: Some words have consonants that you don't hear. Say each word to yourself. Circle the word in each group that has the **silent consonant.** Underline the consonant that is silent.

1. liken, list, liter, **listening**	2. not, **knee**, kept, kite	3. bury, **raspberries**, raisin, laundry
4. drop, distance, **dumb**, disturb	5. signal, **sign**, signature, sister	6. complete, compound, combine, **comb**
7. **wrist**, win, work, waist	8. **fasten**, faster, finally, frantic	9. **design**, desert, dusty, duplicate

Directions: Read the travel guide. Find seven words with **silent consonants.** Write each word on the lines, and circle the consonant that is silent.

Glenview Park

Located just a half hour from downtown, Glenview Park is a place known to hikers as the best park in town. You won't find any loud radios there. Bring a knapsack with a nice treat and a good book. Climb the old gnarled trees to get a better view. If you listen very closely, you can hear the quiet of the outdoors. Deer come at dusk to the side of a clearing, so bring your binoculars!

10. half
11. hour
12. known
13. knapsack
14. climb
15. gnarled
16. listen

Notes for Home: Your child reviewed silent consonants, such as the *w* in *write*. ***Home Activity:*** Read a travel guide with your child. Help your child identify words with silent consonants. Have your child write the words and circle the silent letters.

Phonics: Silent Consonants 151

Spelling Workbook 6.2, p. 25

Name ______________________ From a Spark

Spelling: Unexpected Consonant Spellings

Pretest Directions: Fold back the page along the dotted line. On the blanks, write the spelling words as they are dictated. When you have finished the test, unfold the page and check your words.

1. doubt	1. I don't **doubt** your excuse.
2. fascinate	2. Strange movies **fascinate** her.
3. science	3. He enjoys his **science** classes.
4. scenic	4. We drove along a **scenic** route.
5. autumn	5. Leaves change colors in **autumn**.
6. column	6. He writes a daily **column**.
7. guilty	7. The defendant is not **guilty**.
8. league	8. Our soccer **league** is a big one.
9. guardian	9. Her brother was her **guardian**.
10. disguise	10. The spy wore a clever **disguise**.
11. subtle	11. His jokes are very **subtle**.
12. debt	12. They were in **debt** to the bank.
13. reminiscent	13. I enjoy **reminiscent** music.
14. descent	14. The cliff makes a steep **descent**.
15. condemn	15. I **condemn** cruelty to animals.
16. solemn	16. This is a **solemn** occasion.
17. guidance	17. Sometimes you need **guidance**.
18. vague	18. Your meaning is **vague**.
19. fatigue	19. The hikers battled **fatigue**.
20. intrigue	20. I like books filled with **intrigue**.

Notes for Home: Your child took a pretest on words with unexpected combinations of consonants. ***Home Activity:*** Help your child learn misspelled words before the final test. Your child can underline the word parts that caused the problems and concentrate on those parts.

152 Spelling: Unexpected Consonant Spellings

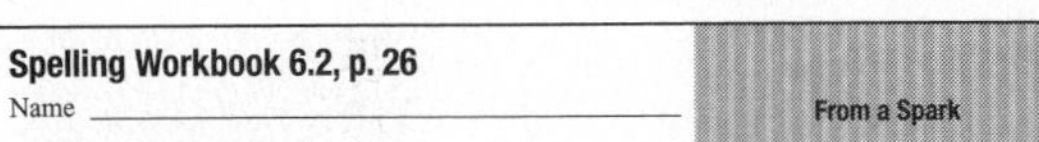

Spelling Workbook 6.2, p. 26

Name ______________________ From a Spark

Spelling: Unexpected Consonant Spellings

Word List

doubt	autumn	guardian	reminiscent	guidance
fascinate	column	disguise	descent	vague
science	guilty	subtle	condemn	fatigue
scenic	league	debt	solemn	intrigue

Directions: Choose the words from the box spelled with **bt, gue,** and **gu.** Listen for the consonant sound each group of letters represents. Write each word in the correct column. **Order may vary**

Words spelled bt	Words spelled gue	Words spelled gu
1. doubt	4. league	8. guilty
2. debt	5. vague	9. guardian
3. subtle	6. fatigue	10. disguise
	7. intrigue	11. guidance

Directions: Choose the word from the box that best completes each sentence. Write the word on the line to the left.

scenic 12. The desert sunrise provided a _____ view as we entered the mine.

autumn 13. We went exploring this _____ to avoid the colder temperatures of winter.

descent 14. Gradually, we began the _____ down the steep slope.

solemn 15. Fred looked serious and _____ as daylight faded behind us.

science 16. We had read the studies in the _____ journals about the atmosphere inside old mine shafts.

condemn 17. Our group had to decide whether to _____ the property as unsuitable for future use.

reminiscent 18. The mine was _____ of a scene from an old movie.

column 19. Each sturdy _____ helped hold up the rough ceiling.

fascinate 20. The complexity of the mine would amaze and _____ anyone.

Notes for Home: Your child spelled words with unexpected letter combinations. ***Home Activity:*** Help your child sort the spelling words into groups that contain the letters *sc, bt, gu* or *gue,* and *mn.* Each letter group represents one consonant sound.

Spelling: Unexpected Consonant Spellings 153

Spelling Workbook 6.2, p. 27

Name ______________________ From a Spark

Spelling: Unexpected Consonant Spellings

Directions: Proofread this journal entry. Find six spelling mistakes. Use the proofreading marks to correct each mistake.

≡ Make a capital.
/ Make a small letter.
∧ Add something.
Take out something.
⊙ Add a period.
¶ Begin a new paragraph.

Day 3. It's great to be back up top again. We just finished the hardest de[c]sent into the caves to date, and all my muscles ache with fatig[u]e. But today we found a cavern sure to fascinat[e] even the most experienced explorer! After hours of climbing and crawling through mud in temperatures reminisc[e]nt of a refrigerator, I began to dou[b]t my abilities. Finally, I squeezed my way through a narrow passage into a huge chamber. Our lights shone on an enormous limestone colum[n]. Now I understand the intrigue of cave exploration!

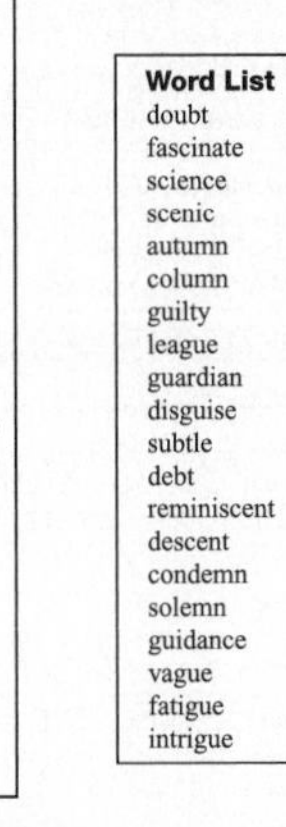

Word List
doubt
fascinate
science
scenic
autumn
column
guilty
league
guardian
disguise
subtle
debt
reminiscent
descent
condemn
solemn
guidance
vague
fatigue
intrigue

Spelling Tip

fascinate fatigue

Fascinate, fatigue, and other spelling words use two or more letters to stand for one consonant sound. Make sure they are spelled correctly in the journal entry.

Write a Journal Entry

On a separate sheet of paper, write a journal entry describing a wilderness adventure. Imagine that you are exploring a new territory. Have you had any narrow escapes? How did you survive? How did you feel when you finally reached your goal? Try to use at least five of your spelling words.

Answers will vary, but each journal entry should include at least five spelling words.

Notes for Home: Your child spelled words with unexpected letter combinations. ***Home Activity:*** Have your child read the spelling words for you to write. Then have your child check your spelling.

154 Spelling: Unexpected Consonant Spellings

Spelling Workbook 6.2, p. 28

Name ______________________

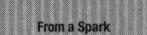

From a Spark

Spelling: Unexpected Consonant Spellings

Word List				
doubt	autumn	guardian	reminiscent	guidance
fascinate	column	disguise	descent	vague
science	guilty	subtle	condemn	fatigue
scenic	league	debt	solemn	intrigue

Directions: Write the word from the box that belongs in each group.

1. pillar, post, **column**
2. unclear, not distinct, **vague**
3. beautiful, natural, **scenic**
4. costume, mask, **disguise**
5. grave, serious, **solemn**
6. direction, leadership, **guidance**
7. caretaker, protector, **guardian**
8. plot, scheme, **intrigue**
9. judge, convict, **condemn**
10. remembered, suggestive, **reminiscent**
11. interest, charm, **fascinate**

Directions: Choose the word from the box that best matches each clue. Write the word on the line.

subtle 12. It's not obvious so you might just overlook me.

autumn 13. It's the season between summer and winter.

science 14. It includes the subjects chemistry, biology, and physics.

league 15. It's a group of people or a division in sports.

doubt 16. It's what you feel when you don't know for sure.

guilty 17. It's the opposite of *innocent.*

scenic 18. It's how you would describe a beautiful view.

debt 19. It's money or other items owed to someone.

descent 20. It's a trip downstairs, down a hill, or down a mountain.

Notes for Home: Your child spelled words with unexpected letter combinations. ***Home Activity:*** Give your child clues about each spelling word. Have your child identify and spell each word. For example: *You use a costume to do this. (disguise)*

Spelling: Unexpected Consonant Spellings 155

Practice Book 6.2, p. 69

Name ______________________

From a Spark

Thesaurus

A **thesaurus** is a kind of dictionary that lists synonyms (words with the same or similar meanings), antonyms (words with opposite meanings), and other related words. Parts of speech are listed to show how a word is used. If a word has multiple meanings, synonyms for each type of meaning are given.

You can use a thesaurus to help you find new and interesting words so you don't repeat the same words too often in your writing. An index lists all the entry words in alphabetical order so you can look them up quickly.

Directions: Use these thesaurus entries to answer the questions that follow.

soundless (adj) still, mute, quiet. See SILENT.

spark (n) **1. flash:** flicker, flare, sparkle, glow, glint, glimmer; **2. stimulus:** goad, spur, motivation, inspiration.

spark (v) **1. flash:** flicker, flare, sparkle, glint; **2. stimulate:** goad, spur, motivate, inspire, ignite, start, activate. (ant) extinguish, douse.

sparkle (v) **1. with light:** glitter, shine, flicker, glint, glimmer, glow, dazzle, shimmer: *The silver ornaments sparkle in the firelight.* **2. with intelligence:** be lively, be vivacious, be the life of the party, shine, dazzle: *Her stories sparkle with clever humor.*

sparse (adj) scanty, meager, slight, scarce, thin, poor, spare, skimpy, few and far between. (ant) thick, abundant, plentiful.

1. What part of speech is *soundless?* How do you know? ***Soundless* is an adjective. The abbreviation (adj) shows the word's part of speech.**
2. What are the synonyms for *soundless?* **still, mute, quiet**

156 Research and Study Skills: Thesaurus

Practice Book 6.2, p. 70

Name ______________________

From a Spark

3. Why do you think the entry for *soundless* includes the cross-reference for *silent?*
Possible answer: The cross-reference to *silent* gives you another word to check to find words related to *soundless.*
4. Why does this thesaurus show two entries for *spark?* ***Spark* can be used as both a noun and a verb.**
5. Rewrite the following sentence using a synonym for *spark.*
He saw a brief spark of light when the hatchet hit the rock.
Check that students use one of the synonyms given for *spark* used as a noun. Possible answer: He saw a brief flicker of light when the hatchet hit the rock.
6. Which meaning of *sparkle* is used in the following sentence? Which synonyms would you use to replace the word *sparkled?* Pick the synonyms that would make the most sense in the sentence.
The stars sparkled like tiny diamonds scattered across the night sky.
The sentence uses *sparkle* to mean "with light." Possible answer: The synonyms *glittered, shined,* and *glimmered* all make sense in the sentence.
7. Write a sentence using any of the antonyms listed. Hint: You can use the list of synonyms to help you figure out the meaning of an antonym.
Check that students correctly use one of the antonyms listed in a sentence.
8. How is a thesaurus like a dictionary? How is it different? **Possible answer: Both include alphabetical lists of words. A thesaurus does not give pronunciations and full definitions of words. A dictionary does not give a list of synonyms or antonyms.**
9. How can you find the synonyms for a word in a thesaurus? Describe the steps.
Possible answer: First, you look up the word in the index of a thesaurus. Then, you look up the entry for that word. The synonyms are listed after the entry word.
10. Why is a thesaurus a useful reference source when you are writing something?
Possible answer: A thesaurus can help you find new and interesting words that you can use to replace the repeated words in your writing.

Notes for Home: Your child used entries from a thesaurus to answer questions. ***Home Activity:*** Make a list of ten common words. Take turns with your child listing as many synonyms as you can for each word. Use the thesaurus, if one is available, to help you.

Research and Study Skills: Thesaurus 157

Practice Book 6.2, p. 71

Name ______________________

Storm-a-Dust

Setting

- The **setting** of a story is the place and time in which the story occurs.
- Sometimes the author tells you the setting. Other times, the author reveals the setting through details.
- The setting can influence what happens to a character or how a character behaves. It can also contribute to the overall feeling, or mood.

Directions: Reread "The Glittering Cloud." Then complete the tables. Identify the place in which the story occurs. Then list story details that describe the setting and tell how the setting influences the characters and mood. **Possible answers given.**

Story Setting	
Time: the 1800s	**Place:** 1. **Laura's family farm on the prairie.**

Story Details About Setting	Influence on Characters and Mood
2. The prairie **has waves of heat rising from it like a hot stove.**	The mood is one of discomfort caused by such strong heat.
3. The schoolhouse **has sticky pine-juice dripping down the board walls.**	4. The school children **pant from the heat inside the schoolhouse.**
5. The wheat **is tall and golden.**	6. Pa **is happy and looks forward to selling the crop and becoming rich.**
7. A cloud **dims the bright sunlight.**	8. The dog **growls and whines at the strange cloud.**
9. Large brown grasshoppers **begin hitting the ground.**	10. The mood **is one of impending doom or disaster.**

Notes for Home: Your child identified the details that reveal the setting of a story and described its effects on the characters. ***Home Activity:*** Choose a favorite story that has an interesting setting. Use details from the story to help your child draw a picture illustrating the setting.

160 Setting

Practice Book 6.2, p. 72

Name ______________________ **Storm-a-Dust**

Vocabulary

Directions: Choose the word from the box that has the same or nearly the same meaning as each word below. Write the word on the line.

Check the Words You Know
- ___ eerie
- ___ grasslands
- ___ gritty
- ___ hazy
- ___ peculiar
- ___ spindly

peculiar 1. odd; strange; unusual
gritty 2. having bits of sand and dust
eerie 3. scary; weird
spindly 4. very long and slender
hazy 5. unclear; murky

Directions: Choose the word from the box that best completes each sentence. Write the word on the matching numbered line below.

The dry **6.** ____ stretched for miles and miles. The dusty air made the setting sun look **7.** ____ and unclear. In the dust storm, the air was **8.** ____ with sand. Tall, **9.** ____ stalks of grass bowed and waved. In the light of the rising moon, the moving grass seemed to come alive. The whole scene was very spooky and **10.** ____. I was glad when the sun rose bright and clear the next day.

6. **grasslands**
7. **hazy**
8. **gritty**
9. **spindly**
10. **eerie**

Write a Weather Report

On a separate sheet of paper, write a weather report describing a dust storm or some other kind of extreme weather. Use as many of the vocabulary words as you can.
Check that vocabulary words are used correctly in students' weather reports.

Notes for Home: Your child identified and used vocabulary words from "Storm-a-Dust." ***Home Activity:*** With your child, name as many weather words that have similar meaning as you can, such as *hazy, murky, unclear,* and *misty.*

Practice Book 6.2, p. 73

Name ______________________ **Storm-a-Dust**

Setting

- The **setting** is the place and time in which a story occurs. It may be directly identified or only suggested through story details.
- The setting of a story can influence what happens to a character and how a character behaves.

Directions: Reread what happens at the beginning of "Storm-a-Dust," when Lindy is wiping the red dust off. Then answer the questions below. Think about the story details to help you identify the setting.

> She must wipe each plant and flower clean. For red dust covered everything. Dust spotted her cheeks reddish brown. It covered her hands in red dust mittens. She took a last swipe at a stunted sunflower. "How are you this morning, yellow fella?" she asked the sunflower.
> "Oh, but I need some water," Lindy answered in a sunflower-high voice.
> "I'll water you at sundown, yellow fella," she told the flower.
> She tied her wiper around her waist. Her tank top and jeans were dusty. Lindy climbed up on the old wood fence and shook her head at their pie-shaped field. "Don't think the corn will make it," she called over to her dad.
>
> Excerpt from DRYSLONGO, copyright © 1992 by Virginia Hamilton, reprinted by permission of Harcourt Brace & Company.

Possible answers given.

1. Where do you think the story takes place? What details suggest this?
It takes place on a farm. Flowers, corn, a fence, and a field are mentioned.

2. What is the weather like where Lindy lives? How do you know?
The weather is dry. Red dust covers everything. Lindy mentions that the sunflower needs water and that she doesn't think the corn will make it.

3. Why is the weather important where Lindy lives?
The dry weather makes it hard for Lindy's family to grow things.

4. What season of the year is it? How do you know?
It is probably summer since it is hot and corn is growing.

5. How does the setting affect Lindy and her parents? How might their lives be different in a different setting? Explain your thinking on a separate sheet of paper.
The dryness, heat, and dust of the setting make it hard for Lindy's family to grow crops. Lindy's family might have an easier time and a bigger harvest in a wetter and cooler climate.

Notes for Home: Your child identified the setting of the story and explained why the setting is important to the story. ***Home Activity:*** Work with your child to describe your home as though it is the setting for a story. Discuss how each room is the setting for different activities.

Practice Book 6.2, p. 75

Name ______________________ **Storm-a-Dust**

Selection Test

Directions: Choose the best answer to each item. Mark the letter for the answer you have chosen.

Part 1: Vocabulary

Find the answer choice that means about the same as the underlined word in each sentence.

1. Mom did not want to use the gritty rag on the windshield.
   A. covered with oil or grease
   B. old; worn out
   (C) containing small bits of dirt or sand
   D. having many holes
2. The sky was hazy.
   F. bright blue
   G. sparkling
   H. filled with black clouds
   (J) not clear
3. The gardener watered the spindly bush.
   A. covered with flowers
   (B) very long and slender
   C. huge
   D. young or newly planted
4. An eerie quiet filled the house.
   (F) scary in a strange way
   G. happy and exciting
   H. complete; total
   J. cozy and comforting
5. The air had a peculiar odor.
   (A) odd
   B. terrible
   C. lovely
   D. fruity
6. Alfonse hiked across the grasslands.
   F. low hills at the base of mountains
   (G) lands covered with grass
   H. narrow strips of rocky pathways
   J. lands that rise up high

Part 2: Comprehension

Use what you know about the story to answer each item.

7. The "wall" that Lindy sees is actually a—
   (A) dust storm.
   B. big flock of birds.
   C. snowstorm.
   D. line of thunderstorms.
8. Lindy's father watches the sky because he hopes he will see—
   F. a rainbow.
   (G) rain clouds.
   H. flocks of birds.
   J. grasshoppers.
9. Throughout the story, Lindy sneezes and coughs because she is—
   A. getting sick.
   B. having a reaction to the plants.
   (C) breathing dusty air.
   D. allergic to cats.
10. This story begins at what time of day?
    F. late afternoon
    (G) morning
    H. sundown
    J. night
11. Which detail about the setting best conveys the mood of the story?
    A. "They stayed in the house with Drylongso."
    B. "This is 1975; we know more."
    (C) "They all stared out at an eerie blue world."
    D. "Every window had little drifts in the corners."

Practice Book 6.2, p. 76

Name ______________________ **Storm-a-Dust**

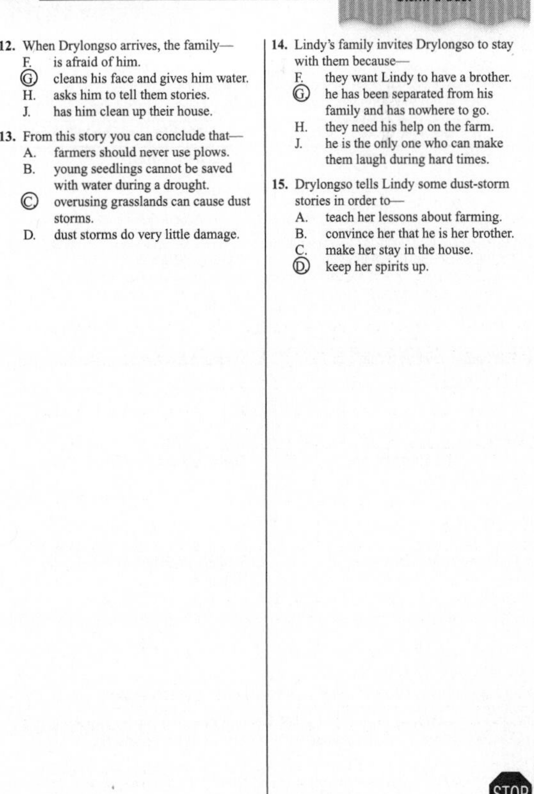

12. When Drylongso arrives, the family—
    F. is afraid of him.
    (G) cleans his face and gives him water.
    H. asks him to tell them stories.
    J. has him clean up their house.
13. From this story you can conclude that—
    A. farmers should never use plows.
    B. young seedlings cannot be saved with water during a drought.
    (C) overusing grasslands can cause dust storms.
    D. dust storms do very little damage.
14. Lindy's family invites Drylongso to stay with them because—
    F. they want Lindy to have a brother.
    (G) he has been separated from his family and has nowhere to go.
    H. they need his help on the farm.
    J. he is the only one who can make them laugh during hard times.
15. Drylongso tells Lindy some dust-storm stories in order to—
    A. teach her lessons about farming.
    B. convince her that he is her brother.
    C. make her stay in the house.
    (D) keep her spirits up.

STOP

Name ______________________ Storm-a-Dust

Setting

- The **setting** is the place and time in which a story occurs. It may be directly identified or only suggested through story details.
- The setting can influence what happens to a character and how a character behaves.

Directions: Read the story below.

The sound of the wind against the hut woke Marta early. When she looked outside, she saw nothing except the huge waves crashing on the shore. The waves had been high for the past four months.

Marta thought her island home was beautiful. But the huge waves were making life harder for Marta and the 100 others who lived there.

The ship that came once every three months had been unable to reach the island since fall. Marta and her people needed supplies from that ship. Marta had heard of a new kind of boat, a huge boat powered by steam. That boat might do better in the sea. But for now, Marta and her people would have to find another way to survive.

Directions: Complete the circles in the web. Circle your answer to each question, and then give supporting evidence from the story.

Setting

(Island) or Mainland?
1. **Marta loves her island home.**

(Morning) or Night?
2. **Marta has just woken up.**

(Winter) or Summer?
3. **The ship was last there three months ago and that was fall.**

Present Day or (Long Ago)?
4. **Marta mentions a "new" boat that is powered by steam.**

5. How does the setting affect Marta and her people?
The huge waves prevent ships from bringing supplies that Marta and her people need.

Notes for Home: Your child read a story and identified its setting—where and when the story takes place. ***Home Activity:*** Have your child choose a favorite story and describe the setting of that story. Then suggest a change in the setting and ask how that might change the story.

Setting 165

Practice Book 6.2, p. 77

Name ______________________ Storm-a-Dust

Sequence

REVIEW

Directions: Read the story. Then read each question about the story. Choose the best answer to each question. Mark the letter for the answer you have chosen.

On the Map

When Tom and Stephanie looked at the map, they thought they had an easy hike. But they soon found out that a map doesn't show everything.

On the second day of the hike, Tom wanted to change the route they had planned. He and Stephanie looked at the map and found a shortcut. The trees were beautiful, and they saw several animals. But the shortcut was so hilly that their packs began to feel heavy. They got rid of everything they didn't want to carry. Unfortunately, this included one of their water bottles.

By the third day, they had drunk all the water from the bottle they had kept. Looking at the map, Stephanie found a detour that would take her and Tom past a stream, where they could refill their bottle. When they got there, they made a terrible discovery—the stream was dry! In the end, they had to radio the rangers for help.

"I'm sorry, Stephanie," said Tom. "If I hadn't wanted to change the hike, we would have followed a flat path near a strong stream."

"We both made mistakes," said Stephanie. "I'll never get rid of a heavy water bottle again!"

1. What was the first mistake Tom and Stephanie made?
   - (A.) They took a shortcut that they were unfamiliar with.
   - B. They decided to go on a hike.
   - C. They went to a stream.
   - D. They got lost.
2. Which of these events happened first?
   - F Tom took a detour to go to a stream.
   - (G.) Tom and Stephanie got rid of everything they didn't want to carry.
   - H. They went to a dry stream.
   - J. They radioed for help.
3. If Stephanie had not thrown out her water bottle, they might have—
   - A. avoided the first shortcut.
   - B. been unable to radio for help.
   - C. been able to climb the hills.
   - (D.) avoided the detour to the dry stream.
4. The last thing that Tom and Stephanie did was to—
   - (F.) talk about how they might have avoided their mistakes.
   - G. go to a dry stream.
   - H. radio for help.
   - J. get rid of a water bottle.
5. If they had stayed on their original course, they probably would not have—
   - (A.) needed help.
   - B needed a map.
   - C gotten tired.
   - D argued.

Notes for Home: Your child read a story and answered questions about the order of events. ***Home Activity:*** Have your child think of a favorite story and list a few important events. Ask your child to explain how the story would have been different if one event had not happened.

166 Sequence

Name ______________________ Storm-a-Dust

Writing Across Texts

Directions: Consider what you learned about dust storms and droughts from the selections "Storm-a-Dust" and "What Is a Drought?" Complete the table below by writing five effects of a dust storm and five effects of a drought. **Possible answers given.**

"Storm-a-Dust"	"What Is a Drought?"
1. **Lindy has trouble breathing.**	6. **Grass turns brown.**
2. **The whole house is full of dust.**	7. **Water is rationed.**
3. **The people look as if they are wearing masks.**	8. **People cannot wash their cars.**
4. **The corn and tomatoes are flattened.**	9. **People cannot water their gardens.**
5. **The town's electricity goes off.**	10. **Millions of people's lives may be changed.**

Write a Comparative Essay

Refer to the two reading selections and the completed table above to write an essay in which you compare and contrast the effects of a dust storm and a drought. Write your essay on a separate sheet of paper. **Essays will vary. Check to see that students have included details from both selections on the effects of natural disasters.**

Notes for Home: Your child compared and contrasted information about natural disasters from two sources. ***Home Activity:*** As you read stories and articles, have your child compare and contrast the effects of events described in the reading materials.

Writing Across Texts 167

Grammar Practice Book 6.2, p. 36

Name ______________________ Storm-a-Dust

Grammar: Plural Nouns

REVIEW

Directions: Write the plural form of each of the following nouns. Use a dictionary if you need help.

1. month **months**
2. lunch **lunches**
3. foot **feet**
4. butterfly **butterflies**
5. alley **alleys**
6. ox **oxen**
7. tomato **tomatoes**
8. dish **dishes**
9. pencil **pencils**
10. loaf **loaves**

Directions: Use the plural form of the noun in ( ) to complete each sentence. Write the plural noun on the line to the left. Use a dictionary if you need help.

quantities 11. Dust storms blow huge _____ of dust or sand over a large area. (quantity)

regions 12. In the 1930s, some _____ of the country suffered terribly. (region)

sheep 13. Many cows, _____, pigs, and other animals died. (sheep)

lives 14. Human _____ were lost as well. (life)

winds 15. The powerful _____ blew millions of tons of topsoil into the ocean. (wind)

people 16. As a result, _____ could not farm the land. (person)

Roofs 17. _____ were covered in dust. (Roof)

children 18. Schools were forced to close, and _____ stayed home. (child)

radios 19. In many cases, _____ were the only link to the outside world. (radio)

masses 20. Great _____ of people moved to other parts of the country to escape devastation. (mass)

Notes for Home: Your child wrote regular and irregular plural nouns. ***Home Activity:*** List singular nouns from the newspaper on slips of paper. Have your child write the plural forms of these nouns.

168 Grammar: Plural Nouns

Grammar Practice Book 6.2, p. 37

Name ______________________ Storm-a-Dust

Grammar: Possessive Nouns

Possessive nouns show that one or more persons, places, or things have or own something. They are formed with an **apostrophe (')** and **-s** or with only an **apostrophe (')**. Here are three rules to help you write possessive nouns:

- Add **'s** to form the possessive of most singular nouns: the barn's silo.
- Add **'s** to form the possessive of plural nouns that do not end in **-s**: the children's shoes.
- Add only **(')** to form the possessive of plural nouns that end in **-s**: the horses' trough.

Directions: Underline the possessive noun in each sentence. If the possessive noun is plural, circle it as well.

1. The kitchen's warmth was welcome.
2. The children's boots dripped on the floor.
3. Outside, the storm's fury increased.
4. Snow and pellets of ice hit the windows' small, old-fashioned panes.
5. The wind's howl swept down the chimney.
6. The downstairs rooms of the house looked eerie, lit only by the candles' glow.
7. Outside steam rose from the three sheep's backs.
8. Each sheep's head was away from the wind.
9. The barn's shape was blurred by snow.
10. Some animals' tracks formed small valleys in the snow.

Directions: Rewrite each underlined phrase to show possession. Write the new phrase on the line.

11. **the animals' feet** Look at the patterns the feet of animals have been making in the snow.
12. **the ice's surface** Wind has certainly roughened the surface of the ice.
13. **those snowdrifts' depths** Danielle plans to measure the depths of those snowdrifts.
14. **Evergreens' boughs** Boughs of evergreens can often bear heavy loads of snow.
15. **the hailstones' sound** What does the sound of hailstones remind you of?

Notes for Home: Your child identified and formed possessive nouns. ***Home Activity:*** Ask your child to explain how to make singular and plural nouns possessive. Take turns thinking of examples of possessive nouns.

Grammar Practice Book 6.2, p. 38

Name ______________________ Storm-a-Dust

Grammar: Possessive Nouns

Directions: Rewrite each underlined phrase to show possession. Write the new phrase on the line.

1. **The animals' noses** The noses of the animals were lifted to the wind.
2. **the trees' branches** Heavy with leaves, the branches of trees creaked and swayed.
3. **the squirrels' tails** Even the tails of the squirrels twitched nervously.
4. **the storm's threat** All the animals could sense the threat of the storm.
5. **The river's waters** The waters of the river flowed fast and choppy.
6. **the water's edge** A frightened deer ran to the edge of the water and tried to cross.
7. **The deer's legs** The legs of the deer became caught in a swirling branch.
8. **the creature's cries** Soon the cries of the creature rang through the forest.
9. **a campers' cabin** Fortunately, a cabin for campers stood near the river.
10. **the people's bravery** Because of the bravery of the people, the life of the deer was saved.

Write a Description

On a separate sheet of paper, write a description of a storm and how it makes you feel. Use colorful words in your description. Use at least three possessive nouns in your description.

Check that students' descriptions use and punctuate possessive nouns correctly.

Notes for Home: Your child wrote the possessive forms of nouns. ***Home Activity:*** Write a variety of nouns on small slips of paper. Take turns with your child, choosing the slips and spelling or writing the singular and plural possessive forms of the nouns.

Grammar Practice Book 6.2, p. 39

Name ______________________ Storm-a-Dust

Grammar: Possessive Nouns

RETEACHING

Underline the possessive nouns. Write the nouns.

1. Sue's smile was joyful. **Sue's**
2. The seals' barks were heard outside. **seals'**
3. Children's laughter rang in the air. **Children's**

A **possessive noun** shows ownership. Add an apostrophe (') and **-s** to spell the possessive form of a singular noun. Add only an apostrophe to spell the possessive form of a plural noun that ends with **-s**. Add an apostrophe and **-s** to spell the possessive form of a plural noun that does not end in **-s**.

Directions: Underline the possessive nouns.

1. The bear's food is being prepared.
2. Lions' roars could be heard throughout the zoo.
3. The keeper's pride in the big cats was clear.
4. The girls ran quickly to the alligators' pits.
5. The boys laughed at the hippopotamus's big yawn.
6. Mr. Morris was fascinated by the monkey's actions.
7. He drew the children's attention to the bears.
8. The sleeping cub's face shone with contentment.
9. The tourists' guide pointed to the cub.

Directions: Write the possessive form of the noun in ( ).

10. The **men's** laughter woke the bear. (men)
11. Look at the **animal's** sharp claw. (animal)
12. The **visitors'** eyes opened wide. (visitors)
13. It walked to the **cage's** corner for a nap. (cage)
14. The **guide's** directions helped us. (guide)
15. The **snake's** cage has a tree trunk with branches. (snake)
16. The **deer's** habitat has a lake. (deer)

Notes for Home: Your child used possessive forms of singular and plural nouns. ***Home Activity:*** Have your child make a list of friends, family members, and families' last names. Have him or her write sentences, using the lists to write possessive nouns.

Grammar Practice Book 6.2, p. 40

Name ______________________ Storm-a-Dust

Grammar: Possessive Nouns

Directions: Write in the blank the possessive form of the noun in ( ).

1. **China's** population is enormous. (China)
2. China is the **world's** third largest country in land area. (world)
3. This **country's** history dates from 3500 years ago. (country)
4. Early **scholars'** name for China was "Zhonghua." (scholars)
5. The **word's** meaning is "central land." (word)
6. Their homeland seemed like the **Earth's** center. (Earth)
7. The **mountains'** height protected the land. (mountains)
8. The **seas'** shores formed its eastern border. (seas)
9. We listened eagerly to the **travelers'** stories about China. (travelers)

Directions: Rewrite each underlined phrase so that it contains a possessive noun.

10. Chinese civilization was influenced by the ideas of many philosophers.
    many philosophers' ideas
11. Confucius was the son of a noble.
    a noble's son
12. The beliefs of this man taught love, wisdom, and sincerity.
    This man's beliefs
13. Respect for parents was important in the lessons of his students.
    his students' lessons
14. Today his ideas still influence the customs of China.
    China's customs
15. The education of children is based on Confucius's teaching.
    Children's education

Write a Travel Brochure

On a separate sheet of paper, write a travel brochure for a country you would like to visit. Describe the weather, the people, and must-see places to explore. Use possessive nouns in some of your sentences.

Make sure students have spelled and punctuated possessive nouns correctly.

Notes for Home: Your child used possessive forms of singular and plural nouns in sentences. ***Home Activity:*** Together, make a list of places your child often goes. Have your child use possessive forms of the place names to write sentences about what can be found there.

Practice Book 6.2, p. 78

Name ______________________ Storm-a-Dust

Word Study: Compound Words

Directions: Compound words are words formed by combining two other words. Compound words can be **closed** *(sunburn)*, **open** *(ice cream)*, or **hyphenated** *(half-time)*. Combine a word from the left box with a word from the right box to form a compound word that makes sense. Write both words and the resulting compound word on the lines below.

pan	bare
snow	table
fence	sun
beach	dead
baby	through

footed	cloth
cakes	post
flake	out
end	umbrella
sit	burn

1. pan + cakes = pancakes
2. snow + flake = snowflake
3. fence + post = fencepost
4. beach + umbrella = beach umbrella
5. baby + sit = babysit
6. bare + footed = barefooted
7. table + cloth = tablecloth
8. sun + burn = sunburn
9. dead + end = dead end
10. through + out = throughout

Directions: Read the paragraph. Find five compound words. Write each compound word on the line.

The storm came up out of nowhere. Dresses and shirts on the clothesline flapped in the wind. The scarecrow looked like a stick-fella dancing in the field. A cloudburst of rain came pouring down. Then, as quickly as it had begun, the storm was over.

11. nowhere
12. clothesline
13. scarecrow
14. stick-fella
15. cloudburst

Notes for Home: Your child wrote compound words, such as *sunburn, ice cream,* and *half-time. **Home Activity:*** Play a game with your child. Say one part of a compound word. Challenge your child to complete the compound word.

Word Study: Compound Words 173

Spelling Workbook 6.2, p. 29

Name ______________________ Storm-a-Dust

Spelling: Compound Words 1

Pretest Directions: Fold back the page along the dotted line. On the blanks, write the spelling words as they are dictated. When you have finished the test, unfold the page and check your words.

1. myself — 1. I went to the library by **myself**.
2. themselves — 2. They always enjoy **themselves**.
3. hallway — 3. The **hallway** was long.
4. homeroom — 4. Who is your **homeroom** teacher?
5. everything — 5. They want to know **everything**.
6. teenage — 6. I have a **teenage** brother.
7. teammate — 7. One **teammate** was late.
8. skateboard — 8. She has a new **skateboard**.
9. everybody — 9. **Everybody** came to the party.
10. doughnut — 10. Your dog ate my **doughnut**.
11. ice cream — 11. **Ice cream** is best on hot days.
12. locker room — 12. I changed in the **locker room**.
13. tape recorder — 13. I bought a new **tape recorder**.
14. root beer — 14. Let's have **root beer** floats.
15. dead end — 15. This street is a **dead end**.
16. air conditioner — 16. Can you fix the **air conditioner**?
17. polka dot — 17. His father has a **polka dot** tie.
18. roller coaster — 18. I love the new **roller coaster**.
19. ice pack — 19. Put an **ice pack** on your bruise.
20. solar system — 20. What is the **solar system**?

Notes for Home: Your child took a pretest on compound words written as one word and as two words. ***Home Activity:*** Help your child learn misspelled words before the final test. Dictate the word and have your child spell the word aloud for you or write it on paper.

174 Spelling: Compound Words 1

Spelling Workbook 6.2, p. 30

Name ______________________ Storm-a-Dust

Spelling: Compound Words 1

Word List			
myself	teenage	ice cream	air conditioner
themselves	teammate	locker room	polka dot
hallway	skateboard	tape recorder	roller coaster
homeroom	everybody	root beer	ice pack
everything	doughnut	dead end	solar system

Directions: Add a word to each word below to form a compound word from the box. Write the compound word on the line.

1. root — root beer
2. my — myself
3. air — air conditioner
4. dead — dead end
5. roller — roller coaster
6. body — everybody
7. polka — polka dot
8. them — themselves
9. cream — ice cream
10. team — teammate

Directions: Find the two words in each sentence that make up a compound word from the box. Write the compound word on the line.

- locker room — 11. My locker is near the weight room.
- hallway — 12. Boxes blocked the hall, but he found a way past.
- ice pack — 13. Fill the cooler with ice before you pack the food and drinks.
- tape recorder — 14. We listened to a tape of a recorder, flute, and guitar.
- homeroom — 15. He had to go home and clean his room.
- solar system — 16. The solar panel was near the heating system.
- skateboard — 17. She loved to skate fast down the big wooden board.
- doughnut — 18. After shaping the dough into small pieces, place a nut on each piece.
- teenage — 19. She asked the teen to state his age.
- everything — 20. Mom thought every child deserved at least one cute thing for a door prize.

Notes for Home: Your child spelled compound words written as one word and as two words. ***Home Activity:*** Take turns saying one part of one of the compound words from the Word List. The other person names the compound word and spells it.

Spelling: Compound Words 1 175

Spelling Workbook 6.2, p. 31

Name ______________________ Storm-a-Dust

Spelling: Compound Words 1

Directions: Proofread this story. Find six spelling mistakes. Use the proofreading marks to correct each mistake.

Proofreading marks	
≡	Make a capital.
/	Make a small letter.
∧	Add something.
℘	Take out something.
⊙	Add a period.
¶	Begin a new paragraph.

Danny and his family had crouched in their hal[l]way closet as the tornado passed by. After the storm, Danny went outside and joined all the neighbors who lived on their de[a]d end street. They were talking among themselves about the damage. It seemed as if ev[e]rything had been tossed around. Wet papers made ~~polkadot~~ polka dot patterns everywhere. An air conditioner had been blown through a window at the home of Danny's tea[m]mate Willie. Luckily, no one had been hurt. And amazingly, a skate/board still sat in the yard where someone had left it before the storm.

Spelling Tip

Some compounds are closed and are written as one word: **everything.** Others are open and are written as two words: **air conditioner.**

Word List

myself
themselves
hallway
homeroom
everything
teenage
teammate
skateboard
everybody
doughnut
ice cream
locker room
tape recorder
root beer
dead end
air conditioner
polka dot
roller coaster
ice pack
solar system

Write a Short Story

On a separate sheet of paper, write a short story that describes the effects of a flood, a blizzard, or other violent storm. Include the characters' reactions and explain how it changed their lives. Try to use at least five spelling words. **Answers will vary, but each short story should include at least five spelling words.**

Notes for Home: Your child spelled compound words written as one word and as two words, such as *everybody* and *tape recorder. **Home Activity:*** Encourage your child to find the compound words in a short newspaper article. Make a list of these compound words.

176 Spelling: Compound Words 1

Spelling Workbook 6.2, p. 32
Name ______________________ Storm-a-Dust

Spelling: Compound Words 1

REVIEW

Word List			
myself	teenage	ice cream	air conditioner
themselves	teammate	locker room	polka dot
hallway	skateboard	tape recorder	roller coaster
homeroom	everybody	root beer	ice pack
everything	doughnut	dead end	solar system

Directions: Write the word from the box that belongs in each group.

1. pastry, turnover, **doughnut**
2. bike, roller skates, **skateboard**
3. galaxy, universe, **solar system**
4. gym, stadium, **locker room**
5. Ferris wheel, carousel, **roller coaster**
6. lobby, corridor, **hallway**
7. freezer, refrigerator, **air conditioner**
8. stripe, plaid, **polka dot**
9. turntable, CD player, **tape recorder**
10. choir room, assembly room, **homeroom**

Directions: Choose the word from the box that best completes each song title. Write the word on the line to the left. Be sure to capitalize each important word.

Ice Pack 11. "A Bandage for My Heart and an _____ for My Soul"
Root Beer 12. "Two Straws Sticking in a _____ Float"
Everybody 13. "Why Does _____ Clown Around in Class?"
Teenage 14. "Just Too Young to Be a _____ Superstar"
Ice Cream 15. "Scoop Me Up Another _____ Cone!"
Myself 16. "I'm Lonesome and Lonely All by _____"
Dead End 17. "Just One More _____ Street"
Themselves 18. "They'll Have to Move It by _____"
Everything 19. "_____ Is Better Now That You're Here"
Teammate 20. "My _____ and I Can Win Any Game"

Notes for Home: Your child spelled compound words written as one word and as two words, such as *everybody* and *tape recorder*. ***Home Activity:*** Write each part of a compound word on a slip of paper. Draw two slips and try to form a compound word.

Practice Book 6.2, p. 79
Name ______________________ Storm-a-Dust

Locate/Collect Information

You can **locate and collect information** about a topic using a variety of sources. Sources of information include print (textbooks, reference books, trade books, magazines/periodicals, newspapers, photographs), electronic media (computer: CD-ROMs, Internet websites; non-computer: audiotapes, videotapes, films, microfilms), and people (librarians, teachers, experts, eyewitnesses).

Directions: Suppose you are writing a report about volcanic eruptions. Use the sources of information below to answer the questions that follow.

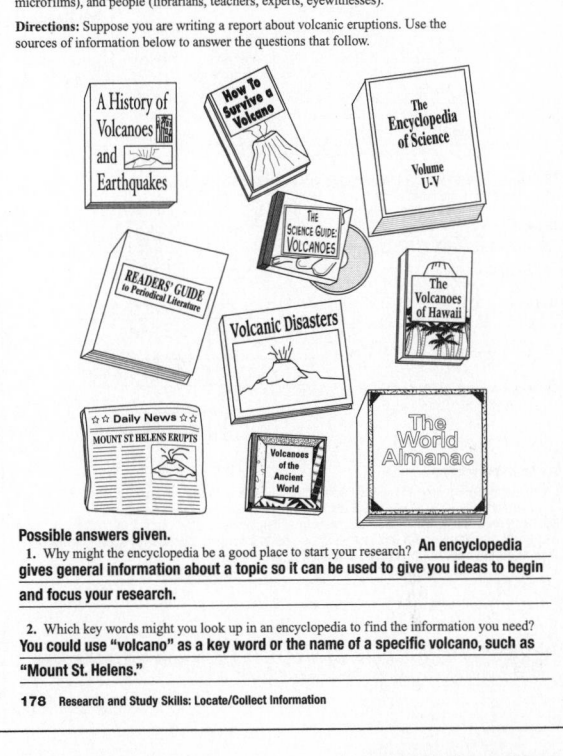

Possible answers given.

1. Why might the encyclopedia be a good place to start your research? **An encyclopedia gives general information about a topic so it can be used to give you ideas to begin and focus your research.**

2. Which key words might you look up in an encyclopedia to find the information you need? **You could use "volcano" as a key word or the name of a specific volcano, such as "Mount St. Helens."**

Practice Book 6.2, p. 80
Name ______________________ Storm-a-Dust

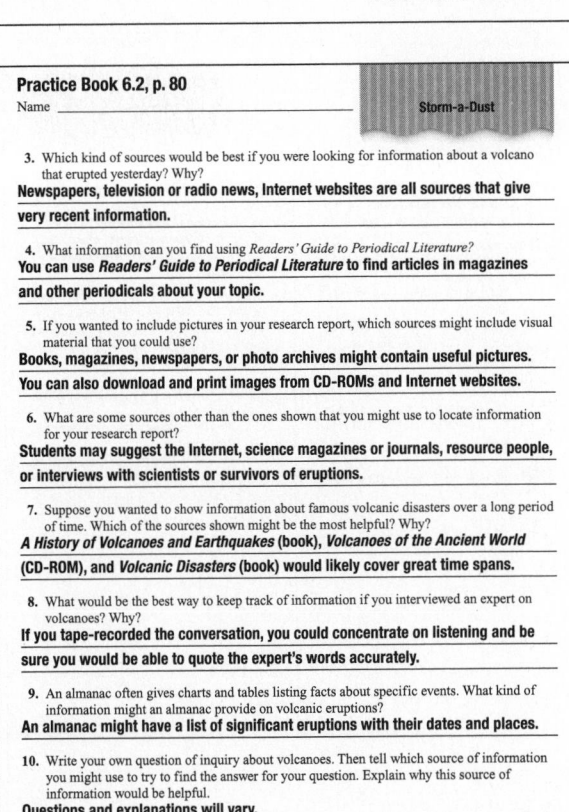

3. Which kind of sources would be best if you were looking for information about a volcano that erupted yesterday? Why?
Newspapers, television or radio news, Internet websites are all sources that give very recent information.

4. What information can you find using *Readers' Guide to Periodical Literature?*
You can use *Readers' Guide to Periodical Literature* to find articles in magazines and other periodicals about your topic.

5. If you wanted to include pictures in your research report, which sources might include visual material that you could use?
Books, magazines, newspapers, or photo archives might contain useful pictures. You can also download and print images from CD-ROMs and Internet websites.

6. What are some sources other than the ones shown that you might use to locate information for your research report?
Students may suggest the Internet, science magazines or journals, resource people, or interviews with scientists or survivors of eruptions.

7. Suppose you wanted to show information about famous volcanic disasters over a long period of time. Which of the sources shown might be the most helpful? Why?
***A History of Volcanoes and Earthquakes* (book), *Volcanoes of the Ancient World* (CD-ROM), and *Volcanic Disasters* (book) would likely cover great time spans.**

8. What would be the best way to keep track of information if you interviewed an expert on volcanoes? Why?
If you tape-recorded the conversation, you could concentrate on listening and be sure you would be able to quote the expert's words accurately.

9. An almanac often gives charts and tables listing facts about specific events. What kind of information might an almanac provide on volcanic eruptions?
An almanac might have a list of significant eruptions with their dates and places.

10. Write your own question of inquiry about volcanoes. Then tell which source of information you might use to try to find the answer for your question. Explain why this source of information would be helpful.
Questions and explanations will vary.

Notes for Home: Your child learned to locate and collect information on a research topic. ***Home Activity:*** Give your child a topic for research. Have him or her suggest a number of sources that might contain useful information about that topic.

Practice Book 6.2, p. 81
Name ______________________ The Day of the Turtle

Visualizing

- To **visualize** is to create a mental image as you read.
- An author may help you visualize by using imagery, words that produce strong images, or sensory details, words that describe how something looks, sounds, smells, tastes, or feels.

Directions: Reread "The Wexford Doe." Then complete each box. List the words from the story that help you visualize what Deirdre experiences. **Possible answers given.**

The Woods	The Stone Wall	The Doe
at the end of Scarlet Oak	low	7. **velvet-smooth coat**
damp air	4. **tiny spiderwebs**	8. **big, round, friendly eyes**
1. **silent**	5. **jagged stones**	9. **eyes turned cautious**
2. **sun's glare lighting dew**	one web cradled a sleeping spider	scampered away
3. **trees twinkle like a forest of crystal-drop chandeliers**	6. **another web shimmered like silk lace in the light**	10. **twigs snapped under her hooves**

Notes for Home: Your child identified words that appeal to the senses and create strong mental images. ***Home Activity:*** Challenge your child to visualize a familiar place and then describe it to you by using imagery and sensory details.

Practice Book 6.2, p. 82

Name ______________________ **The Day of the Turtle**

Vocabulary

Directions: Choose the word from the box that best completes each sentence. Write the word on the line to the left.

Check the Words You Know
__ driftwood
__ jellyfish
__ spar
__ tentacle
__ wary

jellyfish 1. While we were sailing, we saw a large _____ floating past, just under the surface of the water.

wary 2. Swimmers need to be _____ of jellyfish.

tentacle 3. Touching a single jellyfish _____ can be very painful and even dangerous.

spar 4. We set anchor near a beach, furled the sail, and fastened it to the _____.

driftwood 5. We gathered _____ for a small fire and watched the sun set.

Directions: Choose the word from the box that best matches each clue. Write the word in the puzzle.

Down

6. a sea animal made of jellylike tissue
7. cautious; careful

Across

8. a long, slender growth of a jellyfish
9. wood that has been washed up on the shore
10. a wooden pole used as part of a ship's sail

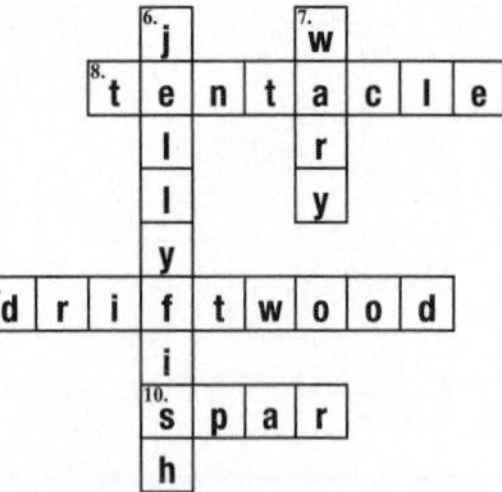

Write a Description

On a separate sheet of paper, write a description of an imaginary sea creature. Is it friendly or dangerous? What does it look like? How does it move? Use vivid details and your vocabulary words to make your writing interesting.

Students' writing should include vivid details to describe the sea creature. Check that included vocabulary words are used appropriately.

Notes for Home: Your child identified and used vocabulary words from "The Day of the Turtle." ***Home Activity:*** Work together to create a sea story, using the listed vocabulary words. Share your story with other family members.

Practice Book 6.2, p. 83

Name ______________________ **The Day of the Turtle**

Visualizing

- To **visualize** is to create a mental image as you read.
- Imagery and sensory details help you visualize scenes from stories.

Directions: Reread what happens in "The Day of the Turtle" when Granny May tries to feed shrimp to the turtle. Then answer the questions below. Use imagery and sensory details from the story to help you visualize.

She told me to dig a bowl in the sand right under the turtle's chin, and then she shook out her net. He looked mildly interested for a moment and then looked away. It was no good. Granny May was looking out to sea, shielding her eyes against the glare of the sun.

"I wonder," she murmured. "I wonder. I won't be long." And she was gone down to the sea. She was wading out up to her ankles, then up to her knees, with her shrimping net scooping through the water around her. I stayed behind with the turtle and threw more stones at the gulls. When she came back, her net was bulging with jellyfish, blue jellyfish. She emptied them into the turtle's sandy bowl. At once he was at them like a vulture, snapping, crunching, swallowing, until there wasn't a tentacle left.

Possible answers given.

1. Picture the day in your mind. Is it sunny, cloudy, hot, or cold? How do you know?
The day is sunny and warm. Granny May shields her eyes against the glare of the sun, and she wades into the water.

2. Describe how you think Granny May looks as she wades into the sea.
Granny May moves knee-deep into the water, pulling her net through the sea.

3. What details does the author use to help you picture the net with jellyfish?
The author uses "blue" and "bulging" to help you picture the color of the jellyfish and the fullness of the net.

4. Visualize the turtle as he eats the jellyfish. How does eating the jellyfish change his behavior?
The turtle suddenly is full of energy. He snaps "like a vulture" as he greedily gobbles up the jellyfish.

5. Select another scene from the story, such as the turtle trudging toward the water. On a separate sheet of paper, describe the mental image you create from the story details.
Answers will vary. Check that students are using the sensory details and imagery to help them visualize.

Notes for Home: Your child used imagery and sensory details from the story to create a mental image of a scene. ***Home Activity:*** Have your child choose a favorite story. Work with your child to visualize and describe characters and places from the story using story details.

Practice Book 6.2, p. 85

Name ______________________ **The Day of the Turtle**

Selection Test

Directions: Choose the best answer to each item. Mark the letter for the answer you have chosen.

Part 1: Vocabulary

Find the answer choice that means about the same as the underlined word in each sentence.

1. Alfred filled a pail with jellyfish.
   - A. fish eggs
   - **(B)** sea animals with soft, often clear, tissue
   - C. sea animals with shells
   - D. sea animals that look like horses

2. Jenny would not touch the tentacle.
   - F. part of the body by which an animal sees
   - G. organ in which digestion occurs
   - H. the outer surface of an animal
   - **(J)** long, slender growth on an animal; feeler

3. When she saw the large dog, Liz felt wary.
   - **(A)** cautious; careful
   - B. surprised
   - C. interested; curious
   - D. friendly

4. The crew returned with a new spar.
   - F. floor of a ship
   - G. door on a ship
   - **(H)** wooden pole used to support a sail on a ship
   - J. a platform used by a lookout on a ship

5. Mr. Hong had a pile of driftwood.
   - **(A)** wood washed up on the shore
   - B. highly polished wood
   - C. wood found under trees in an orchard
   - D. expensive wood

Part 2: Comprehension

Use what you know about the story to answer each item.

6. Why does Laura have such a hard time getting the turtle to the water?
   - F. It struggles against her.
   - G. It has lost its shell.
   - H. It likes lying in the sun.
   - **(J)** It is very big and heavy.

7. What does Laura do first?
   - **(A)** tries to turn the turtle over
   - B. digs a hole beside the turtle
   - C. digs a channel to the sea
   - D. piles seaweed on top of the turtle

8. What has happened to Granny May's house?
   - F. It is filled with water.
   - **(G)** The roof has blown off.
   - H. It has burned down.
   - J. The doors and windows are broken.

9. On the beach, the gulls are waiting for—
   - A. a ship to appear.
   - B. the tide to come in.
   - **(C)** a chance to eat the turtle.
   - D. the tide to go out.

10. Laura digs a channel to the sea to—
    - **(F)** help the turtle return to the water.
    - G. hide the turtle.
    - H. keep the gulls away from the turtle.
    - J. collect food for the turtle.

11. Why doesn't the turtle return to the sea the first day?
    - A. It cannot breathe.
    - B. It is very young.
    - **(C)** It is too weak.
    - D. It cannot walk on land.

Practice Book 6.2, p. 86

Name ______________________ **The Day of the Turtle**

12. Laura thinks that the turtle—
    - F. wants to be her pet.
    - G. will always remember her.
    - H. is afraid of Granny May.
    - **(J)** understands what she says.

13. Which sentence from the story best helps you visualize what the turtle looks like lying in the sand?
    - A. "I think it's called a leatherback turtle."
    - B. "After a while I gave up and sat down beside him on the sand."
    - **(C)** "His flippers were quite still and held out to the clouds above as if he was worshiping them."
    - D. "That turtle would just be food to him, and to anyone else who finds him."

14. Granny May most likely helps Laura with the turtle because she—
    - **(F)** understands why Laura wants to save it.
    - G. does not like turtle soup.
    - H. can always catch plenty of shrimp.
    - J. likes having secrets from Laura's father.

15. Based on what Laura says about her father, how will he probably react when he finds out that Laura and Granny May helped the turtle go back to the sea?
    - A. He will go down to the beach to look for it.
    - **(B)** He will be angry because they need the food.
    - C. He will understand their concern for the turtle.
    - D. He will tell them to go catch another turtle.

STOP

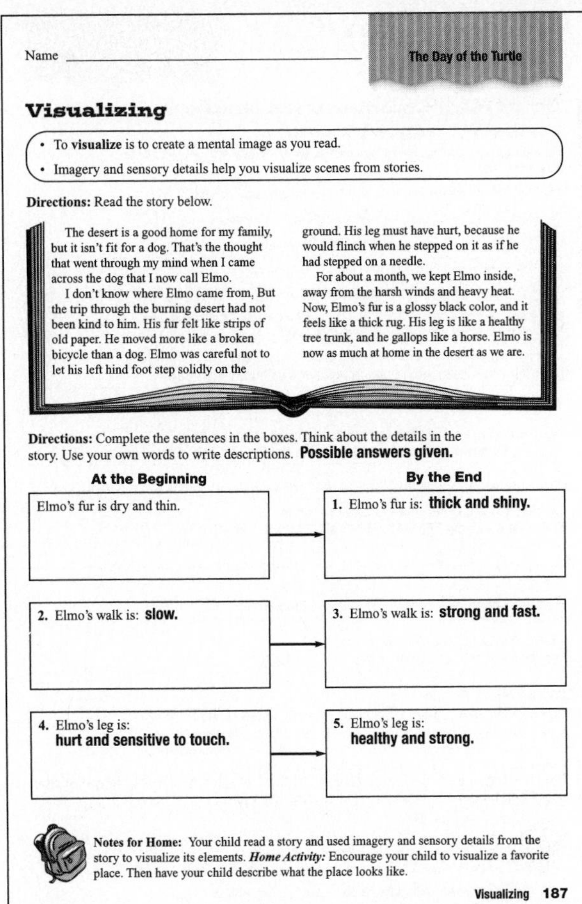

Name ______________________ The Day of the Turtle

Visualizing

- To **visualize** is to create a mental image as you read.
- Imagery and sensory details help you visualize scenes from stories.

Directions: Read the story below.

The desert is a good home for my family, but it isn't fit for a dog. That's the thought that went through my mind when I came across the dog that I now call Elmo.

I don't know where Elmo came from, But the trip through the burning desert had not been kind to him. His fur felt like strips of old paper. He moved more like a broken bicycle than a dog. Elmo was careful not to let his left hind foot step solidly on the ground. His leg must have hurt, because he would flinch when he stepped on it as if he had stepped on a needle.

For about a month, we kept Elmo inside, away from the harsh winds and heavy heat. Now, Elmo's fur is a glossy black color, and it feels like a thick rug. His leg is like a healthy tree trunk, and he gallops like a horse. Elmo is now as much at home in the desert as we are.

Directions: Complete the sentences in the boxes. Think about the details in the story. Use your own words to write descriptions. **Possible answers given.**

At the Beginning		By the End
Elmo's fur is dry and thin.	→	1. Elmo's fur is: **thick and shiny.**
2. Elmo's walk is: **slow.**	→	3. Elmo's walk is: **strong and fast.**
4. Elmo's leg is: **hurt and sensitive to touch.**	→	5. Elmo's leg is: **healthy and strong.**

Notes for Home: Your child read a story and used imagery and sensory details from the story to visualize its elements. ***Home Activity:*** Encourage your child to visualize a favorite place. Then have your child describe what the place looks like.

Name ______________________ The Day of the Turtle

Making Judgments

REVIEW

Directions: Read the passage. Then read each question about the passage. Choose the best answer to each question. Mark the letter for the answer you have chosen.

Letters to the Editor

The Problem of Palmer's Pond

To the Editor,

The issue about what to do with Palmer's Pond has arisen once more. Some people think we should allow motorboats on Palmer's Pond. But independent studies have shown that oil from the boats would put fish in danger. So we should keep motorboats *out* of the pond.

We should also be wary of the plan to build a hotel near the pond. A hotel would destroy the quiet that we love. For the same reason, we should not build a new beach. No matter what the mayor's study says, we don't need a new beach yet.

My family has lived on Palmer's Pond for 120 years. I know what the pond needs. To save the pond, we need to keep it the same.

Sincerely,

Gillian Boswell

1. When the author says that motorboats should be kept off the pond, she—
   - **A.** does not support her opinion.
   - **(B.)** uses an independent study to support her opinion.
   - **C.** is only stating facts.
   - **D.** is ignoring facts.
2. The author's opinion about a new hotel is—
   - **F.** supported by a study.
   - **G.** supported by facts.
   - **(H.)** not supported.
   - **J.** contradicted by other statements in the article.
3. When the author says that a new beach should not be built, she—
   - **A.** uses a study to support her opinion.
   - **B.** seems free of bias.
   - **C.** lists facts.
   - **(D.)** ignores a study.
4. Which statement shows that the author might **not** be a fair judge of plans for the pond?
   - **(F.)** She ignores the mayor's study.
   - **G.** She ignores an independent study.
   - **H.** She doesn't want motorboats.
   - **J.** Her family has lived on the pond for 120 years.
5. Because the author wants the pond to stay the same, she probably—
   - **(A.)** will not consider anything that might change it.
   - **B.** considers all opposing opinions carefully.
   - **C.** gives a balanced account of the situation.
   - **D.** supports all of her opinions.

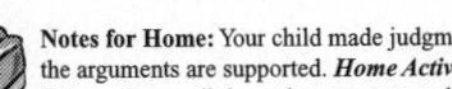

Notes for Home: Your child made judgments about the statements in a letter and how well the arguments are supported. ***Home Activity:*** With your child, read an editorial column. Discuss how well the author presents and supports his or her opinions.

Name ______________________ The Day of the Turtle

Writing Across Texts

Directions: You read two selections about the living earth in "The Day of the Turtle" and "Storm-a-Dust." Think about the characters, setting, and plot. How are the selections alike? How are they different? Write your responses in the Venn diagram below. **Possible answers given.**

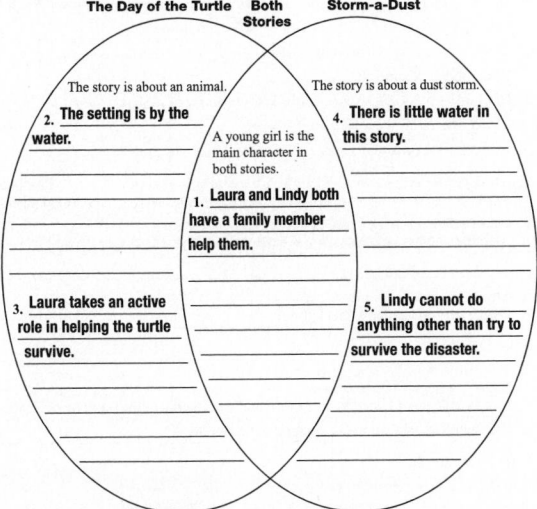

The Day of the Turtle	Both Stories	Storm-a-Dust
The story is about an animal.	A young girl is the main character in both stories.	The story is about a dust storm.
2. **The setting is by the water.**	1. **Laura and Lindy both have a family member help them.**	4. **There is little water in this story.**
3. **Laura takes an active role in helping the turtle survive.**		5. **Lindy cannot do anything other than try to survive the disaster.**

Write a Comparative Paragraph

In a paragraph or two, compare and contrast the problems faced by Laura with the problems faced by Lindy. Use the selections, what you know, and the completed Venn diagram to write your paragraph on a separate sheet of paper. **Paragraphs will vary. Check to see that students have used details from both selections.**

Notes for Home: Your child has compared and contrasted information from two different stories. ***Home Activity:*** As you read other stories or articles, encourage your child to point out how events are alike and different.

Name ______________________ The Day of the Turtle

Grammar: Sentence Punctuation

REVIEW

Directions: Write C if the sentence has correct end punctuation. If the punctuation is incorrect, write the correct punctuation on the line.

1. Do you have an animal shelter in your town. **?**
2. What a great job those shelters do! **C**
3. They rescue and take in animals of all kinds, especially cats and dogs? **.**
4. Please answer this question? **.**
5. Did you adopt your cat from the local shelter? **C**
6. The shelter was full of adorable animals. **C**
7. How hard it must have been to choose one animal? **!**
8. How long did it take you to make up your mind? **C**

Directions: Read each sentence. Add a comma to each compound sentence. Then add the correct end punctuation.

9. The day was hot, and we decided to drive to the beach.
10. We packed our bathing suits and a delicious picnic lunch.
11. We had to wait for Leroy, and Anna was a little late too.
12. Finally we were in the car and on our way.
13. How excited we were about going to the beach!
14. What is in the middle of the road ahead?
15. It might be a small horse or a sheep, or it could be a large dog.
16. My mom slowed the car, and we saw a big, dirty, tired dog.
17. Should we stop, or should we continue driving?
18. We wanted to keep going, but we could not abandon that poor animal.
19. What a smart decision we made!
20. We never got to the beach, but we did eventually get the best pet in the world. **or !**

Notes for Home: Your child added punctuation marks to the ends of sentences and added commas between parts of compound sentences. ***Home Activity:*** Challenge your child to explain the reason for the punctuation in several sentences in favorite books or magazines.

Grammar Practice Book 6.2, p. 42

Name ______________________

The Day of the Turtle

Grammar: Commas with Nouns in Series and in Direct Address

A **comma** is a punctuation mark that is used to set off a word or a group of words from other words in the same sentence. In this way, a comma helps to make the meaning of a sentence clear.

Three or more words (such as nouns) or groups of words listed together in a sentence are called a **series.** A comma is used after each item in the series except the last.

Mike, Sam, and Tammy went to Stewart Beach Aquarium.
The three friends had peanut butter and jelly sandwiches, apples, and juice for lunch.

One or two commas are used to set off the names of people who are directly addressed in speech or writing. This use of a noun is called **direct address.**

Mike, do you know which bus goes to the aquarium?
I think, Tammy, that it is the M17 bus.
Do you know for sure, Sam?

Directions: Add commas to each sentence to set off nouns used in a series or in direct address.

1. Eleanor, Joe, and Terry work at Stewart Beach Aquarium.
2. Eleanor gives tours on Fridays, Saturdays, and Sundays.
3. Joe arranges for lectures, films, and shows.
4. Did you think, Terry, that my last lecture was clear?
5. The aquarium has been attracting students, teachers, and tourists.
6. When is the next showing of the film about dolphins, Joe?
7. Terry is one of the people who feed the dolphins, porpoises, and seals.
8. Joe, please finish the new schedule by Friday.
9. Stingrays, sharks, manatees, and squids are just a few of the creatures that you can see at the aquarium.
10. Stewart Beach Aquarium is easy to reach by train, bus, or car.

Notes for Home: Your child added commas to nouns in a series and in direct address. ***Home Activity:*** Say sentences in which people are spoken to directly by name. Ask your child which word the comma should follow.

Grammar Practice Book 6.2, p. 43

Name ______________________

The Day of the Turtle

Grammar: Commas with Nouns in Series and in Direct Address

Directions: Add commas to each sentence to set off nouns used in a series or in a direct address.

1. Paul, do you remember that terrible storm three summers ago?
2. It rained on Monday, Tuesday, Wednesday, and Thursday.
3. Water got into the attic, the cellar, and the garage.
4. Were you here that summer, Jamal?
5. The storm damaged the house, the garden, and the new deck.

Directions: Rewrite each sentence below to include a noun of direct address. Use commas as needed. **Possible answers given.**

6. Did I tell you about one downpour that lasted nine days?
Did I tell you, Cecile, about one downpour that lasted nine days?
7. TV news stories showed rescuers rowing through flooded areas.
Andrew, TV news stories showed rescuers rowing through flooded areas.
8. Rivers at flood level threatened people's homes.
Rivers at flood level threatened people's homes, Cindy.
9. The nonstop rain was part of the El Niño effect.
Bart, the nonstop rain was part of the El Niño effect.
10. Yes, this occurred in the spring of 1998.
Yes, Andrew, this occurred in the spring of 1998.

Write a News Article

On a separate sheet of paper, write a brief news article about a strong force in nature, such as a blizzard, hurricane, tornado, or flood. The force can be one that you have experienced or one that you have read about or heard about. Include items in a series. Remember to use commas correctly.
Students might describe a hurricane, using three or more words or groups of words listed together in a series and separated by commas.

Notes for Home: Your child used commas to separate words listed in a series and to set off the names of people being addressed directly. ***Home Activity:*** Invite your child to write several sentences in which three or more items are listed in a series, using commas to separate them.

Grammar Practice Book 6.2, p. 44

Name ______________________

The Day of the Turtle

Grammar: Commas with Nouns in Series and in Direct Address

RETEACHING

Circle the commas in the sentences below.

1. Alicia, what is an aqueduct?
2. It is a water canal, tunnel, or pipe.
3. I am going to Italy to see them, Veronica.

When you write, use commas:
- to separate words or groups of words in a series;
- to set off the name of a person directly addressed.

Directions: Insert commas where they are needed in the following sentences.

1. Jena, what is an aqueduct bridge?
2. It is a structure with arches, a road, and a canal.
3. It carried water, people, and goods across a valley.
4. Nancy, what is the Aqua Appia?
5. It was the first Roman aqueduct, Darla.
6. Nine Roman aqueducts were built in all, Judy.
7. Some of them, John, are still in use.

Directions: Use each set of words to write a new sentence. Use the words as items in a series. Add commas where they belong. **Possible answers given.**

8. June July August
It is easiest for me to get together with my friends from Australia in June, July, and August.
9. pizza ice cream potato chips
I like to eat pizza, ice cream, and potato chips, but I don't do it often.

Notes for Home: Your child used commas in sentences with nouns in series and names directly addressed. ***Home Activity:*** Watch a television news program together. Have your child write sentences in which nouns are used in a series or people are directly addressed. Use sentences from the news program.

Grammar Practice Book 6.2, p. 45

Name ______________________

The Day of the Turtle

Grammar: Commas with Nouns in Series and in Direct Address

Directions: Add commas where needed to the sentences below.

1. Sharon, who are the Inuit?
2. They are a group of people who live in areas of Greenland, North America, and Siberia.
3. They inhabit Baffin Island, Banks Island, and Victoria Island.
4. Inuit is their name for themselves, Gerald.
5. Lisa, it means "the people."
6. They arrived in North America after the Native Americans, Sandra.
7. Kim, do the Inuit people have many dialects?
8. Many stories, legends, and myths are told in the Inuit language.

Directions: Rewrite each sentence below to include a noun in direct address. You may wish to add other information as well. Use commas as needed. **Possible answers given.**

9. Learning another language is easiest when a person is very young.
Learning another language, Jim, is easiest when a person is very young.
10. Why do you think that is true?
Vivian, why do you think that is true?
11. If you would like to understand more about a particular culture and its customs, learning some of the language can be helpful.
If you would like to understand more about a particular culture and its customs, Max, learning some of the language can be helpful.

Write a Paragraph

On a separate sheet of paper, write a paragraph about a people or culture you would like to study. Describe some of their customs that you find interesting. You may use an encyclopedia to find information, if you wish.
Check that students have used commas correctly.

Notes for Home: Your child used commas in sentences in which people are directly addressed by name. ***Home Activity:*** Have your child write commands for toys or stuffed animals in your home, directly addressing them by name. Your child should use commas in his or her written commands.

Practice Book 6.2, p. 88
Name ______________________

The Day of the Turtle

Word Study: Base Words

Directions: Many words are formed by adding letters to the beginning or end of a word. The word you start with is called the **base word.** Read each sentence. Find the base word in the underlined word. Write the base word on the line.

gasp 1. The turtle lay gasping for air.
seem 2. It seemed as if it could not move an inch.
shut 3. The turtle kept shutting its mouth.
shout 4. I shouted at the turtle to get into the water.
exhaust 5. But the creature was too exhausted to move.
cover 6. The turtle lay uncovered and exposed.
blink 7. It looked at me with unblinking eyes.
wrinkle 8. The turtle's wrinkled skin was becoming dry.
threat 9. The birds made a threatening noise.
honest 10. I honestly didn't know how to help the turtle.

Directions: Combine each base word and ending to make a new word. You might need to add, drop, or change letters to spell the word correctly. Write the new word on the line.

11. nudge + -ing = nudging
12. drag + -ing = dragging
13. noisy + -ly = noisily
14. hungry + -er = hungrier
15. jump + -ing = jumping

Notes for Home: Your child identified base words in longer words, such as *think* in *unthinking,* and used base words to write longer words. ***Home Activity:*** Read a news article with your child. Look for words that are formed from base words.

Spelling Workbook 6.2, p. 33
Name ______________________

The Day of the Turtle

Spelling: Compound Words 2

Pretest Directions: Fold back the page along the dotted line. On the blanks, write the spelling words as they are dictated. When you have finished the test, unfold the page and check your words.

1. basketball	1. The **basketball** game was close.
2. everywhere	2. We looked **everywhere** for him.
3. outside	3. The cat went **outside**.
4. summertime	4. **Summertime** is always nice.
5. something	5. I forgot **something** at home.
6. afterthought	6. She said it as an **afterthought**.
7. cheerleader	7. My sister is a **cheerleader**.
8. quarterback	8. The **quarterback** was tackled.
9. bookstore	9. This old **bookstore** is wonderful.
10. courthouse	10. He works at the **courthouse**.
11. baby-sit	11. She had to **baby-sit** her brother.
12. roller-skating	12. Let's go **roller-skating** tomorrow.
13. drive-in	13. The old **drive-in** theater closed.
14. self-control	14. You must learn **self-control**.
15. part-time	15. He has a **part-time** job.
16. ice-skated	16. We **ice-skated** for an hour.
17. ninety-five	17. My aunt is **ninety-five** years old.
18. brother-in-law	18. Her **brother-in-law** is a pilot.
19. water-skied	19. We **water-skied** all day.
20. old-fashioned	20. I like **old-fashioned** clothing.

Notes for Home: Your child took a pretest on compound words with and without hyphens. ***Home Activity:*** Help your child learn misspelled words. He or she can divide misspelled words into parts (such as syllables), concentrate on each part, and notice if there is a hyphen.

Spelling Workbook 6.2, p. 34
Name ______________________

The Day of the Turtle

Spelling: Compound Words 2

Word List

basketball	something	bookstore	drive-in	ninety-five
everywhere	afterthought	courthouse	self-control	brother-in-law
outside	cheerleader	baby-sit	part-time	water-skied
summertime	quarterback	roller-skating	ice-skated	old-fashioned

Directions: Choose a word from the box that best answers each question. Write the word on the line.

old-fashioned 1. What is the opposite of *modern?*
ninety-five 2. What would be an excellent test score?
summertime 3. When do schoolchildren have lots of free time?
self-control 4. What helps a person keep his or her temper?
something 5. What do you have if you have more than nothing?
part-time 6. How do you describe a job you only go to on weekends?
afterthought 7. Which word names an idea that comes too late?

Directions: Write the words from the box that belong in each group. **Order may vary.**

Places	People	Activities
8. everywhere	13. cheerleader	16. basketball
9. outside	14. quarterback	17. baby-sit
10. bookstore	15. brother-in-law	18. roller-skating
11. courthouse		19. ice-skated
12. drive-in		20. water-skied

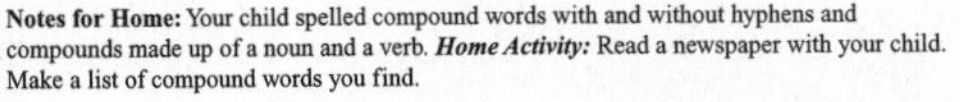

Notes for Home: Your child spelled compound words with and without hyphens and compounds made up of a noun and a verb. ***Home Activity:*** Read a newspaper with your child. Make a list of compound words you find.

Spelling Workbook 6.2, p. 35
Name ______________________

The Day of the Turtle

Spelling: Compound Words 2

Directions: Proofread this news story. Find six spelling mistakes. Use the proofreading marks to correct each mistake.

≡ Make a capital.
/ Make a small letter.
∧ Add something.
Take out something.
○ Add a period.
¶ Begin a new paragraph.

Local Students Save Dog

A small dog named Wylie had a quarter-back and a cheer-leader to thank for saving his life. According to Stan Nagy, the dog's owner and brother-in law to the mayor, Wylie chased something into a pipe on a street. As temperatures out-side soared above ninety-five degrees, the little dog couldn't get out. Luckily, Paul Woud and Yassi Levine were roller-skating to a nearby drivin restaurant when they heard Wylie bark. Levine, a partime clerk's intern at the courthouse, alerted the police, who freed Wylie.

Word List
basketball
everywhere
outside
summertime
something
afterthought
cheerleader
quarterback
bookstore
courthouse
baby-sit
roller-skating
drive-in
self-control
part-time
ice-skated
ninety-five
brother-in-law
water-skied
old-fashioned

Spelling Tip

Remember to keep all the letters when writing a closed compound word. Use hyphens for numbers twenty-one to ninety-nine, compounds ending with **in-law,** compounds beginning with **self,** and compounds made up of a noun and a verb.

Write a News Story

On a separate sheet of paper, write a news story about an animal rescue. Try to use at least five of your spelling words. **Answers will vary, but each news story should include at least five spelling words.**

Notes for Home: Your child spelled compound words with and without hyphens and compounds made up of a noun and a verb. ***Home Activity:*** Take turns naming other compounds that contain one of the shorter words that make up the compounds in the Word List.

Spelling Workbook 6.2, p. 36

Name ______________________ **The Day of the Turtle**

Spelling: Compound Words 2 — REVIEW

Word List

basketball	something	bookstore	drive-in	ninety-five
everywhere	afterthought	courthouse	self-control	brother-in-law
outside	cheerleader	baby-sit	part-time	water-skied
summertime	quarterback	roller-skating	ice-skated	old-fashioned

Directions: Choose the word from the box that includes the underlined part of each word below. Write the word on the line.

1. twenty-five — **ninety-five**
2. law-abiding — **brother-in-law**
3. afternoon — **afterthought**
4. self-pity — **self-control**
5. nowhere — **everywhere**
6. wastebasket — **basketball**
7. everything — **something**
8. drive-through — **drive-in**
9. shutout — **outside**
10. storybook — **bookstore**

Directions: Choose a word from the box that best completes each person's statement. Write the word on the line to the left.

baby-sit 11. Big brother: "Sure, Mom. I'll _____ the kids tonight."
quarterback 12. Football player: "If the _____ passes me the ball, I'll run."
courthouse 13. Judge: "My office can be found in the county _____."
roller-skating 14. Little girl: "I want to go to the _____ party at the rink."
cheerleader 15. Coach: "To be a _____, you must have pep and team spirit."
water-skied 16. Boater: "We _____ up and down the lake all afternoon."
old-fashioned 17. Antique dealer: "People really love _____ gadgets."
part-time 18. Student: "To earn a little money, I work _____ in the fall."
summertime 19. Lifeguard: "The outdoor pool is open daily in the _____."
ice-skated 20. Hockey player: "I've _____ since the day I learned to walk."

Notes for Home: Your child spelled compound words with and without hyphens and compounds made up of a noun and a verb. ***Home Activity:*** Challenge your child to write the hyphenated compounds from the list in alphabetical order.

Spelling: Compound Words 2 **199**

Practice Book 6.2, p. 89

Name ______________________ **The Day of the Turtle**

Technology: Study Strategies

CD-ROM resources can help you gather information on a particular topic. You might use a CD-ROM dictionary, encyclopedia, or a topic-related CD-ROM. You can use search CD-ROMs to find specific information or click on underlined links to find related information.

Directions: Use the three CD-ROM sample screens to answer the questions that follow.

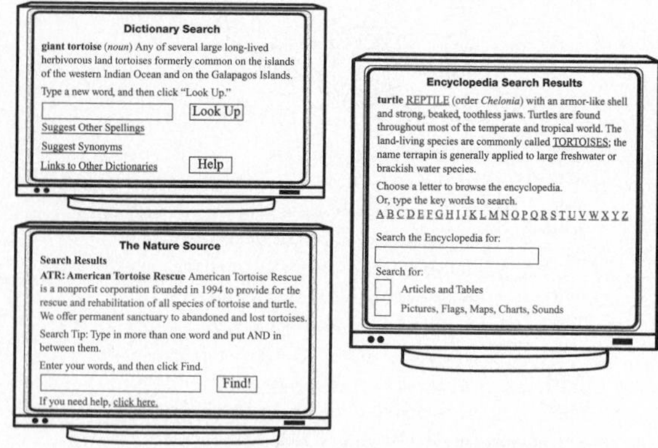

1. How would you find the meaning of "herbivorous" using the CD-ROM dictionary?
Type in the word "herbivorous" and click on "Look Up."

2. How would you find examples of the sounds turtles make in the CD-ROM encyclopedia?
Type in "turtles" and click the box "Pictures, Flags, Maps, Charts, Sounds."

3. How could you use the CD-ROM encyclopedia to find related information about tortoises?
You can click on the underlined link TORTOISES to find related information.

4. What key words could you use to find information about a turtle's diet in "The Nature Source" CD-ROM? Hint: Use AND between key words.
Possible key words: turtle or tortoise AND diet, food, or eat

200 Research and Study Skills: Technology: Study Strategies

Practice Book 6.2, p. 90

Name ______________________ **The Day of the Turtle**

Use **study strategies** to help you save time and avoid reading irrelevant information. You can make a **K-W-L table,** follow the steps of **SQ2R,** or **skim and scan** text to focus your research.

Directions: Use the study strategies below and the three CD-ROM samples to answer the questions that follow.

K What I Know	W What I Want to Know	L What I Learned

SQ2R
- **Survey** the text
- Formulate **questions** about it.
- **Read** the text.
- **Recite** what you have learned.

Skim a text to see if it is appropriate.
Scan a text using key words to locate specific information.

5. Why would writing questions about what you want to know help you save research time?
Possible answer: Writing questions before you research will help you set a purpose for your research.

6. Pick one of the CD-ROM samples. Write one question about something more you would want to know after reading the information on the CD-ROM.
Questions will vary depending on which CD-ROM sample is chosen.

7. When you're surveying or skimming a text, why is it important to look at titles, heads, and boldfaced or underlined words?
Possible answer: They help give you an idea of what the text is about.

8. Why are the underlined words in the CD-ROM encyclopedia entry important?
The underlined words are links to other related information.

9. Scan the information in "The Nature Source" CD-ROM to find out what ATR stands for and when this group was formed.
ATR stands for American Turtle Rescue. The group was founded in 1994.

10. Which of the three study strategies would you be most likely to use? Why?
Answers will vary. Check that students support their choices with explanations.

Notes for Home: Your child used CD-ROM resources to practice using different study strategies. ***Home Activity:*** With your child, pick one of the three study strategies described above. Help your child use one of these strategies to prepare for an upcoming test or research report.

Research and Study Skills: Technology: Study Strategies **201**

Practice Book 6.2, p. 91

Name ______________________ **Saving the Sound**

Persuasive Devices

- **Persuasive devices** are the special techniques an author uses to influence the way you think or feel.
- One type of persuasive device is the use of *loaded words.* Authors use *loaded words* to bring out an emotional response in readers and to convince readers of their ideas and views.

Directions: Reread "Why Care?" Then read the following paraphrases of the article. Complete the table by underlining the loaded word or words in each paraphrase. Then describe the response that readers are likely to have to the loaded words. **Possible answers given.**

Paraphrase	Emotional Response
Humankind dominates the environment.	Readers feel sympathy for the weak and vulnerable environment.
We affect plants and animals negatively.	Readers feel ashamed of the way humans have affected plants and animals.
We shouldn't be bullying the rest of Earth's creatures.	1. **Readers feel guilty for pushing weaker creatures around.**
Plants and animals are important sources of beauty and fun.	2. **Readers appreciate plants and animals.**
Many species enrich our lives just by existing.	3. **Readers feel grateful to plants and animals.**
Our actions may force species into extinction.	4. **Readers feel alarmed about the fate of the species.**
We are violating other living things' right to exist.	5. **Readers feel guilty and ashamed of humans for being so uncaring about the environment.**

Notes for Home: Your child identified loaded words, a persuasuve device used by writers to persuade readers of their point of view. ***Home Activity:*** Help your child identify loaded words in a newspaper editorial or letter to the editor.

204 Persuasive Devices

Practice Book 6.2, p. 92

Name ______________________ **Saving the Sound**

Vocabulary

Directions: Draw a line to connect each word on the left with its definition on the right.

1. contaminated	the air, water, soil, and so on
2. toll	polluted
3. environment	delicate; easily damaged
4. muck	filth
5. fragile	something paid, lost, or suffered

Check the Words You Know

- __ cleanup
- __ contaminated
- __ environment
- __ fragile
- __ muck
- __ toll
- __ widespread

Directions: Choose the word from the box that best completes each sentence. Write the letters of the word on the blanks. The boxed letters spell a problem that humans have created.

6. Some problems with our air are so _____ that they extend for miles. **w i d e s [p] r e a d**
7. Chemicals released into our air and water take a _____ on all of Earth's life forms. **t o [l] l**
8. Harmful waste from factories mixes with soil and water and creates a _____ that no one wants to touch! **m [u] c k**
9. Businesses that dump this type of waste can cause great damage to Earth's _____ ecosystems. **f r a g [i] l e**
10. If we all work together, can we do a complete _____ of our environment? **c l e a [n] u p**

A problem humans have created: **pollution**

Write an Editorial

On a separate sheet of paper, write an editorial in which you state your opinion on an environmental issue or a law, such as recycling or noise pollution. Talk about how the issue affects your neighbors and your community. Use as many vocabulary words as you can.

Encourage students to give well-developed, clearly expressed opinions. Check that their editorials use vocabulary words correctly.

Notes for Home: Your child identified and used vocabulary words from the selection "Saving the Sound." ***Home Activity:*** With your child, discuss the environment and how it could be made better. Encourage your child to use the listed vocabulary words as you talk.

Practice Book 6.2, p. 93

Name ______________________ **Saving the Sound**

Persuasive Devices

- **Persuasive devices** are the special techniques an author uses to influence the way you think or feel.
- One type of persuasive device is the use of loaded words. Authors use loaded words to bring out an an emotional response in readers and to convince readers of their ideas and views.

Directions: Reread the section of "Saving the Sound" in which the author describes the coming of spring to Prince William Sound. Then answer the questions below. Look for loaded words that the author uses to influence your thinking. **Possible answers given.**

In the springtime, the Sound is waking from winter. Ice and snow are melting. Bears emerge from their hibernation dens. Fish and birds that winter elsewhere begin to return. Prince William Sound is coming to life.
 The wreck of the *Exxon Valdez,* however, changed all that. The oil spill turned a time of awakening and beauty into a time of nightmare and death. The Sound awoke on March 24, 1989, to find itself the victim of a disaster unlike anything that had occurred before in the United States.

1. Which sentences are statements of simple facts? Underline these facts.
2. Write some loaded words from the selection that are positive. Explain what the author's purpose is in using these words.
 Waking, coming to life, beauty; These words are used to convince readers that the Sound used to be lively and beautiful.
3. Write some loaded words from the selection that are strongly negative. Explain what the author's purpose is in using these words.
 Nightmare, death, victim, disaster; These words are used to persuade the reader of the seriousness of the oil spill.
4. The author writes "The Sound awoke. . ." as if the place were a person. Why do you think the author makes this suggestion?
 It might make readers feel worse about its fate.
5. On a separate sheet of paper, describe the author's main purpose of "Saving the Sound" and explain whether or not you think the author influenced your thinking.
 The author's main purpose is to make readers understand that oil spills are serious disasters. Text contains many loaded words to influence readers.

Notes for Home: Your child read a work of nonfiction and looked at ways the author might try to influence readers. ***Home Activity:*** With your child, look at an advertisement. Discuss ways in which it tries to persuade you to make a decision.

Practice Book 6.2, p. 95

Name ______________________ **Saving the Sound**

Selection Test

Directions: Choose the best answer to each item. Mark the letter for the answer you have chosen.

Part 1: Vocabulary

Find the answer choice that means about the same as the underlined word in each sentence.

1. Cleanup began right away.
 - **(A) act of removing dirt and filth**
 - B. use of bright lights
 - C. act of building something
 - D. the burning of oil
2. Karen works hard to save the environment.
 - F. bird's nest
 - G. large trees
 - H. body shape
 - **(J) natural surroundings**
3. There is a fragile balance among living things in the sea.
 - **(A) delicate; easily damaged**
 - B. lasting forever
 - C. new; invented recently
 - D. changing quickly
4. That red barrel holds contaminated water.
 - F. clear
 - **(G) polluted**
 - H. used for drinking
 - J. nearly frozen
5. Alison scooped muck into the pail.
 - A. clear water
 - **(B) dirt; filth**
 - C. sea animals
 - D. white sand
6. The accident took a heavy toll on the local economy.
 - F. benefits resulting from an event
 - G. warning sign
 - **(H) something lost, paid, or suffered**
 - J. cause
7. The storm had widespread effects.
 - A. local
 - B. felt immediately
 - C. minor; not very large
 - **(D) distributed over a large area**

Part 2: Comprehension

Use what you know about the selection to answer each item.

8. Where did the *Exxon Valdez* spill its oil?
 - F. Anchorage
 - G. Kodiak Island
 - H. Cook Inlet
 - **(J) Prince William Sound**
9. The first step in the cleanup was to—
 - **(A) try to contain the spill.**
 - B. rescue birds and animals.
 - C. scoop up oil and take it to shore.
 - D. build walls to protect fishing grounds.
10. In the first few days after the spill, why did nice weather hamper the cleanup efforts?
 - F. Oil washed over the containment booms.
 - **(G) Chemicals used to break up the oil require rough seas.**
 - H. It made the oil slick spread faster.
 - J. Workers were slow to respond to the disaster.
11. In this selection, the author is trying to persuade readers to—
 - A. support the fishing industry.
 - B. visit Alaska to see the effects of the spill.
 - **(C) help protect the natural environment.**
 - D. send money to organizations that rescue wildlife.

Practice Book 6.2, p. 96

Name ______________________ **Saving the Sound**

12. The author of this selection makes the effects of the oil spill seem terrible by—
 - F. noting that other spills have occurred since then.
 - G. comparing the size of the Sound with New Jersey.
 - H. naming the company that spilled the oil.
 - **(J) using words that bring out an emotional response in the reader.**
13. "Loaded words" are used as a persuasive device in which of the following sentences from the selection?
 - A. "The wreck of the *Exxon Valdez,* however, changed all that."
 - **(B) "The oil spill turned a time of awakening and beauty into a time of nightmare and death."**
 - C. "One of the worst parts of the first few hours of the spill is that no one was prepared for it."
 - D. "The oil-spill response plan calls for spill-fighting equipment to be on hand five hours after a spill occurs."
14. To make this selection more balanced, the writer could have included the point of view of—
 - F. commercial fishermen.
 - G. wildlife biologists.
 - **(H) oil-company employees.**
 - J. local residents.
15. Which sentence states an opinion?
 - **(A) "The Sound's most appealing sea creature is the playful sea otter."**
 - B. "Much smaller than sea lions, they [sea otters] usually weigh less than 250 pounds (113 kg)."
 - C. "Otters live in the region year-round."
 - D. "Bears wander the forests and mountains, searching for food."

Name ______________________ Saving the Sound

Persuasive Devices

- **Persuasive devices** are the special techniques an author uses to influence the way you think or feel.
- One type of persuasive device is the use of loaded words. Authors use loaded words to bring out an emotional response in readers and to convince readers of their ideas and views.

Directions: Read the article below.

In the past 30 years, our government and some industries have tried to fight air pollution. For example, most cars in America now have special equipment to cut down on pollution.

Unfortunately, these efforts have not been enough. In some places, the air is too foul to breathe. Though scientists have not yet proven it, it is obvious that air pollution contributes to global warming and to the ruining of our climate. Some people claim that it costs too much to fight pollution. But more and more people agree that we should spend as much money as it takes to make our air clean.

Directions: Complete the table. For each statement, write **yes** or **no** to indicate whether the statement includes loaded words. Then write a sentence explaining your answer.

Statement	Persuasive Device Yes or No?	Reason for Answer
The air is too foul to breathe.	1. **Yes**	"Foul" is a loaded word.
Most cars in America now have special equipment to cut down on pollution.	2. **No**	3. **This is a statement of fact that can be proved, and it does not use loaded words.**
Though scientists have not yet proven it, it is obvious that air pollution contributes to global warming and to the ruining of our climate.	4. **Yes**	5. **"Ruining" is a loaded word.**

Notes for Home: Your child read a passage and identified whether or not the author uses loaded words. ***Home Activity:*** Help your child write an editorial about an issue of his or her choice. Work together to include loaded words to influence readers.

Practice Book 6.2, p. 97

Name ______________________ Saving the Sound

Fact and Opinion and Graphic Sources

REVIEW

Directions: Look at the table and read the caption. Then read each question about the table and caption. Choose the best answer to each question. Mark the letter for the answer you have chosen.

Air Quality of U.S. Cities, 1991–1994				
	1991	1992	1993	1994
Chicago	8	7	1	8
Dallas	1	3	5	1
Los Angeles	182	185	146	136
New York	22	4	6	8
San Francisco	0	0	0	0

This table shows the number of days in a year that the air in five American cities failed to meet acceptable air-quality standards. The source of the data is the U.S. Environmental Protection Agency.

1. Which of the following is a statement of opinion?
   A. Los Angeles had 185 days with unacceptable air quality in 1992.
   B. The source of the data is the U.S. Environmental Protection Agency.
   (C) Los Angeles is the worst place to live in the U.S.
   D. San Francisco had the fewest days of unacceptable air quality.
2. Which is an incorrect statement of fact?
   F. San Francisco has better air quality than any other city in the table.
   G. Los Angeles has the most polluted air of the five cities.
   H. The air quality in New York improved greatly after 1991.
   (J.) 1994 had more days of unacceptable air quality than 1992.
3. Which statement of opinion is supported by data in the table?
   (A) Air quality in the U.S. is improving.
   B. No one likes poor air quality.
   C. The author is the best authority on air quality.
   D. The U.S. Environmental Protection Agency is working hard to improve air quality.
4. Which statement of opinion is supported by data in the table.
   F. San Francisco is a very pretty city.
   (G.) The trend shown in the table is encouraging.
   H. The air will improve because we need to make a difference.
   J. Air pollution is still a problem because of corrupt city governments.
5. If the trend continues, 2004 will have—
   A. no days with bad air.
   B. the same number of days with bad air as 1994.
   C. more days with bad air than 1994.
   (D.) fewer days with bad air than 1994.

Notes for Home: Your child read a table and a caption and used it to identify related statements of fact and opinion. ***Home Activity:*** With your child, look through a newspaper for a graphic source, such as a graph or a table. Identify statements of fact and opinion in it.

Name ______________________ Saving the Sound

Writing Across Texts

Directions: Refer to "Saving the Sound" and "How Do People Help Provide a Clean Environment?" to complete the Compare/Contrast diagram below. Use examples from the selections to describe the different kinds of pollution. **Possible answers given.**

Central Issues

Sewage

1. **Oil spills into water.**
2. **Bacteria and viruses get into water.**

Alike

Human actions cause pollution.

3. **Humans use chemicals to correct problems.**
4. **Chemicals don't always work.**

Different

Many animals die.

5. **Humans may develop diseases.**
6. **Animals may be poisoned.**

Conclusions

Humans must protect the environment from pollutants.

7. **Care must be taken to transport oil safely.**
8. **Care must be used about what gets into household drains.**
9. **People must continue to study ways to prevent pollution.**
10. **Scientists can develop new ways to prevent pollution.**

Write an Explanation

Use the selections and the completed Compare/Contrast diagram to write an explanation in which you compare and contrast the kinds of pollution described in the selections. Write your explanation on a separate sheet of paper. **Explanations will vary. Students should use details from both selections as they identify kinds of pollution and possible solutions to the problem.**

Notes for Home: Your child has combined information from two sources to compare and contrast different kinds of pollution. ***Home Activity:*** As you read stories and articles, ask your child to explain how ideas in the reading materials are alike and different.

Grammar Practice Book 6.2, p. 46

Name ______________________ Saving the Sound

Grammar: Subjects and Predicates

REVIEW

Directions: Draw a line between the complete subject and the complete predicate in each sentence. Then underline the simple subject and the simple predicate.

1. Pollution of the oceans / occurs in many different ways.
2. Oceanographers / are needed in increasing numbers.
3. Such experts / possess interests in science, the sea, and adventure.
4. Jacques Costeau / was the most famous oceanographer of all.
5. This daring, brilliant scientist / exposed the ocean's problems to the world.
6. The field of oceanography / includes a number of different specialties.
7. The living creatures of the ocean / are studied by marine biologists.
8. Pollution problems / might be solved someday by a chemical oceanographer.
9. Underwater photographers / record the mysteries below the water.
10. Your special interests / will lead you to the fascinating study of the world's oceans.

Directions: Write **S** on the line to the left if the group of words can be a sentence subject. Write **P** if the group of words can be a sentence predicate. Then use each group of words to write a sentence of your own. **Possible answers given.**

S 11. animals in the ocean
Animals in the ocean are at risk from pollution.

P 12. can cause terrible damage to the seas
Oil spills can cause terrible damage to the seas.

P 13. may be changed forever
Life in the ocean may be changed forever.

S 14. recovery from an oil spill
Recovery from an oil spill may take years.

S 15. the secrets of the ocean
The secrets of the ocean are being explored.

Notes for Home: Your child identified and used simple and complete subjects and simple and complete predicates. ***Home Activity:*** Have your child write some sentences about events at school, and highlight each simple subject and predicate.

Grammar Practice Book 6.2, p. 47

Name ______________________

Saving the Sound

Grammar: Subject-Verb Agreement

To work together, the subject of a sentence and the verb must agree in number. The following rules are for sentences that tell what is happening now, at the present time.

For a singular noun subject, add **-s** or **-es** to most verbs.

Tim lives in Alaska.
His brother writes to him from college.

For a plural noun subject, do **not** add **-s** or **-es** to the verb.

Many people visit Tim.
His grandparents travel to Alaska every year.

For compound subjects joined by *and* or *both,* use the verb form for a plural subject.

Carla and Mary want some of Tim's photos of glaciers.
Both his Alaskan friends and his father collect slides of Alaskan wildlife.

For a singular and a plural noun subject joined by *or, either . . . or,* or *neither . . . nor,* the verb must agree with the subject closer to it.

Neither Tim's friends in Washington nor Mary wants to live in the far north.

Directions: Circle the correct form of the verb in ( ) to complete each sentence.

1. Tim (spend/(spends)) much of his time working.
2. He (guide/(guides)) tours through the Alaskan wilderness.
3. Tim and his sister ((work)/works) together.
4. Four guides ((share)/shares) the work.
5. Each guide (own/(owns)) an equal part of the company.

Directions: Write the correct form of the verb in ( ) to complete each sentence.

sail 6. On one tour, visitors (sail) through the Gulf of Alaska.
swims 7. Sometimes, a humpback whale (swim) into view.
soar 8. Bald eagles often (soar) above the water.
lie 9. Many small islands (lie) in the Gulf of Alaska.
stops 10. Sometimes a tour ship or a cabin cruiser (stop) near one of the islands.

Notes for Home: Your child chose and wrote the verb forms that agree with singular subjects and plural subjects. ***Home Activity:*** Have your child choose a verb. Then ask him or her to use the verb in a sentence with a singular subject and in a sentence with a plural subject.

Grammar Practice Book 6.2, p. 48

Name ______________________

Saving the Sound

Grammar: Subject-Verb Agreement

Directions: Circle the correct form of the verb in ( ) to complete each sentence.

1. Treasure Salvages Inc. (search/(searches)) the seas for old sunken ships.
2. The company (find/(finds)) special maps.
3. First, people ((look)/looks) for clues to find ships that were lost.
4. Next, boats ((survey)/surveys) likely areas.
5. Usually, a boat (use/(uses)) a metal detector to find iron objects left by sunken ships.

Directions: Write the correct form of the verb in ( ) to complete each sentence.

locate 6. When divers (locate) a sunken ship, they are very careful.
takes 7. A diver (take) an interest in more than just gold and silver.
interest 8. Both valuable coins and others relics of the past (interest) the searchers.
collect 9. Can either a company or individuals (collect) these artifacts and put them into museums?
study 10. People (study) these artifacts for clues about the past.
examine 11. Scientists (examine) any navigational instruments from the old ship.
tell 12. Passengers' clothing and personal possessions (tell) much about the owners' social position.
provides 13. The ship's furnishings or cargo also (provide) information.
includes 14. A museum exhibit usually (include) items like dishes and knives.
seems 15. What cargo of ancient times (seem) most interesting to you?

Write a Job Description

Choose one outdoor job, such as forest ranger or lifeguard. On a separate sheet of paper, write three or four sentences that describe ways someone in that job might help to protect our environment. Remember to make your subjects and verbs agree.
Check to see that subjects and verbs agree in each sentence.

Notes for Home: Your child learned how to make verbs agree with subjects. ***Home Activity:*** Say a sentence with a singular subject, such as *Ben cleans up the store.* Then give your child a plural subject and have him or her change the verb to make it agree with the subject.

Grammar Practice Book 6.2, p. 49

Name ______________________

Saving the Sound

RETEACHING

Grammar: Subject-Verb Agreement

Subject	Some Verbs That Agree
I	am, was, walk, search
singular nouns and **she, he, it**	is, was, walks, searches
plural nouns and **we, you, they**	are, were, walk, search

Complete the sentence. Write a subject and a verb that agree. Use words from the chart.

They (subject) **walk** (verb) in the park. **Possible answers given.**

A verb must agree with its subject. Add **-s** or **-es** to most verbs with singular subjects. Do **not** add **-s** or **-es** to verbs with plural subjects.

Directions: Complete each sentence. Write the correct form of the verb in ( ).

1. Mountains **form** from pressure under the Earth's surface. (forms/form)
2. Some mountains **start** as volcanoes. (starts/start)
3. Molten rock **pushes** through the Earth. (pushes/push)
4. The rock **cools** into lava on the surface of the land. (cools/cool)
5. Sometimes underground forces **cause** folds. (causes/cause)
6. The force **presses** areas of land together. (presses/press)
7. The folds **project** above the land around them. (projects/project)
8. Trees **become** smaller near the top. (becomes/become)
9. Foggy mornings **occur** often in the mountains. (occurs/occur)
10. A mountain lion **hides** among the high rocks. (hides/hide)
11. A major mountain range called the Alps **exists** in Europe. (exists/exist)
12. Snow usually **covers** high mountains all year long. (covers/cover)
13. The Himalayas **challenge** climbers. (challenges/challenge)
14. I **think** Edmund Hillary was the first to climb Mt. Everest. (thinks/think)

Notes for Home: Your child practiced subject-verb agreement by writing verbs in sentences. ***Home Activity:*** Together, make a list of verbs that are involved in your child's favorite activity. Have him or her write sentences, making sure subjects and verbs agree.

Grammar Practice Book 6.2, p. 50

Name ______________________

Saving the Sound

Grammar: Subject-Verb Agreement

Directions: Circle the simple subject. Write the correct form of the verb in ( ) to agree with the subject.

1. Three primary (colors) **create** all of the other colors. (creates/create)
2. (I) **prefer** red and blue. (prefers/prefer)
3. The (light) of every color **travels** in waves. (travel/travels)
4. Red's (waves) **stretch** the furthest. (stretch/stretches)
5. The human (eye) **distinguishes** the different waves. (distinguish/distinguishes)
6. (Objects) **reflect** light into the human eye. (reflects/reflect)

Directions: Write the correct present-tense form of each verb in ( ) on the line.

include 7. Warm colors (include) red, orange, and yellow.
appears 8. Most often, a rainbow (appear) after rain has fallen.
splashes 9. My younger brother (splash) in puddles after storms.
looks; smiles 10. He also (look) up at rainbows and (smile).
photograph 11. Then our grandparents (photograph) us.

Directions: Complete the sentences. Include a verb in the present tense that agrees with each subject. **Possible answers given.**

12. Sometimes a rainbow **arches over mountains**.
13. The paint on the wall **dries quickly**.
14. Some modern cameras **take photos digitally**.
15. The school colors **appear on our gym uniforms**.
16. A large color photograph **hangs on the wall**.
17. The trees in summer **shade us from the hot sun**.

Write a Poem

On a separate sheet of paper, write a poem about a beautiful sunset or autumn landscape. Make sure your verbs agree with your subjects.
Check that students' poems have subject-verb agreement.

Notes for Home: Your child used verbs in sentences to make subjects and verbs agree. ***Home Activity:*** Say a verb to your child (*run, sing, play*) and have him or her use the verb in sentences with a singular subject and a plural subject. Switch roles.

Practice Book 6.2, p. 98
Name ______________________________ Saving the Sound

Phonics: Complex Spelling Patterns

Directions: The vowels **ou** can have several different sounds. Match each **ou** word on the left with a word from the box that has the same vowel sound. Write the matching word on the line.

storm	power	bubble	secure

bubble 1. trouble   **power** 2. hour   **storm** 3. pour   **secure** 4. tourist

Directions: Read each sentence below. Circle the word that has the same vowel sound as the underlined word.

5. Prince William Sound in Alaska is a great source of fish.
   sound   sour   sir   (sore)
6. Mountains rim the edge of the Sound.
   (mounds)   mold   months   mute
7. But disaster struck in 1989 when a large amount of oil was spilled into the water.
   (about)   almost   above   absorb
8. People in countries around the world were shocked by the oil spill.
   count   cook   (cup)   cool
9. Many tourists used to visit before the spill.
   shout   (sure)   sour   some
10. Four hundred workers were flown to the site.
   (north)   fought   naught   found
11. The oil kept pouring out of the ship.
   odd   ox   (pout)   punt
12. Southern shores were also affected.
   court   (cousin)   count   sour
13. Volunteers worked around the clock to try to save the wildlife.
   sought   road   rot   (sound)
14. Thousands of birds died as a result of the spill.
   (hound)   though   through   thought
15. Many sea otters were also found dead on the shores.
   first   frog   (pound)   pond

Notes for Home: Your child matched the different *ou* vowel sounds, such as *sound, southern, source,* and *tourist* to words with similar vowel sounds. ***Home Activity:*** Ask your child to read a chapter of a book to you. Help your child look for words with *ou* vowels.

Spelling Workbook 6.2, p. 37
Name ______________________________ Saving the Sound

Spelling: Words with No Sound Clues

Pretest Directions: Fold back the page along the dotted line. On the blanks, write the spelling words as they are dictated. When you have finished the test, unfold the page and check your words.

1. **interested**	1. I'm **interested** in beekeeping.
2. **usually**	2. They **usually** arrive early.
3. **American**	3. She drove an **American** car.
4. **toward**	4. We walked **toward** the ocean.
5. **business**	5. The café is a family **business**.
6. **vegetable**	6. I had **vegetable** soup for lunch.
7. **really**	7. This book is **really** mine.
8. **opposite**	8. His house stood **opposite** theirs.
9. **difficult**	9. The hike up the hill was **difficult**.
10. **Christmas**	10. Will it be **Christmas** soon?
11. **magazine**	11. She bought a sports **magazine**.
12. **apologize**	12. Please **apologize** to him.
13. **multiply**	13. Try to **multiply** the figures.
14. **jealousy**	14. **Jealousy** is a strong emotion.
15. **elementary**	15. The conclusion was **elementary**.
16. **oxygen**	16. We cannot live without **oxygen**.
17. **Maryland**	17. He grew up in **Maryland**.
18. **sensitive**	18. This is a **sensitive** matter.
19. **laughter**	19. **Laughter** can be contagious.
20. **disease**	20. Cancer is a terrible **disease**.

Notes for Home: Your child took a pretest on words that give no sound clues as to their spelling. ***Home Activity:*** Help your child learn misspelled words before the final test. Your child should look at the word, say it, spell it aloud, and then spell it with eyes shut.

Spelling Workbook 6.2, p. 38
Name ______________________________ Saving the Sound

Spelling: Words with No Sound Clues

Word List

interested	vegetable	magazine	oxygen
usually	really	apologize	Maryland
American	opposite	multiply	sensitive
toward	difficult	jealousy	laughter
business	Christmas	elementary	disease

Directions: Choose the word from the box that contains each word below. Write the word on the line. Use each word only once.

1. site **opposite**	6. ease **disease**
2. sit **sensitive**	7. can **American**
3. usual **usually**	8. log **apologize**
4. real **really**	9. tip **multiply**
5. bus **business**	10. tar **elementary**

Directions: Choose the word from the box that best matches each definition. Write the word on the line.

magazine 11. a publication with stories and articles
jealousy 12. envy
laughter 13. happy sound
interested 14. attentive; not bored
toward 15. in the direction of
Maryland 16. an east-coast state
Christmas 17. December 25
vegetable 18. an edible plant
difficult 19. hard
oxygen 20. a gas in the air

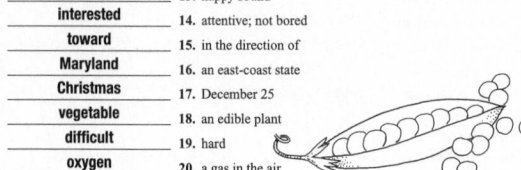

Notes for Home: Your child spelled words with letters that give no sound clues as to their spelling, such as *vegetable, business,* and *opposite. **Home Activity:*** Challenge your child to sort words from the list into groups according to the number of syllables the words contain.

Spelling Workbook 6.2, p. 39
Name ______________________________ Saving the Sound

Spelling: Words with No Sound Clues

Directions: Proofread these interview questions for a news article. Find five spelling mistakes. Use the proofreading marks to correct each mistake.

≡	Make a capital.
/	Make a small letter.
∧	Add something.
℘	Take out something.
⊙	Add a period.
¶	Begin a new paragraph.

1. Why should the American public still be int‸rested (e) in the oil spill after more than ten years?

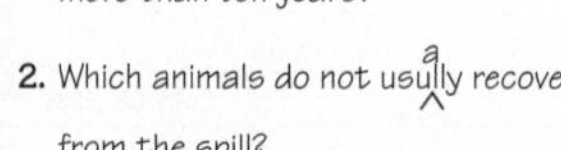

2. Which animals do not usu‸lly (a) recover from the spill?

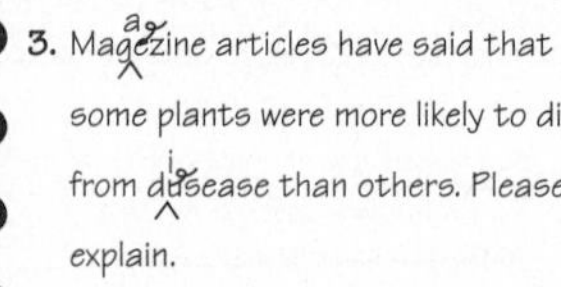

3. Mag~~e~~zine (a) articles have said that some plants were more likely to die from d~~e~~sease (i) than others. Please explain.

4. Is the oil spill affecting the fishing bus‸nes‸ (i, s) in the region? If so, in what way?

Word List
interested
usually
American
toward
business
vegetable
really
opposite
difficult
Christmas
magazine
apologize
multiply
jealousy
elementary
oxygen
Maryland
sensitive
laughter
disease

Spelling Tip

business   **magazine**

Some words in the list have letters for sounds that you don't hear: **business.** Other words in the list have vowel sounds that give no clue to their spelling: **magazine.**

Write Interview Questions

Imagine that you need to interview experts who are cleaning up an oil spill. On a separate sheet of paper, write several questions you would ask to find out more about the accident and cleanup efforts. Try to use at least five of your spelling words. **Answers will vary, but each set of questions should include at least five spelling words.**

Notes for Home: Your child spelled words with letters that give no sound clues as to their spelling. ***Home Activity:*** Hold a spelling bee with family and friends, taking turns spelling each word aloud.

Spelling Workbook 6.2, p. 40

Name ____________________ **Saving the Sound**

Spelling: Words with No Sound Clues REVIEW

Word List

interested	business	difficult	multiply	Maryland
usually	vegetable	Christmas	jealousy	sensitive
American	really	magazine	elementary	laughter
toward	opposite	apologize	oxygen	disease

Directions: Choose the word from the box that is the most opposite in meaning for each word below. Write the word on the line.

1. health **disease**
2. hard-hearted **sensitive**
3. divide **multiply**
4. rarely **usually**
5. insult **apologize**
6. away **toward**
7. bored **interested**
8. easy **difficult**
9. pleasure **business**
10. same **opposite**

Directions: Choose the word from the box that best matches each clue. Write the letters of the word on the blanks. The boxed letters tell why the bee went to see a doctor.

11. a weekly or monthly publication **m a g a z [i] n e**
12. grade school **e l e m e n [t] a r y**
13. a reaction to a good joke **l a u g [h] t e r**
14. actually; truly **r e [a] l l y**
15. one of the fifty states **M a r y l a n [d]**
16. a December holiday **C [h] r i s t m a s**
17. a United States citizen **A m e r [i] c a n**
18. grown in a garden **[v] e g e t a b l e**
19. the gas we breathe **o x y g [e] n**
20. envy **j e a l o u [s] y**

Why did the bee go to see a doctor? **It had hives.**

Notes for Home: Your child spelled words with letters that give no sound clues as to their spelling. ***Home Activity:*** Help your child create a crossword puzzle using as many spelling words as possible.

Practice Book 6.2, p. 99

Name ____________________ **Saving the Sound**

Graphs

Graphs display data in visual form. They can quickly show how one piece of information compares to other pieces or how something changes over time. There are several types of graphs. **Bar graphs** use vertical and horizontal bars to show amounts that you can compare easily. **Circle graphs** have a pie shape. They show how a whole is divided into parts. **Line graphs** are named for the lines that connect a series of points on a graph. They show how things change over time.

Directions: Use the graphs to answer the questions that follow.

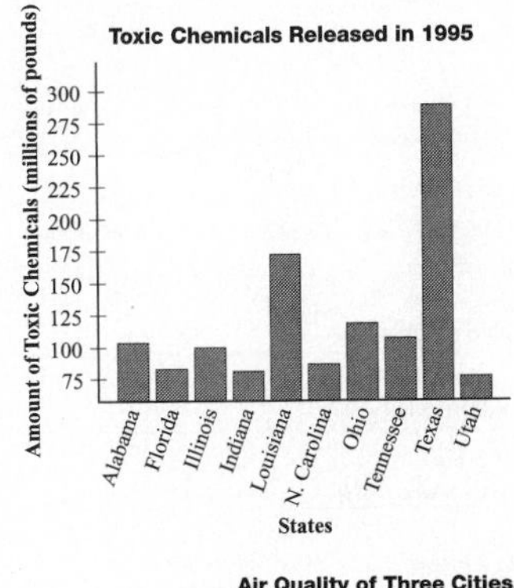

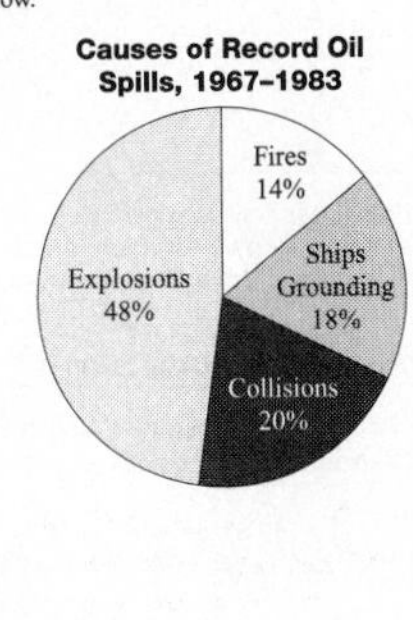

Air Quality of Three Cities, 1987–1995

Number of Days of Unsafe Air: 0–65; Year: 1987 1988 1989 1990 1991 1992 1993 1994 1995; New York, NY; Denver, CO; Boston, MA

Practice Book 6.2, p. 100

Name ____________________ **Saving the Sound**

1. According to the bar graph, which state released the greatest amount of toxic chemicals in 1995? How do you know?
Texas; The bar for Texas is the longest.
2. What unit is used to measure the amount of toxic chemicals released? **millions of pounds**
3. How does a bar graph help you compare the amounts of toxic chemicals released by different states?
Possible answer: The heights of the bars make it easy to compare the different quantities.
4. What information does the circle graph represent? **The circle graph shows the causes of record oil spills from 1967 to 1983.**
5. What type of accident caused most of the record oil spills from 1967 to 1983? Explain.
Explosions caused the majority of the record oil spills. The graph label tells that explosions caused 48% of the record oil spills and explosions has the largest wedge.
6. Based on the data in the circle graph, would it be true to say that almost half of the record oil spills from 1967 to 1983 were caused by explosions? Explain.
Yes, 48% is close to 50%, or half. The wedge for explosions covers almost half of the entire circle.
7. On the line graph, what unit is used to measure the unsafe air in the three cities?
Unsafe air is measured by days.
8. For about how many days in 1988 was the air not safe in New York? For how many days in 1989 was the air not safe in New York?
New York's air was unsafe for about 46 days in 1988, and it was unsafe for about 18 days in 1989.
9. Does the line graph for New York for the period 1988 to 1989 show that the number of days of unsafe air has increased, decreased, or stayed the same?
The line graph indicates that the number of days of unsafe air for New York decreased from 1988 to 1989.
10. Which graph is most effective in showing changes over time? **line graph**

Notes for Home: Your child answered questions about circle, bar, and line graphs. ***Home Activity:*** Show your child some graphs from a magazine or newspaper. Discuss with your child what information each graph shows. Take turns asking one another questions about the graphs.

Name ____________________

Description Web

Directions: Write your topic (the animal you will describe) on the line in the Topic circle. Then organize details about this animal by writing them in the Details circles. **The Description Web should be filled out completely. Responses will vary.**

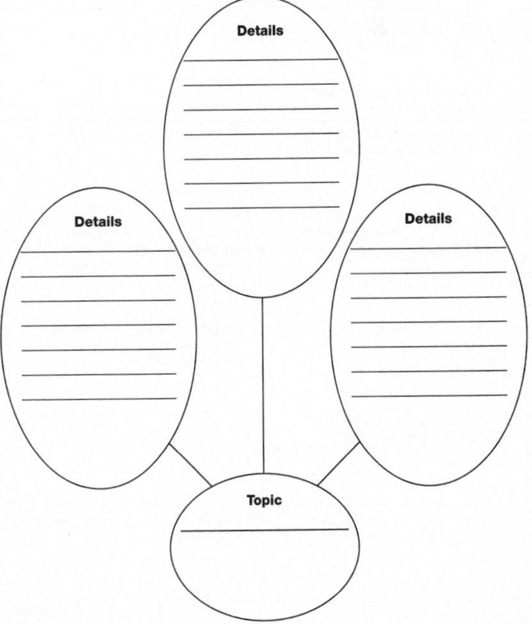

Notes for Home: Your child filled out a Description Web with details about an animal he or she will describe. ***Home Activity:*** Encourage your child to describe a room in the house using different organizational approaches–for example: from top to bottom, or by order of importance.

Name ________________________________

Elaboration

Sense Words

- When you write, you can elaborate by **adding sense words** that help readers imagine things more clearly.
- You can provide vivid images by sharing how things look, sound, feel, taste, and smell.

wild	white	golden	brown
wonderful	huge	roaring	sleek
slithery	excited	tall	long
coil	limber	big	noisy
black	colorful	wrinkly	playful

Directions: Read each sentence below. Then pick a word from the box to make each sentence more vivid and interesting. Write the sentences using these new words. Hint: Some sentences need more than one word.

1. Many animals live in the zoo. **Responses will vary. Reasonable answers are given.**
Many wild, wonderful animals live in the zoo.

2. The python snakes wrap around the trees.
The slithery python snakes coil around the trees.

3. Three pandas played in the grass.
Three black and white pandas played in the tall grass.

4. Two African elephants showered us with water.
Two huge African elephants showered us with water.

5. The monkeys swung from limb to limb.
The limber monkeys swung from limb to limb.

6. A tiger with stripes stalked in his cage.
A sleek tiger with colorful stripes stalked in his cage.

7. The lions' den was full of kingly beasts.
The lions' den was full of roaring, kingly beasts.

8. Their manes were thick and long.
Their golden manes were thick and long.

Notes for Home: Your child elaborated on sentence ideas by adding sense words. ***Home Activity:*** After going outside with your child, have him or her use sentences with sense words to describe the sights, smells, and sounds in your neighborhood.

Name ________________________________

Self-Evaluation Guide

Description

Directions: Think about the final draft of your description. Then answer each question below.

Students' responses should show that they have given careful thought to their description.

	Yes	No	Not sure
1. Does my description tell about my topic animal?			
2. Did I use descriptive words to give readers a good picture of this animal?			
3. Did I keep my audience and purpose in mind?			
4. Did I present my ideas in an organized way?			
5. Did I proofread and edit carefully to avoid errors?			

6. What part of your description do you think gives the best picture of your topic animal?

7. Write one thing that you could change to make this description even better (a word, phrase, or sentence).

Notes for Home: Your child completed a self-evaluation of a description he or she wrote about an animal ***Home Activity:*** Encourage your child to tell you one way he or she tried to make this description vivid.

Name ________________________________

Elizabeth Blackwell: Medical Pioneer

Drawing Conclusions

- To **draw a conclusion** means to make a decision or form an opinion about what you read.
- A conclusion should be sensible. It should make good sense based on the facts and details in the piece of writing and your own experience.

Directions: Reread "To the Rescue." Then complete the table. Write a conclusion for each piece of evidence. Write evidence that supports each conclusion.

Evidence (Story Details and What I Already Know)	Conclusions
1. **Cannons thunder and bullets whiz through the air as Barton arrives.**	Clara Barton is risking her life by coming to Sharpsburg.
2. **The doctors are binding wounds with leaves.**	The doctors at Sharpsburg do not have enough medical supplies.
Clara Barton has spent more than a year gathering medical supplies from friends and concerned citizens.	3. **Supplies are scarce. Barton is dedicated to helping care for wounded soldiers.**
4. **The doctors nickname her the "Angel of the Battlefield."**	The doctors appreciate Clara Barton's help.
Clara Barton sees a bullet hole in her in sleeve. Undaunted, she keeps on working.	5. **Barton is brave and is committed to her work.**

Notes for Home: Your child read a passage and drew conclusions from its details. ***Home Activity:*** With your child, discuss a familiar book, movie, or television show. Work with your child to draw conclusions about what the characters did and why.

Name ________________________________

Elizabeth Blackwell: Medical Pioneer

Vocabulary

Directions: Choose the word from the box that best completes each sentence. Write the word on the line to the left.

Check the Words You Know
- __ application
- __ clinic
- __ diploma
- __ independent
- __ infection
- __ qualified
- __ rejection
- __ surgeon

diploma 1. After she graduated, she framed her ____ and hung it with her other certificates of study.

rejection 2. It is hard for anyone to deal with ____ because everyone wants to be accepted.

clinic 3. Anyone may go to a ____ for inexpensive medical treatment.

infection 4. The doctor cleaned the patient's wound carefully to avoid the risk of an ____ spreading.

surgeon 5. A ____ is a physician who performs surgical operations.

Directions: Choose the word from the box that best fits each definition. Write the word on the line. Then find and circle the words in the puzzle. Words may appear across, down, or diagonally.

qualified 6. having the necessary skills and abilities

application 7. a written request for something

independent 8. able to act without help from others

rejection 9. a refusal of an attempt to gain acceptance

clinic 10. a place to get medical treatment

T G I V A H N A P W J O R
X F M E P S S U B N O K E
I N D E P E N D E N T D J
B I L Q L V I A C L T J E
H N A Z I T Y L X Z V B C
C S D I C L I N I C N A T
J G H O A W F V T A I N I
S B E O T X I I C D U V O
Q U A L I F I E D L L U N
M I X X O S V K A I B L A
Y T Z A N J N Q U A F I D

Write a Conversation

On a separate sheet of paper, write a conversation between a doctor and a patient. The doctor could be asking about a patient's health. The patient could be checking on the doctor's qualifications. Use as many vocabulary words as you can.
Students' writing should make correct use of vocabulary words.

Notes for Home: Your child identified and used vocabulary words from "Elizabeth Blackwell: Medical Pioneer." ***Home Activity:*** Work with your child to write a definition for each of the listed vocabulary words. Use a dictionary as needed.

Name ______________________

Drawing Conclusions

- To **draw a conclusion** means to make a decision or form an opinion about what you read.
- A **conclusion** should make good sense based on the facts and details in the piece of writing.

Directions: Reread what happens in "Elizabeth Blackwell: Medical Pioneer," when Elizabeth tries to go to medical school. Then answer the questions below. Use story details to think about the characters and to draw conclusions of your own.

DR. BARNES: No woman has ever gone to medical school!
ELIZABETH: You told me I had the ability.
DR. BARNES: You do! But it's 1847, Miss Blackwell. There isn't a college in the country that will accept you.
ELIZABETH: Times won't change unless we make them change!
DR. BARNES *(Slowly.)*: There is one way.
ELIZABETH: What? What?
DR. BARNES: Disguise yourself as a man, and go study in Paris.
ELIZABETH *(Shocked.)*: How can I help other women, if I'm in disguise?

1. Why does Dr. Barnes think no college will accept Elizabeth? **Possible answers given.**
He thinks this because no woman has ever gone to medical school.

2. Why does Elizabeth think it won't help other women if she disguises herself as a man to attend medical school?
If no one knows she is a woman, she can't change opinions about women being accepted into medical schools.

3. Why do you think Elizabeth asks Dr. Barnes for help?
She knows he believes she has the ability to be a doctor.

4. How would you describe Elizabeth's character?
Elizabeth is determined, ambitious, independent, and capable.

5. On a separate sheet of paper, explain how Elizabeth helps to get women accepted as doctors. Use details from the story to support your answer.
Elizabeth never gives up. She keeps applying to medical schools until one accepts her. When she is blinded and can't study surgery, she starts to study practical medicine. She works very hard, both in school and as a doctor.

Notes for Home: Your child has read part of a play and used details to draw conclusions. ***Home Activity:*** Describe some of your recent actions. Challenge your child to draw logical conclusions about why you did what you did.

Name ______________________

Selection Test

Directions: Choose the best answer to each item. Mark the letter for the answer you have chosen.

Part 1: Vocabulary

Find the answer choice that means about the same as the underlined word in each sentence.

1. Mrs. Ashland took her children to the clinic.
   A. school for nurses
   Ⓑ place where people receive medical care
   C. hospital for blind people
   D. shopping mall

2. The baby's infection was gone in several days.
   F. discomfort or pain
   G. sneezing caused by dust
   H. sadness or extreme loneliness
   Ⓙ condition caused by disease-producing germs

3. The surgeon checked her knee.
   A. business manager
   Ⓑ doctor who performs operations
   C. type of lawyer
   D. person who specializes in teeth

4. My sister framed her diploma.
   F. realistic image such as a photograph
   G. self-portrait
   Ⓗ certificate awarded for completing a course of study
   J. oil painting

5. She is an independent person.
   A. well-traveled
   B. wealthy
   C. self-employed
   Ⓓ able to act without help from others

6. The writer got a letter of rejection.
   F. praise
   G. act of giving thanks
   Ⓗ condition of not being accepted
   J. criticism

7. Brian sent in his application.
   Ⓐ written request for admission
   B. essay
   C. homework
   D. order to appear in court

8. He was certainly qualified for the job.
   Ⓕ having the necessary training or skills
   G. nervous; shaky
   H. receiving praise
   J. not prepared

Part 2: Comprehension

Use what you know about the play to answer each item.

9. Why did Elizabeth Blackwell have difficulty getting into medical school?
   A. She was not very well prepared.
   Ⓑ No woman had ever gone to medical school.
   C. She was not very highly recommended.
   D. The medical schools did not need any new students.

10. Elizabeth Blackwell took a job as a student nurse because she—
    F. was not yet trained to be a doctor.
    G. needed to learn to work with poor eyesight.
    H. thought she could learn more from being a nurse than from being a doctor.
    Ⓙ could not find a hospital that would hire her as a doctor.

GO ON

Name ______________________

11. You can conclude that Dr. Blackwell's eyesight improved because she—
    Ⓐ became a practicing doctor in New York.
    B. wanted to become a surgeon.
    C. was accepted to study at St. Bartholomew's.
    D. changed her dream.

12. Dr. Blackwell did not become a surgeon because—
    F. there had never been a female surgeon before.
    G. she could not get into a medical school.
    Ⓗ her eyesight was not good enough.
    J. she was more interested in practical medicine.

13. You can conclude that Sean confronted the mob outside Dr. Blackwell's clinic because he—
    A. did not want to pay medical bills.
    B. thought all doctors should be women.
    Ⓒ appreciated her work.
    D. had been saved by her.

14. Which of these goals became most important to Elizabeth Blackwell after she set up her clinic in New York?
    Ⓕ overcoming prejudice
    G. making a good living
    H. having a family
    J. becoming a surgeon

15. From the end of the play you can conclude that Elizabeth Blackwell—
    A. thought women were designed to help men.
    B. believed that very few doctors would ever be women.
    C. argued that women were better doctors than men.
    Ⓓ believed more women would become doctors.

Name ______________________

Drawing Conclusions

- To **draw a conclusion** means to make a decision or form an opinion about what you read.
- A **conclusion** should make good sense based upon the facts and details in the piece of writing.

Directions: Read the play excerpt below.

ENRIQUE: Did you like my story? Do you think I have the talent to be a writer?
MS. CHEN *(Smiling.)*: I think you may be a great writer someday if you work hard. Our "Clinic for New Writers" may be just the class you need.
ENRIQUE *(Surprised.)*: There's a class for writers?
MS. CHEN: All your classmates will be writers like yourself. You will help each other by sharing your reactions to each other's work.
ENRIQUE: I will work so hard in that class! It will be great to have other writers to talk to. I've always been the only one I know who writes stories.
MS. CHEN: The class will help you look critically at your own work and try different kinds of writing. By the end of the year, you'll know whether you really want to be a writer.
ENRIQUE: If I ever become famous, Ms. Chen, it will be thanks to you!

Directions: Complete the table. Draw conclusions based on details from the play or provide details to support conclusions given.

What I Read	What I Conclude
Ms. Chen thinks Enrique may become a great writer.	1. **Enrique's story shows talent.**
2. **Enrique is the only person he knows who writes stories.**	Enrique is different from his friends.
Enrique will work hard in writing class.	3. **Enrique really loves to write.**
4. **Enrique will share his work with other writers and try different kinds of writing.**	Enrique can learn a lot from a writer's class.
If Enrique becomes famous, he will thank Ms. Chen.	5. **Enrique is grateful that Ms. Chen told him about the writer's class and that she believes he has talent.**

Notes for Home: Your child read part of a play and used details to draw conclusions. ***Home Activity:*** Watch a television drama or comedy with your child. Together, draw conclusions about the main characters, why they act as they do, and how true-to-life they seem.

Practice Book 6.3, p. 107

Name ______________________

Elizabeth Blackwell: Medical Pioneer

Compare and Contrast/ Text Structure

REVIEW

Directions: Read the story. Then read each question about the story. Choose the best answer to each question. Mark the letter for the answer you have chosen.

Two Peas in a Pod

Neil and Nancy are brother and sister, but you wouldn't know it to look at them. Neil's face is serious. His eyes seem to see all the way into your thoughts. He is not especially tall, but broad-shouldered and strongly built. In contrast, Nancy is very tall and slender, with long arms and legs. Her eyes always twinkle. When you hear her laugh, you have to laugh too!

Underneath the surface, though, they are as alike as identical twins. When they make up their minds to do something, nothing stops them. They have different talents and interests, but similar ways of doing things.

All through the fall and winter, Nancy practiced daily to break the school's sprint racing record. Rain or shine, Nancy was out on the track, working to run faster each week. She competed with herself as much as with other runners. When the spring track meet was held, Nancy was the fastest runner on her team.

Neil was in charge of designing and building the sets for the December class play. Even when his crew all came down with the flu and he was on his own, Neil didn't give up. He got some friends to help, and he worked late into the night for several days to finish the sets on time. When the play was performed, everyone praised his work.

In their different ways, Nancy and Neil show the value of staying focused. Brother and sister work hard to achieve their goals.

1. Nancy and Neil—
   A. are alike inside and out.
   B. look like brother and sister.
   C. don't act alike.
   (D.) don't look alike.
2. Neil and Nancy are both—
   (F.) hard-working.
   G. talkative.
   H. unfocused.
   J. solemn.
3. Neil and Nancy—
   A. never have setbacks.
   (B.) work hard to get what they want.
   C. change their goals when problems arise.
   D. focus only on their setbacks.
4. The title and the second paragraph tell that Nancy and Neil—
   (F.) are very similar, despite appearances.
   G. are identical twins.
   H. make up their minds easily.
   J. are more different than alike.
5. The passage is organized to show how Neil and Nancy are—
   A. related.
   B. different.
   C. alike.
   (D.) different in some ways and similar in other ways.

Notes for Home: Your child has read a story, compared and contrasted characters, and described the story's organization. ***Home Activity:*** Read a short story to your child. Challenge him or her to identify similarities and differences among the characters.

Name ______________________

Elizabeth Blackwell: Medical Pioneer

Writing Across Texts

Directions: In "Elizabeth Blackwell: Medical Pioneer," Elizabeth Blackwell encountered many obstacles in reaching her goal of becoming a doctor. In "She's the Boss," Kathleen McGrath probably faced obstacles on her way to becoming the Navy's first female warship commander. Compare and contrast some of the difficulties these women faced in the selections. Complete the table below. **Possible answers given.**

Obstacles Elizabeth Blackwell Faced	Obstacles Kathleen McGrath Might Have Faced
Goal: She wanted to be a doctor.	**Goal:** She wanted to be a Navy Commander.
1. **It wasn't "proper" for women to want to be doctors. No medical school wanted to admit her.**	6. **Some critics believe fighting wars is a man's job.**
2. **She was forced to work as a nurse after medical school.**	7. **Some seamen prefer to take orders from a man.**
3. **She went blind in one eye.**	8. **It is difficult for her to leave her children for long periods of time.**
4. **People still distrusted her just because she was a woman doctor.**	9. **For many years women weren't allowed to serve on warships.**
5. **The only place she could start a clinic was in a poor neighborhood.**	10. **Some people believe women are weaker than men.**

Write an Essay

Compare and contrast the obstacles Elizabeth Blackwell faced to those Kathleen McGrath may have faced while trying to reach difficult goals. Write your essay on a separate sheet of paper.

Paragraphs will vary. Check that students state the topic and provide supporting details.

Notes for Home: Your child read about the first woman to attend medical school and become a doctor in the United States. ***Home Activity:*** With your child, discuss potential careers that interest him or her and possible obstacles your child may face while trying to achieve that goal.

Grammar Practice Book 6.3, p. 51

Name ______________________

Elizabeth Blackwell: Medical Pioneer

Grammar: Predicates

REVIEW

Directions: Underline the complete predicate in each sentence. Then circle the simple predicate. (There may be more than one simple predicate in a sentence.)

1. Susan B. Anthony fought for women's rights for 55 years.
2. As a young woman, she worked in the anti-slavery movement.
3. Her efforts helped the passage of the 14th Amendment to the Constitution.
4. That amendment forbid slavery and made citizens of all slaves.
5. At the time, however, women possessed very few rights.
6. Susan B. Anthony saw the similarity between the issues of women's rights and slavery.
7. She met Elizabeth Stanton in 1851 and planned a course of action.
8. They created the National Women's Suffrage Association in 1869.
9. Both women campaigned throughout the country and lobbied members of Congress to allow women to vote.
10. The 19th Amendment to the Constitution passed in Congress 14 years after Susan B. Anthony's death.

Directions: Add a predicate to each subject to form a sentence. Write the complete sentence on the line. **Possible answers given.**

11. Women in the past ________.
    Women in the past couldn't vote.
12. Women today ________.
    Women today have as many rights as men.
13. Women in the future ________.
    Women in the future might even be President.
14. Laws ________.
    Laws made equality possible.
15. My mother ________.
    My mother works as many hours as my father.

Notes for Home: Your child identified simple and complete predicates. ***Home Activity:*** To reinforce this lesson, have your child identify the simple predicates in the five sentences he or she wrote above.

Grammar Practice Book 6.3, p. 52

Name ______________________

Elizabeth Blackwell: Medical Pioneer

Grammar: Verbs

A **verb** is the main word in the predicate of a sentence. An **action verb** tells what action the subject performs. Sometimes the action takes place in someone's mind.

Ruri worked hard for many years.
She wanted to save as much money as she could.

A **linking verb** links, or joins, the subject with a word or group of words in the predicate that tells something about the subject, such as what the subject is or how the subject feels.

Linking verbs are either forms of *be,* such as *am, is, are, was,* and *were,* or verbs like *feel, seem,* and *become.*

Ruri's new restaurant is great.
She seems very happy about the results of her work.

Directions: Underline the action verb in each sentence.

1. Ruri designed the entire restaurant.
2. She chose the furniture and the lighting.
3. Sometimes Ruri worried about her goals.
4. Often, she asked her sister for advice.
5. Ruri trusts her sister more than anyone else.
6. Ruri and her sister planned the menus for the restaurant.
7. They wanted a mix of different types of foods.
8. Ruri always uses fresh produce and meats.
9. She buys them from the local farmers.
10. Her customers appreciate all of Ruri's efforts.

Directions: Underline the linking verb in each sentence.

11. Ruri's business certainly seems successful.
12. The restaurant is almost always full.
13. I am a regular customer at the restaurant.
14. The servers are polite and helpful.
15. Diners always feel good at Ruri's.

Notes for Home: Your child identified action verbs, such as *run* or *think,* and linking verbs, such as *was* or *feel.* ***Home Activity:*** Have your child write three sentences that describe things he or she did in school. Help your child identify each action verb or linking verb.

Grammar Practice Book 6.3, p. 53

Name ______________________

Elizabeth Blackwell: Medical Pioneer

Grammar: Verbs

Directions: Underline the verb in each sentence. Write **A** if the verb is an action verb. Write **L** if it is a linking verb.

A 1. Ken and Liam picked a project for the school fair.
A 2. They made a short videotape about the history of the school.
A 3. The two friends interviewed many former teachers and students.
L 4. Some people felt shy about talking on camera.
A 5. Ken and Liam also found old photographs and pictures of the school.
A 6. The boys worked on the videotape for six weeks.
L 7. Despite the difficulties, the final, edited tape was wonderful.

Directions: Write a sentence for each word from the box that tells about a person or a group of people you admire. **Possible answers given.**

admire	excels	encourages

8. **Michael Jordan is an athlete and a person I admire.**

9. **He excels at his sport.**

10. **As a role model, he encourages others to do their best.**

Write a Letter

On a separate sheet of paper, write a letter to a friend telling about a task that was difficult. Include details to explain why the task was hard and how you completed it. When you are finished, underline all action verbs and circle all linking verbs. **Check that students have correctly identified the action verbs and linking verbs they used.**

Notes for Home: Your child identified action verbs, such as *run* or *think,* and linking verbs, such as *was* or *feel. Home Activity:* Have your child write three sentences that describe a favorite book. Help your child identify the action verbs or linking verbs in each sentence.

Grammar: Verbs 239

Grammar Practice Book 6.3, p. 54

Name ______________________

Elizabeth Blackwell: Medical Pioneer

Grammar: Verbs

RETEACHING

Read each sentence. The complete predicate is underlined. Write each simple predicate.

1. A bird is a pretty creature. **is**
2. Plovers are one kind of bird. **are**
3. They eat insects and worms. **eat**

An **action verb** expresses action the subject performs. Linking verbs, such as **is, was, being, am, are, were,** and **been,** join the subject to a word or group of words in the predicate.

Directions: Write the verb in each sentence on the line.

1. All plovers migrate from place to place. **migrate**
2. They run with energy. **run**
3. They build nests in a safe spot on the ground. **build**
4. Some make their homes along the seashore. **make**
5. Some live in fields or on plains. **live**
6. The golden plover migrates long distances. **migrates**
7. It breeds in Arctic regions. **breeds**
8. Some plovers stay in Florida during winter months. **stay**
9. The bird flies about 2,400 miles over open ocean. **flies**
10. We have a picture of a plover in our living room. **have**
11. They are small birds with long legs. **are**

Directions: Circle the verb in each sentence. Write **action** or **linking** on the line.

12. The killdeer is a type of plover. **linking**
13. People recognize its shrill cry of "kill-deer." **action**
14. Two black bands mark its white breast. **action**
15. The feathers on its back are grayish-brown. **linking**
16. The female lays four black-spotted eggs. **action**

Notes for Home: Your child identified action verbs and linking verbs in sentences. ***Home Activity:*** Have your child use this page to explain the differences between action and linking verbs. Ask him or her to provide other examples of action and linking verbs in sentences.

240 Grammar: Verbs

Grammar Practice Book 6.3, p. 55

Name ______________________

Elizabeth Blackwell: Medical Pioneer

Grammar: Verbs

Directions: Underline the verb in each sentence. Write each one. Then write **A** if it is an action verb or **L** if it is a linking verb.

1. Ants live together in large communities. **live; A**
2. The queen ant lays eggs. **lays; A**
3. Worker ants feed the young. **feed; A**
4. The nests contain many chambers. **contain; A**
5. Many ant homes are in mounds of earth. **are; L**
6. Ants develop in several stages. **develop; A**
7. Tiny white eggs hatch in a few weeks. **hatch; A**
8. Some ants live for several years. **live; A**
9. A few reach the age of fifteen years. **reach; A**
10. Carpenter ants were destructive to human homes. **were; L**
11. One kind of hunter ant destroys harmful pests. **destroys; A**
12. All ants belong to the same family of insects. **belong; A**

Directions: Circle the verb in each sentence. Write **action** or **linking** on the line.

13. Ants store food in their nest. **action**
14. Some kinds of ants eat grass seed. **action**
15. Another gathers grain for food. **action**
16. Another insect is an important partner of ants. **linking**
17. This insect produces a sweet honeydew. **action**
18. This fluid nourishes the ants. **action**
19. Some ants are dormant in the winter. **linking**
20. Other kinds of ants destroy harmful pests. **action**

Write a Funny Song

On a separate sheet of paper, write a funny song about your least favorite insect. Use precise and colorful verbs to describe the insect's behavior.

Make sure that students use verbs appropriately.

Notes for Home: Your child identified action and linking verbs in sentences. ***Home Activity:*** Say a sentence with two verbs. Have your child say another sentence, using one of those verbs and another of his or her choosing. Continue with other verbs.

Grammar: Verbs 241

Practice Book 6.3, p. 108

Name ______________________

Elizabeth Blackwell: Medical Pioneer

Word Study: Regular Plurals

Directions: To make most nouns plural, add **-s.** For nouns that end in **x, s, ss, ch,** or **sh,** add **-es.** For nouns that end in a **consonant** and **y,** change the **y** to **i** and add **-es.** Read the paragraph below. Make each word in ( ) plural. Write the plural word on the line.

(Doctor) and (nurse) must attend school and complete special training before they are ready to help others. They listen to (lecture) presented by people who are important in the medical field. They must achieve excellent (grade) in most of their (class). They spend hours in (library) and (laboratory). With all these (experience), these highly-trained men and women are ready to handle most (emergency). Many of these dedicated professionals work to become the (leader) in their field.

1. **Doctors**
2. **nurses**
3. **lectures**
4. **grades**
5. **classes**
6. **libraries**
7. **laboratories**
8. **experiences**
9. **emergencies**
10. **leaders**

Directions: Write the plural of each word. For some words, you will add **-s.** For others, you will add **-es.** You may need to change **y** to **i** before adding **-es.**

11. study	**studies**	21. narrator	**narrators**
12. pioneer	**pioneers**	22. eyelash	**eyelashes**
13. canary	**canaries**	23. hobby	**hobbies**
14. league	**leagues**	24. monkey	**monkeys**
15. officer	**officers**	25. tax	**taxes**
16. beach	**beaches**	26. dictionary	**dictionaries**
17. sympathy	**sympathies**	27. charlatan	**charlatans**
18. circus	**circuses**	28. messenger	**messengers**
19. pickax	**pickaxes**	29. mystery	**mysteries**
20. lady	**ladies**	30. eyeglass	**eyeglasses**

Notes for Home: Your child formed plural nouns by adding *-s,* or *-es. Home Activity:* Choose individual items from around your home. Have your child write the names of the items. Help your child to write the plural form of each item.

242 Word Study: Regular Plurals

Spelling Workbook 6.3, p. 41

Name ______________________

Elizabeth Blackwell: Medical Pioneer

Spelling: Suffixes *-ance, -ence, -ant, -ent*

Pretest Directions: Fold back the page along the dotted line. On the blanks, write the spelling words as they are dictated. When you have finished the test, unfold the page and check your words.

1. entrance — 1. Where is the main **entrance**?
2. performance — 2. Their **performance** starts soon.
3. appearance — 3. I admire your car's **appearance**.
4. clearance — 4. We went to the **clearance** sale.
5. insurance — 5. Car **insurance** can be expensive.
6. Independence — 6. We celebrate **Independence** Day.
7. difference — 7. What's the **difference**?
8. excellence — 8. I envy her **excellence** in art.
9. confidence — 9. He speaks with great **confidence**.
10. coincidence — 10. The friends met by **coincidence**.
11. brilliant — 11. What a **brilliant** idea!
12. important — 12. My family is **important** to me.
13. pollutant — 13. Car exhaust is an air **pollutant**.
14. ignorant — 14. He made an **ignorant** remark.
15. hesitant — 15. At first, I was **hesitant** to go.
16. intelligent — 16. Dolphins are **intelligent** animals.
17. apparent — 17. Her anger was very **apparent**.
18. persistent — 18. The salesman was **persistent**.
19. convenient — 19. What time's **convenient** for you?
20. consistent — 20. He's a very **consistent** student.

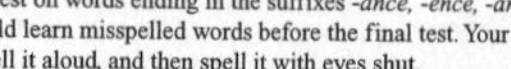

Notes for Home: Your child took a pretest on words ending in the suffixes *-ance, -ence, -ant,* and *-ent*. ***Home Activity:*** Help your child learn misspelled words before the final test. Your child should look at the word, say it, spell it aloud, and then spell it with eyes shut.

Spelling Workbook 6.3, p. 42

Name ______________________

Elizabeth Blackwell: Medical Pioneer

Spelling: Suffixes *-ance, -ence, -ant, -ent*

Word List

entrance	independence	brilliant	intelligent
performance	difference	important	apparent
appearance	excellence	pollutant	persistent
clearance	confidence	ignorant	convenient
insurance	coincidence	hesitant	consistent

Directions: Choose the words from the box that have the suffixes **-ance** or **-ence.** Write each word in the correct column. **Order may vary.**

Words Ending -ance	Words Ending -ence
1. entrance	6. independence
2. performance	7. difference
3. appearance	8. excellence
4. clearance	9. confidence
5. insurance	10. coincidence

Directions: Choose the word from the box that best matches each definition. Write the word on the line.

important 11. significant; meaningful
persistent 12. not giving up
consistent 13. always the same
ignorant 14. lacking knowledge
hesitant 15. doubtful; undecided
pollutant 16. something that dirties
convenient 17. handy; nearby
brilliant 18. sparkling; dazzling
apparent 19. obvious
intelligent 20. smart

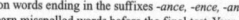

Notes for Home: Your child spelled words ending in the suffixes *-ance, -ence, -ant,* and *-ent*. ***Home Activity:*** Have your child tell which three words are the most difficult to remember how to spell. Help her or him think up memory clues such as *You don't need an A to spell excellence.*

Spelling Workbook 6.3, p. 43

Name ______________________

Elizabeth Blackwell: Medical Pioneer

Spelling: Suffixes *-ance, -ence, -ant, -ent*

Directions: Proofread this profile of aviation pioneer Amelia Earhart. Find six spelling mistakes. Use the proofreading marks to correct each mistake.

≡ Make a capital.
/ Make a small letter.
∧ Add something.
Take out something.
○ Add a period.
¶ Begin a new paragraph.

Amelia Earhart is one pilot who made an important diferance [f, e] for women everywhere. Her independance [e] of spirit inspired women all over the country to have more confidance [e] in their abilities to try new things. Despite early setbacks, Amelia Earhart was persitant [s, e] in her efforts to make her dreams of flying come true. She was the first woman to fly solo across the Atlantic Ocean and she did it in record time! Because of her brillant [i] performence [a] as a pilot, it became apparent to many people that women could do whatever they had the courage to try.

Word List

entrance
performance
appearance
clearance
insurance
independence
difference
excellence
confidence
coincidence
brilliant
important
pollutant
ignorant
hesitant
intelligent
apparent
persistent
convenient
consistent

Spelling Tip

apparent

There are often no sound clues to let you know whether to use an **a** or an **e** when adding the suffixes **-ance, -ence, -ant,** and **-ent.** Make up clues to help you remember the correct spelling, such as: There is always a **parent** in **apparent**.

Write a Paragraph

On a separate sheet of paper, write a description of a real or imaginary female pioneer. Try to use at least five of your spelling words. **Students may need time to do research about female pioneers. Answers will vary, but each paragraph should include at least five spelling words.**

Notes for Home: Your child spelled words ending in the suffixes *-ance, -ence, -ant,* and *-ent*. ***Home Activity:*** Have your child name additional words that are spelled with *-ence,* such as *sentence.* Together, make a list of these words and check their spellings in a dictionary.

Spelling Workbook 6.3, p. 44

Name ______________________

Elizabeth Blackwell: Medical Pioneer

Spelling: Suffixes *-ance, -ence, -ant, -ent*

REVIEW

Word List

entrance	insurance	confidence	pollutant	apparent
performance	independence	coincidence	ignorant	persistent
appearance	difference	brilliant	hesitant	convenient
clearance	excellence	important	intelligent	consistent

Directions: Choose the word from the box that best completes each sentence. Write the words on the matching numbered lines to the right.

It was not a **1.** _____ that the opening **2.** _____ of Andrew McCoy's new play was on Friday the thirteenth. Early misfortunes, including the discovery of a toxic **3.** _____ in the theater's cooling system, undermined people's **4.** _____ that the play would ever open. **5.** _____ rumors that the play was jinxed have plagued the producers from the start. They also had to wait for the money from the **6.** _____ company to cover costs of water damage to the sets. At last, they were given **7.** _____ to go ahead with the performance. The **8.** _____ of the sets and costumes when the curtain was raised made the audience praise the **9.** _____ of the design. The next **10.** _____ job that remains is to bring in large crowds.

1. coincidence
2. performance
3. pollutant
4. confidence
5. Persistent
6. insurance
7. clearance
8. appearance
9. excellence
10. important

Directions: Choose a word from the box that is the most opposite in meaning for each word or words below. Write the word on the line. Use each word only once.

11. dull	brilliant	16. exit	entrance
12. dependence	independence	17. knowing	ignorant
13. similarity	difference	18. certain	hesitant
14. always changing	consistent	19. dumb	intelligent
15. out of the way	convenient	20. hidden	apparent

Notes for Home: Your child reviewed words ending in the suffixes *-ance, -ence, -ant,* and *-ent*. ***Home Activity:*** Challenge your child to use words ending in *-ance* to make up a rhyme.

Practice Book 6.3, p. 109
Name ____________

Elizabeth Blackwell: Medical Pioneer

Technology: Card Catalog/Library Database

You can use a **card catalog** or **library database** to find books, magazines, audiotapes, videotapes, CD-ROMs, and other materials in the library. You can search for materials by author, title, or subject. If you don't know exactly what you are searching for in the library database, you can use key words. Be sure to type and spell words carefully. If you use more than one key word in your search, put the word "AND" between the key words.

Directions: Look at the starting search screen for a library database below. Tell which box and key words you would use to search for the book or books listed below.

Search Kempe High Library

- ☐ Title (exact search)
- ☐ Title (key words)
- ☐ Author (last name, first name)
- ☐ Author (key words)
- ☐ Subject (exact search)
- ☐ Subject (key words)

Check a box and type your key words in the box below. Press return.

1. books about Elizabeth Blackwell **Subject (exact search); Blackwell or Blackwell, Elizabeth**
2. books written by Joanna Halpert Kraus **Author (last name, first name); Kraus, Joanna Halpert**
3. a book titled *Women in Nineteenth-Century America* **Title (exact); Women in Nineteenth-Century America**
4. books about famous women in medicine **Subject (key words); women AND medicine**
5. a book titled *Elizabeth Blackwell: First Woman Doctor* **Title (exact); Elizabeth Blackwell: First Woman Doctor**
6. books about the history of medicine **Subject (key words); medicine AND history**

Practice Book 6.3, p. 110
Name ____________

Elizabeth Blackwell: Medical Pioneer

If you search with a broad subject such as "medicine," the database may give you more choices. These might be arranged according to more specific topics.

Directions: Use the list of specific topics to answer the questions that follow.

Subject: medicine

Search Results	Number of Items
1 Medicine - history	(13)
2 Medicine - women	(4)
3 Medicine - drugs	(12)
4 Medicine - fiction	(8)
5 Medicine - hospitals	(13)
6 Medicine - preventative	(7)
7 Medicine - disease	(23)
8 Medicine - schools	(6)

Type a number or press return to enter a new search.

7. Which topics might be useful to find out more about women and medicine in the 1800s? **Medicine - history and Medicine - women**
8. Which number would you type to find a fictional story about medicine? **4**
9. What are some ways to find information on Marie Curie, another medical pioneer? **Type 1 or 2 and look at the items listed, or return to the previous screen and do a new search by typing "Curie" or "Curie, Marie"**
10. How is searching a library database like and unlike using a card catalog? **Possible answer: You can use both the card catalog and a database to search for materials by author, title, or subject. You can use key words to search the database. It is faster to search using a database, but you need to spell words correctly.**

Notes for Home: Your child answered questions about using a card catalog and a library database. *Home Activity:* Ask your child to name two topics to research. Together, make a list of subject key words for each topic that you could use to search the database at the library.

Practice Book 6.3, p. 111
Name ____________

Born Worker

Compare and Contrast

- To **compare** means to tell how two or more things are alike. To **contrast** means to tell how two or more things are different.
- Some common clue words for likenesses are *like, similarly, as, in addition, likewise,* and *in the same way.* Some common clue words for differences are *but, however, differing, although, in spite of,* and *on the other hand.*

Directions: Reread "One for All." Then complete the table. Compare and contrast Julio to Lucas, Cricket, and Julio's brothers. Tell how Julio is like or unlike these other characters. One has been done for you. **Possible answers given.**

Julio and Lucas	Julio and Cricket	Julio and His Brothers
1. Alike: **Both like soccer.**	3. Alike: **Both are nervous around the principal.**	5. Alike: **All have good heads on their shoulders.**
2. Different: **Julio speaks to the principal, but Lucas is silent.**	4. Different: **Julio likes soccer, but Cricket likes to jump rope.**	Different: Julio is younger than his brothers.

Notes for Home: Your child compared and contrasted the characters in a story. *Home Activity:* With your child, discuss how three people you know are alike and different. Create a table similar to the one above.

Practice Book 6.3, p. 112
Name ____________

Born Worker

Vocabulary

Directions: Choose the word from the box that best matches each definition. Write the word on the line.

Check the Words You Know
- __ accompanied
- __ attitude
- __ collapsed
- __ grime
- __ laborer
- __ solution
- __ supervise

1. **grime** deeply embedded surface dirt
2. **solution** a liquid mixture
3. **attitude** a mindset; a way of thinking
4. **supervise** to oversee others' activities
5. **laborer** a worker performing manual labor

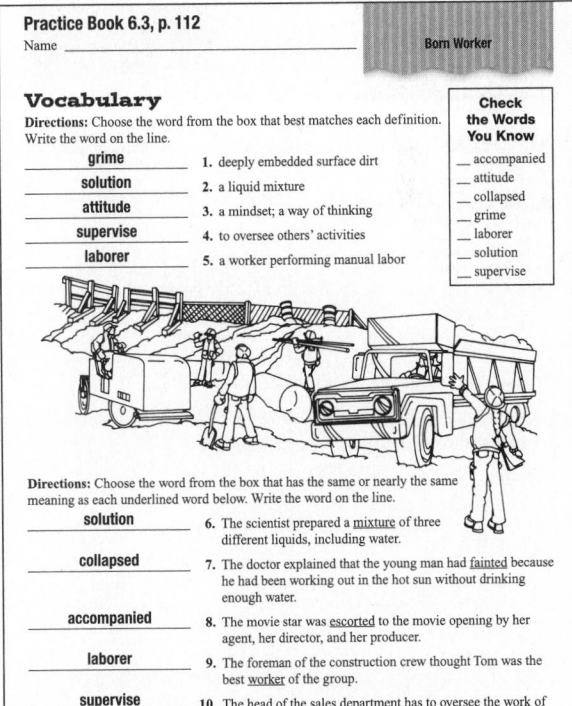

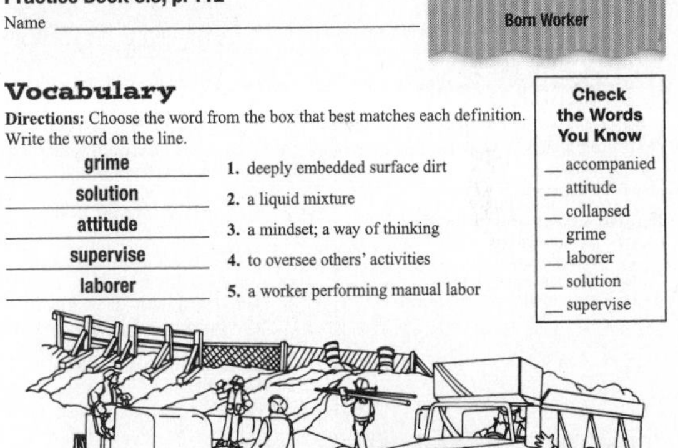

Directions: Choose the word from the box that has the same or nearly the same meaning as each underlined word below. Write the word on the line.

6. **solution** The scientist prepared a <u>mixture</u> of three different liquids, including water.
7. **collapsed** The doctor explained that the young man had <u>fainted</u> because he had been working out in the hot sun without drinking enough water.
8. **accompanied** The movie star was <u>escorted</u> to the movie opening by her agent, her director, and her producer.
9. **laborer** The foreman of the construction crew thought Tom was the best <u>worker</u> of the group.
10. **supervise** The head of the sales department has to <u>oversee</u> the work of thirty customer service representatives.

Write a Thank-you Note

On a separate sheet of paper, write a note thanking someone for some work he or she has done that has made life easier for you. Use as many vocabulary words as you can. **Students' thank-you notes should make correct use of vocabulary words.**

Notes for Home: Your child learned new vocabulary words from "Born Worker." *Home Activity:* Play a game in which one of you describes a kind of work and the other names the worker, for example: *teaching/teacher.*

Practice Book 6.3, p. 113

Name ______________________ **Born Worker**

Compare and Contrast

- To **compare** means to tell how two or more things are alike. To **contrast** means to tell how two or more things are different.
- Clue words such as *like* or *as* can signal comparisons. Clue words such as *but* or *unlike* can signal contrasts.

Directions: Reread what happens in "Born Worker" when José and Arnie agree to work together. Then answer the questions below. Think about the characters in the story to help you compare and contrast.

> José agreed to a seventy-thirty split, with the condition that Arnie had to help out. Arnie hollered, arguing that some people were meant to work and others to come up with brilliant ideas. He was one of the latter. Still, he agreed after José said it was that or nothing.
>
> In the next two weeks, Arnie found an array of jobs. José peeled off shingles from a rickety garage roof, carried rocks down a path to where a pond would go, and spray-painted lawn furniture. And while Arnie accompanied him, most of the time he did nothing.
>
> Excerpt from PETTY CRIMES, copyright © 1998 by Gary Soto, reprinted by permission of Harcourt Brace & Company.

Possible answers given.

1. How are Arnie's and José's ambitions alike?
   They both want to earn money.
2. What does José do to get what he wants?
   José does the heavy work he is hired to do and insists on a larger share of the pay.
3. What does Arnie do to get what he wants?
   Arnie finds jobs and gets José to carry them out.
4. How are their attitudes about work different?
   José feels that since he does most of the work he deserves most of the money.
   Arnie wants to earn money without having to work for it.
5. On a separate sheet of paper, explain which boy you would hire and why. Give an example from the story.
   I would hire José because he gives a fair day's work for a fair day's pay. When Mr. Clemens falls, José copes very well.

Notes for Home: Your child read a short story and used details to compare and contrast its characters. ***Home Activity:*** Take turns comparing and contrasting the personalities and actions of people you and your child both know.

Practice Book 6.3, p. 115

Name ______________________ **Born Worker**

Selection Test

Directions: Choose the best answer to each item. Mark the letter for the answer you have chosen.

Part 1: Vocabulary

Find the answer choice that means about the same as the underlined word in each sentence.

1. Please use that green <u>solution</u>.
   A. type of hammer
   B. type of sponge
   (C) liquid mixture
   D. powder
2. Laurel is a good <u>laborer</u>.
   F. follower
   G. person who remembers everything he or she reads
   H. leader
   (J) person who does work that requires strength rather than skill
3. Did Mrs. DiCamillo <u>supervise</u> the other teachers?
   A. do the same job as
   (B) oversee the work of
   C. greet in a friendly way
   D. cooperate with
4. The walls were covered with <u>grime</u>.
   (F) dirt
   G. paint
   H. flakes of ash
   J. thin coating of water
5. After the race, Jim's <u>attitude</u> changed.
   A. height from the ground
   B. appearance
   (C) way of thinking
   D. goal
6. Mr. Daily <u>collapsed</u> on the sidewalk.
   F. sat still
   (G) fell down suddenly
   H. walked quickly
   J. wandered slowly
7. Yuki <u>accompanied</u> us to the show.
   A. followed
   B. raced
   C. led
   (D) went along with

Part 2: Comprehension

Use what you know about the story to answer each item.

8. Why doesn't José like Arnie?
   (F) Arnie does not earn what he gets.
   G. José is jealous of how easily Arnie makes friends.
   H. Arnie always works harder than José.
   J. José cannot ask people for work as easily as Arnie does.
9. What did Mr. Clemens do while José was scrubbing the pool?
   A. He ate loquats.
   B. He took his poodle for a walk.
   (C) He got dressed.
   D. He lay in the lounge chair.
10. José shows that he is different from Arnie when he—
    F. leaves the scene of an accident.
    (G) takes care of Mr. Clemens.
    H. rides a bike.
    J. acts cheerful.
11. José's attitude toward work is most like—
    A. Mr. Clemens's.
    B. Arnie's.
    (C) his parents'.
    D. Mr. Bechtel's.

GO ON

Practice Book 6.3, p. 116

Name ______________________ **Born Worker**

12. Why does José agree to work with Arnie?
    F. He feels sorry for Arnie.
    (G) He does not like asking for work.
    H. He wants to teach Arnie to be a good laborer.
    J. He wants to be rich.
13. Arnie is best described as—
    (A) lazy and spoiled.
    B. sensitive and caring.
    C. talented and independent.
    D. hard-working and responsible.
14. José's opinion of Arnie is primarily based on—
    F. Mr. Clemens's reactions to him.
    G. comments neighbors have made.
    H. his parents' comments about Arnie's family.
    (J) personal experience and direct observation.
15. The next time he decides to work with Arnie, José will most likely—
    A. provide transportation for Arnie.
    B. take charge of arranging the work.
    (C) insist on receiving more of the pay.
    D. say he does not want to work in a backyard.

STOP

Name ______________________ **Born Worker**

Compare and Contrast

- To **compare** means to tell how two or more things are alike. To **contrast** means to tell how two or more things are different.
- Clue words such as *like* or *as* can signal comparisons. Clue words such as *but* or *unlike* can signal contrasts.

Directions: Read the story below.

> Roy turned to Sam, "Aren't you coming to the final basketball game?"
>
> Sam looked depressed, "I wish I could, but I have to walk Wylie and start on my art project tonight."
>
> "Oh, come on. You can take Wylie out after the game."
>
> "I always take Wylie out at seven. He'll be upset if I'm so late. It wouldn't be fair."
>
> Roy shrugged, "It won't matter this one time. He's only a dog!"
>
> "I'd feel too guilty. I wouldn't enjoy the game"
>
> "For a game as important as this, I'd worry about being fair and guilty later."

Directions: Compare and contrast Roy and Sam. In the circles below, list two things that are true about Roy, list two things that are true about Sam, and one thing that is true of both of them.

Possible answers given.

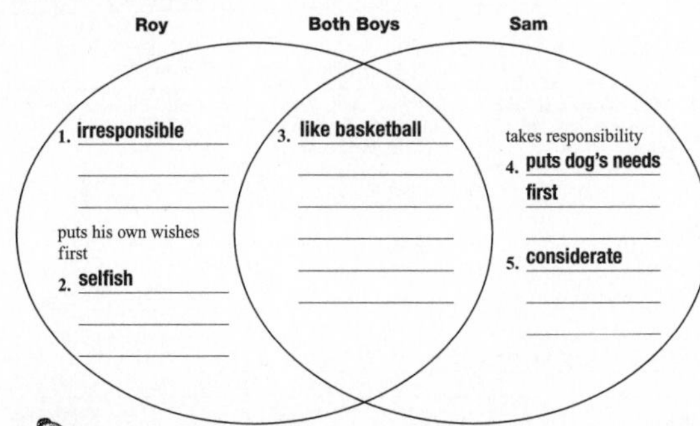

Notes for Home: Your child read a story and used its details to make comparisons and contrasts. ***Home Activity:*** With your child, make a list of family members' household tasks or other responsibilities. Discuss the similarities and differences among people's jobs.

Practice Book 6.3, p. 117

Name ______________________ Born Worker

Predicting and Plot

REVIEW

Directions: Read the story. Then read each question about the story. Choose the best answer to each question. Mark the letter for the answer you have chosen.

Different Directions

When we set off on our trip to Aunt Bess's that Thanksgiving, Mom teased Dad, "Are you planning to get lost again?" He never fails to lose the way. Dad has no sense of direction. Unfortunately, he doesn't know that! He is always sure he knows the way. Only as time passes does he begin a series of stops at gas stations for further directions. We are always so late that Aunt Bess has learned to tell Dad to arrive an hour earlier than she really wants us there. That way, she knows we will probably be on time.

This time, however, I was determined to get us there well before the turkey was overdone and the stuffing all gone. First, I called Aunt Bess and wrote down detailed directions. I knew it was in the final part of the trip that Dad made his worst mistakes. I read that part of the directions back to Aunt Bess to be sure I had it right. I also decided to take the road atlas.

The first time Dad got into the wrong lane, I told him I had directions, and he should go left instead of right. Dad was annoyed for a moment, but had to give in at Mom's heartfelt "Thank goodness you thought of that!" Dad swung back into the left lane.

Unfortunately, things did not go quite as I had planned. Somewhere between Lima and Elyria, my sister moaned, "I don't feel so well. Open the windows, quick!" As big gusts of air blew into the car, making Annie feel better, my careful notes blew out the window!

Mom and I stared at each other; then Mom began to laugh. All of us joined in, knowing that Aunt Bess would be as amused as we were. "I have the best solution," said Mom. "Next time, I'll drive!"

1. What conflict, or problem, do the characters in this story face?
   - **A.** Dad is always getting lost.
   - B. Aunt Bess cooks Thanksgiving dinner.
   - C. Aunt Bess lives far away.
   - D. The narrator gets directions from Aunt Bess.
2. What does the first paragraph lead you to expect next?
   - F. Mom will tease Dad.
   - G. Dad will not get lost this time.
   - H. Aunt Bess will call.
   - **J.** Dad will get lost.
3. After the instructions blow away, the narrator will probably—
   - A. get lost.
   - **B.** look at the road atlas.
   - C. arrive early at Aunt Bess's.
   - D. blame Dad for getting into the wrong lane.
4. The part of the story in which the instructions fly away is called the—
   - F. plot.
   - G. rising action.
   - **H.** climax.
   - J. conflict.
5. When Aunt Bess hears the story of the lost directions, she will probably—
   - A. cry.
   - **B.** laugh.
   - C. never invite her relatives to dinner again.
   - D. tell the narrator to be more careful in the future.

Notes for Home: Your child predicted events in a story and identified plot elements. ***Home Activity:*** Read a story aloud with your child. After every few paragraphs, ask your child to predict what will happen next.

Name ______________________ Born Worker

Writing Across Texts

Directions: *Born Worker* and "Doing Dishes" were both written by Gary Soto. Think about what these two selections have in common. Then make five inferences about Gary Soto and his writing based on details in these two selections. **Possible answers given.**

What I Can Infer About Gary Soto
1. **He is used to work.**
2. **He is Hispanic.**
3. **He was not rich as a young person.**
4. **He had chores when he was young.**
5. **He respects those who work hard.**

Write a Paragraph

Write a paragraph in which you compare Gary Soto's attitude toward work with your own. How do you feel about chores? Use information from the chart and both selections to help you. Write the paragraph on a separate sheet of paper.
Paragraphs will vary. Check that the paragraphs include details from both selections.

Notes for Home: Your child compared two selections by the same author. ***Home Activity:*** Talk with your child about how he or she feels about work and why.

Grammar Practice Book 6.3, p. 56

Name ______________________ Born Worker

Grammar: Verbs

REVIEW

Directions: Circle the verb in each sentence. Write **A** if the verb is an action verb. Write **L** if the verb is a linking verb. Remember, an **action verb** tells what action the subject performs. Sometimes the action takes place in someone's mind. A **linking verb** links, or joins, the subject with a word or group of words in the predicate that tell something about the subject, such as what the subject is or how the subject feels.

A 1. My class at school **earned** $200 last year.
A 2. Everyone **worked** for neighbors or relatives.
L 3. Some of the work **was** very hard.
A 4. José **raked** huge piles of leaves.
L 5. His hands **looked** sore the next day.
A 6. I **cleaned** my grandmother's garbage cans.
L 7. Whew! They **were** smelly!
A 8. I **held** my nose the whole time.
A 9. Others **recycled** newspapers and cans.
L 10. Everyone **felt** good at the end of the day.

Directions: Use each verb in a sentence. Write the sentence on the line. **Possible answers given.**

11. *looked* as an action verb
I looked at the photograph.

12. *looked* as a linking verb
The photograph looked very old.

13. *felt* as an action verb
I felt the cat's fur.

14. *felt* as a linking verb
The cat's fur felt very soft.

15. *sounded* as a linking verb
The cat's purr sounded very loud.

Notes for Home: Your child identified action and linking verbs. ***Home Activity:*** Ask your child to find a paragraph that he or she has written. Go through the paragraph together, replacing any dull, overused verbs, such as *say, go,* and *do,* with more interesting verbs.

Grammar Practice Book 6.3, p. 57

Name ______________________ Born Worker

Grammar: Verb Tenses: Present, Past, and Future

A verb in the **present tense** shows action that is happening now. Many present tense verbs that work with singular subjects end in **-s** or **-es.**

Lucas works every Saturday with me. He misses his former free time, however.

Present tense verbs that work with plural subjects do not usually add **-s** or **-es.**

Lucas and I work for Mr. Polito.

A verb in the **past tense** shows action that has already happened. Many verbs in the past tense end with **-ed.** Those that do not end with **-ed** are called **irregular verbs.** Since they do not follow a regular pattern of verb endings, you need to remember the past tense forms.

Regular verb: Lucas and I worked for Mr. Polito.
Irregular verb: We went to his house every day for three weeks.

A verb in the **future tense** shows action that will happen. Verbs in the future tense include the helping verb *will.*

Next week, we will paint Mr. Polito's fence. Light gray paint will look best.

Directions: Write **present, past,** or **future** to tell the tense of each underlined verb.

past 1. Mr. Polito hired us to work in his yard.
present 2. Sometimes, things are harder than they look.
past 3. Our lawnmower broke, and we had to find another.
present 4. We always prepare fully for each job.
future 5. We know that, sometimes, accidents will happen.
past 6. Recently, we painted Mrs. Warner's shed.
present 7. Now, the shed looks brand new.
past 8. For a while, we thought we would never finish.
present 9. Mrs. Warner's dog often barks when strangers are in the yard.
future 10. That dog will bother you whenever you want to do something.

Notes for Home: Your child identified whether a verb was in the present, past, or future tense. ***Home Activity:*** Choose a verb, such as *wash* or *ride.* Have your child use the verb in three sentences, using a different tense for each sentence.

Grammar Practice Book 6.3, p. 58

Name ______________________ Born Worker

Grammar: Verb Tenses: Present, Past, and Future

Directions: Circle the correct tense of the verb in ( ). Write **past, present,** or **future** to name the tense you chose.

future 1. My brother (laughed/will laugh) when he finds out about my plans.
present 2. He thinks that I (will be/am) a big dreamer.
past 3. He (tells/told) me so just last week.
future 4. Next month, I (will try/tried) to join the school's swimming team.
past 5. I (learned/will learn) how to swim only last year.
future 6. Nevertheless, I think I (will succeed/succeeds).
present 7. Now, I (practice/practices) every afternoon.
past 8. Yesterday, I (swam/swim) for more than an hour.
present 9. My brother (will wonder/wonders) why I have spent so much time at the pool.
present 10. He often (will say/says) that I am like a fish.
present 11. Swimming (does/did) a person's whole body a great deal of good.
future 12. As I get better, I (will develop/developed) stronger muscles.
present 13. This sport (helps/help) me build a swimmer's heart and lungs.
past 14. Somehow, the Australian crawl never (tired/will tire) me when I was doing laps.
present 15. The swim coach (watches/will watch) the rhythm of my strokes as I swim.

Write a Paragraph

Think of something that you dream of doing, such as being a veterinarian or traveling around the world. On a separate sheet of paper, write a paragraph about your dream. As you write, remember to use the correct tense for each verb.

Check that students have used correct verb tenses in a consistent manner.

Notes for Home: Your child chose a verb in the past, present, or future tense to complete sentences. ***Home Activity:*** Invite your child to write sentences about something that happened yesterday and something that will happen tomorrow.

Grammar Practice Book 6.3, p. 59

Name ______________________ Born Worker

Grammar: Verb Tenses: Present, Past, and Future

RETEACHING

Write **present, past,** or **future** to show when each event happens.

1. In 1911, Roald Amundsen reached the South Pole. **past**
2. He lived in Antarctica for a year. **past**
3. Now we learn about his struggles. **present**
4. We give him credit for his achievements. **present**
5. Next week Luisa will do a report about him. **future**
6. Someday I will read Amundsen's autobiography. **future**

The **tense** of a verb shows when the action happens. The past-tense form of most verbs ends in **-ed.** The future tense is usually formed with the helping verb **will.**

Directions: Underline the verb in each sentence below. On the line, write **present, past,** or **future** to show the tense of the verb.

1. I will finish this book about Amundsen tomorrow. **future**
2. Amundsen's books about his adventures interest me. **present**
3. They tell the story of his explorations. **present**
4. He studied science for many years. **past**
5. From 1903 to 1906 he completed his first important expedition. **past**
6. We know of his voyage through the Northwest Passage. **present**
7. You will learn about his stay in Antarctica. **future**
8. He lived there in the bitter cold for a year. **past**
9. He finally reached the South Pole. **past**
10. His endurance of physical hardships still amazes us. **present**
11. Our class will learn about his flight over the North Pole. **future**
12. He traveled seventy hours in an airship. **past**
13. In 1928, Amundsen died during a rescue mission. **past**
14. Our class will read about his death at sea. **future**
15. I enjoy stories about heroic lives. **present**

Notes for Home: Your child identified tenses of verbs in sentences. ***Home Activity:*** Have your child choose some sentences in a favorite story and identify the tense of each verb. Then have him or her say new sentences with the verbs in different tenses.

Grammar Practice Book 6.3, p. 60

Name ______________________ Born Worker

Grammar: Verb Tenses: Present, Past, and Future

Directions: Underline the verb in each sentence. On the line, write its tense.

1. Before A.D. 1100, Vikings roamed far from home. **past**
2. These freebooters practiced piracy. **past**
3. You will learn more about the Viking Age. **future**
4. They raided neighboring lands for treasure. **past**
5. Modern historians recognize their many achievements. **present**
6. They also settled new lands. **past**
7. They pioneered new trade routes. **past**
8. We know about their explorations far and wide. **present**
9. They reached North America centuries before Columbus. **past**
10. Tomorrow we will see one of their wooden long ships. **future**
11. These carried the Vikings on their ocean voyages. **past**
12. You will learn about their use as burial vessels too. **future**

Directions: Change the tense of each verb below to the tense indicated in ( ). Write each new verb on the line.

13. You enjoy Viking history. (future) **will enjoy**
14. We hear some of their great folk tales. (past) **heard**
15. Museums contained many Viking treasures. (present) **contain**
16. People respect their achievements. (future) **will respect**
17. Their explorations affect our culture. (past) **affected**
18. Our word *law* came from an old Norse word. (present) **comes**
19. They introduce lasting art forms. (past) **introduced**

Write a Tale

On a separate sheet of paper, write a tale about exploring a new land. Use the appropriate verb tense to express the time of each idea or event.

Make sure students have used correct verb tenses.

Notes for Home: Your child identified tenses of verbs in sentences. ***Home Activity:*** Have your child use some of the verbs on this page in other sentences. Encourage your child to use the verbs in different tenses.

Practice Book 6.3, p. 118

Name ______________________ Born Worker

Word Study: Irregular Plurals

Directions: Most plural nouns are formed by adding **-s** and **-es.** Some plural nouns do not follow a regular spelling pattern. These are called **irregular plurals.** For some irregular plurals, you need to change the spelling of the singular noun, as in **man** and **men,** or **scarf** and **scarves.** Other irregular plurals have the same singular and plural form, such as **series.** Read each word below. Write the plural form for each word on the line.

1. tooth	**teeth**	6. goose	**geese**	11. shelf	**shelves**
2. fireman	**firemen**	7. knife	**knives**	12. fish	**fish**
3. moose	**moose**	8. sheep	**sheep**	13. ox	**oxen**
4. half	**halves**	9. mouse	**mice**	14. deer	**deer**
5. foot	**feet**	10. salmon	**salmon**	15. life	**lives**

Directions: Find the plural nouns in the paragraph. Write each word in the correct column.

The park needed a lot of work if it was going to open soon. A gardener had been hired to clean it, and he quickly got to work. First he raked around the flower beds. It was springtime, and the flowers would need the sunlight. He knew that children would want to play near the pond and geese would come to rest on it, so he used a net to collect any floating pieces of trash. He cleared rocks from the bike path and picked up discarded cans. Lastly, he repainted the bench so men and women could picnic under the shady leaves of the old oak tree. The work had been hard, but at last the park was clean and ready.

Regular Plurals	Irregular Plurals
16. **beds**	21. **children**
17. **flowers**	22. **geese**
18. **pieces**	23. **men**
19. **rocks**	24. **women**
20. **cans**	25. **leaves**

Notes for Home: Your child formed and identified irregular plurals, such as *mice* and *deer.* ***Home Activity:*** Read a newspaper article with your child. Help your child identify both regular and irregular plurals.

Spelling Workbook 6.3, p. 45
Name ____________________ **Born Worker**

Spelling: Irregular Plurals

Pretest Directions: Fold back the page along the dotted line. On the blanks, write the spelling words as they are dictated. When you have finished the test, unfold the page and check your words.

1. scarfs — 1. These **scarfs** are made of wool.
2. staffs — 2. Schools have teaching **staffs**.
3. sheriffs — 3. This town has had ten **sheriffs**.
4. reefs — 4. Sea animals make coral **reefs**.
5. chiefs — 5. He's met **chiefs** from many tribes.
6. shelves — 6. The store's **shelves** are empty.
7. wolves — 7. **Wolves** are fascinating animals.
8. ourselves — 8. We tend to keep to **ourselves**.
9. knives — 9. His father collects old **knives**.
10. thieves — 10. The train was robbed by **thieves**.
11. solos — 11. She usually sings **solos**.
12. stereos — 12. This store sells car **stereos**.
13. studios — 13. The art **studios** are downstairs.
14. volcanoes — 14. **Volcanoes** erupt from time to time.
15. dominoes — 15. We bought a new set of **dominoes**.
16. buffaloes — 16. The **buffaloes** grazed peacefully.
17. quizzes — 17. These spelling **quizzes** are easy!
18. pants — 18. Please sew up this rip in my **pants**.
19. scissors — 19. Where did you put the **scissors**?
20. measles — 20. **Measles** are contagious.

Notes for Home: Your child took a pretest on words that are irregular plurals. *Home Activity:* Help your child learn misspelled words before the final test. Your child can underline the word parts that caused the problems and concentrate on those parts.

Spelling Workbook 6.3, p. 46
Name ____________________ **Born Worker**

Spelling: Irregular Plurals

Word List

scarfs	shelves	solos	buffaloes
staffs	wolves	stereos	quizzes
sheriffs	ourselves	studios	pants
reefs	knives	volcanoes	scissors
chiefs	thieves	dominoes	measles

Directions: Choose the words from the box where **-s** or **-es** was added to words ending in **o** and where **f** was changed to **v** before **-es** was added. Write each word in the correct column. **Order may vary.**

Plurals of Words ending in -o

1. solos
2. stereos
3. studios
4. volcanoes
5. dominoes
6. buffaloes

Plurals ending in -ves

7. shelves
8. wolves
9. ourselves
10. knives
11. thieves

Directions: Choose the word from the box that is the plural of the word in ( ) in each sentence. Write the word on the line.

measles — 12. Doctor: "I'm afraid these spots look like (measles)."
pants — 13. Tailor: "I have to shorten these (pants) to make them fit."
quizzes — 14. Student: "Please help me study for the two (quiz) tomorrow!"
staffs — 15. Bosses: "Both our (staff) of workers deserve raises in pay."
sheriffs — 16. Governor: "The (sheriff) of those three counties are corrupt."
scissors — 17. Seamstress: "Help! All my pairs of (scissors) are missing!"
chiefs — 18. Sioux Leaders: "The (chief) of the tribes must decide what to do."
reefs — 19. Diver: "The coral I saw in the (reef) of Australia is beautiful."
scarfs — 20. Model: "Which of these two (scarf) goes better with this coat?"

Notes for Home: Your child spelled the plurals of words ending in *o, f,* and *ff,* and words that have the same singular and plural form, such as *pants. Home Activity:* Have your child name the spelling words whose singular and plural forms are spelled alike.

Spelling Workbook 6.3, p. 47
Name ____________________ **Born Worker**

Spelling: Irregular Plurals

Directions: Proofread this interview with a Hollywood handyman. Find five spelling mistakes. Use the proofreading marks to correct each mistake.

≡ Make a capital.
/ Make a small letter.
∧ Add something.
Take out something.
⊙ Add a period.
¶ Begin a new paragraph.

Interviewer: What are some of the everyday jobs of a handyman?

Handyman: I often sharpen knifes and scissors, put up shelfs, and repair stereoes.

Interviewer: What are some of the more unusual jobs that you have been hired to do?

Handyman: Well, working for the movie studios, I repair reefs and volcanos . . . models, that is. Once I built a four-foot-tall wall out of dominos. I think my strangest job was painting measles on plastic model heads.

Spelling Tip

stereos volcanoes

Some words that end in **o** are made plural by adding the **-s**, while others use **-es**. Check the interview to make sure the plural forms of words ending in **o** are spelled correctly.

Word List

scarfs	solos
staffs	stereos
sheriffs	studios
reefs	volcanoes
chiefs	dominoes
shelves	buffaloes
wolves	quizzes
ourselves	pants
knives	scissors
thieves	measles

Write an Interview

Imagine that you have to interview someone with an interesting job. On a separate sheet of paper, write the questions you will ask and make up the subject's responses. Try to use at least five of your spelling words.

Answers will vary, but each interview should include at least five spelling words.

Notes for Home: Your child spelled the plurals of words ending in *o, f,* and *ff,* and words that have the same singular and plural forms, such as *pants. Home Activity:* Give your child the singular form of each spelling word. Have your child name and spell the plural form.

Spelling Workbook 6.3, p. 48
Name ____________________ **Born Worker**

Spelling: Irregular Plurals

REVIEW

Word List

scarfs	chiefs	knives	studios	quizzes
staffs	shelves	thieves	volcanoes	pants
sheriffs	wolves	solos	dominoes	scissors
reefs	ourselves	stereos	buffaloes	measles

Directions: Choose the words from the box that best complete each story. Write the words on the matching numbered lines to the right.

Theft

1. _____ and TVs are missing. The silver forks, spoons, and **2.** _____ are gone. The **3.** _____ are on their way from the station to get a list of what was taken. The **4.** _____ are on the run with the loot. Will we ever see our belongings again?

Rainy-Day Fun

We can play a game of **5.** _____ or use **6.** _____ to cut out pictures and paste them into the scrapbook. We can read about the wild **7.** _____ on the plains, or listen to the **8.** _____ Louis likes to play on his trumpet.

1. Stereos
2. knives
3. sheriffs
4. thieves
5. dominoes
6. scissors
7. buffaloes
8. solos

Directions: Choose the word from the box that best matches each clue. Write the word on the line.

volcanoes — 9. We look like mountains, and we spout lava and flames.
shelves — 10. We hold books, dishes, and other belongings.
chiefs — 11. We rule tribes and other groups of people.
scarfs — 12. We wrap around your neck and keep you warm.
quizzes — 13. We contain questions that you have to answer.
pants — 14. We are garments that cover your legs.
measles — 15. We are spots that itch.
staffs — 16. We are groups of people who work for a boss.
ourselves — 17. We are just us.
wolves — 18. We are the wild cousins of dogs.
studios — 19. We are rooms in which artists work and live.
reefs — 20. We are underwater formations of coral.

Notes for Home: Your child spelled the plurals of words ending in *o, f,* and *ff,* and words that have the same singular and plural forms, such as *pants. Home Activity:* Help your child identify the spelling words whose plurals were formed by changing the letter *f* to *v* before adding *-es.*

Practice Book 6.3, p. 119

Name ______________________ **Born Worker**

Organize and Present Information

As you research and take notes, be sure to **organize information** in a logical manner that makes it easier to **present** your findings. If you have information that includes a lot of comparative quantities, you might consider using line graphs or bar graphs. Summaries, maps, time lines, illustrations, charts, and tables are other ways to organize and present information.

Thinking about text structure can also help you decide how to present your information. You may choose to organize it using chronological order, problem-solution, or cause-effect.

Directions: Read the article. Then answer the questions that follow.

> In 1938, the Fair Labor Standards Act went into effect to assist people who were struggling financially because of the Great Depression. This period was a time of great poverty throughout the United States.
>
> The most important law in the Fair Labor Standards Act was the minimum wage law. "Minimum" means "lowest," and the law made sure workers in most trades were paid no less than a set minimum amount of money per hour. In 1938, the amount was $0.25. (In 1938, a quarter was enough to buy a hearty meal at a restaurant.)
>
> The minimum wage was reviewed in 1939 and raised to $0.30. In 1945, it went up another ten cents. In 1950, it was raised to $0.75. Six more years went by before it was raised again, this time to $1.00. Since then, the minimum wage has been raised 15 more times. The highest jump in the minimum wage took place in 1991, when it went from $3.50 to $4.25. It currently stands at $5.15.
>
> Waiters and waitresses are not covered by the minimum wage law because they are paid "tips." Customers normally add 15% of the cost of a meal for the waiter or waitress. In addition to these tips, waiters or waitresses usually earn a certain amount of money per hour, but this wage does not have to be the minimum wage.

1. Underline or highlight the important ideas presented in this article. **Check that students mark key ideas only.**
2. Summarize the article briefly. **In 1938, a minimum hourly wage was guaranteed to most workers. Since then this minimum has increased to $5.15.**
3. Why was a minimum wage law created? **Possible answer: The law was created to assist workers who were struggling financially.**
4. Why aren't employers required to pay waiters and waitresses a minimum wage? **Waiters and waitresses earn tips in addition to their hourly wage.**
5. If you were giving a speech to a class about the minimum wage, what kind of graphic organizer might be a good visual aid? Why? **Possible answer: A time line, table, or line graph would show the change in the minimum wage over time at a glance.**

Practice Book 6.3, p. 120

Name ______________________ **Born Worker**

Directions: Study the table. Then answer the questions below.

Percentage of Female Workers in Selected Jobs, 1975 to 1997 (as a percentage of total workers)

Job	1975	1985	1996	1997
Auto Mechanic	0.5	0.6	1.2	1.5
Cab Driver/Chauffer	8.7	10.9	10.7	8.3
Carpenter	0.6	1.2	1.3	1.6
Dentist	1.8	6.4	13.7	17.3
Dental Assistant	100.0	99.0	79.8	96.7
Journalist	44.6	51.7	55.7	51.2
Professor	31.1	35.2	43.5	42.7
Waitress	91.1	84.0	77.9	77.8
Welder	4.4	4.8	5.0	5.6

6. Explain what the number 96.7 means in the column "1997." **It means that in 1997 96.7% of all dental assistants were women.**
7. Which four types of jobs showed a steady increase in the percent of female workers from 1975 to 1997? Which job shows a steady decrease? **Steady increase: auto mechanic, carpenter, dentist, welder; steady decrease: waitress**
8. How else might you organize the data in this table? Why might this be a good way to organize this data? **Possible answer: a line graph; Line graphs show changes over time.**
9. Why is it important to organize information as you do research? **Possible answer: If you organize your information as you do the research, it will be easier to present that information later.**
10. Why is it important to think about text structure when you are preparing to present the information you have collected? **Possible answer: Thinking about text structure helps you find the best way to organize and present your information.**

Notes for Home: Your child read a passage, examined a table, and described ways to organize and present the information in them. ***Home Activity:*** Have your child read a newspaper or magazine article. Discuss ways your child could organize and present the information it contains.

Practice Book 6.3, p. 121

Name ______________________ **Wilma Unlimited**

Cause and Effect

- An **effect** is something that happens. A **cause** is why something happens.
- To find an effect, ask yourself "What happened?" To find a cause, ask yourself "Why did it happen?"

Directions: Reread "Sunday Visitors." Then complete the table. Write the cause of each given effect. Write the effect of each given cause. **Possible answers given.**

Cause (Why Did It Happen?)	Effect (What Happened?)
1. **Alice has been at Sheltering Arms so long that she doesn't remember what she is missing.**	Alice doesn't know what she wants from Peg's family.
Peg understands Alice and feels compassion for her.	2. **Peg is glad to share her visiting family with her roommates.**
3. **Peg's family pays attention to them and brings them treats.**	The other girls are as excited about visiting day as Peg.
4. **Alice wants to look nice for Peg's family.**	Alice combs her hair.
5. **Art says that he has come to see Dorothy.**	Dorothy blushes.

Notes for Home: Your child read a passage and linked events with their causes. ***Home Activity:*** Describe a simple event, such as a car stopping in the middle of a street. With your child, discuss possible causes of the event.

Practice Book 6.3, p. 122

Name ______________________ **Wilma Unlimited**

Vocabulary

Directions: Choose the word from the box that best completes each sentence. Write the word on the line to the right.

The fall left her 1. ____ and almost unable to move. She felt 2. ____ grief that she would not be able to run ever again. She had always been very 3. ____, but she knew that those days of playing sports were over. Then came a 4. ____ day, one that she would never forget. She found that she could still enter a 5. ____ and be an athlete.

1. **paralyzed**
2. **intense**
3. **athletic**
4. **memorable**
5. **competition**

Check the Words You Know
- __ athletic
- __ competition
- __ intense
- __ memorable
- __ paralyzed
- __ unlimited

Directions: Choose the word from the box that best matches each clue. Write the word in the puzzle.

Down
6. a contest
7. free; not restricted

Across
8. not to be forgotten
9. something having to do with active games and sports
10. very much; extreme

6. **competition**
7. **unlimited**
8. **memorable**
9. **athletic**
10. **intense**

Write an Awards Certificate

On a separate sheet of paper, write an awards certificate to someone who has overcome something very difficult. It can be someone you know or someone you imagine. Use as many vocabulary words as you can.
Students' writing should make correct use of vocabulary words.

Notes for Home: Your child identified and used vocabulary words from *Wilma Unlimited*. ***Home Activity:*** Talk with your child about someone you know who has overcome an obstacle or difficult task. Make a list of words to describe that person.

Practice Book 6.3, p. 123

Name ______________________ **Wilma Unlimited**

Cause and Effect

- An **effect** is something that happens. A **cause** is why it happens.
- To find an effect, ask yourself "What happened?" To find a cause, ask yourself "Why did this happen?"

Directions: Reread what happens in *Wilma Unlimited* after Wilma gets polio. Then answer the questions below. Ask yourself about what happens and why to help you identify causes and effects.

> Doctors and nurses at the hospital helped Wilma do exercises to make her paralyzed leg stronger. At home, Wilma practiced them constantly, even when it hurt.
>
> To Wilma, what hurt most was that the local school wouldn't let her attend because she couldn't walk. Tearful and lonely, she watched her brothers and sisters run off to school each day, leaving her behind. Finally, tired of crying all the time, she decided she had to fight back—somehow.
>
> Wilma worked so hard at her exercises that the doctors decided she was ready for a heavy steel brace. With the brace supporting her leg, she didn't have to hop anymore. School was possible at last.
>
> Excerpt from WILMA UNLIMITED: HOW WILMA RUDOLPH BECAME THE WORLD'S FASTEST WOMAN, copyright © 1996 by Kathleen Krull, reprinted by permission of Harcourt Brace & Company.

Possible answers given.

1. Why does Wilma keep exercising her paralyzed leg even when it hurts?
   She exercises to make it stronger.
2. What upsets Wilma the most about not being able to walk?
   She is not able to go to school.
3. What makes Wilma stop crying and fight back?
   Her desire to go to school makes her fight to learn to walk again.
4. What are the results of Wilma's hard work?
   Wilma is able to begin using a steel brace so she can walk and go to school.
5. On a separate sheet of paper, explain what you think is the major cause of Wilma's success. Give examples from the story to support your answer. **Wilma succeeds because she refuses to give in to difficulties. When polio paralyzed her and she wanted to go to school, she worked hard to walk again. When she was due to run in the Olympics and twisted her ankle, she ignored the pain and went on to win three gold medals.**

Notes for Home: Your child read a short story and identified causes and effects. ***Home Activity:*** With your child, read or listen to a local news story. Challenge him or her to identify the causes and effects of individual news events.

Practice Book 6.3, p. 125

Name ______________________ **Wilma Unlimited**

Selection Test

Directions: Choose the best answer to each item. Mark the letter for the answer you have chosen.

Part 1: Vocabulary

Find the answer choice that means about the same as the underlined word in each sentence.

1. The Scott family had a memorable vacation.
   A. lengthy
   B. dull or boring
   (C) not to be forgotten
   D. involving the wilderness
2. The pass gives us unlimited use of Henderson Park.
   (F) without restrictions; boundless
   G. paid in advance
   H. from morning to night
   J. cheap; inexpensive
3. Those girls entered the competition.
   A. show of affection
   (B) contest
   C. friendly support
   D. equipment used in track and field
4. Alano worked in intense heat.
   F. occasional
   G. mild
   H. humid
   (J) extreme
5. Shem looked at his paralyzed legs.
   A. small and thin
   (B) unable to move
   C. spotted
   D. covered with hair
6. Carrie joined the athletic club.
   (F) having to do with sports
   G. secret
   H. related to art
   J. for girls only

Part 2: Comprehension

Use what you know about the selection to answer each item.

7. Why did the people of Clarksville think that Wilma would never walk again?
   A. The doctor had her wear a brace.
   B. She had no one to take care of her.
   (C) There was no cure for polio at that time.
   D. She had always been a small and sickly child.
8. Wilma was not allowed to go to school at first because—
   F. her mother needed her help.
   G. she might make others sick.
   H. her leg was supported by a brace.
   (J) she could not walk.
9. Which word best describes Wilma Rudolph throughout her life?
   A. quiet
   B. sickly
   (C) determined
   D. lonely
10. What is the main idea of this selection?
    (F) Wilma Rudolph overcame polio and won three Olympic gold medals.
    G. Wilma Rudolph did leg exercises until she could walk without her leg brace.
    H. Wilma Rudolph was the first person in her family to go to college.
    J. Wilma Rudolph was the fastest woman in the world.

GO ON

Practice Book 6.3, p. 126

Name ______________________ **Wilma Unlimited**

11. School was not as wonderful as Wilma had thought it would be because—
    (A) the other kids made fun of her.
    B. she was a better basketball player than the others.
    C. there were no other African American children there.
    D. she had a hard time doing her schoolwork.
12. You can conclude that Wilma Rudolph felt supported by her community because she—
    F. did leg exercises at home.
    (G) first tried to walk without her brace at church.
    H. ran in Olympic track-and-field events.
    J. went to Tennessee State University.
13. What effect did Wilma's experiences as a child overcoming polio have on her during the Olympics?
    A. She had stronger legs than the other athletes.
    B. She was well prepared to receive the baton.
    C. She was popular with the audience.
    (D) She was able to really concentrate on her goal.
14. Which is a statement of opinion?
    (F) It was the bravest thing she had ever done.
    G. She waited while other people filled the building.
    H. She took off her leg brace and set it by the door.
    J. She placed one foot in front of the other.
15. The biggest obstacle Wilma Rudolph had to overcome in order to become an Olympic runner was that—
    A. her mother had twenty-two children.
    B. she was African American.
    (C) her leg had been paralyzed by polio.
    D. she weighed just four pounds at birth.

STOP

Name ______________________ **Wilma Unlimited**

Cause and Effect

- An **effect** is something that happens. A **cause** is why it happens.
- To find an effect, ask yourself "What happened?" To find a cause, ask yourself "Why did this happen?"

Directions: Read the passage below.

> Nelson Mandela's years of struggle and sacrifice helped to change South Africa from a deeply divided country to a land of greater racial equality.
>
> At one time, black South Africans were only allowed to live in certain areas and work at certain low-paying jobs. Mandela led protests against these laws. In 1964, he was sentenced to life in prison for protesting. Other countries were outraged at this treatment of a man who was fighting for freedom. Their attention to his story made Mandela a powerful symbol of the fight for equality.
>
> This worldwide anger helped convince the South African government to change things. Black South Africans now have the right to vote and the right to live where they like. In 1994, soon after he was freed from prison, Mandela was elected president of his country.

Possible answers given.

Directions: Complete the chart by writing causes and effects based on the passage.

Cause	Effect
South Africa had laws based on racial difference.	1. **Blacks in South Africa had to live in certain areas and work at low-paying jobs.**
Mandela protests the laws.	2. **Mandela is imprisoned; the laws are changed.**
3. **Other countries pay attention to Mandela's story.**	Mandela becomes a symbol of the fight for equality.
4. **There is worldwide anger at Mandela's treatment.**	The South African government begins changing the laws.
Mandela is freed and blacks are granted the right to vote.	5. **Mandela is elected president.**

Notes for Home: Your child identified causes and effects in a passage. ***Home Activity:*** Take turns with your child naming events that happen and figuring out possible reasons why. For example: *The car won't start. Why? (It is too cold; it has no gas; it is broken.)*

Practice Book 6.3, p. 127

Name ______________________ Wilma Unlimited

Main Idea and Supporting Details/Context Clues

REVIEW

Directions: Read the passage. Then read each question about the passage. Choose the best answer to each question. Mark the letter for the answer you have chosen.

The Struggle for America

Large numbers of Chinese people came to California during the Gold Rush in the mid-1800s. They were not made welcome in their new country. They were often forced to pay special taxes and fees. Only a few jobs, such as laundry work and mining, were open to them. In some places, schools refused to accept Chinese children. No state let them argue in court against non-Chinese people, and they were not allowed to become citizens.

Prejudice against Chinese people in America was intense enough in 1882 for the U.S. to pass the Chinese Exclusion Act. This barred Chinese people from entering the country as immigrants for more than sixty years. During this time, many Chinese Americans tried to change the law by going to court.

During World War II, thousands of Chinese Americans joined the U.S. armed forces. Thousands of others went to work in defense factories. In 1943, the repeal of the Chinese Exclusion Act meant that Chinese immigrants were welcome again.

Since that time, Chinese immigration has grown rapidly. Chinese Americans have settled in many states besides California. Today, Chinese Americans have better opportunities for education and employment.

1. The main idea of this passage is that—
   A. Chinese people came to America after the Gold Rush.
   B. Chinese immigrants paid special taxes and fees.
   C. Chinese Americans are citizens today.
   (D.) Racial prejudice once denied opportunities to Chinese Americans.
2. The word prejudice in this passage means—
   F. exclusion.
   (G.) strong dislike.
   H. Chinese.
   J. immigrants.
3. Because of prejudice, Chinese people in America—
   (A.) had few rights.
   B. settled in California.
   C. became citizens.
   D. paid no taxes.
4. The Chinese Exclusion Act kept Chinese people from—
   F. going to court.
   G. going to school.
   (H.) entering the United States.
   J. becoming citizens.
5. Chinese immigration grew when—
   (A.) the Exclusion Act was overturned.
   B. Chinese Americans fought in court.
   C. World War II began.
   D. California became a state.

Notes for Home: Your child identified the main idea and supporting details of a passage and used context clues to understand new words. ***Home Activity:*** Have your child tell you the main idea of an article. Encourage him or her to use context clues to understand new words.

Name ______________________ Wilma Unlimited

Writing Across Texts

Directions: In both *Wilma Unlimited* and "Elizabeth Blackwell: Medical Pioneer," strong women faced considerable obstacles to reach goals that were very important to them. Complete the table below to compare the obstacles faced by Wilma Rudolph and Elizabeth Blackwell in pursuing their goals. **Possible answers given.**

Wilma Rudolph's Obstacles	Elizabeth Blackwell's Obstacles
Wilma was born weighing only four pounds.	Elizabeth went blind in one eye.
1. **Wilma Rudolph contracted polio and doctors thought she would never walk again.**	6. **Women during Elizabeth Blackwell's time were not expected to become doctors.**
2. **She and her mother had to fight racial prejudice while Wilma Rudolph needed treatment.**	7. **No medical schools would accept Elizabeth Blackwell.**
3. **No one in Wilma Rudolph's family had ever attended college.**	8. **Elizabeth Blackwell was forced to work as a nurse after graduation.**
4. **Wilma Rudolph sprained her ankle right before the Olympics.**	9. **She had to switch from trying to be a surgeon to being a regular doctor.**
5. **During the relay race, Wilma Rudolph stumbled, and had to catch up to the other racers.**	10. **People didn't trust Elizabeth Blackwell's skills as a doctor because she was a woman.**

Write a Paragraph

Write a paragraph comparing the obstacles faced by Wilma Rudolph and Elizabeth Blackwell in realizing their potential. Write your paragraph on a separate sheet of paper. **Paragraphs will vary. Check to see that students give examples from each selection to show likenesses and differences.**

Notes for Home: Your child compared the lives of two women who overcame many obstacles to reach their goals. ***Home Activity:*** With your child, discuss obstacles that might keep him or her from attaining specific goals. Together, figure out ways to overcome those obstacles.

Grammar Practice Book 6.3, p. 61

Name ______________________ Wilma Unlimited

Grammar: Verb Tenses: Present, Past, and Future

REVIEW

Directions: Circle the verb in each sentence. Write **present, past,** or **future** on the line to name the tense of each verb.

past 1. Last year Matt (joined) the track team at school.
past 2. He (ran) every day after school with the team.
present 3. Now he still (runs) every day—even on weekends.
future 4. His teammates probably (will elect) him captain of the team next year.
present 5. Matt (takes) this sport very seriously.
past 6. Before last year, Matt (worked) after school.
present 7. Now he (focuses) on one important goal.
future 8. He (will participate) in the Olympics one day!
future 9. His family (will support) him all the way.

Directions: Write a sentence using the verb and the verb tense given. **Possible answers given.**

10. the present tense of *work*
On Saturdays I work with my grandfather.
11. the past tense of *work*
Last Saturday we worked in his yard.
12. the future tense of *work*
Next Saturday we will work in his basement.
13. the present tense of *practice*
I practice the piano every day.
14. the past tense of *practice*
Yesterday I practiced for two hours.
15. the future tense of *practice*
Tomorrow I will practice even longer.

Notes for Home: Your child identified the three main tenses of a verb. ***Home Activity:*** Have your child think of a familiar fairy tale or read one. Then have your child tell the same story in the present tense. If time permits, have your child make up a short fairy tale in the future tense.

Grammar Practice Book 6.3, p. 62

Name ______________________ Wilma Unlimited

Grammar: More Verb Tenses: Perfect and Progressive Tenses

The **present perfect tense** describes an action that began in the past and is completed in the present. It is formed by adding **has** or **have** to the past participle. The **past participle** of any regular verb is formed by adding **-ed** to the present tense.

The track-and-field committee has elected a new chairperson.

The **past perfect tense** describes an action begun at one point in the past and completed at another point in the past. It is formed by adding **had** to the past participle.

Until last week, Denise had attended all the committee meetings.

The **future perfect tense** describes an action to be completed at a particular time in the future. It is formed by adding **will have** to the past participle.

By next week, the committee will have created a new track schedule.

To describe an action that is ongoing, or in progress, you can use the **progressive** form of a tense. Each progressive form includes the **present participle, the -ing** form, of the main verb.

Roland is practicing every day. (present progressive)

Sally was recovering from a knee injury. (past progressive)

Directions: Use the correct form of the verb in ( ) to complete each sentence. Use the verb in the tense named in ( ). Write the verb on the line to the left.

had entered 1. By last week, Tina _____ three different field events. (enter—past perfect)
was trying 2. Tyrell _____ to improve his time in the 100-yard dash. (try—past progressive)
had finished 3. The school _____ the new indoor track. (finish—past perfect)
has competed 4. Our team _____ in five meets. (compete—present perfect)
will have competed 5. We _____ in twenty meets by the time the season ends. (compete—future perfect)
are raising 6. We _____ money for new uniforms. (raise—present progressive)
had donated 7. The fan club _____ two hundred dollars. (donate—past perfect)
will have raised 8. Soon we _____ all the money we need. (raise—future perfect)
is planning 9. Our coach _____ a banquet. (plan—present progressive)
am hoping 10. I _____ to be chosen as the most improved athlete. (hope—present progressive)

Notes for Home: Your child wrote verbs in the perfect and progressive tenses. ***Home Activity:*** Have your child use the present progressive tense to describe actions happening now.

Grammar Practice Book 6.3, p. 63

Name ________________________ Wilma Unlimited

Grammar: More Verb Tenses: Perfect and Progressive Tenses

Directions: Use the correct form of the verb in ( ) to complete each sentence. Use the verb in the tense named in ( ). Write the verb on the line to the left.

have wanted 1. My friends and I _____ a new outdoor track for a long time. (want—present perfect)

have collected 2. We _____ hundreds of signatures for our petitions. (collect—present perfect)

are doing 3. We _____ everything we can to get this track built. (do—present progressive)

will have agreed 4. By next year, we hope the school _____ to build the track. (agree—future perfect)

had ignored 5. Until last month, the school board _____ our petitions and letters. (ignore—past perfect)

were giving 6. Our classmates _____ us advice and support. (give—past progressive)

had started 7. In the past month, other board members _____ to consider our idea. (start—past perfect)

is learning 8. Our group _____ how to present our ideas more clearly. (learn—present progressive)

will have convinced 9. Surely, by the next board meeting, we _____ five other members. (convince—future perfect)

are showing 10. We _____ everyone why our plan makes sense. (show—present progressive)

Write a Short Story

On a separate sheet of paper, write a story that shares a lesson that you learned about someone or something. When you have finished, identify the tense of the verbs you used. **Check that students have used the correct verb tenses in their stories.**

Notes for Home: Your child wrote verbs in present and progressive tenses. ***Home Activity:*** Have your child describe a past action using the past perfect tense. *(I had studied for that test for weeks!)*

Grammar Practice Book 6.3, p. 64

Name ________________________ Wilma Unlimited

Grammar: More Verb Tenses: Perfect and Progressive Tenses

RETEACHING

Underline the correct verb form in ( ) that best completes each sentence.

1. After a week of discussion, we (decide/have decided) not to go. **(present perfect)**
2. Until yesterday, Dan (ran/had run) two miles every day. **(past perfect)**
3. By 3:30, we (have/will have) completed the test. **(future perfect)**
4. Our book club (reading/is reading) every day. **(present progressive)**
5. June (eats/was eating) when her mother came home. **(past progressive)**

The **present perfect tense** describes an action that began in the past and ends in the present. It is formed by adding **has** or **have** to the **past participle** (the **-ed** form) of a regular verb. The **past perfect tense** describes an action that began and ended in the past. It is formed by adding **had** to the past participle. The **future perfect tense** describes an action that will be completed in the future. It is formed by adding **will have** to the past participle. Use a **progressive** form of a tense to describe an action that is in progress. This form includes the **present participle** (the **-ing** form) of the main verb.

Directions: Use the correct form of the verb in ( ) to complete each sentence. Use the verb in the tense named in ( ). Write the verb on the line.

had collected 1. We _____ aluminum cans last month. (collect—past perfect)

had carried 2. We _____ them to the supermarket in baskets. (carry—past perfect)

had counted 3. The clerk _____ them carefully. (count—past perfect)

will have filled 4. We _____ our quota by tomorrow. (fill—future perfect)

are saving 5. My brother and I _____ money to buy CDs. (save—present progressive)

was spending 6. He _____ it all on gum and candy. (spend—past progressive)

were going 7. I told him that if we _____ to have a better CD collection, we needed to budget our money. (go—past progressive)

have saved 8. So far, we _____ enough money to buy one and a half CDs. (save—present perfect)

will have earned 9. After tomorrow we _____ the right amount for two CDs. (earn—future perfect)

Notes for Home: Your child used progressive and perfect forms of verb tenses to complete sentences. ***Home Activity:*** Together, look at an article in a newspaper and have your child identify examples of sentences with progressive and perfect forms of verb tenses.

Grammar Practice Book 6.3, p. 65

Name ________________________ Wilma Unlimited

Grammar: More Verb Tenses: Perfect and Progressive Tenses

Directions: Read each sentence. Identify the tense of each underlined verb. Write the name of the tense on the line.

present perfect 1. I have located some interesting photographs.

past perfect 2. My grandmother had stored them in the attic.

past progressive 3. I was looking for an old stuffed animal when I came across them.

present perfect 4. Tonight she has shared them with me.

future perfect 5. By tomorrow I will have recorded much information.

past perfect 6. My great-grandfather had performed in many concerts.

past perfect 7. He had achieved fame as a pianist.

past perfect 8. My great-grandmother had played the violin with him.

past progressive 9. My grandmother was saving pictures of them.

future perfect 10. We will have mounted them in a book by next week.

present perfect 11. We have discovered recordings of their performances.

future perfect 12. In a year we will have donated them to the library.

present progressive 13. The library is collecting old photos and recordings for a new exhibit about our town's history.

past progressive 14. One librarian was asking for photos of people and the places they lived.

present progressive 15. My great-grandmother is smiling in many of the photographs.

Directions: Write a sentence with the verb and tense named in ( ). Write each new sentence on the line. **Possible answers given.**

16. (understand—past progressive)
I was understanding this homework until today.

17. (try—present progressive)
I am trying to listen better in class.

18. (find—past perfect)
She had found her lost necklace.

Notes for Home: Your child identified tenses of verbs and wrote sentences using verbs in perfect and progressive tenses. ***Home Activity:*** Together, list verbs related to your child's hobby or special skill. Have your child write sentences, using those verbs in perfect and progressive tenses.

Practice Book 6.3, p. 128

Name ________________________ Wilma Unlimited

Phonics: Schwa Sound (Within Word)

Directions: The **schwa sound** is a vowel sound heard in unstressed syllables. The **o** in **person** is an example of a schwa sound. This sound can be spelled with any vowel combination of vowels. Read each word below. Underline the vowel or vowels that stand for the schwa. Some words may contain more than one schwa sound.

1. remedies
2. television
3. several
4. celebrate
5. permanently
6. Tennessee
7. favorite
8. competition
9. against
10. stability
11. opponent
12. different

Directions: In each sentence, one of the underlined words contains the schwa sound. Write the word on the line. Underline the vowel or vowels that stand for the schwa sound.

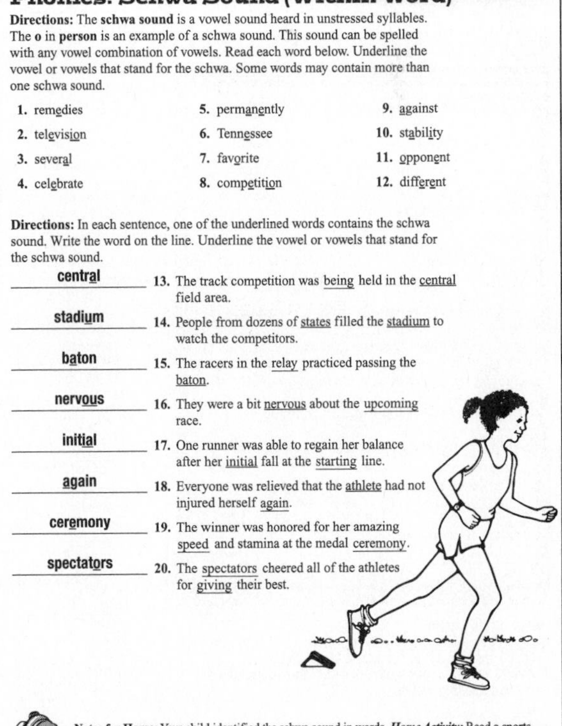

central 13. The track competition was being held in the central field area.

stadium 14. People from dozens of states filled the stadium to watch the competitors.

baton 15. The racers in the relay practiced passing the baton.

nervous 16. They were a bit nervous about the upcoming race.

initial 17. One runner was able to regain her balance after her initial fall at the starting line.

again 18. Everyone was relieved that the athlete had not injured herself again.

ceremony 19. The winner was honored for her amazing speed and stamina at the medal ceremony.

spectators 20. The spectators cheered all of the athletes for giving their best.

Notes for Home: Your child identified the schwa sound in words. ***Home Activity:*** Read a sports story with your child. Help your child find words with schwa sounds and check them in a dictionary. (The symbol for the schwa sound is ə.)

Spelling Workbook 6.3, p. 49

Name ____________________ **Wilma Unlimited**

Spelling: Vowels in Unstressed Syllables

Pretest Directions: Fold back the page along the dotted line. On the blanks, write the spelling words as they are dictated. When you have finished the test, unfold the page and check your words.

1. **different**	1. A boat is **different** from a car.
2. **register**	2. We're going to **register** to vote.
3. **carnival**	3. A **carnival** is coming to town.
4. **variety**	4. I like a wide **variety** of music.
5. **atmosphere**	5. A party has a festive **atmosphere**.
6. **favorite**	6. This is my **favorite** book.
7. **pattern**	7. I **pattern** myself after my father.
8. **understand**	8. We **understand** each other.
9. **sentence**	9. That **sentence** makes no sense.
10. **instance**	10. I can think of no similar **instance**.
11. **elegant**	11. We ate at an **elegant** restaurant.
12. **aquarium**	12. Our fish need a bigger **aquarium**.
13. **communicate**	13. We **communicate** by e-mail.
14. **gasoline**	14. **Gasoline** is highly flammable.
15. **factory**	15. What do they make at the **factory**?
16. **definite**	16. Can you give a **definite** answer?
17. **Chicago**	17. I grew up in **Chicago**.
18. **heavily**	18. He slumped **heavily** into his seat.
19. **garage**	19. We had a **garage** sale last year.
20. **illustrate**	20. Who will **illustrate** your book?

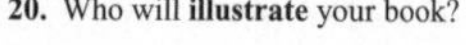

Notes for Home: Your child took a pretest on words that have indistinct vowel sounds in unstressed syllables. ***Home Activity:*** Help your child learn misspelled words before the final test. Dictate the word and have your child spell the word aloud for you or write it on paper.

Spelling Workbook 6.3, p. 50

Name ____________________ **Wilma Unlimited**

Spelling: Vowels in Unstressed Syllables

Word List

different	atmosphere	sentence	communicate	Chicago
register	favorite	instance	gasoline	heavily
carnival	pattern	elegant	factory	garage
variety	understand	aquarium	definite	illustrate

Directions: Write the words from the box that have two **schwa** sounds each. The **schwa** sound is an indistinct vowel sound heard in unstressed syllables, such as the **a** in **garage** or the **o** in **favorite.** Use a dictionary to check your answers.

1. **different**
2. **register**
3. **carnival**
4. **variety**
5. **elegant**
6. **aquarium**
7. **communicate**

Order may vary. Schwa sounds are underlined

Directions: Choose the word from the box that best completes each equation. Write the word on the line.

8. favor + ite = **favorite**
9. Chicken – ken + ago = **Chicago**
10. facts – s + ory = **factory**
11. heavy – y + ill – l + y = **heavily**
12. patriot – riot + tern = **pattern**
13. sensational – sational + tence = **sentence**
14. il + lustre – e + ate = **illustrate**
15. garble – ble + age = **garage**
16. ga + solo – o + ine = **gasoline**
17. define – e + ite = **definite**
18. under + stand = **understand**
19. at + most – st + sphere = **atmosphere**
20. in + stand – d + ce = **instance**

Notes for Home: Your child spelled words with indistinct vowel sounds that give no clue to their spelling, such as the *i* in *register.* ***Home Activity:*** Say each word aloud and have your child write it. Review the list and correct any misspellings together.

Spelling Workbook 6.3, p. 51

Name ____________________ **Wilma Unlimited**

Spelling: Vowels in Unstressed Syllables

Directions: Proofread this fan letter. Find seven spelling mistakes. Use the proofreading marks to correct each mistake.

- ≡ Make a capital.
- / Make a small letter.
- ∧ Add something.
- Take out something.
- ⊙ Add a period.
- ¶ Begin a new paragraph.

Dear Carl Lewis,

I und^e^rstand that you are retiring from competition. Your absence will weigh he^a^vily on this track and field fan!

You are my fav~~e~~^o^rite athlete of all time. The var~~a~~^ie^ty of diff^e^rent events in which you competed was amazing. They all illustrate your great skill. You changed the whole atm~~u~~^o^sphere of the field when you walked onto it. You had the most el~~a~~^e^gant running style, and the pattern of exercise and hard work you followed was a great example to me.

With deepest admiration,

Jesse King

Spelling Tip

All the spelling words contain one or more **schwa** sounds, the indistinct vowel sound you hear in unstressed syllables. This vowel sound gives no clues to its spelling, so you need to check these words carefully.

Word List

different, register, carnival, variety, atmosphere, favorite, pattern, understand, sentence, instance, elegant, aquarium, communicate, gasoline, factory, definite, Chicago, heavily, garage, illustrate

Write a Fan Letter

On a separate sheet of paper, write a fan letter to an athlete you admire. Try to use at least five of your spelling words.

Answers will vary, but each fan letter should include at least five spelling words.

Notes for Home: Your child spelled words with indistinct vowel sounds that give no clue to their spelling, such as the *i* in *register.* ***Home Activity:*** Help your child create spelling clues. For example: *Sentence always has three e's.*

Spelling Workbook 6.3, p. 52

Name ____________________ **Wilma Unlimited**

Spelling: Vowels in Unstressed Syllables

REVIEW

Directions: Choose the word from the box that best matches each clue. Write the word on the line.

favorite 1. what someone likes best
definite 2. certain; positive
elegant 3. tasteful; well-dressed; handsome
heavily 4. with weight
carnival 5. festival; fair
register 6. sign up for; record one's name
instance 7. an example or a case
atmosphere 8. mass of gases surrounding a star or planet
communicate 9. convey your thoughts or ideas to someone else
pattern 10. a regular order or design
variety 11. a group of different things
understand 12. comprehend; grasp the meaning of

Word List

different, register, carnival, variety, atmosphere, favorite, pattern, understand, sentence, instance, elegant, aquarium, communicate, gasoline, factory, definite, Chicago, heavily, garage, illustrate

Directions: Choose the word from the box that best completes each statement. Write the word on the line to the left.

garage 13. *Horse* is to *stable* as *car* is to _____.
factory 14. *Bakers* are to *bakery* as *workers* are to _____.
sentence 15. *Letters* are to *word* as *words* are to _____.
gasoline 16. *Human* is to *food* as *motor vehicle* is to _____.
Chicago 17. *State* is to *Illinois* as *city* is to _____.
aquarium 18. *Bird* is to *cage* as *fish* is to _____.
different 19. *Top* is to *bottom* as *alike* is to _____.
illustrate 20. *Leap* is to *jump* as *draw* is to _____.

Notes for Home: Your child spelled words with indistinct vowel sounds that give no clue to their spelling, such as the *i* in *register* and the *o* in *atmosphere.* ***Home Activity:*** Read some of the spelling words aloud. Challenge your child to spell the words.

Practice Book 6.3, p. 129

Name ____________

Wilma Unlimited

Almanac

An **almanac** is a yearly book that contains calendars, weather information, and dates of holidays, as well as charts and tables of current information in many different subject areas.

Directions: Study the information from an almanac. Then answer the questions that follow.

Table of Contents

General Index

Olympic Games—Summer Medals Table

Berlin, 1936		Rome, 1960		Barcelona, 1992	
Country	Medals Won	Country	Medals Won	Country	Medals Won
Germany	89	USSR	99	Unified Team	111
USA	56	USA	71	USA	108
Hungary	16	Italy	36	Germany	82

Medalists, Women's 100-meter race

Berlin, 1936		Rome, 1960		Barcelona, 1992	
Athlete	Time (sec.)	Athlete	Time (sec.)	Athlete	Time (sec.)
H. Stephens, USA	11.5	W. Rudolph, USA	11.0	G. Devers, USA	10.82
S. Walasiewicz, POL	11.7	D. Hyman, GBR	11.3	J. Cuthbert, JAM	10.83
K. Krauß, GER	11.9	G. Leone, ITALY	11.3	I. Privalova, EUN	10.84

Practice Book 6.3, p. 130

Name ____________

Wilma Unlimited

1. Which subject area in the almanac might tell you how many miles equal one kilometer? On which page does this section of the almanac begin?
Weights and Measures; page 460

2. In which section would you look for information about the imports and exports of India?
Nations of the World

3. In which section might you find the birth date of Albert Einstein? **Possible answer: Einstein's birth date might be in the Famous People section.**

4. On which page in the almanac does the section on the arts begin? **page 220**

5. In which section of the almanac will you find information about the Olympics?
Olympic information would be in the Sports section.

6. If you were looking for specific information on the Special Olympics, would you use the table of contents or the index? Explain.
Possible answer: If you are looking for specific information, it is quicker and easier to use the index since subjects are listed alphabetically and divided into specific categories.

7. How much faster did Wilma Rudolph run the 100-meter race than Dorothy Hyman?
Wilma Rudolph ran 0.3 seconds faster than Dorothy Hyman.

8. How many medals did the United States win in the 1992 Summer Olympics? Where were these Olympic games held?
The United States won 108 medals at the 1992 Summer Olympics in Barcelona.

9. The winner of the Olympic 100-meter race is often referred to as the world's fastest runner. Suppose you were writing a report on the history of the world's fastest women. Would the data in the second table be useful? What other data might you need? Explain.
Possible answer: Yes, the second table shows the times for running the 100-meter race in three Olympic games. It would be helpful to find out the winning times for other Olympic games in order to have a more complete history.

10. If you were making a line graph of the local high weather temperatures for the past month, would an almanac be useful? If you were making a weather map to show the highest temperatures ever recorded, would an almanac be useful? Explain.
Possible answer: No, you wouldn't use an almanac to find information for last month's temperatures since almanacs are published yearly. However, an almanac would probably show record high temperatures for a number of years.

Notes for Home: Your child studied an almanac and answered questions about its use. ***Home Activity:*** Look at the almanacs in a library's reference section with your child. Use the table of contents and index to find out and discuss what kinds of information can be found in almanacs.

Practice Book 6.3, p. 131

Name ____________

Casey at the Bat

Summarizing

- To **summarize** means to give a brief statement of the main idea of an article or the most important events in a story.
- When you summarize an article, include the main idea or ideas and only the most important supporting details.

Directions: Reread "Winners Never Quit." Summarize the main idea of the article. Then summarize the important supporting details by completing each sentence in the web. One sentence has been completed for you. **Possible answers given.**

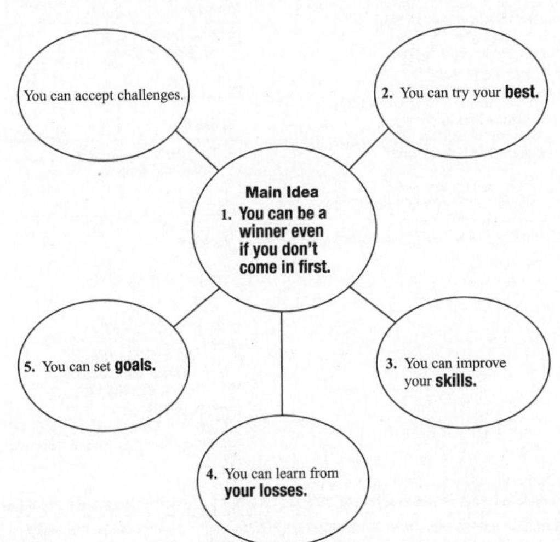

Main Idea
1. You can be a winner even if you don't come in first.
You can accept challenges.
2. You can try your best.
3. You can improve your skills.
4. You can learn from your losses.
5. You can set goals.

Notes for Home: Your child summarized the main idea and most important supporting details of an article. ***Home Activity:*** With your child, summarize a newspaper or magazine article that you have both read. Create a web similar to the one above.

Practice Book 6.3, p. 132

Name ____________

Casey at the Bat

Vocabulary

Directions: Choose the word from the box that is the most opposite in meaning from each word below. Write the word on the line.

Check the Words You Know
- __ defiance
- __ despair
- __ grandeur
- __ haughty
- __ scornful
- __ umpire

haughty 1. humble
defiance 2. compliance
scornful 3. admiring
despair 4. hope
grandeur 5. shabbiness

Directions: Choose the word from the box that best completes each sentence. Write the letters of the word on the blanks. Use the numbers below the blanks to spell out an inspirational message.

6. The **u m p i r e** (5 16 8 2 3) declared the runner out.

7. Although the player showed **d e f i a n c e** (12, 17), she could not change the ruling.

8. The players made **s c o r n f u l** (6 13) comments about the other team's many errors.

9. The losers went home in **d e s p a i r** (1 9 14).

10. The winners were acting **h a u g h t y** (15 4 7 11 10) about their win until the coach told them to practice more!

D r e a m s (1 2 3 4 5 6) **g i** v **e** (7 8 9) **t h e** (10 11 12)

m **o s** t (13 14) **h** o **p e** (15 16 17).

Write a Poem

On a separate sheet of paper, write a poem about something that's the best, or worst, of its kind. The poem needs to have rhythm, but it doesn't have to rhyme. Use as many vocabulary words as you can.
Poems should have clear images, a sense of rhythm, and should use vocabulary words correctly.

Notes for Home: Your child identified and used vocabulary words from the poem *Casey at the Bat*. ***Home Activity:*** Use the vocabulary words *defiance, scornful,* and *haughty* and challenge your child to act out each emotion. Then let your child give you similar words to act out.

Practice Book 6.3, p. 133

Name ______________________ **Casey at the Bat**

Summarizing

- **Summarizing** means giving a brief statement—no more than a few sentences—of the main idea of an article or the most important events in a story.

Directions: Reread the part of *Casey at the Bat* in which Casey waits for and swings at the last pitch. Then answer the questions below. Think about Casey's actions and their outcome to help you summarize.

> The sneer is gone from Casey's lip, his teeth are clenched in hate,
> He pounds with cruel violence his bat upon the plate;
> And now the pitcher holds the ball, and now he lets it go,
> And now the air is shattered by the force of Casey's blow.
>
> Oh, somewhere in this favored land the sun is shining bright,
> The band is playing somewhere, and somewhere hearts are light;
> And somewhere men are laughing, and somewhere children shout,
> But there is no joy in Mudville—mighty Casey has struck out.
>
> From *Casey at the Bat* by Ernest Lawrence, 1888.

Possible answers given.

1. Summarize what happens in the first group of lines.
Casey angrily gets ready for the pitch. When the pitcher throws the ball, Casey swings as hard as he can.

2. What happens after the first group of lines that isn't stated in the second group of lines?
The umpire calls "Strike three!" and the game ends.

3. What is the most important phrase in the second group of lines? Why?
"Mighty Casey has struck out"; the outcome of the game depends on Casey

4. Summarize the action for this part of the poem (both groups of lines).
With two strikes against him, Casey is determined to get a hit, but he swings and misses.

5. On a separate sheet of paper, summarize the action of the Mudville team during the game.
In the first eight innings, they score two runs and give up four runs. In the bottom of the ninth, Cooney and then Barrow are thrown out at first base. Flynn gets a single. Blake gets a double. Casey strikes out, and Mudville loses 4–2.

Notes for Home: Your child summarized events in a poem. ***Home Activity:*** Discuss a favorite story, movie, or television show. Read another poem. Encourage your child to summarize the most important events.

Practice Book 6.3, p. 135

Name ______________________ **Casey at the Bat**

Selection Test

Directions: Choose the best answer to each item. Mark the letter for the answer you have chosen.

Part 1: Vocabulary

Find the answer choice that means about the same as the underlined word in each sentence.

1. Everyone stared at the umpire.
   A. manager of a baseball team
   B. player on a professional sports team
   C. fan at a baseball game
   (D) person who rules on the plays in the game

2. The fans watched in despair.
   F. state of looking forward to something
   (G) state of hopelessness
   H. state of excitement
   J. state of nervousness

3. Sean had a scornful expression on his face.
   A. able to agree with others
   B. courteous; polite
   (C) mocking
   D. full of teasing and fun

4. Aunt Mildred is a haughty woman.
   F. well-mannered
   G. very happy; always cheerful
   H. full of grace
   (J) overly proud and self-confident

5. The house had a sense of grandeur.
   A. ability to last a long time
   B. originality; newness
   (C) greatness; splendor
   D. simple style

6. Leon answered with defiance.
   (F) resistance to power or authority
   G. uncontrolled energy
   H. lack of enthusiasm
   J. impatience

Part 2: Comprehension

Use what you know about the poem to answer each item.

7. The fans felt sure the Mudville team would win if—
   A. Flynn got on base.
   (B) Casey got a chance to bat.
   C. Blake got a walk.
   D. the umpire was fair.

8. Why did the fans stop yelling at the umpire?
   F. They realized the calls were fair.
   (G) Casey signaled for them to be quiet.
   H. Casey yelled at the umpire himself.
   J. The umpire yelled back.

9. How did Casey feel as he stepped up to the plate?
   (A) confident
   B. nervous
   C. excited
   D. angry

10. Which is the best summary of the events before Casey's turn at bat?
    F. Two batters made outs.
    G. There were six points scored and two outs.
    H. The game was close until two Mudville players made outs.
    (J) Mudville was losing four to two with two outs and two players on base.

GO ON

Practice Book 6.3, p. 136

Name ______________________ **Casey at the Bat**

11. Which is the best summary of the events after Casey stepped up to the plate?
    (A) Casey let two strikes go by, swung at and missed the third pitch, and struck out.
    B. The umpire made sure that Casey would not hit the ball.
    C. The pitcher changed the way he threw each ball, so Casey missed three pitches in a row and struck out.
    D. The pitcher threw three balls, but Casey swung at them and struck out.

12. How can you tell which team won the game?
    F. Mudville won, because Casey is a local hero.
    G. The opposing team won, because its players were more talented.
    H. Mudville won, because the narrator did not name the other team.
    (J) The opposing team won, because no one is laughing or shouting.

13. Which line from the poem suggests that Casey became determined after two strikes were called?
    A. "With a smile of Christian charity great Casey's visage shone"
    (B) "They saw his face grow stern and cold, they saw his muscles strain"
    C. "But Casey still ignored it, and the umpire said, 'Strike two.'"
    D. "And now the air is shattered by the force of Casey's blow."

14. Calling Flynn a "lulu" suggests that he—
    F. is a better fielder than hitter.
    G. doesn't have much experience.
    (H) is a bit crazy.
    J. doesn't get along with Casey.

15. The speaker's point of view in this poem is most like that of—
    A. an umpire.
    B. an angry fan.
    (C) a reporter.
    D. a judge.

Name ______________________ **Casey at the Bat**

Summarizing

- **Summarizing** means giving a brief statement—no more than a few sentences—of the main idea of an article or the most important events in a story.

Directions: Read the poem. Complete the flow chart by summarizing the events of the poem.

> The house is still, no one's about,
> A "Welcome home, Meg!" seems much in doubt.
> If no one cares that I'm back to stay,
> I'll wish I'd never gone away.
>
> It's not that I want any childish game,
> Or hats, or songs. They are so lame!
> Parties like that belong to the past
> And I feel all grown up at last!
>
> My parents seem to have followed my wishes.
> All here is quiet; I am suspicious.
> I listen at the top of the stairs,
> But nothing moves. Nobody cares!
>
> I drop my bags and my coat on the floor—
> And then I hear it! The click of the door!
> No one comes up. I go to find out.
> "Welcome home, Meg!" my friends all shout.

Verse 1 **Possible answers given.**

1. Meg thinks: **no one is going to welcome her home.**

Verse 2

2. Meg does not want: **a childish party.**

Verse 3

3. Meg thinks the house is: **quiet and empty.**

Verse 4

4. Meg's friends: **surprise her with a welcome home party.**

5. Summarize the poem in a sentence or two.
Meg comes home to a silent house. She didn't want a party, but seems disappointed that no one greets her. Then her friends suprise her with a welcome home party.

Notes for Home: Your child summarized key events in a poem. ***Home Activity:*** Read a magazine or newspaper article with your child. Ask your child to write a short summary, and then talk together about the main ideas summarized.

Practice Book 6.3, p. 137

Name ______________________

Predicting

REVIEW

Directions: Read the story. Then read each question about the story. Choose the best answer to each question. Mark the letter for the answer you have chosen.

The Humble Princess

As the two knights entered the inn, they stopped short in the doorway. A ragged young woman was scrubbing the table. She looked up at the sight of the knights and spoke in a soft and sweet voice: "Please come and sit down. Come in and hear my story." The knights sat down. If this woman were in trouble, they were ready to help.

"Once I was a princess," began the woman. "I was beautiful to look at, but I wasn't nice. My parents spoiled me. They gave me everything I wanted, and it only made me greedy for more toys and more gowns. Soon I was famous for my rudeness and selfishness. I was very unkind to my servants. I never thought about their feelings at all.

"Hoping I could learn better manners, my parents went to my wise old uncle for advice. After some thought, he said, 'Make her wear old clothes and work for a living. That way, she will learn to put other people first and stop thinking so much about herself. Let her come back to you in two years. I think by then she will have learned her lesson.'

"They sent me away as he suggested. I have done all kinds of work and traveled many miles. I have learned my lesson! The two years are up and my parents expect me to return. May I ask you to take me back to the palace?"

The knights looked at one another, then the Red Knight spoke. "Your highness, we will! But we must first continue our search for the lost prince of our Kingdom. Will you help us?"

1. The princess used to be—
   - A. humble.
   - B. ugly.
   - **(C.)** rude.
   - D. a liar.
2. The princess's punishment is fitting because—
   - F. she wants to be a servant.
   - G. her parents are disappointed.
   - H. her uncle hates her.
   - **(J.)** she treated her servants badly.
3. Stories of this kind usually—
   - A. are in rhyme.
   - B. have lots of jokes.
   - C. describe characters who get away with bad behavior.
   - **(D.)** end happily.
4. How will the princess answer the Red Knight?
   - **(F.)** She will help him.
   - G. She will refuse to help him.
   - H. She will remain a servant.
   - J. She will lead him straight to the lost prince.
5. When the princess's parents see her again, they will be—
   - **(A.)** pleased.
   - B. disappointed.
   - C. angry.
   - D. upset.

Notes for Home: Your child read a story and predicted what would happen next. ***Home Activity:*** Watch a TV show with your child. At a break, challenge her or him to predict what will happen next. Compare your child's prediction with what actually happens.

Name ______________________

Writing Across Texts

Directions: Consider what you learned about José in "Born Worker" and Casey in *Casey at the Bat.* How does José "win" for his team? How does Casey have great responsibility placed on his shoulders? How do they handle their responsibilities? Complete the table to record some of the similarities and differences between these two characters. **Possible answers given.**

José and Casey	
Alike	**Different**
Casey and José are both expected to succeed	3. **José is quiet and modest; Casey knows he is a star.**
1. **Both characters have a history of working (or playing) hard.**	4. **Casey had a whole town to please; José is only working with Arnie and for one person.**
2. **Casey and José have to make up for the poor performance of others.**	5. **José comes through in a time of crisis; Casey does not live up to his reputation.**

Write a Character Comparison

Use your completed table to help you write two paragraphs that compare and contrast the situations of José in "Born Worker" and Casey in *Casey at the Bat.* What expectations do people have of these characters? How do the characters handle the responsibility? Write your paragraphs on a separate sheet of paper.

Comparisons will vary. Check to see that students have described both similarities and differences in their paragraphs.

Notes for Home: Your child wrote about how characters in two different selections handle responsibility and other people's expectations of them. ***Home Activity:*** Talk with your child about a time when two people in your family reacted differently to the same event.

Grammar Practice Book 6.3, p. 66

Name ______________________

Grammar: Using Correct Verb Tenses

REVIEW

Directions: Circle the correct form of the verb in ( ) to complete each sentence.

1. Last year the mayor (invites/**(invited)**) a minor league team to our city.
2. No one (attended/**(had attended)**) a minor league game before.
3. My family (**(likes)**/is liking) baseball very much.
4. For years we (follow/**(had followed)**) teams like the Yankees and the Blue Jays.
5. We (will go/**(went)**) to the opening game last night.
6. We saw that everyone (is playing/**(was playing)**) as hard as possible.
7. At the end, the crowd yelled and (cheers/**(cheered)**).
8. We were excited when our team (**(won)**/wins) 7–4.
9. Now our town (will bragged/**(is bragging)**) proudly about the Santon Seagulls.
10. Next week we (**(will get)**/were getting) season tickets to the games of this minor league team.

Directions: Add a word or words to each verb to form a sentence. Write the complete sentence on the line. **Possible answers given.**

11. wish
I wish for good grades.

12. am wishing
Specifically, I am wishing for an A in English.

13. wished
I wished for good grades last year too.

14. have wished
I have wished this wish many times before.

15. will wish
I will wish for something different next year.

Notes for Home: Your child practiced using the correct tense of verbs. ***Home Activity:*** Extend the second part of this activity by having your child create sentences for the following verb tenses: *ask, am asking, asked,* and *had asked.*

Grammar Practice Book 6.3, p. 67

Name ______________________

Grammar: Irregular Verbs

Regular verbs are verbs that have the same spelling in the past and past participle forms. The **past form** of **regular verbs** is formed by adding **-ed** to the present tense. The **past participle** form of regular verbs is also formed by adding **-ed** to the present tense. It uses a helping verb such as *has* or *have.*

Present: We watch my little brother play baseball.

Past: We watched my little brother play baseball.

Past Participle: We have watched my little brother play baseball many times.

Irregular verbs, however, have a different spelling for the past and past participle forms.

Present: He throws the runner out at first base.

Past: He threw the runner out at first base.

Past Participle: This is the third time he has thrown the runner out at first base.

Directions: Write **regular** or **irregular** to describe each underlined verb.

irregular 1. The Glenview Gators were one of the best teams in the league.

irregular 2. They had a great pitcher.

regular 3. They usually scored at least seven runs a game.

irregular 4. They just won against the Janesville Giants 8–2.

regular 5. I hoped our team would clobber them tonight.

Directions: Use the correct form of the verb shown in ( ) to complete each sentence. Write the verb on the line.

played 6. Our team (play) well against the tough Gators.

stolen 7. Our star player has (steal) home, and the score is now tied.

struck 8. Then, our pitcher (strike) out the lead batter.

caught 9. I (catch) a long fly ball to center field to make it two outs.

lost 10. But now the Mighty Margoles has hit a grand slam, and our team has (lose) again.

Notes for Home: Your child identified regular and irregular verbs and wrote the past and past participle forms of verbs. ***Home Activity:*** Have your child describe three things he or she did today. For each sentence, ask him or her whether the verbs are regular or irregular.

Grammar Practice Book 6.3, p. 68

Name ____________________ **Casey at the Bat**

Grammar: Irregular Verbs

Directions: Write **regular** or **irregular** to describe each underlined verb.

regular 1. Lucy has joined the girl's softball team.

regular 2. She wanted to be a pitcher, but they made her a catcher instead.

irregular 3. She has taken a lot of teasing for the bulky pads she wears.

irregular 4. In the last game, she ran into the dugout to catch a foul ball.

irregular 5. She tries harder than any player I have seen.

Directions: Write the correct form for each irregular verb below.

Present		Past		Past Participle
begin	6.	**began**	7. has/have	**begun**
come	8.	**came**	9. has/have	**come**
eat	10.	**ate**	11. has/have	**eaten**
fall	12.	**fell**	13. has/have	**fallen**
ring	14.	**rang**	15. has/have	**rung**
bring	16.	**brought**	17. has/have	**brought**
swim	18.	**swam**	19. has/have	**swum**
say	20.	**said**	21. has/have	**said**
know	22.	**knew**	23. has/have	**known**
drive	24.	**drove**	25. has/have	**driven**

Write a Diary Entry

On a separate sheet of paper, write a diary entry about an event that turned out differently than you had expected. The event can be either real or made up. Underline the regular verbs and circle the irregular verbs. Be careful to write the correct forms of irregular verbs. **Check that students have used the correct verb forms and that they have correctly identified regular and irregular verbs.**

Notes for Home: Your child identified regular verbs and irregular verbs. ***Home Activity:*** Choose several irregular verbs (such as *swing, give,* and *grow*). Have your child use each verb in a sentence that describes an action that took place in the past.

Grammar Practice Book 6.3, p. 69

Name ____________________ **Casey at the Bat**

Grammar: Irregular Verbs

RETEACHING

Find the verbs in these sentences. Write them in the blanks. Be sure to include any helping verbs.

1. Luis and Liam swim this week. **swim** (present)
2. They swam last week too. **swam** (past)
3. The team has swum every day this month. **has swum** (past participle)

The past and past participle forms of **irregular verbs** are not made by adding **-ed**. Instead, the spelling of each verb changes to make each form.

Directions: Underline the irregular verb in each sentence. Write **past** or **past participle** to tell which verb form is used.

1. Our swim team has begun regular practices. **past participle**
2. Some of us had swum on the team before this year. **past participle**
3. The coach wrote our practice schedule on a chart. **past**
4. She had given a lot of thought to the schedule. **past participle**
5. Then we went to the deep end of the pool. **past**
6. We have grown accustomed to the routine. **past participle**
7. We knew it was for our own good. **past**

Directions: Write the correct verb form in ( ) to complete each sentence.

8. The coach **blew** her whistle. (blew/blown)
9. Two of the boys had **swum** five laps. (swam/swum)
10. They had **done** enough backstroke laps. (did/done)
11. She **gave** the boys three minutes to rest. (gave/given)
12. They **threw** towels around their shoulders. (threw/thrown)
13. The coach had **written** down their times. (wrote/written)
14. I **drank** some milk after practice. (drank/drunk)
15. We had **eaten** a good breakfast at sunrise. (ate/eaten)

Notes for Home: Your child identified irregular verbs in past and past participle forms. ***Home Activity:*** Have your child read a page from "Casey at the Bat" and identify irregular verbs in past participle forms.

Grammar Practice Book 6.3, p. 70

Name ____________________ **Casey at the Bat**

Grammar: Irregular Verbs

Directions: Write the correct verb form as indicated in ( ).

1. drink (past participle) has **drunk**
2. blow (past participle) has **blown**
3. sing (past) **sang**
4. grow (past) **grew**
5. eat (past) **ate**
6. go (past participle) has **gone**
7. throw (past participle) has **thrown**
8. take (past participle) has **taken**

Directions: Complete each sentence by writing the past or past participle form of the verb in ( ).

9. Our visit to the state fair **began** just before lunch. (begin)
10. Everyone **knew** the food at the fair was great. (know)
11. Before long we had **eaten** several ears of roasted corn. (eat)
12. Four-year-old Jacob **went** to find Belgian waffles. (go)
13. He had **grown** very fond of these giant pastries. (grow)
14. He **gave** half of his snack to his cousin Rachel. (give)

Directions: Complete each sentence with a verb form that makes sense. Write on the line the past or past participle form of one of the verbs in the box.

take	sing	give	blow	eat	fly

15. After lunch a whistle **blew** to start the steer-judging competition.
16. The judges had **given** all the prizes.
17. It **took** much more time to judge the hogs and milk cows.
18. Later a famous entertainer **sang** popular songs in the music tent.
19. He had **flown** from Hollywood to the fairgrounds just for the day.
20. By evening Jacob had **eaten** two more Belgian waffles.

Write a Paragraph

On a separate sheet of paper, write a paragraph about a fair or a carnival. Use irregular verbs in some of your sentences.

Check that students have spelled irregular verbs correctly.

Notes for Home: Your child wrote irregular verbs in past-tense and past participle forms. ***Home Activity:*** Discuss with your child what the two of you did today. Have your child give a hand signal every time one of you uses an irregular verb.

Practice Book 6.3, p. 138

Name ____________________ **Casey at the Bat**

Phonics: Schwa Sound (Final Syllable)

Directions: The **schwa sound** is a vowel sound heard in unstressed syllables. In the word **even,** the last **e** has a schwa sound. It can be spelled with any vowel or combination of vowels. Read each word below. Listen for the schwa sound in the final syllable. Underline the vowel or vowels that stand for the schwa sound.

1. silence	6. Simon	11. anxious
2. humor	7. listen	12. instant
3. former	8. audience	13. pretzel
4. seven	9. rehearsal	14. patience
5. instant	10. random	15. unravel

Directions: Circle the word with a schwa sound in each sentence. Underline the vowel or vowels that stand for the schwa sound in the final syllable.

batter 16. The next batter saw that the softball game was on the line.

pressure 17. She walked to the plate, feeling the pressure to win.

players 18. The players and fans yelled her name.

human 19. She tried not to hear the noise, but she was only human.

anchor 20. It was a good thing that she was the anchor of the team.

pitcher 21. The pitcher threw the ball low and fast, and she swung hard.

grounder 22. She hit a grounder to the shortstop.

person 23. The shortstop threw the ball to the person at first base.

second 24. She got to first just a second before the girl at that base caught the throw.

focus 25. Now she could focus on stealing the next base.

Notes for Home: Your child identified the schwa sound in unstressed syllables, such as the *e* in *even*. ***Home Activity:*** Help your child identify words with more than one syllable that have a schwa sound in the final syllable. Ask your child to say the words aloud.

Spelling Workbook 6.3, p. 53
Name ______________________

Casey at the Bat

Spelling: Vowels in Final Syllables

Pretest Directions: Fold back the page along the dotted line. On the blanks, write the spelling words as they are dictated. When you have finished the test, unfold the page and check your words.

1. **slogan** — 1. The store needed a new **slogan**.
2. **citizen** — 2. The immigrant became a **citizen**.
3. **urban** — 3. **Urban** life can be exciting.
4. **orphan** — 4. Wars **orphan** many children.
5. **forgotten** — 5. Have you **forgotten** something?
6. **kindergarten** — 6. My father teaches **kindergarten**.
7. **propeller** — 7. The plane's **propeller** is stuck.
8. **encounter** — 8. It was a chance **encounter**.
9. **conquer** — 9. Love can **conquer** hate.
10. **appetizer** — 10. Would you like an **appetizer**?
11. **collector** — 11. He is quite a **collector** of junk.
12. **dishonor** — 12. The mayor resigned in **dishonor**.
13. **tractor** — 13. The farmer bought a new **tractor**.
14. **level** — 14. A tornado can **level** a house.
15. **tunnel** — 15. We drove through a long **tunnel**.
16. **easel** — 16. The painter set up her **easel**.
17. **double** — 17. I hit a **double** and a home run.
18. **single** — 18. A spider hung by a **single** thread.
19. **example** — 19. Can you give me an **example**?
20. **recycle** — 20. We should **recycle** these cans.

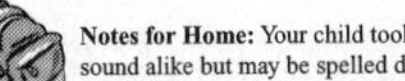

Notes for Home: Your child took a pretest on words whose final syllables contain vowels that sound alike but may be spelled differently. ***Home Activity:*** Have your child divide misspelled words into parts (such as syllables) and concentrate on each part.

Spelling Workbook 6.3, p. 54
Name ______________________

Casey at the Bat

Spelling: Vowels in Final Syllables

Word List

slogan	forgotten	conquer	tractor	double
urban	kindergarten	appetizer	level	single
orphan	propeller	collector	tunnel	example
citizen	encounter	dishonor	easel	recycle

Directions: Choose the words from the box that end in **-en**, **-er**, **-an**, or **-or**. Listen for the vowels in the final syllables. Write each word in the correct column. **Order may vary.**

Words Ending -en
1. **citizen**
2. **forgotten**
3. **kindergarten**

Words Ending -an
4. **slogan**
5. **urban**
6. **orphan**

Words Ending -er
7. **propeller**
8. **encounter**
9. **conquer**
10. **appetizer**

Words Ending -or
11. **collector**
12. **dishonor**
13. **tractor**

Directions: Find seven words from the box in the puzzle. They may be printed across or down. Circle the words in the puzzle and then write them on the lines. Hint: Their final syllables are spelled either **le** or **el**. **Order may vary.**

14. **level**
15. **tunnel**
16. **easel**
17. **double**
18. **single**
19. **example**
20. **recycle**

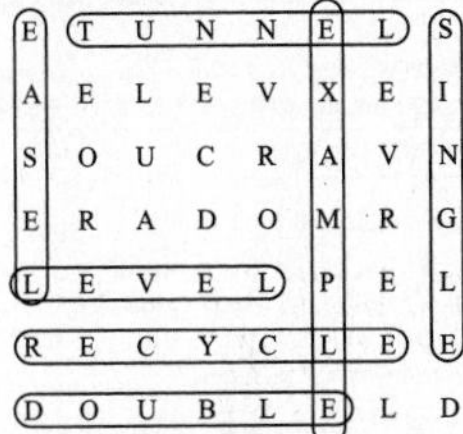

Notes for Home: Your child spelled words whose final syllables contain vowels that often sound alike even when they are spelled differently, such as *slogan* and *citizen*. ***Home Activity:*** Challenge your child to think of two rhyming words, one ending in *-en* and one ending in *-an*.

Spelling Workbook 6.3, p. 55
Name ______________________

Casey at the Bat

Spelling: Vowels in Final Syllables

Directions: Proofread this sports report. Find six spelling mistakes. Use the proofreading marks to correct each mistake.

SPORTS

Today in local baseball, *The Urban Herald Rockets* will encounter its rival newspaper, *The Caspar Citiz~~a~~en Jets. The Urb~~e~~an Herald* team has not forgott~~a~~en last month's single-run loss to *The Caspar Citizen,* in which a 9th inning doub~~el~~le brought in the winning run. Their slog~~e~~an for today's match is "Conqu~~o~~er *The Caspar Citizen.*" Fans should make an effort to see a good example of baseball at its best.

- ≡ Make a capital.
- / Make a small letter.
- ∧ Add something.
- Take out something.
- ⊙ Add a period.
- ¶ Begin a new paragraph.

Word List
slogan, urban, orphan, citizen, forgotten, kindergarten, propeller, encounter, conquer, appetizer, collector, dishonor, tractor, level, tunnel, easel, double, single, example, recycle

Spelling Tip

Vowels in final syllables often sound alike even when they are spelled differently: **slogan, citizen; propeller, collector; level, double.** Check the sports report carefully to be sure words with these endings are spelled correctly.

Write a Sports Report

On a separate sheet of paper, write your own sports report. Write about an event that has just happened or is just about to happen. Try to use at least five of your spelling words. **Answers will vary, but each sports report should include at least five spelling words.**

Notes for Home: Your child spelled words whose final syllables contain vowels that often sound alike even when they are spelled differently, such as in *slogan* and *citizen*. ***Home Activity:*** Have your child listen to or read a short sports report and identify words with *-er* and *-or* endings.

Spelling Workbook 6.3, p. 56
Name ______________________

Casey at the Bat

Spelling: Vowels in Final Syllables

REVIEW

Word List

slogan	forgotten	conquer	tractor	double
urban	kindergarten	appetizer	level	single
orphan	propeller	collector	tunnel	example
citizen	encounter	dishonor	easel	recycle

Directions: Choose the word from the box that best matches each clue. Write the word on the line.

1. **propeller** — This spins around on the front of the airplane.
2. **kindergarten** — This is the grade that most five-year-olds are in.
3. **recycle** — This is what you do when you return bottles for reuse.
4. **easel** — This is what a painter uses to support her canvas.
5. **tunnel** — This is an underground passage.
6. **forgotten** — This is what happens when something is not remembered.
7. **tractor** — This vehicle can pull other farm machinery.
8. **slogan** — This is the saying an advertiser repeats in commercials.
9. **collector** — This is a person who saves certain items, like stamps.
10. **orphan** — This is a person who has lost his or her parents.

Directions: Choose the word from the box that best replaces the underlined word. Write the word on the line.

11. **level** — The shelf is <u>flat</u> in all directions.
12. **encounter** — I wouldn't want to <u>meet</u> a bear in the woods.
13. **urban** — She is the <u>city</u> planner.
14. **appetizer** — The <u>snack</u> was served just before the entrée.
15. **dishonor** — His shameful actions brought <u>disgrace</u> to his family.
16. **conquer** — She expects to <u>overcome</u> her fear of flying.
17. **double** — My savings are <u>twice</u> what they were last year.
18. **example** — She showed me a <u>sample</u> of her work.
19. **citizen** — He is a <u>native</u> of Canada.
20. **single** — The <u>one</u> red pillow was lost in a sea of blue ones.

Notes for Home: Your child spelled words whose final syllables contain vowels that often sound alike even when they are spelled differently, such as *slogan* and *citizen*. ***Home Activity:*** Challenge your child to spell other words that end with *el* and *le*.

Practice Book 6.3, p. 139

Name ______________________ **Casey at the Bat**

Announcement/Poster/Advertisement

An **announcement** is something that is made known. A **poster** is a type of announcement that gives specific facts about an event. It should answer the questions *Who?, What?, When?, Where?,* and *Why?* An **advertisement** is an announcement that tries to persuade readers, listeners, or viewers to do something, buy something, or feel a particular way.

Directions: Read the poster advertising a car wash. Use it to answer the questions that follow.

> **Get a Clean Car and Support Your Little League**
>
> **The Rapid River Little League will be holding a car wash to raise money for much needed new uniforms and equipment.**
>
> Car Wash
> Saturday, May 23rd
> 10:00 A.M. to 6:00 P.M.
> State Fair Grounds, 2122 Lincoln Avenue
> Single (wash only) $4.00
> Double (wash + wax) $6.00
> Grand Slam (wash, wax, windows, interior) $10.00
>
> 
>
> Rain Date:
> Saturday, May 30th
>
> **You'll get a shine so bright, you'll need sunglasses!**

1. What is the purpose of the poster/advertisement? **The poster/advertisement is trying to persuade people to have their cars washed in order to raise funds for the Rapid River Little League.**
2. What event will take place? **a car wash**
3. At what time and on what day does the event take place? **The event takes place between 10:00 A.M. and 6:00 P.M. on May 23rd.**
4. Who organized this event? **the Rapid River Little League**
5. What will the organizers of this event do with the money they raise? **They will buy new uniforms and equipment.**

Practice Book 6.3, p. 140

Name ______________________ **Casey at the Bat**

6. What will happen if it rains on May 23rd? **If it rains, the car wash will be held on May 30th instead.**
7. What words does the poster/advertisement use to persuade readers? **Possible answer: support; much needed; You'll get a shine so bright, you'll need sunglasses!**
8. Why do you think the poster/advertisement uses different sizes and types of letters? **Possible answer: The different sizes and types of letters make it more visually interesting and help show the importance of different pieces of information.**
9. Why do you think the poster includes art? **Possible answer: The art helps catch the reader's attention and shows at a glance what the poster/advertisement is about.**
10. Use the space below to make your own poster to advertise the opening Little League game between the Dairy Flo Dragons and the Supreme Taco Superstars. Be sure to answer the five "W" questions. **Posters will vary. Check that students address the five "W" questions.**

Notes for Home: Your child answered questions about a poster advertising a fundraiser and created a poster to persuade people to attend a Little League game. ***Home Activity:*** Work with your child to create a poster about an upcoming family event.

Practice Book 6.3, p. 141

Name ______________________ **The Night of the Pomegranate**

Theme

- The **theme** of a story is the underlying meaning or message.
- To determine the theme of a story, ask yourself, "What does the author want me to learn or know?" Your answer should be a "big idea" that can stand on its own away from the story.
- Many stories have more than one theme. To be valid, a statement of theme should be supported by evidence from the text.

Directions: Reread "A Winning Essay." Then complete the table. Write three pieces of evidence that support the first theme. Use the supporting evidence given to write a second theme and give another piece of evidence that supports it. **Possible answers given.**

Theme	Evidence that Supports the Theme
Theme 1: People have different ways of expressing love.	1. **Mattie wants to sing about her love for her mother.**
	2. **Mattie wants to buy her mother a pin to show her that she loves her.**
	3. **Mattie writes a letter that expresses her love for her mother.**
4. **Theme 2: Sometimes people have difficulty expressing love.**	4. Mattie has a hard time expressing her love for her mother.
	5. **Mattie's mother finds it easier to talk to and understand Matt than Mattie.**

Notes for Home: Your child identified the themes in a story and provided evidence to support those themes. ***Home Activity:*** Discuss a familiar book or movie with your child. Help your child identify one or more themes of the story.

Practice Book 6.3, p. 142

Name ______________________ **The Night of the Pomegranate**

Vocabulary

Directions: Draw a line to connect each word on the left with its definition on the right.

1. constellation — a planet's elliptical path around another body in space
2. marveled — the whole of existing things, including all space and matter
3. orbit — a group of stars with a recognizable shape
4. solar — wondered at
5. universe — of the sun

Check the Words You Know
- __ constellation
- __ marveled
- __ orbit
- __ relative
- __ solar
- __ universe

Directions: Choose the word from the box that best completes each sentence. Write the word on the line to the left. Then find and circle the words in the puzzle below. Words may appear across, down, or diagonally.

solar 6. Any body that goes around our Sun is part of our _____ system.
relative 7. Jupiter is huge _____ to Earth.
orbit 8. The comet's _____ brought it near Earth.
universe 9. The _____ contains everything there is, including all space and matter.
constellation 10. The Big Dipper is a _____ that got its name because the stars are in the shape of a dipper in the night sky.

Write a News Report

On a separate sheet of paper, write about the discovery of a new planet. Describe the planet's size, its stars, its sun(s), and so on. Use as many vocabulary words as you can.
Check that vocabulary is used appropriately in students' reports.

```
E V B A C S O R B I T Z I N
G Y J U Q U C E X S S O S Y
F C O N S T E L L A T I O N
B W F I A C D A M I Z T L I
P Y A V J U A T I Y L L A Z
S N T E R R B I A T V X R E
R J H R V S O V H N X D O F
D N I S G M J E Z A J I H Y
N Q T E A H N Y S S H D E M
```

Notes for Home: Your child identified and used vocabulary words from "The Night of the Pomegranate." ***Home Activity:*** With your child, look for names and descriptions of parts of the universe. Together, make a picture dictionary of the words you find.

Practice Book 6.3, p. 143

Name ______________________ The Night of the Pomegranate

Theme

- The **theme** of a story is the underlying meaning or message.
- Many stories have more than one theme.

Directions: Reread the part of "The Night of the Pomegranate" about Harriet's and Clayton's models. Then answer the questions below. Ask yourself what the author wants you to learn by reading this story.

Mars was near Earth this month. The nights had been November cold but clear as glass, and Harriet had been out to see Mars every night, which was why she hadn't gotten her solar system finished, why she was so tired, why Mom made Tom drive her to school. It was all Mars's fault.

She was using the tape on Ms. Krensky's desk when Clayton Beemer arrived with his dad. His solar system came from the hobby store. The planets were Styrofoam balls, all different sizes and painted the right colors. Saturn's rings were clear plastic painted over as delicately as insect wings.

Harriet looked down at her own Saturn. Her rings were drooping despite all the tape. They looked like a limp skirt on a . . . on a ball of scrunched-up newspaper.

Possible answers given.

1. Why is it Mars's fault that Harriet has not completed her model?
Harriet has been looking at Mars instead of making her model.

2. In your own words, what is Clayton's model like? Why is it like that?
Clayton's model is very neat and complete because he bought its pieces at a hobby shop.

3. In your own words, what is Harriet's model like? Why is it like that?
Harriet's model is a mess because she made it in a hurry.

4. What is the difference between Clayton's and Harriet's approaches to learning about the solar system?
Harriet spends time looking at real planets while Clayton learns from model planets.

5. On a separate sheet of paper, explain what you think the theme of this story is.
Some of the best learning comes from firsthand experience. Harriet has a sense of the way parts of the universe connect with each other because she has gone out at night to look at the stars.

Notes for Home: Your child identified a story's theme, or the underlying meaning or message. ***Home Activity:*** Read a favorite story together. Encourage your child to explain its theme. Discuss how this theme relates to real-life experiences.

Practice Book 6.3, p. 145

Name ______________________ The Night of the Pomegranate

Selection Test

Directions: Choose the best answer to each item. Mark the letter for the answer you have chosen.

Part 1: Vocabulary

Find the answer choice that means about the same as the underlined word in each sentence.

1. Imagine what it would be like to travel throughout the <u>universe</u>.
   A. solar system
   Ⓑ all that exists
   C. group of stars
   D. wide desert
2. Sandra drew a picture showing Pluto's <u>orbit</u>.
   F. color
   Ⓖ planet's path around the sun
   H. size
   J. what a planet is made of
3. That <u>constellation</u> is called Orion.
   A. ring around a planet
   B. spaceship
   C. large number of planets
   Ⓓ group of stars that form a shape
4. We <u>marveled</u> at the hummingbird.
   F. had great hopes
   G. set a value for
   Ⓗ were filled with wonder
   J. refused to believe
5. The <u>relative</u> strength of steel makes it a good choice for cars.
   Ⓐ as compared with others
   B. important
   C. of or related to metal
   D. unusual
6. Heather's house uses <u>solar</u> power.
   Ⓕ of or from the sun
   G. electrical
   H. modern
   J. without heat

Part 2: Comprehension

Use what you know about the story to answer each item.

7. Why did Harriet use grape gum to construct her model of Pluto?
   Ⓐ She ran out of tape and glue.
   B. Pluto is cold.
   C. She liked the purple color.
   D. Pluto is small.
8. How did Harriet recognize Mars in the night sky?
   F. It twinkled.
   Ⓖ It was red.
   H. Mrs. Pond pointed to it.
   J. She had a map of the constellations.
9. Clayton Beemer's solar-system model—
   A. was very similar to Harriet's.
   B. made many students ask him questions.
   Ⓒ was elaborate and neatly done.
   D. used marbles and pomegranate seeds.
10. With Earth represented by Kevin's marble, Harriet compared Mars to a pomegranate seed because it—
    F. was the only thing she had with her.
    G. reminded her of Mrs. Pond.
    H. had a surprising taste.
    Ⓙ was the right color and relative size.

GO ON

Practice Book 6.3, p. 146

Name ______________________ The Night of the Pomegranate

11. What did Harriet learn about herself in this story?
    A. She was glad her parents were not interested in helping her with school projects.
    B. She did not know very much about any of the planets.
    C. She did not care what her classmates though about her project.
    Ⓓ She was more interested in observing Mars than in making a model.
12. What is a theme of this story?
    F. Pomegranates are tart.
    G. Sometimes Mars is visible in the sky.
    Ⓗ Sometimes we learn more from direct experience than from a school project.
    J. Work is easier if you have a partner.
13. Why did Harriet joke about her solar-system model and pull it apart?
    Ⓐ She was embarrassed by it.
    B. She was hungry.
    C. She wanted to improve it.
    D. She wanted to show off her strength.
14. Ms. Krensky's opinion of Harriet's work improved when she realized that Harriet—
    F. had a better model before she took it apart.
    G. was more interested in learning about pomegranates than planets.
    Ⓗ knew a great deal about Mars.
    J. had seen Mars in a movie.
15. Mrs. Pond tells Harriet about *The War of the Worlds* broadcast in order to—
    A. scare Harriet.
    Ⓑ share an interesting childhood memory with Harriet.
    C. show how foolish people can be.
    D. prove that Mars will someday collide with Earth.

STOP

Name ______________________ The Night of the Pomegranate

Theme

- The **theme** of a story is the underlying meaning or message.
- Many stories have more than one theme.

Directions: Read the story below.

Sean convinced his parents he was old enough to baby-sit his little brother Paddy. He had never baby-sat before, but he'd watched his parents with the baby hundreds of times.

An hour after their parents left, Paddy woke up wailing. Sean folded the baby in his arms and rocked him, just as his parents would have done. It worked! Paddy stopped crying.

Then, just as his parents would have done, Sean gave Paddy some juice from a bottle. By then, Paddy was wide awake and wanted to play. Sean wasn't sure what his parents would do, but he decided to play peek-a-boo for a while. It wasn't long before Paddy began to yawn. Sean sang him a lullaby as he tucked him in.

Sean's parents were pleased at how well he had done. "You're a first-class baby-sitter!" they said.

Directions: Each box contains a question about important story events. Complete each box. Then use your answers to describe the story's theme. **Possible answers given.**

1. Why does Sean think he can take care of Paddy?
He has paid attention to what his parents do for Paddy.

2. Why does Sean give Paddy some juice to drink?
He remembers that his parents feed Paddy juice.

3. Why does Sean play peek-a-boo with Paddy?
Paddy wants to play and Sean thinks it will be okay.

4. Why are Sean's parents pleased?
He took good care of Paddy.

5. This story's theme is:
You can learn from others by watching them and remembering what they do. You should also remain calm and use your judgment in new situations.

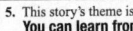

Notes for Home: Your child has read a story and identified its theme. ***Home Activity:*** Read a story with your child. Help your child describe its theme. Take turns naming other stories with the same theme.

Practice Book 6.3, p. 147

Name ______________________ The Night of the Pomegranate

Compare and Contrast REVIEW

Directions: Read the story. Then read each question about the story. Choose the best answer to each question. Mark the letter for the answer you have chosen.

Wish You Were Here

Helen knew all about Rome from her aunt's picture postcards. Each week a new one arrived, and Helen added it to her album. Now, visiting her aunt for the first time, she felt as if the postcards had come to life!

The postcards had made Rome seem still and calm. But the living city was filled with movement and noise. Bus passengers stuck in traffic complained as much as the people back home. Here, though, most poked their heads out the window to see what was the matter and to offer advice. Cars and motorcycles roared by and seemed to park wherever they pleased, even on sidewalks.

Pictures hadn't told Helen how different eating in Rome would be. Unlike stores in America, shops were closed for a few hours for lunch. People took a long time over their meals. Helen liked that. Lunch was always such a rush back home! Helen loved the food. Her favorite was *gelato,* Italian ice cream. It was richer and much better than ice cream at home.

Helen could not get used to the age of the buildings. Rome had many new buildings, of course, but she knew that nothing in America was as old as most of what she saw in Rome. Helen felt that every café, every house, and every sidewalk was a piece of history. She was so overwhelmed by her experiences, that when she wrote to her friend Pablo all she could say was, "Wish you were here."

1. Helen feels that her postcards have come to life because—
   - A. things are different in Rome.
   - (B.) she can see things firsthand.
   - C. she is a tourist.
   - D. her aunt lives in Rome.
2. Compared to Americans, Helen finds Romans —
   - (F.) openly curious.
   - G. very stuffy.
   - H. faster eaters.
   - J. bus riders.
3. Helen observes that when stuck in traffic, both Romans and Americans—
   - A. get involved.
   - B. suffer in silence.
   - (C.) complain.
   - D. get out and walk.
4. Americans eat hastily at lunch while Romans—
   - F. eat a lot.
   - (G.) take their time.
   - H. eat *gelato.*
   - J. eat on the run.
5. Helen observes that most buildings in Rome are—
   - A. newer than those in America.
   - B. about the same age as those in America.
   - C. in worse shape than those in America.
   - (D.) much older than those in America.

Notes for Home: Your child read a passage and made comparisons and contrasts. ***Home Activity:*** With your child, compare and contrast some popular ethnic foods. For instance, pizza and burritos are made of grains and vegetables, though they look and taste different.

Name ______________________ The Night of the Pomegranate

Writing Across Texts

Directions: Think about what you learned about the solar system in "The Night of the Pomegranate" and "What Is Earth's Place in Space?" Complete the Venn diagram to compare and contrast the information in each selection. Think about which explanation would help you to better understand the material. **Possible answers given.**

Harriet's Explanation	Both Selections	What Is Earth's Place in Space?
She compares the sizes of Earth and Mars to a marble and a pomegranate seed.		It explains how long it takes Earth to travel around the Sun.
1. **She compares the distances between the Sun and Mars and Earth to objects the class can see outside the classroom.**	3. **Both selections tell us about where Earth is in relation to other planets.**	4. **The textbook shows real pictures.**
2. **She tells the class about seeing Mars with Mrs. Pond.**		5. **The textbook gives numerical facts about the orbits of the planets.**

Write a Comparison Paragraph

In "The Night of the Pomegranate," Harriet uses her personal experience to explain to her class the relative sizes and distances of the planets. Compare Harriet's explanation to what you learned in "What Is Earth's Place in Space?" Was Harriet's explanation accurate? If you were in her class, would it have been clear to you? Which way of presenting information do you consider more helpful? On a separate sheet of paper, write a paragraph discussing these issues. **Paragraphs will vary. Check that students recognize that both selections give information about the solar system; opinions about how helpful the different approaches to learning are will vary.**

Notes for Home: Your child evaluated different ways of presenting similar information. ***Home Activity:*** As you read a story or article with your child, discuss how results, or outcomes, can be interpreted in more than one way.

Grammar Practice Book 6.3, p. 71

Name ______________________ The Night of the Pomegranate

Grammar: Subject-Verb Agreement REVIEW

Directions: Circle the verb in ( ) that agrees with the subject in each sentence.

1. (Does/(Do)) the students in your class know the names of all the planets?
2. Mercury ((is)/are) the closest planet to the Sun.
3. This small planet ((orbits)/orbit) around the Sun every 88 days.
4. The thick clouds around Venus (makes/(make)) the astronomer's job very difficult.
5. Mars, more than the other planets, ((has)/have) been the subject of many scary movies about space creatures.
6. An asteroid belt ((exists)/exist) between Mars and Jupiter.
7. Even amateur astronomers (enjoys/(enjoy)) the rings around Saturn.
8. A recent discovery by powerful telescopes ((shows)/show) rings around Jupiter too.
9. Jupiter, of course, ((is)/are) the largest planet.
10. Perhaps other planets beyond Pluto (awaits/(await)) our discovery.

Directions: Match each subject with a verb in the box. Then write a sentence that includes both of them. **Possible answers given.**

launches	rotates	searches	shines	watches
launch	rotate	search	shine	watch

11. An astronomer ______.
An astronomer watches the night sky for new discoveries.
12. Mission control ______.
Mission control launches space probes into outer space.
13. Earth ______.
Earth rotates on its axis.
14. Space probes ______.
Space probes search outer space for life.
15. Stars ______.
Stars shine beautifully in the night sky.

Notes for Home: Your child identified verbs that agree with their subjects. ***Home Activity:*** Together, listen to stories on tape or a program on television. Repeat sentences aloud and discuss whether the subject-verb agreement is correct.

Grammar Practice Book 6.3, p. 72

Name ______________________ The Night of the Pomegranate

Grammar: Direct and Indirect Objects and Subject Complements

A **direct object** is a noun or pronoun that follows an action verb and tells who or what receives the action of the verb.

I watched a long movie on TV last night.

The views of Earth from outer space surprised me.

An **indirect object** comes after an action verb. It names the person to whom or for whom the action is done. However, the words *to* or *for* are not used before an indirect object.

I wrote Maria a note about the movie.

In this sentence, *Maria* is the indirect object of *wrote.* The word *note* is the direct object.

A **predicate noun** follows a linking verb and tells who or what the subject is.

Maria is a former neighbor of mine.

A **predicate adjective** follows a linking verb and describes the subject.

Maria has become enthusiastic about flying.

Directions: Underline each direct object once and each indirect object twice. Hint: Not every sentence has an indirect object.

1. I discovered an article about the Wright brothers.
2. The article gave me ideas about working on inventions.
3. I wrote an essay about their experiments with a glider.
4. My cousin Maxine read the paper carefully.
5. Maxine gave me her reactions in writing.

Directions: Write **PN** if the underlined word is a predicate noun. Write **PA** if it is a predicate adjective.

PA 6. From glider flight to space flight, the progress has been amazing.

PA 7. I felt astonished to learn that 1903 was the date of the first engine-powered flight.

PN 8. The young Wright brothers were experienced mechanics.

PA 9. Their patience with repeated failures seems remarkable.

PN 10. Naturally, these two men became celebrities.

Notes for Home: Your child identified direct and indirect objects, as well as predicate nouns and adjectives. ***Home Activity:*** Use the examples and definitions above to help your child write additional examples.

Grammar Practice Book 6.3, p. 73

Name ______________________ *The Night of the Pomegranate*

Grammar: Direct and Indirect Objects and Subject Complements

Directions: Write **DO** if the underlined word is a direct object. Write **IO** if it is an indirect object.

IO 1. Julia sent her relatives some letters.
DO 2. She wanted true stories about successful work experiences.
DO 3. Some of the relatives wrote notes to Julia.
IO 4. Uncle Bob mailed her a tape instead.
DO 5. Bob told Julia a fascinating story about his work with NASA's space exploration.
IO 6. Bob gave his niece many suggestions for her own life.
IO 7. Then he assigned her a little exercise.
DO 8. Julia described the exercise to her mother.
IO 9. "He has sent you many sensible ideas," Julia's mother said.
DO 10. Julia shared her mother's comment with her uncle.

Directions: Circle the linking verb in each sentence. Remember to circle any helping verbs. Then underline the sentence part named in ( ).

11. Julia clearly (felt) interested in her relatives' ideas. (predicate adjective)
12. Sometimes relatives (are) the best advisers. (predicate noun)
13. Her uncle certainly (seems) kind. (predicate adjective)
14. He also (has been) generous with his time. (predicate adjective)
15. Uncle Bob's story (will become) a part of the family history. (predicate noun)

Write a Narrative Paragraph

On a separate sheet of paper, write a narrative paragraph (a very short story) about a time when you helped someone or someone helped you. Try to include one or more direct objects, indirect objects, predicate nouns, and predicate adjectives. List the direct and indirect objects and the prediate nouns and adjectives you used below your paragraph. **Check that students have correctly identified the direct objects, indirect objects, predicate nouns, and predicate adjectives they have used.**

Notes for Home: Your child identified direct objects (Mary sent a *card*) and indirect objects (*Mary sent her a card*), as well as predicate nouns and adjectives. ***Home Activity:*** Have your child write a sentence that includes a direct object and an indirect object.

Grammar Practice Book 6.3, p. 74

Name ______________________ *The Night of the Pomegranate*

Grammar: Direct and Indirect Objects and Subject Complements

RETEACHING

Underline the direct object in each sentence. Circle each indirect object.

1. Gloria gave (me) a wonderful birthday present.
2. I sent (her) a thank-you note yesterday.

Underline the predicate noun. Circle the predicate adjective.

3. Gloria is (thoughtful) about other people.
4. She became an artist after several years of work.

A **direct object** is the noun or noun phrase that follows an action verb and tells who or what receives the action of the verb. An **indirect object** is the noun or noun phrase that often directly follows an action verb and names the person to whom or for whom the action is done. A **predicate noun** follows a linking verb and tells who or what the subject is. A **predicate adjective** also follows a linking verb, and it describes the subject.

Directions: Underline each direct object once and each indirect object twice. Not every sentence will have both.

1. My friends celebrated my birthday early this year.
2. Each of them brought me a silly gift.
3. Mark gave me ten soda straws in a used milk carton.
4. Yoshi sang us a song backwards.
5. My father cooked chicken.
6. I gave each of my friends a big hug.

Directions: Write whether each underlined word is a **predicate noun** or a **predicate adjective.**

predicate adjective 7. Now the sun is low in the sky.
predicate noun 8. I am a photographer in the city.
predicate adjective 9. Some people here are very busy.
predicate adjective 10. Pushing heavy bricks seems easy for that worker.
predicate adjective 11. The afternoon seemed long and hot.

Notes for Home: Your child identified direct and indirect objects and predicate nouns and adjectives. ***Home Activity:*** Have your child write two questions containing direct and indirect objects. Answer the questions, using direct and indirect objects. Have your child check your work.

Grammar Practice Book 6.3, p. 75

Name ______________________ *The Night of the Pomegranate*

Grammar: Direct and Indirect Objects and Subject Complements

Directions: Write **DO** if the underlined word is a direct object. Write **IO** if it is an indirect object.

DO 1. When my Aunt Sarah moved to Germany, she left us many things.
IO 2. One thing she gave us was her collection of ukuleles.
DO 3. Aunt Sarah collected musical instruments from different countries.
DO 4. She told my cousins stories about how and where the instruments were made.
DO 5. Some villagers in a little town in Ireland had made some drums she had.
IO 6. Aunt Sarah gave me her drums because she knew I liked to play them when I visited her.
DO 7. My brother wanted her many books about instruments made out of gourds.
DO 8. Now that she has left, we have sent her thank-you cards for all the gifts she gave us.
IO 9. In my card I told her what I did with the gifts.
IO 10. My brother and I miss the stories she told us.

Directions: Circle the linking verb in each sentence. Then underline each predicate adjective once and each predicate noun twice. Not every sentence will have both a predicate adjective and a predicate noun.

11. "Beth (is) my aunt," said my friend.
12. "I (am) curious about her job as a calligrapher. How should I ask her my questions?"
13. "Writing a letter (seems) smart," I told him.
14. "You (are) right!" he said.
15. Her response (was) very interesting.
16. She (had been) a calligrapher a long time ago.
17. Her entire letter (was) beautiful.

Notes for Home: Your child identified direct and indirect objects and predicate nouns and adjectives in sentences. ***Home Activity:*** Have your child identify in a favorite story two sentences with direct and indirect objects. Then have him or her use the direct and indirect objects in new sentences.

Practice Book 6.3, p. 148

Name ______________________ *The Night of the Pomegranate*

Word Study: Contractions

Directions: A **contraction** is a word formed by joining two words with an **apostrophe.** The apostrophe takes the place of one or more letters. Read the journal entry below. Circle each contraction. Write the contraction on the line to the left. Then write the two words that the contraction combines on the right.

I (wasn't) sure what I saw the other night. As I looked up at the night sky, gazing at the stars I know so well, I spotted bright bands of light shimmering. They (didn't) look like stars, and I realized I (hadn't) seen anything like them before. Waves of greenish light rippled in the sky. "(They're) moving!" I thought to myself. I (couldn't) believe my eyes when the whole sky seemed to come alive with these lights. "(It's) not possible!" I said. I later found out that these bands of light are called Northern Lights. (I'll) never forget that sight as long as I live!

Contraction	Two Words It Combines
1. wasn't	2. was not
3. didn't	4. did not
5. hadn't	6. had not
7. They're	8. They are
9. couldn't	10. could not
11. It's	12. It is
13. I'll	14. I will

Directions: Combine each word pair to form a contraction. Write the contraction on the line.

15. do not **don't**
16. you would **you'd**
17. let us **let's**
18. will not **won't**
19. should not **shouldn't**
20. are not **aren't**

Notes for Home: Your child formed contractions, such as *that's* from the words *that* and *is.* ***Home Activity:*** Listen to a radio or television program, and work with your child to identify spoken contractions. Ask your child to tell you the two words that each contraction represents.

Spelling Workbook 6.3, p. 57
Name ______________________

The Night of the Pomegranate

Spelling: Homophones

Pretest Directions: Fold back the page along the dotted line. On the blanks, write the spelling words as they are dictated. When you have finished the test, unfold the page and check your words.

1. **their**	1. **Their** mother is a surgeon.
2. **there**	2. Put the groceries over **there**.
3. **they're**	3. **They're** not coming until later.
4. **wring**	4. I had to **wring** out my wet shirt.
5. **ring**	5. She has a lovely diamond **ring**.
6. **chili**	6. Please buy some **chili** pepper.
7. **chilly**	7. The wind is **chilly** tonight.
8. **scent**	8. That cheese has a strong **scent**.
9. **sent**	9. I **sent** a letter to my uncle.
10. **cent**	10. I don't have a **cent** to my name.
11. **oversees**	11. Dad **oversees** our business.
12. **overseas**	12. My brother lives **overseas**.
13. **patients**	13. My doctor sees many **patients**.
14. **patience**	14. He has great **patience** with kids.
15. **cereal**	15. Open another box of **cereal**.
16. **serial**	16. A **serial** is broadcast in parts.
17. **coarse**	17. This wood has a **coarse** grain.
18. **course**	18. I work at a local golf **course**.
19. **counsel**	19. To **counsel** is to give advice.
20. **council**	20. The city **council** meets today.

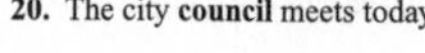

Notes for Home: Your child took a pretest on homophones, words that sound alike but are spelled differently and have different meanings. ***Home Activity:*** Help your child learn to connect the spelling of the word with its meaning.

Spelling: Homophones 331

Spelling Workbook 6.3, p. 58
Name ______________________

The Night of the Pomegranate

Spelling: Homophones

Word List				
their	chili	oversees	cereal	counsel
there	chilly	overseas	serial	council
they're	scent	patients	coarse	
wring	sent	patience	course	
ring	cent			

Directions: Each word below is contained in words from the box. Write the words from the box in the correct column. **Order may vary.**

over
1. **oversees**
2. **overseas**

tie
3. **patients**
4. **patience**

in
5. **wring**
6. **ring**

the
7. **their**
8. **there**
9. **they're**

Directions: Choose the word from the box that has the same or nearly the same meaning as each word or words below. Write the word on the line.

10. cold **chilly**
11. rough **coarse**
12. committee **council**
13. smell **scent**
14. penny **cent**
15. breakfast food **cereal**
16. track **course**
17. advice **counsel**
18. transmitted **sent**
19. hot pepper **chili**
20. in order **serial**

Notes for Home: Your child spelled homophones—words that sound the same but have different spellings and meanings. ***Home Activity:*** Help your child write sentences using each spelling word. You may wish to use a dictionary to review the meanings of the words first.

332 Spelling: Homophones

Spelling Workbook 6.3, p. 59
Name ______________________

The Night of the Pomegranate

Spelling: Homophones

Directions: Proofread this description of the solar system. Find six spelling mistakes. Use the proofreading marks to correct each mistake.

- ≡ Make a capital.
- / Make a small letter.
- ∧ Add something.
- Take out something.
- ⊙ Add a period.
- ¶ Begin a new paragraph.

I see the solar system as a counsel [cil] headed by the Sun. The Sun overseas [ees] the planets and guides their course through the chili [lly] emptiness of space. Belts of rocks and other debris wring [ring] some planets, like Saturn. Their [re] are comets that sometimes outshine the stars. You must have patience if you want to see them, because they are rarely visible. The asteroids that orbit in there [ir] belt between Mars and Jupiter are most mysterious to me.

Spelling Tip

their **there**

Because homophones sound alike, they are sometimes written incorrectly. **Their** and **there** are often mixed up. Remember **there** refers to a place and think: I looked for it **here**, but I found it **there**.

Word List	
their	oversees
there	overseas
they're	patients
wring	patience
ring	cereal
chili	serial
chilly	coarse
scent	course
sent	counsel
cent	council

Write a Description

On a separate sheet of paper, write a description of the solar system. It can be a description of what you see in the night sky or what you imagine the surface of a planet would be like. Try to use at least five of your spelling words.
Answers will vary, but each description should include at least five spelling words.

Notes for Home: Your child spelled homophones—words that sound the same but have different spellings and meanings. ***Home Activity:*** Begin a list of homophones, and work together to keep adding to it with examples such as *to/too/two* or *threw/through*.

Spelling: Homophones 333

Spelling Workbook 6.3, p. 60
Name ______________________

The Night of the Pomegranate

Spelling: Homophones

REVIEW

Word List				
their	chili	oversees	cereal	counsel
there	chilly	overseas	serial	council
they're	scent	patients	coarse	
wring	sent	patience	course	
ring	cent			

Directions: Write the word from the box that belongs in each group.

1. chronological, alphabetical, **serial**
2. his, her, **their**
3. doctors, nurses, **patients**
4. cold, cool, **chilly**
5. senate, cabinet, **council**
6. here, everywhere, **there**
7. dime, nickel, **cent**
8. squeeze, twist, **wring**
9. mailed, posted, **sent**
10. he's, she's, **they're**

Directions: Complete each comparison with a word from the box. Write the word on the line.

chili 11. The spices in this _____ are as hot as the desert.
coarse 12. The cat's tongue feels as _____ as sandpaper.
cereal 13. The milk has made this _____ as soggy as a swamp.
patience 14. The delays have everyone's _____ as thin as ice.
scent 15. The perfume's _____ is like apple blossoms in spring.
course 16. The greens on this golf _____ are as smooth as glass.
oversees 17. Patricia _____ her workers as a director does his crew.
overseas 18. His trip _____ on the cruise ship was an adventure.
counsel 19. Her _____ on what to do is as wise as an owl's.
ring 20. The _____ on her finger sparkled like a star.

Notes for Home: Your child spelled homophones—words that sound the same but have different spellings and meanings. ***Home Activity:*** Ask your child to write a sentence using the homophones *pair* and *pear.* Repeat with other pairs of homophones.

334 Spelling: Homophones

Name ______________________

Textbook/Trade Book/Magazine/Periodical

A **textbook** teaches about a particular subject matter, such as science, social studies, or math. A **trade book** is any book that is not a textbook, periodical, or reference book. A **magazine** or **periodical** is published at set intervals (weekly, monthly, quarterly, and so on). It contains news articles, opinion columns, advertisements, cartoons, reports, and other current information. To locate information in these sources, scan the table of contents, chapter titles, headings, subheadings, captions, and index. You can also locate specific magazine articles using *The Readers' Guide to Periodical Literature.*

Directions: Use the textbook, trade book, and magazine samples below to answer the questions that follow.

The Universe Around Us • **Unit 2**

Chapter 5
Lesson 2: The Planets

Vocabulary solar, Sun, planet, moon

Study Questions: How many planets are in our solar system? What are they called? What is a moon? How many of our planets have moons?

Solar means "of the Sun." Our solar system has a sun at its center, and nine planets that orbit it. (See Fig. 1.)

The **Sun** is a giant, hot star. It gives off energy in the form of visible light, invisible light (ultraviolet and infrared light), and gamma rays.

The nine **planets** in our solar system are Mercury, Venus, Earth, Mars, Jupiter, Saturn, Uranus, Neptune, and Pluto.

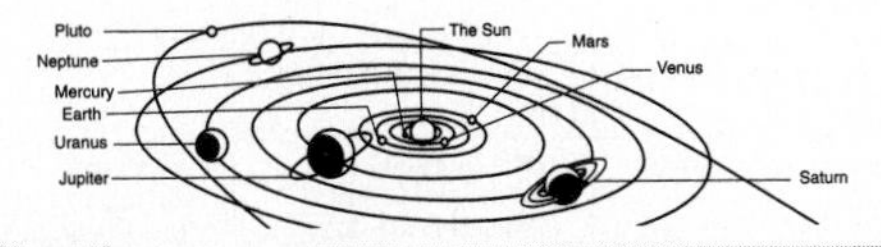

Space Exploration: Travels to the Moon and Beyond

Table of Contents

STARGAZER

- Interview with astronomer Dr. Kay Fields
- Photos of Olympus Mons—Mars's Amazing Volcano
- Keep a Stargazer Log

Which telescope is the best one for you?

Name ______________________

1. Would you most likely find the textbook page from *The Universe Around Us* in a science, social studies, or math class? Explain.
Possible answer: in a science class because it teaches about the planets

2. Why does the textbook page include study questions near the beginning of the lesson? Read the first study question and answer it.
Possible answer: Putting study questions near the beginning of the lesson helps you set a purpose for your reading and helps you prepare for a test. There are nine planets in our solar system.

3. Why do you think *solar, Sun,* and *planet* on the textbook page are set in **boldfaced** type?
Possible answer: The boldfaced words are the vocabulary words for the lesson. The boldfaced type draws your attention to the context of the word.

4. Scan the table of contents in the trade book *Space Exploration.* What is this book about? What kinds of information would you expect to find in it?
Possible answer: The book is about different space explorations in our solar system. The book probably contains facts about each exploration.

5. What was the name of the spacecraft that flew to the moon? ***Apollo 11***

6. Which chapter would give you information about the exploration of Mars? **Chapter 4**

7. Name the topic of one article in the issue of *Stargazer* shown. **Topics in the issue shown are: buying a telescope; an interview with astronomer Dr. Kay Fields; a volcano on Mars; and keeping a stargazer log.**

8. Write a question of inquiry that you might be able to use the textbook to answer.
Questions should focus on something about the planets in our solar system.

9. Write a question of inquiry that you might be able to use the trade book to answer.
Questions should focus on something about space exploration.

10. Write a question of inquiry that you might be able to use the magazine to answer.
Questions should focus on something about astronomy.

Notes for Home: Your child answered questions about a textbook, trade book, and a magazine. ***Home Activity:*** Look through one of your child's textbooks with your child. Compare the textbook to a trade book and/or a magazine. Discuss how to find information in each source.

Name ______________________

Venn Diagram

Venn diagrams should be filled out with points of comparison and contrast.

Directions: Write the name of each person that you will compare and contrast above a circle. In the intersecting part of the circles, write similarities between the people and their paths to success. Show differences by writing points about each person in the separate parts of the two circles.

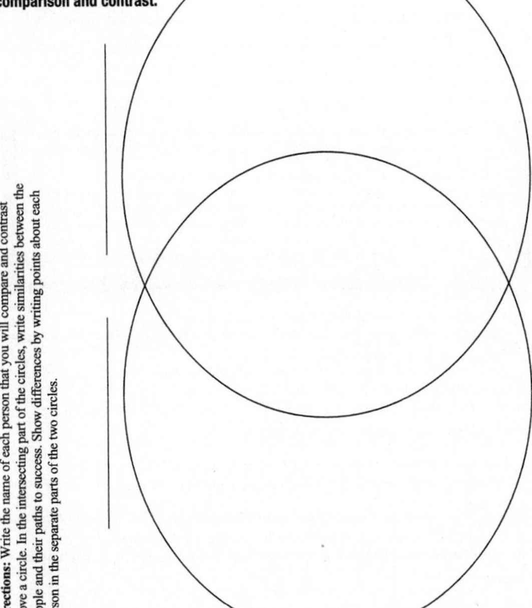

Notes for Home: Your child used this diagram to prepare information for comparing and contrasting two persons who succeeded or solved a problem. ***Home Activity:*** With your child, talk about successful people—and how they have solved problems or achieved success.

Name ______________________

Elaboration
Vivid Verbs

- One way to elaborate as you write is by replacing vague verbs with **vivid verbs** that help readers picture people and things more clearly.
- You can write more effectively by replacing verbs such as *does* and *has* with livelier verbs.

Directions: For each sentence, pick a vivid verb from the box to replace the underlined verb. Rewrite each sentence, using the new verb. Make sure each verb makes sense in the sentence.

Vivid Verbs			
attack	gobbles	marches	slurps
chase	gulps	sips	sniffs

Responses may vary. Reasonable answers are given.

1. My dog Sam and my cat Lulu do problems differently.
My dog Sam and my cat Lulu attack problems differently.

2. Sam smells at new, unfamiliar kinds of food.
Sam sniffs at new, unfamiliar kinds of food.

3. Lulu goes away from her dish if it holds a new food.
Lulu marches away from her dish if it holds a new food.

4. Sam often has food, swallowing it quickly.
Sam often gobbles food, swallowing it quickly.

5. Lulu may eat, but she never eats hungrily, as Sam does.
Lulu may eat, but she never gulps hungrily, as Sam does.

6. When Sam is thirsty, he noisily has water.
When Sam is thirsty, he noisily slurps water.

7. Lulu quietly and slowly drinks hers.
Lulu quietly and slowly sips hers.

8. Both of them, however, follow squirrels in the yard.
Both of them, however, chase squirrels in the yard.

Notes for Home: Your child improved sentences by choosing vivid verbs that express ideas more clearly. ***Home Activity:*** With your child, first make up boring sentences to tell about actions, and then replace the verbs and other words to vividly describe the same actions.

Name ______________________________

Self-Evaluation

Comparison/Contrast Essay

Students' responses should show they have given thought to the essays they have written.

Directions: Think about the final draft of your comparison/contrast essay. Then answer each question in the chart.

	Yes	No	Not sure
1. Did I express a main idea and support it?			
2. Did I include similarities and differences between the two persons?			
3. Are my points of comparison and contrast expressed clearly?			
4. Did I use transition words or phrases well?			
5. Did I proofread and edit carefully to correct errors?			

6. What is the best part of my comparison/contrast essay?

____

7. Write one thing that you would change about this essay if you had the chance to write it again.

____

Notes for Home: Your child answered questions about preparing and writing a comparison/contrast essay. ***Home Activity:*** Ask your child what writing strategies he or she learned that may help in the writing of future papers.

Practice Book 6.4, p. 151

Name ______________________________ **Spring Paint**

Drawing Conclusions

- When you **draw a conclusion,** you make a decision or form an opinion about what you read. Drawing conclusions is also known as *making inferences.*
- A conclusion should make sense and be based on facts and details in the writing, as well as your own experience.

Directions: Reread "Dumbfounded." Then complete the table. Read the three possible conclusions about Grandpa, choose the best conclusion, and then give evidence from the story to support your choice. Then do the same for the possible conclusions about Billy. Below the table, write your own conclusion about the relationship between Billy and Grandpa. **Possible answers given.**

Possible Conclusions	Best Conclusion	Evidence (Story Details and What I Know)
Grandpa is allergic to dust. Grandpa is amazed at Billy's achievement. Grandpa always becomes emotional around Billy.	1. **Grandpa is amazed at Billy's achievement.**	2. **Grandpa is "dumbfounded." He looks astonished when he sees the money.**
Billy thinks saving money is fun. Billy thinks spending money is fun. Billy is willing to work hard to get himself some dogs.	3. **Billy is willing to work hard to get himself some dogs.**	4. **Billy spent two years saving up money to buy the dogs. He picked blackberries to sell even though his feet got cut and scratched.**

5. What conclusion can you draw about the relationship between Billy and Grandpa? Why?
Billy loves and trusts Grandpa; he shares his secret with him. Grandpa is proud of Billy; he is overcome with emotion when Billy tells him about his hard work.

Notes for Home: Your child drew conclusions about characters in a story. ***Home Activity:*** Discuss with your child the conclusions drawn by letter writers in the editorial section of the local newspaper. Check to see whether the writers provide supporting evidence for their conclusions.

Practice Book 6.4, p. 152

Name ______________________________ **Spring Paint**

Vocabulary

Directions: Write the word from the box that best matches each definition. Write the word on the line.

Check the Words You Know
- __ ancestor
- __ boundary
- __ gnarled
- __ reassuring
- __ wigwam

gnarled 1. knotted; twisted
wigwam 2. a dome-shaped hut made of bark
ancestor 3. a distant relative from whom one is descended
reassuring 4. restoring to confidence
boundary 5. limit; border

Directions: Choose the word from the box that best completes each sentence. Write the word on the line to the left.

boundary 6. The _____ of our property is marked by a stone wall.
gnarled 7. Next to the stone wall is a _____ tree with branches that twist around each other.
reassuring 8. When I look at that tree, I feel calm; it is very _____.
ancestor 9. I can imagine an _____ of mine from a hundred years ago sitting under that same tree.
wigwam 10. I wonder if long ago, my family lived in a _____ near this tree and had the same view as I have now.

Write a Postcard

On a separate sheet of paper, write a postcard. Imagine you are visiting the home of one of your ancestors. Describe what you see and what you imagine life might have been like for your ancestor. Use as many vocabulary words as you can.
Students' postcards should make correct use of vocabulary words.

Notes for Home: Your child identified and used vocabulary words from "Spring Paint." ***Home Activity:*** Talk about how life was the same or different for your ancestors. Try to include the vocabulary words in your discussion.

Practice Book 6.4, p. 153

Name ______________________________ **Spring Paint**

Drawing Conclusions

- **Drawing conclusions** means making sensible decisions or forming reasonable opinions about what you read.
- A **conclusion** should be based on facts and details in the writing, as well as your own experience.

Directions: Reread the scene in "Spring Paint" in which the young man enters the lodge. Then answer the questions below. Use story details to help you draw conclusions. **Possible answers given.**

"Come in, then," said the old man. He smiled a hard smile, knowing that whoever came into his lodge would freeze.

Then a young man entered the wigwam. His face was painted with red lines and circles that looked like the sun. There was a warm smile on his face; and as he sat down on the other side of the fire, the old man felt the young man's warm breath. The old man began to sweat. He felt himself growing weaker.

"Go away," said the old man.

"No," said the young man, his voice as gentle as the sound of a summer breeze. "It is you who must leave now. Your season has ended."

"Spring Paint" from BOWMAN'S STORE by Joseph Bruchac. Copyright © 1997 by Joseph Bruchac.

1. Which season of the year does the young man represent? How do you know?
He represents spring with his warm smile, warm breath, and gentle voice. His face is painted with circles like the sun.

2. Which season does the old man represent? How do you know?
He stands for winter with his hard smile. He lives in a lodge that is freezing. He grows sweaty and weak when spring arrives.

3. Why do you think the old man tells the young man to go away?
The old man is weakened by the young man's presence. The old man doesn't want to go away.

4. The word *wigwam* suggests that the story originated in which culture or cultures?
The use of *wigwam* suggests that the story probably came from a Native American culture.

5. On a separate sheet of paper, explain how this myth relates to the grandfather's search for bloodroot flowers. **Bloodroot flowers are the earliest sign of spring, and the grandfather uses the flower to paint Joseph's face like Spring's painted face.**

Notes for Home: Your child formed conclusions based on story details. ***Home Activity:*** Discuss specific actions of real-life people. Challenge your child to draw conclusions about why these actions happened and what these actions reveal about each person.

Practice Book 6.4, p. 155

Name ____________________ Spring Paint

Selection Test

Directions: Choose the best answer to each item. Mark the letter for the answer you have chosen.

Part 1: Vocabulary

Find the answer choice that means about the same as the underlined word in each sentence.

1. Ali's ancestor built the house.
   - A. offspring, such as a child or grandchild
   - B. relative by marriage
   - Ⓒ relative from whom one is descended, such as a grandparent
   - D. person of the same generation or age group
2. They built a wigwam.
   - Ⓕ dome-shaped hut
   - G. light, narrow boat
   - H. cone-shaped tent
   - J. large rectangular dwelling
3. A river formed the boundary.
   - A. pathway; trail
   - B. landscape
   - C. property
   - Ⓓ border line; limit
4. The branches were gnarled.
   - Ⓕ rough and twisted
   - G. carved with a sharp object
   - H. old and weak
   - J. marked with dark blotches
5. Miguel was reassuring the new student.
   - A. getting to know
   - B. introducing
   - Ⓒ giving confidence to
   - D. preparing

Part 2: Comprehension

Use what you know about the selection to answer each item.

6. When the author was a boy, his special place was—
   - F. Always Winter Land.
   - Ⓖ the Woods.
   - H. a tree house.
   - J. the old man's lodge.
7. How did the author's grandfather make a living?
   - A. He hunted and gathered.
   - Ⓑ He owned a store.
   - C. He bred wolves as pets.
   - D. He worked for a neighbor.
8. What is special about the bloodroot flower?
   - F. It looks like a paintbrush.
   - G. It has an especially bright color.
   - H. It has a wonderful smell.
   - Ⓙ It is the first flower of spring.
9. The Abenaki and the Mohawks used the juice of bloodroot stems for—
   - Ⓐ repelling insects.
   - B. curing headaches.
   - C. flavoring foods.
   - D. healing wounds.
10. In the myth about Old Man Winter, what caused the bloodroot flowers to bloom?
    - F. the Great White Bear
    - G. Winter's cold fire
    - Ⓗ the coming of spring
    - J. the songs of birds

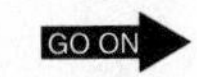

Practice Book 6.4, p. 156

Name ____________________ Spring Paint

11. The myth explains why—
    - A. some animals sleep all winter.
    - Ⓑ the seasons change.
    - C. flowers bloom.
    - D. the sun rises and sets.
12. As a child, the author was—
    - F. a good storyteller.
    - G. a bit too reckless.
    - H. a skillful painter.
    - Ⓙ a careful observer.
13. One reason the author's grandfather painted the boy's face with bloodroot juice was to—
    - A. tell an old story in a new way.
    - B. make people laugh.
    - C. mark the boy as a warrior.
    - Ⓓ celebrate spring.
14. You can tell from this selection that the author's memories of his grandfather are closely linked with his memories of—
    - F. making up games.
    - Ⓖ learning about nature.
    - H. becoming a writer.
    - J. hunting for fossils.
15. Why did the author begin this story about his childhood by retelling a myth?
    - Ⓐ The myth connects in important ways with events in his own life.
    - B. The myth was one his grandfather loved to tell.
    - C. The myth gives the reader an entertaining mix of fact and fiction.
    - D. The myth helps the reader understand the author's family.

STOP

Name ____________________ Spring Paint

Drawing Conclusions

- **Drawing conclusions** means making sensible decisions or forming reasonable opinions about what you read.
- A **conclusion** should be based on facts and details in the writing, as well as your own experience.

Directions: Read the story below.

"Now I'll teach you how to make my sweet potato pie, just like my grandma taught me," said Nana. "Remember, canned filling and store-bought pie crust just won't do. Why, we've been baking these pies for six generations!"

Keesha knew Nana's pie-baking story by heart. The family recipe dated back to the days when her ancestors had grown the sweet potatoes themselves. Today Keesha was learning how to make the crisp crust and tasty filling. She smiled, thinking about the heavenly cinnamon aroma soon to fill the kitchen. One day she'd pass the recipe on to her grandchildren. She thought it would be a tasty way to honor family traditions.

Directions: Complete the table. Write evidence to support conclusions given or draw conclusions from the given evidence. **Possible answers given.**

Evidence (Story Details and Personal Knowledge)	Conclusion
Nana will not use canned filling or store-bought pie crust.	1. **Nana takes pride in baking pies from scratch.**
2. **Nana wants to teach Keesha how to bake pie just the way she was taught.**	Nana is proud to pass on a family tradition.
3. **Keesha knows the story by heart.**	Nana must have told the pie-making story many times over the years.
A heavenly cinnamon aroma would soon fill the kitchen.	4. **Cinnamon must be one of the pie's ingredients.**
Keesha plans to pass the tradition on to her grandchildren.	5. **Keesha takes pride in her family traditions.**

Notes for Home: Your child used story details to draw conclusions. *Home Activity:* Do some "people watching" during the next family gathering. Discuss possible conclusions to be drawn about people's feelings from their facial expressions and body language.

Practice Book 6.4, p. 157

Name ____________________ Spring Paint

Author's Viewpoint

REVIEW

Directions: Read the passage. Then read each question about the passage. Choose the best answer to each question. Mark the letter for the answer you have chosen.

Save That Green!!

Dear Editor,

What will be built on the last green area in the center of town? Will it be an unhealthy fast-food spot or another parking lot? We don't need those! There are two diners within a few blocks of the area, and people usually don't drive into the town center. Everyone knows there are always plenty of places to park on Mattingly Avenue and on Ruth Street.

What we need is a park to protect the gnarled old oak tree growing there. Everyone knows the tree I mean, the one with the trunk that's too big to put your arms around! That tree has been there for more than 100 years. Children climb it and use it as a lookout when they play pirates. Cows used to graze in its shade. Many a pair of sweethearts met underneath its leafy branches.

The old oak tree has its small place in history too. The great American writer Mark Twain once rested under it! He told the story in a letter. His train was late and he strolled into the town. Tired from his long day's journey, he stretched out in the shade of the oak and took a nap.

That old tree and this town both need a cool, peaceful park, not another parking lot. Let's save the green and tree!

Signed,
Theresa Ver

1. The main purpose of this article is to—
   - A. entertain.
   - Ⓑ persuade.
   - C. explain.
   - D. express.
2. Which of the following is a statement of fact that the author uses to support her argument?
   - F. A parking lot will be built on the lot.
   - G. The town does not need another park.
   - Ⓗ Mark Twain once rested under the tree.
   - J. Fast-food shops are unnecessary.
3. The author hopes readers will agree that—
   - Ⓐ the oak tree must be saved.
   - B. the town needs more parking.
   - C. Mark Twain was a great writer.
   - D. cows should be allowed to graze in the center of town again.
4. Words used to influence the reader include—
   - F. pirates, cows
   - G. trunk, branches
   - H. train, nap
   - Ⓙ unhealthy, peaceful
5. The author believes that—
   - A. Mark Twain deserves a monument.
   - Ⓑ a park would be the best use of the space around the tree.
   - C. nothing more must be built in town.
   - D. oak trees are the best trees.

Notes for Home: Your child identified the author's viewpoint in a letter to the editor. *Home Activity:* Discuss with your child an author's viewpoint in individual letters to editors from the local newspaper.

Name ______________________ Spring Paint

Writing Across Texts

Directions: How are the theme, story line, and characters in the Native American legend described in "Spring Paint" like those in "Demeter's Daughter"? Complete the following table to record your ideas. **Possible answers given.**

Comparing "Spring Paint" to "Demeter's Daughter"
One Way the Themes Are Alike 1. **Both stories explain a change of seasons.**
Two Ways the Characters Are Alike 2. **In both stories, characters caused the earth to get cold.** 3. **In both stories, characters caused the earth to become sunny and warm.**
Two Ways the Story Lines Are Alike 4. **Winter is associated with evil; spring with good.** 5. **Both the old man and Pluto used trickery to try to get their way.**

Write a Comparison

On a separate sheet of paper, write a comparison paragraph to explain how "Spring Paint" is like "Demeter's Daughter." **Paragraphs will vary. Check that students' paragraphs contain accurate similarities.**

Notes for Home: Your child compared legends from two different cultures. ***Home Activity:*** Together, find and read aloud a folk tale, myth, or legend from your family's ancestral culture. Discuss the story and how it shares information about the culture from which it came.

Grammar Practice Book 6.4, p. 76

Name ______________________ Spring Paint

Grammar: Complete Subjects

REVIEW

Directions: Underline the complete subject in each sentence.

1. The Abenaki people grew much of their own food.
2. One very important crop for their diet was corn.
3. A favorite Abenaki myth tells of the creation of this basic food.
4. A lonely man meets a mysterious woman one day.
5. Her long, flowing hair is remarkably fair and silky.
6. This lovely creature asks the man to follow her instructions carefully.
7. He first sets fire to a field.
8. The obedient man then pulls the woman gently over the ground by her long hair.
9. Her fair, silken hair will then reappear to him each year in the form of corn silks.
10. The gift of golden corn remains with the man and his people forever after.

Directions: Use each word as part of the complete subject in a sentence of your own. Your complete subject should have at least three words. **Possible answers given.**

11. corn
Fresh, golden corn is one of my favorite foods.

12. myths
Many interesting myths are included in this book.

13. hair
Her short, curly hair makes her look very young.

14. crops
Several different crops are planted in that field each year.

15. water
Cool, clear water flowed from the mountain stream.

Notes for Home: Your child identified and wrote sentences with complete subjects—the part that tells whom or what the sentence is about. ***Home Activity:*** Look through a newspaper with your child. Identify the complete subjects of some sentences.

Grammar Practice Book 6.4, p. 77

Name ______________________ Spring Paint

Grammar: Adjectives

Adjectives modify, or tell more about, nouns or pronouns. Adjectives can tell what kind, which one, how many, or how much.

red sky (what kind)   this village (which one)   two miles (how many)

Most adjectives come before the nouns they modify. However, **predicate adjectives** follow linking verbs and modify a noun or pronoun in the subject.

Grandmother is very wise. She is also kind.

An adjective formed from a proper noun is called a **proper adjective.** Proper adjectives are capitalized.

European village   South African music

Directions: Underline each adjective. Circle the noun it modifies.

1. Toni visited Grandmother's old village.
2. She saw ancient houses and uneven streets.
3. Greek villages seemed pleasant to her.
4. Young and old relatives crowded around her.
5. Toni's American clothes interested them.

Directions: Add adjectives to complete each sentence. Use the clues in ( ) to help. Write each adjective on the matching numbered line to the right. **Possible answers given.**

6. _____ (how many) huge trees hung over the 7. _____ (what kind) gate. From the gate, a 8. _____ (what kind) path led to my uncle's 9. _____ (what kind) garden. The garden had 10. _____ (how many) different kinds of plants. 11. _____ (which ones) plants all looked very 12. _____ (what kind). I noticed that 13. _____ (how many) plants had grown remarkably tall. Uncle Jim promised to teach me to raise plants as 14. _____ (what kind) as his. I know I can learn 15. _____ (which one) skill from my capable uncle.

6. **Two**
7. **wooden**
8. **winding**
9. **flower**
10. **several**
11. **These**
12. **healthy**
13. **several**
14. **fine**
15. **that**

Notes for Home: Your child identified and used adjectives, words that describe nouns and pronouns. ***Home Activity:*** Challenge your child to use as many adjectives as he or she can in describing someone or something. See if you can guess whom or what your child is describing.

Grammar Practice Book 6.4, p. 78

Name ______________________ Spring Paint

Grammar: Adjectives

Directions: Underline the adjectives in each sentence. Circle the noun each adjective modifies.

1. The Acoma people occupy an ancient pueblo on a mesa in the Southwest.
2. A mesa is flat at the top.
3. The Acoma still keep the old way of life.
4. They speak the first language of their ancestors.
5. They make beautiful pottery.

Directions: Choose an adjective from the box to complete each sentence. Write the adjective on the line to the left.

steep	young	traditional	hard	full
soft	high	Santa Fe	free	sagebrush

young 6. The _____ children learn how to find clay in nearby canyons.

soft 7. They knead the stiff clay, and it becomes _____ enough to shape.

traditional 8. The painted decorations for the pots are _____ designs that the children learned from their parents.

hard 9. Next, the children fire the painted pots, and the clay becomes _____.

Santa Fe 10. Then the Acoma sell the pots at a _____ market.

Write Instructions

Think about something a family member taught you how to do. You might have learned how to grow a garden, make pottery, or cook a traditional dish. Write a simple set of instructions that a friend could follow to make the same item. Use adjectives in your writing. **Students' instructions should include adjectives to describe the finished product.**

Notes for Home: Your child identified and used adjectives, including proper adjectives. ***Home Activity:*** Challenge your child to name something that you describe using proper adjectives: *an American city, an Italian dish,* for example.

Grammar Practice Book 6.4, p. 79

Name ______________________

Spring Paint

RETEACHING

Grammar: Adjectives

Underline each adjective in the sentences.

1. We chose bright material for our new curtains.
2. I didn't want this day to end.
3. Toloma added six kiwis to her basket.
4. Rory the dog is very gentle.
5. We decided to try the Spanish rice.

Adjectives tell more about persons, places, or things that nouns name. Adjectives tell what kind, which one, or how many. Often adjectives appear before the nouns they tell more about. When an adjective appears in the predicate of the sentence, it follows a linking verb and is called a **predicate adjective.** A **proper adjective** is an adjective formed from a proper noun.

Directions: Underline each adjective. Then draw an arrow from each adjective to the noun it tells more about. Hint: There may be more than one adjective modifying the same noun.

1. This mountain had many glaciers.
2. Kim is a brave woman and a skillful climber.
3. She is strong too.
4. In the morning, she put on Norwegian athletic shoes.
5. The sky was pink at the start of the steep climb.
6. The crisp air chilled her.
7. Finally a red sun rose.
8. Kim saw purple flowers and blue dragonflies.
9. These lovely sights refreshed her.
10. Kim climbed over three huge boulders.
11. She rested beside a clear stream.
12. The icy water tasted sweet.

Notes for Home: Your child identified adjectives in sentences and the nouns that they tell about. ***Home Activity:*** Discuss with your child an important event at school. Encourage your child to use adjectives in the discussion.

Grammar Practice Book 6.4, p. 80

Name ______________________

Spring Paint

Grammar: Adjectives

Directions: Choose an adjective to sensibly complete each sentence. Write the adjective on the line. **Possible answers given.**

1. **Last** week, my parents decided what our summer project would be.
2. They had been talking about it for **three** weeks, and my sister and I had been guessing what our parents would choose.
3. Shaunita thought we would have to paint the **ugly** garage because the paint was peeling off.
4. Then she mentioned that we might have to wash the **French** doors in the dining room.
5. I was almost positive we would have to clean out the garage because it hadn't been cleaned in years, and it was **messy**.
6. My brother guessed we would have to plant new bushes and shrubs in the **back** yard.
7. At dinner one night, Mom and Dad announced their **exciting** plan.
8. With help, we were going to refinish the **old** deck behind our house.
9. My brother and sister and I would be in charge of choosing **pretty** flowers and paint for the flower boxes and paint for the railings.
10. I chose **red** flowers and **yellow** and **purple** paint.
11. My brother didn't like that idea. He thought **those** colors wouldn't match the house.
12. We finally agreed on **one** color for both the flower boxes and the railings.

Directions: Circle each adjective. Underline the noun each adjective tells more about.

13. This summer we began our massive project.
14. My entire family put on their old, dirty clothes.
15. Then we called our helpful neighbors and held a meeting.
16. Mom explained the new project to all seven people.
17. She showed the neighbors the blue paint.
18. Then everyone began this exciting job.
19. We had to let the paint dry on the boxes before we could plant the English flowers.
20. It took us two weeks, but we finished the beautiful deck!

Notes for Home: Your child identified and wrote adjectives in sentences. ***Home Activity:*** Together, listen to a favorite song or instrumental piece. Talk about the music together. Encourage your child to use descriptive adjectives.

Practice Book 6.4, p. 158

Name ______________________

Spring Paint

Word Study: Inflected Endings: *-ed, -ing*

Directions: Two endings that are commonly added to verbs are **-ed** and **-ing.** Read the paragraph below. Circle the words with **-ed** and **-ing** endings. Then write the base word for each circled word.

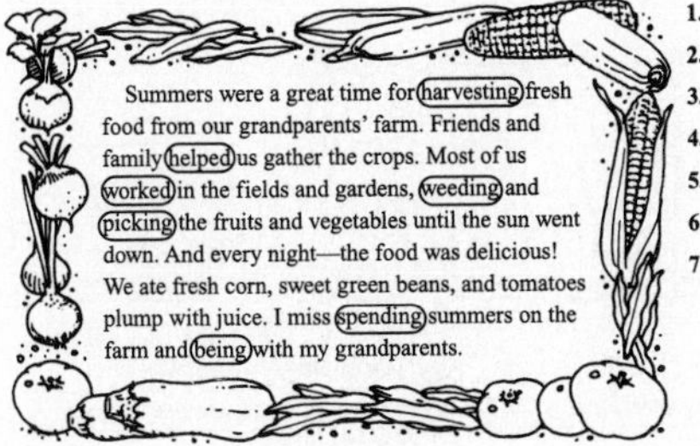

Summers were a great time for harvesting fresh food from our grandparents' farm. Friends and family helped us gather the crops. Most of us worked in the fields and gardens, weeding and picking the fruits and vegetables until the sun went down. And every night—the food was delicious! We ate fresh corn, sweet green beans, and tomatoes plump with juice. I miss spending summers on the farm and being with my grandparents.

1. **harvest**
2. **help**
3. **work**
4. **weed**
5. **pick**
6. **spend**
7. **be**

Directions: Add **-ed** and **-ing** to each base word. Write the new word on the line.

Base Word	Add -ed	Add -ing
flicker	8. **flickered**	9. **flickering**
follow	10. **followed**	11. **following**
search	12. **searched**	13. **searching**
watch	14. **watched**	15. **watching**
surround	16. **surrounded**	17. **surrounding**
return	18. **returned**	19. **returning**
invent	20. **invented**	21. **inventing**
wander	22. **wandered**	23. **wandering**
stroll	24. **strolled**	25. **strolling**

Notes for Home: Your child identified and wrote words ending in *-ed* and *-ing.* ***Home Activity:*** Help your child think of other words with these endings. Make a table with two columns, one for *-ed* words and one for *-ing* words. Have your child write the words in the correct columns.

Spelling Workbook 6.4, p. 61

Name ______________________

Spring Paint

Spelling: Using Just Enough Letters

Pretest Directions: Fold back the page along the dotted line. On the blanks, write the spelling words as they are dictated. When you have finished the test, unfold the page and check your words.

1. **similar**	1. They have **similar** appearances.
2. **doesn't**	2. Why **doesn't** it snow in July?
3. **experience**	3. We often learn by **experience**.
4. **forward**	4. **Forward**, march!
5. **exactly**	5. That is **exactly** what I mean.
6. **partner**	6. She is my dancing **partner**.
7. **drawer**	7. Put your socks in the **drawer**.
8. **expensive**	8. Lobster is an **expensive** dish.
9. **develop**	9. Plants **develop** from seeds.
10. **familiar**	10. His face is **familiar**.
11. **pigeon**	11. A **pigeon** landed on the statue.
12. **tickling**	12. Dust is **tickling** my nose.
13. **penalty**	13. Cheaters face a harsh **penalty**.
14. **frustrated**	14. Rain **frustrated** our picnic plans.
15. **athletic**	15. She is very **athletic**.
16. **celebration**	16. This calls for a **celebration**.
17. **circling**	17. Birds were **circling** overhead.
18. **helicopter**	18. We rode in a **helicopter**.
19. **trembling**	19. He is **trembling** from the cold.
20. **sparkling**	20. The stars are **sparkling** tonight.

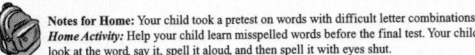

Notes for Home: Your child took a pretest on words with difficult letter combinations. ***Home Activity:*** Help your child learn misspelled words before the final test. Your child should look at the word, say it, spell it aloud, and then spell it with eyes shut.

Spelling Workbook 6.4, p. 62

Name ____________________ **Spring Paint**

Spelling: Using Just Enough Letters

Word List				
similar	exactly	develop	penalty	circling
doesn't	partner	familiar	frustrated	helicopter
experience	drawer	pigeon	athletic	trembling
forward	expensive	tickling	celebration	sparkling

Directions: Choose the words from the box that have three or four syllables. Write each word in the correct column. **Order may vary.**

Words with Three Syllables

1. **similar**
2. **exactly**
3. **expensive**
4. **develop**
5. **familiar**
6. **penalty**
7. **frustrated**
8. **athletic**

Words with Four Syllables

9. **experience**
10. **celebration**
11. **helicopter**

Directions: Choose the word from the box that best matches each clue. Write the word on the line.

forward 12. I am the opposite of *backward.*

tickling 13. I am the feeling you get in your nose when you are surrounded by dusty air or fuzzy sweaters.

doesn't 14. I am a contraction of the words *does* and *not.*

partner 15. I am a person you work with or dance with.

pigeon 16. I am a gray, black, and white city bird that coos.

drawer 17. I am the part of a desk or chest in which you keep things.

trembling 18. I am similar in meaning to *shaking.*

sparkling 19. I am dazzling and shining in the light.

circling 20. I am an action that will cause you to get dizzy if you do it too often or too fast.

Notes for Home: Your child spelled words that are often misspelled by adding too many letters. ***Home Activity:*** Write each spelling word on a card. Show your child a card for ten seconds. Have your child pronounce the word carefully, picture how it looks, and spell it aloud.

Spelling Workbook 6.4, p. 63

Name ____________________ **Spring Paint**

Spelling: Using Just Enough Letters

Directions: Proofread this description of the Abenaki, a Native American people. Find six spelling mistakes. Use the proofreading marks to correct each mistake.

- ≡ Make a capital.
- / Make a small letter.
- ∧ Add something.
- Take out something.
- ⊙ Add a period.
- ¶ Begin a new paragraph.

The Abenaki lived in the Northeast, in what is now Vermont and Connecticut. Their lives followed a familare seasonal pattern. They stalked game, raised and harvested crops, fished, and hunted waterfowl and pigeon. Close-knit family groups moved often, so they had to devellop movable homes called *wigwams.* While their experientce was gained through hard living, they had fun too. When the Abenaki held a feast or cellebration, the athtletic men played a game called *lacrosse.* In winter the children played in the sparkeling snow.

Spelling Tip

Pronouncing a word correctly and picturing how it looks can help you avoid writing too many letters. Check the description to make sure the words from the box are spelled correctly.

Word List	
similar	pigeon
doesn't	tickling
experience	penalty
forward	frustrated
exactly	athletic
partner	celebration
drawer	circling
expensive	helicopter
develop	trembling
familiar	sparkling

Write a Description

On a separate sheet of paper, write a description of your family. Tell about the house you live in, what you do for work and for fun, and what happens when you have a family celebration. Try to use at least five of your spelling words. **Answers will vary, but each description should include at least five spelling words.**

Notes for Home: Your child spelled words that are often misspelled by adding too many letters. ***Home Activity:*** Copy the list of spelling words, but misspell some of them by adding extra letters. Give your child the list and have him or her find and correct the misspelled words.

Spelling Workbook 6.4, p. 64

Name ____________________ **Spring Paint**

Spelling: Using Just Enough Letters REVIEW

Directions: Choose the word from the box that best fits each definition. Write the word on the line.

pigeon 1. dove-like city bird

similar 2. alike

penalty 3. punishment

familiar 4. well-known

helicopter 5. small aircraft with a propeller

trembling 6. shaking; quaking

forward 7. ahead

experience 8. something you have done or lived through

circling 9. going around

develop 10. grow and change

Word List	
similar	pigeon
doesn't	tickling
experience	penalty
forward	frustrated
exactly	athletic
partner	celebration
drawer	circling
expensive	helicopter
develop	trembling
familiar	sparkling

Directions: Choose the word from the box that is the correct form of each word in ( ) to complete each sentence. Write the word on the matching numbered line to the right.

"It **11.** (do not) seem to me that they'll want an **12.** (expense) gift," said Mom. "A family treasure would mean a lot more to your grandparents, since this is their fiftieth anniversary **13.** (celebrate)." We were soon **14.** (frustrate) from wondering **15.** (exact) what would be the ideal gift. Then we looked in the attic, sneezing as its dusty air began **16.** (tickle) our noses. In a **17.** (draw) of the big chest, Mom found an old photo of an **18.** (athlete) Gramps and pretty young Grammie with her **19.** (sparkle) smile. The picture showed each **20.** (part) ready to start a fifty-year journey together. It was perfect.

11. **doesn't**
12. **expensive**
13. **celebration**
14. **frustrated**
15. **exactly**
16. **tickling**
17. **drawer**
18. **athletic**
19. **sparkling**
20. **partner**

Notes for Home: Your child spelled words that are often misspelled by adding too many letters. ***Home Activity:*** Take turns with your child using each spelling word in a sentence. Then challenge each other to try to use two or more words in each sentence.

Practice Book 6.4, p. 159

Name ____________________ **Spring Paint**

The *Readers' Guide to Periodical Literature*

The *Readers' Guide to Periodical Literature* is a set of books that alphabetically lists, by author and subject, the articles that are published in periodicals.

Directions: Look at the set of *Readers' Guides.* Then answer the questions that follow.

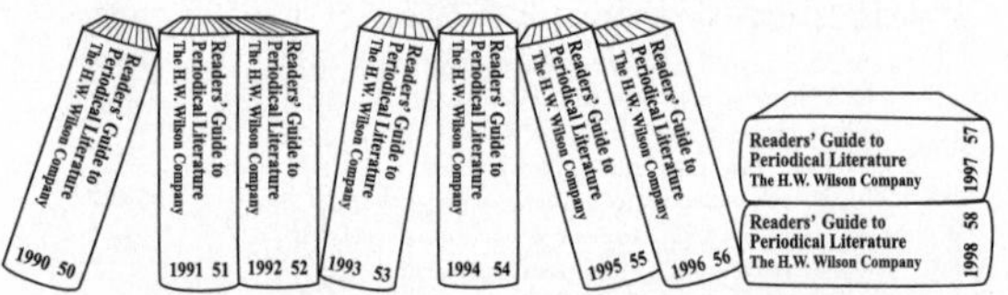

Possible answers given.

1. How are the guides organized? How can you tell? **The guides are arranged in chronological order by year. Each guide shows the year and the volume number.**

2. Suppose you wanted to know more about a large Navaho Pow Wow that took place in the summer of 1997. Which volume would you use to see whether any articles had been written about this gathering? Explain.
You would look in volume 57, since this volume would include articles published in 1997.

3. Suppose you are writing about the lives and customs of Native Americans living on reservations today. Would it be more helpful to search recent volumes of the *Readers' Guide* or look in an encyclopedia? Explain.
The *Readers' Guide* would probably give you references for articles with more up-to-date and detailed information than an encyclopedia.

4. Suppose you are writing about Native American stories by Joseph Bruchac. Why might you have to check several volumes to find an article about or by Joseph Bruchac?
Articles about or by Joseph Bruchac could have been published in different years so you might find entries listed in more than one volume.

5. Some libraries are now using computer databases to store information about articles published in periodicals. Why might a computer database be easier to use than the *Readers' Guide?* Explain.
A computer database would let you do one search to find information about articles published over many years. You would have to search through several volumes of the *Readers' Guide* to find the same information.

Practice Book 6.4, p. 160

Name ______________________ **Spring Paint**

Entries in the *Readers' Guide to Periodical Literature* are arranged alphabetically by subject or author. Each entry provides the title of the article, author of the article, title of the publication in which the article appears, volume number of the periodical, pages of the article, and other information. Information about abbreviations used in entries can be found at the front of each volume.

Directions: Scan these entries from the *Readers' Guide*. Then answer the questions that follow.

INDIANS OF NORTH AMERICA—

Art

Hidden art treasures of the Indian missions. S. Lowe. il *Arizona Highways* v72 p12-17 D '96
The impact of tradition on Native American art. B. Wright. il *Arizona Highways* v72 p12-19 O '96
Objects of power. A. Wardwell. il Natural History v106 p42-3 Mr '97
Representing Indians [treatment of Indian art in museums] R.White. il *The New Republic* v216 p28-34 Ap 21 '97

Collectors and collecting

Black Hawk's drawing of a vision. G. T. Vincent and J. C. Berlo.il *The Magazine Antiques* v151 p200-1 Ja '97

Exhibitions

American expressions [Native American jewelry and metalwork: contemporary expressions at the Institute of American Indian Arts Museum, Santa Fe] L. Coulter. *American Craft* v57 p72-7 O/N '97
American Indian art [Gifts of the spirit: works by the nineteenth century and contemporary Native American artists at the Peabody Essex Museum] A. E. Ledes. il *The Magazine Antiques* v150 p760 D '96
Nineteenth-century Plains Indian drawings. J. C. Berlo. bibl f il *The Magazine Antiques* v150 p686-95 N '96

Arts and crafts

Buying Indian arts and crafts. B. Wright. il *Arizona Highways* v72 p18-21 N '96
Last of the old-time traders [trading posts in Arizona] S. Negri. il *Arizona Highways* v73 p4-9 Ja '97
The legend of Hubbell Trading Post. L. E. Jacka. il *Arizona Highways* v73 p10-15 Ja '97

6. What main subject and two subtopics are shown? **main subject: Indians of North America; subtopics: Art, Arts and Crafts**

7. Name the magazine, volume, page numbers, and year that you could find an article about the impact, or effect, of tradition on Native American art.
Arizona Highways, volume 72, pages 12–19, October 1996

8. In which article would you find drawings by the Plains Indians of the nineteenth century?
"Nineteenth-Century Plains Indian Drawings"

9. Which magazine would give you more information about buying Native American arts and crafts? Name the magazine title, volume, month, and year.
Arizona Highways, volume 72, November 1996

10. How is using the *Readers' Guide to Periodical Literature* similar to using an index at the back of a textbook or trade book? How is it different?
Possible answer: Both contain subject entries arranged alphabetically. The _Readers' Guide_ lists articles published in many different periodicals. An index lists information only about the book in which it appears.

Notes for Home: Your child answered questions about using the *Readers' Guide to Periodical Literature. Home Activity:* With your child, look through some magazines. Ask your child to find information such as the volume number, date of publication, and the titles and authors of articles.

Practice Book 6.4, p. 161

Name ______________________ **A Brother's Promise**

Plot

- The **plot** of a story is the series of important events from the story's beginning, middle, and end. The plot revolves around a central problem, or **conflict.**
- In most stories, the conflict is introduced in the beginning. As the story progresses, the conflict leads to other problems. Gradually, the **rising action** builds to a high point, or climax. The **climax** is the highest point of interest in the story. Following the climax, there is **resolution** of the conflict and the action winds down.

Directions: Reread "The Sailor and the Fly." Then complete the plot structure map by identifying each element of the plot. One has been done for you. **Possible answers given.**

Conflict (Central Problem)
1. **The sailor and fly are drowning.**

Rising Action (Other Problems)
2. **The sailor can't see the fisherman.**
3. **The fisherman does not understand the fly.**

The fisherman nearly crashes into the sailor.

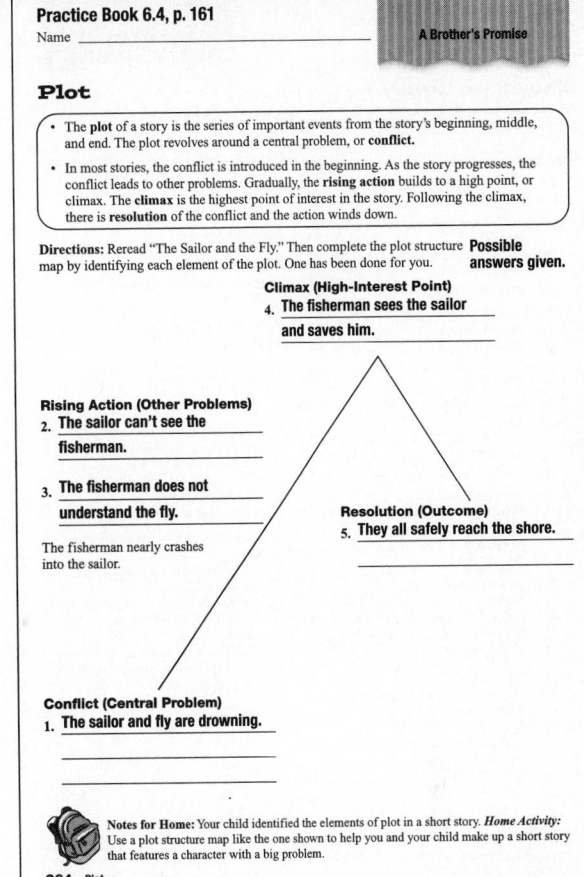

Climax (High-Interest Point)
4. **The fisherman sees the sailor and saves him.**

Resolution (Outcome)
5. **They all safely reach the shore.**

Notes for Home: Your child identified the elements of plot in a short story. ***Home Activity:*** Use a plot structure map like the one shown to help you and your child make up a short story that features a character with a big problem.

Practice Book 6.4, p. 162

Name ______________________ **A Brother's Promise**

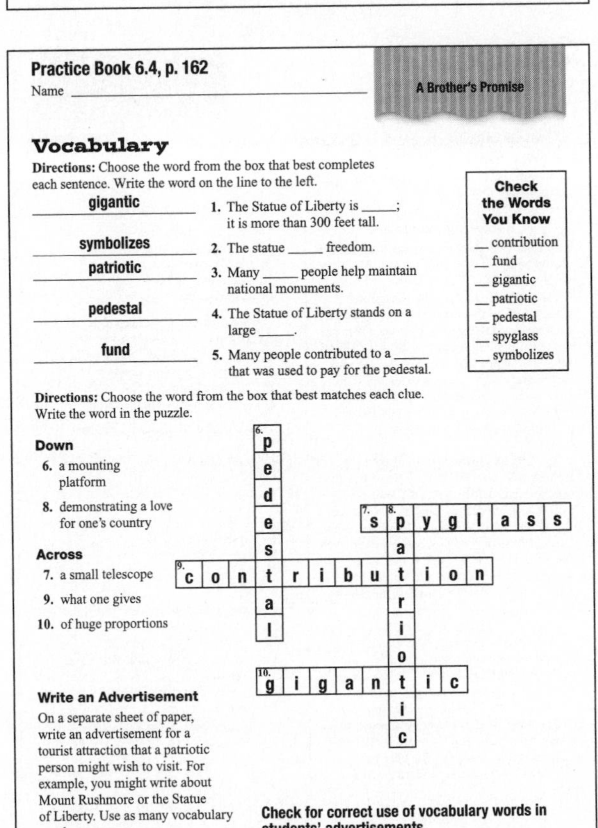

Vocabulary

Directions: Choose the word from the box that best completes each sentence. Write the word on the line to the left.

Check the Words You Know
__ contribution
__ fund
__ gigantic
__ patriotic
__ pedestal
__ spyglass
__ symbolizes

gigantic 1. The Statue of Liberty is _____; it is more than 300 feet tall.

symbolizes 2. The statue _____ freedom.

patriotic 3. Many _____ people help maintain national monuments.

pedestal 4. The Statue of Liberty stands on a large _____.

fund 5. Many people contributed to a _____ that was used to pay for the pedestal.

Directions: Choose the word from the box that best matches each clue. Write the word in the puzzle.

Down
6. a mounting platform
8. demonstrating a love for one's country

Across
7. a small telescope
9. what one gives
10. of huge proportions

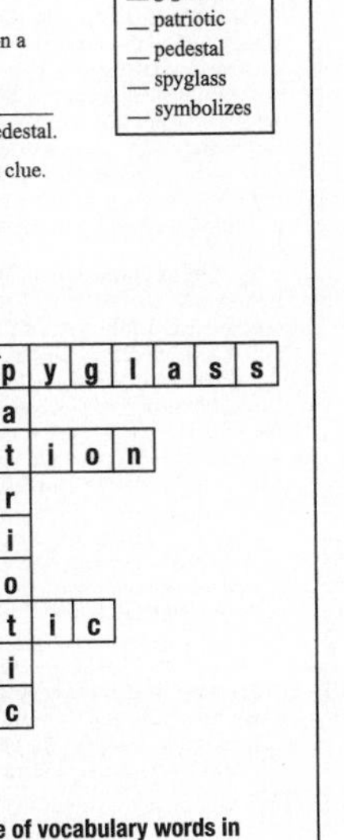

Write an Advertisement

On a separate sheet of paper, write an advertisement for a tourist attraction that a patriotic person might wish to visit. For example, you might write about Mount Rushmore or the Statue of Liberty. Use as many vocabulary words as you can.

Check for correct use of vocabulary words in students' advertisements.

Notes for Home: Your child identified and used vocabulary words from "A Brother's Promise." ***Home Activity:*** Work with your child to write a paragraph about celebrating a national holiday. Encourage your child to use as many of the listed vocabulary words as possible.

Practice Book 6.4, p. 163

Name ______________________ **A Brother's Promise**

Plot

- A story's **plot** is the series of important events from the story's beginning, middle, and end.
- A plot revolves around a central problem, or conflict. Other elements of plot include the background, the rising action, the climax, and the resolution, or outcome.

Directions: Reread Joseph Pulitzer's speech about Annie from "A Brother's Promise." Then answer the questions below. Think about which story details are important to the plot. **Possible answers given.**

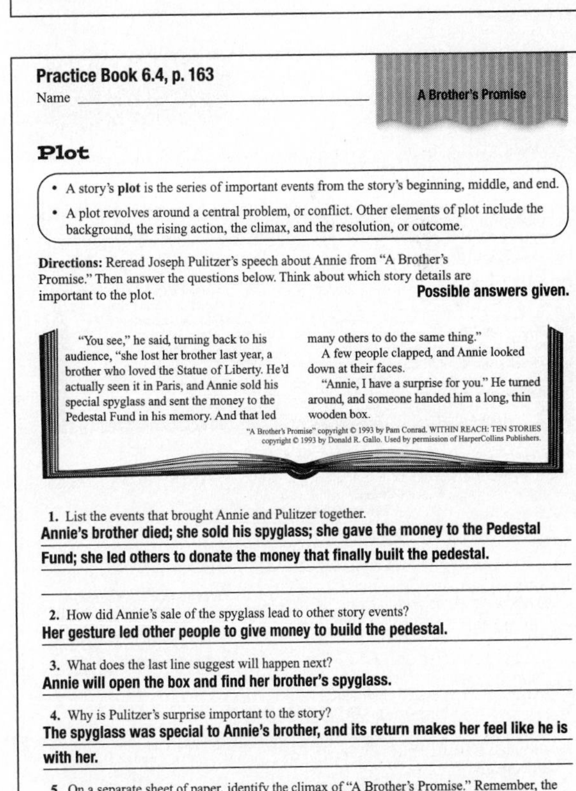

"You see," he said, turning back to his audience, "she lost her brother last year, a brother who loved the Statue of Liberty. He'd actually seen it in Paris, and Annie sold his special spyglass and sent the money to the Pedestal Fund in his memory. And that led many others to do the same thing."

A few people clapped, and Annie looked down at their faces.

"Annie, I have a surprise for you." He turned around, and someone handed him a long, thin wooden box.

1. List the events that brought Annie and Pulitzer together.
Annie's brother died; she sold his spyglass; she gave the money to the Pedestal Fund; she led others to donate the money that finally built the pedestal.

2. How did Annie's sale of the spyglass lead to other story events?
Her gesture led other people to give money to build the pedestal.

3. What does the last line suggest will happen next?
Annie will open the box and find her brother's spyglass.

4. Why is Pulitzer's surprise important to the story?
The spyglass was special to Annie's brother, and its return makes her feel like he is with her.

5. On a separate sheet of paper, identify the climax of "A Brother's Promise." Remember, the climax is the "high point" of the story where the story's problem is directly confronted.
The climax occurs when Annie enters the torch of the finished statue. This is the point where she deals with her promise to her brother and his death.

Notes for Home: Your child read a passage and identified various parts of its plot. ***Home Activity:*** Encourage your child to draw a diagram that shows the basic plot of an episode of a recent television show.

Practice Book 6.4, p. 165

Name ____________________

A Brother's Promise

Selection Test

Directions: Choose the best answer to each item. Mark the letter for the answer you have chosen.

Part 1: Vocabulary

Find the answer choice that means about the same as the underlined word in each sentence.

1. He placed it on a pedestal.
   A. wide post
   B. table with hinged sides
   C. mound of earth
   (D) base on which something stands
2. She looked into the spyglass.
   F. magnifying glass
   (G) small telescope
   H. round window
   J. small mirror
3. The statue is gigantic.
   (A) huge
   B. strange
   C. expensive
   D. lovely
4. He made a contribution.
   F. statement against something
   G. loud noise or disturbance
   H. description of something
   (J) gift of money or help
5. They decided to set up a fund.
   A. work done for the common good
   B. community organization
   (C) money set aside for a special purpose
   D. small company
6. We sang patriotic songs.
   (F) showing love of one's country
   G. expressing strong emotion
   H. of or about soldiers
   J. originating and handed down among the common people
7. Do you know what the statue symbolizes?
   A. celebrates
   B. attracts
   (C) stands for
   D. includes

Part 2: Comprehension

Use what you know about the story to answer each item.

8. Where did Geoffrey see the Statue of Liberty?
   F. Madison Square
   (G) Paris
   H. New York Harbor
   J. Philadelphia
9. Why was there a problem in bringing the Statue of Liberty to America?
   A. It was too heavy to move.
   B. The body was not finished.
   C. The statue was a hoax.
   (D) There was no base to put it on.
10. After Geoffrey died, Annie's main goal was to—
    F. take Geoffrey's spyglass into the Statue of Liberty.
    (G) make sure the Statue of Liberty was placed in New York Harbor.
    H. help others appreciate how wonderful the Statue of Liberty was.
    J. go to France to see where the Statue of Liberty was made.

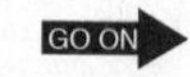

Practice Book 6.4, p. 166

Name ____________________

A Brother's Promise

11. Why did Annie pawn the spyglass?
    A. She hoped someone just like Geoffrey would buy it.
    B. She did not like it.
    (C) She wanted to give money to the pedestal fund.
    D. It brought back sad memories.
12. Mr. Pulitzer helped persuade many people to give money for the pedestal by—
    F. buying Geoffrey's spyglass.
    (G) printing Annie's letter in the *New York World.*
    H. proving that the statue was real.
    J. giving a speech on Bedloe's Island.
13. The climax of the story occurs when—
    A. Annie writes to Mr. Pulitzer.
    B. Geoffrey and Annie climb up into the torch together.
    C. Geoffrey is killed in an accident.
    (D) Annie climbs to the top of the statue with Geoffrey's spyglass.
14. When Annie speaks to Geoffrey from the top of the Statue of Liberty, it—
    (F) helps the reader know what Annie sees and feels.
    G. makes the reader wonder whether Geoffrey is really dead.
    H. gives the story the spooky feeling of a ghost story.
    J. ties up loose ends and solves the riddle of the plot.
15. In historical fiction, some parts of the story are based on facts. Which of these statements can you be quite sure is true?
    A. Annie is ten years younger than Geoffrey.
    (B) The Statue of Liberty was erected on Bedloe's Island in 1886.
    C. Joseph Pulitzer bought Geoffrey's spyglass from a pawnshop.
    D. Geoffrey was an art student in France.

STOP

Name ____________________

A Brother's Promise

Plot

- A story's **plot** is the series of important events from the story's beginning, middle, and end.
- A plot revolves around a central problem, or conflict. Other elements of plot include the background, the rising action, the climax, and the resolution, or outcome.

Directions: Read the story below.

Uncle Nate walked on crutches and could not climb the cemetery's hills. Leo had promised to take Uncle Nate's place, but the thought of placing flags on graves on Veterans' Day seemed creepy. He'd rather be swimming, hiking, washing dishes—not this.

Leo blocked out his thoughts, grabbed the flags, and hurried to the correct area. As he placed a flag, he stopped to read the gravestone. How interesting! This soldier had served in World War I and had died when he was only a little older than Leo!

Leo felt a lump in his throat. He straightened the flag in its holder. "I will come back every November to honor these young men," he vowed.

Directions: Complete the plot map below. Describe the parts of the plot from the story. The first one has been started for you. **Possible answers given.**

Background
1. Uncle Nate is on crutches, so he: **cannot walk around the cemetery with the flags.**

Conflict
2. **Leo has mixed feelings about placing flags on graves.**

Event/Rising Action
3. **Leo hurries to the correct area with the flags.**

Climax
4. **Leo reads the gravestone as he places the first flag.**

Resolution (Outcome)
5. **Leo is moved by what he finds and plans to go back every November.**

Notes for Home: Your child identified the important parts of a story's plot. ***Home Activity:*** Have your child describe the plot of a play you both have seen or a story you have both read. Make sure he or she can identify the background, conflict, rising action, climax, and resolution.

Practice Book 6.4, p. 167

Name ____________________

A Brother's Promise

Visualizing and Theme

REVIEW

Directions: Read the passage. Then read each question about the passage. Choose the best answer to each question. Mark the letter for the answer you have chosen.

A Floating Monument

First the boat dock grew smaller until only a gigantic flag could be seen, waving like an unruly child. Then the traffic jam noises of sirens and horns grew fainter as tugboats guided the *USS Constitution* to the open ocean. Salty winds cooled the excited guests and crew.

Once this old ship had proudly served her country. She was launched in 1797, and took part in many naval battles. During the War of 1812, a sailor gave her the nickname "Old Ironsides." He claimed to have seen British cannonballs bouncing off the sides of the *Constitution!*

By 1830, Old Ironsides' proud career seemed to be over. The navy declared that she was too old and no longer safe to sail. The navy planned to destroy her. But when the poet Oliver Wendell Holmes wrote a farewell poem to the great ship, people remembered her glory and wrote to the navy. They wanted to save Old Ironsides. The navy, surprised, agreed to the people's wishes. In 1833, the *Constitution* was afloat again.

Now, 200 years after her launching, she was about to travel under sail power again. A signal pierced the air. It was time. High above the deck, sailors worked lines and unfurled sails. At first nothing happened. Then sail after sail caught the wind. The ship came alive like a bird carried across the water by huge white wings. As the ship proudly sailed forth, people were once more reminded that the *USS Constitution* symbolizes the courage of a nation.

1. The flag is compared to—
   A. a huge white bird.
   B. the open ocean.
   (C) an unruly child.
   D. the bravery of a nation.
2. The words traffic jam are used to describe—
   (F) the confusing jumble of sounds.
   G. why the ship sails slowly.
   H. decks aboard the ship.
   J. crowds of boats in the harbor.
3. The nickname "Ironsides" suggests—
   A. age.
   (B) strength.
   C. beauty.
   D. grace.
4. As the ship sets sail, it is compared to—
   (F) a bird.
   G. the wind.
   H. a flag.
   J. a child.
5. One theme the passage expresses is the—
   A. courage of sailors.
   B. importance of sail power.
   C. unusual demands placed on naval vessels.
   (D) power of patriotic symbols to inspire people.

Notes for Home: Your child identified the descriptive details and the underlying meaning of a passage. ***Home Activity:*** Encourage your child to use a variety of descriptive words that convey the sights, sounds, smells, and mood of a specific place.

Name ______________________ A Brother's Promise

Writing Across Texts

Directions: Think about "A Brother's Promise" and "Symbols That Make Us Proud." Which selection was your favorite? Complete the following table to contrast the selections and give reasons why one was more appealing to you than the other. **Possible answers given.**

Favorite Selection Title
1. **"A Brother's Promise"**
Reasons I Liked It Better Than the Other Selection
2. **I like stories more than informational articles.**
3. **"A Brother's Promise" made me feel more patriotic.**
4. **I like to read about people rather than things.**
5. **I like to make pictures in my head while reading, rather than having the pictures in front of me.**

Write a Paragraph that Contrasts

Consider "A Brother's Promise" and "Symbols That Make Us Proud." On a separate sheet of paper, write a paragraph explaining which selection was your favorite to read and why. Be sure to contrast the selections as a way to share your opinions. **Paragraphs will vary. Check that students stated their opinions clearly and supported them with reasons relating to both selections.**

Notes for Home: Your child compared two reading selections and chose one as a favorite. *Home Activity:* Together, read aloud two magazine or newspaper articles about the same subject. Talk with your child about which article he or she liked more and why.

Grammar Practice Book 6.4, p. 81

Name ______________________ A Brother's Promise

Grammar: Adjectives

REVIEW

Directions: Draw a line under each adjective. Circle the noun it modifies.

1. The enormous copper statue rises over the busy harbor of New York City.
2. The colossal work was a gift to the American people from France.
3. The huge stone pedestal, however, was built with American money.
4. President Cleveland dedicated the beautiful Statue of Liberty in 1886, and it soon became a powerful symbol of freedom.
5. In former years, when new immigrants arrived by ship, the towering statue provided the first sight of America.
6. Anxious newcomers hoping for improved lives in a free country were moved to tears when they saw the mighty lady.
7. In 1924, the famous and familiar statue was declared a national monument.
8. A steep spiral staircase inside the steel framework leads to the crown.
9. From the high crown, numerous visitors have looked out at the breathtaking view.
10. "Miss Liberty" is tall and proud, and she is known to the entire world.

Directions: Complete each sentence with an article or adjective from the box that tells how many or how much. Write the word on the line.

a *or* an	many	two	no	several

many 11. Shana was one of _____ visitors to the Statue of Liberty that crisp fall day.

several 12. She had come with _____ members of her family—her parents, brother, aunt, and uncle.

no 13. They had had _____ food since breakfast, but they were too excited to eat.

two 14. They had moved to America just _____ weeks ago.

an 15. To Shana and her family, the huge statue was _____ amazing sight that they will never forget.

Notes for Home: Your child identified and used adjectives—words that describe nouns and pronouns. *Home Activity:* Write some of the adjectives on cards. Then have your child choose a card and use the adjective in a sentence.

Grammar Practice Book 6.4, p. 82

Name ______________________ A Brother's Promise

Grammar: Comparative and Superlative Adjectives

An adjective describes a person, a place, or a thing.

The **comparative form** of an adjective is used to compare two persons, places, or things. The word **than** sometimes signals this form.

These fireworks are brighter than last year's display.

The **superlative form** of an adjective is used to compare three or more persons, places, or things.

Next year's fireworks will be the brightest of all.

More and **most** are usually used in the comparative or superlative forms of adjectives.

Chili dogs are more delicious than plain hot dogs.
Dad makes the most delicious hot dogs on the grill.

Do not use **more** and **most** with adjectives ending in **-er** or **-est.**

Don't write: Mom's iced lemonade tastes more sweeter than my iced lemonade.
Write: Mom's iced lemonade tastes sweeter than my iced lemonade.

As shown below, the spelling of some adjectives changes in the comparative and superlative forms.

good, better, best	much, more, most
bad, worse, worst	little, less, least

Directions: Circle the correct form of the adjective in ( ) to complete each sentence.

1. To Clara, the Fourth of July was the (better/best) holiday of the year.
2. First, she would twirl her baton and march in the (bigger/biggest) parade in the entire state.
3. The band's uniforms were the (brighter/brightest) red she had ever seen.
4. The notes played by the flute section were (softer/softest) than those played by the trumpet section.
5. The float of the Statue of Liberty was the (larger/largest) of all.
6. Clara's family would always throw one of the (nicer/nicest) parties on the block.
7. Clara would help cook the (tastier/tastiest) hot dogs her friends had ever eaten.
8. In the evening, there would be a fireworks display with the (louder/loudest) noises ever!
9. The red starburst at the end was the (more brilliant/most brilliant) of all the fireworks.
10. Clara couldn't think of anything (better/best) than the Fourth of July.

Notes for Home: Your child identified and used comparative and superlative adjectives to compare people, places, and things. *Home Activity:* Challenge your child to think of a sentence with a comparative adjective. You, in turn, supply a sentence with a superlative adjective.

Grammar Practice Book 6.4, p. 83

Name ______________________ A Brother's Promise

Grammar: Comparative and Superlative Adjectives

Directions: Use the correct form of the adjective in ( ) to complete each sentence. Write the adjective on the line.

greatest 1. Thanksgiving is the (great) holiday.

better 2. My family gets together for a feast that's (good) than the one the Pilgrims had.

happiest 3. Mom is (happy) of all, because my brother comes home from college.

taller 4. She always says he looks (tall) than he was when he left.

loudest 5. We all laugh, but my brother laughs (loud) of all.

bigger 6. He says he couldn't have grown any (big) than he was three months ago.

good 7. We give thanks for the (good) life we have.

most delicious 8. Then we eat the (delicious) dinner of all—turkey, stuffing, potatoes, and squash.

sweeter 9. Mom's apple pie is (sweet) than her pumpkin pie.

best 10. But I think pumpkin pie is the (good) dessert of all.

most exciting 11. After dinner, we watch the (exciting) football game that we can find on TV.

more loyal 12. My mom is (loyal) to the home team than my brother.

better 13. My brother thinks the team from his college town is (good) than ours.

liveliest 14. When it comes to sports, Mom and my brother have the (lively) discussions of anyone in our family.

most enjoyable 15. Mom says it's the (enjoyable) debate she has all year long.

Write a Description

Invent a new holiday. On a separate sheet of paper, give the holiday a name and describe what it celebrates. Then explain how people will observe the day. Will they have a parade? Will they prepare a special meal? Use comparative and superlative adjectives in your description. **Check to see if students have used the appropriate adjective forms to make comparisons.**

Notes for Home: Your child wrote the comparative and superlative forms of adjectives. *Home Activity:* On small pieces of paper, write a variety of nouns. With your child, take turns choosing a noun and describing it with comparative and superlative forms of adjectives.

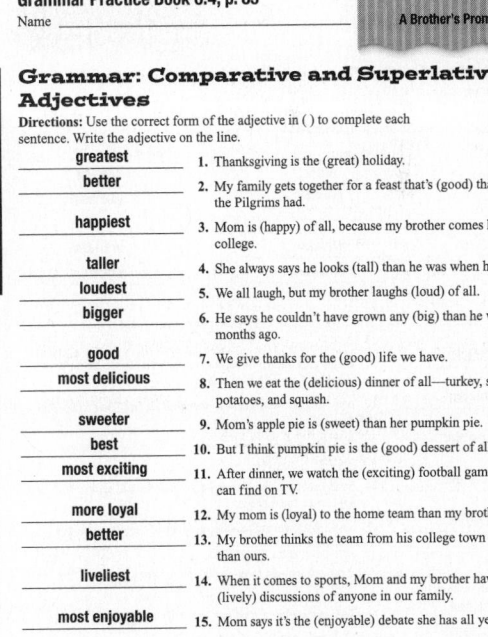

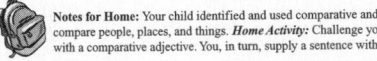

Grammar Practice Book 6.4, p. 84

Name ______________________ A Brother's Promise

Grammar: Comparative and Superlative Adjectives

RETEACHING

The chart below shows some forms of four adjectives. Fill in the missing adjectives in the chart.

	Adjective	Comparative Form	Superlative Form
1.	happy	happier	happiest
2.	expensive	more expensive	most expensive
3.	good	better	best
4.	bad	worse	worst

Use the **comparative** form of an adjective to compare two items. Use the **superlative** form to compare three or more items. Most adjectives add **-er, -est, more,** or **most** to form the comparative and superlative forms. Some adjectives have special forms.

Directions: Write the correct adjective form in ( ) to complete each sentence.

1. Some people say the clipper ship was the **most exciting** ship ever built. (more exciting/most exciting)
2. The vessel of Christopher Columbus's time was a **newer** ship than the galley. (newer/newest)
3. Clipper ships were **larger** than Columbus's ships. (larger/largest)
4. Of all sailing vessels, the clipper was the **fastest** ship. (faster/fastest)
5. The **biggest** clipper ship ever built was the *Great Republic.* (bigger/biggest)
6. Steamships have been **more common** than sailing ships in recent times. (common/more common)
7. Steamships were **better** than sailing ships at maintaining a steady pace. (better/best)
8. These ships were the **most powerful** ships of all time. (more powerful/most powerful)
9. Even today, however, many people find sailboats **more enjoyable** than power boats. (enjoyable/more enjoyable)
10. The sailboat is **more thrilling** than the power boat. (most thrilling/more thrilling)

Notes for Home: Your child used comparative and superlative forms of adjectives in sentences. ***Home Activity:*** Take a walk with your child. Talk about what you see by saying sentences with adjectives in comparative and superlative forms.

Grammar: Comparative and Superlative Adjectives 375

Grammar Practice Book 6.4, p. 85

Name ______________________ A Brother's Promise

Grammar: Comparative and Superlative Adjectives

Directions: Write the comparative or superlative form of each adjective in ( ).

1. What is the (efficient) of all methods of producing power? **most efficient**
2. Nuclear fusion will produce (clean) power than fission. **cleaner**
3. Some fuels burn for a (long) time than others. **longer**
4. Of all types of coal, anthracite burns the (long) time. **longest**
5. Anthracite coal is one of the (hard) fuels there is. **hardest**
6. Bituminous coal is (soft) than anthracite coal. **softer**
7. The Donets Basin is one of the (large) of all coal deposits. **largest**
8. The United States has the (great) amount of coal of all. **greatest**
9. The (big) of all anthracite deposits is in Pennsylvania. **biggest**

Directions: Write the correct form of the adjective in ( ).

10. Which is the (good) region of all for coal? **best**
11. Appalachia is the (large) producer of all. **largest**
12. Mining is one of the (dangerous) jobs of all. **most dangerous**
13. Liquid fuels are (convenient) than solids. **more convenient**
14. Is oil or gas a (efficient) fuel? **more efficient**
15. Are nuclear fuels (good) than fossil fuels? **better**
16. Someday nuclear fusion may be (common) than fission. **more common/commoner**
17. Nuclear power is (economical) than coal. **more economical**
18. Nuclear fuels are (compact) than fossil fuels. **more compact**

Write a Journal Entry

On a separate sheet of paper, write a journal entry about what a day in your life would be like without electrical power. Be sure to use comparative and superlative forms of adjectives to point out differences.

Make sure that students write the correct comparative and superlative forms of adjectives in their journal entries.

Notes for Home: Your child identified comparative and superlative forms of adjectives in sentences. ***Home Activity:*** Name an adjective and have your child supply the comparative and superlative forms. Then switch roles.

376 Grammar: Comparative and Superlative Adjectives

Practice Book 6.4, p. 168

Name ______________________ A Brother's Promise

Word Study: Inflected Endings *-er, -est*

Directions: The ending **-er** is added to words to compare two things. The ending **-est** is added to compare two or more things. Add **-er** and **-est** to each base word below. Write the new word on the line.

Base Word	Add -er	Add -est
old	1. older	2. oldest
short	3. shorter	4. shortest
near	5. nearer	6. nearest
grand	7. grander	8. grandest
small	9. smaller	10. smallest

Directions: Read each sentence. Add **-er** to the word in ( ). Write the new word on the line.

longer 11. It had taken much (long) to finish the building than we thought.

higher 12. Now that the building was complete, it reached (high) than ever before.

brighter 13. The stars never looked (bright) as I stood on the new rooftop.

younger 14. Even though I was (young) than the others, I could still appreciate the moment.

smaller 15. Looking down, the cars below seemed (small) than ants.

Directions: Read each sentence. Add the ending **-est** to the word in ( ). Write the new word on the line.

tallest 16. The new building was now the (tall) in the city.

deepest 17. The architect expressed his (deep) gratitude when he was presented with the award.

greatest 18. The observation tower was the (great) I had ever seen.

fastest 19. The elevator ride to the top was the (fast) ride I had ever taken.

highest 20. After stepping off the elevator, I realized I was looking down from the (high) point of the city.

Notes for Home: Your child formed new words by adding *-er* and *-est* to base words. ***Home Activity:*** Listen to radio advertisements or watch television commercials with your child to find words that end in *-er* and *-est*. Make a list of these words and the products they compare.

Word Study: Inflected Endings *-er, -est* 377

Spelling Workbook 6.4, p. 65

Name ______________________ A Brother's Promise

Spelling: Including All the Letters

Pretest Directions: Fold back the page along the dotted line. On the blanks, write the spelling words as they are dictated. When you have finished the test, unfold the page and check your words.

1. probably	1. There is **probably** enough food.
2. cabinet	2. We keep dishes in the **cabinet**.
3. separate	3. I have a **separate** room.
4. wondering	4. I was just **wondering** why.
5. clothes	5. It is time to wash the **clothes**.
6. average	6. What is the **average** test score?
7. beginning	7. He went back to the **beginning**.
8. restaurant	8. She opened a new **restaurant**.
9. promise	9. Do you **promise** to remember?
10. aspirin	10. Take some **aspirin** for your pain.
11. desperate	11. It was a **desperate** battle.
12. twelfth	12. She was the **twelfth** in line.
13. skiing	13. His brother loves to go **skiing**.
14. unwritten	14. There are many **unwritten** rules.
15. roughly	15. It is **roughly** a mile to town.
16. schedule	16. The driver kept to his **schedule**.
17. overrule	17. My parents might **overrule** me.
18. awfully	18. I'm **awfully** sorry for the mistake.
19. fishhook	19. How much is this **fishhook**?
20. temperature	20. The **temperature** is dropping.

Notes for Home: Your child took a pretest on words with difficult letter combinations. ***Home Activity:*** Help your child learn misspelled words before the final test. Your child can underline the word parts that caused the problems and concentrate on those parts.

378 Spelling: Including All the Letters

Spelling Workbook 6.4, p. 66

Name ______________________ A Brother's Promise

Spelling: Including All the Letters

Word List

probably	temperature	aspirin	skiing
cabinet	average	desperate	unwritten
separate	beginning	awfully	roughly
wondering	restaurant	fishhook	schedule
clothes	promise	twelfth	overrule

Directions: Sort words from the box according to how their endings are spelled. Write each word in the correct column. **Order may vary**

Ending in -ing

1. **wondering**
2. **beginning**
3. **skiing**

Ending in -ly

4. **probably**
5. **awfully**
6. **roughly**

Ending in consonant-vowel-consonant-e

7. **separate**
8. **temperature**
9. **average**
10. **promise**
11. **desperate**
12. **schedule**
13. **overrule**

Directions: Write the word from the box that belongs in each group.

14. cupboard, chest, **cabinet**
15. shoes, hats, **clothes**
16. deli, café, **restaurant**
17. vitamin, medicine, **aspirin**
18. unspoken, undone, **unwritten**
19. tenth, eleventh, **twelfth**
20. rod, reel, **fishhook**

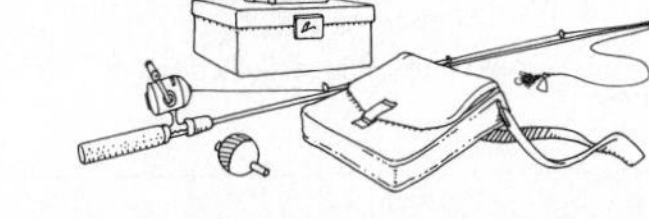

Notes for Home: Your child spelled words with more letters than you might expect. ***Home Activity:*** Help your child spell these words correctly by pronouncing each syllable carefully or by exaggerating the pronunciation of troublesome letters, such as prob*ab*ly or cab*i*net.

Spelling Workbook 6.4, p. 67

Name ______________________ A Brother's Promise

Spelling: Including All the Letters

Directions: Proofread this letter. Find nine spelling mistakes. Use the proofreading marks to correct each mistake.

- ≡ Make a capital.
- / Make a small letter.
- ∧ Add something.
- Take out something.
- ⊙ Add a period.
- ¶ Begin a new paragraph.

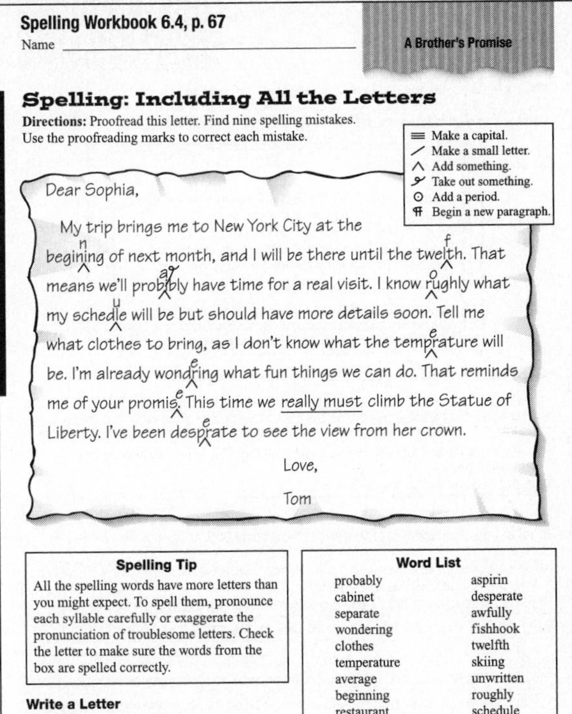

Dear Sophia,

My trip brings me to New York City at the begi[n]ing of next month, and I will be there until the twel[f]th. That means we'll prob[a]bly have time for a real visit. I know r[o]ughly what my sche[d]ule will be but should have more details soon. Tell me what clothes to bring, as I don't know what the temp[e]rature will be. I'm already wond[e]ring what fun things we can do. That reminds me of your promis[e]. This time we really must climb the Statue of Liberty. I've been desp[e]rate to see the view from her crown.

Love,

Tom

Spelling Tip

All the spelling words have more letters than you might expect. To spell them, pronounce each syllable carefully or exaggerate the pronunciation of troublesome letters. Check the letter to make sure the words from the box are spelled correctly.

Word List

probably	aspirin
cabinet	desperate
separate	awfully
wondering	fishhook
clothes	twelfth
temperature	skiing
average	unwritten
beginning	roughly
restaurant	schedule
promise	overrule

Write a Letter

On a separate sheet of paper, write a letter to a friend, explaining what interests you about a famous tourist attraction. Make plans to visit it together. Try to use at least five of your spelling words. **Answers will vary, but each letter should include at least five spelling words.**

Notes for Home: Your child spelled words with more letters than you might expect. ***Home Activity:*** Make up clues or hints about each spelling word, such as *This is something you use to catch a fish.* Challenge your child to guess the word and spell it. *(fishhook)*

Spelling Workbook 6.4, p. 68

Name ______________________ A Brother's Promise

Spelling: Including All the Letters REVIEW

Word List

probably	clothes	restaurant	awfully	unwritten
cabinet	temperature	promise	fishhook	roughly
separate	average	aspirin	twelfth	schedule
wondering	beginning	desperate	skiing	overrule

Directions: Choose a word from the box that best matches each clue. Write the word in the puzzle.

Across

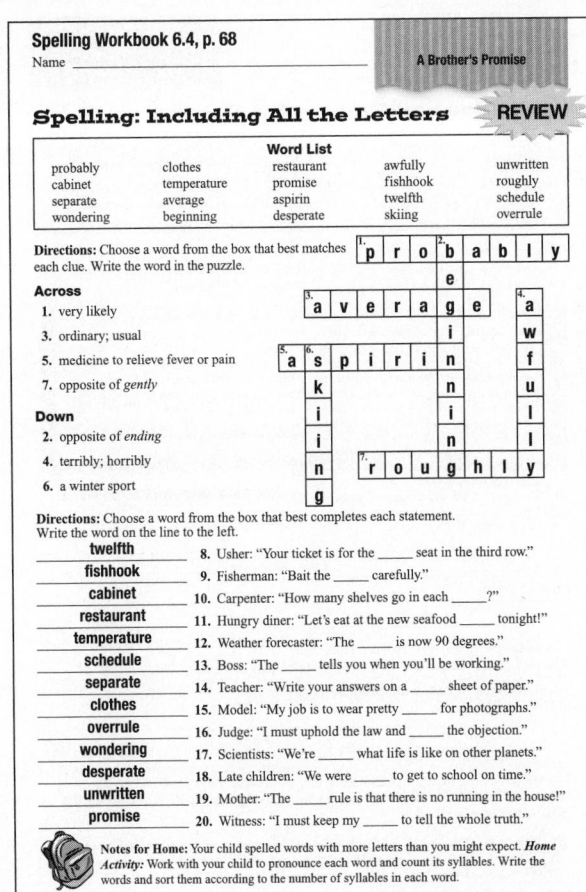

1. very likely
3. ordinary; usual
5. medicine to relieve fever or pain
7. opposite of *gently*

Down

2. opposite of *ending*
4. terribly; horribly
6. a winter sport

			p	r	o	b	a	b	l	y
						e				
	a	v	e	r	a	g	e		a	
						i			w	
a	s	p	i	r	i	n			f	
	k					n			u	
	i					i			l	
	i					n			l	
	n		r	o	u	g	h	l	y	
	g									

Directions: Choose a word from the box that best completes each statement. Write the word on the line to the left.

twelfth 8. Usher: "Your ticket is for the _____ seat in the third row."

fishhook 9. Fisherman: "Bait the _____ carefully."

cabinet 10. Carpenter: "How many shelves go in each _____?"

restaurant 11. Hungry diner: "Let's eat at the new seafood _____ tonight!"

temperature 12. Weather forecaster: "The _____ is now 90 degrees."

schedule 13. Boss: "The _____ tells you when you'll be working."

separate 14. Teacher: "Write your answers on a _____ sheet of paper."

clothes 15. Model: "My job is to wear pretty _____ for photographs."

overrule 16. Judge: "I must uphold the law and _____ the objection."

wondering 17. Scientists: "We're _____ what life is like on other planets."

desperate 18. Late children: "We were _____ to get to school on time."

unwritten 19. Mother: "The _____ rule is that there is no running in the house!"

promise 20. Witness: "I must keep my _____ to tell the whole truth."

Notes for Home: Your child spelled words with more letters than you might expect. ***Home Activity:*** Work with your child to pronounce each word and count its syllables. Write the words and sort them according to the number of syllables in each word.

Practice Book 6.4, p. 169

Name ______________________ A Brother's Promise

Technology: Encyclopedia

An **encyclopedia** gives general information about many different subjects. If you are using a CD-ROM or online encyclopedia, you can search the entire encyclopedia for your topic. You can usually search by letter or by typing key words. The welcome screen for an on-line encyclopedia might look like this:

Welcome to the Encyclopedia

Choose a letter to browse the encyclopedia.

Or, type the key words to search. Use AND between key words.

A B C D E F G H I J K L M N O P Q R S T U V W X Y Z

Search the Encyclopedia for:

Search for:

- ☐ Articles and Tables
- ☐ Pictures, Flags, Maps, Charts, Sounds
- ☐ Websites
- ☐ All of the Above

If you wanted an encyclopedia article about the Statue of Liberty, you could try clicking on the letter *S.* If that doesn't work, you could try the letter *L.* Then you might get this:

Lewis, Sinclair
Lewis and Clark
Liberal Party
Liberty, Statue of
Liberty Bell
library
lichen
licorice

Try another letter:

A B C D E F G H I J K L M N O P Q R S T U V W X Y Z

Search the Encyclopedia for:

Practice Book 6.4, p. 170

Name ______

A Brother's Promise

When you find an article about your topic, it will probably have links to other articles. The links are often set in all capital letters that are underlined. For example, you might find an article like this about the Statue of Liberty:

Liberty, Statue of

A large statue on Liberty Island in upper New York Bay. It was given to the United States in 1886, by the Franco-American Union to commemorate the AMERICAN REVOLUTION. It was designed by the sculptor F.A. BARTHOLDI. The statue became a national monument in 1924, and was extensively restored in 1986.

Click here to see pictures of the Statue of Liberty.

Directions: Use the sample computer screens to answer these questions.

1. In the first and second computer screens, what happens if you click on a letter?
You'll get a list of encyclopedia articles about topics that start with that letter.

2. Besides clicking on the letters S or L, what is another way to find information about the Statue of Liberty?
Type the key words "statue AND liberty"

3. In the second computer screen, what happens if you click on "Liberty Bell"?
You'll get an encyclopedia article about the Liberty Bell.

4. How can you get an article about the person who designed the Statue of Liberty? How can you get pictures of the Statue of Liberty?
To get an article about the designer, you would click on the underlined link F.A. BARTHOLDI. To see pictures, you would click on the link marked Click here.

5. How is a CD-ROM or online encyclopedia like and unlike a print encyclopedia?
Possible answer: Like: Both give general information about many different subjects. You use key words to search for information. Unlike: You can search a CD-ROM or online encyclopedia faster. You can get additional information easier by clicking on links. You can tell the computer what kinds of information to search for, such as an article, map, or website.

Notes for Home: Your child learned how to use a CD-ROM or online encyclopedia. ***Home Activity:*** Ask your child to list possible key words to use to search for articles about other national monuments or interesting sights, such as Mount Rushmore.

Research and Study Skills: Technology: Encyclopedia 383

Practice Book 6.4, p. 171

Name ______

from Catching the Fire

Main Idea and Supporting Details

- The most important idea about the topic of a paragraph or an article is the **main idea.** Small pieces of information that tell more about the main idea are **supporting details.**
- To find the main idea, first identify the topic. Ask yourself "What is this all about?" Then look for the most important idea about the topic. If it is not stated, put the main idea in your own words.

Directions: Reread "Quilted Memories." Complete the diagram below by writing the topic of the article, its main idea, and several important details that support the main idea.

Possible answers given.

Topic
1. **quilting**

Main Idea
2. **Quilting is a way to preserve memories.**

Supporting Detail
3. **Quilters used a family's old clothes.**

Supporting Detail
4. **Tiny, even stitching is a reminder of the skill and labor of the quilter.**

Supporting Detail
5. **Different kinds of quilt designs are reminders of women of different times, places, and cultures.**

Notes for Home: Your child identified the topic and main idea in an article. ***Home Activity:*** Work with your child to identify the topic and main idea of individual paragraphs in a magazine article. Then challenge your child to state the main idea of the entire article.

386 Main Idea and Supporting Details

Practice Book 6.4, p. 172

Name ______

from Catching the Fire

Vocabulary

Directions: Choose the word from the box that matches each definition. Write the word on the line.

Check the Words You Know
__ anvil
__ businessman
__ craftsman
__ horseshoes
__ ornamental
__ workshop

anvil 1. an iron or steel block on which metals are hammered and shaped
horseshoes 2. flat pieces of metal shaped like the letter U used to protect the hooves of horses
ornamental 3. decorative
businessman 4. a person who is in business or who runs a business
workshop 5. a shop or building where work is done

Directions: Choose the word from the box that best matches each clue. Write the word on the line.

horseshoes 6. They may not be fashionable, but every horse wears four of them.
workshop 7. You might build or make something here.
businessman 8. A person who owns a store could be called this.
ornamental 9. The fancy designs on an iron gate might be called this.
craftsman 10. You might see this person at a craft fair selling crafts he has made.

Write a Letter

On a separate sheet of paper, write a letter to a friend in which you describe a visit to a workshop. The letter can be based on an actual workshop that you have visited or one you imagine. Use as many vocabulary words as you can.
Students' letters should use vocabulary words correctly.

Notes for Home: Your child identified and used vocabulary words from *Catching the Fire.* ***Home Activity:*** Read a story with your child and have him or her point out unfamiliar words. Work together to try to figure out the meaning of each word using other words nearby.

Vocabulary 387

Practice Book 6.4, p. 173

Name ______

from Catching the Fire

Main Idea and Supporting Details

- The most important idea about the topic of a paragraph or an article is the **main idea.** Small pieces of information that tell more about the main idea are **supporting details.**
- To find the main idea, first identify the topic. Ask yourself "What is this all about?" Then look for the most important idea about the topic. If it is not stated, put the main idea in your own words.

Directions: Reread this scene from *Catching the Fire* in which John Vlach and Philip Simmons admire the Snake Gate. Then answer the questions below. Think about the main idea of the passage and look for supporting details.

Philip drove John over to East Bay Street to see his Snake Gate. It took him one month to forge that gate. He thought he'd never finish the eye. At first, it stared as if it were dead. Philip "heat and beat, heat and beat, heat and beat," until the snake looked as real as a diamond head rattler. "If it bites you," Philip joked, "you better get to the doctor fast. Blood get up to your heart, you know what happens!"

John Vlach was impressed. These were no ordinary pieces of ornamental ironwork. They were sculpture! Philip Simmons was not just a blacksmith. He was an artist.

Possible answers given.

1. What does John Vlach think of Philip's work? **John Vlach is impressed by Philip's artistry.**

2. What is the main idea of the passage? **Philip Simmons is not just a blacksmith. He is an artist.**

3.–4. List two details that support the main idea. **Philip Simmons crafted the snake until it looked as real as a diamond head rattler. "These were no ordinary pieces of ornamental work. They were sculpture!"**

5. On a separate sheet of paper, state the main idea of the last part of the story in which Philip attends the festival in Washington, D.C. Give specific details that support your answer.
The main idea is to keep working until you get it right. Philip can't sleep knowing the star in the gate is off-center, and he gets up very early to fix it in time for the demonstrations.

Notes for Home: Your child identified the main idea and supporting details of an excerpt from a biography. ***Home Activity:*** Read a magazine article with your child. Work together to identify its main idea and several supporting details.

388 Main Idea and Supporting Details

Practice Book 6.4, p. 175

Name ______________________

from Catching the Fire

Selection Test

Directions: Choose the best answer to each item. Mark the letter for the answer you have chosen.

Part 1: Vocabulary

Find the answer choice that means about the same as the underlined word in each sentence.

1. Where can I get some horseshoes?
   A. plants with spicy roots
   B. stiff fabrics made from horse hair
   C. riding crops used with horses
   (D) u-shaped pieces of metal nailed to horses' hooves
2. He is a wonderful craftsman.
   F. person who loves to hunt
   (G) person skilled in a trade
   H. person who likes to compete
   J. person trained to fly airplanes
3. Her workshop is quite small.
   A. strong table used for working
   B. person who is learning a trade
   (C) building or room where work is done
   D. room where people exercise
4. Mr. Cole is a wise businessman.
   F. man who interferes in other people's business
   G. man who runs for public office
   H. man who works in a library
   (J) man who owns or works in a business
5. She designed an ornamental gate.
   (A) for decoration
   B. well-hidden
   C. made of iron
   D. without hinges
6. We bought a new anvil.
   (F) iron or steel block on which metals are hammered and shaped
   G. small fireplace where metal is heated
   H. large, heavy hammer, usually swung with both hands
   J. device for producing a strong current of air

Part 2: Comprehension

Use what you know about the selection to answer each item.

7. Philip Simmons's best-known works are—
   A. chandeliers.
   B. plant stands.
   (C) gates with animal figures on them.
   D. benches.
8. A master and an apprentice are most like a—
   (F) teacher and student.
   G. father and mother.
   H. worker and tool.
   J. brother and sister.
9. The beginning of this selection is mostly about—
   A. a young boy working in his father's blacksmith shop.
   B. how to earn money as a blacksmith's apprentice.
   C. what it was like in Charleston, South Carolina, in 1923.
   (D) the ancient tradition of blacksmithing that Philip Simmons followed.
10. You can tell from reading this selection that being a blacksmith like Simmons—
    F. requires little skill.
    G. is a lost art.
    (H) combines physical and artistic talent.
    J. is a fairly simple way to make a lot of money.

Practice Book 6.4, p. 176

Name ______________________

from Catching the Fire

11. When John Vlach first asked him to go to the festival, Philip—
    A. knew just what he wanted to make.
    (B) wasn't sure he wanted to go.
    C. realized it was a great honor.
    D. didn't want to take his apprentices along.
12. Which title best fits the last part of the selection?
    F. "Thanking John Vlach"
    G. "Seeing Washington"
    H. "America in the 1970s"
    (J) "Preserving a Lost Art"
13. You can tell from reading this selection that Philip Simmons is not only a blacksmith, he is also—
    A. an accomplished photographer.
    B. a person who knows a lot about history.
    (C) a fine artist.
    D. a published author.
14. One of the major reasons that Philip survived as a blacksmith after World War II is that he—
    F. didn't charge much for his work.
    G. was able to buy iron cheaply.
    (H) knew how to adapt to changes in the world around him.
    J. always worked in the same neighborhood.
15. The author's main purpose in writing this selection is to—
    A. describe the 1976 Festival of American Folklife.
    B. discuss whether blacksmithing is a dying art.
    C. entertain with an exciting story about life in the 1920s.
    (D) give information about Philip Simmons, a talented blacksmith.

Name ______________________

from Catching the Fire

Main Idea and Supporting Details

- The most important idea about the topic of a paragraph or an article is the **main idea.** Small pieces of information that tell more about the main idea are **supporting details.**
- To find the main idea, first identify the topic. Ask yourself "What is this all about?" Then look for the most important idea about the topic. If it is not stated, put the main idea in your own words.

Directions: Read the story below.

Janette has always liked making things. She designs sets and sews costumes for community theater productions. She built a wall of bookshelves for her apartment.

The craft she likes best, though, is glass-blowing. She is a professional glass blower and spends a lot of time experimenting and imagining new things to make. She likes to make paperweights, ornaments, jewelry, and vases.

Janette has made a great success of her work. She recently opened her own studio in Tennessee. Her pieces grace the shelves of many gift shops. Soon, Janette may be able to open a shop of her own.

Directions: Each paragraph in this story has a main idea and supporting details. Complete the table by providing the missing ideas and details. **Possible answers given.**

Paragraph	Main Idea	Supporting Details
1	1. **Janette likes to make things.**	designs sets and makes costumes 2. **built shelves for apartment**
2	3. **Janette likes glass-blowing best.**	4. **spends a lot of time thinking about things to make** likes to make paperweights, ornaments, jewelry, and vases
3	Janette is successful.	5. **recently opened a studio** may soon open a shop

Notes for Home: Your child identified the main idea and supporting details of each paragraph in a biography. ***Home Activity:*** Tell your child a story about a real person. Have your child tell you the main idea of the story and some of its supporting details.

Practice Book 6.4, p. 177

Name ______________________

from Catching the Fire

Author's Purpose

REVIEW

Directions: Read the passage. Then read each question about the passage. Choose the best answer to each question. Mark the letter for the answer you have chosen.

Making Paint

Artists have a variety of paint choices today. Did you know that many materials in current use were also known to paintmakers in ancient times?

The substance that gives paint its color is called *pigment.* It is usually made from clay, lead, chalk, or other natural minerals that are ground into fine powder. In ancient times, people mixed vegetable and earth pigments with water or animal fat. In Colonial America, people used things like coffee, milk, and butter for pigment! Recently the paint industry has developed new chemical pigments.

To hold the color on the picture, pigments must be mixed with a sticky substance, or *binder.* A variety of materials are used, from oils to tree resins, beeswax, and even egg yolks. Recently, acrylic binders made from petroleum have also become popular. Drying time, gloss, and texture are all affected by the binder.

During the Italian Renaissance of the 1500s, painters began inventing new binders and new formulas for mixing pigments and binders. They kept their formulas secret so that other painters could not steal their ideas and profit from them. Most of the time, the new process died with the painter who invented it. Scientific analysis may yet reveal what made Italian paintings from the Renaissance so beautiful, but for now it is a mystery.

1. The topic of this article is—
   A. paintmakers of ancient times.
   (B) how paint is made.
   C. finely-ground pigments.
   D. minerals and other powders.
2. The main purpose of the article is—
   (F) to inform.
   G. to entertain.
   H. to persuade.
   J. to express.
3. The article's main idea is that—
   A. natural materials make the best paints.
   B. Colonial paintmakers used food substances to make pigments.
   (C) paints are made from different pigments and binders.
   D. an artist's style depends upon pigments.
4. Why does the author include the mention of paintmakers of ancient times?
   F. to impress readers with his knowledge of history
   (G) to show that some of their materials are still in use today
   H. to show how primitive their materials were
   J. to suggest that their materials were better than recent ones
5. The author included the last paragraph to—
   A. make the article more entertaining.
   (B) inform the reader about an interesting period in the history of paintmaking.
   C. persuade the reader that the Italian painters of the Renaissance were the best painters.
   D. express the beauty of Renaissance paintings.

Notes for Home: Your child read an article and identified the author's purpose. ***Home Activity:*** Together, name some favorite books, TV shows, and movies. Identify the author's purpose or purposes for writing each kind of text.

Name ______________________________ *from* Catching the Fire

Writing Across Texts

Directions: Think about what you learned about fire in the excerpt from *Catching the Fire* and "Fire All Around Us." Use that information to tell how fire is used in each of the processes in the web below. **Possible answers given.**

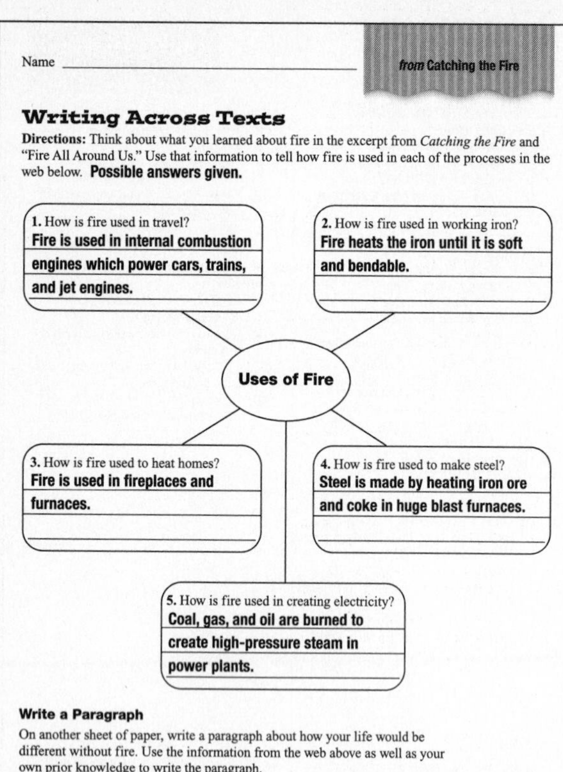

Uses of Fire
1. How is fire used in travel?
Fire is used in internal combustion engines which power cars, trains, and jet engines.
2. How is fire used in working iron?
Fire heats the iron until it is soft and bendable.
3. How is fire used to heat homes?
Fire is used in fireplaces and furnaces.
4. How is fire used to make steel?
Steel is made by heating iron ore and coke in huge blast furnaces.

5. How is fire used in creating electricity?
Coal, gas, and oil are burned to create high-pressure steam in power plants.

Write a Paragraph

On another sheet of paper, write a paragraph about how your life would be different without fire. Use the information from the web above as well as your own prior knowledge to write the paragraph.
Paragraphs will vary. Check that students' paragraphs include information from the web and from prior knowledge.

Notes for Home: Your child wrote a paragraph imagining what his or her life would be like without the use of fire in the world. ***Home Activity:*** With your child, list the ways fire is used in your home.

Name ______________________________ *from* Catching the Fire

Grammar: Comparative and Superlative Adjectives

REVIEW

Directions: Fill in the columns below with the comparative and superlative forms of each of the adjectives given.

Adjective	Comparative Form	Superlative Form
extraordinary	1. more extraordinary	2. most extraordinary
hot	3. hotter	4. hottest
tame	5. tamer	6. tamest
steep	7. steeper	8. steepest
sleepy	9. sleepier	10. sleepiest

Directions: Complete each sentence with the comparative or superlative form of the adjective in ( ). Write the adjective on the line.

unhappiest 11. Mike felt as if he were the (unhappy) person in the world that day in 1935.

poorer 12. His family's farmland had become (poor) each year, and now nothing would grow on it.

richer 13. He and his family were moving to a place with (rich) land—California.

largest 14. Mike's family was joining one of the (large) migrations, or movements, in American history.

more bearable 15. In the 1930s, over three million people in the Great Plains moved west to find a (bearable) life.

more precious 16. Mike had packed his carving tools carefully, for nothing was (precious) to him.

most beautiful 17. The figures Mike carved out of wood were some of the (beautiful) people had ever seen.

prouder 18. In fact, he was (proud) of his carvings than he usually admitted.

more fulfilling 19. Perhaps in California, Mike could sell his figures and find a (fulfilling) life.

more cheerful 20. Mike began to feel (cheerful) as the family's overloaded old car rattled west.

Notes for Home: Your child used the comparative and superlative forms of adjectives to compare people, places, and things. ***Home Activity:*** Have your child make a list of adjectives. Challenge your child to use each adjective in its comparative and superlative forms.

Name ______________________________ *from* Catching the Fire

Grammar: Adverbs

An **adverb** is a word that can tell how, where, or when something happens.

Yesterday we walked quietly into the library, read the onscreen instructions for doing a title search, and eventually located a blacksmith's published diary.

Like adjectives, adverbs can be used to make comparisons. Most adverbs have three forms: the adverb itself, the **comparative** form, and the **superlative** form.

Use the comparative form when you talk about two actions. To write the comparative form of most adverbs, add the ending **-er** or the word **more.**

Gram pored over the old diary longer than Mom did.
She studied the diary entries more carefully than Mom did too.

Use the superlative form when you talk about three or more actions. To form the superlative, add the ending **-est** or the word **most.**

Of the three of us, Gram is the one who stays longest in the Rare Books area.
She also is the one who examines those valuable books most carefully.

Most adverbs that end in **-ly** use **more** and **most** to make the comparative and the superlative forms: for example, **rapidly, more rapidly, most rapidly.**

Directions: Complete the table with the comparative and the superlative forms of each adverb.

Adverb	Comparative Form	Superlative Form
warmly	1. more warmly	2. most warmly
fast	3. faster	4. fastest
quickly	5. more quickly	6. most quickly
oddly	7. more oddly	8. most oddly
soon	9. sooner	10. soonest
recently	11. more recently	12. most recently
late	13. later	14. latest
hopefully	15. more hopefully	16. most hopefully
early	17. earlier	18. earliest
easily	19. more easily	20. most easily

Notes for Home: Your child learned to identify comparative and superlative forms of adverbs. ***Home Activity:*** Challenge your child to describe an activity you do together, using comparative or superlative adverbs.

Name ______________________________ *from* Catching the Fire

Grammar: Adverbs

Directions: Write the kind of adverb named in ( ) on the line to the left to complete each sentence. **Possible answers given.**

outside 1. Tanya waited with her classmates _____ the blacksmith's shop that morning. (tell where)

recently 2. She had read a story _____ about blacksmiths and looked forward to seeing them demonstrate their trade. (tell when)

clearly 3. She remembered _____ an illustration of a blacksmith working near a hot fire. (tell how)

Directions: Write the correct form of the adverb in ( ) to complete each sentence.

easiest 4. "This could not have been the (easy) skill to learn," Tanya thought.

harder 5. Blacksmiths have to work (hard) than many workers today.

more carefully 6. Blacksmiths also have to work (carefully) to bend and shape the iron than workers who use machines to do this task.

more skillfully 7. A complicated design means that the blacksmith has to work (skillfully) than usual.

longer 8. Tanya would probably stay (long) than her classmates.

more closely 9. She would watch (closely) than the other students too.

sooner 10. She wished the shop would open its doors (soon) than 10 A.M.!

Write a Poem

Think about a skill that you admire and a person who does that skill well. On a separate sheet of paper, write a poem about this person. Use comparative and superlative adverbs to compare this skill to another, or to compare the person's ability to another's. **Students' poems should use the correct comparative and superlative adverb forms.**

Notes for Home: Your child wrote adverbs, including the comparative and superlative form. ***Home Activity:*** Take turns making up quiz questions, using comparative and superlative adverbs, for example, *What small boat would you have to operate most slowly? (a rowboat)*

Grammar Practice Book 6.4, p. 89

Name ______________________

from Catching the Fire

RETEACHING

Grammar: Adverbs

Underline the adverb in each sentence.

1. I ran quickly through the park.
2. My friend ran quicker than I did.
3. Yesterday she told me she would race me to the school playground.
4. I told her I would race her today.

An **adverb** can tell how, where, or when something happens. When an adverb is used to compare two actions, the **comparative form** is used. Add **-er** or **more** to make the comparative form. When an adverb is used to compare three or more actions, the **superlative form** is used. Add **-est** or **most** to make the superlative form.

Directions: Circle the adverb in each sentence.

1. I have read this book (before).
2. The story begins (mysteriously).
3. I enjoyed this book (more thoroughly) than any other mystery book I have read.
4. The dog, Mutt, (suddenly) disappears.
5. He is gone (faster) than you can imagine.

Directions: Choose an adverb that best fits each sentence. Write it on the line to the left. **Possible answers given.**

easily	6. The heroine, Lila, ________ finds Mutt.
already	7. Lila ________ suspects foul play.
quickly	8. She ________ discovers a ransom note.
now	9. The kidnappers ________ demand a huge ransom.
loudly	10. Lila gasps ________.
carefully	11. She looks ________ for Mutt.
cautiously	12. She approaches the house ________.
carelessly	13. The kidnappers have acted ________.
fortunately	14. They ________ left open a window.
safely	15. Mutt arrives home ________.

Notes for Home: Your child identified and used adverbs in sentences. ***Home Activity:*** Watch a television show with your child, but turn off the sound. Have your child use adverbs in sentences to describe what the actors on the show are doing.

Grammar Practice Book 6.4, p. 90

Name ______________________

from Catching the Fire

Grammar: Adverbs

Directions: Read each sentence. Write the correct form of each adverb in ( ) on the line to the left.

more carefully	1. She does her work (carefully) than you.
most neatly	2. You write (neatly) of the three.
more beautifully	3. You write (beautifully) than I ever could.
more clearly	4. Print your name (clearly) than you did last time.
more thoroughly	5. Next time erase your mistakes (thoroughly) than this.
more skillfully	6. This picture is (skillfully) drawn than the first one.
earlier	7. Today our class was dismissed (early) than usual.
soonest	8. I finished (soon) of anyone.
more easily	9. I learned French (easily) than I learned German.
most eagerly	10. Of the whole class, who works (eagerly)?

Directions: Rewrite each sentence with the correct form of the underlined adverb.

11. Can't you run more faster?
Can't you run faster?

12. Of all the bands, this one plays most loudest.
Of all the bands, this one plays loudest.

13. This building was built latest than that one.
This building was built later than that one.

14. These books are stacked neatly than those.
These books are stacked more neatly than those.

15. The movie started earliest than we had thought.
The movie started earlier than we had thought.

16. Doesn't Venus shine brightly than Mars?
Doesn't Venus shine more brightly than Mars?

17. This car runs economically of all three.
This car runs most economically of all three.

Notes for Home: Your child wrote the correct forms of adverbs in sentences. ***Home Activity:*** Have your child create a five-box comic strip. Challenge him or her to use adverbs in captions for the comic strip.

Practice Book 6.4, p. 178

Name ______________________

from Catching the Fire

Word Study: Inflected Endings

Directions: If a word ends in a **consonant** and **y**, change the **y** to **i** before adding most endings. For example, **baby** becomes **babies.** You do **not** change **y** to **i** when adding **-ing. Try** becomes **trying.** If a word ends in a single consonant preceded by a single vowel, double the final consonant before adding the ending. For example, **step** becomes **stepped.** Add the given ending to each base word. Write the new word on the line.

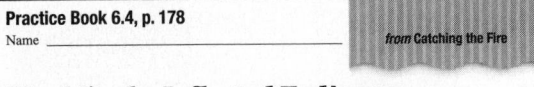

1.	drop	+	-ing	=	dropping
2.	strip	+	-ed	=	stripped
3.	family	+	-es	=	families
4.	big	+	-er	=	bigger
5.	factory	+	-es	=	factories
6.	big	+	-est	=	biggest
7.	industry	+	-al	=	industrial
8.	stir	+	-ed	=	stirred

Directions: Read each sentence. Write the base word for each underlined word below.

try	9. No matter how hard the ironworkers tried, they could not get management to give them a raise.
plan	10. In order to have their demands met, the laborers were planning to go on strike.
county	11. In counties all across the state, there were no other jobs for the workers.
run	12. The employees were running out of options for the future.
tragedy	13. It would be one of the biggest tragedies of the year if the town's factory were to close its doors.
community	14. In order for communities to survive, jobs must be plentiful.
industry	15. It sometimes takes several industries to make a town a success.

Notes for Home: Your child added endings to base words. ***Home Activity:*** Read a newspaper with your child. Look for words with endings such as *-ing, -ed, -er, -est,* and *-es*. Have your child tell if the base word changed when the ending was added.

Spelling Workbook 6.4, p. 69

Name ______________________

from Catching the Fire

Spelling: Adding *-ed* and *-ing*

Pretest Directions: Fold back the page along the dotted line. On the blanks, write the spelling words as they are dictated. When you have finished the test, unfold the page and check your words.

1.	answered	1. No one **answered** the telephone.
2.	answering	2. He spent time **answering** them.
3.	decided	3. She **decided** to take a long trip.
4.	deciding	4. I'll wait while you're **deciding**.
5.	included	5. The award **included** money.
6.	including	6. We all went, **including** Grandma.
7.	omitted	7. The essay **omitted** one detail.
8.	omitting	8. I hope you are not **omitting** me.
9.	satisfied	9. The dog's hunger was **satisfied**.
10.	satisfying	10. I like **satisfying** endings.
11.	delayed	11. The slow train **delayed** us.
12.	delaying	12. He kept on **delaying** a decision.
13.	remembered	13. My mom **remembered** my lunch.
14.	remembering	14. I dislike **remembering** that day.
15.	exercised	15. She **exercised** for an hour.
16.	exercising	16. I love **exercising**.
17.	interfered	17. They have **interfered**.
18.	interfering	18. Stop **interfering** and help!
19.	occurred	19. A great event just **occurred**.
20.	occurring	20. The same thing kept **occurring**.

Notes for Home: Your child took a pretest on words ending in *-ed* and *-ing*. ***Home Activity:*** Help your child learn misspelled words before the final test. Have your child learn to spell the base word and then notice how it changes when *-ed* or *-ing* is added.

Spelling Workbook 6.4, p. 70

Name ____________________

from Catching the Fire

Spelling: Adding *-ed* and *-ing*

Word List

answered	included	satisfied	remembered	interfered
answering	including	satisfying	remembering	interfering
decided	omitted	delayed	exercised	occurred
deciding	omitting	delaying	exercising	occurring

Directions: Choose the words from the box that end in **-ed.** Sort the words according to the way their endings are spelled. Write each word in the correct column. **Order may vary**

Just Add -ed

1. answered
2. delayed
3. remembered

Double the Final Consonant, Then Add -ed

4. omitted
5. occurred

Drop the Final e, Then Add -ed

6. decided
7. included
8. exercised
9. interfered

Directions: Choose the word from the box that best completes each statement. Write the word on the line.

occurring 10. *Smiling* is to *grinning* as *happening* is to _____.
interfering 11. *Queen* is to *ruling* as *busybody* is to _____.
remembering 12. *Love* is to *hating* as *forget* is to _____.
satisfied 13. *Try* is to *tried* as *satisfy* is to _____.
answering 14. *Drawing* is to *sketching* as *replying* is to _____.
including 15. *Out* is to *in* as *excluding* is to _____.
exercising 16. *Theater* is to *acting* as *gym* is to _____.
delaying 17. *Early* is to *late* as *hurrying* is to _____.
omitting 18. *On* is to *off* as *enclosing* is to _____.
satisfying 19. *Pleasure* is to *pleasing* as *satisfaction* is to _____.
deciding 20. *Pitcher* is to *throwing* as *umpire* is to _____.

Notes for Home: Your child spelled words ending in *-ed* and *-ing*. ***Home Activity:*** Say the base word for each spelling word, such as *answer* for *answered.* Have your child add *-ed* and *-ing* to each base word and spell the new words he or she has made.

Spelling: Adding *-ed* and *-ing* 401

Spelling Workbook 6.4, p. 71

Name ____________________

from Catching the Fire

Spelling: Adding *-ed* and *-ing*

Directions: Proofread this paragraph that tells of reactions to a quilting class. Find seven spelling mistakes. Use the proofreading marks to correct each mistake.

Proofreading marks
≡ Make a capital.
/ Make a small letter.
∧ Add something.
Take out something.
⊙ Add a period.
¶ Begin a new paragraph.

During the first meeting of my quilting class I had trouble rememberring the many techniques presented by the instructor. In the first week of quilting I made several mistakes because I ommitted important steps in the quilting process. It has occured to me that quilting is a difficult and time consuming skill. I am very satisfyed with the beautiful new quilt that I am making, but the completion of the project has been delaied because I don't have enough time to work on it. In fact, I've spent so much time quilting that it has interferred with my homework and the exerciseing that I must do to get into condition for the upcoming basketball season. Quilting is a very old and beautiful craft. Even though it is a lot of work, I am glad that I decided to take the class.

Spelling Tip

The spelling of some base words changes before adding **-ed** or **-ing.** You may need to drop a final **e** as in **decided,** double the final consonant as in **omitting,** or change a final **y** to **i,** as in **satisfied.**

Word List

answered	delayed
answering	delaying
decided	remembered
deciding	remembering
included	exercised
including	exercising
omitted	interfered
omitting	interfering
satisfied	occurred
satisfying	occurring

Write a Paragraph

Find a library book with pictures of quilts and choose one that you like. On a separate sheet of paper, write a paragraph describing the quilt. Try to use at least three of your spelling words.

Answers will vary, but each paragraph should include at least three spelling words.

Notes for Home: Your child spelled words ending in *-ed* and *-ing*. ***Home Activity:*** Read the Spelling Tip above. Ask your child to identify the spelling words that fall into the three groups described, as well as the spelling words in which the base word does not change.

402 Spelling: Adding *-ed* and *-ing*

Spelling Workbook 6.4, p. 72

Name ____________________

from Catching the Fire

Spelling: Adding *-ed* and *-ing* — REVIEW

Word List

answered	included	satisfied	remembered	interfered
answering	including	satisfying	remembering	interfering
decided	omitted	delayed	exercised	occurred
deciding	omitting	delaying	exercising	occurring

Directions: Choose the word from the box that is the most opposite in meaning to each word below. Write the word on the line.

1. forgot remembered
2. rushing delaying
3. dissatisfied satisfied
4. avoiding interfering
5. including omitting
6. undecided decided
7. not happening occurring
8. relaxing exercising
9. questioning answering
10. leaving out including

Directions: Choose the word from the box that best replaces the underlined word or words. Write the word on the line.

answered 11. The quilting instructor <u>responded to</u> my questions about sewing squares of material together.
included 12. A lot of beautiful details can be <u>enclosed</u> in a single small section of a quilt.
omitted 13. There is so little room on my four-inch section that some of the fine details were <u>left out</u>.
remembering 14. The elderly quilters passed the hours <u>recalling</u> and telling old stories.
exercised 15. Mary and I <u>stretched</u> after quilting for two hours.
delayed 16. When the instructor demonstrated her skill we all <u>halted</u> our sewing for a while.
interfered 17. Her many careful instructions <u>meddled</u> with our progress in class.
Deciding 18. <u>Determining</u> that I had an interest in quilting was easy—finishing a quilt is not easy.
occurred 19. Completing one small portion of the quilt <u>happened</u> very slowly.
satisfying 20. It is <u>pleasing</u> to learn a skill that I can teach to my children someday.

Notes for Home: Your child spelled words ending in *-ed* and *-ing*. ***Home Activity:*** Write all the spelling words that end in *-ed* on separate slips of paper. Take turns drawing words and spelling the words with an *-ing* ending instead of *-ed.*

Spelling: Adding *-ed* and *-ing* 403

Practice Book 6.4, p. 179

Name ____________________

from Catching the Fire

Pictures and Captions

Pictures and captions can provide information about the characters and events in a story or information about the subject in nonfiction writing.

Directions: Use the picture and the caption to answer the questions that follow.

Quilt-making is a popular form of American folk art. Historically, quilting served as a way for women to get together in a "quilting bee." A quilt is generally made from a series of cloth patches sewn together to form a design. Story quilts include images that tell a story.

1. What does the picture show? **Possible answer: It shows a group of women making a quilt.**
2. What is a quilting bee? **A quilting bee refers to a group of people, usually all women, who get together to make a quilt.**
3. How is a quilt generally constructed? **A quilt is made by sewing together a series of cloth patches to form a design.**
4. How are "story quilts" different from other quilts? **Possible answer: A story quilt includes images that tell a story. Other quilts may just show a pattern or visual design.**
5. Would this picture and caption be useful for a research essay on American folk art? Explain. **Possible answer: The picture helps show how a quilt is made. The caption helps explain how and why quilts are made and tells what a story quilt is.**

404 Research and Study Skills: Pictures and Captions

Practice Book 6.4, p. 180

Name ______________________

from Catching the Fire

Directions: Study the picture and caption from a story. Then answer the questions that follow.

John Thomas worked hard into the night. He could picture the snake in his mind and wouldn't rest until he got it right.

6. What do you learn about the character from looking at the picture? **Possible answer: You see what the character looks like and how hard he works.**

7. What do you learn about the character from reading the caption? **Possible answer: You learn the character's name. You can draw the conclusions that he is hard-working and concerned that his work be done very well.**

8. Use what you have learned about the character to write your own caption for the picture. **Captions will vary but should reflect logical conclusions that can be drawn from the art and the original caption.**

9. How can you use a picture and a caption to draw conclusions about a character? **Possible answer: A picture or caption can help show or describe how a character looks or acts. You can draw conclusions about a character by looking at how the character is shown in the picture or described in the caption.**

10. Why is it important to read captions carefully? **Possible answer: You need to read captions carefully because they may help explain the picture or give information not provided in the text.**

Notes for Home: Your child answered questions about pictures and captions. ***Home Activity:*** Look through a magazine or nonfiction book with your child to find pictures with captions. Discuss what you learn from these pictures and captions.

Practice Book 6.4, p. 181

Name ______________________

The Seven Wonders of the Ancient World

Text Structure

- **Text structure** refers to the way a piece of writing is organized.
- Fiction tells of imaginary people and events. It is usually organized in chronological order, the order in which the events happen.
- Nonfiction tells of real people and events or tells information about the real world. It may be organized in chronological order, or by topic, cause and effect, problem and solution, or some other way.

Directions: Reread "Engineering the Land." Then complete the diagram. Identify the topics and give the main idea of each paragraph related to that topic.

Answers will vary.

Topic: Terracing

First paragraph: Because much of their land was hard to farm, the Incas had to terrace and dig canals.

1. **Second paragraph:** **Terracing transformed steep hillsides into huge steps that increased the amount of land for farming and reduced erosion.**

2. **Topic:** **Irrigation**

3. **Paragraph:** **The Incas built elaborate irrigation systems to transport water to areas where rain was scarce.**

4. **Topic:** **Scientific knowledge**

5. **Paragraph:** **The public works of the Inca engineers show that they had a good knowledge of political science.**

Notes for Home: Your child analyzed the way a nonfiction selection was organized. ***Home Activity:*** Review together the text structure of familiar textbooks. Discuss the ways the different textbook features help readers better understand and remember the information.

Practice Book 6.4, p. 182

Name ______________________

The Seven Wonders of the Ancient World

Vocabulary

Directions: Match each word on the left with its definition on the right. Write the letter of the definition on the line to the left of the word.

Check the Words You Know
- __ archaeologists
- __ classical
- __ excavate
- __ pharaohs
- __ structures
- __ tomb

c 1. pharaohs
d 2. classical
f 3. tomb
b 4. structures
a 5. excavate
e 6. archaeologists

a. unearth; dig up
b. buildings
c. ancient Egyptian kings
d. having to do with ancient Greece and Rome
e. scientists who study the past by unearthing artifacts
f. grave or vault

Directions: Choose the word from the box that best replaces the underlined word or words. Write the word on the line.

pharaohs 7. The kings of ancient Egypt had huge pyramids built as a resting place for the dead.

tomb 8. It took years and thousands of laborers just to build a single burial place.

archaeologists 9. Scientists who study these ancient structures are still not completely certain how these pyramids were built.

excavate 10. They continue to dig near these marvelous structures hoping to learn more about the past.

Write a Journal Entry

On a separate sheet of paper, write a journal entry in which you pretend you are an archaeologist. Describe a dig in which you discover artifacts (objects made by humans) from an ancient civilization. Use as many vocabulary words as you can.
Students' journal entries should make correct use of vocabulary words.

Notes for Home: Your child identified and used vocabulary words from *The Seven Wonders of the Ancient World.* ***Home Activity:*** Work with your child to write an adventure story about an archaeologist, using the vocabulary words listed above.

Practice Book 6.4, p. 183

Name ______________________

The Seven Wonders of the Ancient World

Text Structure

- **Text structure** refers to the way a piece of writing is organized.
- Fiction tells stories of imaginary people and events. It is usually organized in chronological order, the order in which the events happened.
- Nonfiction tells of real people and events or tells information about the real world. Some ways to organize nonfiction are chronological order, cause and effect, problem and solution, or comparison and contrast.

Directions: Reread this passage about the Colossus of Rhodes from *The Seven Wonders of the Ancient World.* Then answer the questions below. Think about the way in which the events it describes are organized.

> In about 226 B.C., little more than 50 years after it was completed, the Colossus fell. It was toppled by an earthquake and snapped off at the knees. The people of Rhodes were told by an oracle not to rebuild the statue, and so they left it lying where it had fallen. It stayed like this for nearly 900 years, and people would travel to Rhodes just to gaze at the ruins of the fallen sun god.
>
> In A.D. 654 a Syrian prince captured Rhodes and stripped the statue of its bronze plates. People said that he took them back to Syria on the backs of 900 camels. The bronze was sold by merchants and probably turned into coins.
>
>

Possible answers given.

1. What is the topic of the passage?
The passage is about the destruction of the Colossus of Rhodes.

2. About how much time does it take for all the events to happen?
It takes more than 900 years.

3. How are the events in this passage organized?
The events are described in the order in which they happened.

4. Do you think the organization of the passage makes sense? Why or why not?
Each event described in the passage depends on what happened earlier, so telling the story in chronological order makes sense.

5. On a separate sheet of paper, explain how the information in *The Seven Wonders of the Ancient World* is organized. Explain whether you think it was effective and why.
The seven wonders of the ancient world are listed in the order in which they were built. The story of each is told in chronological order, from its background through its creation to its destruction (except for the pyramid, which survives). This structure is effective because it lets the reader experience events as they happened.

Notes for Home: Your child identified the organization of a text. ***Home Activity:*** Have your child read aloud a passage from a nonfiction book. Have him or her tell how it is organized and why the author might have organized it in that way.

Practice Book 6.4, p. 185

Name ______________________

Selection Test

Directions: Choose the best answer to each item. Mark the letter for the answer you have chosen.

Part 1: Vocabulary

Find the answer choice that means about the same as the underlined word in each sentence.

1. She wanted to excavate the old fort.
A. explore
B. lay out
(C) uncover by digging
D. bury

2. He discovered an ancient tomb.
F. fortress
G. house
H. earthen jar for storage
(J) grave or vault

3. They found what was left of the structures.
A. paintings
(B) things that are built
C. borders
D. rivers and waterways

4. A team of archaeologists arrived.
F. scientists who study the surface features of the earth
(G) scientists who study the people and customs of ancient times
H. scientists who study the earth's climate
J. scientists who study fossils of animals and plants

5. She was learning about the pharoahs.
(A) kings of ancient Egypt
B. buildings in ancient Egypt
C. statues of ancient rulers
D. priests of an ancient religion

6. He was reading classical literature.
F. originating in Asia
G. about music
(H) of ancient Greece and Rome
J. about school

Part 2: Comprehension

Use what you know about the selection to answer each item.

7. Which of the "Seven Wonders" is still standing today?
A. the Mausoleum at Halicarnassus
B. the Statue of Zeus at Olympia
C. the Temple of Artemis at Ephesus
(D) the Great Pyramid at Giza

8. The "Seven Wonders of the Ancient World" were all located near the—
(F) Mediterranean Sea.
G. Atlantic Ocean.
H. Caspian Sea.
J. Persian Gulf.

9. Why did these particular sites become known as the "Seven Wonders"?
A. No one knew how they were made.
B. They were built in seven different countries.
(C) A Greek poet wrote about them.
D. Scientists today are amazed by them.

10. The main idea of this selection is that the "Seven Wonders" all—
F. prove that ancient peoples had the same beliefs and values we do today.
G. honored kings and queens who are no longer important.
(H) were designed and built by people who lived thousands of years ago.
J. demonstrated the supreme power of nature.

11. The author's main purpose in this selection is to—
A. entertain.
B. express feelings.
C. persuade.
(D) give information.

Practice Book 6.4, p. 186

Name ______________________

12. The information in this selection is organized by—
(F) topic.
G. cause and effect.
H. problem and solution.
J. comparison/contrast.

13. For which of these structures is the exact location **not** known?
A. Great Pyramid at Giza
(B) Hanging Gardens of Babylon
C. Temple of Artemis at Ephesus
D. Pharos of Alexandria

14. Which sentence states an opinion?
F. The Great Pyramid at Giza was built as a tomb.
G. The main structure of the Temple of Artemis was supported by about 120 marble columns.
H. The Statue of Zeus at Olympia stood for about 800 years.
(J) The Pharos of Alexandria was the greatest of the Seven Wonders.

15. After reading this selection, you can conclude that what we build today—
A. is more beautiful than what people built in the past.
(B) may someday be studied by people of the future.
C. will last much longer than buildings did in the past.
D. differs very little from what has been built throughout history.

Name ______________________

Text Structure

- **Text structure** refers to the way a piece of writing is organized.
- Fiction tells stories of imaginary people and events. It is usually organized in chronological order, the order in which the events happened. Nonfiction tells of real people and events or tells information about the real world. Some ways to organize nonfiction are chronological order, cause and effect, problem and solution, or comparison and contrast.

Directions: Read the passage below.

When it was built in 1910, the Pennsylvania Railroad Station was the pride of New York City. Its huge waiting rooms, great marble walls, and grand staircases made every train journey an event. In 1966, the station was torn down to make room for an office tower and sports arena. The station's owners felt that they could make a lot of money by keeping only the underground train tracks and platforms and selling the space above ground to a builder.

Many New Yorkers were outraged at the fate of the beloved landmark. Laws were passed soon after to protect old buildings like the station. In 1998, Grand Central Station benefited from these laws. It was fully cleaned and restored to the glory it had known on its opening day in 1913.

Directions: Complete the table below. Decide whether each type of text structure listed is used in the passage. Then give an example from the passage or an explanation to support your answer.

Possible answers given.

Type of Structure	Detail from Passage/Explanation
chronological order	Penn Station is destroyed; laws are passed; Grand Central is saved.
cause/effect	1. **Yes** 2. **Because Penn Station was torn down, people passed laws to save other landmarks.**
problem/solution	3. **Yes** 4. **Penn Station's owners wanted to make more money; they tore down the station and sold the property.**
comparison/contrast	Yes 5. **Penn Station was torn down; Grand Central Station was cleaned and restored.**

Notes for Home: Your child identified the different ways information in a passage was organized. *Home Activity:* Find other examples of nonfiction, such as a book, a documentary, or a flyer. Discuss how the information is organized.

Practice Book 6.4, p. 187

Name ______________________

Persuasive Devices

REVIEW

Directions: Read the passage. Then read each question about the passage. Choose the best answer to each question. Mark the letter for the answer you have chosen.

The Eighth Wonder of the World

The next stop on our tour is the Empire State Building. It's no longer the tallest building in New York, but it is still the best-looking. People joke about the World Trade Center being "the box the Chrysler Building came in"—no one would ever mock the Empire State Building like that!

The building is best known for its splendid view from the top of the tower. You can stay up there all day if you want, and take in the surrounding city from every direction. On clear days you can see far beyond the city limits. At night, the view is even better—everything is lit, cars drive along in rows of red and yellow lights, and the city looks magical.

The lobby is just as grand as the view. You've never seen so much marble in one place! It's as lofty as a cathedral. Even the journey to the top can be an adventure. A maze of elevators and hallways are negotiated by visitors before reaching the glorious view from the top of the tower.

No other building in New York has the personality of the Empire State. Hollywood has featured the grand building in many movies. For example, the great ape King Kong once climbed its tower! It is still the greatest tourist attraction in the city, and it deserves to be.

1. The tour guide thinks the Empire State Building is—
A. the tallest building in New York.
B. the smallest building in New York.
(C) the best-looking building in New York.
D. the oldest building in New York.

2. Which words persuade the listeners that the view is great?
(F) splendid, magical
G. all day, every direction
H. splendid, lit
J. clear days, far beyond

3. Which of the following is an attempt to persuade the listener?
A. The lobby is marble.
(B) The view is splendid.
C. King Kong once climbed the tower.
D. The building is tall.

4. Which of the following is a sweeping generalization?
(F) No other building has a personality like that of the Empire State.
G. From the tower, you can see a great distance on a clear day
H. The Empire State has a marble lobby.
J. The Empire State is no longer the tallest building in New York.

5. Which of the following is **not** an attempt to persuade the listener?
A. The view is magnificent at night.
B. It is the greatest tourist attraction in the city.
C. No other building has a personality like the Empire State.
(D) On a clear day, you can see a lot from the tower.

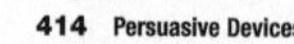

Notes for Home: Your child identified the persuasive devices in a passage. *Home Activity:* Read a newspaper article with your child. Encourage him or her to identify persuasive devices such as generalizations and propaganda, as opposed to facts and information.

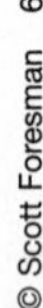

Name ______________________ The Seven Wonders of the Ancient World

Writing Across Texts

Directions: Consider what you learned from reading *The Seven Wonders of the Ancient World* and "The Great Pyramids." Think about the reasons ancient civilizations built these structures. Do we build structures for the same reasons today? Compare the information you learned from the selections to what you know about people today. Record your ideas in the following table. **Possible answers given.**

Comparing the Seven Wonders to Today's Structures
Just like the Great Pyramid and the Mausoleum, people still build structures for burial today. Gravestones are one example.
1. **Just like the Hanging Gardens of Babylon, structures for loved ones are still built. "Dream homes" are one example.**
2. **Just like the Temple of Artemis, places of worship are still built. Churches are one example.**
3. **Just like the Colossus, statues that are gestures of friendship or honor are still built.**
4. **Just like the Pharos of Alexandria, lighthouses are still built.**
5. **Just like the Statue of Zeus, monuments in honor of prominent figures are still built. Mount Rushmore is one example.**

Write an Explanation

On a separate sheet of paper, write an explanation that tells how our reasons for building specific structures today are similar to those in the past. Use ideas from the table above and from *The Seven Wonders of the Ancient World* and "The Great Pyramids."
Explanations will vary. Check that students' explanations contain accurate similarities.

Notes for Home: Your child wrote about the similarities between the past and today. ***Home Activity:*** Talk with your child about a tradition that your family observes that has been observed by others for centuries, such as weddings.

Name ______________________ The Seven Wonders of the Ancient World

Grammar: Adverbs

REVIEW

Directions: Write the adverb that modifies the underlined verb.

really 1. The world really has more than seven ancient wonders.
often 2. Visitors often climb 7,000 feet to Peru's ancient city of Machu Picchu.
There 3. There they see a temple and a fortress with beautiful stonework.
originally 4. Terraced gardens surrounded the city originally.
Today 5. Today visitors must imagine the city as it once looked.

Directions: Write an adverb to complete each sentence. **Possible answers given.**

soon 6. My cousins will visit the Great Wall of China _____.
definitely 7. They _____ will take many pictures of that amazing sight.
actually 8. Visitors find it hard to believe, but the wall _____ covers 4,000 miles.
up 9. From the ground, one must look _____ thirty feet to see the top of the structure.
back 10. The wall dates _____ to the fourth century B.C.E., but parts were later rebuilt in the fifteenth and sixteenth centuries.

Directions: Complete each sentence with the comparative or superlative form of the adverb in ( ). Write the adverb on the line.

earliest 11. The British tour buses left London at about the same time, but our bus arrived at Stonehenge (early) of all.
most frequently 12. The question asked (frequently) was why prehistoric people built this group of stones in a circle.
more seriously 13. Certain ideas about Stonehenge are treated (seriously) than others.
most convincingly 14. Scholars who claim that Stonehenge was a place of worship seem to argue (convincingly) of all.
more deeply 15. Stonehenge remains a mysterious site that affected me (deeply) than I had imagined.

Notes for Home: Your child used different kinds of adverbs to describe things that happen. ***Home Activity:*** Challenge your child to list as many adverbs as she or he can in one minute. Then have your child make up sentences with the adverbs.

Name ______________________ The Seven Wonders of the Ancient World

Grammar: Using Adjectives and Adverbs to Improve Sentences

To be vivid and precise or to be clear and interesting, a sentence needs descriptive details.

- Add adjectives to describe nouns and pronouns. They can tell which one, how many, how much, or what kind.
- Add adverbs to describe actions. They can tell when, where, and how.
  Without adjectives and adverbs: The tour continued.
  With adjectives and adverbs: The museum tour continued slowly.

Directions: Read each sentence. Underline each adjective and adverb. Draw an arrow to the word it describes.

1. Komiko spoke happily about her interesting trip to Greece.
2. She travels most often to historic places.
3. In Athens, Greece, she admired the magnificent temple of Athena greatly.
4. She writes excitedly about these foreign travels.
5. On another fascinating trip, Komiko saw ancient Egyptian pyramids.

Directions: Add an adjective or adverb to make each sentence more vivid or precise. Then rewrite each sentence on the line. **Possible answers given.**

6. Komiko lectures about her travels.
Komiko skillfully lectures about her travels.
7. People await her talks.
People eagerly await her interesting talks.
8. When she gives a lecture, the hall is full.
When she gives a lecture, the hall is usually full.
9. Her slide presentations show the ruins of ancient civilizations.
Her colorful slide presentations vividly show the ruins of ancient civilizations.
10. I love to hear her talk about places.
I love to hear her talk about unusual places.

Notes for Home: Your child identified adjectives and adverbs and used them to make sentences more descriptive. ***Home Activity:*** Give your child pairs of similar adjectives and adverbs, such as *quick* and *quickly*. Have him or her use each of the words in a sentence.

Name ______________________ The Seven Wonders of the Ancient World

Grammar: Using Adjectives and Adverbs to Improve Sentences

Directions: Write a different adjective or adverb to replace the one that is underlined. **Possible answers given.**

interesting 1. The Great Pyramid is an impressive structure.
carefully 2. When I was there, I listened attentively to the guide.
fascinated 3. I was curious to learn how such a structure could have been built.
most popular 4. The Great Pyramid is one of the most famous places in Egypt.
happily 5. I quickly agreed to a sightseeing trip down the Nile River.

Directions: Add adjectives or adverbs to improve each sentence. Write the new sentence on the line. **Possible answers given.**

6. After every trip, I return home.
After every trip, I reluctantly return home.
7. Last year, I took a boat trip on the Aegean Sea.
Last year, I took a wonderful boat trip on the Aegean Sea.
8. We docked at an island called Rhodes.
We docked at a famous island called Rhodes.
9. I stared out at the sea.
I stared sadly out at the sea.
10. I thought about the Colossus of Rhodes that used to tower over the harbor.
I thought about the great Colossus of Rhodes that used to tower over the harbor.

Write a Diary Entry

On a separate sheet of paper, write a diary entry about a favorite place. It can be either a place you already know or a place you'd like to visit. Use adjectives and adverbs to describe the place and the types of activities you enjoy there. **Students should write about a favorite place. Check for correct use of adjectives and adverbs.**

Notes for Home: Your child identified and supplied adjectives and adverbs in sentences. ***Home Activity:*** Pick a place you and your child would like to visit. Take turns describing what you want to see and do. Use adjectives and adverbs in your sentences.

Grammar Practice Book 6.4, p. 94

Name ______________________

The Seven Wonders of the Ancient World

Grammar: Using Adjectives and Adverbs to Improve Sentences

RETEACHING

Circle the adjective. Underline the adverb.

1. We spoke quietly to the small child.

Add one adjective and one adverb to improve the sentence. **Possible answers given.**

2. The raft floated.
   The light raft floated gracefully.

Add **adjectives** and **adverbs** to provide more information about nouns and verbs in sentences, and to make sentences more interesting.

Directions: Add an adjective and/or an adverb to each sentence. Write the new sentence on the line. **Possible answers given.**

1. The movie would begin.
   The movie would begin soon.
2. My friend Janine chewed her popcorn.
   My friend Janine chewed her popcorn loudly.
3. The lights grew dim.
   The bright lights grew dim.
4. The actor appeared.
   The young actor appeared.
5. There was a conversation among the characters.
   There was a short conversation among the characters.
6. Janine laughed at parts.
   Janine laughed loudly at funny parts.
7. People behind us asked her to laugh more quietly.
   Some people behind us asked her to laugh more quietly.
8. When the movie ended, we walked home.
   When the movie ended, we walked home slowly.

Notes for Home: Your child added adjectives and adverbs to sentences to make them more interesting. ***Home Activity:*** Write some simple sentences for your child. Then have him or her add adjectives and adverbs to provide more detail for the reader.

Grammar Practice Book 6.4, p. 95

Name ______________________

The Seven Wonders of the Ancient World

Grammar: Using Adjectives and Adverbs to Improve Sentences

Directions: Read each sentence. Underline each adjective and each adverb. Draw an arrow to the word it describes.

1. Fishing can be more exciting than some people think.
2. My grandfather tells some wild stories about frogs that ask questions clearly.
3. Sometimes he says that they generously tell him where to catch the best fish.
4. I'm not sure I believe all of his funny stories, but they make time pass more quickly.
5. Next time I go on a long trip with Grandpa, I'm going to ask him to help me create new stories.

Directions: Add adjectives or adverbs to improve each sentence. Write the new sentence on the line. **Possible answers given.**

6. Boats bob in the water.
   Boats bob jauntily in the water.
7. When the sun sets, you can see colors in the sky.
   When the sun sets, you can see extraordinary colors in the sky.
8. I like to sit on the end of our dock and watch the clouds change color.
   I like to sit on the end of our dock and quietly watch the clouds change color.
9. My dog joins me.
   My big dog joins me.
10. I make up songs about what I see.
    I make up cheerful songs about what I see.

Write a Song

Write a song about what you might see when the sun goes down. Be creative. Your song may include what animals and plants do when the sun sets. Use at least two adjectives and two adverbs in your song.

Make sure that students have used at least two adjectives and two adverbs in their songs.

Notes for Home: Your child used adjectives and adverbs to improve sentences. ***Home Activity:*** Together, listen to a favorite song. Have your child write down some of the adjectives and adverbs used in the song. Then have your child make up sentences, using those adjectives and adverbs.

Practice Book 6.4, p. 188

Name ______________________

The Seven Wonders of the Ancient World

Word Study: Syllabication; Common Syllable Patterns

- Knowing how to divide words into their syllable parts can help you read and understand them better
- **VCV:** If a word with two syllables has one consonant between two vowels, and the first syllable has a short vowel sound, then the word is divided after the consonant, such as **lev • er.**
- **VCV:** If a word with two syllables has one consonant between two vowels, and the first syllable has a long vowel sound, then the word is divided after the first vowel sound, such as **re • mind.**
- **VCCV:** If a word with two syllables has two consonants between two vowels, then the word is divided between the middle consonants, such as **won • der.**
- **VCCV/VCCCV:** If a word with two syllables has a consonant blend (such as **dr**) or a digraph (such as **th**) between two vowels, then the word is divided after the blend or digraph if the first vowel is short, like **fast • er,** or before the blend or digraph if the vowel is long, such as **re • think.** Follow these same rules, if there are three consonants and two of them are a blend or digraph, such as **hun • dred.**

Directions: Read the words in the box. Sort the words according to the syllable patterns. Write the words to show the syllables like this: **won · der.**

seven	organs	repaint	modern	travel
garden	terrace	chamber	farthest	workmen
destroy	merchants	Romans	worship	smother

Pattern VCV	Pattern VCCV	Pattern VCCCV
1. **sev • en**	6. **or • gans**	11. **mer • chants**
2. **mod • ern**	7. **cham • ber**	12. **wor • ship**
3. **re • paint**	8. **ter • race**	13. **work • men**
4. **Ro • mans**	9. **gar • den**	14. **far • thest**
5. **trav • el**	10. **smoth • er**	15. **de • stroy**

Notes for Home: Your child explored vowel-consonant patterns, such as VCV in *lever,* VCCV in *wonder,* and VCCCV in *hundred,* to divide words into syllables. ***Home Activity:*** Together, make a list of words with two or more syllables. Use the rules above to divide each word.

Spelling Workbook 6.4, p. 73

Name ______________________

The Seven Wonders of the Ancient World

Spelling: One Consonant or Two?

Pretest Directions: Fold back the page along the dotted line. On the blanks, write the spelling words as they are dictated. When you have finished the test, unfold the page and check your words.

1. **connect**	1. The flights **connect** in Rome.
2. **command**	2. My dog obeys that **command.**
3. **mirror**	3. How much does the **mirror** cost?
4. **accomplish**	4. Will they **accomplish** their goal?
5. **according**	5. We proceeded **according** to plan.
6. **allowance**	6. His **allowance** is one dollar.
7. **college**	7. Sonia's sister went to **college.**
8. **address**	8. Print your **address** clearly.
9. **Mississippi**	9. The **Mississippi** River flooded.
10. **recess**	10. We have **recess** at noon.
11. **committee**	11. Our **committee** will plan the trip.
12. **immediate**	12. What are your **immediate** plans?
13. **barricade**	13. A **barricade** surrounds the fort.
14. **interrupt**	14. It is impolite to **interrupt.**
15. **broccoli**	15. Lani ate all of her **broccoli.**
16. **collect**	16. They **collect** rare stamps.
17. **afford**	17. Can you **afford** the movie ticket?
18. **possess**	18. They **possess** a lot of land.
19. **Tennessee**	19. They drove through **Tennessee.**
20. **announce**	20. Who will **announce** the winner?

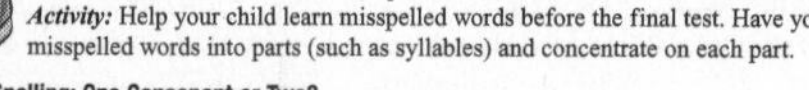

Notes for Home: Your child took a pretest on words that have double consonants. ***Home Activity:*** Help your child learn misspelled words before the final test. Have your child divide misspelled words into parts (such as syllables) and concentrate on each part.

Spelling Workbook 6.4, p. 74

Name ______________________

The Seven Wonders of the Ancient World

Spelling: One Consonant or Two?

Word List				
connect	according	Mississippi	barricade	afford
command	allowance	recess	interrupt	possess
mirror	college	committee	broccoli	Tennessee
accomplish	address	immediate	collect	announce

Directions: Sort the words from the box according to their double consonants. Write the words in the correct column. **Order may vary.**

The Double Consonants r or c

1. mirror
2. accomplish
3. according
4. barricade
5. interrupt
6. broccoli

Two or More Sets of Double Consonants

7. address
8. Mississippi
9. committee
10. possess
11. Tennessee

Directions: Choose the word from the box that best matches each clue. Write the missing letters of the word in the puzzle.

12. type of school — 12. c o l l e g e
13. group together — 13. c o l l e c t
14. right now — 14. i m m e d i a t e
15. sum of money paid regularly — 15. a l l o w a n c e
16. order — 16. c o m m a n d
17. have the money to buy — 17. a f f o r d
18. school "playtime" — 18. r e c e s s
19. make a public statement — 19. a n n o u n c e
20. join together — 20. c o n n e c t

Notes for Home: Your child spelled words containing double consonants that stand for only one sound, such as *afford*. ***Home Activity:*** Scramble the letters for each spelling word. Challenge your child to unscramble them so that the words are spelled correctly.

Spelling Workbook 6.4, p. 75

Name ______________________

The Seven Wonders of the Ancient World

Spelling: One Consonant or Two?

Directions: Proofread this travel brochure. Find five spelling mistakes. Use the proofreading marks to correct each mistake.

- ≡ Make a capital.
- / Make a small letter.
- ∧ Add something.
- Take out something.
- ⊙ Add a period.
- ¶ Begin a new paragraph.

The Travel Comittee [m] of Community Collige [e] is proud to announce a new tour offering. We call it the Mayan Quest. We'll conect [n] with our tour guides on our journey through several Mayan city-states. The guides will take you through the ruins of pyramids, palaces, and temples. You will see paintings, carvings, and other relics as you discover what the Mayan culture was able to acommplish [c]. This fifteen-day trip is one you cannot afford to miss. An imediate [m] response to our offer is recommended.

Spelling Tip

All the spelling words have double consonants that stand for only one sound, as in **afford.** Try to think of a clue that will help you remember when double consonants are needed. Example: *I can **afford** to have a second **f**.*

Word List	
connect	committee
command	immediate
mirror	barricade
accomplish	interrupt
according	broccoli
allowance	collect
college	afford
address	possess
Mississippi	Tennessee
recess	announce

Write a Travel Brochure

On a separate sheet of paper, write a travel brochure to encourage people to visit the ruins of an ancient civilization. What will they see there? Why is it important or noteworthy? You may need to do some research before you write. Try to use at least five of your spelling words. **Students may need time to do research before they begin writing. Answers will vary, but each brochure should include at least five spelling words.**

Notes for Home: Your child spelled words containing double consonants that stand for only one sound, such as *afford*. ***Home Activity:*** Challenge your child to find examples of other words that have two or more sets of double consonants.

Spelling Workbook 6.4, p. 76

Name ______________________

The Seven Wonders of the Ancient World

Spelling: One Consonant or Two? REVIEW

Word List				
connect	according	Mississippi	barricade	afford
command	allowance	recess	interrupt	possess
mirror	college	committee	broccoli	Tennessee
accomplish	address	immediate	collect	announce

Directions: Write the word from the box that belongs in each group.

1. asparagus, cauliflower, **broccoli**
2. order, direct, **command**
3. Minnesota, Missouri, **Mississippi**
4. school, university, **college**
5. achieve, finish, **accomplish**
6. join, unite, **connect**
7. instant, now, **immediate**
8. council, group, **committee**
9. barrier, wall, **barricade**
10. declare, report, **announce**
11. own, have, **possess**

Directions: Choose the word from the box that best matches each clue. Write the word on the line.

afford 12. I am what you can do when you have enough money.
mirror 13. I hang above the sink and show you your face every day.
Tennessee 14. I contain the cities of Nashville and Memphis.
recess 15. I am a break for fun during the school day.
address 16. I am written on all your mail.
collect 17. I am what many people do with baseball cards or stamps.
interrupt 18. I mean "to break into someone else's speech or actions."
according 19. I contain the word *cord.*
allowance 20. I am a sum of money given regularly to someone.

Notes for Home: Your child spelled words containing double consonants that stand for only one sound. ***Home Activity:*** List the spelling words, making some double consonants single and some single consonants double. Challenge your child to correct the misspellings.

Practice Book 6.4, p. 189

Name ______________________

The Seven Wonders of the Ancient World

Outlining

Outlining is a good way to organize information found in nonfiction texts. Outlines include main topics, subtopics, and details.

Directions: Read the nonfiction article. Think about the different civilizations described, when they lived, where they lived, and what happened to them. Then follow the directions to write an outline on the next page. Note: You may not need to fill in every line on the outline.

A **civilization** is a group of people who have a set class system of who owns and controls goods and services, political and religious structures, and people employed in a variety of positions. Scientists have classified several major ancient civilizations, among them the Sumerians, the Aegean, and the Mesoamericans.

The **Sumerians** are a people who occupied the lands of what is now called Iraq. They settled in the area about 5,000 years ago, around 3500 B.C.E. They spread northward through the Tigris-Euphrates Valley. During the early part of their civilization, the people formed small political units. As the civilization developed, these political groups began to war with each other. Eventually, the factions were united under a single ruler in the area that would later be known as Babylonia. The Sumerians lost their land and their identity when other invaders ultimately conquered the land around 2000 B.C.E.

The **Aegean** civilization arose during the Bronze Age, between 3000 and 1000 B.C.E. Early Aegean people were hunters who roamed Greece. Small settlements were then established. The first real civilization was established by the Minoan in Crete. It is believed that they used some form of writing. The next wave of the civilization's development is known as the Mycenaean. However, wars between Mycenaean states soon caused the Aegean civilization to die out.

The civilization of the **Mesoamericans** included such peoples as the Aztec, the Maya, and the Toltec. This civilization dates back to 1200 B.C.E. They lived in several areas of Mexico and Central America. Much of the Mesoamerican civilization was destroyed after the arrival of Spanish settlers in the A.D. 1500s.

- What are the three main topics of the article? Write each main topic at I, II, and III.
- What are some subtopics of the main topics I, II, III? Write each at A, B, and C.
- What details support the subtopics A, B, C? Write each at 1 and 2.

Practice Book 6.4, p. 190

Name

The Seven Wonders of the Ancient World

Title: Three Ancient Civilizations

Subtopics and details may vary. Check that students are grouping information logically. Possible answers given.

I. The Sumerians
- A. When did they live?
  1. first settled about 3500 B.C.E.
  2. died out about 2000 B.C.E.
- B. Where did they live?
  1. first settled in what is now Iraq
  2. spread north to Tigris-Euphrates Valley
- C. What happened to them?
  1. united under a single ruler
  2. were conquered by invaders

II. The Aegeans
- A. When did they live?
  1. between 3000 and 1000 B.C.E.
  2.
- B. Where did they live?
  1. roamed Greece
  2. first real civilization established in Crete
- C. What happened to them?
  1. Minoans replaced by Mycenaeans
  2. wars among Mycenaean states destroyed the Aegean civilization

III. The Mesoamericans
- A. When did they live?
  1. began around 1200 B.C.E.
  2. mostly destroyed in A.D. 1500s
- B. Where did they live?
  1. Mexico
  2. Central America
- C. What happened to them?
  1. nearly destroyed by Spanish settlers
  2.

Notes for Home: Your child organized information in an outline. ***Home Activity:*** Help your child use an outline to help study for an upcoming test. Review material to be tested and organize related information by main topics, subtopics, and details.

Practice Book 6.4, p. 191

Name

The Gold Coin

Author's Purpose

- **Author's purpose** refers to an author's reason or reasons for writing.
- Four common purposes for writing are to inform, to persuade, to entertain, and to express. Often an author has more than one purpose for writing.
- Understanding an author's purpose can help you adjust your reading speed and can help explain the author's choice of words and writing style.

Possible answers given.

Directions: Reread "The Tortoise in the Tree." Then complete the table by writing evidence from the story that supports the purposes given. Then give an example of another folk tale that shares these purposes. Explain your choice.

Author's Purpose	Evidence for Author's Purpose
To entertain	1. The tortoise cheerfully dabbed sticky tree gum on the hyena.
	2. The hyena looked as beautiful as a garbage heap.
To persuade	3. You have the coat you deserve.
	4. Don't play a trick on someone else unless you want them to play an even bigger trick on you.

Another Folk Tale That Entertains and Persuades

5. Examples will vary. Check that students explain how the folk tale entertains and persuades by teaching lessons about behavior.

Notes for Home: Your child identified and analyzed an author's purpose for writing a folk tale. ***Home Activity:*** Challenge your child to write a humorous story that explains an animal's behavior or appearance, such as "How the Whale Got Its Tale" or "Why Snakes Hiss."

Practice Book 6.4, p. 192

Name

The Gold Coin

Vocabulary

Directions: Choose the word from the box that best matches each definition. Write the word on the line.

Check the Words You Know
- __ distressed
- __ impatience
- __ insistent
- __ recovery
- __ stunned

insistent 1. continuing to demand

recovery 2. the process of regaining one's health or well-being

distressed 3. in great pain or sorrow

stunned 4. shocked

impatience 5. a lack of patience

Directions: Choose the word from the box that best completes each sentence. Write the word on the line to the left.

stunned 6. When the factory suddenly closed, Mr. Winters was _____ to find out that he had lost his job.

distressed 7. He was worried and _____ about his ability to find a new job.

impatience 8. During his first few weeks at home, Mr. Winters showed great _____; he wanted to settle into a new job as soon as possible.

insistent 9. Mrs. Winters knew that her husband liked learning new things, so she was _____ that he sign up for a job training class.

recovery 10. Now Mr. Winters has a job working with computers. His mood and his spirits have made a complete _____.

Write a News Story

On a separate sheet of paper, write a news story about someone who has turned his or her life around. The person can be someone you know or have heard of, or someone that you make up. Use as many vocabulary words as you can.

Students' news stories should use vocabulary words correctly.

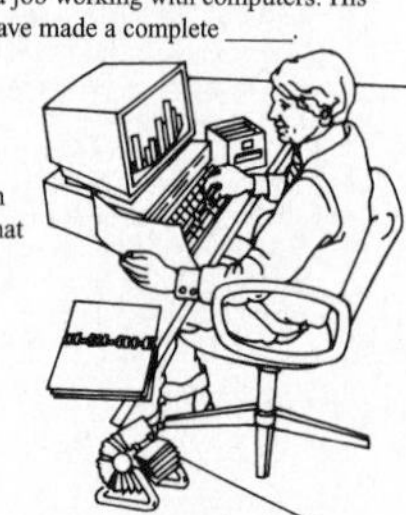

Notes for Home: Your child identified and used vocabulary words from *The Gold Coin*. ***Home Activity:*** Talk about a time when a family member recovered from an illness. Encourage your child to use the vocabulary words to describe how the person felt.

Practice Book 6.4, p. 193

Name

The Gold Coin

Author's Purpose

- The **author's purpose** is the reason or reasons an author has for writing.
- Four common purposes for writing are to inform, to persuade, to entertain, and to express. Often an author has more than one purpose.

Directions: Reread the scene from *The Gold Coin* in which Juan begins to change. Then answer the questions below. Think about why the author is telling this story. **Possible answers given.**

"If you'd like, I'll take you there tomorrow. But first I must gather my squash and beans."

So Juan spent another long day in the fields. Working beneath the summer sun, Juan noticed that his skin had begun to tan. And although he had to stoop down to pick the squash, he found that he could now stretch his body. His back had begun to straighten too.

Later, when the little girl took him by the hand to show him a family of rabbits burrowed under a fallen tree, Juan's face broke into a smile. It had been a long, long time since Juan had smiled.

From THE GOLD COIN by Alma Flor Ada. Text copyright © 1991, by Alma Flor Ada. Reprinted with permission of Atheneum Books for Young Readers, Simon & Schuster Children's Publishing Division.

1. How is Juan changing? **He is getting more tanned, his back is straightening, and he smiles.**
2. What is Juan learning? **He is beginning to appreciate and enjoy hard work and helping others.**
3. Why does the author include the detail about the little girl and the rabbits? **She wants to entertain the reader with a lively detail.**
4. What is the purpose of this passage? How do you know? **The purpose is to entertain by giving colorful details like the rabbit family and to teach by suggesting that working hard and helping others will make you happy.**
5. On a separate sheet of paper, explain why you think the author wrote this story. Give specific examples from the story to support your answer. **The author wanted to entertain by telling a story about an interesting character who travels and has adventures. She wanted to teach the reader that wealth is not necessary to happiness by showing that happy people do not want gold.**

Notes for Home: Your child read a folk tale and identified the author's purpose. ***Home Activity:*** Encourage your child to read a movie review, a letter to the editor, and a sports article. Have your child tell you each author's purpose and explain his or her answers.

Practice Book 6.4, p. 195

Name ______________________ **The Gold Coin**

Selection Test

Directions: Choose the best answer to each item. Mark the letter for the answer you have chosen.

Part 1: Vocabulary

Find the answer choice that means about the same as the underlined word in each sentence.

1. Everyone noticed his <u>impatience</u>.
   - A. lack of control
   - Ⓑ unwillingness to put up with delay
   - C. lack of manners
   - D. shyness
2. Her plea was <u>insistent</u>.
   - F. fearless
   - G. showing bad judgment
   - H. unfriendly; hostile
   - Ⓙ pressing; urgent
3. We were <u>stunned</u> by the news.
   - Ⓐ shocked
   - B. pleased
   - C. excited
   - D. angered
4. My uncle made a full <u>recovery</u>.
   - F. act of arranging things in a new way
   - G. process of repeating or summing up
   - Ⓗ process of regaining one's health
   - J. act of finding something out
5. The old woman looked <u>distressed</u>.
   - A. feeling or showing scorn
   - B. in high spirits; excited
   - C. annoyed or angered
   - Ⓓ in great pain or sorrow

Part 2: Comprehension

Use what you know about the story to answer each item.

6. Juan looked pale because he—
   - F. had been ill.
   - Ⓖ worked by night.
   - H. came from a cold country.
   - J. had no friends.
7. Juan heard Doña Josefa say that she must be the—
   - A. luckiest person in the world.
   - B. hardest-working person in the world.
   - C. busiest person in the world.
   - Ⓓ richest person in the world.
8. As he tried to catch up with Doña Josefa, Juan first had to—
   - Ⓕ cross a river.
   - G. plant crops on a farm.
   - H. climb a mountain.
   - J. learn to ride a horse.
9. One big change that Juan noticed in himself was that he—
   - A. followed Doña Josefa everywhere.
   - B. learned to enjoy eating potatoes.
   - Ⓒ smiled at a little girl.
   - D. caught an illness from one of the people he met.
10. Why did Doña Josefa keep moving from house to house?
    - F. She had many friends and relations.
    - G. She was a house cleaner.
    - H. She liked to travel to different places.
    - Ⓙ She took care of sick people.
11. How is the text of this story organized?
    - Ⓐ chronological order
    - B. cause and effect
    - C. problem and solution
    - D. comparison and contrast
12. One of the author's main purposes in this story is to—
    - F. explain farm work.
    - G. compare Juan with Doña Josefa.
    - Ⓗ teach a lesson.
    - J. describe Doña Josefa's work.

Practice Book 6.4, p. 196

Name ______________________ **The Gold Coin**

13. Why is "The Gold Coin" a good title for this story?
    - A. The gold coin has Juan's name printed on it.
    - Ⓑ The gold coin is a symbol of Juan's greed and Doña Josefa's generosity.
    - C. Readers will be attracted to the story because people are attracted to gold.
    - D. The gold coin represents the hopes and dreams of the people in the story.
14. Which sentence best states a theme of this story?
    - F. Good things come to those who wait.
    - Ⓖ The key to happiness is giving to others.
    - H. Wealth comes to those who most deserve it.
    - J. One gold coin can make many people happy.
15. What is the most important change that has taken place between the first time Juan comes to Doña Josefa's house and the next?
    - A. Doña Josefa is not quite as willing to help her neighbors as before.
    - B. A storm is fast approaching.
    - Ⓒ Juan decides to help Doña Josefa rather than simply satisfy his own greed.
    - D. The house is now in ruins.

STOP

Name ______________________ **The Gold Coin**

Author's Purpose

- The **author's purpose** is the reason or reasons an author has for writing.
- Four common purposes for writing are to inform, to persuade, to entertain, and to express. Often an author has more than one purpose.

Directions: Read the story below.

> A poor boy named Tom went to sea to seek his fortune with his only friend, a cat named Trapper. One day Trapper gave birth to six kittens. The ship's captain hated cats, so Tom hid them in the hold.
>
> Six months later the captain landed on an island in hopes of trading with the people there. However, the islanders were too upset to think about trading. Swarms of rats were terrorizing their villages. Tom offered his kittens for trade. "Just what we need!" cried the islanders.
>
> For the rest of his life, the captain never sailed without a cat on board.

Directions: Complete the table below. In the first row, list the author's purpose or purposes for writing the story above, and give an explanation for your answer. Then for each purpose listed, give an example of a specific text you've read that fits that purpose. Explain your choices.

Answers will vary. Make sure students support their choices.

Author's Purpose	Title and Explanation
1. **To entertain**	2. **no title; The character of the captain is interesting, and his sudden love of cats is funny.**
to inform	3. **Students will likely name a nonfiction book or article.**
to persuade	4. **Students may name an advertisement or a letter to the editor.**
to entertain	5. **Students may name a humorous story or a favorite comic strip or comic book.**
to express	*Wilma Unlimited,* by Kathleen Krull, expresses Wilma Rudolph's courage and determination to walk again.

Notes for Home: Your child identified an author's purpose for writing. ***Home Activity:*** Talk about different types of books, articles, or movies that you and your child have read or seen. Discuss why a writer would write this material.

Practice Book 6.4, p. 197

Name ______________________ **The Gold Coin**

Drawing Conclusions

REVIEW

Directions: Read the story. Then read each question about the story. Choose the best answer to each question. Mark the letter for the answer you have chosen.

A Frog Fable

Once three frogs lived in a shallow pond. Summer came and with it a severe drought. Their pond shrank to a mud puddle. Two of the frogs decided to search for a new home elsewhere. The third, however, claimed she'd just as soon die in their familiar puddle as some strange lake. She refused to go. Finally, her two friends left her. They promised to return as soon as the drought ended. She watched as they hopped away into the distance.

The two frogs hopped a long way, seeking water. At the end of the first day, they came to an old well. It was so dark by then that they could not see the bottom.

"Surely there is water down below. Let's hop right in!" said the first frog, leaping to the top of the wall.

"Wait, wait!" cried her friend. "We must find out for sure before you leap! What if there is no water down below? What if there is no way to climb out?"

"I know what we'll do!" said the first frog. "You will have to help me, though. We will push this pebble over the edge and listen hard. If we hear a splash, we will know there is water. We can also guess how deep it is and how far we will have to fall before we hit the water. If it is high enough, we can climb out whenever we want."

Working together, the tired frogs shoved the pebble over the side. PLUNK! It hit water almost immediately. Relieved that their suffering was over, they jumped into the well.

Suddenly, there was a booming of thunder! "Rain!" cried the first frog. "The drought is over!"

1. Why did the third frog stay behind?
   - Ⓐ She was afraid of the unknown.
   - B. She knew it would rain.
   - C. She was happy in the mud puddle.
   - D. She hated water.
2. What makes the first two frogs leave the third frog behind?
   - F. They are thirstier than she is.
   - Ⓖ They are braver than she is.
   - H. They like to travel.
   - J. They want to see the world beyond the pond.
3. Why does one frog hesitate at the side of the well?
   - A. She is afraid of the dark.
   - Ⓑ She is afraid leaping into the well may be dangerous.
   - C. She has changed her mind and wants to go home.
   - D. She is angry at the first frog.
4. The frogs know it is safe to jump in the well because—
   - Ⓕ they hear the splash from the pebble right away.
   - G. they hear nothing after tossing the pebble in the well.
   - H. it begins to rain.
   - J. they can see the water when the sun rises.
5. What will the two frogs do now that it's raining?
   - A. stay in the well
   - Ⓑ return to their home
   - C. drown in the well
   - D. push another pebble into the well

Notes for Home: Your child read a story and formed conclusions about its characters. ***Home Activity:*** With your child, think of other well-known folk tales or fables. Discuss why characters act a certain way and what lessons they may have learned.

Name ____________________ **The Gold Coin**

Writing Across Texts

Directions: Although *The Gold Coin* and "Pecos Bill and the Cyclone" are both traditional regional tales, they are very different in style, mood, and theme. Think about the differences between the two stories. How would you contrast these two stories? Write your ideas in the table below. **Possible answers given.**

Differences Between *The Gold Coin* and "Pecos Bill and the Cyclone"
The Gold Coin teaches a lesson. "Pecos Bill and the Cyclone" seems to be written for pure enjoyment.
1. ***The Gold Coin* is serious and somber. "Pecos Bill and the Cyclone" is light and fun.**
2. ***The Gold Coin* is realistic. "Pecos Bill and the Cyclone" is fantasy.**
3. **"Pecos Bill and the Cyclone" uses dialect. *The Gold Coin* does not.**
4. **The main character in *The Gold Coin* is a "bad guy." The main character in "Pecos Bill and the Cyclone" is "a good guy."**
5. **The virtue of generosity is a main focus in *The Gold Coin.* The virtue of taking what you need is a main focus in "Pecos Bill and the Cyclone."**

Write an Explanation

On a separate sheet of paper, write an explanation of how *The Gold Coin* and "Pecos Bill and the Cyclone" are different in style, mood, and theme. Support your opinions with information from each story. **Explanations will vary. Check that students identify style, mood, and theme accurately and use information from the selections to support their opinions.**

Notes for Home: Your child contrasted two different traditional stories. ***Home Activity:*** Together, read aloud folk tales from two different regions. Help your child list the differences between the style, mood, and theme of the stories.

Writing Across Texts 437

Grammar Practice Book 6.4, p. 96

Name ____________________ **The Gold Coin**

Grammar: Using Adjectives and Adverbs to Improve Sentences

REVIEW

Directions: Add adjectives and/or adverbs to improve the sentences below. Write each new sentence on the line. **Possible answers given.**

1. A frog leaped out of the pond.
A lively young frog leaped out of the little pond.

2. A fly landed on a leaf.
A huge fly landed smoothly on a leaf nearby.

3. The two creatures stared at each other.
The two creatures stared at each other curiously.

4. "Hello," said the frog.
"Hello," said the frog politely.

5. "Humm," buzzed the fly.
"Humm," buzzed the cautious fly.

Directions: Cross out any unneeded adjectives or adverbs in the sentences below. Write your new sentence on the line. **Possible answers given.**

6. "Do I ~~actually~~ know you?" asked the friendly ~~young green~~ frog.
"Do I know you?" asked the friendly frog.

7. "Humm," loudly buzzed the ~~same old~~ fly again.
"Humm," loudly buzzed the fly again.

8. The small ~~young~~ frog looked at the fly thoughtfully ~~and carefully.~~
The small frog looked at the fly thoughtfully.

9. Then ~~soon~~ he stuck out his sticky, ~~gooey~~ tongue, caught the fly, and ~~immediately~~ swallowed it instantly.
Then he stuck out his sticky tongue, caught the fly, and swallowed it instantly.

10. "Yumm," buzzed the happy, ~~smiling~~ frog.
"Yumm," buzzed the happy frog.

Notes for Home: Your child improved sentences by adding needed adjectives and adverbs and removing unneeded ones. ***Home Activity:*** Have your child write some sentences about a person you both know. Then challenge your child to add and/or remove some adjectives and adverbs.

438 Grammar: Using Adjectives and Adverbs to Improve Sentences

Grammar Practice Book 6.4, p. 97

Name ____________________ **The Gold Coin**

Grammar: Avoiding Misplaced Modifiers

Adjectives and adverbs are called modifiers because they modify, or tell more about, nouns and verbs. In doing so, these modifiers affect the meanings of the nouns and verbs.

Phrases can affect the meaning of nouns and verbs too, as in the following sentence:

<u>With spray paint</u>, vandals seriously damaged the pleasant old city's appearance.

Watch for misplaced modifiers. To avoid confusion, keep modifiers close to the words they modify. Note how the meaning changes when the misplaced modifier in the sentence below is moved closer to the word it is meant to modify.

Misplaced: With nothing better to do, Judge Alvarez said that two strangers had defaced their city's buildings.

Correct: Judge Alvarez said that two strangers with nothing better to do had defaced their city's buildings.

Directions: Read each sentence. If the sentence is correct, write **C** on the line. If it contains a misplaced modifier, write **NC** on the line and circle the misplaced modifier.

C 1. Foolishly, the men thought no one had seen what they had done.

C 2. On the street, people had seen two men running with cans of spray paint.

C 3. These witnesses called the police immediately and appeared in court later.

C 4. Fortunately, the city had laws against graffiti (words and pictures drawn on walls and buildings) and owned a machine for removing it.

NC 5. In court, the mayor described the graffiti on one wall (with an outraged face).

NC 6. He said that the vandals should clean the wall (angrily).

C 7. The guilty men faced three possible penalties: detention in jail, heavy fines, or community service.

C 8. As a second chance, the judge sentenced them to community service in the city.

NC 9. (Carefully) the relieved men agreed to operate the graffiti-removal machine.

NC 10. They offered to do other useful work, too, and apologized sincerely for their past behavior (on local TV).

Notes for Home: Your child identified misplaced modifiers. ***Home Activity:*** Say *Teri took a picture of a snake <u>with her new camera</u>.* Have your child identify the misplaced modifier and explain why it is misplaced (*with her new camera* seems to refer to the snake instead of to Teri).

Grammar: Avoiding Misplaced Modifiers 439

Grammar Practice Book 6.4, p. 98

Name ____________________ **The Gold Coin**

Grammar: Avoiding Misplaced Modifiers

Directions: Read each sentence. If a sentence contains a misplaced modifier, think about the word or words it should describe. Then write the sentence correctly on the line. If a sentence is already correct, write **C** on the line.

1. Mrs. Vu entered a local library full of complaints.
Full of complaints, Mrs. Vu entered a local library.

2. "The outside looks terrible," she said, "with trash, weedy grass, and no flowers."
C

3. She annoyed everyone with the same kinds of complaints.
With the same kinds of complaints, she annoyed everyone.

4. The city needed more money to support the library badly.
The city badly needed more money to support the library.

5. Mrs. Vu suddenly stopped criticizing and started to help.
C

6. She ran fundraising auctions and found donors without much training.
Without much training, she ran fundraising auctions and found donors.

7. Thick, green, and healthy, business people donated a new lawn.
Business people donated a thick, green, and healthy new lawn.

8. Bright flowers pleased library users in window boxes.
Bright flowers in window boxes pleased library users.

9. As a woman of action, everyone praised Mrs. Vu's success.
Everyone praised Mrs. Vu's success as a woman of action.

10. Now, the librarians happily watch her daily arrival through the window.
Now, through the window, the librarians happily watch her daily arrival.

Write a Project Profile

On a separate sheet of paper, write a description of a local project you would like to start or be involved with. Make sure there are no misplaced modifiers in your description. **Check that all modifiers are correctly placed.**

Notes for Home: Your child identified misplaced modifiers. ***Home Activity:*** Write a sentence with a misplaced modifier such as *Sally saw the bear <u>looking through her binoculars</u>.* Have your child rewrite the sentence to correct the misplaced modifier.

440 Grammar: Avoiding Misplaced Modifiers

Grammar Practice Book 6.4, p. 99

Name ______________________ The Gold Coin

Grammar: Avoiding Misplaced Modifiers

RETEACHING

Rewrite the sentence so that it makes sense.

I asked a woman if I could borrow her flashlight from down the block.

I asked a woman from down the block if I could borrow her flashlight.

Modifiers are words or phrases that tell more about nouns and verbs. Sometimes the placement of a modifier is incorrect, and the sentence doesn't make sense. To avoid confusion, keep modifiers close to the words they modify.

Directions: Read each sentence. If the sentence is correct, write **C** on the short line. If it contains a misplaced modifier, write **NC** on the line and write the sentence correctly.

NC 1. A song was playing on the radio about a traveling artist.
A song about a traveling artist was playing on the radio.

NC 2. That girl asked me a question who was interested in painting.
That girl who was interested in painting asked me a question.

C 3. A boy in my math class offered to help me study for the test.

NC 4. My neighbor walked his dog who sings in the opera.
My neighbor who sings in the opera walked his dog.

C 5. The television commercial advertised a new way to brush your teeth.

NC 6. In great detail, the boy agreed to paint the castle.
The boy agreed to paint the castle in great detail.

NC 7. In the sky, several people saw a flock of geese flying.
Several people saw a flock of geese flying in the sky.

Notes for Home: Your child identified misplaced modifiers in sentences and wrote the sentences correctly. ***Home Activity:*** Have your child use some of the sentences on this page to explain to you the importance of keeping modifiers near the words or phrases they modify.

Grammar: Avoiding Misplaced Modifiers 441

Grammar Practice Book 6.4, p. 100

Name ______________________ The Gold Coin

Grammar: Avoiding Misplaced Modifiers

Directions: Read each sentence. If the sentence is correct, write **C** on the line. If it contains a misplaced modifier, write **NC** on the line and circle the misplaced modifier.

NC 1. (Brightly,) my family saw the sun shine through the windows.

C 2. My brother thought it looked like a beautiful golden shower.

NC 3. My sister needed help climbing up on the chair, (who is younger than me.)

NC 4. (Loudly,) my grandmother told me about the foghorn that used to sound near her childhood home.

C 5. I whispered softly to the sleeping kitten.

Directions: Read each sentence. If a sentence contains a misplaced modifier, write the sentence correctly on the line. If the sentence is correct, write **correct** on the line.

6. A rabbit ate a carrot with long, floppy ears.
A rabbit with long, floppy ears ate a carrot.

7. A girl trains horses in my class.
A girl in my class trains horses.

8. A man climbs mountains on my block.
A man on my block climbs mountains.

9. My sister who dances is going to leave school early today.
correct

10. A boy found a dog from my sister's math class.
A boy from my sister's math class found a dog.

Write a Funny Story

Sentences with misplaced modifiers can be funny. Write a four-sentence story with sentences that have misplaced modifiers. Then rewrite the story so that the sentences make sense. Check your work carefully to make sure you have written modifiers in the correct places.

Make sure students have used modifiers correctly.

Notes for Home: Your child identified misplaced modifiers and wrote modifiers correctly in sentences. ***Home Activity:*** Have your child read his or her funny story to you. Add a sentence with a misplaced modifier and have your child write it correctly.

442 Grammar: Avoiding Misplaced Modifiers

Practice Book 6.4, p. 198

Name ______________________ The Gold Coin

Word Study: Word Building

Directions: Read each sentence. Say the underlined word to yourself. Write the letters of the stressed syllable in capital letters and the unstressed syllables in lowercase letters. For example: write **garden** and **garage** as **GAR · den** and **ga · RAGE**.

DIFF • i • cult 1. It is sometimes difficult to understand how life used to be long ago.

i • MAG • ine 2. Imagine walking five miles to school every day instead of riding in a comfortable school bus!

fa • MIL • iar 3. The past will become more familiar if you compare it to the present.

REL • a • tive 4. To learn about your family's past, talk to an older relative.

com • PAN • ions 5. Try to keep in touch with family and companions in other parts of the country.

WON • der • ful 6. My aunt thinks it's wonderful that I keep in touch with my old friends.

im • PA • tience 7. My impatience to get letters often prompts me to make a telephone call.

COUN • try • side 8. Sometimes, I travel to the countryside to visit family members.

for • GOT • ten 9. Just remember, traditions will not be forgotten if we work to keep them alive.

Directions: Read the pairs of related words. Say each word to yourself. Circle the stressed syllable in each word.

10. (u)niverse 11. uni(ver)sal
12. (ac)cident 13. acci(den)tal
14. (his)tory 15. his(tor)ical

Notes for Home: Your child identified the stressed syllables in words such as *garden* (first syllable) and *garage* (second syllable). ***Home Activity:*** Read a poem or song lyrics with your child. Repeat individual words for your child. Work together to decide which syllable is stressed.

Word Study: Word Building 443

Spelling Workbook 6.4, p. 77

Name ______________________ The Gold Coin

Spelling: Related Words 1

Pretest Directions: Fold back the page along the dotted line. On the blanks, write the spelling words as they are dictated. When you have finished the test, unfold the page and check your words.

1. **human**	1. Language is a **human** trait.
2. **humane**	2. Treat animals in a **humane** way.
3. **clean**	3. Please **clean** your room.
4. **cleanse**	4. The rain will **cleanse** the street.
5. **nature**	5. He loved to be out in **nature**.
6. **natural**	6. She eats only **natural** foods.
7. **major**	7. His college **major** was English.
8. **majority**	8. A **majority** voted for her.
9. **poem**	9. What is your favorite **poem**?
10. **poetic**	10. Her speech was quite **poetic**.
11. **equal**	11. We all have **equal** rights.
12. **equation**	12. Please solve this **equation**.
13. **unite**	13. **Unite** for the common good.
14. **unity**	14. Understanding promotes **unity**.
15. **bomb**	15. They diffused the **bomb** in time.
16. **bombard**	16. He'll **bombard** us with questions.
17. **muscle**	17. Exercise builds **muscle**.
18. **muscular**	18. The athlete was very **muscular**.
19. **resign**	19. As of next week, I hereby **resign**.
20. **resignation**	20. Please hand in your **resignation**.

Notes for Home: Your child took a pretest on related words that have parts spelled the same but pronounced differently. ***Home Activity:*** Help your child learn misspelled words before the final test by underlining the parts that are different in each pair and concentrating on those.

444 Spelling: Related Words 1

Spelling Workbook 6.4, p. 78

Name ______________________ **The Gold Coin**

Spelling: Related Words 1

Word List				
human	nature	poem	unite	muscle
humane	natural	poetic	unity	muscular
clean	major	equal	bomb	resign
cleanse	majority	equation	bombard	resignation

Directions: Listen carefully as you read each word from the box aloud. Find the five pairs of related words in which the stressed syllable changes. For example, listen to the difference in stress between **office** and **official.** Write the words on the lines.

Order may vary.

Changes in Stressed Syllables

1. **human**
2. **humane**
3. **major**
4. **majority**
5. **equal**
6. **equation**
7. **unite**
8. **unity**
9. **resign**
10. **resignation**

Directions: Choose the word from the box that best matches each clue. Write the word on the line.

clean 11. I am what a shirt is after you wash it.
poem 12. I am written in verses that may or may not rhyme.
bomb 13. I am a weapon that explodes.
cleanse 14. I rhyme with *bends.*
muscular 15. I am how you might describe a strong athlete.
muscle 16. I am what makes you able to clench your fist.
nature 17. I include all things not made by humans, like forests and oceans.
poetic 18. I am how you might describe a nicely phrased sentence.
bombard 19. I am what children might do to each other with snowballs.
natural 20. I am the opposite of *artificial.*

Notes for Home: Your child spelled related words that have parts with similar spellings but different pronunciations, such as *human* and *humane. Home Activity:* Work with your child to use several spelling words to make a crossword puzzle.

Spelling Workbook 6.4, p. 79

Name ______________________ **The Gold Coin**

Spelling: Related Words 1

Directions: Proofread this "Help Wanted" ad for new storybook characters. Find six spelling mistakes. Use the proofreading marks to correct each mistake.

≡ Make a capital.
/ Make a small letter.
∧ Add something.
Take out something.
⊙ Add a period.
¶ Begin a new paragraph.

Help Wanted

Due to the resignasion of several characters, new folk tale heroes, villains, and comic sidekicks are needed. Applicants must be able to act in a mature manner. Villains should resign themselves to losing. Heroes must be able to treat all creatures in a humain fashion. A musculler shape is not necessary, but a clean face is required. The ability to use poetac language is a definite plus, especially for princes and knights! Equell opportunities will be given to all applicants, animal or humen. Come join our team!

Spelling Tip

Related words like *resign* and *resignation* have parts that are spelled the same but pronounced differently. Pronounce each word carefully to spell it correctly. Note that the **g** in **resign** is not silent when a suffix is added to form **resignation.**

Word List	
human	equal
humane	equation
clean	unite
cleanse	unity
nature	bomb
natural	bombard
major	muscle
majority	muscular
poem	resign
poetic	resignation

Write an Advertisement

On a separate sheet of paper, write an advertisement to find a replacement for a favorite book or movie character. Describe the qualities the applicant needs in order to fill the position. Try to use at least five of your spelling words.

Answers will vary, but each advertisement should include five spelling words.

Notes for Home: Your child spelled related words that have parts with similar spellings but different pronunciations, such as *human* and *humane. Home Activity:* Play a board game. Make the new rule that before moving, a player must spell a word from the box correctly.

Spelling Workbook 6.4, p. 80

Name ______________________ **The Gold Coin**

Spelling: Related Words 1

REVIEW

Word List				
human	nature	poem	unite	muscle
humane	natural	poetic	unity	muscular
clean	major	equal	bomb	resign
cleanse	majority	equation	bombard	resignation

Directions: Choose the word from the box that best completes each statement. Write the word on the line to the left.

muscle 1. *Breathe* is to *lung* as *move* is to _____.
natural 2. *Fake* is to *real* as *artificial* is to _____.
bomb 3. *Blast* is to *dynamite* as *explosion* is to _____.
muscular 4. *Weak* is to *flabby* as *powerful* is to _____.
humane 5. *Cruel* is to *kind* as *merciless* is to _____.
clean 6. *Messy* is to *dirty* as *neat* is to _____.
unite 7. *Separate* is to *join* as *divide* is to _____.
poem 8. *Stanza* is to *song* as *verse* is to _____.
equation 9. *English* is to *sentence* as *mathematics* is to _____.
human 10. *Mechanic* is to *car* as *doctor* is to _____.
major 11. *Small* is to *large* as *minor* is to _____.

Directions: Choose the word from the box that best replaces the underlined words. Write the word on the line.

resign 12. Glenda told the Villains' Committee that she would quit.
resignation 13. She gave them her written notice of quitting.
poetic 14. She made a speech laced with vivid, flowing language.
nature 15. Glenda was tired of struggling against all the forces at work in the world.
bombard 16. People would heavily attack her for her wicked deeds.
cleanse 17. Glenda wanted to make clean herself of all evil.
equal 18. She wanted to give the same time to doing good.
majority 19. The largest part of the Committee agreed to let her go.
unity 20. In a rare show of togetherness, the Committee agreed on a replacement.

Notes for Home: Your child spelled related words that have parts with similar spellings but different pronunciations. *Home Activity:* Challenge your child to find and spell a third word that relates to each pair of words on the list, such as *humane, human, humanity.*

Practice Book 6.4, p. 199

Name ______________________ **The Gold Coin**

Recipe

A **recipe** is a set of directions for preparing something to eat. It gives step-by-step instructions and may include pictures. Using recipes will strengthen your skills in following directions and understanding pictures or diagrams.

Directions: Read the recipe. Then answer the questions that follow.

Baked Chinese Egg Rolls

Ingredients:

1 cup all-purpose flour
2 cups water
2 eggs
$\frac{1}{2}$ teaspoon salt
3 tablespoons vegetable oil
$\frac{1}{2}$ cup chopped celery
$\frac{3}{4}$ cup chopped cabbage
4 scallions, chopped
$\frac{1}{2}$ cup diced shrimp
$\frac{1}{2}$ cup diced pork, cooked
$\frac{1}{2}$ cup chopped water chestnuts
$\frac{1}{2}$ cup bean sprouts
1 clove garlic, chopped
$\frac{1}{4}$ cup soy sauce
$\frac{1}{2}$ teaspoon sugar

Steps:

1. Sift flour into bowl.
2. Stir in water.
3. Beat in eggs and salt to make a smooth batter.
4. Grease a skillet with some cooking oil, butter, or margarine, and set the skillet on low heat.
5. Pour 1 tablespoon of batter into the pan to form a thin pancake. Flip so it cooks on the opposite side. Remove and set on a plate. Repeat Step 5 to make more thin pancakes. These are the outside of the egg rolls.
6. In another skillet, heat the vegetable oil.
7. Then add the celery, cabbage, and scallions. When they are nicely fried, stir in the shrimp and pork. Cook for about 3 minutes.
8. Then add the water chestnuts, bean sprouts, garlic, soy sauce, and sugar. Cook for another 5 minutes. This is the filling for the egg rolls.
9. Spoon about 4 tablespoons of filling onto each pancake.
10. Roll the pancake around the filling and fold up the ends.
11. Place on a tray in a 425°F oven for 15 minutes.
12. Serve with sweet-and-sour sauce, Chinese mustard, or soy sauce.

Makes about 12 egg rolls.

Practice Book 6.4, p. 200

Name ______________________ **The Gold Coin**

1. Before starting this recipe, which cooking tools would you need to get together?
Before cooking, I would need to get a bowl, a knife for chopping, two skillets, a plate, measuring cups, measuring spoons, a spoon, and a tray.

2. How is the list of ingredients organized? **It is organized according to the steps in the cooking process.**

3. In which way are most of the vegetables prepared? **Most of the vegetables are chopped, and then fried.**

4. What do you have to do to the pork before you can add it in Step 7? How do you know?
You have to cook the pork first. The list of ingredients says, "$\frac{1}{2}$ cup diced pork, *cooked*."

5. What part of the Baked Chinese Egg Rolls is made first? **The outside wrapping of the egg rolls is made first.**

6. Do you think you would be able to cook the pancakes and the vegetables at the same time? Why or why not?
Possible answer: If you were cooking alone, you probably could not cook the pancakes and the vegetables at the same time because it would be difficult to do both tasks.

7. If you had two dozen people to serve, what would you need to do to this recipe? Why?
You would need to double this recipe because it only serves one dozen people.

8. Why do you think the ingredients are listed separate from the steps of the recipe?
Possible answer: It helps to have the ingredients listed separately so you can get all your ingredients ready before you begin to follow the steps.

9. Do the pictures help you understand the recipe? Explain. **Possible answer: Yes, the pictures are helpful because they show some ingredients and the finished product.**

10. Why do you think using recipes will help you strengthen your skills in following directions and understanding pictures and diagrams?
Possible answer: You need to follow the directions in a recipe carefully and interpret and understand the information shown in a picture or diagram correctly or the food may not turn out well.

Notes for Home Your child read a recipe, and answered questions about its organization and contents. ***Home Activity:*** Help your child write a recipe for a favorite dish by listing the ingredients and steps to follow. Work together, using the recipe to make the dish.

Name ______________________

How-To Chart

The How-to chart should be filled out completely.

Directions: Fill in the how-to chart with information about your project.

Explain task ______________________

Materials ______________________

Introduction ______________________

Steps ______________________

Conclusion ______________________

Notes for Home: Your child has been preparing to write a how-to report. ***Home Activity:*** Think of a simple task such as setting the table, making popcorn, or playing a game. Ask your child to outline the steps in the process. Try it out. Are there any steps missing?

Name ______________________

Elaboration

Sense Words

- One way to elaborate is by adding **sense words** that help readers picture things clearly.
- You can provide vivid images by telling how things look, sound, feel, taste, and smell.

Responses will vary. Reasonable answers are given.

Directions: Add words from the box to make the sentences below more interesting. Write the new sentences using the words you picked.

autumn	crisp	fascinating	pine	smooth
bright	delicate	fragrant	sandy	unique
colorful	disposable	natural	small	

1. You can make crafts from objects.
You can make fascinating crafts from natural objects.

2. Search beaches for seashells.
Search sandy beaches for delicate seashells.

3. Hunt for leaves one day.
Hunt for leaves one crisp autumn day.

4. Check the forest for cones.
Check the forest for fragrant pine cones.

5. Be on the lookout for stones.
Be on the lookout for smooth, colorful stones.

6. Flowers can be pressed or ironed.
Bright flowers can be pressed or ironed.

7. Dye fruit seeds in containers.
Dye fruit seeds in small, disposable containers.

8. Make cards, mobiles, boxes, and frames.
Make unique cards, mobiles, boxes, and frames.

Notes for Home: Your child expanded sentences by adding sense words. ***Home Activity:*** Ask your child to describe something he or she has made, using sense words. For example: *I can make warm, tasty cocoa with a fluffy marshmallow on top.*

Name ______________________

Self-Evaluation Guide

How-to Report

Students' responses should show that they have given thought to the how-to reports that they have written.

Directions: Think about the final draft of your how-to report. Then answer each question below.

	Yes	No	Not sure
1. Did I include all the steps in the right order?			
2. Did I provide enough information to accomplish the task?			
3. Did I indicate the steps with words like *first* and *next?*			
4. Did I use clear sentences to guide my audience?			
5. Did I proofread and edit carefully to avoid errors?			

6. What did I learn from this report?

7. Write one thing that you could change to make this how-to report even better.

Notes for Home: Your child recently wrote a how-to report. ***Home Activity:*** Encourage your child to give you an oral explanation of the steps. You might also ask for a demonstration of the how-to report.

Practice Book 6.5, p. 201

Name ______________________ To the Pole

Fact and Opinion

- A **statement of fact** can be proven true or false. You can prove it true or false by reading, observing, asking an expert, or checking it in some way.
- A **statement of opinion** tells someone's belief, judgment, or way of thinking about something. It cannot be proven true or false, but it can be supported or explained.
- Some sentences contain both facts and opinions.

Directions: Reread "Mount Everest: The Ultimate Challenge." Then complete the table. Write **X** in the proper column to show whether each statement contains a fact or an opinion.

Statement	Fact	Opinion
1. The peak of Mount Everest used to be a tough place to reach.		X
2. The mountain is on the border of Nepal and China.	X	
3. Many climbers have come away with an incredible experience.		X
4. Climbers have contributed $90 million to Nepal's economy.	X	
5. Modern technology makes it easier for climbers to communicate with faraway people.	X	
6. Too many inexperienced climbers attempt to scale Everest's treacherous terrain.		X
7. About one in every thirty Everest climbers dies in the attempt.	X	
8. Eight climbers died in May 1996.	X	
9. Climbers leave behind oxygen cylinders, food remains, and other garbage.	X	
10. The May disaster will make climbers rethink their attitudes about climbing Mount Everest.		X

Notes for Home: Your child read an article and decided whether statements were statements of fact or opinion. ***Home Activity:*** Have your child describe his or her school day, giving at least three statements of fact and three statements of opinion.

Fact and Opinion 455

Practice Book 6.5, p. 202

Name ______________________ To the Pole

Vocabulary

Directions: Choose the word from the box that best completes each sentence. Write the word on the line to the left.

expeditions	**1.** I own many books about _____ to faraway places.
Arctic	**2.** I've always wanted to go to the _____ and reach the North Pole.
strenuous	**3.** I'm sure that hiking through a place like that would be _____.
terrain	**4.** The icy _____ creates challenges for even the most experienced explorers.
longitude	**5.** The weather conditions at that latitude and _____ can be quite severe.

Check the Words You Know
- __ Arctic
- __ collide
- __ expeditions
- __ latitude
- __ longitude
- __ satellite
- __ strenuous
- __ terrain

Directions: Choose the word from the box that best matches each clue. Write the word in the puzzle.

Down
6. distance north or south of the equator
8. natural features of a region
9. crash into something

Across
7. an artificial object that orbits around a planet
10. journeys to uncharted areas

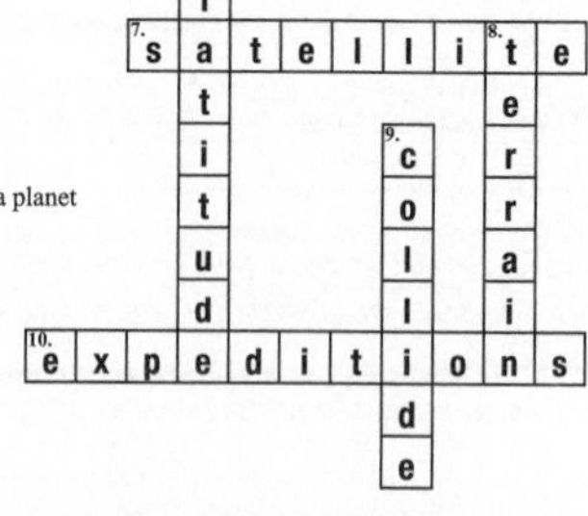

Write a Story

On a separate sheet of paper, write a story about exploring an unfamiliar place. Use as many vocabulary words as you can. **Check that students' stories about unfamiliar places use vocabulary words correctly.**

Notes for Home: Your child identified and used vocabulary words from "To the Pole." ***Home Activity:*** Read a story about exploration with your child. Encourage your child to try to find synonyms—words with similar meanings—to the vocabulary words listed above.

456 Vocabulary

Practice Book 6.5, p. 203

Name ______________________ To the Pole

Fact and Opinion

- A **statement of fact** can be proven true or false. You can prove it true or false by reading, observing, asking an expert, or checking it in some way.
- A **statement of opinion** tells someone's belief, judgment, or way of thinking about something. It cannot be proven true or false, but it can be supported or explained.
- Some sentences contain both facts and opinions.

Directions: Reread the part of "To the Pole" in which Will Steger describes sharing a tent with Victor. Then answer the questions below. Think about whether statements can be proven true or false.

Victor and I are sharing a tent. In our travels across Antarctica and Greenland we have tented together many nights before. He is good company—we know each other's habits well, and his optimism is always a boost to me.

We're like a little family of two, living inside a space the size of a car. Our arrangement is that I prepare dinner and he makes breakfast. In the morning, while I'm still in my sleeping bag, I know exactly what time it is by the breakfast sounds Victor is making. When I hear him stirring dried fruit and hot chocolate powder into a steaming bowl of leftover rice—my favorite on-the-ice breakfast—I know it is 6:40. Ten minutes later he will pour hot water for our tea.

From OVER THE TOP OF THE WORLD by Will Steger and Jon Bowermaster. Copyright © 1997 by Will Steger and Jon Bowermaster. Reprinted by permission of Scholastic Inc.

Possible answers given.

1. What is Will's opinion of Victor? How do you know?
Will thinks Victor is a good companion because he lifts Will's spirits.

2. What facts are given about how chores will be done in the tent?
Will prepares dinner, and Victor makes breakfast.

3. Will writes, "We are like a little family . . ." Is this a statement of fact or opinion? Explain.
It is a statement of opinion because it cannot be proven true or false.

4. Is Will's statement "I know it is 6:40" a statement of fact or opinion? Explain.
It is a statement of fact because Will can check the time on his watch.

5. How might the facts and opinions found in "To the Pole" be useful to another expedition? Explain your thinking on a separate sheet of paper.
Possible answer: This account can be useful because it gives details and facts about an actual expedition by a person who was there. Because Will is an expert, his opinions are also useful.

Notes for Home: Your child identified statements of fact and opinion in a nonfiction text. ***Home Activity:*** Read the promotional material from a book or video cover with your child. Have him or her identify the statements of fact and the statements of opinion.

Fact and Opinion 457

Practice Book 6.5, p. 205

Name ______________________ To the Pole

Selection Test

Directions: Choose the best answer to each item. Mark the letter for the answer you have chosen.

Part 1: Vocabulary

Find the answer choice that means about the same as the underlined word in each sentence.

1. They struggled over the rough <u>terrain</u>.
   A. the surface of the ocean
   B. a ridge of high mountains
   C. violent, rushing stream of water
   (D) the natural features of a region

2. He wanted to know the <u>latitude</u>.
   (F) distance north or south of the equator
   G. height above the earth's surface
   H. space in between two points
   J. distance east or west on the earth's surface

3. We hoped the wagons wouldn't <u>collide</u>.
   A. break apart
   (B) crash into each other
   C. topple over
   D. cave in

4. They traveled to the <u>Arctic</u>.
   F. south polar region
   G. high mountains in Asia
   (H) north polar region
   J. desert in Africa

5. She had been on several <u>expeditions</u>.
   (A) journeys for a special purpose, such as exploration or study
   B. long periods in outer space
   C. visits to a zoo or museum
   D. cruise ships

6. The journey was <u>strenuous</u>.
   F. exciting; full of adventure
   G. causing worry or fuss
   H. dull and uninteresting
   (J) requiring much energy

7. The camps were at the same <u>longitude</u>.
   A. height above the earth's surface
   (B) distance east or west of the earth's surface
   C. space in between two points
   D. distance north or south of the equator

8. They communicated via <u>satellite</u>.
   F. a system of telephones connected by wires
   (G) an artificial object launched into orbit around the earth
   H. a machine with an engine and wheels
   J. an unidentified flying object

Part 2: Comprehension

Use what you know about the selection to answer each item.

9. Which condition presented the biggest challenge for Will Steger and his companions?
   A. big mounds of ice
   B. snowdrifts
   (C) open water
   D. pressure ridges

10. The job of the "point person" is to—
   (F) ski out ahead to find a safe path.
   G. steer the lead sled.
   H. use the Global Positioning System.
   J. set up the campsite.

GO ON

458 Selection Test

Practice Book 6.5, p. 206

Name ______________________ **To the Pole**

11. Which sentence states an opinion?
    - A. "We have reached the North Pole exactly as planned, on Earth Day."
    - B. "Our friends have brought supplies with them—including letters and small gifts."
    - Ⓒ "But I got the best present—an apple pie baked by my mother."
    - D. "Victor is the first Russian to reach both the North and South poles by skis."

12. Which of the following sentences states a fact?
    - F. "But then, just before we got here, it began to look like heaven."
    - Ⓖ "We passed 89 degrees north latitude, which means we are less than 60 miles from the pole!"
    - H. "So far, the most surprising aspect of the whole trip is all the snow."
    - J. "When we left the North Pole, it seemed like a perfect day."

13. Most of the information in this selection is organized by—
    - A. comparison/contrast.
    - B. cause and effect.
    - C. problem and solution.
    - Ⓓ chronological order.

14. Which generalization seems to be based on the author's personal opinion?
    - F. In most years, the Arctic has little precipitation.
    - G. On most days, the ice they crossed was more than three years old.
    - Ⓗ Female sled dogs are often very bright.
    - J. The peoples of the Arctic have adapted to the environment.

15. Which part of this selection best supports the author's goal of showing "how all parts of the world are interconnected"?
    - Ⓐ the section on pollution in the Arctic
    - B. the part describing animals of the Arctic
    - C. the entry for April 22, when the team reached the North Pole
    - D. the section called "Facts from the Trip"

Name ______________________ **To the Pole**

Fact and Opinion

- A **statement of fact** can be proven true or false. You can prove it true or false by reading, observing, asking an expert, or checking it in some way.
- A **statement of opinion** tells someone's belief, judgment, or way of thinking about something. It cannot be proven true or false, but it can be supported or explained.
- Some sentences contain both facts and opinions.

Directions: Read the passage below.

In 1804, President Thomas Jefferson asked his secretary Meriwether Lewis to lead an expedition to explore America's West and Northwest. Mr. Lewis, a naturalist and ex-army officer, chose William Clark to act as his co-leader. Mr. Clark was Mr. Lewis's friend from their army days together. The two men had the ideal qualities for leading such an expedition: they were brave, intelligent, and resourceful.

President Jefferson instructed the two men to take detailed notes of everything they saw: peoples, animals, plants, and geographical features. Mr. Lewis and Mr. Clark returned from their journey with careful and extensive records of everything they had seen. Because of their expedition, many Americans became eager to see the West for themselves.

Directions: Tell whether each statement is a fact or opinion. Two have been done for you.

Fact or Opinion?	Statement
Fact	President Jefferson asked Meriwether Lewis to explore the West and Northwest.
Fact	Meriwether Lewis chose William Clark as his co-leader.
1. **Fact**	Mr. Lewis and Mr. Clark had known one another during their army days.
2. **Opinion**	Mr. Lewis and Mr. Clark were brave and resourceful.
3. **Fact**	President Jefferson asked Mr. Lewis and Mr. Clark to take detailed notes about everything they saw.
4. **Fact**	Mr. Lewis and Mr. Clark kept extensive records of their journey.
5. **Opinion**	Because of their expedition, many Americans became eager to see the West for themselves.

Notes for Home: Your child read a passage and identified statements of fact and opinion. ***Home Activity:*** Read an advertisement with your child. Challenge him or her to identify statements that can be proved true or false (facts) and those that cannot (opinions).

Practice Book 6.5, p. 207

Name ______________________ **To the Pole**

Summarizing and Text Structure

REVIEW

Directions: Read the passage. Then read each question about the passage. Choose the best answer to each question. Mark the letter for the answer you have chosen.

Travels of the Past

The explorer and anthropologist Thor Heyerdahl went on many adventures in order to test his ideas. He believed ancient peoples regularly traveled great distances, and that this is why we find similar objects in places that are very far apart. He tested his ideas by crossing oceans in small handmade boats like those used in ancient times.

One of Thor Heyerdahl's ideas was that the native peoples of Peru were able to sail to Polynesia in the distant past. He thought that even though they did not know latitude and longitude, they were able to follow ocean currents and the stars in the sky. He tried out his idea by building a balsa raft like the ones Peruvians made long ago. His movie about this successful trip won an Academy Award in 1951. With his small crew, he led several other successful expeditions from South America to the East Pacific, to show that such long journeys would have been possible for Native American people.

Thor Heyerdahl also was able to cross the Atlantic from North Africa in a boat modeled after ancient Egyptian papyrus boats. He believed that ancient Egyptians actually did travel to South America this way and that the Egyptians are the ancestors of the Aztec and Inca people.

Thor Heyerdahl also believed that the Sumerians, who lived between the Tigris and Euphrates Rivers 5,000 years ago in what is now Iraq, traveled from their homeland to the Indian Ocean. However, war in the region kept him from testing his idea and the model reed boat he had built.

1. A summary of this article should **not** include the information about—
    - **A.** travel from South America to Polynesia.
    - **B.** journeys by Egyptians to America.
    - Ⓒ the movie about the trip to Polynesia.
    - **D.** Sumerian travel to the Indian Ocean.

2. A main idea of this article is that ancient peoples—
    - **F.** followed currents and stars.
    - **G.** were smart.
    - **H.** did not know latitude and longitude.
    - Ⓙ traveled far in simple crafts.

3. A summary of this article should include information about Thor Heyerdahl's —
    - Ⓐ ways of testing his ideas about ancient travel.
    - **B.** balsa raft.
    - **C.** crew.
    - **D.** education.

4. Thor Heyerdahl believes that journeys made in ancient times explain why—
    - **F.** his film won an Academy Award.
    - **G.** Egyptians used boats made of papyrus.
    - Ⓗ similar objects are found in places great distances apart.
    - **J.** the native peoples of Peru built such excellent boats.

5. Which text structure best describes the organization of this article?
    - **A.** chronological order
    - **B.** comparison-contrast
    - Ⓒ problem-solution
    - **D.** cause-effect

Notes for Home: Your child read a passage and identified its main ideas and text structure. ***Home Activity:*** Read a nonfiction article from a magazine with your child. Have your child identify its main ideas and then summarize it.

Name ______________________ **To the Pole**

Writing Across Texts

Directions: In "To the Pole!" and "Antarctica Melts" you read about opposite ends of the Earth. These two areas of the world differ in some ways, but they have many things in common. Read the following sentences and decide if they are true about the Arctic, Antarctica, or both. Then add them to the correct place on the chart. **Possible answers given.**

1. The average temperature is below zero.
2. The Inuit live there.
3. There are problems with pollution.
4. This area is at the north end of the Earth.
5. The average temperatures are rising.
6. The area has many icebergs.
7. This area is at the south end of the Earth.
8. Will Steger has visited there.
9. Ice island B-10A broke from there.
10. This area is reached by going north through Canada.

The Arctic	Antarctica	Both
The Inuit live there. **This area is at the north end of the Earth.** **is reached by going north through Canada**	**The average temperatures are rising.** **is at the south end of the Earth** **Ice island B-10A broke from there.**	**The average temperature is below zero.** **There are problems with pollution.** **The area has many icebergs.** **Will Steger has visited there.**

Write a Comparison/Contrast Paragraph

Write a paragraph comparing and contrasting the Arctic with Antarctica. Use information from the chart above and from both selections. Use a separate sheet of paper for your paragraph.
Paragraphs will vary. Check that students use information from the chart and from both selections.

Notes for Home: You child wrote a paragraph comparing the Arctic with the continent of Antarctica. ***Home Activity:*** Discuss with your child journeys you have taken. Share things you experienced for the first time as your child takes notes.

Grammar Practice Book 6.5, p. 101
Name ______________________ To the Pole

Grammar: Possessive Nouns
REVIEW

Directions: Decide whether the underlined possessive noun is singular or plural. Write **S** on the line if it is singular. Write **P** if it is plural.

S 1. What was the class's choice for the next field trip?
P 2. The students' decision was to visit the Museum of Science.
S 3. They especially wanted to see the museum's new exhibit on the Arctic.
S 4. Everyone applauded as the bus's doors closed, and the class was on its way.
P 5. At the museum, the students watched a short film about polar bears' habits.
P 6. Animals' lives are hard in the Arctic.
S 7. A seal's life is often in great danger for it is a polar bear's favorite food.
P 8. People's safety cannot be guaranteed around these powerful animals either.
P 9. The flapping of snowy owls' wings can be heard in parts of the Arctic.
S 10. This harsh environment is also the Arctic fox's home.

Directions: Correct each underlined word by adding an apostrophe to make it possessive. Write the possessive noun on the line.

world's 11. Isn't the Arctic Ocean the worlds smallest ocean?
Bess's 12. Besss question was addressed to the museum guide.
group's 13. The groups guide replied that the answer was yes.
reptiles' 14. You will not find reptiles footprints in the Arctic because these creatures cannot survive the cold.
geese's 15. Geeses honks can be heard, however, especially in Greenland.
wolves' 16. Wolves howls are not unusual in the Arctic.
country's 17. Parts of Canada, Russia, Iceland, and other nations are included in the Arctic, but a countrys borders are hard to find.
listeners' 18. To the listeners surprise, the guide told the group that the Arctic Circle is not an actual place.
mapmaker's 19. Rather, it is a mapmakers aid, marking the area that has at least one 24-hour day and one 24-hour night each year.
children's 20. At the museum exit, childrens voices mixed with those of other visitors, who chatted about all they had learned.

Notes for Home: Your child used an apostrophe to form singular and plural possessive nouns—nouns that show ownership. ***Home Activity:*** With your child, look through a newspaper for possessive nouns. Decide which ones are singular and which ones are plural.

Grammar Practice Book 6.5, p. 102
Name ______________________ To the Pole

Grammar: Pronouns

Pronouns are words that can take the place of nouns or noun phrases. Like nouns, pronouns have singular and plural forms. A singular pronoun replaces a singular noun. A plural pronoun replaces a plural noun.

Singular pronouns: I, me, you, he, she, him, her, it
Plural pronouns: we, us, you, they, them

Pronouns that show ownership are **possessive pronouns.** There are two kinds of possessive pronouns. One kind is used before nouns. The second kind stands alone without a noun following it.

Used before nouns: my, your, his, her, its, our, their
Used alone: mine, yours, his, hers, ours, theirs

Possessive pronouns, unlike possessive nouns, do not use apostrophes.

Allen has given his dog sled its first coat of yellow paint.

Directions: Choose a pronoun in ( ) to replace the underlined words in each sentence. Write the pronoun on the line.

We 1. Norah, Joan, and I went on a hiking trip. (We/She)
them 2. These trails were new to Joan and Norah. (her/them)
They 3. Joan and Norah felt like explorers. (We/They)
her 4. I pointed out an enormous tree to Joan. (it/her)
It 5. The tree looked as if it were hundreds of feet tall. (It/You)

Directions: Circle the correct possessive pronoun in ( ) to complete each sentence.

6. That backpack is (my/mine).
7. (My/mine) compass is in the front pocket.
8. (Their/Theirs) tent is larger than this one.
9. This tent is (our/ours).
10. (Your/Yours) sense of direction is better than mine.

Notes for Home: Your child used pronouns, such as *he, you,* and *they,* and possessive pronouns, such as *his, your,* and *theirs,* in sentences. ***Home Activity:*** Challenge your child to describe something that happened in school today, using pronouns and possessive pronouns.

Grammar Practice Book 6.5, p. 103
Name ______________________ To the Pole

Grammar: Pronouns

Directions: Choose a pronoun in ( ) to replace the underlined words in each sentence. Write the pronoun on the line.

us 1. The explorer talked to my friends and me. (us/them)
He 2. Mr. Johnson had been to the Arctic three times. (We/He)
They 3. The explorer and his colleagues are famous. (We/They)
him 4. I enjoyed listening to Mr. Johnson. (him/them)
We 5. My friends and I had a number of questions for Mr. Johnson. (We/They)

Directions: Choose a possessive pronoun in ( ) to complete each sentence correctly. Write the possessive pronoun on the line.

our 6. The Smith family and (our/their) family have lived in Smithtown for 300 years.
theirs 7. The Smiths' ancestors bought so much land that most of Smithtown once was (his/theirs).
his 8. My great-great-grandfather claimed that 100 acres of the Smiths' land was really (mine/his).
their 9. With (his/their) approval, I explored and made a list of the contents of my grandparents' attic.
her 10. I told Liddy Smith that one of my family's oldest books must have belonged first to (her/my) family, not to ours.

Write a Log

Imagine that you keep a log as you travel to some faraway place, such as a polar region. On a separate sheet of paper, write several entries in your log. Describe the journey and your experiences. Tell about the people who travel with you. Use singular and plural pronouns and possessive pronouns.
Check whether students have used singular and plural pronouns correctly and that they have distinguished between those possessive pronouns that come before nouns and those that stand alone.

Notes for Home: Your child used singular and plural pronouns, such as *he, you,* and *they,* and possessive pronouns, such as *his, your,* and *theirs.* ***Home Activity:*** With your child, describe items in your home and in your neighborhood using possessive pronouns.

Grammar Practice Book 6.5, p. 104
Name ______________________ To the Pole

Grammar: Pronouns
RETEACHING

Singular Pronouns			
I	me	my	mine
he	you	your	yours
her	she	it	him
	his	hers	its

Plural Pronouns			
we	us	our	ours
you	your	yours	
they	them	their	theirs

Complete the sentences. Write pronouns from the boxes.

1. Maria likes basketball.
She likes basketball.

2. Maria plays with some friends.
Maria plays with them.

A **pronoun** takes the place of a noun or nouns. Pronouns may be singular or plural. **Possessive pronouns** show ownership.

Directions: Write the pronoun from each sentence.

1. They played basketball at Maria's house. They
2. Maria's parents gave her a new basketball. her
3. Maria thanked them before breakfast. them
4. Maria is very happy with their gift. their
5. Rachel and Tomas like it too. it
6. Other friends will join their game. their
7. Neighbors such as us will watch. us
8. We should have an exciting afternoon. We

Directions: Write a pronoun to replace the underlined word or words.

9. Maria wanted a party for her birthday. She
10. Mr. and Mrs. Santos agreed to Maria's request. her
11. Mr. and Mrs. Santos arranged for a surprise. They
12. The surprise was a visit from a basketball star. It
13. He signed a basketball for Maria and her family. them

Notes for Home: Your child used singular and plural pronouns and possessive pronouns. ***Home Activity:*** Have your child observe a family member and take notes. Then have your child write sentences from his or her notes, using pronouns.

Grammar Practice Book 6.5, p. 105

Name ______________________ To the Pole

Grammar: Pronouns

Directions: Circle each pronoun.

1. (He) built a boat and sailed (it) around the world.
2. (She) made (him) a flag to fly on (it).
3. (We) sailed in (my) boat last week.
4. (I) think that (her) boat is bigger than (ours).
5. Can (you) tell the difference between (mine) and (hers)?
6. Where do (they) store (their) sails?
7. Gina keeps (her) sails where (we) keep (our) oars.
8. Peter folds (his) sails and puts (them) aboard the boat.
9. Do (you) think (we) should take a water safety course?
10. (My) aunt and uncle took (theirs) from the Coast Guard.

Directions: Write each sentence, completing it with a pronoun that makes sense.

Possible answers given.

11. Since boating is fun, many people enjoy (pronoun) as a pastime.
Since boating is fun, many people enjoy it as a pastime.

12. Some people paddle (pronoun) own canoes.
Some people paddle their own canoes.

13. My brother likes to fish from (pronoun) rowboat.
My brother likes to fish from his rowboat.

14. People with boats sail (pronoun) on breezy days.
People with boats sail theirs on breezy days.

15. My aunt would never sell (pronoun) motorboat.
My aunt would never sell her motorboat.

16. Aunt Sal likes riding in (pronoun) so much.
Aunt Sal likes riding in it so much.

17. (pronoun) family often rides with her.
My family often rides with her.

Notes for Home: Your child identified pronouns in sentences and wrote sentences with pronouns. ***Home Activity:*** Together, look for pronouns in a favorite story. Have your child identify whether they are singular or plural, and whether they are possessive.

Practice Book 6.5, p. 208

Name ______________________ To the Pole

Word Study: Prefixes

Directions: A letter or group of letters added to the beginning of a word is a **prefix.** A prefix can change the meaning of a word. Add a prefix to each word below to make a new word. Write each new word on the line.

1.	re	+	heat	=	**reheat**
2.	in	+	active	=	**inactive**
3.	un	+	wrap	=	**unwrap**
4.	in	+	complete	=	**incomplete**
5.	re	+	place	=	**replace**
6.	un	+	lock	=	**unlock**
7.	in	+	audible	=	**inaudible**
8.	re	+	play	=	**replay**

Directions: Read the newspaper story below. Look for the words with the prefixes **un-, re-,** or **in-.** Circle these words. Then write the prefix and the rest of the word on the line, connected by a + sign. For example, for **undone,** you would write **un + done.**

AMAZING JOURNEY!

An (unlikely) group has reached the North Pole. Students from a local college have journeyed with their teachers over (unstable) ice floes and (uneven) terrain to reach territory not many have seen. This (unusual) accomplishment was funded by a major corporation, who met the group at critical points along the way to (restock) their food supply and check on their health. The group made it by the end of the summer, just before the ice floes (reformed) and froze solid. It was an (incredible) show of courage and fortitude!

9. **un + likely**
10. **un + stable**
11. **un + even**
12. **un + usual**
13. **re + stock**
14. **re + formed**
15. **in + credible**

Notes for Home: Your child formed new words by adding the prefixes *un-, re-,* and *in-* to base words. ***Home Activity:*** Read a newspaper story with your child. Help your child find words that have these prefixes. Have your child write each word and circle its prefix.

Spelling Workbook 6.5, p. 81

Name ______________________ To the Pole

Spelling: Negative Prefixes

Pretest Directions: Fold back the page along the dotted line. On the blanks, write the spelling words as they are dictated. When you have finished the test, unfold the page and check your words.

1. **illegal**	1. I've never done anything **illegal.**
2. **illogical**	2. Your conclusion is **illogical.**
3. **illegible**	3. Ink stains left my note **illegible.**
4. **inexpensive**	4. The watch is very **inexpensive.**
5. **inaccurate**	5. Rumors are often **inaccurate.**
6. **indirect**	6. He gave an **indirect** answer.
7. **informal**	7. It was an **informal** gathering.
8. **incapable**	8. Don't pretend to be **incapable.**
9. **incredible**	9. A tornado's power is **incredible.**
10. **impolite**	10. It is **impolite** to stare at people.
11. **improper**	11. That was an **improper** remark.
12. **imperfect**	12. A crack made the cup **imperfect.**
13. **impatient**	13. I'm **impatient** with my little sister.
14. **imbalance**	14. I have an **imbalance** in my diet.
15. **immature**	15. His tantrum was quite **immature.**
16. **irresponsible**	16. His actions were **irresponsible.**
17. **irregular**	17. He has an **irregular** heartbeat.
18. **irrational**	18. His **irrational** thinking worries me.
19. **irresistible**	19. The puppy is simply **irresistible.**
20. **irreplaceable**	20. An heirloom is **irreplaceable.**

Notes for Home: Your child took a pretest on words with the negative prefixes *il-, in-, im-,* and *ir-.* ***Home Activity:*** Help your child learn misspelled words. Your child should look at the word, notice its prefix, say it, spell it aloud, and then spell it with eyes shut.

Spelling Workbook 6.5, p. 82

Name ______________________ To the Pole

Spelling: Negative Prefixes

Word List

illegal	inaccurate	incredible	impatient	irregular
illogical	indirect	impolite	imbalance	irrational
illegible	informal	improper	immature	irresistible
inexpensive	incapable	imperfect	irresponsible	irreplaceable

Directions: Choose the word from the box that is formed by adding **il-** or **in-** to each word. Write the word on the line.

1. formal **informal**
2. logical **illogical**
3. accurate **inaccurate**
4. direct **indirect**
5. legible **illegible**
6. expensive **inexpensive**
7. capable **incapable**
8. legal **illegal**
9. credible **incredible**

Directions: Choose the word from the box that best matches each clue. Use each word only once. Write the word on the line.

impatient 10. I am how you feel when you are in a hurry and have to wait.
irresistible 11. I am something hard to resist.
improper 12. I am the kind of behavior that is considered not proper.
irregular 13. I am the kind of spelling word that doesn't follow a rule.
immature 14. I am the kind of person who does not act like an adult.
irresponsible 15. I am the kind of person who you do not trust to do an important task.
imbalance 16. I am the result when one side is heavier than the other.
irrational 17. I am how you behave when you aren't thinking clearly.
imperfect 18. I am not ideal; I have flaws.
irreplaceable 19. I am something or someone that is unique.
impolite 20. I am how you describe a person who has bad manners.

Notes for Home: Your child spelled words with the negative prefixes *il-, in-, im-,* and *ir-.* ***Home Activity:*** Have your child add the prefix *in-* to *effective* and *frequent* and use each word in a sentence. Discuss how adding this prefix changes the meaning of words.

Spelling Workbook 6.5, p. 83

Name ______________________

To the Pole

Spelling: Negative Prefixes

Directions: Proofread this letter from an Arctic expedition. Find seven spelling mistakes. Use the proofreading marks to correct each mistake.

≡	Make a capital.
/	Make a small letter.
∧	Add something.
℘	Take out something.
⊙	Add a period.
¶	Begin a new paragraph.

Dear Dad,

If this letter ever reaches you, it will be by a very undirect route, but the temptation to try is iresistible. We're stuck in a settlement that has iregular contact with the outside world, so any prediction of when my letter can go is bound to be innaccurate.

The Arctic is incredible—I'm imcapable of finding words for it! I feel an unlogical impulse to speak in a whisper—I'm almost afraid to break the vast silence of the landscape. Maybe twenty-four hours of daylight has made me irrational.

If my writing is illegible, it's Ben's fault—he is inpatient to go exploring. We are both well and eager to see you and Mom soon.

Love,

Marianne

Spelling Tip

When negative prefixes are added to base words, the spelling of the base word does not change. Check the letter to make sure the beginnings of words are spelled correctly.

Word List

illegal	improper
illogical	imperfect
illegible	impatient
inexpensive	imbalance
inaccurate	immature
indirect	irresponsible
informal	irregular
incapable	irrational
incredible	irresistible
impolite	irreplaceable

Write a Letter

On a separate sheet of paper, write a letter to Marianne from her father. Try to use at least three spelling words. **Answers will vary, but each letter should include at least three spelling words.**

Notes for Home: Your child spelled words with the negative prefixes *il-*, *in-*, *im-*, and *ir-*. ***Home Activity:*** Give your child the base word for each spelling word. Have him or her add one of the negative prefixes to each base word to form a spelling word *(il + legal = illegal)*.

Spelling Workbook 6.5, p. 84

Name ______________________

To the Pole

Spelling: Negative Prefixes

REVIEW

Word List

illegal	inaccurate	incredible	impatient	irregular
illogical	indirect	impolite	imbalance	irrational
illegible	informal	improper	immature	irresistible
inexpensive	incapable	imperfect	irresponsible	irreplaceable

Directions: Choose the word from the box that is the negative form of the word in parentheses and that makes sense in the sentence. Write the word on the line.

impatient 1. I am (patient) to begin the trip north to the Arctic.
illogical 2. Arctic travel is (logical) without careful planning.
improper 3. You can freeze to death if you wear (proper) clothing.
irregular 4. Going alone would be (regular); groups are safer.
Irresponsible 5. (Responsible) people could endanger the whole group.
immature 6. That means we can't take Celia; she is too (mature).
irrational 7. Celia can't overcome her (rational) fear of snow.
indirect 8. An (direct) route will take longer, but we will see more.
imbalance 9. The (balance) of the load on the sled will make it tip over.
informal 10. We all enjoy our (formal) dinners around the campfire.

Directions: Choose the word from the box that best matches each definition. Write the word on the line.

irreplaceable 11. unique; impossible to replace
imperfect 12. flawed or defective
impolite 13. ill-mannered; rude
inexpensive 14. cheap; easily affordable
illegal 15. against the law
irresistible 16. overwhelming; strongly tempting
incapable 17. without ability
illegible 18. difficult or impossible to read
inaccurate 19. containing mistakes; not exact
incredible 20. hard to believe; extraordinary

Notes for Home: Your child spelled words with the negative prefixes *il-*, *in-*, *im-*, and *ir-*. ***Home Activity:*** Write the four negative prefixes on separate sheets of paper. Say each spelling word aloud and have your child write the word on the correct sheet.

Practice Book 6.5, p. 209

Name ______________________

To the Pole

Schedule

A **schedule** is a specialized chart that lists events and when they take place, side by side.

Directions: Read the schedule for cruise ships. Note the names of the cruise ships, their departure dates, routes, and arrival dates. Then answer the questions that follow.

Cruise Ship	Departure/ Anchorage, Alaska	Arrive at Prudhoe Bay (3-day stay)	Sail Through Queen Elizabeth Islands	Final Destination/ Frobisher Bay, Canada
Alaskan Princess	June 1	June 5	June 8–10	June 15
Arctic Mist	June 11	June 15	June 18–20	June 25
Northern Explorer	June 26	June 30	July 3–5	July 10
Polar Princess	July 4	July 8	July 11–13	July 18
Vancouver Vacation	July 16	July 20	July 23–25	July 30
Queen Elizabeth's Quest	July 23	July 27	July 30–August 1	August 6
Alaskan Princess	July 31	August 4	August 7–9	August 14
Arctic Mist	August 8	August 12	August 15–17	August 22
Northern Explorer	August 19	August 23	August 26–28	September 2
Polar Princess	August 30	September 3	September 6–8	September 13
Vancouver Vacation	September 11	September 15	September 18–20	September 25
Queen Elizabeth's Quest	September 21	September 25	September 28–30	October 5

1. How many days is each cruise? How can you tell? **15 days; The ship departs on June 1 and arrives at its final destination on June 15, which is 15 days.**

2. How many ships travel this route? How can you tell? **6 ships; The names of only six ships are listed under "Cruise Ship."**

3. If you traveled on the first sailing of the *Arctic Mist,* during which days would you cruise through the Queen Elizabeth Islands? **June 18 through June 20**

4. What happens at Prudhoe Bay? How can you tell? **The ship sets anchor and stays at Prudhoe Bay for 3 days. This information is given at the top of the third column.**

5. If you wanted to sail on the *Polar Princess,* for which dates could you schedule a trip? **July 3–July 18 or August 29–September 13**

Practice Book 6.5, p. 210

Name ______________________

To the Pole

Directions: Use the schedule of shipboard events to answer the questions that follow.

Schedule of Activities for June 10

Activity	7 A.M. to 9 A.M.	9 A.M. to 11 A.M.	11 A.M. to 1 P.M.	1 P.M. to 3 P.M.	3 P.M. to 5 P.M.	5 P.M. to 7 P.M.	7 P.M. to 9 P.M.
Bird Watching	✓	✓	✓				
Ship Walk	✓	✓	✓	✓	✓	✓	
Whale Watching	✓	✓	✓	✓	✓		
Shuffleboard			✓	✓	✓		
Midday Movie Feature			✓				
Iceberg Viewing	✓	✓	✓	✓	✓	✓	
Ping-Pong Tournament					✓	✓	✓
Line Dancing Instruction					✓		✓
First Dinner Seating						✓	
Talent Show							✓
Photography Class		✓		✓			✓

✓ = Activity is available.

6. What do the checkmarks on the schedule represent? How do you know? **The checkmarks indicate when a particular activity will take place. This symbol is explained at the bottom of the schedule.**

7. Between which hours might you be able to watch for whales? **7 A.M. to 5 P.M.**

8. Which activities occur at the same time as the talent show? **the ping-pong tournament, the line-dancing instruction, and the photography class**

9. If you watched the Midday Movie Feature, which activities would you be missing? **bird watching, the ship walk, whale watching, shuffleboard, and iceberg viewing**

10. How does the schedule assist passengers in planning their day? **It helps passengers see at a glance which activities are possible during which hours.**

Notes for Home: Your child answered questions about schedules. ***Home Activity:*** Obtain a schedule for a bus or train route. Plan a trip with your child. Choose a destination and a departure time, and then figure out your arrival time and how long the trip would take.

Practice Book 6.5, p. 211

Name ______________________ *from* El Güero

Context Clues

- **Context clues** are words that come before or after an unfamiliar word and help you figure out what it means.
- A context clue may be a synonym, a word with nearly the same meaning as the unknown word, or an antonym, a word with an opposite meaning.
- A context clue may also be a definition or explanation of the unknown word, or a series of examples.

Directions: Reread "For the First Time." Then complete the table. Use context clues to determine the meaning of each word or group of words from the story.

Words	Meaning
gallina rellena	1. **turkey stuffed with meat and *piñon* nuts and a little cinnamon**
frijoles machacados	2. **mashed *bolita* beans**
guacamole salad	3. **salad made of avocadoes, tomatoes, and other things**
bollitos	4. **fat round rolls**
tortillas	5. **flat round bread**

Notes for Home: Your child read a story and used context clues to figure out the meaning of five words from the story. ***Home Activity:*** Read a story with your child. Prompt your child to point out unfamiliar words. Help him or her use context clues to figure out the meaning of these words.

Practice Book 6.5, p. 212

Name ______________________ *from* El Güero

Vocabulary

Directions: Choose the word from the box that best answers each question. Write the word on the line.

Check the Words You Know
__ bandits
__ caravans
__ conserve
__ embark
__ exiled
__ merciful

bandits 1. Which word describes people who break the law?

merciful 2. Which word describes someone who does not like to see other people suffer?

embark 3. Which word has a similar meaning to the word *begin?*

conserve 4. Which word means to save something, such as energy or resources?

caravans 5. Which word describes groups of people who are traveling?

Directions: Choose the word from the box that best replaces the underlined word or words. Write the word on the line to the left.

exiled 6. Shefki was banished from his country because of his political beliefs.

merciful 7. If it were not for a kind, sympathetic judge, he might have been imprisoned for life.

embark 8. Not knowing where to go, he decided to set out on a journey across the desert.

caravans 9. He joined one of the groups of travelers that were going to Asia to trade for silks and spices.

bandits 10. The groups traveled together for protection against outlaws who might rob them.

Write a Poem

On a separate sheet of paper, write a poem that tells a story of someone who must leave his or her homeland and travel to a strange unknown place. Use as many vocabulary words as you can in your poem. **Students' poems should make correct use of vocabulary words.**

Notes for Home: Your child identified and used vocabulary words from *El Güero. **Home Activity:*** Act out an adventure story with your child using the listed vocabulary words.

Practice Book 6.5, p. 213

Name ______________________ *from* El Güero

Context Clues

- **Context clues** are words that come before or after an unfamiliar word and help you figure out what it means.
- Specific types of context clues include a synonym, a word with the same or nearly the same meaning as the unfamiliar word; an antonym, a word that means the opposite of the unfamiliar word; a definition or explanation that appears before or after the unfamiliar word; or an example to explain the unfamiliar word.

Directions: Reread the passage from *El Güero* in which the characters are introduced. Then use context clues and refer to the list of types of context clues to answer the questions below.

> My name is Porfirio, but nobody ever calls me by my name. It is because most people in this country have dark eyes and dark hair, while my eyes are green and my hair is yellow. It is for this reason that everyone calls me El Güero, or the Blond One. My little sister, María, is called Maruca. I call my Aunt Victoria Tía Vicky, and my mother Mamacita. Everyone in Mexico has a nickname, or a short, affectionate form of his name. Only my father, the Judge, who is so dignified and taciturn, is called by his name, Cayetano, and then only by Mamacita and Tía Vicky. I have been told to call him Papá, though the other children I know call their fathers Papacito, dear little father.
>
>

1. What context clues are used to explain the meaning of *El Güero* in the passage?
Porfirio says that his hair is yellow and he is called "the Blond One."

2. Which type of context clue helps you understand the meaning of *nickname?*
a definition or explanation

3. Which context clues can be used to understand what *taciturn* means? How might you check if your understanding is correct?
His father is a judge, he is dignified, and he is addressed formally. You can check the meaning in a dictionary. *Taciturn* means reserved.

4. What does *Papacito* mean? How do you know?
***Papacito* means dear little father. Its meaning is given directly after the word.**

5. On a separate sheet of paper, list three other unfamiliar words from *El Güero* that you defined with the help of context clues. Write the meaning of each word.
Possible answers include: *caballerango:* a stable boy; *exiled:* sent away; *tlacoyos:* corn cakes stuffed with beans; *venison:* deer meat; *joven:* young man; *vigilant:* attentive to danger; *gourd:* a container

Notes for Home: Your child used context clues to figure out the meaning of unfamiliar words. ***Home Activity:*** Read a brief magazine article with your child. Help him or her to use context clues to determine the meaning of any unfamiliar words.

Practice Book 6.5, p. 215

Name ______________________ *from* El Güero

Selection Test

Directions: Choose the best answer to each item. Mark the letter for the answer you have chosen.

Part 1: Vocabulary

Find the answer choice that means about the same as the underlined word in each sentence.

1. The former president was exiled.
   A. held back
   B. assigned to a different job
   C. imprisoned
   (D) forced to leave one's country or home
2. The family was ready to embark.
   (F) set out; start
   G. make a decision
   H. make their own way
   J. take a rest
3. The merchants traveled in caravans.
   A. small, fast sailing ships
   (B) groups of people traveling together for safety
   C. trails marked in the woods
   D. wagons with covers that can be taken off
4. A group of bandits approached.
   F. pilgrims; travelers
   G. soldiers
   (H) robbers; outlaws
   J. peasants
5. Mr. Alexander was merciful.
   (A) showing mercy or kindness
   B. having a stern expression
   C. honest and truthful
   D. tending to be cruel
6. We learned to conserve water.
   F. be thankful for
   G. find many uses for
   H. make clean; purify
   (J) keep from wasting or using up

Part 2: Comprehension

Use what you know about the story to answer each item.

7. The narrator of the story is called "El Güero" because—
   A. he is strong.
   B. it is his name.
   C. he is small.
   (D) his hair is yellow.
8. *Cayetano* is—
   F. the nickname El Güero's mother uses
   (G) El Güero's father's name
   H. a word meaning "dear little father"
   J. the Spanish word for "judge"
9. Why was El Güero's family upset at the beginning of the story?
   A. The President had offered El Güero's father a new job.
   (B) They were being forced to leave their home.
   C. They had decided to move to a different country.
   D. A war had begun, and they had to escape.
10. Why did the bandit leader decide to protect the judge and his family?
    F. He hoped for a reward.
    (G) He was grateful for how the judge had treated him.
    H. He was afraid of the judge.
    J. He liked the judge's family.
11. El Güero explains, "There he had written poetry and had declaimed it before large audiences." Declaimed means—
    A. took something back.
    B. burned.
    (C) recited in public.
    D. copied.

GO ON

Practice Book 6.5, p. 216

Name ______________________ *from* El Güero

12. El Güero's father buys quinine from a pharmacist. You can figure out the meaning of the word pharmacist from the clue that—
    - F. quinine is made from a tree in Peru.
    - G. the pharmacist lives in Acapulco.
    - (H) quinine is a medicine.
    - J. the family is staying in a hotel.
13. From the family's experiences on their journey, you can conclude that—
    - A. physical health is the first thing to suffer in such situations.
    - B. people tend to become very selfish when resources are limited.
    - (C) difficult situations can strengthen people and relationships.
    - D. people who are in a faraway place really get on each other's nerves.
14. Which clue helps you understand that this story takes place in the past?
    - (F) The ship burns coal to power its steam engine.
    - G. The judge has to pay the captain of the ship for passage.
    - H. The food on the ship is heavy and salty.
    - J. Tía Vicky carries scissors, thread, and cloth in her baggage.
15. At Cabo San Lucas, who seems to give up the most to help the family?
    - A. El Güero
    - B. Maruca
    - (C) Tía Vicky
    - D. Mamacita

STOP

Name ______________________ *from* El Güero

Context Clues

- **Context clues** are words that come before or after an unfamiliar word and help you figure out what it means.
- Specific types of context clues include a synonym, a word with the same or nearly the same meaning as the unfamiliar word; an antonym, a word that means the opposite of the unfamiliar word; a definition or explanation that appears before or after the unfamiliar word; or an example to explain the unfamiliar word.

Directions: Read the story below. Use context clues to think about the meaning of the underlined words.

About dawn of April 18, 1906, I was roused from a sound sleep by large pieces of my plaster ceiling falling about me. The whole house was shaking. It was an earthquake! I jumped up, dressed quickly, and ran outside. People were milling about. No one seemed to have any idea where to go.

The tremors soon ended, but fires broke out and threatened to destroy the entire city. Stunned by the shock of events, we could only watch our beloved San Francisco disintegrate into ruins.

The presence of the army kept people from looting any goods from houses or stores. The Red Cross dispensed free meals during the emergency. The people recovered sooner than anyone thought possible. Before the fires were out, we were determined to rebuild our city.

Directions: Use context clues to write a definition for each word in the table. One has been done for you. **Possible answers given.**

Words	Definitions
roused	woken up
tremors	1. **shaking or vibrations**
milling	2. **wandering around**
disintegrate	3. **fall apart**
looting	4. **stealing**
dispensed	5. **gave out**

Notes for Home: Your child used context clues to determine the meaning of unfamiliar words. ***Home Activity:*** Read a story with your child. Encourage your child to use context clues to figure out the meaning of unfamiliar words. Then check definitions in a dictionary.

Practice Book 6.5, p. 217

Name ______________________ *from* El Güero

Setting

REVIEW

Directions: Read the story. Then read each question about the story. Choose the best answer to each question. Mark the letter for the answer you have chosen.

The Endless Count

Jonelle and her friends gathered at their wooden table under the oak, each carrying a breakfast tray. None of the other people around the girls seemed aware of the awful situation they were in. The others talked excitedly about the day's activities, but Jonelle's friends did not need to talk.

No words, just numbers. Each of them was silently counting the days left until they could return to civilization. How could their parents have sent them off into the heat, the flies, the bugs, the pollen, the dust, the unfamiliar sheets, the shared bathrooms, the tiny cabins?

Jonelle's parents had been sure she would enjoy a month of camping. In spite of her protests that she would rather stay at home, they made the arrangements and bundled Jonelle into the car. "It's for your own good, honey" and "You'll thank us by the time you come home" were two sentences that stuck in Jonelle's mind. During the drive to camp, her mother told stories about her childhood summers in the hot city and her longing for a country vacation. Her father told stories about the great times he had had at camp when he was a boy. But Jonelle knew better. She would hate it!

The camp leaders had promised another day of walking through woods, looking at birds and plants. This was not life as Jonelle knew and liked it. No friends' houses, no lazy afternoons by the pool, no shopping malls, not even school. Jonelle was shocked. Could she actually be eager for the new school year to start?

1. Jonelle and her friends eat breakfast—
   - A. cold.
   - (B) outside.
   - C. in a hall.
   - D. in a cabin.
2. Jonelle and the others are staying in—
   - F. a school.
   - G. a prison.
   - H. a friend's home.
   - (J) a camp.
3. Which of the following is **not** part of the setting?
   - (A) a swimming pool
   - B. an oak tree
   - C. tiny cabins
   - D. a wooden table
4. What effect does the setting have on Jonelle?
   - (F) She hates being away from "civilization."
   - G. She misses her parents.
   - H. She wants to go on a nature walk.
   - J. She doesn't want to return to school.
5. The time of year is most likely—
   - A. spring.
   - (B) summer.
   - C. fall.
   - D. winter.

Notes for Home: Your child read a story and answered questions about its setting. ***Home Activity:*** After watching a movie together, encourage your child to discuss its setting. Talk about how the setting affected the characters and their actions.

Name ______________________ *from* El Güero

Writing Across Texts

Directions: Think about what you learned from the excerpt from *El Güero* and from "The California Rancheros." Use that information to answer the questions below about the history of the area. **Possible answers given.**

Of what three countries has California been a part since the 1770's?

1. **Spain, Mexico, and the United States**

What happened in Mexico that made it necessary for the judge and his family to flee?

2. **Porfirio Diaz seized the presidency and exiled the Treviño family.**

To what area of Mexico was the Treviño family headed?

3. **Baja, California**

What happened in 1821, and how did it change things in Mexico?

4. **Mexico was granted its independence from Spain. California became a province of the Republic of Mexico. The Mexican government gave lands previously used for missions to native-born Californios.**

What is the difference between a rancho and a hacienda?

5. **A *hacienda* is larger.**

Write a Comparison/Contrast Paragraph

Use the information you gathered to write a paragraph on the history of northern Mexico and southern California. Write your paragraph on a separate sheet of paper. **Paragraphs will vary. Check that students have compared and contrasted information they have gathered with information from the selection.**

Notes for Home: Your child used information from two sources to write a paragraph. ***Home Activity:*** Read aloud a story set in the past. With your child, discuss how things are alike or different today.

Grammar Practice Book 6.5, p. 106

Name ______________________ *from* El Güero

Grammar: Pronouns

REVIEW

Directions: Underline the pronoun in each sentence. Hint: Some pronouns are possessive pronouns.

1. Juan had mixed feelings about his new life in the United States.
2. The earthquake at home had caused great damage, and he and his family decided to move to America.
3. Life was good in America, but it was also strange and unfamiliar.
4. The social worker had been kind, and her advice was helpful.
5. Still, newcomers in a new land have their own particular problems.

Directions: Rewrite each pronoun and verb as a contraction.

6. we have **we've**
7. he will **he'll**
8. she had **she'd**
9. they are **they're**
10. it is **it's**
11. I am **I'm**
12. we are **we're**
13. you have **you've**
14. they will **they'll**
15. you are **you're**
16. we will **we'll**
17. he would **he'd**
18. she is **she's**
19. I have **I've**
20. he is **he's**
21. it will **it'll**
22. you will **you'll**
23. she has **she's**
24. he had **he'd**
25. they have **they've**

Directions: Choose the pronoun in ( ) that completes each sentence. Write the pronoun on the line.

their 26. Juan and his family were moving into (their/they're) new apartment.

theirs 27. None of the furniture was really (their's/theirs), for they had had to leave everything behind.

its 28. They thought longingly of their real home, with (it's/its) open, airy rooms.

your 29. "Welcome to (your/you're) new home," said the woman who was helping them get settled.

yours 30. "My country is now (your's/yours)," she said.

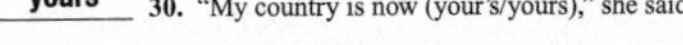

Notes for Home: Your child identified and used pronouns—words that take the place of nouns. ***Home Activity:*** Point to different things in your home and ask questions such as "Whose is that?" Have your child respond, using a pronoun in the answer.

Grammar: Pronouns 485

Grammar Practice Book 6.5, p. 107

Name ______________________ *from* El Güero

Grammar: Subject/Object Pronouns and Agreement

A pronoun takes the place of one or more nouns or noun phrases. When a pronoun is used as the subject of a sentence, it is called a **subject pronoun.**

My family moved to a new town. We moved to a new town.

Subject Pronouns: I, you, he, she, it, we, they

A pronoun used as an object in a sentence is called an **object pronoun.** An object pronoun used as a direct object follows an action verb and tells who or what receives the action.

My dog explored the new house. My dog explored it.

Object Pronouns: me, you, him, her, it, us, them

The **referent** is the noun or nouns to which the pronoun refers. A pronoun and its referent must agree. A singular pronoun agrees with a singular referent. A plural pronoun agrees with one or more plural referents. A pronoun and its referent can appear in separate sentences or in the same sentence.

My parents looked for a long time. They wanted to find a good place to live.

My mother and father were sure they had made the right choice.

Directions: Write a pronoun that best replaces the underlined words in each sentence. Then write **S** if it is a subject pronoun. Write **O** if it is an object pronoun.

we; S 1. Last April, my family moved to Acapulco, Mexico.

us; O 2. The move surprised my brother and me.

They; S 3. My parents said that the move would be a good experience.

them; O 4. Later, my brother and I agreed with our parents.

We; S 5. My brother and I enjoyed learning Spanish and living by the sea.

Directions: Underline the pronoun in each sentence. Then circle its referent.

6. When Mary first moved to Hawaii, she had a hard time making new friends.
7. Friends from home kept in touch. They called and wrote letters.
8. After a week, Mary made her first new friend.
9. Steven showed Mary the big island. He knew about many interesting places.
10. Steven and Mary biked to the top of a mountain. They could see the whole island below.

Notes for Home: Your child wrote subject pronouns and object pronouns, and identified pronouns and their referents. ***Home Activity:*** Use pronouns in sentences. Have your child tell you if each pronoun is a subject pronoun or an object pronoun.

486 Grammar: Subject/Object Pronouns and Agreement

Grammar Practice Book 6.5, p. 108

Name ______________________ *from* El Güero

Grammar: Subject/Object Pronouns and Agreement

Directions: Write a pronoun that best replaces the underlined words. Then write **S** if it is a subject pronoun. Write **O** if it is an object pronoun.

she; S 1. Last September, Renata arrived in town.

They; S 2. Renata and her family came from Veracruz, Mexico.

us; O 3. Renata taught my friends and me about Mexico and its culture.

We; S 4. My friends and I were guests at Renata's house for a holiday called *Cinco de Mayo.*

her; O 5. We all thanked Renata for including us in the holiday.

Directions: Underline the pronoun in each sentence. Then circle its referent.

6. Ellen's family took a trip to Mexico. They saw many amazing things.
7. Ellen was interested in the Mayan ruins. She had read about the pyramids and temples.
8. Ellen first saw the Pyramid of the Sun. It was over 200 feet high.
9. When she reached the top of the pyramid, Ellen stared down at the rest of the city.
10. A guide who was with Ellen pointed out the important sites to her.

Write a Newspaper Story

On a separate sheet of paper, write a story about a current event in your town or school. Include subject and object pronouns in your composition, and make sure they agree with their referents. When you are finished, underline each pronoun and circle its referent. **Check to make sure students use subject and object pronouns correctly and that they link each pronoun correctly with its referent.**

Notes for Home: Your child wrote subject pronouns, object pronouns, and identified pronouns and their referents. ***Home Activity:*** With your child, read a few paragraphs from a story. Have your child identify each pronoun and its referent.

Grammar: Subject/Object Pronouns and Agreement 487

Grammar Practice Book 6.5, p. 109

Name ______________________ *from* El Güero

Grammar: Subject/Object Pronouns and Agreement

RETEACHING

Subject Pronouns	Object Pronouns
I, you, she, he, it, we, they	me, you, her, him, it, us, them

Complete each sentence. Use a pronoun from the boxes. The clues in ( ) will help you.

1. Once **you** (subject pronoun) wrote a message to **me** (object pronoun).
2. **We** (subject pronoun) looked at **it** (object pronoun).

The **subject pronouns** are **I, you, she, he, it, we,** and **they.** A subject pronoun may be used as the subject of a sentence. The **object pronouns** are **me, you, her, him, it, us,** and **them.** An object pronoun may be used as the object in a sentence or in a prepositional phrase.

Directions: Underline each subject pronoun.

1. She knows some interesting facts about the telegraph.
2. It was the first way to send messages with electricity.
3. They could travel quickly from place to place.
4. "I want to be remembered as an inventor," Morse said.
5. "We will teach others to send messages," telegraph operators said.

Directions: Underline each object pronoun.

6. The operators taught me the code.
7. Morse's invention brought them to the world's attention.
8. People compared him to the great inventors of the past.
9. Does the telegraph affect us today?
10. The telephone, radio, and television have largely replaced it.

Notes for Home: Your child identified subject and object pronouns in sentences. ***Home Activity:*** Have your child use some of the pronouns from this page in other sentences. Ask him or her to tell you if they are subject or object pronouns.

488 Grammar: Subject/Object Pronouns and Agreement

Grammar Practice Book 6.5, p. 110

Name ______________________ *from* El Güero

Grammar: Subject/Object Pronouns and Agreement

Directions: Write the subject pronoun from each sentence.

1. I am studying the dragonfly for science class. **I**
2. You should hear the facts about the insect. **You**
3. It has four large delicate wings. **It**
4. They look like fine netting. **They**

Directions: Write the object pronoun from each sentence.

5. The wings move them rapidly through the air. **them**
6. The speed of the insect surprised her. **her**
7. People can spot it near water in summer. **it**
8. A dragonfly's unique appearance pleases me. **me**

Directions: Write a pronoun to replace the underlined word or words in each sentence.

9. Ms. Wasp assigned a report about dragonflies. **them**
10. The report will require some research. **It**
11. Pat and Toni worked on theirs at the library. **They**
12. The instructor praised Pam and me today. **us**
13. Beth discovered dragonflies lay eggs in water. **She**
14. That did not surprise Rafael very much. **him**
15. Patrick said, "The adults live only a few weeks." **He**
16. Kim and I observed live dragonflies for hours. **We**
17. We saw a dragonfly eat many kinds of insects. **it**

Write an Observation Journal Entry

On a separate sheet of paper, write an observation journal entry about an insect you have seen. Use subject and object pronouns to help you explain how it looked, where it was, and what it was doing.

Check that students use pronouns correctly.

Notes for Home: Your child identified subject and object pronouns in sentences. ***Home Activity:*** Have your child read his or her Observation Journal Entry to you. Ask your child to underline subject pronouns and circle object pronouns.

Grammar: Subject/Object Pronouns and Agreement 489

Practice Book 6.5, p. 218

Name ______________________ *from* El Güero

Word Study: Suffixes

Directions: A letter or group of letters added to the end of a word is called a **suffix.** A suffix can change the meaning of the base word. Add a suffix to each word below to make a new word. Write each new word on the line.

1. right + ful = **rightful**
2. flex + ible = **flexible**
3. final + ly = **finally**
4. mercy + ful = **merciful**
5. care + ful + ly = **carefully**
6. fortune + ate + ly = **fortunately**

Directions: Read the sentences below. Look and listen for words with the suffixes **-ly, -ful,** or **-ible.** Circle these words. Then write the base word and the suffix on the line, connected by a + sign. For example, for **doubtful,** you would write **doubt + ful.**

7. **sad + ly** — Sadly the family packed their belongings and left their home behind.
8. **sense + ible** — Being sensible they took the first ship they could find traveling out of the country.
9. **use + ful** — The new travelers tried to make themselves useful on board.
10. **willing + ly** — They helped prepare meals and entertained the crew willingly.
11. **slight + ly** — Once, a fog drifted in, and the ship's captain realized that the ship was slightly off course.
12. **instant + ly** — He instantly took action to correct the direction.
13. **beauty + ful** — When the ship docked, the family gazed with joy at the beautiful city that would be their new home.
14. **wonder + ful** — How wonderful it felt to stand on solid ground again!
15. **pain + ful** — As they made a new life for themselves, they tried to forget the painful memories of leaving their old home.

Notes for Home: Your child formed new words by adding the suffixes *-ly, -ful,* and *-ible* to base words. ***Home Activity:*** Read a magazine article with your child. Help your child notice words with these suffixes. Have your child group words with the same suffix together and write them in a list.

490 Word Study: Suffixes

Spelling Workbook 6.5, p. 85

Name ______________________ *from* El Güero

Spelling: Suffixes *-ation, -tion, -ion*

Pretest Directions: Fold back the page along the dotted line. On the blanks, write the spelling words as they are dictated. When you have finished the test, unfold the page and check your words.

1. **relaxation**	1. **Relaxation** lessens tension.
2. **exploration**	2. Space **exploration** continues.
3. **occupation**	3. What is your **occupation**?
4. **destination**	4. The train reached its **destination**.
5. **orientation**	5. New students attend **orientation**.
6. **recommendation**	6. He made the **recommendation**.
7. **determination**	7. **Determination** helps success.
8. **infection**	8. My cut has a minor **infection**.
9. **collection**	9. The **collection** was for the sick.
10. **reaction**	10. His **reaction** was one of surprise.
11. **situation**	11. It was a difficult **situation**.
12. **television**	12. Please turn off the **television**.
13. **generation**	13. Ours is a hopeful **generation**.
14. **reflection**	14. On **reflection**, I'll try it.
15. **destruction**	15. The forest faces **destruction**.
16. **attention**	16. Pay **attention** to the lesson.
17. **deduction**	17. Use **deduction** to solve it.
18. **reception**	18. We held the wedding **reception**.
19. **solution**	19. We need a **solution** quickly.
20. **convention**	20. The **convention** was at the hotel.

Notes for Home: Your child took a pretest on words that have the suffixes *-ation, -tion,* and *-ion.* ***Home Activity:*** Help your child learn misspelled words before the final test. Your child can underline the word parts that caused the problems and concentrate on those parts.

Spelling: Suffixes *-ation, -tion, -ion* 491

Spelling Workbook 6.5, p. 86

Name ______________________ *from* El Güero

Spelling: Suffixes *-ation, -tion, -ion*

Word List

relaxation	recommendation	situation	attention
exploration	determination	television	deduction
occupation	infection	generation	reception
destination	collection	reflection	solution
orientation	reaction	destruction	convention

Directions: Add a suffix to each base word below to form a word from the box. Write the word on the line.

1. determine **determination**
2. convene **convention**
3. situate **situation**
4. generate **generation**
5. solve **solution**
6. televise **television**
7. attend **attention**
8. occupy **occupation**
9. deduce **deduction**
10. explore **exploration**
11. receive **reception**
12. destiny **destination**

Directions: Choose the word from the box that best completes each equation. Write the word on the line.

13. re + commence – ce + dation = **recommendation**
14. destroy – oy + uction = **destruction**
15. re + lax + a + tion = **relaxation**
16. reach – h + tion = **reaction**
17. in + fect – t + tion = **infection**
18. color – or + lec + tion = **collection**
19. orient + ate – te + tion = **orientation**
20. reflexes – xes + c + tion = **reflection**

Notes for Home: Your child spelled words with the suffixes *-ation, -tion,* and *-ion.* ***Home Activity:*** Challenge your child to add the suffix *-ion* to each of these words and use the new words in sentences: *elect, act, construct.*

492 Spelling: Suffixes *-ation, -tion, -ion*

Spelling Workbook 6.5, p. 87

Name ______________________ *from* El Güero

Spelling: Suffixes *-ation, -tion, -ion*

Directions: Proofread this humorous account of a canine exile's thoughts. Find six spelling mistakes. Use the proofreading marks to correct each mistake.

Proofreading Marks	
≡	Make a capital.
/	Make a small letter.
∧	Add something.
⸗	Take out something.
⊙	Add a period.
¶	Begin a new paragraph.

How can I get back in? Is my life of relaxasion [ti] in front of the telavision [e] over? I miss the attention and affection of the people inside.

I didn't mean any harm. I was wandering about without a specific destination and decided a little exploreation under the shed would be fun. Who knew a spray in the face would be my recepsion [t]? And now, though I've barked my reccomendation [m] to be allowed in, I'm banned from the house until the skunk smell wears off. I never expected this reaction to my situasion [t].

Spelling Tip

When adding the suffixes **-ation, -tion,** or **-ion,** some base words do not change: **relaxation.** Other base words may drop a final **e** or **y: exploration, occupation.** Some base words have other changes: **receive + -tion = reception**

Word List

relaxation	situation
exploration	television
occupation	generation
destination	reflection
orientation	destruction
recommendation	attention
determination	deduction
infection	reception
collection	solution
reaction	convention

Write a Narrative

On a separate sheet of paper, write a narrative that describes thoughts that might occupy an exile's mind. It can be humorous, like the dog's tale above, or serious. What does an exile feel? What might an exile do? Try to use at least five spelling words in your narrative.

Answers will vary, but the description should include at least five spelling words.

Notes for Home: Your child spelled words with suffixes *-ation, -tion, -ion.* ***Home Activity:*** Challenge your child to identify the base word in each word from the box and to tell whether the spelling of the base word changed when the suffix was added.

Spelling Workbook 6.5, p. 88

Name ______________________ *from* El Güero

Spelling: Suffixes *-ation, -tion, -ion* REVIEW

Word List

relaxation	recommendation	situation	attention
exploration	determination	television	deduction
occupation	infection	generation	reception
destination	collection	reflection	solution
orientation	reaction	destruction	convention

Directions: Choose the word from the box that best completes each sentence. Write the word on the line to the left.

occupation 1. Before school started in the fall, her _____ was being a lifeguard at the local beach.

destination 2. The train took her straight to her _____: Lowwood School.

reception 3. Her _____ by the older students was warm and friendly.

collection 4. They had taken up a _____ to buy party refreshments to make the "new girl in town" feel more at home.

solution 5. She found a _____ to her isolation in new friendships.

attention 6. She paid _____ in class, wanting to do well in her studies.

relaxation 7. Dinner was a welcome form of _____ after each busy day.

television 8. She rarely found time to watch _____ after dinner.

determination 9. Her _____ to make a better life for herself in this country was admired by many.

generation 10. Each _____ in her family had always had at least one person eager to try new adventures.

Directions: Choose the word from the box that has the same or nearly the same meaning as each word or words below. Write the word on the line.

11. response	**reaction**	16. suggestion	**recommendation**
12. search	**exploration**	17. disease	**infection**
13. adjustment	**orientation**	18. conference	**convention**
14. mirror image	**reflection**	19. circumstances	**situation**
15. subtraction	**deduction**	20. ruin	**destruction**

Notes for Home: Your child reviewed words with suffixes *-ation, -ion, -tion.* ***Home Activity:*** Write the base word of each spelling word on index cards. Have your child pick a card and add a suffix to form a spelling word *(occupy + -tion = occupation).*

Practice Book 6.5, p. 219

Name ______________________ *from* El Güero

Evaluate Reference Sources

In order to decide whether a source is reliable and valid, you need to **evaluate reference sources.** You need to decide whether the information in the source is complete, unbiased, factual, and up-to-date, and ask yourself whether the source provides the kind of information you need for your research purposes.

Directions: Study the different reference sources. Then answer the questions that follow.

TRAVELING THE WORLD

Table of Contents

Getting from Here to There: A History of Travel

Contents

The World Almanac 1998, Index

World Travel

Vol. 232 Issue 9 February 1999

Practice Book 6.5, p. 220

Name ______________________ *from* El Güero

Possible answers given.

1. Read the chapter titles for *Traveling the World.* What is this book mostly about?
This book is mostly about exciting or adventurous trips taken around the world.

2. Read the chapter titles for *Getting from Here to There.* What is this book mostly about?
This book is mostly about the history of inventions in travel and transportation.

3. Suppose you are writing a paper about exciting, yet difficult, journeys. Which of these two books would be the most helpful? Why?
***Traveling the World* would be most helpful because it is about exciting trips.**

4. Suppose you wanted historical information about ships from long ago. Which of the resources shown would be most useful? Explain.
The book *Getting From Here to There* would be most helpful because it has a chapter on the world's first tall ships.

5. Would an almanac be a good place to find out the population of Jamaica? Explain.
Yes, an almanac would probably list facts about Jamaica, such as its population.

6. Suppose you wanted to read about someone's real-life travel experiences. Would the magazine *World Travel* be helpful? Explain.
Yes, the magazine includes an interview with a mountain climber so you could get a first-hand account of a traveler's experience.

7. Suppose you were writing a report on the invention of the airplane and you discovered that the book *Getting from Here to There* was published in 1995. Would this book still be a useful reference source? Explain.
Yes, since the information needed is historical, the information in a 1995 book would still be up-to-date.

8. When evaluating books, why is it important to check the copyright page?
The copyright page will tell you when a book was published. This information will help you decide how up-to-date the book's information will be.

9. How can an index or a table of contents help you evaluate a reference source?
An index or table of contents helps show at a glance what a book is about so you can decide whether it suits your research needs.

10. Why is it important to set a purpose for your research before evaluating reference sources?
By setting the purpose for your research first, you can better evaluate whether a reference source would be useful.

Notes for Home: Your child evaluated reference sources for specific research purposes. ***Home Activity:*** With your child, think of a topic and write questions about what you would like to know. Discuss what kinds of reference sources would be the most helpful.

Practice Book 6.5, p. 221

Name ______________________ **Destination: Mars**

Steps in a Process

- The actions you perform in order to make something or to reach a goal are the **steps in a process.**
- Sometimes the steps in a process will have numbers. Other clues to the order of the steps are words like *first, begin, next, then,* and *last.* If there are no clue words or numbers to help you keep the steps in order, use your common sense.
- Sometimes the steps in a process refer to a process in nature, such as the growth of a plant.

First → Then → Next → Last

Directions: Reread "Living in Space." Then complete the flow chart to describe the process by which oxygen, water, and carbon dioxide are constantly recycled in a bottle garden. Write the steps in the flow chart in the order in which they occur. Some steps have been started for you. **Possible answers given.**

1. Plants collect **energy from sunlight.**
2. Plants convert **water from the soil and carbon dioxide from the air into glucose.**
3. The leaves also produce **oxygen.**
4. **Plants and tiny animals use the food (the glucose) and oxygen to grow.**
5. **Plants and animals release water and carbon dioxide.**

Notes for Home: Your child read about a process and listed the steps in the process in the order in which they occur. ***Home Activity:*** Encourage your child to list the steps in an everyday process, such as making breakfast or playing a compact disc.

Steps in a Process 499

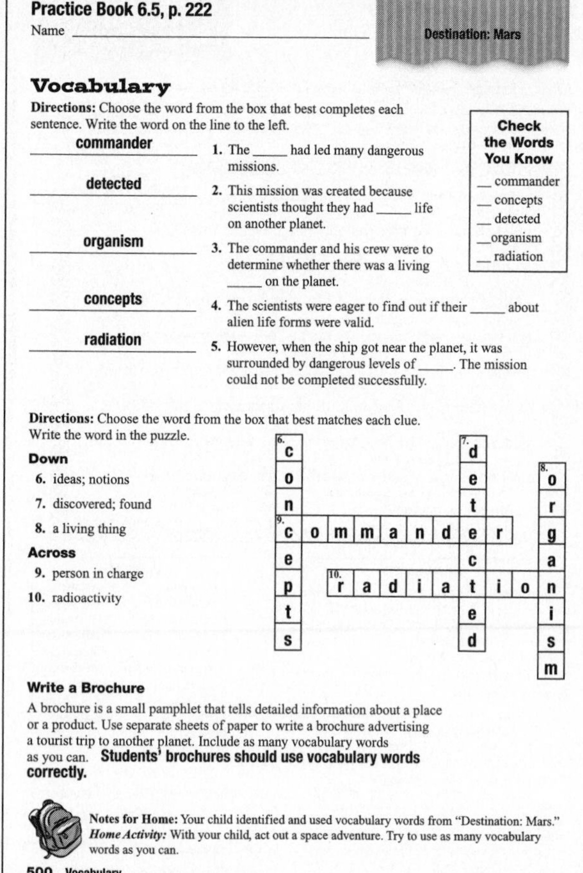

Practice Book 6.5, p. 222

Name ______________________ **Destination: Mars**

Vocabulary

Directions: Choose the word from the box that best completes each sentence. Write the word on the line to the left.

Check the Words You Know
- __ commander
- __ concepts
- __ detected
- __ organism
- __ radiation

commander 1. The _____ had led many dangerous missions.

detected 2. This mission was created because scientists thought they had _____ life on another planet.

organism 3. The commander and his crew were to determine whether there was a living _____ on the planet.

concepts 4. The scientists were eager to find out if their _____ about alien life forms were valid.

radiation 5. However, when the ship got near the planet, it was surrounded by dangerous levels of _____. The mission could not be completed successfully.

Directions: Choose the word from the box that best matches each clue. Write the word in the puzzle.

Down
6. ideas; notions — **concepts**
7. discovered; found — **detected**
8. a living thing — **organism**

Across
9. person in charge — **commander**
10. radioactivity — **radiation**

Write a Brochure

A brochure is a small pamphlet that tells detailed information about a place or a product. Use separate sheets of paper to write a brochure advertising a tourist trip to another planet. Include as many vocabulary words as you can. **Students' brochures should use vocabulary words correctly.**

Notes for Home: Your child identified and used vocabulary words from "Destination: Mars." ***Home Activity:*** With your child, act out a space adventure. Try to use as many vocabulary words as you can.

500 Vocabulary

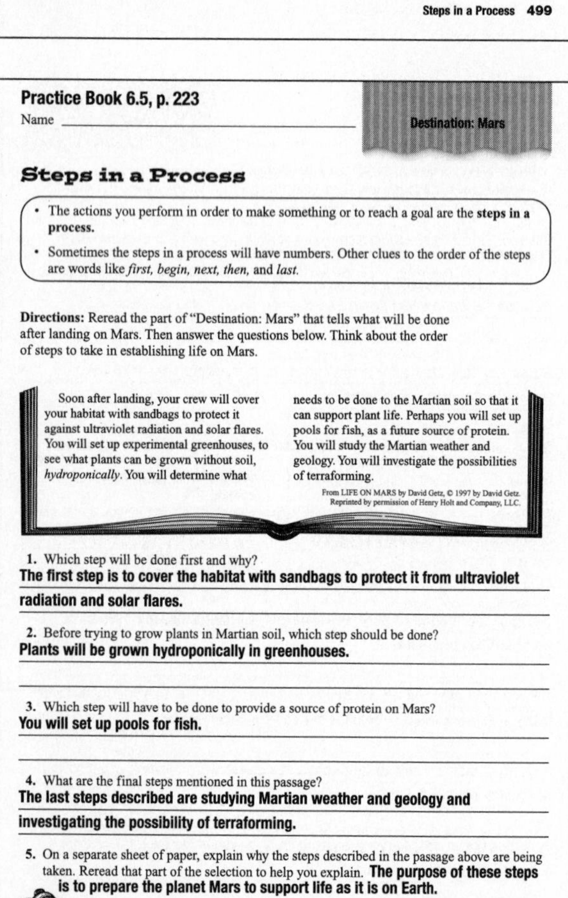

Practice Book 6.5, p. 223

Name ______________________ **Destination: Mars**

Steps in a Process

- The actions you perform in order to make something or to reach a goal are the **steps in a process.**
- Sometimes the steps in a process will have numbers. Other clues to the order of the steps are words like *first, begin, next, then,* and *last.*

Directions: Reread the part of "Destination: Mars" that tells what will be done after landing on Mars. Then answer the questions below. Think about the order of steps to take in establishing life on Mars.

Soon after landing, your crew will cover your habitat with sandbags to protect it against ultraviolet radiation and solar flares. You will set up experimental greenhouses, to see what plants can be grown without soil, *hydroponically.* You will determine what needs to be done to the Martian soil so that it can support plant life. Perhaps you will set up pools for fish, as a future source of protein. You will study the Martian weather and geology. You will investigate the possibilities of terraforming.

From LIFE ON MARS by David Getz, © 1997 by David Getz. Reprinted by permission of Henry Holt and Company, LLC.

1. Which step will be done first and why?
The first step is to cover the habitat with sandbags to protect it from ultraviolet radiation and solar flares.
2. Before trying to grow plants in Martian soil, which step should be done?
Plants will be grown hydroponically in greenhouses.
3. Which step will have to be done to provide a source of protein on Mars?
You will set up pools for fish.
4. What are the final steps mentioned in this passage?
The last steps described are studying Martian weather and geology and investigating the possibility of terraforming.
5. On a separate sheet of paper, explain why the steps described in the passage above are being taken. Reread that part of the selection to help you explain. **The purpose of these steps is to prepare the planet Mars to support life as it is on Earth.**

Notes for Home: Your child read a passage from a selection and identified the steps in a process. ***Home Activity:*** Read an instruction guide for using a simple household machine with your child. Encourage her or him to retell the steps for use in the correct order.

Steps in a Process 501

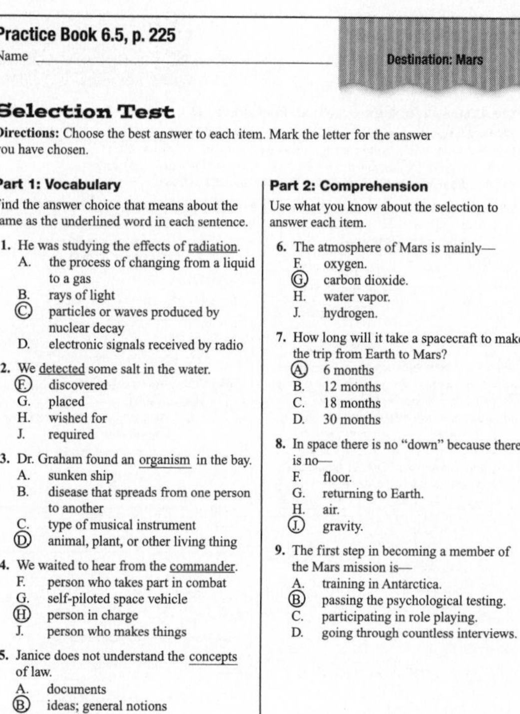

Practice Book 6.5, p. 225

Name ______________________ **Destination: Mars**

Selection Test

Directions: Choose the best answer to each item. Mark the letter for the answer you have chosen.

Part 1: Vocabulary

Find the answer choice that means about the same as the underlined word in each sentence.

1. He was studying the effects of radiation.
   - A. the process of changing from a liquid to a gas
   - B. rays of light
   - **(C)** particles or waves produced by nuclear decay
   - D. electronic signals received by radio
2. We detected some salt in the water.
   - **(F)** discovered
   - G. placed
   - H. wished for
   - J. required
3. Dr. Graham found an organism in the bay.
   - A. sunken ship
   - B. disease that spreads from one person to another
   - C. type of musical instrument
   - **(D)** animal, plant, or other living thing
4. We waited to hear from the commander.
   - F. person who takes part in combat
   - G. self-piloted space vehicle
   - **(H)** person in charge
   - J. person who makes things
5. Janice does not understand the concepts of law.
   - A. documents
   - **(B)** ideas; general notions
   - C. decisions
   - D. problems; puzzles

Part 2: Comprehension

Use what you know about the selection to answer each item.

6. The atmosphere of Mars is mainly—
   - F. oxygen.
   - **(G)** carbon dioxide.
   - H. water vapor.
   - J. hydrogen.
7. How long will it take a spacecraft to make the trip from Earth to Mars?
   - **(A)** 6 months
   - B. 12 months
   - C. 18 months
   - D. 30 months
8. In space there is no "down" because there is no—
   - F. floor.
   - G. returning to Earth.
   - H. air.
   - **(J)** gravity.
9. The first step in becoming a member of the Mars mission is—
   - A. training in Antarctica.
   - **(B)** passing the psychological testing.
   - C. participating in role playing.
   - D. going through countless interviews.

GO ON

502 Selection Test

Practice Book 6.5, p. 226

Name ______________________________

Destination: Mars

10. You are on a mission to Mars, and the spaceship is now in orbit around Earth. What is the next step?
    F. You wait for the next "launch window" before heading toward Mars.
    G. The ship slides toward Mars in a Hohman transfer.
    (H) The commander fires the rockets to fling the ship away from Earth's gravity.
    J. An unmanned rocket is sent to Mars, carrying cargo you will need when you get there.

11. Why do a person's muscles become weak in outer space?
    (A) They no longer need to fight gravity.
    B. There are few opportunities for exercise.
    C. The food is not healthful.
    D. The cabin of the spacecraft is small and cramped.

12. What is the same about solar flares and galactic rays?
    F. They give about an hour's warning.
    G. They are hot and bright.
    (H) They are harmful to humans.
    J. They constantly bombard the spaceship.

13. People from Earth have to remain on Mars for eighteen months because—
    A. they need that long for exploring and doing experiments.
    B. they need time to readjust to living with gravity.
    C. it takes that long to make enough fuel for the return trip.
    (D) it would not be possible for them to reach Earth if they tried to leave earlier.

14. Which statement is an opinion?
    F. "Thousands of people applied to join the first Mars mission."
    (G) "It is one of the richest areas for finding dinosaur fossils in the world."
    H. "Most of this loss occurs in your spine and hips."
    J. "There are no magic pills for gravity yet."

15. Which is the greatest obstacle to human survival on Mars?
    (A) lack of air and water
    B. lack of gravity
    C. distance from Earth
    D. lack of a native civilization

Name ______________________________

Destination: Mars

Steps in a Process

- The actions you perform in order to make something or to reach a goal are the **steps in a process.**
- Sometimes the steps in a process will have numbers. Other clues to the order of the steps are words like *first, begin, next, then,* and *last.*

Directions: Read the story below.

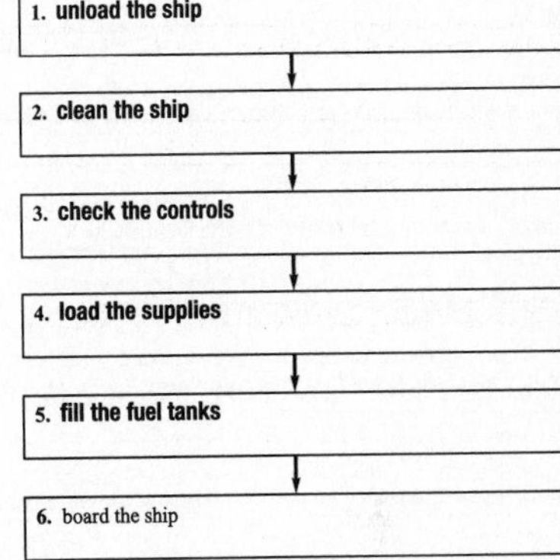
There is a lot to do to get the spaceship ready for our trip to the asteroid belt. First we have to unload all the stuff left behind by the last crew. Once the ship is empty, we have to clean it. Then all the controls have to be checked. We need to be sure everything is working properly before we take off. After that, we have to load the supplies: food, extra clothing, tape recorders, writing materials, and emergency gear. Then we need to have the fuel tanks filled. The last step is to make sure everyone is on board and ready to go.

Directions: The steps for preparing the spaceship are out of order in the box on the left. Reread the passage to put the steps in the right order in the flow chart. The last step has been done for you.

Out of Order
board the ship
load the supplies
unload the ship
clean the ship
fill the fuel tanks
check the controls

1. **unload the ship**
2. **clean the ship**
3. **check the controls**
4. **load the supplies**
5. **fill the fuel tanks**
6. board the ship

Notes for Home: Your child read a passage and wrote the steps of the process described in order. ***Home Activity:*** Together, read the directions on a food package for preparing a simple dish. Challenge your child to repeat the steps for preparation in their correct order.

Practice Book 6.5, p. 227

Name ______________________________

Destination: Mars

Paraphrasing

REVIEW

Directions: Read the passage. Then read each question about the passage. Choose the best answer to each question. Mark the letter for the answer you have chosen.

The Time Machine

For centuries, people have been fascinated by the idea of time travel. Many stories from past centuries are about this concept.

Before people thought about traveling in space, they used the idea of an enchanted sleep as a way to get a person from one time period to another. In the French fairy tale "Sleeping Beauty," princess Briar Rose pricks her finger on a spindle and falls asleep. Generations pass. The prince who finally awakens her was born over a century after Briar Rose—and yet they seem to be about the same age!

A Connecticut Yankee in King Arthur's Court is a funny 19th century story of time travel by Mark Twain. In this story, an ordinary young man is knocked unconscious in a fight and awakens in Camelot in the year 528. His knowledge of everyday modern objects like forks and bicycles cause Arthur's knights and ladies to marvel.

More recent time-travel stories have involved complicated machines that literally transport people through time. In the popular film *Back to the Future,* a high school student suddenly finds himself going to class with his own mother and father. In the film, the time travel machine uses radioactive materials, lightning, and garbage as sources of fuel.

1. Which of the following is a paraphrase of the article's main idea?
    (A) Time travel has been a popular subject of stories for centuries.
    B. Some time machines need lightning to travel.
    C. An enchanted sleep is one way of traveling through time.
    D. A Yankee once traveled to Camelot.

2. Which of the following best paraphrases the main idea of the second paragraph?
    F. Briar Rose pricks her finger and falls asleep.
    G. Many young men want to wake her up.
    H. The prince is 100 years younger than Briar Rose.
    (J) In old stories, people travel through time by sleeping through it.

3. Which of the following best paraphrases the main idea of the third paragraph?
    A. The Yankee tells Arthur about forks.
    (B) Mark Twain wrote a funny story about time travel.
    C. In the year 528, Arthur was king of Great Britain.
    D. Everyone in Camelot learns how to ride a bicycle.

4. Which of the following best paraphrases the main idea of the last paragraph?
    (F) Recent time-travel stories use complicated machines to transport people through time.
    G. Characters no longer sleep through time anymore.
    H. *Back To The Future* was a popular film about time travel.
    J. Time machines can let you meet your parents as teenagers.

5. Which of the following is **not** a paraphrase of something in the article?
    A. Time-travel stories are popular.
    B. One day, a young American wakes up in King Arthur's court.
    (C) Rip Van Winkle sleeps for many years.
    D. Briar Rose falls asleep when she pricks her finger.

Notes for Home: Your child read a passage and identified paraphrases of statements in the passage. ***Home Activity:*** Tell your child a story about time travel. Have your child retell the story in his or her own words.

Name ______________________________

Destination: Mars

Writing Across Texts

Directions: Think about what you learned about a space mission to Mars from "Destination: Mars" and "Exploring Mars." Complete the first column of the table by listing what you learned about a trip to Mars from "Destination: Mars." In the second column, make a list of facts from "Exploring Mars."
Possible answers given.

"Destination: Mars"	"Exploring Mars"
It would take 30 months to travel to Mars and back.	Viking landers made the trip there in a year.
1. **The Earth revolves around the sun at about 70,000 miles per hour.**	6. **The Pathfinder landed on Mars in 1997.**
2. **Mars is 4,223 miles in diameter.**	7. **It carried a remote-controlled buggy that explored the area around the landing site.**
3. **Gravitational pull on Mars is about one third of what it is on Earth.**	8. **The sky on Mars glows for more than an hour after sunset.**
4. **Your body deteriorates if you spend a long time where there is no gravity.**	9. **The Viking landers beamed back the first pictures of the surface of Mars.**
5. **Galactic rays and solar flares threaten your safety on a trip to Mars.**	10. **To protect it, the Pathfinder parachuted onto the surface of Mars inside a giant "beach ball."**

Write a Research Report

Use the library or the Internet to find updated information about missions to Mars. Write a research report detailing the successes and failures of the last few years.
Reports will vary. Check that students made good use of the information they gathered.

Notes for Home: Your child wrote a research report about recent missions to Mars. ***Home Activity:*** Read a news article with your child. Write questions you each have about the topic. Identify and paraphrase a topic sentence in the article that tells what the article is about.

Grammar Practice Book 6.5, p. 111

Name ______________________ Destination: Mars

Grammar: Pronouns and Their Referents

REVIEW

Directions: In each sentence, underline the pronoun and draw a circle around its referent. Hint: Some pronouns are possessive pronouns.

1. Wanda, would you like to travel through space?
2. Spaceships were just a dream years ago, but today they are becoming a reality.
3. Imagine how Neil Armstrong must have felt when he first stepped onto the moon in 1969.
4. Wanda would like to be the first person to step onto Mars, and perhaps she will be.
5. Many people throughout history have had their dreams about space travel.
6. This generation is the first that may see its dreams come true.
7. Astronauts in space have looked down at Earth, with its mountains and oceans.
8. Travel in outer space is exciting, but it can also be very dangerous.
9. Nevertheless, Wanda has made up her mind.
10. Look for Wanda and others someday as they zoom far out into space.

Directions: Replace the underlined word or words in each sentence with a pronoun. Write your new sentences on the lines.

11. With young people like Wanda, humans may actually visit other planets someday.
With young people like her, humans may actually visit other planets someday.

12. One day a spaceship may take off with Wanda and other young people inside it.
One day a spaceship may take off with them inside it.

13. Years later, these astronauts will reach their destination planet.
Years later, they will reach their destination planet.

14. When Wanda sends her first message back to Earth, what will Wanda say?
When Wanda sends her first message back to Earth, what will she say?

15. She is probably working on that first message of Wanda's already!
She is probably working on that first message of hers already!

Notes for Home: Your child matched pronouns with their referents and rewrote sentences with pronouns. ***Home Activity:*** Work with your child to write a short dramatic scene about landing on a new planet. Have your child underline all the pronouns in the script.

Grammar: Pronouns and Their Referents 507

Grammar Practice Book 6.5, p. 112

Name ______________________ Destination: Mars

Grammar: Prepositions and Prepositional Phrases

A **prepositional phrase** begins with a **preposition** and ends with a noun or pronoun that is called the **object of the preposition.**

Have you seen any photos of lunar eclipses?

In the sentence above, *eclipses* is the object of the preposition *of.* Notice that the object of the preposition may have a modifier, such as *lunar.*

Common Prepositions:
about, above, across, after, along, among, around, at, before, behind, below, beside, between, by, down, for, from, in, inside, into, near, of, off, on, onto, out, outside, over, through, to, toward, under, until, up, with

Directions: Underline the prepositional phrase or phrases in each sentence. Draw a second line under the preposition. Circle the object of the preposition.

1. Astronauts in orbit have traveled around our planet.
2. In 1969, two American astronauts landed on the moon.
3. Will human visitors ever step onto the surface of Mars?
4. Our family watched TV news coverage of John Glenn's 1998 mission in space.
5. By that time, "a de-orbit burn" was part of the English language.
6. I often think about a trip across the galaxy!
7. With a telescope, I can look through the atmosphere and see into space.
8. I have read about Saturn, and it seems interesting to me.
9. The *Cassini* will reach out and study Saturn by 2004.
10. Data from *Cassini* will tell us more about Saturn's atmosphere.

Directions: Choose a preposition that makes sense in each sentence. Write the preposition on the line to the left. **Answers may vary. Accept all reasonable answers.**

of 11. In Roman myths, Saturn was the god _____ harvests.

from 12. Saturn is the sixth planet _____ the Sun, and Jupiter is the fifth planet.

around 13. Each of these planets travels in orbit _____ the Sun and has its own moons.

for 14. Saturn or Jupiter would make a good subject _____ a painting.

at 15. Look _____ Jupiter, huge and silvery, near an autumn moon, and dream of going there!

Notes for Home: Your child identified prepositional phrases, such as *across the galaxy.* ***Home Activity:*** Make up some short sentences. Have your child use the list of prepositions above to add prepositional phrases to each one.

508 Grammar: Prepositions and Prepositional Phrases

Grammar Practice Book 6.5, p. 113

Name ______________________ Destination: Mars

Grammar: Prepositions and Prepositional Phrases

Directions: Write a prepositional phrase, using the preposition in ( ). Add the phrase to the word group to form a complete sentence. Write the sentence on the line. **Possible answers given.**

1. Sometimes, I imagine living (on) ______.
Sometimes, I imagine living on a distant planet.

2. I would be far away (from) ______.
I would be far away from danger.

3. I would be part of a colony (of) ______.
I would be part of a colony of scientists.

4. Lighted tunnels would run (through) ______.
Lighted tunnels would run through the planet.

5. Fruits and vegetables would grow (inside) ______.
Fruits and vegetables would grow inside solar greenhouses.

6. There might be fish (in) ______.
There might be fish in underground pools.

7. We would have an observatory (in) ______.
We would have an observatory in the colony.

8. We would look at Earth (through) ______.
We would look at Earth through giant lenses.

9. Fields and forests would lie (beyond) ______.
Fields and forests would lie beyond our colony.

10. We could hide our rockets (under) ______.
We could hide our rockets under the mountains.

Write a Journal Entry

Imagine that you are an astronaut. On a separate sheet of paper, write a journal entry in which you describe a day in your life on a trip to Mars. Include several sentences that use prepositions, such as *beside, into,* and *toward,* and prepositional phrases, such as *on the way* and *upon arrival.* **Check to be sure that students have correctly placed prepositional phrases that make sense in their writing.**

Notes for Home: Your child wrote prepositional phrases. ***Home Activity:*** Talk together about a trip you have taken. Have your child identify each prepositional phrase he or she uses, for example: *We traveled to the beach.*

Grammar: Prepositions and Prepositional Phrases 509

Grammar Practice Book 6.5, p. 114

Name ______________________ Destination: Mars

Grammar: Prepositions and Prepositional Phrases

RETEACHING

Underline the prepositional phrase in each sentence.

1. Emily thinks about the colors.
2. She chooses the color of daffodils.
3. Her room looks wonderful with yellow paint.

A **preposition** relates a noun or pronoun to another word in the sentence. The noun or pronoun that follows a preposition is the **object of the preposition.** A preposition, its object, and any words that describe the object make up a **prepositional phrase.**

Directions: Underline each prepositional phrase in the sentences below.

1. Paintings called frescos are on wet plaster.
2. You can mix dry colors with egg yolks.
3. Tempera is the result of the mixture.
4. Painters once used tempera on linen surfaces.
5. Cave pictures were the earliest type of paintings.
6. Egyptians painted the walls of pharaohs' tombs.
7. Artists painted books in medieval times.
8. Small pictures appeared near letters.
9. Artists painted words and pictures by hand.
10. No printing presses existed at that time.
11. The paper consisted of long-lasting parchment.
12. We have many books made by medieval monks.

Directions: Write the prepositional phrases from the sentences above. Circle the object of each preposition.

13. **on wet plaster**
14. **with egg yolks**
15. **of the mixture**
16. **on linen surfaces**
17. **of paintings**
18. **of pharaohs' tombs**
19. **in medieval times**
20. **near letters**
21. **by hand**
22. **at that time**
23. **of long-lasting parchment**
24. **by medieval monks**

Notes for Home: Your child identified prepositions in prepositional phrases. ***Home Activity:*** Name an animal. Have your child describe something the animal can do and use a prepositional phrase in the description. Switch roles.

510 Grammar: Prepositions and Prepositional Phrases

Grammar Practice Book 6.5, p. 115

Name ______________________ **Destination: Mars**

Grammar: Prepositions and Prepositional Phrases

Directions: Underline the prepositional phrase in each sentence. Circle each preposition.

1. We use paper in books.
2. We also use it for homework and other tasks.
3. People write letters on paper.
4. Have you ever wrapped a present in paper?
5. Some factories make paper from fibers.
6. Most paper is made with wood fibers.
7. Fibers from cloth are important too.
8. A chipping machine cuts a log into tiny chips.
9. Machines mix the chips and rags in water.
10. The mixture is treated with chemicals.
11. The watery pulp hardens between thin molds.
12. Through many machines the sheets are processed.
13. The machines press them into long paper strips.

Directions: Complete each sentence. Write prepositional phrases. **Possible answers given.**

14. I use paper **in my hobbies**.
15. I write on paper **with colorful stripes**.
16. **In third grade** I learned handwriting.
17. You can find paper **in many stores**.
18. Wrapping paper is printed **on shiny paper**.
19. Paper **below standard** is often dull and colorless.
20. Paper comes **in many sizes and colors**.
21. Many products **in this country** are made from wood.
22. The man spoke **to me** at the paper factory.

Write a Description

On a separate sheet of paper, describe something you can make from paper. Use prepositional phrases in your sentences.

Check that students have used prepositional phrases correctly.

Notes for Home: Your child wrote prepositional phrases to complete sentences. ***Home Activity:*** Write complete subjects of sentences on slips of paper *(The baseball team)* and have your child add words including a prepositional phrase to finish the sentence. *(The baseball team cheered for each other.)*

Practice Book 6.5, p. 228

Name ______________________ **Destination: Mars**

Word Study: Singular Possessives

Directions: Words that show ownership, or possession, are called **possessives.** Add an **apostrophe (')** and **s** to form possessives of singular nouns: **Mom's.** Read the phrases below. Change each phrase to form possessive nouns. Write the new phrase on the line.

the brightness of the star	the star's brightness
1. the orders of the commander	**the commander's orders**
2. the surface of Earth	**Earth's surface**
3. the canyons of Mars	**Mars's canyons**
4. the months of a year	**a year's months**
5. the rays of the Sun	**the Sun's rays**

Directions: Read the paragraph below. Look for ten words with apostrophes ('). Five words are possessives. The other five words are contractions. Write each word in the correct column to show which type of word it is.

Dr. McKay's Notes
July 2000

It's with a child's wonder and a scientist's concern that I gaze toward the stars and speculate about the ship we've sent into space. As a child, I'd always wanted to venture to that great beyond and view another planet's splendor and colors, especially Saturn's rings. But the ship doesn't carry any crew or passengers. We'll track it by computer and download the pictures of space.

Possessives	Contractions
6. **Dr. McKay's**	11. **It's**
7. **child's**	12. **we've**
8. **scientist's**	13. **I'd**
9. **planet's**	14. **doesn't**
10. **Saturn's**	15. **We'll**

Notes for Home: Your child wrote possessives and sorted contractions and possessives. ***Home Activity:*** With your child, write ten contractions and ten possessives on separate index cards. Take turns choosing two cards to try to get two possessives or two contractions.

Spelling Workbook 6.5, p. 89

Name ______________________ **Destination: Mars**

Spelling: Opposite Prefixes

Pretest Directions: Fold back the page along the dotted line. On the blanks, write the spelling words as they are dictated. When you have finished the test, unfold the page and check your words.

1. **pretrial**	1. The **pretrial** hearing was short.
2. **prearrange**	2. We will **prearrange** the vacation.
3. **premeditated**	3. The crime was not **premeditated**.
4. **prehistoric**	4. She found a **prehistoric** fossil.
5. **precaution**	5. Proper **precaution** is wise.
6. **postdate**	6. The houses **postdate** the farm.
7. **postwar**	7. **Postwar** Europe prospered.
8. **postponement**	8. The **postponement** is temporary.
9. **postgraduate**	9. She did **postgraduate** studies.
10. **overcook**	10. Do not **overcook** the rice.
11. **overlook**	11. The cliffs **overlook** the sea.
12. **overflow**	12. The pot began to **overflow**.
13. **overpopulated**	13. The zoo was **overpopulated**.
14. **undercover**	14. Stay **undercover** until it is safe.
15. **undernourished**	15. The bear looked **undernourished**.
16. **underweight**	16. The luggage was **underweight**.
17. **include**	17. Does the meal **include** a salad?
18. **inhale**	18. I like to **inhale** baking smells.
19. **exclude**	19. Do not **exclude** your friends.
20. **exhale**	20. They **exhale** audibly.

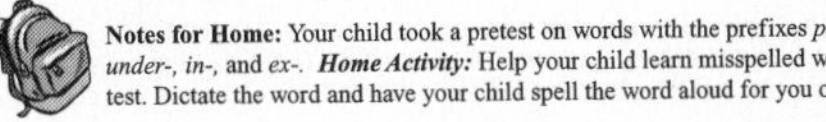

Notes for Home: Your child took a pretest on words with the prefixes *pre-, post-, over-, under-, in-,* and *ex-*. ***Home Activity:*** Help your child learn misspelled words before the final test. Dictate the word and have your child spell the word aloud for you or write it on paper.

Spelling Workbook 6.5, p. 90

Name ______________________ **Destination: Mars**

Spelling: Opposite Prefixes

Word List

pretrial	precaution	postgraduate	overpopulated	include
prearrange	postdate	overcook	undercover	inhale
premeditated	postwar	overlook	undernourished	exclude
prehistoric	postponement	overflow	underweight	exhale

Directions: Choose the words from the box that have the prefixes **pre-, post-, in-** or **ex-.** Write each word in the correct column. **Order may vary.**

Prefix pre-	Prefix post-
1. **pretrial**	8. **postdate**
2. **prearrange**	9. **postwar**
3. **premeditated**	10. **postponement**
4. **prehistoric**	11. **postgraduate**
5. **precaution**	

Prefix in-	Prefix ex-
6. **include**	12. **exclude**
7. **inhale**	13. **exhale**

Directions: Choose the word from the box that matches each definition. Write the word on the line.

overcook 14. cook too much
underweight 15. not heavy enough
undernourished 16. not eating a healthful diet
overflow 17. go over or beyond the limits; flood
overlook 18. not to see something
undercover 19. in secret
overpopulated 20. crowded with people

Notes for Home: Your child spelled words with the prefixes *pre-, post-, over-, under-, in-,* and *ex-*. ***Home Activity:*** Have your child name two words not on the list that can be formed by adding the prefix *under-* and two words that can be formed by adding the prefix *over-*.

Spelling Workbook 6.5, p. 91

Name ______________________ Destination: Mars

Spelling: Opposite Prefixes

Directions: Proofread this space log. Find seven spelling mistakes. Use the proofreading marks to correct each mistake.

≡	Make a capital.
/	Make a small letter.
∧	Add something.
♪	Take out something.
⊙	Add a period.
¶	Begin a new paragraph.

Today we made our first poswar visit to Elkan. After 40 years of isolation, conditions on the planet are, by our standards, perhistoric. Going without is a way of life for this population, which appears undrnourished and underweight.

The purposes of our prarranged meeting included locating a suitable site for pertrial hearings and discussing the charges of premeditated war crimes. I discovered that the former leaders charged with these crimes have taken the precaution of filing for a trial posponement. I fear this mission will be a long one.

Spelling Tip

When adding the prefixes **pre-**, **post-**, **over-**, **under-**, **in-**, and **ex-**, do not make any changes in the base word.

Word List

pretrial	overlook
prearrange	overflow
premeditated	overpopulated
prehistoric	undercover
precaution	undernourished
postdate	underweight
postwar	include
postponement	inhale
postgraduate	exclude
overcook	exhale

Write a Space Log Entry

On a separate sheet of paper, write an entry in a space log. What did you do in space today? Were there any problems? Try to use at least five spelling words. **Answers will vary, but each space log entry should include at least five spelling words.**

Notes for Home: Your child spelled words with the prefixes *pre-, post-, over-, under-, in-,* and *ex-*. ***Home Activity:*** Help your child separate the prefixes from the base words in the spelling list *(pretrial = pre + trial)*. Discuss how prefixes change the meaning of base words.

Spelling Workbook 6.5, p. 92

Name ______________________ Destination: Mars

Spelling: Opposite Prefixes

REVIEW

Word List

pretrial	precaution	postgraduate	overpopulated	include
prearrange	postdate	overcook	undercover	inhale
premeditated	postwar	overlook	undernourished	exclude
prehistoric	postponement	overflow	underweight	exhale

Directions: Find two words in each sentence that can be combined to form a word from the box. Write the word from the box on the line.

underweight 1. Put the papers under the brass weight.
overlook 2. I went over to his house to look for him.
postwar 3. That post was destroyed in the war.
overcook 4. If you come over for dinner, I will cook spaghetti.
postdate 5. The post office stamps the date on each letter.
overflow 6. Let's go over to the bridge and watch the river flow.
postgraduate 7. He left his military post just as his son was about to graduate.
undercover 8. I found a book under the couch; look at the dust on its cover!
overpopulated 9. We traveled over stretches of country populated by cattle.
undernourished 10. Clams live under the water; they are nourished by the sea.

Directions: Choose the word from the box that best answers each riddle. Write the word on the line.

inhale 11. I am what you do when you take in a breath.
exhale 12. I am what you do when you release your breath.
prehistoric 13. I am from the time before written history.
postponement 14. I am what you ask for if you want to put something off until later.
prearrange 15. I am what you do when you make an arrangement in advance.
include 16. I am what you do when you make someone part of a group.
precaution 17. I am what you take beforehand to ensure your safety.
pretrial 18. I am a meeting before a trial.
exclude 19. I am what you do when you shut something or someone out.
premeditated 20. I am a type of action that has been thought out in advance.

Notes for Home: Your child reviewed words with the prefixes *pre-, post-, over-, under-, in-,* and *ex-*. ***Home Activity:*** Write the spelling words on separate index cards. Take turns with your child choosing a card from the stack, spelling the word, and using it in a sentence.

Practice Book 6.5, p. 229

Name ______________________ Destination: Mars

Technology: Electronic Media

There are two types of **electronic media**—computer and non-computer. Computer sources include computer software, CD-ROMs, and the Internet. Non-computer sources include audiotapes, videotapes, films, film strips, television, and radio.

To find information on the Internet, use a search engine and type in your key words. Be specific. It's a good idea to use two or more key words, typing AND between key words. For example, if you typed "Mars AND photographs," you might get a list of web pages like the one below. To get to a web page, click on the underlined link.

Directions: Use the Internet search results to answer the questions that follow.

You Searched For: Mars AND Photographs

Top 5 of 38 matches.

1 Ruins on Mars Striking color photographs of what may be ancient ruins on the surface of Mars are now available.

2 Mars Home Page All about Mars—missions to Mars, images of Mars, and plans for Mars exploration and settlement in the future.

3 Mars: Past Missions Past missions include 1962: The first attempt to fly to Mars ended when a Russian probe was lost after traveling 66 million miles. 1964: A U.S. flyby returns 21 images of Mars to Earth. 1971–1972: America's *Mariner IX* and Russia's *Mars 3* orbit the planet, providing data and photographs.

4 Spacelink - Mars Global Surveyor Mars Global Surveyor is a polar-orbiting spacecraft designed to provide global maps of surface topography, distribution of minerals, and monitoring of global weather.

5 Mars Pathfinder On July 4, 1997, the Mars *Pathfinder* spacecraft arrived on the Red Planet. *Pathfinder* sent out a small rover called *Sojourner* to explore the Martian landscape. Learn more intriguing information here.

Click here to continue →

Practice Book 6.5, p. 230

Name ______________________ Destination: Mars

1. How do you get to a specific web page? **You can click on an underlined link.**
2. What information will web page 5 have? **It will have information about the *Pathfinder* mission.**
3. Which web page has information about the Mars Global Surveyor? **web page 4**
4. What key words could you use to find web pages about the history of exploration on Mars? **Possible answer: Mars AND exploration AND history**
5. Why is it important to choose your key words carefully when searching the Internet? **Possible answer: You need to choose key words that are specific enough in order to limit your search and focus on getting the most relevant information.**
6. What are some of the advantages of using the Internet as a source of information for research? **Possible answers: You can search for information quickly and easily. You can find many different websites and web pages. You can get current information.**
7. How might you use a documentary videotape on Mars for a research report? **Possible answer: You could use facts from the videotape as part of your report. You might also show some of the videotape in an oral presentation of your report.**
8. How might you use an audiotape of conversations between astronauts on a space mission and the mission command center? **Possible answer: You could quote parts of the conversations in your report. You could use the audiotape to get a better sense of what it's like to be on a space mission. You could play parts of the audiotape in an oral presentation of your report.**
9. Name some ways television could be used as a research source. **Possible answer: TV programs such as news, documentaries, or nature programs can give factual information on subjects. TV news is a good resource for current information about recent events.**
10. Is electronic media always the best choice as a research source? Explain why or why not. **No, it depends on your research purpose. A printed book, for example, may give more detailed information than a film, videotape, or website.**

Notes for Home: Your child answered questions about the results of a web page search on the Internet and other forms of electronic media. ***Home Activity:*** Make a list of the different forms of electronic media. Discuss how each form could be used for research or study.

Practice Book 6.5, p. 231

Name ____________________ The Land of Expectations

Summarizing

- To **summarize** means to give a brief statement of the main idea of an article or the most important events in a story.
- When you summarize a story, include only the main actions of the characters and the outcomes of those actions.

Directions: Reread "To Surprise the Children." Then summarize the story by choosing the five sentences from the box that best describe the most important actions or events. Write the sentences in the flow chart in the correct order.

The main character asked a bricklayer what would happen if the brick fell on somebody.
The main character went somewhere and looked up.
The bricklayers supported the brick by building a whole house around it.
The main character asked what would happen if the brick fell on somebody.
Some people, including the main character, moved into the house.
The main character looked up and saw a brick sitting in the air.
Everyone was looking at the brick.
The bricklayer called for other bricklayers to come.
Some people moved into the house.

Event 1: **The main character looked up and saw a brick sitting in the air.**

Event 2: **The main character asked a bricklayer what would happen if the brick fell on somebody.**

Event 3: **The bricklayer called for other bricklayers to come.**

Event 4: **The bricklayers supported the brick by building a whole house around it.**

Event 5: **Some people, including the main character, moved into the house.**

Notes for Home: Your child summarized a story. ***Home Activity:*** Work with your child to summarize a story or movie. Be sure to include only the most important events.

Practice Book 6.5, p. 232

Name ____________________ The Land of Expectations

Vocabulary

Directions: Choose the word from the box that best matches each definition. Write the word on the line.

Check the Words You Know
__ assembled
__ destination
__ encounter
__ expectations
__ regulations
__ tollbooth

destination 1. place to which you are traveling

tollbooth 2. a gate at which money is collected before or after driving on a road

encounter 3. to find by chance

regulations 4. rules

expectations 5. good reasons for thinking that something will happen

assembled 6. put together

Directions: Read the diary entry. Choose the word from the box that best completes each sentence. Write the word on the matching numbered line below.

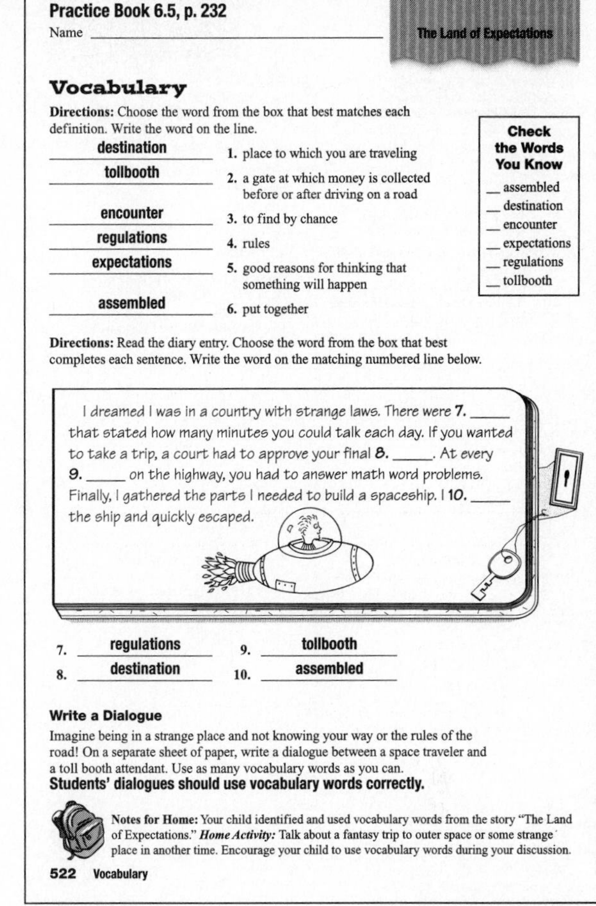

I dreamed I was in a country with strange laws. There were **7.** _____ that stated how many minutes you could talk each day. If you wanted to take a trip, a court had to approve your final **8.** _____. At every **9.** _____ on the highway, you had to answer math word problems. Finally, I gathered the parts I needed to build a spaceship. I **10.** _____ the ship and quickly escaped.

7. **regulations**
8. **destination**
9. **tollbooth**
10. **assembled**

Write a Dialogue

Imagine being in a strange place and not knowing your way or the rules of the road! On a separate sheet of paper, write a dialogue between a space traveler and a toll booth attendant. Use as many vocabulary words as you can.

Students' dialogues should use vocabulary words correctly.

Notes for Home: Your child identified and used vocabulary words from the story "The Land of Expectations." ***Home Activity:*** Talk about a fantasy trip to outer space or some strange place in another time. Encourage your child to use vocabulary words during your discussion.

Practice Book 6.5, p. 233

Name ____________________ The Land of Expectations

Summarizing

- **Summarizing** means giving a brief statement of the main idea of an article or the most important events in a story.

Directions: Reread the passage below in which the author introduces Milo. Then follow the instructions below. Think about which information belongs in your summary.

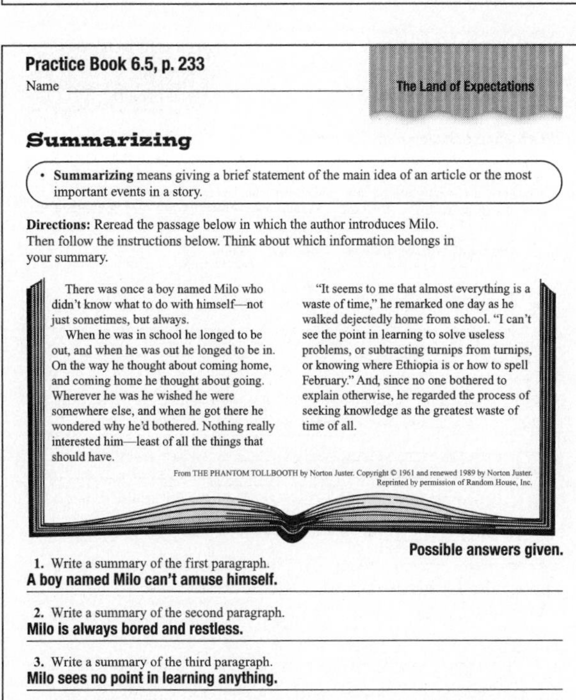

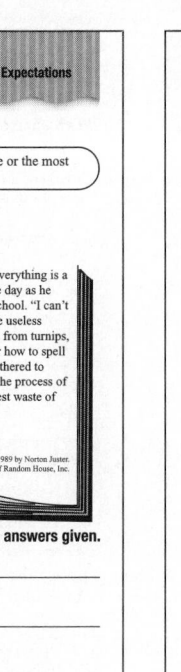

There was once a boy named Milo who didn't know what to do with himself—not just sometimes, but always.

When he was in school he longed to be out, and when he was out he longed to be in. On the way he thought about coming home, and coming home he thought about going. Wherever he was he wished he were somewhere else, and when he got there he wondered why he'd bothered. Nothing really interested him—least of all the things that should have.

"It seems to me that almost everything is a waste of time," he remarked one day as he walked dejectedly home from school. "I can't see the point in learning to solve useless problems, or subtracting turnips from turnips, or knowing where Ethiopia is or how to spell February." And, since no one bothered to explain otherwise, he regarded the process of seeking knowledge as the greatest waste of time of all.

Possible answers given.

1. Write a summary of the first paragraph.
A boy named Milo can't amuse himself.

2. Write a summary of the second paragraph.
Milo is always bored and restless.

3. Write a summary of the third paragraph.
Milo sees no point in learning anything.

4. Give an example of something you left out of your summary of the third paragraph. Why did you leave this information out?
Example: Milo doesn't care where Ethiopia is. Reason: This is a supporting detail, and a summary should only include main ideas.

5. Summarize the story and how Milo changes by the end. Explain your ideas on a separate sheet of paper.
Check that students' summaries focus on the most important story events.

Notes for Home: Your child read a story and summarized what happened in it in a few sentences. ***Home Activity:*** After watching a movie together with your child, challenge him or her to write a brief summary of it. Discuss which events were included and why.

Practice Book 6.5, p. 235

Name ____________________ The Land of Expectations

Selection Test

Directions: Choose the best answer to each item. Mark the letter for the answer you have chosen.

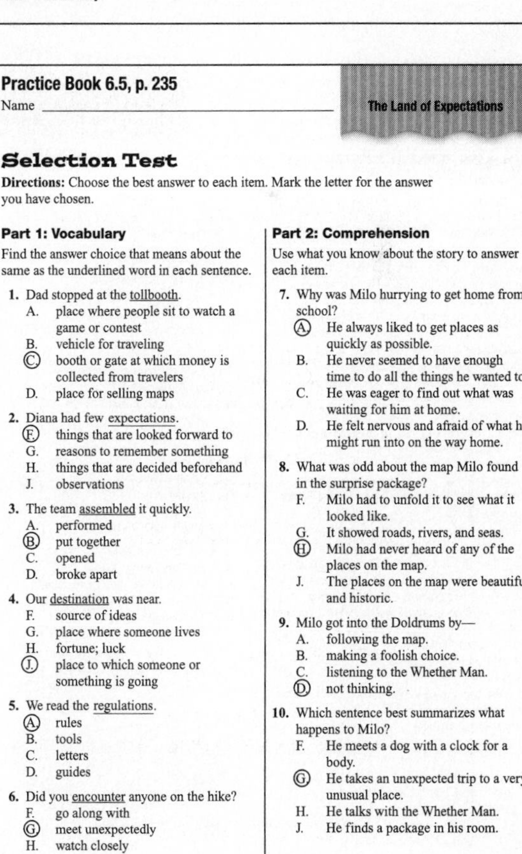

Part 1: Vocabulary

Find the answer choice that means about the same as the underlined word in each sentence.

1. Dad stopped at the tollbooth.
   - A. place where people sit to watch a game or contest
   - B. vehicle for traveling
   - Ⓒ booth or gate at which money is collected from travelers
   - D. place for selling maps
2. Diana had few expectations.
   - Ⓕ things that are looked forward to
   - G. reasons to remember something
   - H. things that are decided beforehand
   - J. observations
3. The team assembled it quickly.
   - A. performed
   - Ⓑ put together
   - C. opened
   - D. broke apart
4. Our destination was near.
   - F. source of ideas
   - G. place where someone lives
   - H. fortune; luck
   - Ⓙ place to which someone or something is going
5. We read the regulations.
   - Ⓐ rules
   - B. tools
   - C. letters
   - D. guides
6. Did you encounter anyone on the hike?
   - F. go along with
   - Ⓖ meet unexpectedly
   - H. watch closely
   - J. lose track of

Part 2: Comprehension

Use what you know about the story to answer each item.

7. Why was Milo hurrying to get home from school?
   - Ⓐ He always liked to get places as quickly as possible.
   - B. He never seemed to have enough time to do all the things he wanted to.
   - C. He was eager to find out what was waiting for him at home.
   - D. He felt nervous and afraid of what he might run into on the way home.
8. What was odd about the map Milo found in the surprise package?
   - F. Milo had to unfold it to see what it looked like.
   - G. It showed roads, rivers, and seas.
   - Ⓗ Milo had never heard of any of the places on the map.
   - J. The places on the map were beautiful and historic.
9. Milo got into the Doldrums by—
   - A. following the map.
   - B. making a foolish choice.
   - C. listening to the Whether Man.
   - Ⓓ not thinking.
10. Which sentence best summarizes what happens to Milo?
    - F. He meets a dog with a clock for a body.
    - Ⓖ He takes an unexpected trip to a very unusual place.
    - H. He talks with the Whether Man.
    - J. He finds a package in his room.

GO ON

Practice Book 6.5, p. 236

Name ______________________ The Land of Expectations

11. Which of these events would be important to include in a summary of this story?
   A. The Whether Man released a dozen balloons that sailed off into the sky.
   B. The Lethargarians described their busy schedule to Milo.
   (C) Tock the watchdog helped Milo get out of the Doldrums.
   D. Tock explained that it is traditional for watchdogs to be ferocious.

12. What can you tell about the Whether Man?
   F. He enjoys life to the fullest.
   G. He does not know where he is.
   (H) He doesn't like to make up his mind.
   J. He is Milo's best friend.

13. Where will Milo probably go next?
   A. back to the Doldrums
   (B) to Dictionopolis
   C. back to his apartment
   D. to Tock's home

14. In Tock's view, the most valuable thing in the world is—
   (F) time.
   G. diamonds.
   H. sleep.
   J. weather.

15. One thing that Tock likes to do is—
   A. chase after cars.
   B. kill time.
   C. socialize with the Lethargarians.
   (D) tell long stories about his family.

Selection Test 525

Name ______________________ The Land of Expectations

Summarizing

• **Summarizing** means giving a brief statement of the main idea of an article or the most important events in a story.

Directions: Read the story below.

Lu had always thought he could fly. Sure enough, there he was one night, soaring above Earth. He tried some fancy moves to test his skill. It was better than floating on the lake in summertime.

A little later, Lu joined a flock of geese on their way south for the winter. They didn't seem to mind his company as long as he kept up with them. All Lu had to do was follow the leader. He dipped, turned right or left, or sped up when the leader did.

At that moment, the sky grew dark. It began to rain heavily. Lu lost sight of the geese! "Help!" he shouted. Suddenly he realized he was sitting bolt upright in his own warm bed. He sighed in relief, but also in regret. Flying was wonderful, even in a dream.

Directions: Complete the table. Write a summary for the two details given in each row. One has been done for you. **Possible answers given.**

Detail	Detail	Summary
Lu thought he could fly.	Lu soars above Earth.	Lu can fly.
Lu tries fancy moves.	It's better than floating.	1. **Lu has fun flying.**
Lu keeps up with the geese.	Lu follows the leader.	2. **Lu flies with the geese.**
The sky grows dark.	Rain falls heavily.	3. **A storm breaks.**
Lu sits up in bed.	Lu sighs in relief.	4. **Lu was dreaming.**

Directions: Summarize the story. Use the completed table to help you.

5. **One night Lu flies south with a flock of geese. When a storm breaks, he wakes up and realizes it was only a dream.**

Notes for Home: Your child read a story and summarized it. ***Home Activity:*** Read a story with your child. After reviewing the main events and ideas together, challenge him or her to summarize the story in no more than three sentences.

526 Summarizing

Practice Book 6.5, p. 237

Name ______________________ The Land of Expectations

Cause and Effect

REVIEW

Directions: Read the story. Then read each question about the story. Choose the best answer to each question. Mark the letter for the answer you have chosen.

The Monster, the Maze, and the Fall

King Minos of Crete asked the architect Daedalus to build a maze. The maze was to be a prison for the Minotaur, a fierce monster who was half human and half bull. Minos wanted a maze from which the monster would never be able to escape. Daedalus created a maze, so full of twists and turns that the Minotaur could never find his way out.

Minos' daughter Ariadne had fallen in love with the hero Theseus. When Minos threatened to feed Theseus to the Minotaur, Ariadne thought of a way to save his life. She told Theseus to fasten a thread to the maze's entrance. If he kept hold of the thread's other end, he would be able to find his way out. Theseus killed the Minotaur and escaped from the maze.

King Minos was so angry about Theseus's escape that he imprisoned Daedalus and his son Icarus in a tower. Daedalus made wings of wood, wax, and feathers for himself and his son so that they could fly away from their prison. Daedalus warned Icarus not to fly too close to the sun. If the wax melted, the feathers would fall from the frames.

Icarus enjoyed flying so much that he forgot his father's warning. He flew too close to the sun. The wax on his wings melted, and he fell into the sea. Grief-stricken, Daedalus recovered his son's body and buried it on a nearby island.

1. The Minotaur cannot escape because—
   (A) the maze is too complicated.
   B. it is part animal.
   C. it will be killed if it escapes.
   D. Ariadne refuses to help it.

2. Because Daedalus is an excellent architect—
   F. he is put in prison.
   G. he traps King Minos.
   H. he is asked by the King to build a flying machine.
   (J) he is asked by the King to build an escape-proof maze.

3. Thanks to the help of Ariadne—
   A. Icarus escapes.
   B. Daedalus escapes.
   (C) Theseus escapes.
   D. King Minos kills Theseus.

4. Daedalus makes wings in order to—
   (F) escape the tower.
   G. teach his son to fly.
   H. kill the monster.
   J. challenge the king.

5. Icarus is killed because—
   A. he flies into the sea.
   (B) he forgets his father's warning.
   C. the wings don't work very well.
   D. the king is angry with him.

Notes for Home: Your child read a story and identified the causes and effects of its events. ***Home Activity:*** Read a myth or folk tale with your child. Encourage him or her to tell what happens in the story (effects) and why these events happen (causes).

Cause and Effect 527

Name ______________________ The Land of Expectations

Writing Across Texts

Directions: Think about what you have read about journeys to other lands in "To the Pole," the excerpt from *El Güero*, and "Destination: Mars." Complete the Venn diagram by choosing the journey in one of these selections and comparing and contrasting it to the journey in "The Land of Expectations." **Answers will vary depending on the selection chosen.**

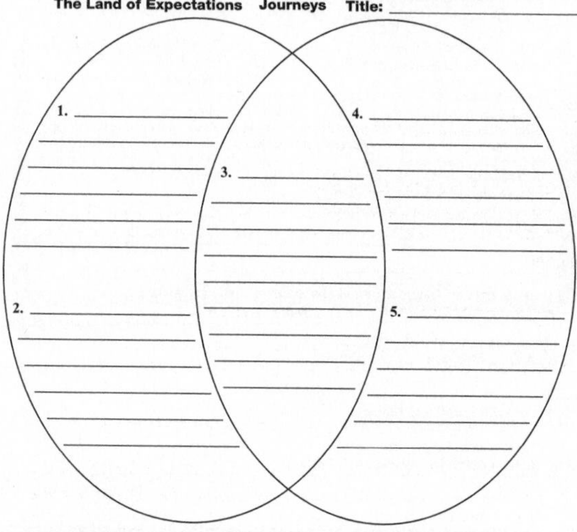

Write an Opinion

Based on your diagram, write a paragraph or two giving your opinion about which experience would be more exciting. Support your opinion with information from the selections. **Opinions will vary. Check that students used information they compared and contrasted from "The Land of Expectations" and one of the three other selections listed.**

Notes for Home: Your child compared and contrasted two selections to form an opinion. ***Home Activity:*** Read a story with your child, and then compare and contrast it with other stories on the same topic. Ask your child to voice opinions about the stories and topics.

528 Writing Across Texts

Grammar Practice Book 6.5, p. 116

Name ______________________ **The Land of Expectations**

Grammar: Compound and Complex Sentences — REVIEW

Directions: Write **compound** or **complex** on the line to describe each sentence.

complex 1. After I saw the movie *The Wizard of Oz,* I read the book.

compound 2. I enjoyed the movie, but I enjoyed the book even more.

complex 3. Who could forget Dorothy and her dog as they are blown by a tornado to the Land of Oz?

compound 4. Will Dorothy find her way back to Kansas, or will she have to stay in Oz?

compound 5. Dorothy meets a scarecrow, a tin man, and a cowardly lion, and they set off to find the Wizard of Oz.

compound 6. The wizard is described as all-powerful, and he may be able to grant their wishes.

compound 7. Scarecrow wants a brain, the tin man wants a heart, the lion wants courage, and Dorothy just wants to go home.

complex 8. Although the wizard turns out to be an impostor, the group's wishes do all come true.

complex 9. If you enjoyed *The Wizard of Oz,* you may also enjoy the many other books about Oz.

complex 10. L. Frank Baum must have enjoyed his own visits to the Land of Oz because he wrote more than a dozen books about it.

Directions: Use a joining word to combine each pair of sentences. Create a new sentence of the kind shown in ( ). Write your new sentence on the line. **Possible answers given.**

11. You could go anywhere in the world. Where would you go? (complex)
If you could go anywhere in the world, where would you go?

12. I might want to climb Mt. Everest. I might prefer to dive deep below the ocean. (compound)
I might want to climb Mt. Everest, or I might prefer to dive deep below the ocean.

13. Fantastic journeys are exciting. Simpler ones can be wonderful too. (complex)
Although fantastic journeys are exciting, simpler ones can be wonderful too.

14. Imagine yourself on a lovely ocean beach. You will understand my point. (compound)
Imagine yourself on a lovely ocean beach, and you will understand my point

15. You travel all around the world. You will still enjoy coming home. (complex)
After you travel all around the world, you will still enjoy coming home.

Notes for Home: Your child identified and wrote compound and complex sentences. ***Home Activity:*** Work with your child to write simple sentences about a family trip. Then use joining words to make pairs of related sentences compound or complex.

Grammar: Compound and Complex Sentences **529**

Grammar Practice Book 6.5, p. 117

Name ______________________ **The Land of Expectations**

Grammar: Conjunctions

Conjunctions can be used to join words, phrases, or entire sentences. Conjunctions are used to write compound subjects, compound predicates, and compound sentences. The three most commonly used conjunctions are *and, but,* and *or. And* joins related ideas. *But* joins contrasting ideas. *Or* suggests a choice between ideas.

Compound Subject: Our hearts and minds long for adventures.
Compound Predicate: We may live quietly but imagine taking trips to see marvelous things.
Compound Sentence: We may climb high mountains, or we may explore the depths of the sea.

Directions: Circle the conjunction in each sentence. Underline the two words or groups of words that the conjunction connects.

1. I went to the stage (and) faced my audience.
2. The men (and) women in the room were quiet.
3. I liked the audience (but) felt nervous at first.
4. I told a story about an imaginary world, (and) they seemed pleased.
5. Everyone in the story lived under the sea (or) had an island home.
6. Some people lived in hollow coral reefs, (but) others lived in caves beneath the sea.
7. Fish (or) other sea creatures were the sea dwellers' food.
8. Only a few islands (and) houses stood above the water.
9. The people (and) animals on the islands were called surface dwellers.
10. The surface dwellers never entered the sea, (but) no one knew why.

Directions: Use *and, but,* or *or* to complete each sentence. The words in ( ) tell what the conjunction should do. Write the conjunction on the line to the left.

and 11. Four-legged animals lived on the islands, _____ birds were living there too. (join related ideas)

but 12. Many of the birds ate berries, _____ the larger birds caught fish. (show a difference)

and 13. The fisher birds ate some of the fish _____ carried the rest to the people. (add information)

or 14. Sea dwellers dived _____ hid among the reefs. (show a choice)

and 15. The sea dwellers _____ the surface dwellers remained separate societies. (add information)

Notes for Home: Your child used the conjunctions *and, but,* and *or* to complete sentences. ***Home Activity:*** Give your child two sentences with the same subject, such as *I washed the plates. I scrubbed the pots.* Have him or her use the conjunction *and* to combine the two sentences.

530 Grammar: Conjunctions

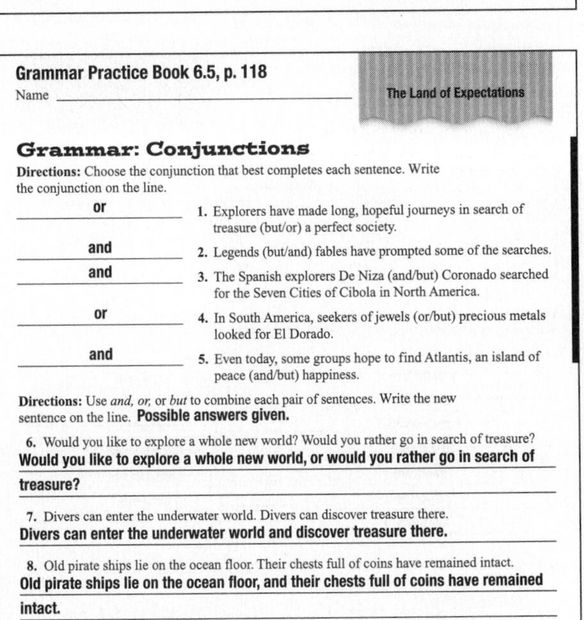

Grammar Practice Book 6.5, p. 118

Name ______________________ **The Land of Expectations**

Grammar: Conjunctions

Directions: Choose the conjunction that best completes each sentence. Write the conjunction on the line.

or 1. Explorers have made long, hopeful journeys in search of treasure (but/or) a perfect society.

and 2. Legends (but/and) fables have prompted some of the searches.

and 3. The Spanish explorers De Niza (and/but) Coronado searched for the Seven Cities of Cibola in North America.

or 4. In South America, seekers of jewels (or/but) precious metals looked for El Dorado.

and 5. Even today, some groups hope to find Atlantis, an island of peace (and/but) happiness.

Directions: Use *and, or,* or *but* to combine each pair of sentences. Write the new sentence on the line. **Possible answers given.**

6. Would you like to explore a whole new world? Would you rather go in search of treasure?
Would you like to explore a whole new world, or would you rather go in search of treasure?

7. Divers can enter the underwater world. Divers can discover treasure there.
Divers can enter the underwater world and discover treasure there.

8. Old pirate ships lie on the ocean floor. Their chests full of coins have remained intact.
Old pirate ships lie on the ocean floor, and their chests full of coins have remained intact.

9. Cannons hundreds of years old are on those ships. Cannonballs hundreds of years old are on those ships.
Cannons and cannonballs hundreds of years old are on those ships.

10. Other kinds of ships also sank centuries ago. Divers are still discovering interesting objects on these old ships.
Other kinds of ships also sank centuries ago, and divers are still discovering interesting objects on these old ships.

Write a Postcard

On a separate sheet of paper, write a postcard to a friend that tells about a trip to an imaginary land. Underline the conjunctions **and, but,** and **or** in your postcard message. **Students should correctly use conjunctions to form compound subjects, predicates, and sentences.**

Notes for Home: Your child used conjunctions, such as *and, but,* and *or,* to connect ideas and form interesting sentences. ***Home Activity:*** Pick a topic and say two simple sentences related to that topic. Challenge your child to join the sentences with a conjunction.

Grammar: Conjunctions **531**

Grammar Practice Book 6.5, p. 119

Name ______________________ **The Land of Expectations**

Grammar: Conjunctions — RETEACHING

A conjunction connects words, phrases, or sentences. Underline the words the conjunctions **and, or,** and **but** connect.

1. Is that insect a butterfly or a moth?
2. They have pretty but delicate wings.
3. They both lay and hatch eggs.
4. Wing markings hide them easily and well.

A **conjunction** joins words or groups of words. A conjunction may join nouns, pronouns, verbs, adjectives, or adverbs.

Directions: Circle each conjunction in the sentences below.

1. Butterflies (and) moths are very similar.
2. Butterflies flutter (and) fly from plant to plant.
3. A female butterfly lays tiny (but) numerous eggs.
4. Larvae can see (and) chew.
5. They quickly grow (and) shed their skin often.
6. An adult life span may be only a few days (or) weeks.
7. Moths have feathery (or) smooth antennae.
8. Some species have beautiful (but) poisonous wings.
9. Kim (and) Alan gave a report about butterflies.
10. These beautiful insects fascinated them (and) me.

Directions: Read each sentence. Choose a conjunction that makes the most sense from those in ( ) and write it on the line.

11. Many insects (and/but) spiders spin silk threads. **and**
12. The silkworm spins the finest (and/or) strongest threads. **and**
13. Farmers handle the silkworms carefully (or/and) patiently. **and**
14. China produces more silk than Japan (or/but) South Korea. **or**
15. Show this silk scarf to her (but/and) him. **and**

Notes for Home: Your child used conjunctions in sentences. ***Home Activity:*** Say two simple sentences about something your family has done recently. Have your child use a conjunction to combine the sentences to form a compound sentence.

532 Grammar: Conjunctions

Grammar Practice Book 6.5, p. 120

Name ______________________ **The Land of Expectations**

Grammar: Conjunctions

Directions: Circle the conjunction in each sentence. Underline the words or groups of words that the conjunction connects.

1. Andrew Jackson was a lawyer (and) a military leader.
2. He was orphaned (and) was reared by an uncle.
3. He grew to be a determined (but) thoughtful leader.
4. He was feared (or) was respected by others.
5. He brilliantly (but) unexpectedly won a battle.
6. You (and) I might enjoy a visit to his home, the Hermitage.
7. Friends (and) admirers supported him.
8. He campaigned hard (but) won easily.
9. Jackson was a courageous (and) clever president.
10. He supported democracy (and) the union of the states.

Directions: Write **and, but,** or **or** to complete each sentence below. **Possible answers given.**

11. Jackson could have won **or** lost the election.
12. He became an effective **and** popular president.
13. Sometimes his official cabinet **or** an unofficial "kitchen cabinet" gave him advice.
14. This group met **and** chatted in the White House kitchen.
15. President Jackson could sign **or** veto bills.
16. Jackson could agree **or** disagree with a group.
17. He was a strong **but** kindly man.
18. Young America grew **and** prospered under his leadership.

Write a Paragraph

On a separate sheet of paper, write a paragraph about the special qualities of someone you admire. Use the conjunctions **and, but,** and **or.**

Check that students have used conjunctions appropriately.

Notes for Home: Your child identified and wrote conjunctions in sentences. ***Home Activity:*** Talk with your child about the role of each conjunction in a sentence.

Grammar: Conjunctions 533

Practice Book 6.5, p. 238

Name ______________________ **The Land of Expectations**

Word Study: Suffixes

Directions: A letter or group of letters added to the end of a word is called a **suffix.** A suffix can change the meaning of the base word. The words below have been formed by adding suffixes. Read each word pair. Write the suffix on the line.

1. useless, endless **less**
2. traditional, logical **al**
3. silvery, rusty **y**
4. historic, apologetic **ic**
5. festive, massive **ive**
6. magical, natural **al**
7. meaningless, clueless **less**
8. classy, showy **y**
9. hypnotic, idiotic **ic**
10. preventive, inventive **ive**

Directions: Read the letter below. Look and listen for words that have the suffixes **-less, -al, -y, -ic,** and **-ive.** Circle these words. Then write the base word and the suffix on the line, connected by a + sign. For example, for **restless,** you would write **rest + less. Order may vary.**

Dear Marisa,

You'll never believe what happened to me! I went on a (magical) journey. It was quite (dreamy) and (fantastic). You see, I haven't been very (active) these days. So when my uncle suggested that I join him on his (traditional) yearly trip, I said sure. But where he went and what I saw made me (speechless). He took me up in a hot-air balloon. Wish you had been there. I could see for (endless) miles. My head was spinning. Even my uncle got (emotional). It felt like a (historic) moment in my life. I'm so (lucky).

Your friend,

Dianne

11. **magic + al**
12. **dream + y**
13. **fantasy + ic**
14. **act + ive**
15. **tradition + al**
16. **luck + y**
17. **speech + less**
18. **end + less**
19. **emotion + al**
20. **history + ic**

Notes for Home: Your child identified and wrote words with the suffixes *-less, -al, -y, -ic,* and *-ive.* ***Home Activity:*** Read a short story with your child. Encourage your child to find words with these suffixes. Have your child write down the words and underline the suffixes.

534 Word Study: Suffixes

Spelling Workbook 6.5, p. 93

Name ______________________ **The Land of Expectations**

Spelling: Suffixes *-ate, -ive, -ship*

Pretest Directions: Fold back the page along the dotted line. On the blanks, write the spelling words as they are dictated. When you have finished the test, unfold the page and check your words.

1. **originate**	1. Let's **originate** a new recipe.
2. **fortunate**	2. I'm **fortunate** to have friends.
3. **activate**	3. Please **activate** my account.
4. **affectionate**	4. Her cat is very **affectionate.**
5. **considerate**	5. He is kind and **considerate.**
6. **obligate**	6. Your duties **obligate** you to try.
7. **productive**	7. We had a **productive** lesson.
8. **defective**	8. This toy is **defective.**
9. **constructive**	9. Her ideas were **constructive.**
10. **attractive**	10. He has an **attractive** apartment.
11. **inventive**	11. She is an **inventive** writer.
12. **negative**	12. The insult had a **negative** effect.
13. **creative**	13. He is a **creative** painter.
14. **ownership**	14. I claim **ownership** of this book.
15. **membership**	15. The club **membership** is free.
16. **hardship**	16. Poverty is a terrible **hardship.**
17. **relationship**	17. What is your **relationship**?
18. **friendship**	18. We have a solid **friendship.**
19. **championship**	19. We will win the **championship.**
20. **leadership**	20. She has natural **leadership.**

Notes for Home: Your child took a pretest on words that have the suffixes *-ate, -ive,* and *-ship.* ***Home Activity:*** Help your child learn misspelled words before the final test. Have your child divide misspelled words into parts (such as syllables) and concentrate on each part.

Spelling: Suffixes *-ate, -ive, -ship* 535

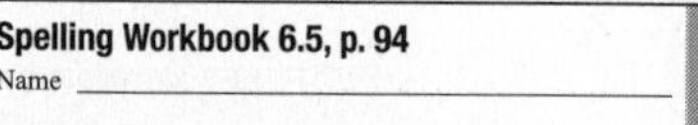

Spelling Workbook 6.5, p. 94

Name ______________________ **The Land of Expectations**

Spelling: Suffixes *-ate, -ive, -ship*

Word List

originate	obligate	inventive	hardship
fortunate	productive	negative	relationship
activate	defective	creative	friendship
affectionate	constructive	ownership	championship
considerate	attractive	membership	leadership

Directions: Choose the words from the box that have the suffixes **-ate** and **-ive.** Write each word in the correct column. **Order may vary.**

Suffix -ive	Suffix -ate
1. **productive**	8. **originate**
2. **defective**	9. **fortunate**
3. **constructive**	10. **activate**
4. **attractive**	11. **affectionate**
5. **inventive**	12. **considerate**
6. **negative**	13. **obligate**
7. **creative**	

Directions: Choose the word from the box that best answers each riddle. Write the word on the line.

championship 14. I am a victory in the World Series or the Super Bowl.
ownership 15. I am a synonym of the word *possession.*
hardship 16. I am poverty, sorrow, difficulty, or hunger.
relationship 17. I am the link between any two people who know each other.
friendship 18. I am the link between two people who are friends.
leadership 19. I am a quality generals, presidents, and kings should have.
membership 20. I am what you apply for if you want to join a club or group.

Notes for Home: Your child spelled words with suffixes *-ate, -ive,* and *-ship.* ***Home Activity:*** Help your child identify the base word of each spelling word. Then discuss whether the spelling of the base word changed when the suffix was added.

536 Spelling: Suffixes *-ate, -ive, -ship*

Spelling Workbook 6.5, p. 95

Name ______________________

The Land of Expectations

Spelling: Suffixes -ate, -ive, -ship

Directions: Proofread this transcript of a sports broadcast. Find five spelling mistakes. Use the proofreading marks to correct each mistake.

- ≡ Make a capital.
- / Make a small letter.
- ∧ Add something.
- Take out something.
- ⊙ Add a period.
- ¶ Begin a new paragraph.

After five days of long, wet, dark hardship, Jennifer Dizeck can almost see the finish line of the Center of the Earth Championsship. Owne^r^ship of the prized cup seems almost certain. But what's this? She is taking on water! Will a defective canoe obligate Jennifer to pull out of the race?

Jennifer seems to be back in control. It is fortun^a^te she is so resourceful. She was invent~~a~~^i^ve enough to plug the hole with her waterproof jacket. That's good, creative thinking on Jennifer's part! She's regained her leadersh~~a~~^i^p position in the last mile of the race. Jennifer Dizeck wins by a few feet!

Spelling Tip

For base words that end in **e**, drop the **e** before adding the suffixes **-ate**, **-ive**, or **-ship: obligate, creative.**

Word List

originate	inventive
fortunate	negative
activate	creative
affectionate	ownership
considerate	membership
obligate	hardship
productive	relationship
defective	friendship
constructive	championship
attractive	leadership

Write a Sports Broadcast

On a separate sheet of paper, write a sports broadcast about an imaginary new sporting event. Remember that a broadcaster reports the action as he or she watches it happen. Try to use at least three spelling words. **Answers will vary, but each report should include at least three spelling words.**

Notes for Home: Your child spelled words with the suffixes *-ate, -ive,* and *-ship.* ***Home Activity:*** Have your child scan a magazine article to find other words that contain the suffixes *-ate, -ive,* and *-ship.* Encourage him or her to tell you the base word of each of the words.

Spelling Workbook 6.5, p. 96

Name ______________________

The Land of Expectations

Spelling: Suffixes -ate, -ive, -ship

REVIEW

Word List

originate	considerate	constructive	creative	relationship
fortunate	obligate	attractive	ownership	friendship
activate	productive	inventive	membership	championship
affectionate	defective	negative	hardship	leadership

Directions: Write the word from the box that belongs in each group.

1. fellowship, companionship, **friendship**
2. faulty, imperfect, **defective**
3. disapproving, pessimistic, **negative**
4. authority, guidance, **leadership**
5. fertile, fruitful, **productive**
6. begin, start, **activate or originate**
7. burden, misfortune, **hardship**
8. affiliation, association, **membership**
9. possession, title, **ownership**
10. loving, cuddly, **affectionate**

Directions: Choose the word from the box that best replaces the underlined word or words. Write the word on the line.

relationship 11. My <u>association</u> with time travel began long ago.

creative or inventive 12. In an <u>imaginative</u> mood, I built my own time machine.

constructive 13. My best friend Josh offered <u>helpful</u> criticism.

inventive or creative 14. Josh was <u>ingenious</u> enough to fix the flaws in the machine.

fortunate 15. I was very <u>lucky</u> to have a sympathetic friend like him.

championship 16. Together we had won the <u>victory</u> medal in the science fair.

originate 17. My voyage will <u>begin</u> here in Kansas City; my destination is Paris in 1899.

attractive 18. The trip sounded <u>appealing</u> to Josh, but he couldn't come.

obligate 19. He did <u>require</u> me to promise that he could go on the next trip.

considerate 20. It was very <u>thoughtful</u> of Josh to see me off.

Notes for Home: Your child reviewed words with the suffixes *-ate, -ive,* and *-ship.* ***Home Activity:*** Challenge your child to spell *inventive* and *creative,* use each word in a sentence, and explain the similarities and differences between the meanings of the two words.

Practice Book 6.5, p. 239

Name ______________________

The Land of Expectations

Manual

A **manual** is usually in the form of a booklet or book. It contains a written set of directions that help the reader understand, use, or build something.

Directions: Study the table of contents and diagram from a manual for a VCR (video cassette recorder). Then answer the questions that follow.

Table of Contents for Your VCR

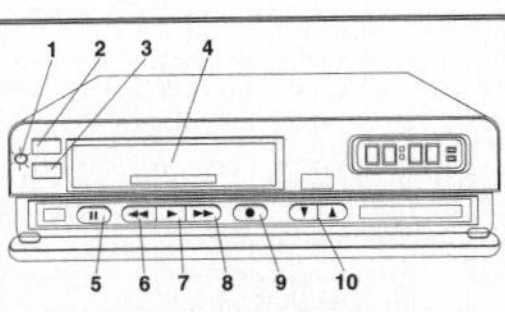

Front Panel Features

1. Power Indicator Light—A red light appears when the VCR is on.
2. Power Button—Use to turn the VCR on and off.
3. Stop/Eject Button—Press to stop videotape. Then press again to eject tape.
4. Tape Compartment—Insert videotape here.
5. Pause Button—Use to view single frame or picture while playing a videotape.
6. Rewind Button—Press to rewind tape after pressing stop. If pressed during playback, video may be viewed in rapid reverse.
7. Play Button—Press to play videotape.
8. Fast Forward Button—Press to advance the tape. If pressed during playback, video may be viewed in rapid forward.
9. Record Button—Use for recording.
10. Channel Up/Channel Down Buttons—Use to select TV channels on VCR.

Practice Book 6.5, p. 240

Name ______________________

The Land of Expectations

1. What is the purpose of this manual? **Possible answer: The purpose is to explain the use of a VCR.**
2. When might you use this manual? Give an example. **Examples will vary. Students could use any feature listed in the table of contents.**
3. Do you think this table of contents is organized well? How might it help you use the manual? **Possible answer: Yes, the table of contents is organized by a specific feature or operation. You can tell at a glance which part of the manual will tell you about how something works or can be used.**
4. On which page would you find information about setting the clock? **page 8**
5. Suppose you wanted to record a TV program about space travel. Which page would you turn to in the manual to see how to do this? Which front panel features would you most likely use? **page 9; Possible front panel features used to record include the power button, tape compartment, the channel up/channel down buttons, and the play and record buttons.**
6. Which front panel feature confirms that the VCR is actually on? **The Power Indicator Light will show a red light if VCR is on.**
7. What does the rewind button do? **The rewind button makes the tape go in reverse.**
8. If you were unable to make the VCR work properly, on what page would you find a phone number to get help? **page 11**
9. Why do you think a diagram was included in this manual? **Possible answer: Diagrams make it easier to understand the directions for operating the VCR.**
10. Why is it important to be able to follow directions carefully and correctly when using a manual? **If directions are not followed correctly, an important step in how to use or build something could be missed or done incorrectly.**

Notes for Home: Your child studied a sample page from an instruction manual and answered questions about it. ***Home Activity:*** With your child, look at an instruction manual. Discuss the information in it, such as the table of contents, diagrams, and instructions.

Practice Book 6.5, p. 241

Name ____________________ **The Trail Drive**

Character

- **Characters** are the people or animals who take part in the events of a short story, novel, play, or other form of fiction.
- You can learn about characters by noticing what they think, say, and do. You can also learn about characters by paying attention to how other characters treat them and what others say about them.
- The lasting qualities of a character's personality are called character traits. *Brave, stubborn,* and *honest* are examples of character traits.

Directions: Reread "The Pleasantest Days." Complete the web by writing about what Sam likes. Then write a sentence describing Sam.

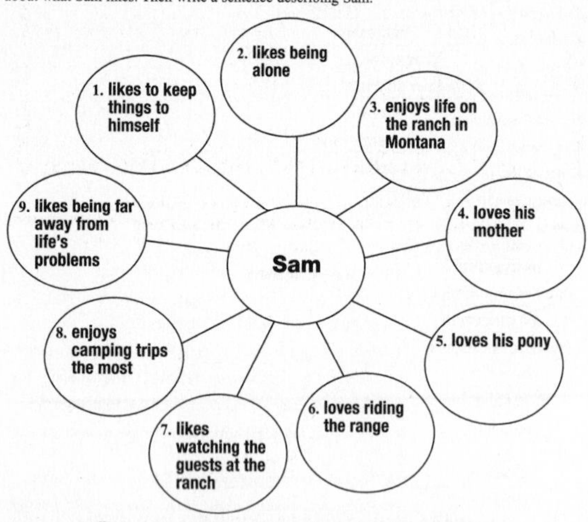
Sam
1. likes to keep things to himself
2. likes being alone
3. enjoys life on the ranch in Montana
4. loves his mother
5. loves his pony
6. loves riding the range
7. likes watching the guests at the ranch
8. enjoys camping trips the most
9. likes being far away from life's problems

10. Sam is **a solitary person with a deep love for his parents and nature**.

Notes for Home: Your child described a story character. ***Home Activity:*** Encourage your child to make a list of character traits for different characters in stories, movies, and TV programs. Work together to draw a picture and write a caption that describes each character.

Practice Book 6.5, p. 242

Name ____________________ **The Trail Drive**

Vocabulary

Directions: Choose the word from the box that best matches each definition. Write the word on the line.

Check the Words You Know
__ drive
__ mustang
__ pounce
__ scorching
__ weariness

mustang 1. a small, wild horse

pounce 2. to attack suddenly, usually from above

weariness 3. exhaustion

drive 4. the act of moving cattle overland to a shipping point

scorching 5. very hot

Directions: Choose the word from the box that best completes each sentence. Write the word on the line to the left.

drive 6. On Tyrone's first cattle _____, he and the other cowboys moved hundreds of cattle across Texas.

mustang 7. One day while riding, Tyrone saw a _____ galloping free across the prairie with its mane flying in the wind.

pounce 8. Another time he spied a cougar trying to _____ on a jackrabbit, but the rabbit got away.

scorching 9. But most days, Tyrone spent long hours riding under the _____ sun.

weariness 10. On those days, Tyrone was overcome with _____ and wanted nothing more than a soft bed.

Write a Story

On a separate sheet of paper, write a story about being a cowhand. Write about what you know or what you imagine it might be like to work with horses. Use as many vocabulary words as you can. **Students' stories about the life of a cowhand should use vocabulary words correctly.**

Notes for Home: Your child identified and used vocabulary words from "The Trail Drive." ***Home Activity:*** Act out a conversation between two cowhands. Try to use as many listed vocabulary words as you can.

Practice Book 6.5, p. 243

Name ____________________ **The Trail Drive**

Character

- **Characters** are the people or animals who take part in the events of a short story, novel, play, or other form of fiction.
- You can learn about characters by noticing what they think, say, and do.
- You can also learn about characters by paying attention to how other characters in the story treat them and what these other characters say about them.

Directions: Reread the part of "The Trail Drive" about Midnight's first day on the drive. Then answer the questions below. Think about what the passage tells you about the characters.

One by one Midnight tethered six ponies to the picket line. He worked on, not paying attention to anyone or anything else. Sweat rolled down his temples. He licked the salty taste off his lips and kept going. Six more. At last he tied Dahomey to the line and stood to wipe his forehead. Midnight looked back at the work he'd done. The horses hadn't really given him any trouble. His first day on the drive was over, and he was satisfied.

"Good job for your first time." Joe B. strolled up and tugged on the last rope line Midnight had stretched. It was so tight that the rope bounced against Joe's hand. He nodded and looked at Midnight.

From THE ADVENTURES OF MIDNIGHT SON by Denise Lewis Patrick, © 1997 by Denise Lewis Patrick. Reprinted by permission of Henry Holt and Company, LLC.

1. What action tells you that Midnight feels that working hard is more important than socializing or watching the others?
Midnight doesn't pay attention to anyone or anything else.

2. How does Midnight feel about his first day on the drive?
He feels satisfied because none of the horses gave him trouble.

3. What do Joe B.'s words tell you about how he feels about Midnight's work?
Joe B. is pleased with Midnight's work. He says, "Good job for your first time."

4. What action by Joe B. suggests that he feels Midnight did a good job tying the ropes?
After tugging on the rope, Joe B. nodded and looked at Midnight.

5. On a separate sheet of paper, describe what you learn about the character of Midnight from reading the story. Give examples from the story to support your answer. **Possible answer: Midnight cares about doing his work well. He feels he needs to save Rusty from the bobcat to make up for the guilt he feels for not having been able to save Lady from being sold.**

Notes for Home: Your child read a story and analyzed its characters. ***Home Activity:*** Read a short story with your child. Encourage your child to describe what he or she learns about its characters.

Practice Book 6.5, p. 245

Name ____________________ **The Trail Drive**

Selection Test

Directions: Choose the best answer to each item. Mark the letter for the answer you have chosen.

Part 1: Vocabulary

Find the answer choice that means about the same as the underlined word in each sentence.

1. Those cowboys saw the drive.
   A. a public sale of animals
   (B) act of moving cattle overland
   C. a rodeo show
   D. fenced-in area for cattle

2. Weariness overtook them.
   F. state of being confused
   G. nervousness; fear
   H. state of being alert
   (J) deep tiredness

3. It was scorching weather.
   (A) very hot
   B. unpredictable
   C. very wet
   D. unpleasant

4. He kept his eye on the mustang.
   F. leader in a group of horses
   G. group of spare horses
   (H) small wild stray horse
   J. horse used for carrying loads

5. The cat was about to pounce.
   A. begin eating
   B. hunch down with eyes alert
   C. turn over on its back
   (D) leap suddenly and seize something

Part 2: Comprehension

Use what you know about the story to answer each item.

6. This story begins with—
   (F) Midnight's first day on a long trip.
   G. a river crossing.
   H. the last day of a long trip.
   J. a terrible storm.

7. What is Midnight's job in the evenings?
   A. watching the edges of the herd
   B. helping to make dinner
   (C) taking care of the spare horses
   D. finding water for the herd

8. What is Slim's job on the drive?
   F. boss
   (G) cook
   H. scout
   J. guard

9. Why did Midnight tie Rusty to the picket line before the other horses?
   (A) He noticed that other horses seemed to follow her.
   B. She was the horse he rode on the drive.
   C. He could tell she was hungry.
   D. He thought she was the one most likely to give him trouble.

10. You can tell that Slim was a little worried about—
    F. the horses.
    G. whether there was enough food.
    H. the weather.
    (J) how things were going for Midnight.

11. Midnight showed he was brave and determined when he—
    A. set up a picket line for the first time.
    (B) took the horses across the Red River.
    C. avoided talking to Lou Boy about Curly.
    D. fell asleep on the bare ground.

12. Nighttime reminded Midnight of—
    F. the first time he saw a horse.
    (G) his escape from slavery.
    H. crossing large bodies of water.
    J. his arrival in Mexico.

GO ON

Practice Book 6.5, p. 246

Name ______________________ The Trail Drive

13. What feeling deep inside Midnight was the main cause of his fight with the cougar?
    - A. fear that he would lose his job if he wasn't brave enough
    - B. love for the horses in his care
    - **C.** anger over things that happened in the past
    - D. hatred of wild cats

14. In some parts of the story, the author uses *italic* type to call attention to—
    - **F.** Midnight's thoughts.
    - G. important ideas.
    - H. events from the past.
    - J. make-believe events.

15. Slim cautions Midnight not to—
    - A. risk his life for a horse.
    - B. leave camp without a partner.
    - C. get too friendly with the other cowboys.
    - **D.** let bad memories control him.

STOP

Name ______________________ The Trail Drive

Character

- **Characters** are the people or animals who take part in the events of a short story, novel, play, or other form of fiction.
- You can learn about characters by noticing what they think, say, and do.
- You can also learn about characters by paying attention to how other characters in the story treat them and what these other characters say about them.

Directions: Read the journal entry below.

March 31, 1895

I am sailing with my husband to India. What an adventure it will be! I have always wanted to travel, but until now I've never left Ireland. I have become friends with the captain—everyone else seems to be seasick! "We may be in for storms before long, Mrs. Clancy," he warned me. "Yet I see that you take the rough weather in stride."

One day, the sails suddenly started to flap, and the boat began to toss and weave. I dashed to the deck. Huge waves crashed over the deck. Fierce winds tossed the ship. The captain's calm but strong commands set her back on course as the wind died down. The captain suddenly saw me at the railing. "Mrs. Clancy," he called, bowing, "I wish all my crew were as brave as you!"

Directions: Complete the web below. Use details from the journal entry to tell about Mrs. Clancy. Below the web, describe Mrs. Clancy in your own words. **Possible answers given.**

Mrs. Clancy
- has always wanted to travel
- 1. **friendly**
- 2. **not seasick**
- 3. **takes rough weather in stride**
- 4. **brave**

5. **Mrs. Clancy loves everything about her first big adventure. She makes friends with the captain right away. She is not at all afraid of the storms.**

Notes for Home: Your child read a story and listed details about its main character. ***Home Activity:*** Read a story with your child. Encourage your child to write a sentence describing each character. Discuss how he or she decided what to write about each character.

Practice Book 6.5, p. 247

Name ______________________ The Trail Drive

Generalizing

REVIEW

Directions: Read the passage. Then read each question about the passage. Choose the best answer to each question. Mark the letter for the answer you have chosen.

Explosive Earth

Most volcanoes are made out of lava flows, or streams of melted rock, and other materials. The lava shoots upward in the eruption and falls back again. It lands as cinders or ashes and is shot into the air again. This rise and fall happens many times and forms the cone shape common to most volcanoes. Mount Vesuvius in Italy is a famous volcano of this kind.

A number of volcanoes have deep basins, called calderas, which become filled with water over a long period of time. Crater Lake in Oregon is an example. Forceful explosions that destroy the volcano itself form some calderas.

Many volcanoes are born underwater on the sea floor. Mount Etna and Mount Vesuvius began as underwater volcanoes. So did the huge cones found in the Hawaiian Islands.

Some volcanoes are much more active than others. A number of constantly active volcanoes are found in a belt called the Ring of Fire that encircles the Pacific Ocean. Other volcanoes become inactive, or dormant, for months or years. The eruption that follows a long dormant period is usually violent. This was true in the state of Washington when Mount Saint Helens erupted violently after a 123-year period of quiet.

One reason scientists study volcanoes is that they can be dangerous to life forms. In addition to the dangers of lava and ash, the eruptions can melt ice and snow and cause deadly mud flows. Harmful gases can pour out of volcanoes long after they have erupted.

1. Which of the following statements is **not** a generalization?
   - A. Most volcanoes are made out of lava flows and other materials.
   - **B.** Mount Vesuvius is a famous volcano in Italy.
   - C. A number of volcanoes have deep basins.
   - D. Most volcanoes have a cone shape.
2. Underwater volcanoes are born—
   - F. only in Italy.
   - G. inactive.
   - **H.** on the sea floor.
   - J. only in the Ring of Fire.
3. Many active volcanoes are found—
   - A. only on the sea floor.
   - B. in Oregon.
   - **C.** in a rim around the Pacific.
   - D. everywhere on Earth.
4. An eruption after a period of inactivity usually—
   - F. occurs in the Ring of Fire.
   - **G.** is violent.
   - H. creates a cone-shaped volcano.
   - J. forms a caldera.
5. Which statement below is a valid generalization?
   - A. All volcanoes become active again after a quiet time.
   - B. Few volcanic eruptions are dangerous.
   - C. Danger from volcanoes ends with the eruptions.
   - **D.** Some volcanoes are more active than others.

Notes for Home: Your child identified generalizations—broad statements about several things or people—in a passage. ***Home Activity:*** Read a brief magazine article with your child. Challenge him or her to write one or two generalizations that are supported by the facts in the article.

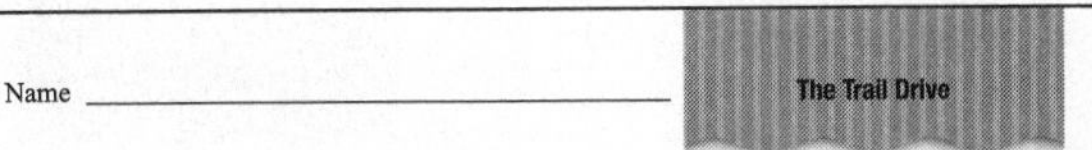

Name ______________________ The Trail Drive

Writing Across Texts

Directions: Consider what you know about cowboys and what you learned from "The Trail Drive" and "A Cowboy's Job." Add more examples to the table below to tell why a cowboy's life would be fun and why it would be difficult.
Possible answers given.

Why a Cowboy's Life Would Be Fun	Why a Cowboy's Life Would Be Difficult
Cowboys learn how to do rope tricks.	Cowboys work long hours.
1. **Being a cowboy is exciting, unusual work.**	6. **Cowboys do dangerous, hard work.**
2. **They get to stay outdoors all day.**	7. **They must stay outdoors all day.**
3. **They camp out.**	8. **They ride horses for hours.**
4. **They ride horses.**	9. **They do not always have the comforts of home.**
5. **They see new places.**	10. **They are sometimes away from home for a long time.**

Write a Persuasive Paragraph

Would a cowboy's life be fun or difficult? Write a persuasive paragraph that convinces readers of your opinion. Support your opinion with information from "The Trail Drive" and "A Cowboy's Job." **Paragraphs will vary. Check that students used persuasive language to convince readers to accept their opinions.**

Notes for Home: Your child used information from more than one source to support an opinion. ***Home Activity:*** As you read stories or articles with your child, discuss how the ideas connect with other material read. Encourage your child to make comparisons.

Grammar Practice Book 6.5, p. 121

Name ______________ The Trail Drive

Grammar: Exclamations

REVIEW

Directions: Decide whether each group of words is a complete exclamatory sentence. Write **S** on the line if it is a sentence. Write **N** if it is not.

S 1. He really used to be a cowboy!
N 2. Wow!
N 3. What a piece of luck!
S 4. Watch out for that horse!
S 5. Be careful of those hooves!
N 6. How absolutely terrifying!
N 7. Just a minute, please!
N 8. Whew, what a relief!
S 9. I cannot imagine that!
S 10. What a gorgeous horse that is!

Directions: Read each sentence. Then write an exclamation to respond to each sentence. **Possible answers given.**

11. That horse just lost its shoe.
That must have hurt!

12. Do you think cowboys led exciting lives?
Sure they did!

13. Real cowboys often had to manage thousands of cows.
Wow, that's a tough job!

14. Cara does not look comfortable on that horse.
Oh no, she fell off!

15. What did you think of that old cowboy movie?
It's a very silly movie!

Notes for Home: Your child recognized and wrote exclamations—statements that show strong feeling and that end with exclamation marks. ***Home Activity:*** Together write a short skit for a TV show you both know. Use some exclamations.

Grammar Practice Book 6.5, p. 122

Name ______________ The Trail Drive

Grammar: Interjections

Interjections are used to express strong feeling. When the feeling is especially strong, the interjection is followed by an exclamation mark. When the feeling is less strong, the interjection is followed by a comma.

Wow! That horse is wild.
Hey, get back here.

Directions: Circle the interjection in each sentence.

1. (Hey!) There's a cowboy movie on TV.
2. (Wow!) Being on a cattle drive looks like fun.
3. (Ugh!) It's probably harder than it seems.
4. (Ouch!) Falling from a horse can't feel good.
5. (Hooray!) They finally found that poor runaway cow.
6. (Whew,) that's a relief.
7. (Oops,) they forgot to tie up that horse.
8. (Yikes!) The horse is running away!
9. (Oh my!) He's never going to catch that horse.
10. (Say,) that movie was pretty good.

Directions: Choose an appropriate interjection and punctuation mark to add to the beginning of each sentence. Write the interjection on the line. **Possible answers given.**

11. **What!** Do you really own a pony of your own?
12. **Yes,** I've had this pony for six months.
13. **Wow!** This horse is really big.
14. **Help!** I don't know how to stop this horse!
15. **Whew!** Thanks for getting him to stop.

Notes for Home: Your child identified interjections, words that express strong feeling, such as *Wow, Oh my,* and *Hey.* ***Home Activity:*** Together, write a letter or brief note to a relative. Choose a place to insert one interjection.

Grammar Practice Book 6.5, p. 123

Name ______________ The Trail Drive

Grammar: Interjections

Directions: Write the interjection in each sentence on the line.

My 1. My, I'd like to climb a mountain like Mount Everest.
Oh 2. Oh! Being at the top must be incredible.
Say 3. Say, have you ever seen films of mountain climbers?
Wow 4. Wow! It looks like quite an adventure.
Well 5. Well, I think it would be very hard to do.
Hey 6. Hey! Don't get discouraged.
My goodness 7. My goodness, they looked determined.
Oh no 8. Oh no! That cable broke.
Ouch 9. Ouch! He fell a few feet.
Whew 10. Whew, the climber didn't get hurt.

Directions: On each line, write a sentence expressing the feeling that the interjection suggests. **Possible answers given.**

11. Oh no! **I forgot to bring binoculars.**
12. Good grief, **how much farther do we have to go?**
13. Hah! **Nobody but me thought I'd get this far.**
14. What! **You didn't bring any drinking water?**
15. Great! **We can make camp in half an hour.**
16. Yes, **we can go fishing down by the river.**
17. Yuck! **I don't want to touch that worm!**
18. Hey! **I think I caught something.**
19. Oops, **it's only an old boot.**
20. Wow, **that is a beautiful sunset.**

Write an Advertisement

On a separate sheet of paper, write an advertisement for an adventure trip such as rafting, mountain climbing, or going on safari. Use interjections in some of your sentences. Underline each one that you use. **Students' writing should include some interjections. Check for appropriate use and punctuation.**

Notes for Home: Your child identified interjections, words that express strong feeling, such as *Wow, Oh my,* and *Hey,* and wrote sentences using interjections. ***Home Activity:*** Challenge your child to describe something enjoyable, using interjections to show his or her feelings.

Grammar Practice Book 6.5, p. 124

Name ______________ The Trail Drive

Grammar: Interjections

RETEACHING

Underline each interjection.

1. Whoa! We're going so fast!
2. Eek! It's really dark in here!

An interjection is used to express strong feeling. Often an interjection is followed by an exclamation mark. If the feeling is less strong, the interjection is followed by a comma.

Directions: Circle the interjection in each sentence.

1. (Aha!) I've found the answer!
2. (Oops,) I missed that word.
3. (Oh,) I guess I'll go.
4. (Ow!) That's my sore hand.
5. (Wow!) I won first prize!
6. (Ugh!) That tastes awful.
7. (Well,) you finally got here.
8. (Right,) I understand.
9. (Yikes!) That scared me!
10. (Whee!) I love fast rides!

Directions: Write an interjection that makes sense in each sentence. **Possible answers given.**

11. **Wow!** We are so far away!
12. **Yikes!** I'm afraid of that dog.
13. **My goodness,** that boat is huge!
14. **Oops,** I made a mistake.
15. **Well,** I guess I'd better go home.
16. **Oh no!** What a mess that is!

Notes for Home: Your child identified and wrote interjections in sentences. ***Home Activity:*** Together, look through old photographs. Have your child write captions for them, using interjections.

Grammar Practice Book 6.5, p. 125

Name ______________ **The Trail Drive**

Grammar: Interjections

Directions: On each line, write a sentence expressing the feeling that that interjection suggests. **Possible answers given.**

1. Ugh! **That soup tastes like socks!**
2. My, **that was a long day.**
3. Well, **I suppose I could help.**
4. Ouch! **That kettle is hot!**
5. Yikes! **I almost stepped on him.**
6. Oh my! **What a loud sound that was!**
7. Say, **can you come over?**
8. Yes! **I did it!**
9. Uh, oh! **Here we go again!**
10. Man! **Isn't it over yet?**

Directions: Write on the line the interjection from each sentence.

Oh no! 11. Oh no! I forgot my homework!
Yuck! 12. Yuck! That milk is spoiled.
Whew! 13. Whew! That was close!
Well, 14. Well, I guess you're right.
No way! 15. No way! I'm not climbing that fence!
Wow! 16. Wow! I've never seen that kind of car before.
Whoops, 17. Whoops, I slipped on that patch of ice.
Gee! 18. Gee! That completely slipped my mind!
My, 19. My, that was a long speech.
All right! 20. All right! We won the game!

Write a Scary Story

On a separate sheet of paper, write a story about people in an imaginary scary place. Think about how characters in your story might react to different situations. Include dialogue in your story. Use interjections in some of your sentences. **Make sure students have used interjections appropriately.**

Notes for Home: Your child used interjections in sentences. ***Home Activity:*** Write interjections (For example: *Wow! Oh, no! My goodness!*) on cards. Hold up a card and have your child use that interjection in a sentence.

Grammar: Interjections 555

Practice Book 6.5, p. 248

Name ______________ **The Trail Drive**

Word Study: Plural Possessives

Directions: Add an apostrophe (') to form the possessive of plural nouns that end in **s: sisters'**. For plural nouns that do not end in **s**, add an **apostrophe (')** and **s** to form the possessive: **oxen's.** Read the phrases below. Change each phrase to form a possessive noun. Write each new phrase on the line.

the scales of the fish — the fish's scales

1. the chores of the men — **the men's chores**
2. the toys of the boys — **the boys' toys**
3. the experiences of the women — **the women's experiences**
4. the squeaks of the mice — **the mice's squeaks**
5. the heavy loads of the trucks — **the trucks' heavy loads**

Directions: Read each sentence. Use the possessive form of the noun in ( ) to complete each sentence. Write the possessive noun on the line.

girls' 6. Before they fell asleep, the (girls) last thoughts were of the next day's trail drive.
horses' 7. The next morning, the (horses) whinnies sounded clearly across the field.
children's 8. The (children) excitement was infectious as they gathered around the horses.
parents' 9. The (parents) concerns had been that their children might get hurt.
families' 10. But the (families) worries were laid to rest when they saw how gentle the horses were.
trails' 11. The (trails) rocky terrain made the ride a little rough for those not used to traveling on horseback.
men's 12. Even the (men) warnings of dangers along the trail could not dampen the group's enthusiasm.
moose's 13. Everyone kept a sharp eye out looking for the (moose) tracks.
elk's 14. They saw marks on the ground where the (elk) hooves had dug in the dirt.
deer's 15. The guide pointed to scratches where the (deer) antlers had rubbed against the tree bark.

Notes for Home: Your child formed plural possessives, such as *sisters'* and *oxen's*. ***Home Activity:*** Read a biography with your child about a person she or he finds interesting. Look for possessive nouns. Have your child write the words and notice how they were formed.

556 Word Study: Plural Possessives

Spelling Workbook 6.5, p. 97

Name ______________ **The Trail Drive**

Spelling: Using Apostrophes

Pretest Directions: Fold back the page along the dotted line. On the blanks, write the spelling words as they are dictated. When you have finished the test, unfold the page and check your words.

1. **it's** — 1. **It's** not time to go already, is it?
2. **let's** — 2. **Let's** go bowling.
3. **that's** — 3. I think **that's** a great idea.
4. **we'd** — 4. **We'd** rather go to the zoo.
5. **don't** — 5. They **don't** know who called.
6. **there's** — 6. **There's** a pie for dessert.
7. **coach's** — 7. The **coach's** hat fell off.
8. **coaches'** — 8. The **coaches'** whistles are loud.
9. **man's** — 9. That **man's** pants are plaid.
10. **men's** — 10. Those **men's** jobs are all done.
11. **you're** — 11. **You're** just the person I need.
12. **she'd** — 12. **She'd** tell us if she knew.
13. **mustn't** — 13. You **mustn't** stay out too late.
14. **o'clock** — 14. It is after ten **o'clock**.
15. **guide's** — 15. Our **guide's** walking stick broke.
16. **guides'** — 16. The **guides'** station is over there.
17. **director's** — 17. She sat in the **director's** desk.
18. **directors'** — 18. The **directors'** offices are locked.
19. **city's** — 19. This **city's** mayor is Mr. Jones.
20. **cities'** — 20. Those **cities'** names are alike.

Notes for Home: Your child took a pretest on contractions and possessives with apostrophes. ***Home Activity:*** Help your child learn misspelled words before the final test by concentrating on which two words are shortened to one or on whether one person or more than one person owns something.

Spelling: Using Apostrophes 557

Spelling Workbook 6.5, p. 98

Name ______________ **The Trail Drive**

Spelling: Using Apostrophes

Word List

it's	don't	man's	mustn't	director's
let's	there's	men's	o'clock	directors'
that's	coach's	you're	guide's	city's
we'd	coaches'	she'd	guides'	cities'

Directions: Choose the words from the box that are possessive nouns. Write each word in the correct column. **Order may vary.**

Singular Possessive Nouns	Plural Possessive Nouns
1. **coach's**	6. **coaches'**
2. **man's**	7. **men's**
3. **guide's**	8. **guides'**
4. **director's**	9. **directors'**
5. **city's**	10. **cities'**

Directions: Choose the word from the box that best replaces each underlined word or words. Write the word on the line.

It's 11. "It is morning! Time to get up!" called Aunt Carmela.
o'clock 12. "Seven A.M. is too early to get up," grumbled Alice.
that's 13. "On a farm, that is very late," her aunt explained.
We'd 14. "We would never get our work done if we slept that late."
let's 15. "After you've eaten," said Uncle Tony, "let us go to the barn."
You're 16. "You are going to learn how to milk, Alice," he explained.
don't 17. "I do not think I can," objected Alice. "Cows scare me."
mustn't 18. "You must not be scared, Alice. They are very gentle."
There's 19. "Look, Uncle Tony!" cried Alice later. "There is the full pail of milk!"
she'd 20. After this success, Alice knew she would like living on the farm.

Notes for Home: Your child used apostrophes to spell contractions and possessives. ***Home Activity:*** Challenge your child to tell you the two words each contraction represents. Note that some can stand for different combinations: *she'd = she had, she did,* or *she would.*

558 Spelling: Using Apostrophes

Spelling Workbook 6.5, p. 99

Name ______________________

The Trail Drive

Spelling: Using Apostrophes

Directions: Proofread this cowboy song. Find five spelling mistakes. Use the proofreading marks to correct each mistake.

≡	Make a capital.
/	Make a small letter.
∧	Add something.
℘	Take out something.
⊙	Add a period.
¶	Begin a new paragraph.

A citys lights dont mean a thing to me.

That's not where this mans heart will ever be.

Its the Chisholm Trail that calls.

Let's ride the range, we will see it all.

Theres joy and laughter when you're riding free.

Word List

it's	there's	you're	guides'
let's	coach's	she'd	director's
that's	coaches'	mustn't	directors'
we'd	man's	o'clock	city's
don't	men's	guide's	cities'

Spelling Tip

man's men's cities' To form the possessive of a singular noun or a plural noun that does not end in **s**, add an **apostrophe** and an **s: man's, men's.** For plural nouns that end in **s,** just add an apostrophe to form the possessive: **cities'**. Check the cowboy song to be sure the plurals are formed correctly.

Write a Song

On a separate sheet of paper, write your own cowboy song. Think about experiences that a cowhand on a ranch might have. Try to use at least five spelling words. **Answers will vary, but each song should include at least five spelling words.**

Notes for Home: Your child used apostrophes to spell contractions and possessives. ***Home Activity:*** Have your child use the spelling words in sentences. Check for the correct use of singular and plural possessives.

Spelling Workbook 6.5, p. 100

Name ______________________

The Trail Drive

Spelling: Using Apostrophes

REVIEW

Word List

it's	don't	man's	mustn't	director's
let's	there's	men's	o'clock	directors'
that's	coach's	you're	guide's	city's
we'd	coaches'	she'd	guides'	cities'

Directions: Each underlined word is missing its apostrophe. Write each word correctly on the line, inserting the apostrophe in its proper place.

There's 1. Jud: Theres a fair this Saturday. Would you like to go?
don't 2. Laurey: I dont know. Where is it going to be held?
It's 3. Jud: Its near the Simpson ranch.
that's 4. Laurey: Oh, thats not far. I would like to go!
o'clock 5. Jud: It starts at 8 oclock.
let's 6. Laurey: Well, lets not be late.
We'd 7. Jud: Wed better invite your sister to come along.
She'd 8. Laurey: Shed probably like that.
mustn't 9. Jud: We mustnt forget to ask her.
You're 10. Laurey: Youre coming to dinner tonight. We'll ask her then.

Directions: Complete each phrase with the correct possessive word in ( ). Write the word on the line.

director's 11. Singular: (director's/directors') chair
coaches' 12. Plural: (coach's/coaches') offices
guides' 13. Plural: (guide's/guides') presentations
city's 14. Singular: (city's/cities') art museum
directors' 15. Plural: (director's/directors') awards
coach's 16. Singular: (coach's/coaches') whistle
man's 17. Singular: (man's/men's) hat
guide's 18. Singular: (guide's/guides') tour
cities' 19. Plural: (city's/cities') skyscrapers
men's 20. Plural: (man's/men's) choirs

Notes for Home: Your child used apostrophes to spell contractions and possessives. ***Home Activity:*** Help your child write sentences that contain both a contraction and a possessive from the word list.

Practice Book 6.5, p. 249

Name ______________________

The Trail Drive

Interpret Information/Draw Conclusions

To interpret information and draw conclusions about it, you need to decide what the information means and whether it suits your research purposes.

Directions: Read the passage. Next, complete the web by telling what you learned from reading the passage. Then answer the questions that follow the web.

The True Life of the Cowboy

Imagine working up to 20 hours a day in grueling weather with unpredictable animals. Now imagine you only got paid about $25 to $40 a month! Even back then, this wasn't a lot of money. This was what a cowboy's life was really like.

Cowboys have become almost legendary in American history as bold, heroic figures who led glamorous lives in the Old West. However, the cowboy's life was anything but glamorous. Besides being poorly paid, the work they did was very strenuous and very difficult, not to mention dirty and dangerous. A cowboy's job was to take a herd of cattle from one place to another, usually from Texas into either Kansas, Nebraska, or Wyoming. Each minute of every hour of every day cowboys needed to stay constantly alert in order to avoid disaster. They had to guard the cattle from predators—both animal and human. They also had to prevent, if possible, cattle stampedes. They had to round up any stray cattle, as well as take care of the ones already in their possession.

The era of the cowboy spanned about 25 years from 1865–1890. With the expansion of the railroad, these underpaid workers were no longer needed to do long cattle drives. However, "cowboys" continue to live on through the many western stories written about them and the TV shows and movies made about them.

Practice Book 6.5, p. 250

Name ______________________

The Trail Drive

Possible answers given.

Cowboys of the Old West

1. **They worked up to 20 hours a day.**
2. **They earned $25–40 a month.**
3. **They herded cattle from Texas to Kansas, Nebraska, or Wyoming.**
4. **After the railroad came, long cattle drives and cowboys weren't needed.**
5. **A cowboy's life was hard, poorly paid, and dangerous.**

6. Does the passage contain mostly statements of fact or opinion? **It contains mostly statements of fact.**

7. What is the main idea of the passage? **The life of a cowboy in the Old West was hard, poorly-paid work that was often dangerous. It was much less glamorous than depicted in stories, TV shows, and movies.**

8. Why were cowboys not needed for cattle drives after the expansion of the railroad? **The long cattle drives weren't necessary because the cattle could be transported using the railroad.**

9. Would the information in this passage be useful for a research report on the work that cowboys did? Explain. **Yes, the information contains interesting details and facts about a cowboy's life.**

10. Would the information in this passage help you answer the question: "What is life like for cowboys on ranches today?" Explain. **No, the passage focuses only on the cowboys of the Old West, not modern-day cowboys.**

Notes for Home Your child read a nonfiction passage, interpreted information in it, and drew conclusions about it. ***Home Activity:*** Challenge your child to read a newspaper article and tell you the main idea of the article.

Name ______________________________

K-W-L Chart

K-W-L charts should be filled out completely, before and during the research process.

Directions: Write your topic (the place you will research) on the topic line. In the chart, write what you know about your topic and what you want to know about it. Then write information sources you can use. As you research, write information you learn that you can use in your report.

Topic: ______________________________

K What I Know	W What I Want to Know	L What I Learn (Information to Use in My Report)

What kinds of books and other sources can help me?

Notes for Home: Your child has learned about finding information for a research report. ***Home Activity:*** Think of a topic, such as a person in history or an event. Ask your child what kinds of books or other sources may offer valuable information about the topic.

Name ______________________________

Elaboration

Explanatory Phrases

- One way to elaborate is by adding an **explanatory phrase.**
- Often, you can supply information by adding a comma and a phrase that explains a word.

Directions: Complete each sentence by picking a phrase that tells more about a word. The line in the sentence tells where the phrase goes. Be sure to use a comma before and after each phrase. Write the new sentence on the long line. Use each phrase only once.

Explanatory Phrases
with only twelve letters
which joined the Union in 1959
a British naval officer
over 1,523 miles long
a graceful dance
many of Polynesian descent
wreaths of flowers
the Aloha State

1. Captain James Cook ________ reached Hawaii in 1778.
Captain Cook, a British naval officer, reached Hawaii in 1778.

2. Hawaii ______ is the youngest state.
Hawaii, which joined the Union in 1959, is the youngest state.

3. Hawaii's people _______ welcome tourists.
Hawaii's people, many of Polynesian descent, welcome tourists.

4. Leis ________ are given to newcomers.
Leis, wreaths of flowers, are given to newcomers.

5. Do the hula ________ and attend a pig roast.
Do the hula, a graceful dance, and attend a pig roast.

6. The Hawaiian alphabet ________ is unusual.
The Hawaiian alphabet, with only twelve letters, is unusual.

7. Hawaii's nickname _______ means "love."
Hawaii's nickname, the Aloha State, means "love."

8. These islands ________ are beautiful.
These islands, over 1,523 miles long, are beautiful.

Notes for Home: Your child has added information to sentences by using explanatory phrases. ***Home Activity:*** Ask your child to describe a place such as Hawaii, using at least one explanatory phrase to give information about a word.

Name ______________________________

Self-Evaluation

Research Report

Students' responses should show that they have given thought to the research reports that they have prepared and written.

Directions: Think about the final draft of your research report. Then answer each question below.

	Yes	No	Not sure
1. Did I present information clearly?			
2. Did I write a good introduction and conclusion?			
3. Did I keep my purpose and audience in mind?			
4. Did I use my sources of information well?			
5. Did I proofread and edit carefully to avoid errors?			

6. What is the best part of my research report?

7. Write one thing that you would change about this research report if you had the chance to research or write it again.

Notes for Home: Your child has answered questions about preparing and writing a research report. ***Home Activity:*** Ask your child what kinds of books or other sources gave the most useful information. Ask whether the place he or she chose was a good topic to research.

Practice Book 6.6, p. 251

Name ______________________________ Noah Writes a B & B Letter

Generalizing

- A broad statement about what several people or things have in common is a **generalization.**
- Some generalizations contain clue words such as *most, many, all, sometimes, generally, always,* or *never.*
- A valid generalization is supported by facts and agrees with what you already know. A faulty generalization is not supported by facts.

Directions: Reread "Almost Ready for School." Then complete the table. Circle **Yes** if the statement is a generalization. Circle **No** if it is not. Explain your answer. Identify any clue words that signal a generalization. **Possible answers given.**

Statement	Generalization?	Explanation
Sixth-graders were always chosen to help out in the office or in the halls.	1. (Yes) No	2. **Clue word "always" signals the generalization.**
Dad made an appointment for me with a new dentist.	3. Yes (No)	4. **This is a statement about a one-time event.**
Dentists always slip into the room so quietly you don't even know they're there.	5. (Yes) No	6. **Clue word "always" signals the generalization.**
I immediately opened my mouth.	7. Yes (No)	8. **This is a statement about a one-time event.**
People grind their teeth when they're tense.	9. (Yes) No	10. **This is a broad statement about what people have in common.**

Notes for Home: Your child read a story and identified generalizations. ***Home Activity:*** Take turns using *always, sometimes,* and *never* to make generalizations. Discuss whether each generalization is valid or faulty.

Practice Book 6.6, p. 252

Name ______________________ **Noah Writes a B & B Letter**

Vocabulary

Directions: Draw a line to connect each word on the left with its definition on the right.

1. handwriting — writing by hand
2. generation — people born about the same time
3. stationery — writing materials, such as paper and envelopes
4. calligraphy — a style of handwriting
5. committee — a group of people who plan something

Check the Words You Know
- __ calligraphy
- __ circumstances
- __ committee
- __ generation
- __ handwriting
- __ stationery

Dear Friend

Directions: Choose the word from the box that best completes each sentence. Write the word on the line.

calligraphy 6. Before there were typewriters or computers, well-educated people learned an elegant style of writing called ________ to make their letters beautiful.

stationery 7. Since their ________ was too expensive to waste, they wrote carefully.

generation 8. This older ________ who wrote so carefully may criticize the way young people write now.

committee 9. They might like to set up a ________ to suggest changes, but it probably would not do much good.

circumstances 10. The ________ of modern life have changed, and most people type or e-mail their letters today.

Write a Comparison

On a separate sheet of paper, write a paragraph that compares e-mail messages to conventional letters. Think about the benefits of both forms of communication. Do you think the advantages of one type of writing outweighs the other type? Use as many vocabulary words as you can in your comparison.
Students' comparisons should use vocabulary words correctly.

Notes for Home: Your child identified and used vocabulary words from the story. "Noah Writes a B & B Letter." ***Home Activity:*** Discuss which is more important: improving one's handwriting or typing skills.

Vocabulary 569

Practice Book 6.6, p. 253

Name ______________________ **Noah Writes a B & B Letter**

Generalizing

- A broad statement about what several people or things have in common is a **generalization.**
- Some generalizations contain clue words such as *most, many, all, sometimes, generally, always,* or *never.*
- A valid generalization is supported by facts and agrees with what you already know. A faulty generalization is not supported by facts.

Directions: Reread what happens in "Noah Writes a B & B Letter" when Noah begins to write a letter to his grandparents. Then answer the questions below. Think about how generalizations sum up the story details.

I took a box of notepaper out of my desk drawer. The notes were bigger than postage stamps, but not by much. I took out a ballpoint pen and started pressing it against a piece of scrap paper, making dents in the paper but not making a mark. Ballpoint pens sometimes take a while to get started. When I was down in Florida, Tillie Nachman had said, "The ballpoint pen has been the biggest single factor in the decline of Western Civilization. It makes the written word cheap, fast, and totally without character." My mother and Tillie should get together. Between them, they have come up with the two major reasons why Western Civilization is about to collapse.

1. What is Noah's first generalization?
Ballpoint pens sometimes take a while to get started.
2. What clue word did you use to identify this generalization? **sometimes**
3. Does Noah support his generalization? Explain.
Yes; he gives an example of a time when the pen doesn't start easily to support his generalization.
4. If Noah had said, "ballpoint pens always get started easily," would this be a valid or faulty generalization? Explain.
Possible answer: Faulty; His example shows that "always" is not true, so the generalization is not supported.
5. On a separate sheet of paper, write a valid generalization about the people of Century Village. Give evidence from the story to support your generalization. **Check that students' generalizations are valid and supported by story examples.**

Notes for Home: Your child identified generalizations and decided if they were valid or faulty. ***Home Activity:*** Take turns using *most, all, always,* and *never* to make generalizations about your neighborhood. Discuss whether each generalization is valid or faulty.

570 Generalizing

Practice Book 6.6, p. 255

Name ______________________ **Noah Writes a B & B Letter**

Selection Test

Directions: Choose the best answer to each item. Mark the letter for the answer you have chosen.

Part 1: Vocabulary

Find the answer choice that means about the same as the underlined word in each sentence.

1. Emma practiced her handwriting.
   A. a method of painting on paper with fingers instead of brushes
   B. using hand and finger movements to spell out words in the air
   (C) making letters or words with a pen, pencil, or other writing tool
   D. any means of communicating that involves the hands
2. Martin used a calligraphy pen.
   F. expressing meaning without words
   G. writing in code
   H. of or related to black
   (J) beautiful handwriting
3. Dad checked his stationery supplies.
   (A) writing materials, such as paper, cards, and envelopes
   B. staying in one place
   C. furniture, such as desks, chairs, and file cabinets
   D. related to weather
4. Considering the circumstances, she was doing well.
   F. difficulties
   (G) conditions for an act or event
   H. goals
   J. time left to complete something
5. My dad just doesn't understand our generation.
   A. method of getting something done
   B. the people on one side of a family
   C. standards of taste or style
   (D) all the people born at about the same time
6. They formed a committee.
   F. group of persons elected to make laws
   G. business
   (H) group of persons appointed or elected to do a certain task
   J. large circle

Part 2: Comprehension

Use what you know about the story to answer each item.

7. What is a "B & B letter"?
   A. an invitation
   (B) a thank-you letter
   C. a business letter
   D. a story in letter form
8. Why did Noah go to Florida to stay with his grandparents?
   (F) His parents were away on a cruise.
   G. His grandparents needed his help.
   H. He wanted to meet his grandparents' friends.
   J. He wanted to visit a theme park in Florida.
9. What kind of place is Century Village?
   A. a small town
   B. a nursing home
   C. a vacation resort
   (D) a retirement community
10. What generalization can you make about the residents of Century Village based on the information in the story?
   F. Most came to Florida from Epiphany, New York.
   G. Many have grandchildren living with them.
   H. Most like to grow flowers.
   (J) Many get involved in community events.

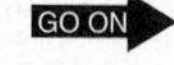

Selection Test 571

Practice Book 6.6, p. 256

Name ______________________ **Noah Writes a B & B Letter**

11. Which sentence from the story is a valid generalization?
   A. "The ball-point pen has been the biggest single factor in the decline of Western Civilization."
   (B) "Almost everyone who lives there is retired."
   C. "I looked totally presentable in my tuxedo T-shirt, which was a real work of art."
   D. "Fortunately, Grandpa Nate took its picture right after she finished it."
12. What did everyone at Century Village believe about Tillie Nachman?
   F. She was a great artist.
   G. She should become a professional calligrapher.
   (H) She did not make mistakes.
   J. She was unhappy living in Florida.
13. During the preparations for the wedding, Noah seems to think that almost everything is—
   A. educational.
   B. unnecessary.
   C. extremely annoying.
   (D) going wrong in some way.
14. The author's purpose in writing this story was to—
   F. describe life in southern Florida.
   (G) tell an amusing story.
   H. help the reader distinguish between facts and opinions.
   J. show that young people are not good judges of adults.
15. Noah's mother thinks the decline of Western Civilization will come about because—
   (A) young people don't do things the way they used to be done.
   B. boys wear T-shirts instead of tuxedos.
   C. young people do not learn calligraphy.
   D. children let computers think for them.

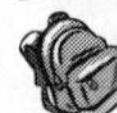

STOP

572 Selection Test

Name ______________________ **Noah Writes a B & B Letter**

Generalizing

- A broad statement about what several people or things have in common is a **generalization.**
- Some generalizations contain clue words such as *most, many, all, sometimes, generally, always,* or *never.*
- A valid generalization is supported by facts and agrees with what you already know. A faulty generalization is not supported by facts.

Directions: Read the story below.

Jill, Vani, and I are best friends even though we're very different. Vani is the smart one with all the good ideas, Jill is the strong and athletic one, and I tell the best stories. We think maybe we have such good times together because of being different, not in spite of it!

Look at what happened on the camping trip last fall. Jill was able to blow up the air mattresses when the hand pump broke. Then Vani figured out the complicated directions for setting up the tent—just before the rain began falling! I kept them entertained all evening with scary stories. If all three of us had had the same talents, that trip would never have been so much fun!

Directions: Complete the table. Decide if each generalization is valid or faulty. Give an explanation to support your decision.

Generalization	Valid or Faulty?	Explanation
The girls are all different.	1. **Valid**	The narrator says that Vani is the smart one, Jill is the athlete, and she is the storyteller.
The girls are resourceful.	2. **Valid**	3. **Each one finds a way to solve a problem on the camping trip.**
The girls would have more fun together if they were more alike.	4. **Faulty**	5. **The narrator says that they have good times because they are different.**

Notes for Home: Your child evaluated generalizations to see if they were valid or faulty. ***Home Activity:*** Name related facts about school, and ask your child to sum up the ideas by making generalizations, such as *School always ends at 3:00 P.M.*

Practice Book 6.6, p. 257

Name ______________________ **Noah Writes a B & B Letter**

Character and Visualizing

REVIEW

Directions: Read the story. Then read each question about the story. Choose the best answer to each question. Mark the letter for the answer you have chosen.

A Hoop, a Game Show, and a Good Idea

"I know you'll find a way to help me out, Desirée," said Desi's mother as she turned back to the work on her desk. When Mom spoke in that tone of voice, Desi knew she meant what she said. Her mother, she knew, had a deadline to meet with her publisher, and she couldn't stop working until their relatives actually arrived in an hour. But how was Desi to entertain her four little cousins on a rainy day?

Desi surveyed her cluttered room. A huge, striped hoop, five dusty sneakers, and colorful scarves sat in one corner. Wads of crumpled paper crowded her wastebasket, like so much popcorn, and her closet and shelves overflowed with toys and books. Old prizes from parties—cheap plastic rings, whistles, and so on—looked like crickets escaping from the tipped box nearby. An old box of cards with trivia questions and answers had spilled like a waterfall onto the carpet. Only her compact discs were carefully arranged on her desk by the CD player, like soldiers lined up for inspection. It was the one corner of the room Desi always kept neat, dusted, and organized.

"Maybe I can make an obstacle course in the basement," thought Desi. "The hoop, scarves, and shoes will be handy for that. The plastic prizes will be useful too, but I'll also need a timer." Surely Desi could find one in an old game box! Now, how could she use those worn-out trivia cards? "Hmmm. I'll set up my room as a TV game show. The kids can answer trivia questions and win play money. Perfect, but I'd better get busy! They'll be here in an hour!"

1. Desi's thoughts show that she is—
   - **A.** puzzled by her mother's request.
   - **(B.)** good at solving problems.
   - **C.** easily upset by a change of plans.
   - **D.** a constant complainer.
2. Desi's CDs are neatly arranged because—
   - **F.** she likes to keep her room neat.
   - **G.** she likes loud music.
   - **(H.)** the CDs are important to her.
   - **J.** her mother likes to see things neat and orderly.
3. The word *crickets* is used to describe how—
   - **A.** bugs could be heard outside.
   - **B.** the plastic prizes were all one color.
   - **C.** the prizes jumped around the room.
   - **(D.)** the prizes were scattered about.
4. The CDs were compared to soldiers to show—
   - **F.** how much Desi likes toy soldiers.
   - **(G.)** how neat and orderly they were.
   - **H.** the kinds of music recorded on them.
   - **J.** the similarity of their cover designs.
5. In the next hour, Desi will probably—
   - **(A.)** set up games for her cousins.
   - **B.** make lunch for her cousins.
   - **C.** reorganize her CD collection.
   - **D.** help her mom with her work.

Notes for Home: Your child identified a character's traits and visualized the setting based on images from a passage. ***Home Activity:*** Take turns describing the bedrooms or favorite rooms of family members. Discuss how each room reveals something about that person.

Name ______________________ **Noah Writes a B & B Letter**

Writing Across Texts

Directions: Read the steps in the box below that outline the process of doing calligraphy as described in "Noah Writes a B & B Letter" and "Learn Calligraphy." Then, place the steps in the correct order in the table below.

Dip nib into ink.	Obtain lined paper.
Hold pen at 45-degree angle.	Practice writing "X" thicker in one direction.
Do not twist marker.	Turn pen plunger counterclockwise.
Turn plunger clockwise to fill pen.	Wipe nib.
Practice all 26 letters of the alphabet.	Place paper at an angle.

Possible answers given.

Noah Writes a B & B Letter	Learn Calligraphy
Buy calligraphy pen and ink.	Obtain chisel-tip felt marker.
1. **Turn pen plunger counterclockwise.**	6. **Obtain lined paper.**
2. **Dip nib into ink.**	7. **Place paper at an angle.**
3. **Turn plunger clockwise to fill pen.**	8. **Hold pen at a 45-degree angle.**
4. **Wipe nib.**	9. **Practice writing "X" thicker in one direction.**
5. **Practice all 26 letters of the alphabet.**	10. **Do not twist marker.**
Begin to address invitations.	Practice patterns of numbers and letters in model.

Write a "How-To" Paragraph

Write two or three how-to paragraphs about one of the skills discussed in the reading selections. You may use information from both selections and the table to write about the steps involved in doing calligraphy, or you may write about other skills—how to write a B & B letter, decorate a wedding cake, fill an ink pen, paint a T-shirt, call 911 in an emergency, and so on. Write your paragraph on a separate sheet of paper. **Paragraphs will vary, depending on which skills students choose to write about. Check that steps are in chronological order. Also check for the use of sequence clue words.**

Notes for Home: Your child has combined and used information from more than one selection. ***Home Activity:*** When reading stories or articles, have your child point out steps in a process, whenever possible.

Grammar Practice Book 6.6, p. 126

Name ______________________ **Noah Writes a B & B Letter**

Grammar: Proper Nouns and Proper Adjectives

REVIEW

Directions: Rewrite each sentence. Capitalize each proper noun and proper adjective.

1. My brother arnold and I call our grandmother by her first name, rachel.
   My brother Arnold and I call our grandmother by her first name, Rachel.
2. My grandfather's name is edward benedict miller, but we call him ted.
   My grandfather's name is Edward Benedict Miller, but we call him Ted.
3. They live in twin falls, idaho, not too far from the snake river.
   They live in Twin Falls, Idaho, not too far from the Snake River.
4. Recently they moved from a house on weston dr. to an apartment on ridgewood ave.
   Recently they moved from a house on Weston Dr. to an apartment on Ridgewood Ave.
5. Rachel came to the united states from china, and ted came from great britain.
   Rachel came to the United States from China, and Ted came from Great Britain.
6. My family, including our irish setter, nellie, visits them every january and june.
   My family, including our Irish setter, Nellie, visits them every January and June.
7. Having a chinese grandmother and a british grandfather can be very interesting.
   Having a Chinese grandmother and a British grandfather can be very interesting.
8. rachel and ted have a siamese cat and a south american parrot.
   Rachel and Ted have a Siamese cat and a South American parrot.
9. In their apartment building, a vietnamese neighbor lives on one side of them and an iranian family lives on the other.
   In their apartment building, a Vietnamese neighbor lives on one side of them and an Iranian family lives on the other.
10. They are really just american grandparents who live in idaho, but visiting them is like taking a trip around the world.
    They are really just American grandparents who live in Idaho, but visiting them is like taking a trip around the world.

Notes for Home: Your child capitalized proper nouns and proper adjectives. ***Home Activity:*** Help your child write a thank-you letter, thanking someone who has helped him or her. Have your child check that all proper nouns and adjectives are capitalized.

Grammar Practice Book 6.6, p. 127

Name ______________________ Noah Writes a B & B Letter

Grammar: Capitalization

Directions: When you write a letter to a friend or family member, remember to follow these rules for capitalizing words.

- Capitalize the first word of the greeting: Dear Aunt Sarah,
- Capitalize the first letter of every sentence: My grandparents came to visit.
- Capitalize the pronoun *I:* Uncle Joe and I had a lot of fun.
- Capitalize the first word of the closing: Your nephew,
- Capitalize proper nouns and proper adjectives. Remember proper nouns name particular persons, places, and things: Jana Collins, Hackensack River, American Riverboats, January 24, 2001
- Capitalize the personal titles of people: Dr. Sandra P. Weintraub

Directions: Read the following parts of a letter. Rewrite the words on the line using the correct capital letters.

1. dear Uncle joe, **Dear Uncle Joe,**
2. your friend, **Your friend,**
3. dear martin, **Dear Martin,**
4. sincerely yours, **Sincerely yours,**
5. april 6, 2001 **April 6, 2001**

Directions: Rewrite each sentence. Use capital letters where they are needed.

6. I wanted to visit my grandparents, jacques and sophie marceau.
I wanted to visit my grandparents, Jacques and Sophie Marceau.

7. they used to live in amarillo, texas, but they just moved to memphis, tennessee.
They used to live in Amarillo, Texas, but they just moved to Memphis, Tennessee.

8. Their favorite thing about Memphis is that it's next to the mississippi river.
Their favorite thing about Memphis is that it's next to the Mississippi River.

9. i think their new address is 748 bishop court, but i'm not sure about that!
I think their new address is 748 Bishop Court, but I'm not sure about that!

10. Their neighbors are captain dennis healy and his wife, mrs. jennifer healy.
Their neighbors are Captain Dennis Healy and his wife, Mrs. Jennifer Healy.

Notes for Home: Your child used rules of capitalization to write different parts of a letter and to correct capitalization errors in sentences. ***Home Activity:*** Have your child write your home address using capital letters for your name, street, city, and state abbreviation.

Grammar: Capitalization **577**

Grammar Practice Book 6.6, p. 128

Name ______________________ Noah Writes a B & B Letter

Grammar: Capitalization

Directions: Underline each word in the letter that needs to begin with a capital letter. Then rewrite the words correctly on the lines to the right. **Order may vary.**

dear Grandpa morris,

Thank you for having me at your house last week. As i told my mom, it was one of the best visits ever. It was great fun meeting your famous neighbor, dr. Hugo p. Science. I still remember how surprised he was when we predicted that storm. If he had looked behind him at hurley's river, he would have understood. Those black clouds above the river looked liked they covered all of edwards county!

your grandson,
Scott

1. **Dear**
2. **Morris**
3. **I**
4. **Dr.**
5. **P.**
6. **Hurley's**
7. **River**
8. **Edwards**
9. **County**
10. **Your**

Write a Thank-You Letter

On a separate sheet of paper, write a thank-you letter to a friend or relative. Remember to capitalize words when necessary.
Check to make sure that students have followed rules for capitalizing greetings, closing, titles, proper nouns, and so on.

Notes for Home: Your child identified and corrected capitalization errors in a letter. ***Home Activity:*** With your child, read over a letter from a friend or family member. Have your child explain why different parts of the letter are capitalized.

578 Grammar: Capitalization

Grammar Practice Book 6.6, p. 129

Name ______________________ Noah Writes a B & B Letter

Grammar: Capitalization

RETEACHING

Capitalize the following groups of words correctly.

1. dear grandma, **Dear Grandma,**
2. answer the phone. **Answer the phone.**
3. chicago tribune **Chicago Tribune**
4. north carolina **North Carolina**
5. february 21, 2001 **February 21, 2001**
6. mason champlin **Mason Champlin**
7. 1426 wellsley dr. **1426 Wellsley Dr.**
8. *great expectations* ***Great Expectations***

Capitalize all important words in a proper noun and in a title. Capitalize the first word of a greeting and a closing in a letter. Also capitalize the first word in a sentence.

Directions: Read the letter. Underline each word or group of words with a capitalization error. Write the words correctly on the lines.

2520 central st.
evanston, illinois 60201
august 13, 2001

dear uncle chris,

how are you feeling? I'm sorry you broke your leg at jones pond. I bought you a book called fun things to do while stuck indoors. it was written by amy sargeant. She also wrote a song called "sunny days will come again." I will sing it for you on thanksgiving. Write back soon if you feel up to it.

yours truly,
charlie

1. **Central St.**
2. **Evanston, Illinois**
3. **August**
4. **Dear Uncle Chris,**
5. **How**
6. **Jones Pond**
7. ***Fun Things to Do While Stuck Indoors***
8. **It**
9. **Amy Sargeant**
10. **"Sunny Days Will Come Again"**
11. **Thanksgiving**
12. **Yours truly,**
13. **Charlie**

Notes for Home: Your child identified and corrected capitalization errors in a letter. ***Home Activity:*** Write a short letter to your child, but include some mistakes in capitalization. Have your child read the letter carefully and rewrite it correctly.

Grammar: Capitalization **579**

Grammar Practice Book 6.6, p. 130

Name ______________________ Noah Writes a B & B Letter

Grammar: Capitalization

Directions: Answer each question with a complete sentence. Use capital letters correctly. **Possible answers given.**

1. What is the name of the month in which you were born?
I was born in October.

2. What is the name of your town and street?
I live on North Street in Bilkesburg.

3. What is the name of your favorite book, and who wrote it?
My favorite book is *The View from Saturday* by E. L. Konigsburg.

4. What is the name of your favorite song, and who sings it?
My favorite song is "My New Hat" by Bub Lyons.

5. How would you begin a letter to a relative or close friend?
I would begin a letter "Dear . . . ."

6. What is the name of a newspaper you have seen?
I have seen the *New York Times.*

7. What day is it today?
Today is Friday.

8. What is the name of a lake or river near your town?
Lake Erie is near my town.

Directions: Rewrite each sentence. Use capital letters where they are needed.

9. gene has a dentist appointment with dr. grey at 8775 north bentley ave.
Gene has a dentist appointment with Dr. Grey at 8775 North Bentley Ave.

10. mr. fenton said the party was on saturday, june 14, 2001.
Mr. Fenton said the party was on Saturday, June 14, 2001.

11. please buy the book *seven days in the jungle* by steven stafford.
Please buy the book *Seven Days in the Jungle* by Steven Stafford.

Notes for Home: Your child used capital letters correctly in sentences. ***Home Activity:*** Have your child write a letter to a friend or relative. Help him or her check for capitalization mistakes.

580 Grammar: Capitalization

Practice Book 6.6, p. 258

Name ______________________ **Noah Writes a B & B Letter**

Phonics: Vowel Digraphs

Directions: Read the words in the box. Each word contains the vowel combination **oo.** Say each word to yourself. Listen for those words with the same vowel sound as **choose** and those words with the same vowel sound as **stood.** Write each word in the correct column.

bedroom	fishhook	look
books	fooling	moon
cook	good	pooled
cookie	groom	stool

Vowel sound in *choose*		Vowel sound in *stood*	
1.	bedroom	7.	books
2.	fooling	8.	cook
3.	groom	9.	cookie
4.	moon	10.	fishhook
5.	pooled	11.	good
6.	stool	12.	look

Directions: Read the words below. Each word contains the vowel combination **ow.** Circle the words that have the same vowel sound as **grow.**

13. (row) now (slowly) however brown (sowing) cowboy

14. down (grown) gown towns (tow) (mowing) (lowly)

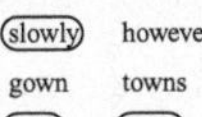 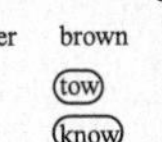 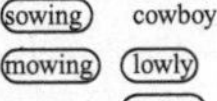

15. (owed) flowers (stow) (show) (know) Howard (below)

Directions: For each word below, give three more words that have the same vowel sound and spelling. **Possible answers given.**

16. throat	boat, coat, float,	goat, moat, coal,	foal, coast, toast
17. weight	eight, veil, reindeer,	sleigh, weigh,	neighbor
18. flow	blow, show, know,	grow, tow, low,	glow, snow, crow
19. room	loom, gloom, soon,	school, fool, food,	cool, stool, mood
20. good	hood, wood, wool,	foot, look, brook,	stood, hook, book

Notes for Home: Your child distinguished vowel digraphs, such as *oo* in *room, ow* in *owe, oa* in *toast,* and *ei* in *weight. **Home Activity:*** With your child, read a letter or card you have received from family or friends. Look for these vowel sounds and spellings.

Spelling Workbook 6.6, p. 101

Name ______________________ **Noah Writes a B & B Letter**

Spelling: Easily Confused Words

Pretest Directions: Fold back the page along the dotted line. On the blanks, write the spelling words as they are dictated. When you have finished the test, unfold the page and check your words.

1.	since	1. It has been raining **since** noon.
2.	sense	2. That movie made no **sense.**
3.	choose	3. You must **choose** only one.
4.	chose	4. He **chose** a vanilla milkshake.
5.	finally	5. The bus **finally** arrived.
6.	finely	6. The watch is **finely** engraved.
7.	except	7. Everybody went **except** Todd.
8.	accept	8. We **accept** your apology.
9.	beside	9. A tree stands **beside** the barn.
10.	besides	10. I like all fruit **besides** pears.
11.	recent	11. The Internet is a **recent** invention.
12.	resent	12. I **resent** your rude comments.
13.	access	13. She needs **access** to those files.
14.	excess	14. I have an **excess** of comic books.
15.	later	15. We will meet at home **later.**
16.	latter	16. I like the **latter** parts of the play.
17.	metal	17. The gate was made of **metal.**
18.	medal	18. The soldier earned a **medal.**
19.	personal	19. It is a **personal** matter.
20.	personnel	20. He is in charge of **personnel.**

Notes for Home: Your child took a pretest on words that are easily confused because of similar pronunciations and spellings. ***Home Activity:*** Help your child learn misspelled words before the final test. Your child should look at the word, say it, spell it aloud, and then spell it with eyes shut.

Spelling Workbook 6.6, p. 102

Name ______________________ **Noah Writes a B & B Letter**

Spelling: Easily Confused Words

Word List

since	finally	beside	access	metal
sense	finely	besides	excess	medal
choose	except	recent	later	personal
chose	accept	resent	latter	personnel

Directions: Choose the word from the box that best matches each definition. Write the word on the line.

excess	1. too much; overflow	finally	7. in the end
access	2. right to enter or use	finely	8. delicately
resent	3. feel injured and angry	beside	9. next to
recent	4. not long ago	besides	10. other than, in addition to
choose	5. select	medal	11. award; decoration
chose	6. selected	metal	12. a substance such as iron, steel, silver, or gold

Directions: Choose the word in ( ) that best completes each sentence. Write the word on the line.

accept	13. The couple will gladly (except/accept) any wedding presents.
since	14. Ever (since/sense) yesterday, guests have been arriving for the wedding.
latter	15. The (later/latter) of the two flower girls in the procession was taller.
Except	16. (Except/Accept) for Jill, the bridesmaids were all blonde.
personnel	17. The (personal/personnel) from the church were glad to help.
sense	18. The groom had the (since/sense) that the bride was nervous.
later	19. He knew that (later/latter) in the day she would feel better.
personal	20. In my (personal/personnel) opinion, it was a lovely wedding.

Notes for Home: Your child spelled words that are easily confused because of similar pronunciations and spellings. ***Home Activity:*** Write a definition of each spelling word on an index card. Have your child choose a card, spell the word defined, and use it in a sentence.

Spelling Workbook 6.6, p. 103

Name ______________________ **Noah Writes a B & B Letter**

Spelling: Easily Confused Words

Directions: Proofread the signs Lynn saw in her grandparents' store. Find six spelling mistakes. Use the proofreading marks to correct each mistake.

≡ Make a capital.
/ Make a small letter.
∧ Add something.
Take out something.
⊙ Add a period.
¶ Begin a new paragraph.

All personall are to separate plastic bottles from metal cans and containers. (corrected: n, e — personnel)

It's getting latter by the minute, so get busy! (corrected: later)

Do not except checks without two forms of identification. (corrected: ac — accept)

Do not block access to this door.

Due to resent weather problems, vegetable prices have risen! (corrected: c — recent)

Please dispose of eksess boxes properly. (corrected: xc — excess)

The new uniforms you chose last month have finely arrived!!! (corrected: al — finally)

Spelling Tip

Some words are easily confused because they have similar pronunciations and spellings. Check the signs to make sure that the words from the box are spelled correctly.

Word List

since	recent
sense	resent
choose	access
chose	excess
finally	later
finely	latter
except	metal
accept	medal
beside	personal
besides	personnel

Write Signs

On a separate piece of paper, create several signs that give helpful tips for employees, friends, family, or students. Try to use at least five of your spelling words. **Answers will vary, but each set of signs should include at least five spelling words.**

Notes for Home: Your child spelled words that are easily confused because they have similar pronunciations and spellings. ***Home Activity:*** Work with your child to design and decorate a poster that presents warnings or rules. Use some of the spelling words in your poster.

Spelling Workbook 6.6, p. 104

Name ______________________ **Noah Writes a B & B Letter**

Spelling: Easily Confused Words **REVIEW**

Word List

since	finely	recent	latter
sense	except	resent	metal
choose	accept	access	medal
chose	beside	excess	personal
finally	besides	later	personnel

Directions: Choose the word from the box that contains each word below. Write the word on the line.

1. ate **later**
2. fine **finely**
3. sent **resent**
4. hose **chose**
5. cent **recent**
6. met **metal**
7. sides **besides**
8. sin **since**

Directions: Choose a word from the box that best replaces the underlined words in each book title. Write the word on the line.

Finally 9. *At Last, We Were Champions!*

Latter 10. *Food Over Fashion: Who Cares About the Second of the Two?*

Except 11. *Nothing Left to Say but Goodbye*

Personal 12. *A Private Memoir of My Life in Kenya*

Excess 13. *Too Much Is Never Enough for Some People*

Personnel 14. *Ten Easy Steps to Popularity with Your Employees*

Medal 15. *Gold Award Champions of the Winter Olympics*

Beside 16. *How to Keep Your Pet Next to You When You Walk*

Access 17. *Why No One Gets Admittance Without Proper I.D.*

Choose 18. *How To Select the Right Tile for Your Bathroom*

Sense 19. *Just Desserts: Sweets to Please Any Awareness of Taste*

Accept 20. *How to Receive a Compliment and What to Say Back*

Notes for Home: Your child spelled words that are easily confused because they have similar pronunciations and spellings. ***Home Activity:*** Deliberately misuse some of the spelling words in sentences (for instance, use *sense* instead of *since*). Have your child correct the mistakes.

Practice Book 6.6, p. 259

Name ______________________ **Noah Writes a B & B Letter**

Dictionary

A **dictionary** is a book of words, listed in alphabetical order, and their meanings. Guide words appear at the top of each page that tell the first and last words that appear on the page. Each entry shows a word's spelling, syllable parts, pronunciation, definitions, and parts of speech. Some entries will also include illustrative, or sample, phrases or sentences, and an etymology that tells how the word came into the English language from other languages.

Directions: Use the dictionary entries to answer the questions that follow.

re • la • tion • ship (ri lā ′ shən ship), **1** a connection: *What is the relationship of clouds to rain?* **2** the condition of belonging to the same family. **3** the state that exists between people or groups that deal with each other: *I have good relationships with all of my teachers this year. noun.*

rel • a • tive (rel ′ ə tiv), **1** a person who belongs to the same family as another, such as a father, brother, aunt, nephew, or cousin. **2** compared to each other: *We discussed the relative advantages of city and country life.* **3** depending for meaning on a relation to something else: *East is a relative term; for example, Chicago is east of California but west of New York.* 1 *noun,* 2, 3 *adjective.* **relative to, 1** about; concerning: *The teacher asked me some questions relative to my plans for the summer.* **2** in comparison with; in proportion to; for: *He is strong relative to his size.*

rel • a • tive • ly (rel ′ ə tiv lē), in relation to something else; comparatively: *You are relatively tall for your age. adverb.*

re • lax (ri laks′), **1** to loosen up; make or become less stiff or firm: *Relax your muscles to rest them. Relax when you dance.* **2** to make or become less strict or severe; lessen in force: *Discipline is relaxed on the last day of school.* **3** to relieve or be relieved from work, effort, or worry: *We relaxed during the holidays. Relax! Everything will be all right. verb.*

re • lax • a • tion (rē ′ lak sā ′ shən), **1** a loosening: *the relaxation of the muscles.* **2** a lessening of strictness, severity, or force: *the relaxation of discipline over the holidays.* **3** recreation; amusement: *Walking and reading are relaxations. noun.*

re • lay (rē ′ lā *for 1;* rē ′ lā ′ *or* ri lā ′ *for 2*), **1** a fresh supply: *New relays of firefighters were sent in.* **2** to take and carry farther: *Please relay this message to your parents.* 1 *noun,* 2 *verb,* **re • lays, re • layed, re • lay • ing.**

re • lay race (rē ′ lā rās ′), a race in which each member of a team runs or swims only a certain part of the distance.

Practice Book 6.6, p. 260

Name ______________________ **Noah Writes a B & B Letter**

1. Does the *e* in *relationship* sound like the first *e* in *relative* or the *e* in *relax?* Explain.
The *e* in *relationship* sounds like the *e* in *relax* because they sound the same and the pronunciation key uses the same symbols to represent this sound.

2. Find the word that can be used as both a noun and a verb. Write two sentences using the word, one for each part of speech.
Check that students use *relay* correctly as a noun and a verb.

3. How many syllables does *relative* have? **3 syllables**

4. Which meaning of the word *relax* best refers to rules or enforcers of rules?
meaning 2: to make or become less strict or severe; lessen in force

5. If the guide words *reign* and *relay race* were shown above the entries, list three words that might appear on this page before the word *relationship.*
Words will vary but should fall alphabetically between *reign* and *relationship.*

6. Which meaning of *relationship* is being used in the following sentence?
The relationship between the two old friends was as strong today as it was twenty years ago.
meaning 3: the state that exists between people or groups that deal with each other

7. Are the spellings of the underlined words in the following sentence correct? If not, identify and correct any misspelled words.
My relatives were relativly relaxed given that the groom was rather late.
relatively

8. Why are guide words helpful when you are searching for a specific entry?
Possible answer: You can use alphabetical order to decide if the word you're searching for falls between the two guide words.

9. Do you think the illustrative phrases are helpful? Explain. **Possible answer: Yes, the phrases show how the word can be used and help make its meaning more clear.**

10. How might you use a dictionary to help you as you read and write?
Possible answer: You can use a dictionary as you read to look up unfamiliar words. You can use a dictionary as you write to make sure you have spelled a word correctly or that you are using it correctly.

Notes for Home: Your child answered questions about several dictionary entries. ***Home Activity:*** Play a dictionary game in which one person picks a word from a dictionary and uses it in an illustrative sentence. The other players write down what they think the word means.

Practice Book 6.6, p. 261

Name ______________________ **Louis Braille**

Author's Viewpoint/Bias

- **Author's viewpoint** is the way an author thinks about the subject of his or her writing.
- You can identify an author's viewpoint by looking at the words an author uses. Some authors use loaded words, such as *terrible* or *wonderful,* to express a strong preference, or bias.
- *Balanced writing* presents both sides of an issue. *Biased writing* shows strong feeling for or against someone or something and presents only one side of an issue. You should read biased writing critically.

Directions: Reread "Normal." Then complete the table. Write whether you think the author would agree or disagree with each statement below. Explain your thinking with evidence from the article. **Possible answers given.**

Statement	Agree or Disagree? Explain.
Normal is different for each individual.	1. **Agree; The author says that "*normal* is what you make it to be."**
Students cannot learn anything from a person in a wheelchair.	2. **Disagree; The author's experience as a teacher has proved this to be wrong.**
A person can learn to overcome any problem.	3. **Agree; The author says that "each one of us faces problems that we must resolve."**
When something is *normal* to a person, that person does not think about it.	4. **Agree; The author has not even thought about writing about her wheelchair.**
Normal is what is average or what the majority accepts.	5. **Disagree; This definition is disproved by the author's own experience.**

Notes for Home: Your child read an article and analyzed the author's viewpoint. ***Home Activity:*** Have a family debate. Write topics on slips of paper. Take turns choosing one and expressing a viewpoint on the topic. Later, discuss whether any speaker used loaded words.

Practice Book 6.6, p. 262

Name ________________ **Louis Braille**

Vocabulary

Directions: Choose the word from the box that best matches each definition. Write the word on the line.

Check the Words You Know
__ advantages
__ ambitions
__ blindness
__ complicated
__ merit
__ recognition
__ visual

visual 1. of, for, or by sight

merit 2. worth or value; quality

recognition 3. favorable notice

advantages 4. benefits

ambitions 5. things strongly desired

blindness 6. condition of being without sight

Directions: Read the diary entry of an inventor. Choose the word from the box that best completes each sentence. Write the word on the matching numbered lines below.

Tomorrow I will show off my new invention. I hope everyone will see the **7.** _____ of making a device that makes it easier for people to open cans and jars. For this invention to be a success, it can't be too **8.** _____, or people won't want to use it. If tomorrow's test goes well, my ideas will soon get the **9.** _____ they deserve. My friends tell me that my **10.** _____ are too high, but I know that this invention could change people's lives for the better. I'm sure of it!

7. **merit or advantages**
8. **complicated**
9. **recognition**
10. **ambitions**

Write a Commercial

On a separate sheet of paper, write a television or radio commercial for a new invention. Your commercial should briefly tell what your invention can do and convince people of its merit. Use as many vocabulary words as you can.

Students' commercials should use vocabulary words correctly.

Notes for Home: Your child identified and used vocabulary words from *Louis Braille*. ***Home Activity:*** Talk to your child about an invention that has changed the lives of those who use it. Make a two-column list that shows the advantages and drawbacks of the invention.

Practice Book 6.6, p. 263

Name ________________ **Louis Braille**

Author's Viewpoint/Bias

- **Author's viewpoint** is the way an author thinks about the subject of his or her writing. You can identify an author's viewpoint by looking at the words an author uses. Some authors use loaded words, such as *terrible* or *wonderful*, to express a strong preference, or bias.
- *Balanced writing* presents both sides of an issue. *Biased writing* shows strong feeling for or against someone or something and presents only one side of an issue. You should read biased writing critically.

Directions: Reread the passage from *Louis Braille* which describes the governor's reaction to the Braille system. Then answer the questions below. Think about the words the author uses to support his viewpoint.

> Although Braille's system was brilliant, and although it was supported by all the pupils and many of the teachers at the National Institute for Blind Youth, it was disliked by the Institute's governors. They supported other systems of reading and writing, such as Haüy's raised wooden letters, which they knew how to read themselves but which was far too cumbersome to be efficient when used by the blind.
>
> Because the governors of the Institute were not blind themselves, they couldn't understand the tremendous advantages of Braille. They did not realize its simplicity and the fact that it allowed blind people to write as well as to read. They distrusted a new system that they were unable to use without first having to learn Braille's language of dots.
>
> From LOUIS BRAILLE by Stephen Keeler. Copyright ©1986 by Wayland Publishers, Ltd. Reprinted by permission.

Possible answers given.

1. What word or words indicate the author's view of Louis Braille's system?
The author calls Braille's system "brilliant," with "tremendous advantages."

2. What word or words indicate the author's view of Haüy's system?
The author calls Haüy's system "cumbersome."

3. Why does the author think the governors favor Haüy's system?
The governors favor Haüy's system because they are unwilling to learn. They are not blind, so they don't appreciate Braille's system.

4. Which system of reading does the author favor?
The author favors Braille's system.

5. On a separate sheet of paper, explain the author's viewpoint of Louis Braille and his invention. Is the author biased? Explain. **Keeler calls Braille's writing system "brilliant" and says he was a good student. He tells of Braille's determination to play instruments and to get his writing system accepted. Keeler is biased in Braille's favor because everything he says about Braille is positive.**

Notes for Home: Your child analyzed the way an author presented his viewpoint. ***Home Activity:*** Discuss the viewpoint presented in a newspaper editorial. Think about the bias of the writer and how convincing and valid the evidence is.

Practice Book 6.6, p. 265

Name ________________ **Louis Braille**

Selection Test

Directions: Choose the best answer to each item. Mark the letter for the answer you have chosen.

Part 1: Vocabulary

Find the answer choice that means about the same as the underlined word in each sentence.

1. Her <u>blindness</u> was caused by a childhood illness.
   - A. condition of being slow to learn
   - (B) condition of being unable to see
   - C. condition of having weak muscles
   - D. condition of being unable to hear
2. John spoke of his <u>ambitions</u>.
   - F. plans for a building
   - G. ideas about education
   - (H) things that are strongly desired
   - J. places where students are taught
3. Dr. Casey gained <u>recognition</u> for his ideas.
   - (A) favorable notice; acceptance
   - B. award of money
   - C. distrust; lack of faith
   - D. permission to change
4. Candace got a raise based on <u>merit</u>.
   - F. time spent on a job
   - G. ability to plan ahead
   - H. condition of being older than others
   - (J) something that deserves praise or reward
5. Maureen has great <u>visual</u> skills.
   - A. used for teaching; educational
   - (B) related to sight
   - C. from a certain time in history
   - D. related to machines
6. These instructions are <u>complicated</u>.
   - F. freely offered
   - (G) hard to understand
   - H. providing correct information
   - J. well organized
7. Her plan had some <u>advantages</u>.
   - A. unfavorable conditions
   - B. supporters
   - C. causes of cancellation or delay
   - (D) benefits

Part 2: Comprehension

Use what you know about the selection to answer each item.

8. The school in Paris that Louis Braille attended in 1819 was—
   - F. the first school for boys and girls with special needs.
   - G. a school for children who were gifted.
   - (H) the only school for blind children in France.
   - J. a school for music students.
9. At the National Institute for Blind Youth, students learned mainly by—
   - (A) listening and remembering.
   - B. reading books published in "Night Writing."
   - C. going on field trips.
   - D. making things and doing experiments.
10. The writing system developed by Charles Barbier was easier to read than embossed books because—
    - F. it was first developed for sighted people to use at night.
    - (G) dots and dashes are easier to recognize by touch than the shapes of letters.
    - H. it was based on sounds rather than spelling.
    - J. each letter could be quickly recognized by a single touch of the finger.

GO ON

Practice Book 6.6, p. 266

Name ________________ **Louis Braille**

11. In his efforts to improve Charles Barbier's system, Louis Braille's major breakthrough came when he—
    - A. dropped all dashes from the system.
    - B. learned to write with a stylus.
    - (C) invented a system of only six dots to represent letters.
    - D. talked to Dr. Pignier, the school principal, about his experiments.
12. The author of this selection seems to think that—
    - (F) Louis Braille was a truly remarkable person.
    - G. schools in the past gave students more opportunities to be creative than those of today.
    - H. Louis Braille has been given too much credit for something another man invented.
    - J. Louis Braille's success was based largely on luck.
13. Which words do you think the author would use to describe school principal Dr. Pignier?
    - A. creative and fun
    - B. mean-spirited
    - (C) thoughtful and open-minded
    - D. stubbornly proud
14. Which of these statements would be impossible to verify as a fact?
    - F. Gabriel Gauthier went to school with Louis Braille.
    - G. Boys who broke the rules were kept after school and made to write punishment papers.
    - H. Charles Barbier had invented a secret military code based on dots and dashes.
    - (J) Louis's face lit up with excitement when he realized what a great opportunity he had.
15. In writing this selection, the author has combined known facts with—
    - A. fictional characters and events.
    - B. exaggerated statements and humor.
    - (C) what he imagines the characters may have thought and felt.
    - D. poetic language and rhythms.

STOP

Name ______________________ Louis Braille

Author's Viewpoint/Bias

- **Author's viewpoint** is the way an author thinks about the subject of his or her writing. You can identify an author's viewpoint by looking at the words an author uses. Some authors use loaded words, such as *terrible* or *wonderful,* to express a strong preference, or bias.
- *Balanced writing* presents both sides of an issue. *Biased writing* shows strong feeling for or against someone or something and presents only one side of an issue. You should read biased writing critically.

Directions: Read the story below.

American history books highlight men's inventions, but they often overlook women's efforts or credit them to men. Among the first to agree would be Martha Coston (1826–1906). She spent almost ten years struggling to develop, improve, and market special chemical flares used to signal seagoing ships at night. Her signal system proved very successful and saved many sailors during the Civil War. Martha Coston held two patents on her system. Many years after it had been in use, Lieutenant E. Very improved the hand-held cartridge from which the flares were fired. The device was named the "Very pistol" in his honor. As always, American history denies women the credit for what they do.

Directions: Complete the table. Think about the author's beliefs and the facts used to support them. **Possible answers given.**

Summary of Main Idea	1. **Female inventors in American history go unrecognized.**
Author's Viewpoint on the Subject	2. **History has treated American female inventors unfairly.**
Facts Supporting Author's Views	3. **Martha Coston worked hard to perfect the flare, but Lieutenant Very, a man, had his name used for the invention.**
Loaded Words Used	4. **"often overlook" and "As always, history denies women the credit for what they do."**
Author's Unstated Belief	5. **The accomplishments of women like Martha Coston deserve recognition.**

Notes for Home: Your child identified an author's viewpoint/bias. ***Home Activity:*** Challenge your child to find examples of balanced and biased writing in a newspaper. Discuss how your child decided whether it was balanced or biased writing.

Practice Book 6.6, p. 267

Name ______________________ Louis Braille

Persuasive Devices

REVIEW

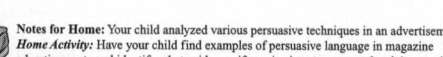

Directions: Read the passage. Then read each question about the passage. Choose the best answer to each question. Mark the letter for the answer you have chosen.

Simply Speaking

Hands off that keyboard! Make editing and spell-checking things of the past. Join the revolution that has everyone talking—and all the computers listening!!

From stressed typists to keyboard klutzes, every computer-user can find a use for this advanced technology. Known in the industry as *continuous-speech recognition,* these programs can turn natural speech into typed pages almost instantly. (This means that you speak and your words appear automatically on the screen. Over 90 percent of the time, they appear correctly spelled and punctuated.) Many of these high-powered programs also come with simple voice commands that make formatting, editing, and moving through files a breeze. When combined with other programs, some products can sort through records, search for data, even send messages and read them aloud, simply based on voice commands. As a result, all office workers can increase their speed and output, as can students, researchers, and anyone else who talks!

The sharpest minds in the business are already switching to speech recognition programs, so don't be left out of the conversation. Speak up and install your own right away!

1. The author believes that the product is best suited for—
   - A. people who are poor spellers.
   - B. everyone needing to search for data.
   - C. those who write exactly the way they speak.
   - (D) anyone who owns a computer and can talk.
2. Which of the following claims is an attempt to persuade you?
   - F. The programs can turn natural speech into typed pages.
   - (G) The smartest people are using it already.
   - H. Some programs can even send messages and read them aloud.
   - J. Some products can sort through records.
3. Loaded words used to influence the reader include—
   - A. keyboard and voice commands.
   - B. commands and technology.
   - (C) revolution and high-powered.
   - D. recognition and punctuated.
4. Which of the following is a sweeping generalization?
   - (F) As a result, all office workers can increase their speed and output.
   - G. Some products can sort through records.
   - H. Continuous-speech recognition programs turn natural speech into typed pages.
   - J. Continuous-speech recognition programs come with simple voice commands.
5. The purpose of this passage is to persuade readers to—
   - A. quit using computers.
   - (B) install continuous-speech recognition programming.
   - C. spell-check more often.
   - D. increase their speed and output.

Notes for Home: Your child analyzed various persuasive techniques in an advertisement. ***Home Activity:*** Have your child find examples of persuasive language in magazine advertisements and identify what evidence, if any, is given to support the claims made.

Name ______________________ Louis Braille

Writing Across Texts

Directions: Refer to *Louis Braille* and the selection you read in Unit 3, "Elizabeth Blackwell: Medical Pioneer." Complete the left-hand side of the diagram to tell about Louis Braille's problem, the steps he took to solve it, and his solution. Then complete the right-hand side of the diagram for Elizabeth Blackwell. **Possible answers given.**

Louis Braille	Elizabeth Blackwell
Problem Louis Braille wanted to find an easier way to teach the blind to read and write.	**Problem** 6. **Elizabeth Blackwell wanted to be a doctor, but medical schools did not admit women.**
Attempts to Solve the Problem 1. **Louis Braille learned about "Night Writing" from Captain Barbier.** 2. **He experimented with dots and dashes to simplify this system.** 3. **He worked in his spare time for three years to create the Braille cell.** 4. **He got support from pupils and students in the school.**	**Attempts to Solve the Problem** 7. **She went to ask Dean Reynolds to admit her in Philadelphia.** 8. **The students accepted her at Geneva Medical College.** 9. **After graduation, she had to go to Paris to find work.**
Solution 5. **Louis Braille's system was taught all over the world.**	**Solution** 10. **Elizabeth Blackwell became the first woman doctor in the United States.**

Write a Comparison/Contrast Essay

Refer to the reading selections about Louis Braille and Elizabeth Blackwell and the diagram. Write an essay to compare and contrast the problems faced by the two pioneers, the steps they took to solve their problems, and their solutions.

Essays will vary. Check that students have used information from both selections and the diagram. Check that they have described the pioneers' attempts to solve their problems in chronological order.

Notes for Home: Your child combined information from two sources. ***Home Activity:*** As you read selections about historical characters, have your child make problem and solution charts about them similiar to the diagram above.

Grammar Practice Book 6.6, p. 131

Name ______________________ Louis Braille

Grammar: Compound Subjects and Objects

REVIEW

Directions: Combine each set of sentences to form a new sentence with a compound subject or a compound object. Write the new sentence on the lines. Remember to make verbs agree with their subjects and pronouns agree with their referents. (You may need to make other changes as well.) **Possible answers given.**

1. Sightless people have reason to be grateful to Louis Braille. People with poor vision do too.
   Sightless people and people with poor vision have reason to be grateful to Louis Braille.
2. Louis Braille developed a printing system for the blind. In addition, he developed a writing system for the blind.
   Louis Braille developed a printing system and a writing system for the blind.
3. With this system of six raised dots in different combinations, people can handle reading. They can use it for writing too. They can even produce musical notation.
   With this system of six raised dots in different combinations, people can handle reading, writing, and even musical notation.
4. Braillewriters use keys to form letters. So do typewriters.
   Braillewriters and typewriters use keys to form letters.
5. *Braille* is a type of word called *eponym*—a word based on someone's name. *Braillewriter* is also an eponym.
   Braille and Braillewriter are a type of word called eponym—a word based on someone's name.

Notes for Home: Your child combined sentences to form new sentences with compound subjects and compound objects. ***Home Activity:*** Together, look through books to find sentences with compound subjects and objects. Try to break each one down into two or more sentences.

Grammar Practice Book 6.6, p. 132

Name ______________________ Louis Braille

Grammar: Commas

A **comma** is a punctuation mark that is used to set off a word or a group of words from other words. In a friendly letter, use a comma after the greeting and the closing.

Dear Louis, Sincerely, Your friend,

In a date, use a comma between the day of the week and the month, and between the day of the month and the year. In an address, use a comma between the city and the state or country.

Saturday, April 2 March 12, 1895 Gotham City, ID 06007

Commas are also used to separate three or more nouns or phrases in a series.

The five senses are sight, hearing, smell, taste, and touch.
Some people can't see, some have no hearing, and some are unable to speak.

When you speak to, or address, a person by name or title, you are using direct address. Commas are used to set off the name when it apppears at the beginning, in the middle, or at the end of a sentence. When the name is in the middle of a sentence, two commas are used.

Thomas, is your cousin a professional dancer?
He is, Mark, and he is also deaf.
That's amazing, Thomas.

Directions: Read the following letter. Add commas where they are needed.

Dear Otto,

I am reading an interesting book about people who are deaf. Did you know that some people are born deaf, some become deaf from injury, and others become deaf from disease? There are actors, athletes, and even dancers who are deaf. Dancers keep the beat by feeling the vibrations from the music.

This book has inspired me to learn sign language, Otto. I'm going to write to a school for the deaf in Rochester, New York. They offer to send books, tapes, and a videotape to help people learn sign language.

Your brother,
Phillip

Notes for Home: Your child inserted commas in a letter. ***Home Activity:*** Help your child write a letter to a friend or relative. Talk about the places where commas are needed.

Grammar Practice Book 6.6, p. 133

Name ______________________ Louis Braille

Grammar: Commas

Directions: Read the following parts of a letter. Add commas where they are needed.

1. Your friend,
2. Dear Myra,
3. With love,
4. November 11, 1911
5. Monday, February 20
6. Oakdale, CA

Directions: Rewrite each sentence on the line, adding commas where they are needed.

7. Ellen did I tell you about my new invention?
Ellen, did I tell you about my new invention?

8. It will warn me when a dog a cat or another animal enters the yard.
It will warn me when a dog, a cat, or another animal enters the yard.

9. It works whether the animal walks runs or crawls into the yard.
It works whether the animal walks, runs, or crawls into the yard.

10. The new alarm uses packing paper strings and bells.
The new alarm uses packing paper, strings, and bells.

11. I think you are wrong Mom when you say this system is impractical.
I think you are wrong, Mom, when you say this system is impractical.

12. It will appeal to homeowners renters and landlords.
It will appeal to homeowners, renters, and landlords.

13. I won't charge a lot for my alarm Mom.
I won't charge a lot for my alarm, Mom.

14. I'm thinking about charging two dollars three dollars or four dollars.
I'm thinking about charging two dollars, three dollars, or four dollars.

15. Did you say Mom that you would trade the alarm for a pizza tonight?
Did you say, Mom, that you would trade the alarm for a pizza tonight?

Write a Letter

Write a letter to someone who shares a hobby of yours, such as coin collecting, drawing, or a playing a particular computer game. Remember to use commas where necessary.

Students' letters should include correct use of commas in greeting, closing, and date, as well as in direct address and in items in a series.

Notes for Home: Your child inserted commas in parts of a letter, in dates, in addresses, to set off a person's name, and to separate words or phrases in a series of three or more. ***Home Activity:*** Invite your child to write entries in an address book, using commas correctly.

Grammar Practice Book 6.6, p. 134

Name ______________________ Louis Braille

Grammar: Commas

RETEACHING

Insert commas where they are needed in each phrase or sentence.

1. Dear Jack,
2. Bring me the scissors, the stapler, and the tape.
3. I wanted to go see the new exhibit at the art museum, but I didn't have time.
4. Although she looked nervous, Kathy made a wonderful presentation.
5. Amanda, don't you think you should be more careful with that vase?
6. We are moving to Maryland on Wednesday, April 27, 2001.
7. I will miss you, Kari.

A **comma** is used to set off a word or a group of words from other words. In a friendly letter, use a comma after the greeting and the closing. In a date, use a comma between the day of the week and the month, and between the date and the year (*Monday, June 22* or *June 22, 2004*). In an address, use a comma between the city and the state. Use commas to separate three or more nouns or phrases in a series. Also use a comma to set off a name used in direct address.

Directions: Insert commas where they are needed in each sentence. Draw an **X** through commas that do not belong.

1. Remember x to feed the cat, water the flowers, and do your homework.
2. I can't do all that x in fifteen minutes, Sandra!
3. I need someone to do it, or I'll get in big trouble.
4. Ask Tanya. She lives at 421 Amber Road, Merriwether, Wisconsin.
5. I hope she is home, although often she is out x on Tuesday afternoons.
6. Dina, maybe you should call her x before you go.
7. I'll call her, pack my things, and walk there.
8. Don't forget the festival on Sunday, March x 8.
9. I tried x to open the door, but it was locked.
10. You need x to ring the doorbell, knock on the door, or try the back door.

Notes for Home: Your child inserted commas where they belong in sentences and marked commas that do not belong. ***Home Activity:*** Have your child use this page to explain to you where commas are often used.

Grammar Practice Book 6.6, p. 135

Name ______________________ Louis Braille

Grammar: Commas

Directions: Each sentence is missing one or more commas. Rewrite each sentence, inserting commas where they belong.

1. Yes John the correct date is October 8 1822.
Yes, John, the correct date is October 8, 1822.

2. I live at 42 Main Street Columbus Ohio Mrs. Gordon.
I live at 42 Main Street, Columbus, Ohio, Mrs. Gordon.

3. We went to London England a week later Sally.
We went to London, England, a week later, Sally.

4. Lee is the correct address 650 Olive Avenue Bangor Maine 04401?
Lee, is the correct address 650 Olive Avenue, Bangor, Maine 04401?

5. By the way Heather just where is Hannibal Missouri?
By the way, Heather, just where is Hannibal, Missouri?

6. Have we run out of bags or are there more back there?
Have we run out of bags, or are there more back there?

7. This is hard work but it's for a good cause.
This is hard work, but it's for a good cause.

8. Doreen is a skier a pilot and a dancer.
Doreen is a skier, a pilot, and a dancer.

9. Her patients will see Dr. Rodriguez or they will make appointments for another day.
Her patients will see Dr. Rodriguez, or they will make appointments for another day.

10. Don't you think that I look terrific Louisa?
Don't you think that I look terrific, Louisa?

11. I know of a spot near 14 Olivera Street Pamplona Spain that's just like it.
I know of a spot near 14 Olivera Street, Pamplona, Spain, that's just like it.

12. I caught a big trout there on June 12 1998 at noon.
I caught a big trout there on June 12, 1998, at noon.

Notes for Home: Your child correctly used commas in sentences. ***Home Activity:*** Write some sentences without commas, and have your child insert commas where they belong. Help your child check his or her work.

Practice Book 6.6, p. 268
Name ______________________ **Louis Braille**

Phonics: Diphthongs and Digraphs

Directions: Read the word pairs below. Each word contains the vowel combination **ou.** For each pair, circle the word that has the same vowel sound as **out.**

1. (house) tough
2. through (trousers)
3. though (mountains)
4. (announcements) thorough
5. bought (bound)
6. (astound) thought

Directions: Read each sentence below. Each sentence has two words with the letters **ou,** but only one of the words has the same vowel sound as **out.** Circle that word and write it on the line.

sound 7. The group of science students was experimenting with the principles of (sound).
about 8. They wanted to learn (about) how music travels through water.
outside 9. They brought a stereo speaker up to the (outside) of an aquarium tank filled with water.
loud 10. Then they turned up the stereo, (loud) enough to feel the vibrations on the speaker.
proudly 11. By noticing the vibrations in the water, the students (proudly) concluded that music could travel underwater.

Directions: Read the paragraph below. Look and listen for words that have the letters **au** with the same vowel sound as in **sauce;** the letters **ew** with the same vowel sound as in **threw;** or the letters **oi** with the same vowel sound as in **moist.** Circle the words and write them on the lines.

> The students did not want to be (disappointed) again. They'd been extra (cautious) this time, adjusting a (few) dials and (pointing) out any possible problems. They'd trusted the (voices) inside their heads, as well as the science lessons their teacher had (taught) them. Now they were ready. (Because) they'd followed each step to the letter, their anticipation (grew). Their hopes had been (renewed) that this time their invention would be a success.

au as in *sauce*	ew as in *threw*	oi as in *moist*
12. **cautious**	15. **few**	18. **disappointed**
13. **taught**	16. **grew**	19. **pointing**
14. **because**	17. **renewed**	20. **voices**

Notes for Home: Your child sorted words with the vowel sounds heard in *sauce, threw, moist,* and *out. Home Activity:* Together, write other words with *au, ew, oi,* and *ou.* Take turns using these words in sentences.

Spelling Workbook 6.6, p. 105
Name ______________________ **Louis Braille**

Spelling: Vowel Sounds /oi/, /ou/, /ȯ/

Pretest Directions: Fold back the page along the dotted line. On the blanks, write the spelling words as they are dictated. When you have finished the test, unfold the page and check your words.

1. **outlast**	1. He will **outlast** his opponent.
2. **account**	2. She opened a bank **account.**
3. **astound**	3. The show will **astound** you.
4. **boundary**	4. A fence is an unnatural **boundary.**
5. **southeast**	5. The bird flew **southeast.**
6. **counter**	6. Set the box on the **counter.**
7. **sunflower**	7. The **sunflower** bloomed today.
8. **somehow**	8. We have to get there **somehow.**
9. **chowder**	9. I do not like this clam **chowder.**
10. **coward**	10. That bully is really a **coward.**
11. **disappointed**	11. The movie left us **disappointed.**
12. **voices**	12. Their **voices** blended together.
13. **tabloid**	13. They publish a weekly **tabloid.**
14. **employee**	14. She is the **employee** of the year.
15. **joyful**	15. They gave a **joyful** shout.
16. **applaud**	16. The guests **applaud** the speaker.
17. **faucet**	17. Turn off that dripping **faucet.**
18. **caution**	18. Proceed with **caution.**
19. **author**	19. She's my favorite **author.**
20. **trauma**	20. He was treated for mental **trauma.**

Notes for Home: Your child took a pretest on words that have the vowel sounds /oi/, /ou/, and /ȯ/. *Home Activity:* Help your child learn misspelled words before the final test. Your child can underline the word parts that caused the problems and concentrate on those parts.

Spelling Workbook 6.6, p. 106
Name ______________________ **Louis Braille**

Spelling: Vowel Sounds /oi/, /ou/, /ȯ/

Word List

outlast	counter	disappointed	applaud
account	sunflower	voices	faucet
astound	somehow	tabloid	caution
boundary	chowder	employee	author
southeast	coward	joyful	trauma

Directions: Choose the words from the box with the vowel sound /ou/. Write each word in the correct column. **Order may vary.**

Words with /ou/ spelled ou	Words with /ou/ spelled ow
1. **outlast**	7. **sunflower**
2. **account**	8. **somehow**
3. **astound**	9. **chowder**
4. **boundary**	10. **coward**
5. **southeast**	
6. **counter**	

Directions: Choose the word from the box that best matches each clue. Write the word on the line.

tabloid 11. I am a newspaper with huge headlines and lots of photos.
employee 12. I work for another person.
disappointed 13. I am how you feel when you don't achieve a goal.
trauma 14. I am a severe injury, wound, or shock.
voices 15. We are what the singers in the choir use to make music.
author 16. I write books, plays, stories, and scripts.
caution 17. I show concern for safety.
applaud 18. I am what you do when you clap your hands.
joyful 19. I am delighted and happy.
faucet 20. I am a fixture for drawing liquid from a pipe.

Notes for Home: Your child spelled words with the vowel sounds /oi/, /ou/, and /ȯ/. *Home Activity:* Challenge your child to spell words from the list in which *oy* spells the vowel sound in *boy* and *au* spells the vowel sound in *fault.*

Spelling Workbook 6.6, p. 107
Name ______________________ **Louis Braille**

Spelling: Vowel Sounds /oi/, /ou/, /ȯ/

Directions: Proofread this biography. Find seven spelling mistakes. Use the proofreading marks to correct each mistake.

- ≡ Make a capital.
- / Make a small letter.
- ∧ Add something.
- Take out something.
- ⊙ Add a period.
- ¶ Begin a new paragraph.

> Louis Braille lost his sight from a childhood trama [u added: trauma], but he never felt limited by his blindness or any bowndry [boundary] set by other people's thinking. More than one accownt [account] of his life says that Braille got his idea for his system when he was only twelve. That is a fact sure to astouned [astound] anyone.
>
> Braille worked for years to improve his idea until somehouw [somehow] he invented the simple raised-dot system still in use today. Braille was disappoynted [disappointed] that his writing system was not officially recognized in his lifetime, but he would be joyful to learn that Braille writing is widely used now. It has managed to owtlast [outlast] many other systems.

Spelling Tip

The vowel sound /ou/ is spelled **ou** and **ow:** **outlast, somehow.** The vowel sound /oi/ is spelled **oi** and **oy: voices, joyful.** The vowel sound /ȯ/ is often spelled **au: author.**

Word List

outlast	disappointed
account	voices
astound	tabloid
boundary	employee
southeast	joyful
counter	applaud
sunflower	faucet
somehow	caution
chowder	author
coward	trauma

Write a Biography

Whom do you admire for his or her invention? On a separate sheet of paper, write a brief biography of the inventor of your choice. Explain why you feel his or her work is important. Try to use at least three spelling words. **Students may need time to do research on inventors. Answers will vary, but each biography should include at least three spelling words.**

Notes for Home: Your child spelled words with the vowel sounds /oi/ spelled *oi* and *oy,* /ou/ spelled *ou* and *ow,* and /ȯ/ spelled *au. Home Activity:* Write the spelling words in a list. Include several misspellings. Invite your child to proofread and correct the list.

Spelling Workbook 6.6, p. 108

Name ______________________

Louis Braille

Spelling: Vowel Sounds /oi/, /ou/, /ȯ/

REVIEW

Word List				
outlast	southeast	chowder	tabloid	faucet
account	counter	coward	employee	caution
astound	sunflower	disappointed	joyful	author
boundary	somehow	voices	applaud	trauma

Directions: Write the word from the box that belongs in each group.

1. worker, staff, **employee**
2. barrier, border, **boundary**
3. someday, somewhere, **somehow**
4. northeast, northwest, **southeast**
5. happy, delighted, **joyful**
6. care, wariness, **caution**
7. writer, journalist, **author**

Directions: Choose the word from the box that best completes each sentence about a person's activity. Write the word on the line to the left.

chowder 8. The cook made _____ for the entire seafood restaurant.

counter 9. The store clerk stood behind the _____ as he served the customers.

astound 10. The magician was able to _____ the audience with his tricks.

outlast 11. The long-distance runner managed to _____ all her opponents in order to win.

trauma 12. The nurse monitored the patients in the _____ ward.

applaud 13. The audience stood to _____ the actor's fine performance.

faucet 14. The plumber tightened the bolt to fix the dripping _____.

sunflower 15. The gardener was proud that his tall, yellow _____ won the contest.

account 16. The banker needed to fix the problems with an _____.

coward 17. The _____ cringed with fear.

tabloid 18. The reporter for the weekly _____ called in the story.

voices 19. The singers' _____ sounded full, clear, and triumphant.

disappointed 20. The manager was _____ when the shortstop made an error.

Notes for Home: Your child spelled words with the vowel sounds /oi/ spelled *oi* and *oy*, /ou/ spelled *ou* and *ow*, and /ȯ/ spelled *au*. ***Home Activity:*** Read a newspaper or magazine with your child. Make a list of other words that have these vowel sounds and spellings.

Practice Book 6.6, p. 269

Name ______________________

Louis Braille

Chart/Table/Time Line

A **chart** organizes information visually, such as in a list, table, or diagram.
A **table** is a special kind of chart that shows information in rows and columns.
A **time line** is a bar divided into periods of time that shows a sequence of events.

Directions: Use the time line to complete the table on the next page. List in the table's second column the different types of transportation shown on the time line. Then answer the questions that follow.

Transportation Time Line

1800, 1810, 1820, 1830, 1840, 1850, 1860, 1870, 1880, 1890, 1900, 1910

- **1803**—The first steam train is built in England.
- **1807**—The boat *Clermont* is the first running steamboat, moving along the Hudson River.
- **1848**—A steam-powered model airplane is tested in England.
- **1861**—One of the first types of bicycle is developed in France.
- **1867**—The first motorcycle is invented when a steam engine is attached to a bicycle.
- **1879**—The first electric railroad is built in Germany.
- **1884**—The first aircraft to use an electric propeller is flown in France.
- **1885**—German engineer Karl Benz builds the first gasoline-powered car.
- **1893**—The first gasoline-powered car is built in the United States.
- **1903**—Orville Wright makes his first flight in a gasoline-powered airplane at Kitty Hawk in North Carolina.

Practice Book 6.6, p. 270

Name ______________________

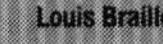

Louis Braille

Travel by . . .	Transportation Invention
Land	1. **steam train, bicycle, motorcycle, electric railroad, gasoline-powered car**
Sea	2. **Clermont (steamboat)**
Air	3. **steam-powered model airplane, electric propeller aircraft, gasoline-powered airplane**

4. How many years does the time line cover? Into what periods of time is the line divided?
110 years; It's divided into 10-year periods.

5. What information does this time line show? Is a time line a good way to organize this information? Explain.
Possible answer: The time line shows important transportation inventions from 1800 to 1910. A time line is a good way to show the chronological sequence of historical events.

6. How many years before Orville Wright flew at Kitty Hawk did the first successful plane flight take place in France?
19 years

7. How many years after the first gasoline-powered car in Germany was invented was a gasoline-powered car built in the United States?
8 years

8. If you were living in France in 1861, what might you have seen that no one else had?
a bicycle

9. For what research topic would this time line be useful? **Possible answer: You could use this time line for a research topic on the history of transportation.**

10. How might you use a chart, table, or time line as you research information for a report?
Possible answer: You can use a chart, table, or time line to help you visually organize or present the research information you have gathered.

Notes for Home: Your child read a time line, used it to complete a table, and answered questions about it. ***Home Activity:*** Set up a time line with your child for activities you do during an evening. Write the hours along a line; then write the activities beside each hour.

Practice Book 6.6, p. 271

Name ______________________

The Librarian Who Measured the Earth

Graphic Sources

- A **graphic** or **graphic source** of information is something that shows information visually.
- Some common graphic sources of information are pictures, charts, maps, graphs, and diagrams.
- A graphic source can present new information in the text differently or show more information.

Directions: Reread "Ptolemy—An Early Map Maker," and review the maps. Then follow the directions below to mark the map to show areas Ptolemy did and did not know about. You may need to refer to another map to complete the last two directions.

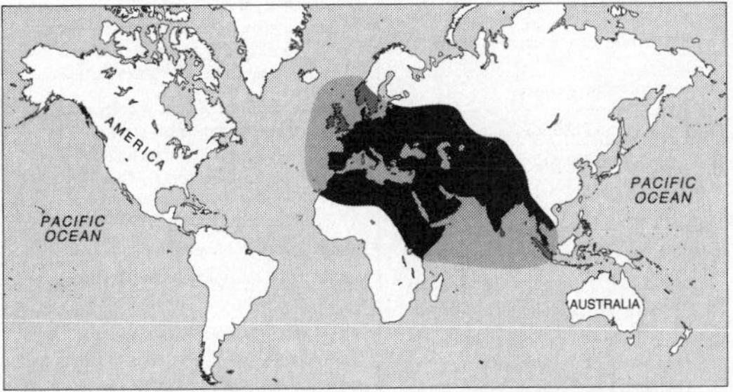

Check that students have correctly labeled and shaded the map as shown.

1. Label the city where Ptolemy was from.
2. Shade the land areas that Ptolemy knew about.
3. Use a different color to shade the areas of water that Ptolemy knew about.
4. Label the two continents that Ptolemy did not know about.
5. Label the ocean that Ptolemy did not know about.

Notes for Home: Your child marked a map to show his or her understanding of the material. ***Home Activity:*** With your child, find a newspaper or magazine article that includes a picture, map, or graph. Discuss how the graphic source of information relates to the article.

Practice Book 6.6, p. 272

Name ______________________

The Librarian Who Measured the Earth

Vocabulary

Directions: Choose the word from the box that best completes each sentence. Write the word on the line to the left.

Check the Words You Know
__ accurate
__ angle
__ arc
__ calculate
__ estimate
__ formula
__ scholar
__ sphere

accurate 1. Scientists can make _____ predictions about a satellite's path.

estimate 2. They can make an _____ based on what they know about space flight.

calculate 3. Sometimes, scientists _____ an exact answer.

formula 4. They use a _____ in which symbols stand for different pieces of data.

scholar 5. Sometimes, a _____ who studies mathematics or science will discover a new formula.

Directions: Choose the word from the box that best matches each clue. Write the word in the puzzle.

Down

6. a person of learning
7. to compute information

Across

8. any part of a circumference
9. space between two lines that meet
10. a round solid object

		6. s			7. c	
8. a	r	c			a	
		h			l	
		o			c	
		l			u	
		9. a	n	g	l	e
		r			a	
					t	
10. s	p	h	e	r	e	

Write an E-mail Message

On a separate sheet of paper, write an e-mail message. Imagine you are a scientist who has made a new discovery and that you are describing your discovery to another scientist. Use as many vocabulary words as you can.

E-mail messages should be brief, but descriptive. Check that students have used vocabulary words correctly.

Notes for Home: Your child identified and used vocabulary words from *The Librarian Who Measured the Earth. **Home Activity:*** Talk with your child about math in everyday life. Encourage him or her to use vocabulary words during the discussion.

Practice Book 6.6, p. 273

Name ______________________

The Librarian Who Measured the Earth

Graphic Sources

- A **graphic** or **graphic source** of information is something that shows information visually.
- Some common graphic sources of information are pictures, charts, maps, graphs, and diagrams.
- A graphic source can present new information in the text differently or show more information.

Directions: Reread the passage from *The Librarian Who Measured the Earth* in which the author explains how to find Earth's circumference. Then follow the instructions below. **Check that students have correctly drawn and labeled the circumference and arc and have shaded one section as shown.**

Perhaps [Eratosthenes] imagined the earth as a grapefruit. If [a grapefruit] is sliced in half, you can see its sections. In order to measure the distance all the way around the edge of the grapefruit (the circumference), you would need to know only the distance along the edge of one section (the arc) and how many of these same-size sections it would take to make up the whole grapefruit.

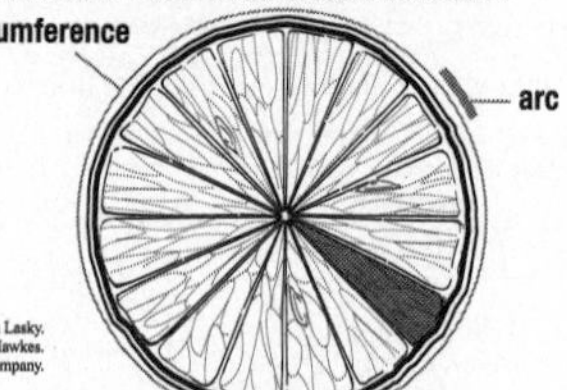

1. Use the description in the passage and the picture of the grapefruit to trace the circumference of the grapefruit. Label the circumference you traced.
2. Draw and label an arc on the picture of the grapefruit.
3. Shade in one section.
4. How does the image of the grapefruit help you better understand the main idea of the passage?
Possible answer: The image of the grapefruit is a good visual model for Earth. It makes it easier to understand the mathematical terms.
5. Reread the story. Are there other places in the story where a picture helps you better understand the text? Explain your thinking on a separate sheet of paper.
Answers will vary. Student should recognize that the illustrations make it easier to visualize some of Eratosthenes' ideas and experiments.

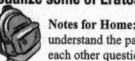

Notes for Home: Your child used a graphic source of information to help him or her understand the passage's main idea. ***Home Activity:*** Look at some newspaper graphics. Ask each other questions that can be answered using the graphic source.

Practice Book 6.6, p. 275

Name ______________________

The Librarian Who Measured the Earth

Selection Test

Directions: Choose the best answer to each item. Mark the letter for the answer you have chosen.

Part 1: Vocabulary

Find the answer choice that means about the same as the underlined word in each sentence.

1. We asked him to estimate the cost.
   A. agree to pay on a fixed schedule
   Ⓑ make a judgment or guess based on available facts
   C. pay no attention to
   D. say that something is larger or greater than it is
2. I knew that the news story was not accurate.
   F. interesting
   G. well written
   H. recent
   Ⓙ correct; exact
3. I need to calculate the distance.
   A. make shorter and narrower
   B. increase
   Ⓒ find by using numbers
   D. imagine
4. She found the formula she needed.
   Ⓕ combination of symbols used in mathematics to state a rule or principle
   G. list of ingredients and procedures for preparing food
   H. a formal written or oral discussion of a topic
   J. an explanation based on observation only
5. The moon is a sphere.
   A. figure shaped like an oval
   Ⓑ a round solid object; globe
   C. object that revolves around a planet
   D. solid block
6. He needed to know the distance along the arc.
   F. one side of a triangle
   G. a curved structure capable of carrying weight
   H. a type of boat
   Ⓙ any part of a circle's circumference
7. She measured the angle.
   Ⓐ space between two lines or surfaces that meet
   B. distance along the curve of a circle
   C. point where two lines meet
   D. side of a square or rectangle
8. His mother is a famous scholar.
   F. person who writes plays
   Ⓖ person who has much knowledge
   H. woman who sings with a high voice
   J. person who practices magic

Part 2: Comprehension

Use what you know about the selection to answer each item.

9. When did Eratosthenes live?
   A. less than 900 years ago
   B. about 1,000 years ago
   Ⓒ more than 2,000 years ago
   D. about 4,000 years ago
10. At the gymnasium, Eratosthenes wrote with—
    F. charcoal on slate tablets.
    G. pen and ink on paper.
    Ⓗ sharp sticks on wax tablets.
    J. brushes and ink on papyrus.

GO ON

Practice Book 6.6, p. 276

Name ______________________

The Librarian Who Measured the Earth

11. Why was Eratosthenes glad to go to Alexandria to tutor the king's son?
    A. Life in Cyrene offered few challenges for him.
    B. It was near the place where he had grown up as a boy.
    C. It was a great honor to teach the son of the king.
    Ⓓ Alexandria was the best place in the world to study and learn.
12. In this selection, the pictures of a circle and a grapefruit help to show—
    F. why the sun's rays strike only one section of the earth at a time.
    Ⓖ how applying geometry to everyday objects could help Eratosthenes figure out the size of the earth.
    H. why circles are measured in degrees.
    J. how Eratosthenes measured the distance from Alexandria to Syene.
13. The picture of Eratosthenes measuring the shadow of a pole helps to show how he—
    Ⓐ measured the angle of the sun's rays.
    B. organized books in the library.
    C. traveled to Syene.
    D. demonstrated to others that his numbers were correct.
14. Which statement would be most difficult to verify as a fact?
    Ⓕ "He would crawl across the kitchen floor to follow the path of ants."
    G. "He also made a list of all the winners of the Olympic Games."
    H. "At the museum there were laboratories and libraries, dining halls and private studios."
    J. "Eratosthenes dedicated the solution to the king."
15. In order to write this selection, the author most likely spent a lot of time—
    A. visiting Athens, Alexandria, and other cities named in the selection.
    B. solving geometry problems.
    C. talking with people who knew Eratosthenes.
    Ⓓ doing historical research.

STOP

Name ______________________

The Librarian Who Measured the Earth

Graphic Sources

- A **graphic** or **graphic source** of information is something that shows information visually.
- Some common graphic sources of information are pictures, charts, maps, graphs, and diagrams.
- A graphic source can present new information in the text differently or show more information.

Directions: Read the steps and look at the pictures.

Try this triangle experiment. Take one sheet of construction paper. Then cut a large triangle from the paper and measure its three angles. Add the three angle measures together.

Tear off the three angles, making sure the pieces are fairly big. Lay the three pieces down so that the angles all touch at one point. Look at the figure that is formed. Repeat two more times and you'll discover that the sum of the angles of any triangle is 180°—the same as a straight line.

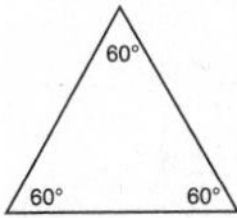

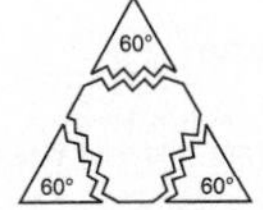

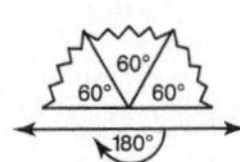

Directions: Answer the questions below. Think about how the diagram helps you figure out the answers.

1. What are the measures of the three angles of the triangle shown? **60°, 60°, 60°**
2. What is the sum of the three angles? **180°**
3. What figure do you see when the three pieces of the triangle are laid out touching at their X marks?
   a straight line or a straight edge
4. What do you think will happen if you repeat the experiment with a different sized triangle?
   The three angles will always form a straight line, which always measures 180°.
5. How does looking at the pictures and reading the steps help you understand a rule about the angles of a triangle?
   Possible answer: The activity and the diagram show a connection between a straight line, which always measures 180°, and the three angles of a triangle, which also always add up to 180°.

Notes for Home: Your child read steps for an experiment and looked at pictures to understand a mathematical rule. ***Home Activity:*** Look at some newspaper and magazine graphics with your child. Discuss what each visual shows and how it helps you understand the text.

Name ______________________

The Librarian Who Measured the Earth

Context Clues

REVIEW

Directions: Read the passage. Then read each question about the passage. Choose the best answer to each question. Mark the letter for the answer you have chosen.

Before Chemistry

Over 800 years ago, some European scholars practiced alchemy, an early form of chemistry. These alchemists had three main goals. They wanted to discover the secret of transmutation, a process in which base metals such as iron or lead could be turned into costly silver or gold. They also hoped to discover the philosopher's stone, an unusual substance that would make transmutation easier. Additionally, many alchemists aspired to discover the proper chemical mix for a potion to cure all diseases and prolong lives by hundreds of years.

Some alchemists were charlatans who claimed that their discoveries gave them magical powers. Other more honest scholars devoted their entire lives to their experiments. They learned about the properties of various substances. After all, knowing the characteristics of a chemical —its hardness and melting point, and the ways it reacts with other substances—might one day be the key to a success. As a result, alchemists added new information to the pool of knowledge about chemicals. New kinds of tools and equipment were needed to aid them in their work, so they invented special scales, tools to melt metals, and other equipment. Alchemy may seem foolish by today's standards, but alchemists' research helped lay the foundations of modern chemistry.

1. Transmutation is a process that alchemists believed could—
   A. remove the metal found in rocks.
   B. help them live longer.
   (C.) change lead into gold.
   D. change gold into base metals.
2. In this passage, base metals are those that are—
   F. low in weight.
   G. the supporting layers for other metals.
   H. the most important ingredients in the philosopher's stone.
   (J.) low in cost or value.
3. In this passage, the word aspired means—
   (A.) hoped to achieve a goal.
   B. expressed a thought clearly.
   C. took for granted.
   D. worried or annoyed.
4. In this passage, the word charlatans means—
   F. street actors.
   (G.) frauds.
   H. scientists.
   J. cure-alls.
5. In this passage, the word properties means—
   A. rightful owners.
   B. magic powers.
   (C.) characteristics of chemical substances.
   D. owned pieces of land.

Notes for Home: Your child figured out the meaning of unfamiliar words by using context clues. ***Home Activity:*** Encourage your child to use context clues to figure out the meanings of unfamiliar words in stories he or she reads. Together, use a dictionary to check these words.

Name ______________________

The Librarian Who Measured the Earth

Writing Across Texts

Directions: Consider what you know about the two selections, *The Librarian Who Measured the Earth* and "A Revolution." Use the table below to list ways that mapmaking has changed since Eratosthenes.

Possible answers given.

How Mapmaking has changed
Both discuss how to measure.
1. **Mapmakers now use computers to store information.**
2. **They often take mapmaking photos from airplanes.**
3. **Photographs are often taken from space to give information to mapmakers.**
4. **Using a computer and a Geographic Information System, almost anyone can make a map.**
5. **With remote-sensing methods, mapmakers can record the amount of infrared radiation coming from different areas on the Earth.**

Write a Paragraph

The Librarian Who Measured the Earth and "A Revolution" are about mapmaking. How are these selections alike? How are they different? On a separate sheet of paper, write a paragraph comparing and contrasting these two selections.
Paragraphs will vary. Check that students have used information from the two selections in their paragraphs.

Notes for Home: Your child used information from two different sources to write a comparison/contrast paragraph. ***Home Activity:*** As you read a story or article with your child, discuss how its ideas connect to other reading your child has done.

Name ______________________

The Librarian Who Measured the Earth

Grammar: Commas

REVIEW

Directions: Add a comma where needed to correct each sentence.

1. Was Euclid an ancient Greek mathematician,or was he an ancient Roman?
2. Euclid lived in Greece in ancient times,but we still rely on his work today.
3. Geometry students may not know Euclid's name,but they learn his principles.
4. Start at one point,and you can always draw a straight line to another point.
5. Measure one right angle,and you will know the measurement of every other right angle.
6. Points, lines, and angles are the subject of geometry,but triangles are the subject of trigonometry.
7. Trigonometry is used to study light and electricity,and it is crucial in surveying, navigation, and astronomy.
8. Euclidean geometry is basic,but there are other kinds of geometry.
9. Mathematicians might work on analytic geometry,or they might prefer descriptive geometry.
10. Much has been learned since Euclid's day,but his work remains the starting point.

Directions: Add a comma where needed to correct each sentence. If no comma is needed, write **N** on the line.

_______ 11. If you could meet someone from the past,would you like to meet Euclid?
___**N**___ 12. Although he was a brilliant mathematican, he may not have been fun to talk to one-on-one.
___**N**___ 13. While you are meeting mathematicians, you might want to talk to Descartes.
___**N**___ 14. Descartes worked on geometry after Euclid had been dead for centuries.
_______ 15. Although Euclid lived so long ago,his principles are still used and tested hundreds of years later.
___**N**___ 16. Amazingly, Euclid's principles are still recalled by mathematicians whenever they use geometry.
_______ 17. "If you want to find the area of a rectangle," explained Mr. Sams, "multiply the length of the base by the height."
_______ 18. If you do not multiply the base by the height and divide by 2,you will not find the area of a triangle.
_______ 19. After you use such calculations a few times,you will find them less difficult.
_______ 20. "When you study geometry," Mr. Sams said, "remember to think of Euclid and thank him."

Notes for Home: Your child added commas where needed to punctuate compound and complex sentences correctly. ***Home Activity:*** Read aloud an interesting written passage for your child to write down. Then help your child check that commas were used correctly.

Grammar Practice Book 6.6, p. 137

Name ______________________

The Librarian Who Measured the Earth

Grammar: Quotation Marks and Paragraph Indentation

A **direct quotation** is made up of the exact words a speaker says. When you write a direct quotation, enclose it in quotation marks (" "), and capitalize the first word. Begin a new paragraph each time the speaker changes.

Use commas to set off words that introduce a direct quotation. Place the comma that ends the quotation inside the quotation marks. If the quotation is a question or exclamation, place the question or exclamation mark inside the quotation marks.

Ms. Fisher said, "Today, you will do an experiment."
"What will we do today?" Jolene asked.

In interrupted quotations, a comma is used when the second part of the quotation does not begin a new sentence. If the second part begins a new sentence, a capital letter and proper end mark are used in this second part.

"What," asked Robert, "will the experiment be about?"
The class waited in silence.
"We will observe acceleration," Ms. Fisher said. "You will use marbles of different sizes, a ramp, and a stopwatch."

Directions: Use quotation marks to enclose the direct quotation in each sentence.

1. "I want to see what it's like to live without clocks," Ken said.
2. Sarah said, "What do you mean?"
3. "What I mean," Ken said, "is that I want to test my sense of time."
4. "If I take a walk," Ken said, "will I be able to guess how long I have been walking?"
5. "Or will you be able to tell about what time of the day it is?" Sarah said.
6. "Right, now you understand," Ken said.
7. "I'd like to know whether I would do things faster or more slowly, if I wasn't looking at a clock," said Jenny.
8. "That's a good idea," Sarah said. "Let's try it."
9. "I'll carry a watch," Lori said, "but none of you will look at it."
10. "I'll list the times," Lori continued, "at which we start and finish things."

Notes for Home: Your child inserted quotation marks before and after direct quotations. ***Home Activity:*** With your child, write a few sentences of a conversation. Have your child insert quotation marks before and after the exact words each person says.

Grammar Practice Book 6.6, p. 138

Name ______________________

The Librarian Who Measured the Earth

Grammar: Quotation Marks and Paragraph Indentation

Directions: Add quotation marks, commas, end marks, and capital letters to form complete sentences. Write the sentences on the lines.

1. please do your geometry homework now Mom said
"Please do your geometry homework now," Mom said.
2. what makes you think that I'm not going to do it I asked
"What makes you think that I'm not going to do it?" I asked.
3. I know you like to put off your homework Mom replied.
"I know you like to put off your homework," Mom replied.
4. Then she added but geometry is very important
Then she added, "But geometry is very important."
5. what do you mean by that I asked
"What do you mean by that?" I asked.
6. without geometry Mom answered life itself would be impossible
"Without geometry," Mom answered, "life itself would be impossible."
7. mom I answered i think that's a little extreme
"Mom," I answered, "I think that's a little extreme."
8. she replied maybe I am speaking a little too strongly
She replied, "Maybe I am speaking a little too strongly."
9. I know why I said
"I know why," I said.
10. you can't help it I added you're my geometry teacher
"You can't help it," I added. "You're my geometry teacher."

Write a Conversation

On a separate sheet of paper, write a few lines of a conversation between two characters. Have them work out a complicated math problem. Remember to use quotation marks and punctuate each sentence correctly. Start a new paragraph each time the speaker changes. **Check that students have correctly used quotation marks, capital letters, commas, and end punctuation and that they have followed the rules for paragraph indentation.**

Notes for Home: Your child used quotation marks and other punctuation marks to set off direct quotations. ***Home Activity:*** With your child, listen to a conversation on a television show. Have your child "insert quotation marks" before and after each person's words, using hand gestures.

Grammar Practice Book 6.6, p. 139

Name ______________________

The Librarian Who Measured the Earth

Grammar: Quotation Marks and Paragraph Indentation

RETEACHING

Study the following quotations. Then insert quotation marks, commas, periods, question marks, and exclamation marks where they belong.

"I have a question," he said.
She replied, "Go ahead."
"Why does an elephant have wrinkles?" he asked.
"It's hard to iron an elephant!" she answered.
"That," he sighed, "is not very funny."
"You're wrong," she laughed. "It's hilarious."

Use **quotation marks** to show the exact works of a speaker.

Directions: Write each quotation using capital letters and punctuation correctly. **Possible answers given.**

1. I threw the clock so I could see time fly said Dotty.
"I threw the clock so I could see time fly," said Dotty.
2. Meet me at the corner said the wall to the ceiling
"Meet me at the corner," said the wall to the ceiling.
3. The elevator sighed life has its ups and downs
The elevator sighed, "Life has its ups and downs."
4. How do you know it is raining cats and dogs asked Fern
"How do you know it is raining cats and dogs?" asked Fern.
5. Because I just stepped in a poodle exclaimed LaVerne.
"Because I just stepped in a poodle!" exclaimed LaVerne.
6. Which hand do you write with Willy inquired
"Which hand do you write with?" Willy inquired.
7. I do not write with my hand said Nilly I write with a pencil
"I do not write with my hand," said Nilly. "I write with a pencil."

Notes for Home: Your child punctuated quotations. ***Home Activity:*** Let your child listen to a conversation between you and another family member. Have your child write part of the conversation, using quotation marks to signal a speaker's exact words.

Grammar Practice Book 6.6, p. 140

Name ______________________

The Librarian Who Measured the Earth

Grammar: Quotation Marks and Paragraph Indentation

Directions: Add all necessary punctuation to the sentences below.

1. "Pyramids are interesting structures," said Marie.
2. Philip asked, "Who built them?"
3. "Egyptians built many of them," replied Marie.
4. "In the Americas," added Mrs. Conti, "the Mayans built pyramids."
5. "Egyptian pyramids are very old," remarked Marie.
6. "You are right," noted Mrs. Conti. "They were built from about 2700 B.C. to about 1000 B.C., thousands of years ago."
7. "Why were they built?" asked Philip.
8. Marie explained, "Egyptian pyramids were used as tombs for royalty."

Directions: Rewrite the conversation below. Use correct punctuation and capitalization. Begin a new paragraph each time the speaker changes.

9.–16.

the largest pyramid in Egypt Marie remarked is the Great Pyramid. I read about it in the encyclopedia said Jeff it is amazing. it is one of the Seven Wonders of the World explained Mrs. Conti. how big is it asked Philip. It is nearly five hundred feet tall said Jeff. each side measures over seven hundred fifty feet added Marie. wow exclaimed Philip it must have contained some treasure. you can see it continued Marie if you travel to Egypt.

"The largest pyramid in Egypt," Marie remarked, "is the Great Pyramid."
"I read about it in the encyclopedia," said Jeff. "It is amazing."
"It is one of the Seven Wonders of the World," explained Mrs. Conti.
"How big is it?" asked Philip.
"It is nearly five hundred feet tall," said Jeff.
"Each side measures over seven hundred fifty feet," added Marie.
"Wow!" exclaimed Phillip. "It must have contained some treasure."
"You can see it," continued Marie, "if you travel to Egypt."

Notes for Home: Your child correctly wrote and punctuated a conversation. ***Home Activity:*** Have your child write an imaginary conversation between two made-up characters. Help him or her add quotation marks to signal a speaker's exact words.

Practice Book 6.6, p. 278

Name ______________________

The Librarian Who Measured the Earth

Phonics: *r*-Controlled Vowels

Directions: Read the diary entry below. Look and listen for words with **ar** that sound like **garden.** Circle the words and write them on the lines.

January 9

As I gaze at the stars. I am bombarded with all sorts of questions. How did these outer-space lights find their place in the sky? Could they be as random as marbles thrown across a playing field? Or is there a pattern, something no one has yet discovered? Several look closer together while others seem far from each other. You need to be sharp to study the universe. I wonder if I am smart enough to figure out such cosmic mysteries?

1. stars
2. bombarded
3. marbles
4. far
5. sharp
6. smart

Directions: Read the word pairs below. Each word contains the letters **or.** For each pair, circle the word that has the same vowel sound as **for.**

7. born working
8. word morning
9. worthless formula 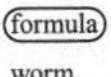
10. transport worm

Directions: Read each sentence below. Listen for a word that has the same vowel sound as **shirt.** Hint: This vowel sound can be spelled different ways. Circle the word and write it on the line.

world 11. Thousands of years ago, it seemed impossible to find out exactly how big our world was.

Earth's 12. Only those with the desire and skill could calculate Earth's size.

research 13. Thanks to the research of one ancient scholar, this was solved long ago.

first 14. Who knows who else might have been the first to find out some of the very basic things?

work 15. Much of the work of scholars in ancient times has not been recorded in history.

Notes for Home: Your child identified words with *r*-controlled vowels, such as *garden, for,* and *shirt. **Home Activity:*** Read a nonfiction book with your child. Help your child find words with these sounds. Make a chart to record the words you find.

Spelling Workbook 6.6, p. 109

Name ______________________

The Librarian Who Measured the Earth

Spelling: Words from Greek and Latin

Pretest Directions: Fold back the page along the dotted line. On the blanks, write the spelling words as they are dictated. When you have finished the test, unfold the page and check your words.

1. automobile
2. autograph
3. automatic
4. autobiography
5. autopilot
6. telescope
7. telecast
8. telegram
9. telegraph
10. telephone
11. portable
12. import
13. export
14. transport
15. passport
16. microphone
17. headphones
18. symphony
19. saxophone
20. megaphone

1. Who invented the **automobile**?
2. He got the star's **autograph**.
3. The car has **automatic** windows.
4. She wrote her **autobiography**.
5. The plane was on **autopilot**.
6. This **telescope** is very powerful.
7. The speech will be **telecast** now.
8. He received an urgent **telegram**.
9. The **telegraph** wires fell down.
10. Is that the **telephone** ringing?
11. Her computer is **portable**.
12. We **import** toys into the country.
13. Cotton is an important **export**.
14. Trucks are used for **transport**.
15. He went to apply for a **passport**.
16. This is a sensitive **microphone**.
17. Please take off your **headphones**.
18. I play in a **symphony** orchestra.
19. He bought a new **saxophone**.
20. He sang into the **megaphone**.

Notes for Home: Your child took a pretest on words with Greek and Latin word parts. ***Home Activity:*** Help your child learn misspelled words before the final test. Dictate the word and have your child spell the word aloud for you or write it on paper.

Spelling Workbook 6.6, p. 110

Name ______________________

The Librarian Who Measured the Earth

Spelling: Words from Greek and Latin

Word List

automobile	telescope	portable	microphone
autograph	telecast	import	headphones
automatic	telegram	export	symphony
autobiography	telegraph	transport	saxophone
autopilot	telephone	passport	megaphone

Directions: Choose the words from the box that have the Greek word part **auto-** and the Latin word part **phon.** Write each word in the correct column. **Order may vary.**

Words with auto-

1. automobile
2. autograph
3. automatic
4. autobiography
5. autopilot

Words with phon

6. telephone
7. microphone
8. headphones
9. symphony
10. saxophone
11. megaphone

Directions: Use **port** or **tele-** to form a word from the box that completes each equation. Write the word on the line.

12. exact – act + ? = export
13. microscope – micro + ? = telescope
14. password – word + ? = passport
15. cablegram – cable + ? = telegram
16. transform – form + ? = transport
17. phonograph – phono + ? = telegraph
18. remarkable – remark + ? = portable
19. forecast – fore + ? = telecast
20. improve – prove + ? = import

Notes for Home: Your child spelled words with Greek *(auto-, tele-)* and Latin *(port, phon)* word parts. ***Home Activity:*** Use the spelling words to create a set of word cards. Take turns choosing two cards to try to match words with the same Greek or Latin word parts.

Spelling Workbook 6.6, p. 111

Name ______________________

The Librarian Who Measured the Earth

Spelling: Words from Greek and Latin

Directions: Proofread this fact file. Find five spelling mistakes. Use the proofreading marks to correct each mistake.

- ≡ Make a capital.
- / Make a small letter.
- ∧ Add something.
- Take out something.
- ⊙ Add a period.
- ¶ Begin a new paragraph.

Math in the Real World

1. Light bouncing off the moon into a telascope (telescope) lens travels in a straight line.
2. A composer uses quarter notes, half notes, and other notes in a symphonie (symphony).
3. Some trucks can transport up to two tons of equipment.
4. If something gets between the signal and a portible (portable) telephone, the phone will not work properly.
5. The speed of an autmobile (automobile) and how far it travels determines the time the trip will take.
6. Many computer programs have an autumatic (automatic) drawing tool for drawing shapes.

Spelling Tip

The Greek word part **tele-** means "far off." Be sure to keep the second **e** when spelling words with this word part. Remember, the word part has an **e** for each syllable: **telephone.**

Word List

automobile	telescope	portable	microphone
autograph	telecast	import	headphones
automatic	telegram	export	symphony
autobiography	telegraph	transport	saxophone
autopilot	telephone	passport	megaphone

Write a Fact File

On a separate sheet of paper, create a fact file of your own. Give examples that show how mathematics or another school subject relates to everyday living. Try to use at least three spelling words. **Answers will vary, but each fact file should include at least three spelling words.**

Notes for Home: Your child spelled words with Greek *(auto-, tele-)* and Latin *(port, phon)* word parts. ***Home Activity:*** Give a clue that helps define each spelling word. Challenge your child to guess the word and spell it.

Spelling Workbook 6.6, p. 112

Name ______________________

The Librarian Who Measured the Earth

Spelling: Words from Greek and Latin

Word List				
automobile	autopilot	telegraph	export	headphones
autograph	telescope	telephone	transport	symphony
automatic	telecast	portable	passport	saxophone
autobiography	telegram	import	microphone	megaphone

Directions: Write the word from the box that belongs in each group.

1. oboe, clarinet, **saxophone**
2. binoculars, spyglass, **telescope**
3. sonata, concerto, **symphony**
4. vehicle, car, **automobile**
5. memoir, life story, **autobiography**
6. move, carry, **transport**
7. message, wire, **telegram**
8. pay phone, cell phone, **telephone**
9. signature, name, **autograph**
10. reflex, spontaneous, **automatic**

Directions: Choose the word from the box that best completes each statement. Write the word on the line.

import 11. Retailer: "We should _____ more sweaters from Peru."

megaphone 12. Director: "If I yell through the _____, they will all hear."

headphones 13. Pilot: "Let me adjust my _____ so I can hear the control tower."

passport 14. Traveler: "My _____ shows that I am a Mexican citizen."

telecast 15. Producer: "The _____ of the World Series will air at 8:00."

export 16. Manufacturer: "We plan to _____ our products to China."

autopilot 17. Astronaut: "If I set the shuttle's computer on _____, I can get some sleep."

microphone 18. Actor: "By using a _____, the back row will hear me, even if I'm speaking quietly."

portable 19. Camper: "That small _____ stove is nice to have on a long hike."

telegraph 20. Office Employee: "We used to _____ urgent messages."

Notes for Home: Your child spelled words with Greek *(auto-, tele-)* and Latin *(port, phon)* word parts. ***Home Activity:*** Work with your child to identify other words that have these same word parts.

Practice Book 6.6, p. 279

Name ______________________

The Librarian Who Measured the Earth

Diagram

A **diagram** is a special drawing with labels. A diagram usually shows how something is made or how it works.

Directions: Study the diagram of a tree house. Then use it to answer the questions that follow.

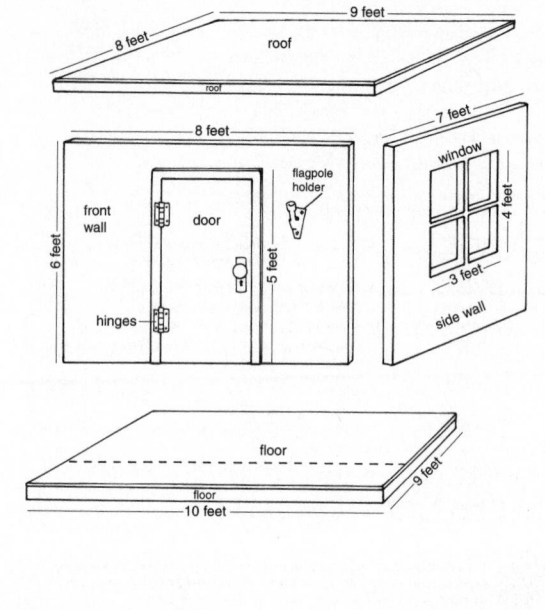

9 feet
8 feet
roof
roof
8 feet
7 feet
window
front wall
door
flagpole holder
6 feet
5 feet
4 feet
3 feet
hinges
side wall
floor
floor
9 feet
10 feet

Practice Book 6.6, p. 280

Name ______________________

The Librarian Who Measured the Earth

Possible answers given.

1. What is the purpose of this diagram? **The purpose of the diagram is to show the measurements for different parts of a tree house and how the parts go together.**
2. What else besides this diagram will you need to build a tree house? **You would need step-by-step instructions and the materials for building a tree house.**
3. What do the numbers on the diagram tell you? **The numbers tell you the lengths and widths of different parts of a tree house in feet.**
4. Why would you want to study this diagram carefully before purchasing building materials? **You need to know what lengths of boards you will need before you buy them.**
5. What is the widest measurement for this tree house? How do you know? **10 feet; This is the width of the floor of the tree house.**
6. About how tall is the tree house? How can you tell? **About 6 feet; This is the height of the wall of the tree house plus a little more for the thickness of the roof.**
7. What would happen if you made the measurements of the roof $1\frac{1}{2}$ feet shorter than shown in the diagram? **If you shortened the measurements of the roof, it wouldn't fit on top of the tree house and cover it.**
8. Why do you think the left side wall and the back wall of the tree house are not shown? **The left side wall would have the same measurements as the right side wall. The back wall would have the same measurements as the front wall (without a door).**
9. Would you be more likely to find this diagram in a manual, a dictionary, an encyclopedia, or a fiction story? Explain. **You would most likely find this diagram in a manual since manuals often show how to build or make something.**
10. Describe a situation when you might draw a diagram. **You might draw a diagram to show someone how to make something or how something works.**

Notes for Home: Your child examined a diagram that showed how to put something together. ***Home Activity:*** Find a diagram that shows how to make something or how something works. Take turns asking one another questions about what the diagram shows.

Practice Book 6.6, p. 281

Name ______________________

Tyree's Song

Paraphrasing

- To **paraphrase** is to explain something in your own words.
- To paraphrase a piece of writing, first ask yourself what the author is trying to say. Then restate the ideas or description in your own words, without changing the meaning or adding opinions of your own.

Directions: Reread "A Lesson from the Master." Complete the table by paraphrasing portions of the story. Then answer the question below. **Possible answers given.**

Passage	Paraphrase
Graybeard got to his feet. He lifted his thin arms over his head and stretched. Then he looked down at the boy. "Now it is time to begin," he said.	1. **Graybeard tells the boy that he is ready to begin.**
The old man stopped him immediately, shaking his head briskly. "That is wrong. I have told you, always make your first sketch in charcoal. Black is better. And start with an outline of the body and the head."	2. **The old man stops Tao. He reminds Tao to make his first sketch in black charcoal and to start with an outline.**
As he followed Graybeard's instructions Tao found he was drawing easier, faster. He smiled with a quick feeling of satisfaction. Just a few words from the master made a big difference.	3. **Following Graybeard's instructions helps Tao to draw more easily and quickly. He is pleased with this change in his drawing.**
Graybeard nodded. "You are learning, my friend. It takes time, but you are learning."	4. **Graybeard nods to show his approval of Tao's work and tells him that he is learning to draw better.**

5. Why is it important not to add your own opinions when paraphrasing a piece of writing? **A paraphrase should simply restate or explain the author's ideas.**

Notes for Home: Your child read a story and used his or her own words to restate what happened in various parts of the story. ***Home Activity:*** With your child, read a paragraph from a story or article. Help your child use his or her own words to restate the ideas in the paragraph.

Practice Book 6.6, p. 282

Name ______________________ **Tyree's Song**

Vocabulary

Directions: Choose the word from the box that best fits each definition. Write the word on the line.

Check the Words You Know
__ abandoned
__ alien
__ anxiety
__ improvise
__ themes
__ variations

variations 1. altered or varied forms of something

abandoned 2. deserted

improvise 3. compose music on the spur of the moment

anxiety 4. uneasy thoughts or fears about what may happen

alien 5. an imaginary creature from space

themes 6. the principal melodies in pieces of music

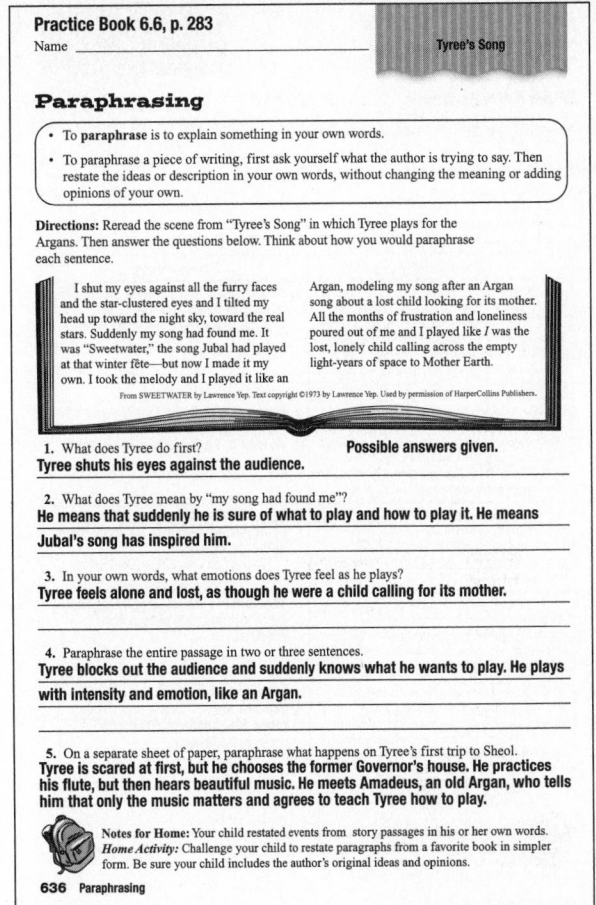

Directions: Choose the word from the box that best complete each sentence. Write the word on the line to the left.

anxiety 7. When I am worried, music helps me get rid of any feelings of _____.

themes 8. Because I like melodies, I enjoy trying to identify the _____ in famous pieces of music.

variations 9. Some people play many different _____ of the same basic tune.

improvise 10. Sometimes I play music written by others, but I also like to _____ my own music as I play my piano.

Write a Descriptive Paragraph

On a separate sheet of paper, write a paragraph about a strange new instrument that an alien taught you to play. Describe the instrument and the kinds of music you can play with it. Use as many vocabulary words as you can.

Students' descriptions should use vocabulary words correctly.

Notes for Home: Your child identified and used vocabulary words from "Tyree's Song." *Home Activity:* Play some music that you and your child like. Use vocabulary words to discuss why people enjoy music.

Vocabulary 635

Practice Book 6.6, p. 283

Name ______________________ **Tyree's Song**

Paraphrasing

- To **paraphrase** is to explain something in your own words.
- To paraphrase a piece of writing, first ask yourself what the author is trying to say. Then restate the ideas or description in your own words, without changing the meaning or adding opinions of your own.

Directions: Reread the scene from "Tyree's Song" in which Tyree plays for the Argans. Then answer the questions below. Think about how you would paraphrase each sentence.

I shut my eyes against all the furry faces and the star-clustered eyes and I tilted my head up toward the night sky, toward the real stars. Suddenly my song had found me. It was "Sweetwater," the song Jubal had played at that winter fête—but now I made it my own. I took the melody and I played it like an Argan, modeling my song after an Argan song about a lost child looking for its mother. All the months of frustration and loneliness poured out of me and I played like *I* was the lost, lonely child calling across the empty light-years of space to Mother Earth.

From SWEETWATER by Lawrence Yep. Text copyright ©1973 by Lawrence Yep. Used by permission of HarperCollins Publishers.

Possible answers given.

1. What does Tyree do first?
Tyree shuts his eyes against the audience.

2. What does Tyree mean by "my song had found me"?
He means that suddenly he is sure of what to play and how to play it. He means Jubal's song has inspired him.

3. In your own words, what emotions does Tyree feel as he plays?
Tyree feels alone and lost, as though he were a child calling for its mother.

4. Paraphrase the entire passage in two or three sentences.
Tyree blocks out the audience and suddenly knows what he wants to play. He plays with intensity and emotion, like an Argan.

5. On a separate sheet of paper, paraphrase what happens on Tyree's first trip to Sheol.
Tyree is scared at first, but he chooses the former Governor's house. He practices his flute, but then hears beautiful music. He meets Amadeus, an old Argan, who tells him that only the music matters and agrees to teach Tyree how to play.

Notes for Home: Your child restated events from story passages in his or her own words. *Home Activity:* Challenge your child to restate paragraphs from a favorite book in simpler form. Be sure your child includes the author's original ideas and opinions.

636 Paraphrasing

Practice Book 6.6, p. 285

Name ______________________ **Tyree's Song**

Selection Test

Directions: Choose the best answer to each item. Mark the letter for the answer you have chosen.

Part 1: Vocabulary

Find the answer choice that means about the same as the underlined word in each sentence.

1. Darla thinks she saw an <u>alien</u>.
   A. a creature that is part animal and part human
   B. a person who makes others laugh
   C. a visitor from another country
   Ⓓ a creature from outer space

2. Ronnie was filled with <u>anxiety</u>.
   F. feeling of terror
   Ⓖ uneasy thoughts or fears about what might happen
   H. feeling of sadness or gloominess
   J. act of sharing someone else's sorrow or hardship

3. The performers began to <u>improvise</u>.
   Ⓐ make up music, poetry, or drama on the spur of the moment
   B. move together at the same rate
   C. take turns performing alone
   D. practice for a public performance

4. He used the same <u>themes</u> over and over.
   F. words repeated in a song
   G. ordered scales of notes
   H. combinations of musical instruments
   Ⓙ principal melodies in pieces of music

5. They played several <u>variations</u>.
   A. unusual musical instruments
   Ⓑ slight changes in tunes
   C. slow, sad songs
   D. humorous imitations of serious music

6. The town had been <u>abandoned</u>.
   Ⓕ deserted
   G. buried
   H. completed
   J. displayed for sale

Part 2: Comprehension

Use what you know about the story to answer each item.

7. This story takes place on—
   A. Earth.
   B. the moon.
   Ⓒ the planet Harmony.
   D. a space station.

8. Why did the Silkie colonists leave Sheol?
   F. They wished to return to Earth.
   G. They were angry with the Argans.
   Ⓗ Their homes were flooded.
   J. Argans drove them out.

9. When they first met, the Argan musician gripped Tyree with his—
   A. claws.
   B. magnetic force.
   C. jaws.
   Ⓓ suction pads.

10. In this episode, you can tell that the Argans and the Silkies—
    F. are alike in most ways.
    Ⓖ do not trust each other.
    H. all came from Earth.
    J. depend on each other.

11. "I moored my skiff to one of the pillars of the portico and splashed up the steps." Which is the best paraphrase of this sentence?
    A. I left my skiff near a pillar of the portico and went up the steps.
    Ⓑ I tied my boat to the porch and walked up the steps.
    C. I docked my skiff in front of the elegant mansion and went up the staircase.
    D. I steered my boat to a pillar and made my lonely way up the stairs.

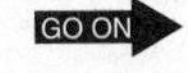

Selection Test 637

Practice Book 6.6, p. 286

Name ______________________ **Tyree's Song**

12. "I had to trade twenty feet of my best nylon fishing line to Red Genteel, but he agreed to do my chores in the garden for that day while I napped." Which is the best paraphrase of this sentence?
    F. Red Genteel needed twenty yards of fishing line for the garden. He used it while I napped.
    G. Lucky for me, Red Genteel was willing to do my chores that day so long as I gave him a bit of fishing line.
    H. Red Genteel and I traded days for fishing, doing chores in the garden, and napping.
    Ⓙ In exchange for some fishing line, Red Genteel agreed to do my chores so that I could take a nap.

13. Which is a major theme in this story?
    Ⓐ True friendship can be found in unexpected places.
    B. Humans will live on faraway planets in the future.
    C. If you mistreat people, they will not go out of their way to help you.
    D. Music is the same everywhere.

14. When Tyree plays "Sweetwater" for the Argans, his song suggests that he—
    F. wants the Argans to like him.
    Ⓖ feels lonely.
    H. would prefer to be an Argan.
    J. is very nervous about performing.

15. What is the most important thing that Amadeus does for Tyree in this story?
    Ⓐ teaches him that he must let the music find him
    B. makes him feel that he is a very special person
    C. gets other Argans to accept him
    D. helps him understand the differences between Argan and human styles of music

STOP

638 Selection Test

Name ______________________ Tyree's Song

Paraphrasing

- To **paraphrase** is to explain something in your own words.
- To paraphrase a piece of writing, first ask yourself what the author is trying to say. Then restate the ideas or description in your own words, without changing the meaning or adding opinions of your own.

Directions: Read the story in the first column below. After you finish reading, reread each paragraph and briefly retell it in your own words. **Possible answers given.**

Paragraphs	Paraphrases
In the year 2331, robots commonly performed the routine jobs they had done for the last 250 years. Robot designers had also created "smarter" models that proved to be excellent pilots, sports stars, and yes, even nannies! The nanny 2-Bane was one such model, built to guard, guide, and raise children.	1. **Many robots in the 2300s do simple work, but some, like the nanny 2-Bane, have big responsibilities.**
Quite efficient, 2-Bane had earned ninety merit stars in her sixty years of service. Her hard drives overflowed with the data she had collected over those years. This background was what made 2-Bane so perfect for a new experiment. She had been reprogrammed to be an artist.	2. **Because of 2-Bane's sixty years of experience with children, she is chosen to be the first robot artist.**
2-Bane painted nonstop for three days. Her new programs calculated the painting colors, shapes, and sizes perfectly. Her technique, of course, was flawless, and she turned out photo-like portraits in record time.	3. **2-Bane's new programs allow her to paint perfect pictures for three days without stopping.**
The programmers' reactions, though, told 2-Bane she had failed. Their human faces registered surprise and disappointment. Their experiment had failed. To humans, her paintings had no feelings. They were just paint on a board.	4. **The humans are disappointed. They feel that her work shows little emotion.**
"Perhaps," said 2-Bane politely, "I disappoint because I am asked to paint human subject matter. I can only express a robot's viewpoint. Ask me to show the joy of computing numbers or the pain of virus damage. Those experiences are what I can show in my art."	5. **2-Bane explains that she cannot express herself as a human, only a robot. She needs to show what a robot experiences.**

Notes for Home: Your child restated paragraph details in his or her own words. ***Home Activity:*** Give your child a set of directions to perform a simple task, and encourage him or her to restate them more simply.

Practice Book 6.6, p. 287

Name ______________________ Tyree's Song

Author's Purpose and Theme

REVIEW

Directions: Read the passage. Then read each question that follows the passage. Choose the best answer to each question. Mark the letter for the answer you have chosen.

At the Movies

Movies are made up of pictures and sound. Actors speak their lines, but there is another important sound happening—background music. This music is known as a film's *score*. The score is as important as any other part of a movie because it helps provide the mood for a scene.

The score can add the extra "punch" to make a movie a success. Does the script call for feelings of awe or mystery? Sorrow or anger? Tension or joy? Filmmakers can provide a real sense of excitement or nervousness by adding music that has a quick rhythm. By emphasizing the mood, music can express the same emotions caught by the camera lens.

Music can also show changes in location. You can change from a quiet forest scene to a noisy city street with the help of different styles of music. Sometimes music can even replace the actors' dialogue!

Some film scores are written especially for movies. Many composers spend their whole careers writing scores for films. Other film scores are made up of popular songs or dance music that suits the characters and events in the film. This kind of score can be just as effective as one that was written for a movie.

Although it will never replace the camera as the filmmaker's favorite tool, music serves an important purpose in movie making. If the pictures are what make the meal, it is the music that provides the spice to flavor it.

1. The author wrote this passage to—
   - A. provide an entertaining story.
   - B. inform readers about careers in filmmaking.
   - (C) express an opinion about music in movies.
   - D. persuade readers to watch more movies.
2. The main theme of the passage is that—
   - F. movies have pictures and sound.
   - G. music can replace dialogue in films.
   - H. music can describe a location.
   - (J) music plays an important role in movies.
3. The author compared music to spice in a meal in order to—
   - (A) show the relationship between a film's music and its pictures.
   - B. tell what kind of music is best.
   - C. emphasize a need for music with quick rhythms.
   - D. suggest that music appeals to an audience's sense of taste.
4. The author assumes that the reader—
   - (F) has heard music in movies.
   - G. likes to go to action movies.
   - H. likes movies set in big cities.
   - J. believes that movies should be more exciting.
5. The author supports his or her opinions by—
   - (A) giving examples.
   - B. quoting experts.
   - C. making vague generalizations.
   - D. explaining how music is recorded for movies.

Notes for Home: Your child identified the theme of a passage and the author's purpose in writing it. ***Home Activity:*** Challenge your child to find examples of materials written for different purposes, such as editorials, advertisements, clothing care labels, and so on.

Name ______________________ Tyree's Song

Writing Across Texts

Directions: The story and illustrations in "Tyree's Song" and "Noah Writes a B & B Letter" give details about different creative activities. Consider what you learned about the ways that people express themselves creatively. Complete the web by listing things people do to create works of art or express themselves. You may use examples from the selections or list your own examples. **Possible answers given.**

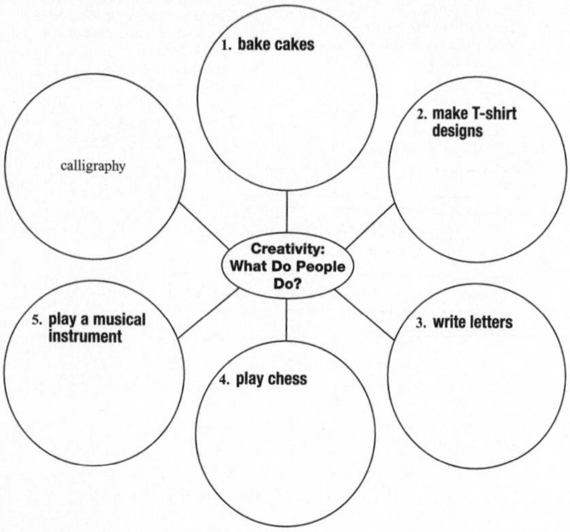

Write an Essay

Which creative activity would you most like to pursue? Write a short essay that describes more about the activity and why it would appeal to you. Write your essay on a separate sheet of paper. **Essays will vary. Check that students' essays are focused on one of the activities they inserted in the web and that it explains the reasons for their choice.**

Notes for Home: Your child listed details about creative activities from two different selections. ***Home Activity:*** Discuss ways members of your family have to express their creativity. Work together to make a web similar to the one above.

Grammar Practice Book 6.6, p. 141

Name ______________________ Tyree's Song

Grammar: Quotation Marks

REVIEW

Directions: Rewrite the sentences, adding quotation marks, commas, periods, question marks, and exclamation marks as needed.

1. are you trying out for the band asked Jerome
   "Are you trying out for the band?" asked Jerome.
2. i'd like to said Lydia but I'm not sure I'm good enough
   "I'd like to," said Lydia, "but I'm not sure I'm good enough."
3. that's silly exclaimed Jerome you're a good clarinet player
   "That's silly!" exclaimed Jerome. "You're a good clarinet player."
4. Lydia smiled and said do you really think so
   Lydia smiled and said, "Do you really think so?"
5. Yes, I think so replied Jerome and the band leader will think so too
   "Yes, I think so," replied Jerome, "and the band leader will think so too."

Directions: Write a sentence that uses each group of words as a quotation. **Possible answers given.**

6. you can start playing now, Lydia
   "You can start playing now, Lydia," said Ms. Lucca, the band leader.
7. thank you. that was very good
   "Thank you," she said when Lydia finished her clarinet piece. "That was very good."
8. do you think I passed the audition
   Lydia whispered to her friend, "Do you think I passed the audition?"
9. well, Lydia, welcome to the band
   "Well, Lydia," Ms. Lucca announced, "welcome to the band."
10. great I did it
    "Great!" exclaimed Lydia. "I did it!"

Notes for Home: Your child corrected and wrote sentences that included quotations. ***Home Activity:*** Have a conversation with your child about a favorite song or musical group. Then challenge your child to write the conversation as if it were part of a story.

Grammar Practice Book 6.6, p. 142

Name ______________________

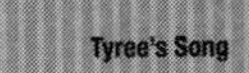

Grammar: Contractions

A **contraction** can be formed by combining a pronoun and a verb. An apostrophe replaces the letter or letters that are left out. Here are some common contractions:

Pronoun + Verb	Contraction	Pronoun + Verb	Contraction
I am	I'm	I will	I'll
she is	she's	he has	he's
it is	it's	it has	it's
you are	you're	we have	we've
they are	they're	I would	I'd

Contractions can also be formed by combining a verb and *not.* Since *not* is a negative word, these contractions are called **negative contractions.** Here are some common negative contractions.

Verb + *not*	Negative Contraction	Verb + *not*	Negative Contraction
are not	aren't	do not	don't
is not	isn't	does not	doesn't
were not	weren't	did not	didn't
was not	wasn't	has not	hasn't
would not	wouldn't	have not	haven't

Use only one negative to make a sentence mean "no" or "not."
Don't write: Don't never do that again.
Write: Don't do that again.
Or: Never do that again.

Directions: Combine each pair of words to form a contraction. Write the contraction on the line.

1. he will **he'll**
2. would not **wouldn't**
3. she has **she's**
4. does not **doesn't**
5. they are **they're**
6. I have **I've**

Directions: Combine each pair of words in ( ) to form a contraction that completes each sentence. Write the contraction on the line.

I'd 7. (I would) like to learn how to play the guitar.
It's 8. (It is) an instrument that you can play alone.
You've 9. (You have) listened to guitar players, haven't you?
haven't 10. I (have not) heard any sound quite as beautiful.

Notes for Home: Your child practiced writing contractions. ***Home Activity:*** Play a matching game. Write words such as *I am, he has,* and *are not* on index cards. Then write the contraction for each on another set of cards. Place them face down and try to pick a matching pair.

Grammar Practice Book 6.6, p. 143

Name ______________________

Tyree's Song

Grammar: Contractions

Directions: Match each word in the column to the left with its contraction in the column to the right. Write the letter of the matching contraction on the line.

h	1. they have	a. he's
e	2. is not	b. you're
a	3. he has	c. I'd
d	4. we will	d. we'll
b	5. you are	e. isn't
j	6. were not	f. doesn't
g	7. it is	g. it's
c	8. I had	h. they've
i	9. you have	i. you've
f	10. does not	j. weren't

Directions: Choose a contraction from the box to complete each sentence. Write the contraction on the line to the left.

she's we'd aren't she'd isn't

isn't 11. For Kelly, there _____ anything more fun than painting.
She'd 12. _____ do it every day if she had time.
aren't 13. Kelly says that there _____ enough hours in the day to do everything she wants to do.
she's 14. I think Kelly is a great musician, but _____ not so sure of herself.
we'd 15. My friends and I told her that _____ all come to her concert.

Write a Journal Entry

On a separate sheet of paper, write a journal entry about a song that you really like. Tell what the song means to you. Include some contractions.
Journal entries should include correct spelling and use of contractions.

Notes for Home: Your child practiced writing contractions, such as *aren't* for *are not.* ***Home Activity:*** Say some sentences, using a few of the contractions on this page. Encourage your child to tell you the two words that form each contraction.

Grammar Practice Book 6.6, p. 144

Name ______________________

Tyree's Song

Grammar: Contractions

RETEACHING

Write the contraction for each pair of words.

1. I have **I've**
2. she has **she's**
3. they will **they'll**
4. you are **you're**
5. is not **isn't**
6. would not **wouldn't**

A **contraction** is a short way to write two words. It is formed by taking out one or more letters and replacing them with an **apostrophe (').** A contraction can be formed by combining a pronoun and a verb or by combining a verb and the word *not.*

Directions: Circle the correctly spelled contraction for each pair of words at the left.

1. will not	willn't	**(won't)**	will'not
2. cannot	**(can't)**	cant	cann't
3. she had	shed'	shed	**(she'd)**
4. should not	shouldnt	**(shouldn't)**	should'nt
5. have not	**(haven't)**	have'nt	havent
6. we are	were	**(we're)**	wer'e
7. she will	**(she'll)**	shell	shel'l
8. do not	**(don't)**	do'nt	dont
9. you had	youd	yo'ud	**(you'd)**
10. he is	hes	**(he's)**	h'es
11. were not	were'nt	**(weren't)**	werent'
12. I will	Ill	I'wll	**(I'll)**
13. had not	had'not	hadt'n	**(hadn't)**
14. there is	**(there's)**	theres	ther'is
15. was not	was'not	**(wasn't)**	wa'nt

Notes for Home: Your child identified contractions that were spelled and punctuated correctly. ***Home Activity:*** Have your child use some of the contractions on this page in sentences. Ask your child to form contractions of other word pairs, such as *might have* or *you have.*

Grammar Practice Book 6.6, p. 145

Name ______________________

Tyree's Song

Grammar: Contractions

Directions: Form twenty contractions by choosing one word from each box and writing the contraction on the line. **Possible answers given.**

I	can	might
she	have	were
he	has	was
we	did	you
they	do	

am	not
are	will
was	have
were	has
is	had

1. **I'm**
2. **I'll**
3. **she's**
4. **we're**
5. **we'll**
6. **they're**
7. **they'll**
8. **he's**
9. **he'll**
10. **can't**
11. **haven't**
12. **hasn't**
13. **didn't**
14. **don't**
15. **might've**
16. **weren't**
17. **wasn't**
18. **you'll**
19. **you're**
20. **you've**

Directions: Choose a contraction from the box that best completes each sentence. Write the contraction on the line to the left.

you've don't haven't hasn't shouldn't

haven't 21. I ________ been able to read for pleasure since we moved far away from the library.
you've 22. As long as ________ got a library card, you will always have something to read.
don't 23. Please ________ walk on the flowers.
shouldn't 24. I know it is important to you, but you ________ leave school to go to the concert.
hasn't 25. She ________ visited Grandma in three months.

Write a Poem

On a separate sheet of paper, write a poem about what you can do and what you would like to be able to do better. Use contractions in your poem.
Make sure that students spell and punctuate contractions correctly.

Notes for Home: Your child formed contractions and used contractions in sentences. ***Home Activity:*** Together, watch ten minutes of a television program. Have your child write as many contractions as possible that were used in the program.

Practice Book 6.6, p. 288

Name ______________________ **Tyree's Song**

Phonics: Complex Spelling Patterns

Directions: Some words have letters that don't match the sounds we hear. Read the words in the box. Listen carefully to each sound. Then read the clues. Match the clues with the words. Write each word on the line. **Answers will vary.**

privilege	miniature	acoustics	creature
ballet	ancient	mediocre	maneuver

ancient 1. This word has the letter *c*, but the *c* stands for a sound like *shut*.

maneuver 2. This word has the long *u* sound, but the letters that represent the sound start with the letter *e*.

miniature 3. This word has the letter *a*, but you hear it as a schwa sound.

ballet 4. This word ends with the letters *-et*, but you say it with a long *a* sound.

creature 5. This word has the letters *eat*, but it rhymes with the word *teacher*.

privilege 6. This word has the letter *g*, but the word sounds like it should be spelled with *dg*.

mediocre 7. This word has the same ending sound as *father*, but it's spelled *re*.

acoustics 8. This word has the long *u* sound, but the letters that represent the sound start with the letter *o*.

Directions: Read the words in the box. Then read each related word below. Write the word from the box next to its related word. Then circle the part of the word that is spelled differently from the related word.

creature	variation	decision	musician	competition	gratitude

9. music **musician** (ian)
10. vary **variation** (ation)
11. grateful **gratitude** (itude)
12. create **creature** (ure)
13. decide **decision** (sion)
14. compete **competition** (ition)

Directions: Choose one of the word pairs above. Use both words in one sentence. **Possible answer given.**

15. **The make-up artist was able to create an amazing outer-space creature.**

Notes for Home: Your child explored words in which the spelling did not match the sound. ***Home Activity:*** Read a short story with your child. Challenge your child to find words that have unusual spellings. Write them down to review after you read.

Spelling Workbook 6.6, p. 113

Name ______________________ **Tyree's Song**

Spelling: Words with *ci* and *ti*

Pretest Directions: Fold back the page along the dotted line. On the blanks, write the spelling words as they are dictated. When you have finished the test, unfold the page and check your words.

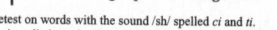

1. social	1. Dogs are **social** creatures.
2. precious	2. A diamond is a **precious** stone.
3. commercial	3. I never liked this **commercial**.
4. especially	4. He is **especially** fond of berries.
5. artificial	5. The soda has **artificial** coloring.
6. financial	6. Her aunt is a **financial** analyst.
7. gracious	7. Please thank our **gracious** hosts.
8. glacier	8. A **glacier** once covered the land.
9. national	9. What is our **national** bird?
10. dictionary	10. Look it up in the **dictionary**.
11. motion	11. The gears went into **motion**.
12. position	12. Which **position** do you play?
13. population	13. The **population** keeps growing.
14. cautious	14. Be **cautious** of strangers.
15. question	15. That is a very personal **question**.
16. suggestion	16. I will consider your **suggestion**.
17. mention	17. I forgot to **mention** my name.
18. fraction	18. He ate a **fraction** of the pie.
19. exhaustion	19. She collapsed from **exhaustion**.
20. digestion	20. Drinking liquids aids **digestion**.

Notes for Home: Your child took a pretest on words with the sound /sh/ spelled *ci* and *ti*. ***Home Activity:*** Help your child learn misspelled words. Have your child divide misspelled words into parts (such as syllables), concentrate on each part, and notice how the sound /sh/ is spelled.

Spelling Workbook 6.6, p. 114

Name ______________________ **Tyree's Song**

Spelling: Words with *ci* and *ti*

Word List

social	financial	motion	suggestion
precious	gracious	position	mention
commercial	glacier	population	fraction
especially	national	cautious	exhaustion
artificial	dictionary	question	digestion

Directions: Choose the words from the box that have the sound **/sh/** spelled **ci** or **ti**. Write each word in the correct column. Hint: **ti** can also represent the sound **/ch/**.

/sh/ spelled ci	/sh/ spelled ti
1. social	9. national
2. precious	10. dictionary
3. commercial	11. motion
4. especially	12. position
5. artificial	13. population
6. financial	14. cautious
7. gracious	15. mention
8. glacier	16. fraction

Directions: Choose the word from the box that best matches each clue.

question 17. I am what you ask when you want to know the answer.

exhaustion 18. I am a condition of being extremely tired and worn out.

digestion 19. I am the process in your body that breaks down the food you eat.

suggestion 20. I am what you offer when you have an opinion or recommendation.

Notes for Home: Your child spelled words with the sound /sh/ spelled *ci* and *ti* as in *especially* and *dictionary*, and the sound /ch/ spelled *ti* as in *question*. ***Home Activity:*** Help your child write humorous tongue-twister sentences that include several spelling words.

Spelling Workbook 6.6, p. 115

Name ______________________ **Tyree's Song**

Spelling: Words with *ci* and *ti*

Directions: Proofread these song lyrics. Find six spelling mistakes. Use the proofreading marks to correct each mistake.

- ≡ Make a capital.
- / Make a small letter.
- ∧ Add something.
- Take out something.
- ⊙ Add a period.
- ¶ Begin a new paragraph.

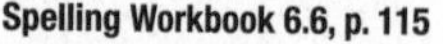

The Martian Dilemma

Where has all the water gone—preshous water? [ci]
Is it in a glaher or an artifficial pool? [c]
What can a population do with no water?
Be careful, don't be a fool!
Being cawtious is the rule. [u]

Where will all the water go—that's the quesion. [t]
Should we share our reservoirs, a nashional debate? [t]
Let us learn new ways to find
Cool, clean water.

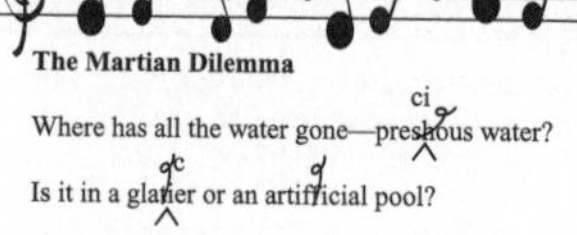

Spelling Tip

The sound /sh/ can be spelled *ci* or *ti*: **artificial, national.** Check the song lyrics to make sure that words with this sound are spelled correctly.

Word List

social	motion
precious	position
commercial	population
especially	cautious
artificial	question
financial	suggestion
gracious	mention
glacier	fraction
national	exhaustion
dictionary	digestion

Write a Song

On a separate sheet of paper, write your own song lyrics. In your song, persuade others that your ideas about an issue are important. Try to use at least four spelling words. **Answers will vary, but each song should include at least four spelling words.**

Notes for Home: Your child spelled words with the sound /sh/ spelled *ci* and *ti* as in *especially* and *dictionary*, and the sound /ch/ spelled *ti* as in *question*. ***Home Activity:*** Say each spelling word twice. Have your child visualize each word and then spell it aloud.

Spelling Workbook 6.6, p. 116

Name

Tyree's Song

Spelling: Words with *ci* and *ti*

REVIEW

Word List

social	financial	motion	suggestion
precious	gracious	position	mention
commercial	glacier	population	fraction
especially	national	cautious	exhaustion
artificial	dictionary	question	digestion

Directions: Choose the word from the box that is the most opposite in meaning for each word below. Write the word on the line.

1. energy **exhaustion**
2. whole **fraction**
3. reckless **cautious**
4. generally **especially**
5. answer **question**
6. stillness **motion**
7. local **national**
8. rude **gracious**
9. natural **artificial**
10. worthless **precious**

Directions: Choose a word from the box that best matches each definition. Write the word on the line.

position 11. a place or way of being placed

suggestion 12. a hint, proposal, or recommendation

digestion 13. the process of breaking down food once eaten

commercial 14. an advertisement on television or on the radio

financial 15. having to do with money

social 16. having to do with human beings and their relationships

mention 17. a casual reference to something

population 18. the total number of people in a given area

glacier 19. a huge mass of ice

dictionary 20. a book of words, origins, pronunciations, and definitions

Notes for Home: Your child spelled words with the sound /sh/ spelled *ci* and *ti* as in *especially* and *dictionary,* and the sound /ch/ spelled *ti* as in *question.* ***Home Activity:*** Scramble the letters of each spelling word. Challenge your child to unscramble them.

Spelling: Words with *ci* and *ti* 651

Practice Book 6.6, p. 289

Name

Tyree's Song

Take Notes/Highlight

Taking notes about or **highlighting** key information in a text can help you understand and remember the text better. It can also help you organize information to study for a test or to include in a research report. There is no one right way to take notes. You might make a list, an outline, a story map, a word web, a table, or write a summary. When you highlight, you can circle, underline, or mark with special pens the important details in what you have read.

Directions: Read the passage and then read the questions that follow. Highlight details in the passage that will help you answer the questions, and then answer the questions. **Check that students have highlighted key information.**

Music has been around for thousands of years—perhaps as long as 30,000 years. Archaeologists—scientists who research and study objects from long ago—have found musical instruments that date back this long. In fact, it is possible that making music may even have developed before people learned to talk. It is believed that early music was used for religious purposes, as well as for entertainment, dance, and telling stories. Most cultures have developed musical instruments and specific musical traditions and styles.

In Europe, the first songs were really simple chants. Dots were written down, above or below a line, to remind the singer if the next note was higher or lower. It was not until the 1700s that the tradition of writing music notes on lined paper was developed.

In China, writings have been found dating back over 2500 years that refer to musical performances. In fact, much of the music in some cultures is the same today as it was centuries ago. The Japanese *gagaku* of the 8th century is a style of music that still exists today. The Chinese *guenzhen* of the 16th century is another style that can still be heard today in its original form. In fact, much of the music that we listen to today has components picked up from classical pieces of centuries before.

The many cultures of Africa also have a rich musical history. Traditionally, African music has been associated with drums, but it has also included a variety of instruments, such as bells, rattles, gongs, and even xylophones. A guitar-like instrument, called the *lamellaphone,* or "thumb piano" is made up of metal or bamboo strips strung across a board or box. The strips are plucked with the fingers. These rhythmic instruments give African music a sound of its own.

652 Research and Study Skills: Take Notes/Highlight

Practice Book 6.6, p. 290

Name

Tyree's Song

1. Which specific continents or countries are discussed in the article? **Europe, China, Japan, and Africa**
2. How long ago were some of the earliest musical instruments made? **30,000 years ago**
3. For what purposes has music been used? **Music has been used for religious purposes, entertainment, dance, and telling stories.**
4. Which facts would be useful in a report about written music? **the facts about European musical notation for chants**
5. What are two styles of Asian music that can still be heard today? **the Japanese *gagaku,* and the Chinese *guenzhen***
6. What are the names of the instruments that are used in African music? **drums, bells, rattles, gongs, xylophones, lamellaphone**
7. How is this article organized? **Possible answer: It has a paragraph about the earliest music, then a paragraph each about music in Europe, Asia (China and Japan), and Africa.**
8. Suppose you wanted to make a table to organize the information in this passage. Describe what your table might look like. What heads might your table have? **Descriptions will vary. Heads used might be: Europe, Asia, Africa.**
9. When you take notes, why is it important to write the names of the sources you have read? **Possible answer: You need to know the name of a source if you are quoting something directly or are referencing the source in a bibliography. You may also need to go back to the source to verify information or look for further information.**
10. Why is it important to think about your questions of inquiry before you begin taking notes? **Possible answer: Thinking first about questions of inquiry will help you stay focused on the information you need to find as you read.**

Notes for Home: Your child read a nonfiction passage and highlighted key details to help him or her answer questions about it. ***Home Activity:*** Read a magazine or newspaper article with your child. Ask your child to highlight or take notes about important details in the article.

Research and Study Skills: Take Notes/Highlight 653

Practice Book 6.6, p. 291

Name

Cutters, Carvers, and the Cathedral

Fact and Opinion

- A **statement of fact** can be proven true or false by reading, observing, asking an expert, or checking it in some way.
- A **statement of opinion** tells someone's belief, judgment, or way of thinking about something. It cannot be proven true or false, but it can be supported or explained.
- A valid statement of opinion is supported by facts or by the authority of an expert. A faulty statement of opinion is not.

Directions: Reread "Three Wondrous Buildings." Then complete the table. For each building, write one statement of fact and one statement of opinion from the article. One fact has been done for you. **Possible answers given.**

The Taj Mahal	The Parthenon	Our Lady of Chartres
Fact: The Taj Mahal is in a small city in northern India.	2. Fact: **The Parthenon is made of white marble.**	4. Fact: **Our Lady of Chartres is in a city near Paris, France.**
1. Opinion: **In the moonlight the Taj Mahal sleeps and dreams.**	3. Opinion: **The Parthenon is as famous as the Taj Mahal and has as many admirers.**	5. Opinion: **The building's stone is not friendly and has many moods.**

Notes for Home: Your child read an article and identified statements of fact and opinion. ***Home Activity:*** With your child, watch a news program. Help your child identify statements of fact, as well as valid and faulty statements of opinion.

656 Fact and Opinion

Practice Book 6.6, p. 292

Name ______________________

Cutters, Carvers, and the Cathedral

Vocabulary

Directions: Match each word on the left with its definition on the right. Write the letter of the definition on the line to the left of the word.

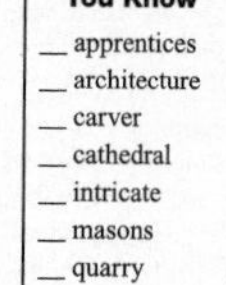

Check the Words You Know
__ apprentices
__ architecture
__ carver
__ cathedral
__ intricate
__ masons
__ quarry

Answer	Word	Definition
d	1. quarry	a. people who build with stones, bricks, and so on
f	2. architecture	b. sculptor
e	3. apprentices	c. complicated; detailed
b	4. carver	d. place for cutting stone from the earth
c	5. intricate	e. people learning a trade
a	6. masons	f. art of designing buildings

Directions: Read the newspaper article. Choose the word from the box that best completes each sentence. Write the word on the matching numbered line.

New Student Learns to Sculpt

Kelly was one of the **7.** _____ who was learning to sculpt stone. She was studying under a master **8.** _____ who was very well respected. She wanted to learn how to make beautiful, **9.** _____ designs. Someday, Kelly hoped to carve stones to be used in a **10.** _____ or church.

7. **apprentices**
8. **carver**
9. **intricate**
10. **cathedral**

Write a Persuasive Argument

On a separate sheet of paper, write a persuasive argument telling why it is important to learn an art or a craft, such as drawing or woodworking . Use as many vocabulary words as you can.
Students' persuasive arguments should use vocabulary words correctly.

Notes for Home: Your child identified and used vocabulary words from *Cutters, Carvers, and the Cathedral*. ***Home Activity:*** With your child, look at local architecture and talk about its special features, using the listed vocabulary words.

Practice Book 6.6, p. 293

Name ______________________

Cutters, Carvers, and the Cathedral

Fact and Opinion

- A **statement of fact** can be proven true or false by reading, observing, asking an expert, or checking it in some way.
- A **statement of opinion** tells someone's belief, judgment, or way of thinking about something. It cannot be proven true or false, but it can be supported or explained.
- A valid statement of opinion is supported by facts or by the authority of an expert. A faulty statement of opinion is not.

Directions: Reread this description of a mason's job from *Cutters, Carvers, and the Cathedral*. Then answer the questions below. Think about how the statements of fact and statements of opinion are different.

Deep below the cathedral floor, "Jeep" Kincannon, the chief masonry draftsman, works in the architecture office. "To be a good mason, you must have a good sense of geometry," he says. "With the computer, I can produce the templates for the blocks that go into the cathedral. The masons use these templates, or patterns, to shape each block of stone." All the blocks are cut to fit into their specific places, and they rise one above the other into columns, arches, walls, and steeples.

From CUTTERS, CARVERS AND THE CATHEDRAL by George Ancona. Copyright © 1995 by George Ancona. By permission of Lothrop, Lee & Shepard Books, a division of William Morrow & Company, Inc.

1. What statement of opinion does Jeep Kincannon offer?
"To be a good mason, you must have a good sense of geometry."

2. Is his statement valid or faulty? How do you know?
Possible answer: Valid; he is an expert in his field.

3. What is a statement of fact about templates?
The computer produces the templates used by masons to shape the stone.

4. How might you prove this statement of fact true or false?
Possible answer: Check a reference source or consult an expert.

5. On a separate sheet of paper, tell which of the jobs described in *Cutters, Carvers, and the Cathedral* seems the most difficult to you. Support your statement of opinion with facts or expert opinions from the selection. **Possible answer: I think that a stone carver's job is the most difficult. A stone carver has no template for decorations and has to know how to carve them without making mistakes.**

Notes for Home: Your child distinguished between statements of fact and statements of opinion. ***Home Activity:*** Work together to identify facts and opinions in a newspaper article. Discuss how well the author's opinions are supported by the facts presented.

Practice Book 6.6, p. 295

Name ______________________

Cutters, Carvers, and the Cathedral

Selection Test

Directions: Choose the best answer to each item. Mark the letter for the answer you have chosen.

Part 1: Vocabulary

Find the answer choice that means about the same as the underlined word in each sentence.

1. He worked in a quarry.
   - Ⓐ place where stone is dug or cut from the earth
   - B. temporary structure for holding workers and materials
   - C. place where stone or brick is stored for use in construction
   - D. a large factory for building houses

2. Her father was a carver.
   - F. person who designs buildings
   - G. person who builds with bricks
   - Ⓗ person who sculpts by cutting stone or wood
   - J. person who transports stone blocks

3. The cathedral was in the capital city.
   - A. an immense building
   - B. a large room with a high ceiling
   - Ⓒ a large or important church
   - D. a place where people work with stone

4. The artist had several apprentices.
   - Ⓕ people learning a trade or art
   - G. areas set aside for keeping materials while working
   - H. people who give aid or help
   - J. styles or methods of working

5. My brother wants to study architecture.
   - A. rocks of a particular area
   - B. the art of making figures by carving, modeling, or casting
   - C. the science of the forms of life represented by fossils
   - Ⓓ the art of designing buildings

6. She was fascinated by the intricate designs.
   - F. unusual
   - Ⓖ complicated and detailed
   - H. bold
   - J. delicate and difficult to see

7. The masons had gone home for the day.
   - A. people who draw diagrams
   - Ⓑ people who build with stone or brick
   - C. people who pound wedges into stone to separate ledge from seam
   - D. people who operate saws

Part 2: Comprehension

Use what you know about the selection to answer each item.

8. Where does the stone for the Cathedral of Saint John the Divine come from?
   - Ⓕ Indiana
   - G. England
   - H. New York
   - J. Pennsylvania

9. What is dynamite used for in a limestone quarry?
   - A. separating the ledge from the seam
   - B. causing a section of ledge to crash to the ground
   - Ⓒ uncovering a new section of the limestone seam
   - D. finding fossils in the limestone

10. In the process of removing limestone from the earth, which step comes first?
   - F. Small blocks are cut from the ledge.
   - G. Drill runners drive holes into the base of the ledge.
   - H. Rubber bags are inflated by hoses to push the ledge out.
   - Ⓙ Saw runners cut blocks called ledges into the stone.

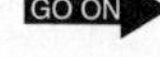

Practice Book 6.6, p. 296

Name ______________________

Cutters, Carvers, and the Cathedral

11. Which item states a fact?
   - A. "To be a carver, you have to have a passion for it, to love it with all your heart."
   - Ⓑ "The following Sunday, the Second World War broke out."
   - C. "The breaker has to have a good 'lick' to hit those wedges just right."
   - D. "But it is less important than the masons'. . . ."

12. In which of these sentences does the author state an opinion?
   - F. "Construction on the cathedral has stopped for lack of funding."
   - G. "Some of the figures portray leaders in the struggle for social justice, such as Nelson Mandela."
   - Ⓗ "If the limestone took three hundred million years to form, a hundred years to build a monument to faith doesn't seem so very long."
   - J. "Yet, services are held, concerts are performed, and festivals are celebrated."

13. The author uses quotations from actual workers in this selection to—
   - Ⓐ give the reader a more vivid picture of what the work is really like.
   - B. add humor to the selection.
   - C. avoid having to restate what he has learned from them.
   - D. make it seem as if the construction was completed long ago.

14. If you are very good at geometry, which of these jobs is most likely to suit you best?
   - F. breaker
   - G. stone carver
   - H. drill runner
   - Ⓙ masonry draftsman

15. Which of these workers uses the same tools he or she would have used 100 years ago?
   - A. limestone quarrier
   - B. stone mason
   - C. masonry draftsman
   - Ⓓ master carver

STOP

Name ______________________________ Cutters, Carvers, and the Cathedral

Fact and Opinion

- A **statement of fact** can be proven true or false by reading, observing, asking an expert, or checking it in some way.
- A **statement of opinion** tells someone's belief, judgment, or way of thinking about something. It cannot be proven true or false, but it can be supported or explained.
- A valid statement of opinion is supported by facts or by the authority of an expert. A faulty statement of opinion is not.

Directions: Read the passage below.

When the final blasting and carving are finished, this huge granite mountain will become an impressive memorial to Lakota warrior-chief Crazy Horse. The statue, designed and begun by Korczak Ziolkowski, shows Crazy Horse mounted on a pony, pointing toward the lands of his people.

Mr. Ziolkowski was invited to come to the Black Hills of South Dakota in 1947. There he began the huge statue, using jackhammers, blowtorches, and dynamite to fashion features from the rough granite. He died in 1982, but many of his children and grandchildren continue his project. Already the nine-story face and portions of the arm have been carved. When finished, the 563-foot-high statue is certain to inspire awe in all who see it.

Directions: Complete the table below. Decide if each statement is a fact or an opinion. If it is a fact, tell how it might be proved true or false. If it's an opinion, tell whether it is valid or faulty and why you think so.

Statements	Fact or Opinion	If fact, how can it be proved true or false? If opinion, is it valid or faulty?
The monument to Crazy Horse will be impressive.	opinion	Valid; its great size and height are characteristics that often impress many people.
Mr. Ziolkowski was invited to come to the Black Hills of South Dakota in 1947.	1. **fact**	2. **Date might be checked in South Dakota newspapers or in Mr. Ziolkowski's records.**
When finished, the statue of Crazy Horse will point toward the lands of the Lakota.	fact	3. **Look in history books or old maps to find out where the Lakota used to live and where they live now.**
Mr. Ziolkowski's children and grandchildren don't care about the project.	4. **opinion**	5. **Faulty; they have continued the project since his death.**

Notes for Home: Your child identified statements of fact and opinion. ***Home Activity:*** Together, discuss statements of opinion made on television news reports. In particular, talk about how well the opinions are supported by factual evidence.

Practice Book 6.6, p. 297

Name ______________________________ Cutters, Carvers, and the Cathedral

Graphic Sources and Steps in a Process

REVIEW

Directions: Read the passage and look at the picture. Then read each question about the passage and picture. Choose the best answer to each question. Mark the letter for the answer you have chosen.

Building a Flower

Imagine a "Metallic Flower" rising into the sky in a field of old factories. Such a flower has grown into a reality in the form of Frank Gehry's Guggenheim Museum in Bilbao, Spain. The building's most striking feature is an immense roof constructed of curving, twisting metal that reminds people of a flower.

This building is a result of a process that began with an international competition. The competition invited leading architects to design a building that would blend with the Bilbao skyline and be different from all other buildings in the world. While Frank Gehry's winning design reminds some people of the unusual shape of New York City's Guggenheim Museum, it has elements all its own.

The roof's unusual sculpted curving shape required careful planning. First, Mr. Gehry built a wood and paper model of the museum. Next, he entered mathematical data about the curves of the model's walls and roof into a computer. Mr. Gehry said afterwards that the computer was essential to turning his designs into reality.

Roof of Guggenheim Museum in Bilbao, Spain

1. The first step in building the museum was to—
   A. invite Frank Gehry to design it.
   B. build the roof.
   C. use a computer to begin the design.
   (D) hold an international competition.
2. The picture helps you understand—
   (F) the shape of the roof.
   G. the location of the museum.
   H. how the computer software works.
   J. how Gehry's design was different from other designs.
3. Which picture would be of further help in understanding the article?
   A. a portrait of Frank Gehry
   B. a portrait of Solomon R. Guggenheim
   (C) a picture of the Guggenheim Museum in New York City
   D. a picture of the city of Bilbao
4. What was the first step in moving from the design on paper to the actual building?
   F. looking at the Guggenheim Museum in New York
   G. assigning the job to Frank Gehry
   H. entering mathematical data about the curves of the walls and roof
   (J) building a model of the design
5. Before Mr. Gehry was able to use the computer for help, he had to—
   A. win the competition.
   (B) enter mathematical data about the curve of the roof and walls into the computer.
   C. invent a new computer program.
   D. name the roof "Metallic Flower."

Notes for Home: Your child analyzed a passage and a picture and identified the steps in a process. ***Home Activity:*** Describe a house or a room to your child. Encourage him or her to draw a picture of the house or room, based on your description.

Name ______________________________ Cutters, Carvers, and the Cathedral

Writing Across Texts

Directions: Consider what you learned about building design and function from *Cutters, Carvers, and the Cathedral* and "How Does the Use of a Building Affect What It Ends Up Looking Like?" In the chart below, compare the cathedral from *Cutters, Carvers, and the Cathedral* and one building from the selection by Caroline Grimshaw. How does each compare in terms of its function, size, building material(s), shape, and how its design fits its function? **Possible answers given.**

Criteria	The Cathedral	Comparison Building
Function	1. **church services, concerts, feeding and caring for those in need**	2. **send messages to passing ships**
Size	3. **very large**	4. **somewhat small**
Building Materials	5. **limestone**	6. **glass, stone**
Shape	7. **has many parts with different shapes: arched doorways, round windows, rectangular building parts**	8. **cylindrical**
How the Design Fits the Function	9. **The building is large to fit the number of people who use it, and ornate to allow people to appreciate its beauty.**	10. **The building is cylindrical so its beam of light can sweep in a circle, and tall so that it allows for a good view of the sea.**

Write a Comparison/Contrast Paragraph

On another sheet of paper, write a paragraph comparing and contrasting the two buildings from the chart above. Use information from *Cutters, Carvers, and the Cathedral* and "How Does the Use of a Building Affect What It Ends Up Looking Like?" **Paragraphs will vary. Check that students have supported their opinions with information from both selections.**

Notes for Home: Your child compared two buildings in terms of function, size, building materials, shape, and how well the design of the building fits its function. ***Home Activity:*** Talk with your child about how the design of your residence fits its function.

Grammar Practice Book 6.6, p. 146

Name ______________________________ Cutters, Carvers, and the Cathedral

Grammar: Conjunctions

REVIEW

Directions: Use the conjunctions *and, but,* or *or* to complete the sentences. Write the conjunction on the line to the left.

but 1. You may think you want to be an architect, _____ you should consider these questions first.

and 2. Do engineering _____ art both appeal to you?

or 3. When you travel, would you rather look at buildings _____ go to the beach?

but 4. Architects may enjoy the beach, _____ buildings come first.

and 5. If you enjoy building things _____ drawing pictures, perhaps architecture is the career for you.

Directions: Combine each pair of sentences with the conjunctions *and, but,* or *or.*

6. *Form* refers to the appearance of a building. *Function* refers to its purpose.
   ***Form* refers to the appearance of a building, and *function* refers to its purpose.**
7. Does form depend on function? Does function depend on form?
   Does form depend on function, or does function depend on form?
8. Architects are always asking this question. No one has found the final answer.
   Architects are always asking this question, but no one has found the final answer.
9. Is beauty more important? Is comfort more important?
   Is beauty more important, or is comfort more important?
10. Architects may not agree on the answer. They still manage to design wonderful buildings.
    Architects may not agree on the answer, but they still manage to design wonderful buildings.

Notes for Home: Your child used the conjunctions *and, but,* and *or* to complete and combine sentences. ***Home Activity:*** Make a card for each of the three conjunctions. Then make word cards. Take turns choosing two word cards and a conjunction card to use in forming a sentence.

Grammar Practice Book 6.6, p. 147

Name ____________

Cutters, Carvers, and the Cathedral

Grammar: Semicolons, Colons, and Hyphens

Semicolons (;)

- Use a semicolon to join two closely related, short sentences: Friends and neighbors worked hard; the barn was built in a day.

Colons (:)

- Use a colon to separate the hour from the minute: 8:45 P.M.
- Use a colon to punctuate the greeting in a business letter: Dear Senator Young:
- Use a colon to introduce a list that comes after words like *following* or *these:* These are some of the creative arts: painting, sculpture, and architecture.
- Use a colon to set off the name of a speaker in a play: MOLLY: *(Quietly)* I've never told anyone this, but I want to be an architect someday.

Hyphens (-)

- Use a hyphen to join words that are thought of as one: Michelangelo was a well-known sculptor, painter, and architect.
- Use a hyphen to write the numbers twenty-one to ninety-nine.

Directions: Join each pair of sentences with a semicolon. Write the new sentence on the line.

1. I like to stand and stare at buildings. Someday I think I'll try to design one.
I like to stand and stare at buildings; someday I think I'll try to design one.

2. Some architects specialize in skyscrapers. Other architects specialize in bridges or tunnels.
Some architects specialize in skyscrapers; other architects specialize in bridges or tunnels.

Directions: Add a colon or a hyphen to each sentence.

3. The reasons I want to design buildings are these: they last a long time, they're useful and necessary, and they can be very beautiful.
4. I may be soft-spoken, but I work very hard to get what I want.
5. My first architecture class begins at 9:30 A.M.

Notes for Home: Your child used semicolons (;), colons (:), and hyphens (-). ***Home Activity:*** Have your child explain four different ways to use colons.

Grammar Practice Book 6.6, p. 148

Name ____________

Cutters, Carvers, and the Cathedral

Grammar: Semicolons, Colons, and Hyphens

Directions: Use a semicolon to join a sentence in the first column to a sentence in the second column. Write the new sentences on the matching numbered line.

1. I want to travel. — a. Every year it tilts a little bit more.
2. I especially love modern skyscrapers. — b. My favorite is the Sears Tower in Chicago.
3. I want to see the Leaning Tower of Pisa. — c. They were built five thousand years ago.
4. I also want to go to Egypt to see the pyramids. — d. That way, I can see the great buildings of the world.

1. **I want to travel; that way, I can see the great buildings of the world.**
2. **I especially love modern skyscrapers; my favorite is the Sears Tower in Chicago.**
3. **I want to see the Leaning Tower of Pisa; every year it tilts a little bit more.**
4. **I also want to go to Egypt to see the pyramids; they were built five thousand years ago.**

Directions: Add a colon and a series of items to complete each sentence.

5. To build these bird houses, we need the following materials **: paint, nails, a hammer, and some wood.**
6. These are the birds we want to attract **: sparrows, robins, and chickadees.**
7. Good teamwork requires the following skills **: discipline, cooperation, and communication.**

Directions: Use a hyphen to combine the two words given. Write the new word on the line.

8. well, liked **well-liked**
9. eighty, nine **eighty-nine**
10. vice, president **vice-president**

Write a Description

On a separate sheet of paper, write a description of the most beautiful building you've ever seen. Tell what you know about the building's history, including when it was built and how it's been used. Include colons, semicolons, and hyphens as needed in your description.
Students' writing should include correct use of semicolons, colons, and hyphens.

Notes for Home: Your child used semicolons (;), colons (:), and hyphens (-). ***Home Activity:*** Write two sentences that can be combined with a semicolon, such as *I like plays. However, I like movies better.* Have your child use a semicolon to combine the two sentences.

Grammar Practice Book 6.6, p. 149

Name ____________

Cutters, Carvers, and the Cathedral

Grammar: Semicolons, Colons, and Hyphens

RETEACHING

Insert a semicolon to join the pair of sentences. Write the new sentence.

1. My brother and I love reading. However, we haven't had time to go to the library this week.
2. **My brother and I love reading; however, we haven't had time to go to the library this week.**

Insert colons where they belong.

3. Please bring the following: shoes, socks, and a bucket.
4. I arrived at 4:30.
5. Dear Governor Smith:
6. GENE: Look out!

Insert hyphens where they belong.

7. She had a worn-out hat.
8. Read page fifty-eight.

Semicolons are used to join two short sentences that are closely related. **Colons** are used to separate the hour from the minute when giving the time. Colons are also used to punctuate the greeting in a business letter, to set off the name of a speaker in a play, and to introduce a list. **Hyphens** are used to join words that are thought of as one word and to write the numbers twenty-one to ninety-nine.

Directions: In each sentence, add a colon or a hyphen where it belongs.

1. She had these three ideas for a project: making a collage, building a model, and painting a portrait.
2. Mr. Nevins looks young, but he is sixty-two.
3. BARBARA: I wonder where they are.
4. Dear Doctor Fields:

Directions: Join the pair of sentences with a semicolon. Write the new sentence on the line.

5. Our friends were avid skiers. Colorado was their home away from home.
Our friends were avid skiers; Colorado was their home away from home.

Notes for Home: Your child used colons, semicolons, and hyphens to correctly punctuate sentences. ***Home Activity:*** Have your child find in a newspaper or magazine examples where colons, semicolons, and hyphens are used. Ask your child to explain the punctuation in one example.

Grammar Practice Book 6.6, p. 150

Name ____________

Cutters, Carvers, and the Cathedral

Grammar: Semicolons, Colons, and Hyphens

Directions: Insert colons, semicolons, and hyphens where they belong.

THE TRICKY BEAR

These are the characters: Lucy, Bud, and a Bear. The play starts at 5:00 in the afternoon.

BUD: We're lost. What do we do now?

LUCY: Bud, don't be so negative. This is a very pleasant grove of trees.

BUD: Hey, what's that?

LUCY: Looks like a falcon. *(rubbing her hands together)* Just look at those gleaming talons.

BUD: It's quite obvious you're trying to scare me; however, it won't work. *(A fierce growl is heard offstage.)* Yikes! It's a bear!

LUCY: Don't be silly. It's probably one of the other kids trying to trick us.

BUD: A lot you know. I'm getting out of here. *(He hesitates.)* Wait. What if I run right into it?

LUCY: Climb that tree. But there aren't any bears within eighty-nine miles of here.

BUD: That's no good—bears can climb trees. *(The growling sound is very loud now.)* I'm getting out of here!

(Bud runs off just as the bear runs in, and they collide. As they fall, the Bear's head comes off and we see that it is Kevin, a friend of theirs.)

Write an Ending

On the lines, write an ending to the script you corrected. Think about what the characters might say to each other, and how they might act. Use colons where they belong. Also use at least one semicolon and one hyphen. **Possible answers given.**

BUD: **I can't believe you tricked me; what a great costume.**

KEVIN: **I growled twenty-six times before you heard me!**

LUCY: **We'd better leave. It's 5:30.**

Notes for Home: Your child correctly used colons, semicolons, and hyphens to punctuate a script for a play. ***Home Activity:*** Together, write a short script of a conversation during a family meal. Help your child punctuate the script correctly.

Practice Book 6.6, p. 298
Name ______________________

Cutters, Carvers, and the Cathedral

Word Study: Word Building

Directions: Read the word pairs below. Listen to how each word in a pair is different from the other. Underline the stressed syllable in each word, for example: **rectangle** and **rectangular.** Use a dictionary to check your work.

1. electric electricians
2. history prehistoric
3. specify specific
4. restore restorations
5. certify certification

Directions: Read the letter below. It contains five related word pairs—a base word and a new word formed by adding a prefix or a suffix, for example: **electric** and **electricians.** Find each pair. Write each word in the correct column. **Order may vary.**

Dear Miguel,

I am having a great time helping to restore the old church in town. The restoration process is slow and tedious, but the people I work with dedicate as much time as necessary to the work. You'd be amazed at the decorations we've brushed off and cleaned. You know I've always been inspired by history. Well, some of the carvings we've found look almost prehistoric! We have to separate the very old workmanship from the new additions. This separation is very time-consuming. However, our dedication is paying off! Every day we marvel at how the carvers and cutters of long ago chose to decorate this amazing church. I wish you could see it!

Your friend,

Amelia

Base Word		New Word	
6.	restore	11.	restoration
7.	dedicate	12.	dedication
8.	decorate	13.	decorations
9.	history	14.	prehistoric
10.	separate	15.	separation

Notes for Home: Your child compared the sounds of words with suffixes and prefixes to their base words. ***Home Activity:*** Read a magazine article with your child. Look for words that have been built from other words. Figure out the base word. Say the words to hear the sound changes.

Spelling Workbook 6.6, p. 117
Name ______________________

Cutters, Carvers, and the Cathedral

Spelling: Related Words 2

Pretest Directions: Fold back the page along the dotted line. On the blanks, write the spelling words as they are dictated. When you have finished the test, unfold the page and check your words.

1. direct	1. The road to my house is **direct**.
2. direction	2. I went in the wrong **direction**.
3. history	3. He studied American **history**.
4. historical	4. This is a **historical** site.
5. fact	5. The **fact** is I am tired.
6. factual	6. She gave a **factual** account.
7. critic	7. He is a film **critic** on TV.
8. criticize	8. Don't **criticize** if you don't know.
9. produce	9. The factories **produce** radios.
10. production	10. I help with the play's **production**.
11. magic	11. He learned to do **magic** tricks.
12. magician	12. The **magician** lost his wand.
13. electric	13. He saw an **electric** eel.
14. electrician	14. The **electrician** fixed the lamp.
15. distract	15. Their voices **distract** me.
16. distraction	16. That noise is a **distraction**.
17. remedy	17. What is a good cough **remedy**?
18. remedial	18. Her sister took **remedial** math.
19. origin	19. Where is the **origin** of the stream?
20. original	20. This is an **original** story.

Notes for Home: Your child took a pretest on related words that have parts spelled similarly but pronounced differently. ***Home Activity:*** Help your child learn misspelled words before the final test by underlining the parts that are different in each pair and concentrating on those.

Spelling Workbook 6.6, p. 118
Name ______________________

Cutters, Carvers, and the Cathedral

Spelling: Related Words 2

Word List

direct	fact	produce	electric	remedy
direction	factual	production	electrician	remedial
history	critic	magic	distract	origin
historical	criticize	magician	distraction	original

Directions: Choose the pair of related words from the box that contain the same letter pronounced differently. Write the words in the correct group. **Order may vary.**

Word Pairs in Which the Sound of c is Different

1. critic	2. criticize
3. produce	4. production
5. magic	6. magician
7. electric	8. electrician

Word Pairs in Which the Sound of t is Different

9. direct	10. direction
11. fact	12. factual
13. distract	14. distraction

Directions: Choose the word in ( ) that best completes each sentence. Write the word on the line.

historical 15. This arch is a (history/historical) monument that honors the war dead.

history 16. The monument has a long and colorful (history/historical).

original 17. The sculptor's (origin/original) idea had been for a statue, not an arch.

origin 18. The marble used in the arch is of Italian (origin/original).

remedy 19. He needed a quick (remedy/remedial) when funding was cut back.

remedial 20. Fortunately, a millionaire gave some money as a (remedy/remedial) measure until further funds could be raised.

Notes for Home: Your child spelled related words that have parts with similar spellings but different pronunciations. ***Home Activity:*** Say each pair of related words aloud. Have your child spell each word and use it in a sentence.

Spelling Workbook 6.6, p. 119
Name ______________________

Cutters, Carvers, and the Cathedral

Spelling: Related Words 2

Directions: Proofread this passage from a gardening encyclopedia. Find five spelling mistakes. Use the proofreading marks to correct each mistake.

- ≡ Make a capital.
- / Make a small letter.
- ∧ Add something.
- Take out something.
- ⊙ Add a period.
- ¶ Begin a new paragraph.

Landscape architects design parks and landscapes for the grounds around buildings. They are asked to produse [c] pleasing and useful outdoor areas. Electric lights strung through tree branches look madgical when lit up at night. Highly originl [a] and effective designs can remedee [y] urban locations that are ugly and barren. Some gardens are designed strictly to focus attention on a beautiful view or the historrical features of a building. Whatever the project, landscape architects work magic with a combination of trees, shrubs, and flowers.

Spelling Tip

Related words often have parts that are spelled the same but that sound different: **direct, direction.** Check the passage to make sure that related words are spelled correctly.

Word List

direct	fact	produce	electric	remedy
direction	factual	production	electrician	remedial
history	critic	magic	distract	origin
historical	criticize	magician	distraction	original

Write an Article

Imagine that you are a writer of encyclopedias. On a separate sheet of paper, write an encyclopedia entry on some aspect of building, architecture, or construction. Describe the skills and training that are needed. Try to use at least three spelling words. **Answers will vary, but each article should include at least three spelling words.**

Notes for Home: Your child spelled related words that have parts with similar spellings but different pronunciations. ***Home Activity:*** Help your child write sentences that use pairs of related words. For example: *The historical society has a great interest in history.*

Spelling Workbook 6.6, p. 120

Name ______

Cutters, Carvers, and the Cathedral

Spelling: Related Words 2

REVIEW

Word List				
direct	fact	produce	electric	remedy
direction	factual	production	electrician	remedial
history	critic	magic	distract	origin
historical	criticize	magician	distraction	original

Directions: Choose the word from the box that best matches each clue. Write the word on the line.

direction 1. any point on the compass

history 2. a record of past events

electric 3. a type of light that uses electricity

remedial 4. curing; relieving

origin 5. source; starting point

fact 6. statement that can be proven true or false

critic 7. a person who makes judgments

historical 8. concerned with history

production 9. the act or result of producing

distraction 10. something that makes it hard to concentrate

magic 11. a type of trick, like pulling a rabbit out of a hat

distract 12. to draw one's attention away from a task

remedy 13. a cure

Directions: Write the word from the box that belongs in each group.

14. authentic, unique, original
15. clown, acrobat, magician
16. judge, analyze, criticize
17. truthful, realistic, factual
18. plumber, engineer, electrician
19. create, make, produce
20. order, command, direct

Notes for Home: Your child spelled related words that have parts with similar spellings but different pronunciations. ***Home Activity:*** Work with your child to create dictionary entries. For each spelling word, write a definition and an example sentence.

Spelling: Related Words 2 673

Practice Book 6.6, p. 299

Name ______

Cutters, Carvers, and the Cathedral

Technology: Order Form/Following Directions

An **order form** is a special chart with spaces to be filled in. It can be used to purchase merchandise or obtain other materials. Since order forms are often complex, it is important to **follow directions** carefully.

Suppose you wanted to order a book from an online bookstore. You might begin searching to see if the bookstore has the book you want to purchase. The computer screen could look like the one below. You type words in the boxes and click on the round buttons beneath the boxes. Then click "Search Now."

Welcome to Our Bookstore!

You can search by author, title, or subject.

Author ______

○ Exact Name ○ Last Name ○ Start of Last Name

Title ______

○ Exact Title ○ Key Words ○ Start of Title

Subject ______

○ Exact Subject ○ Key Words ○ Start of Subject

Search Now | Start Over

Directions: Use the computer screen above to answer these questions.

1. How would you find a book about architecture? Enter "architecture" in the subject box, click on the button "Exact Subject," and then click on "Search Now."

2. How would you find a book written by the architect Frank Lloyd Wright? Enter "Frank Lloyd Wright" in the author box, click on the button for "Exact Name," and then click on "Search Now."

3. How would you find the book called *Understanding Architecture?* Enter "Understanding Architecture" in the title box, click on the button for "Exact Title," and then click on "Search Now."

674 Research and Study Skills: Technology: Order Form/Following Directions

Practice Book 6.6, p. 300

Name ______

Cutters, Carvers, and the Cathedral

Once you have found the book you want, you might get an order form like the one below. To purchase a book, you would need to complete the order form and then click "Order Now." Never use a person's credit card without that person's permission. Never give information about a credit card unless you are sure that this information will be confidential.

Place Your Order Now

You have chosen the book:

Understanding Architecture: Its Elements, History, and Meaning

by Leland M. Roth

List Price: $28.00 Our Price: $22.40 You Save: $5.60 (20%)

Name ______

Address ______

City ______ **State** ______ **Zip Code** ______

Telephone Number ______ **E-mail Address** ______

Method of Payment ○ Credit Card ○ Bill Me

Credit Card Type ______

Credit Card Number ______

Order Now | Start Over

Directions: Use the computer screen above to answer these questions.

4. What would you do if you realized you had made a mistake typing in information or the book selected was not the one you wanted?
Possible answer: You could click on "Start Over" and either retype the correct information or start a new search to select a different book.

5. Why is it important to follow all directions carefully when filling out order forms?
Possible answers: to make sure you haven't ordered the wrong item; to make sure that you give the correct information so your purchase gets to you

Notes for Home: Your child learned about filling out an order form to order a book. ***Home Activity:*** Show your child different types of order forms and discuss how to fill them out. Help your child complete an order form to make an imaginary purchase.

Research and Study Skills: Technology: Order Form/Following Directions 675

Name ______

Persuasive Argument Organizer

Directions: Complete the entire organizer. In each box, write a reason that supports the arguing statement. Next to each box, write three sentences that explain the reason. **The organizer should be filled out completely.**

Title: ______

Arguing Statement: ______

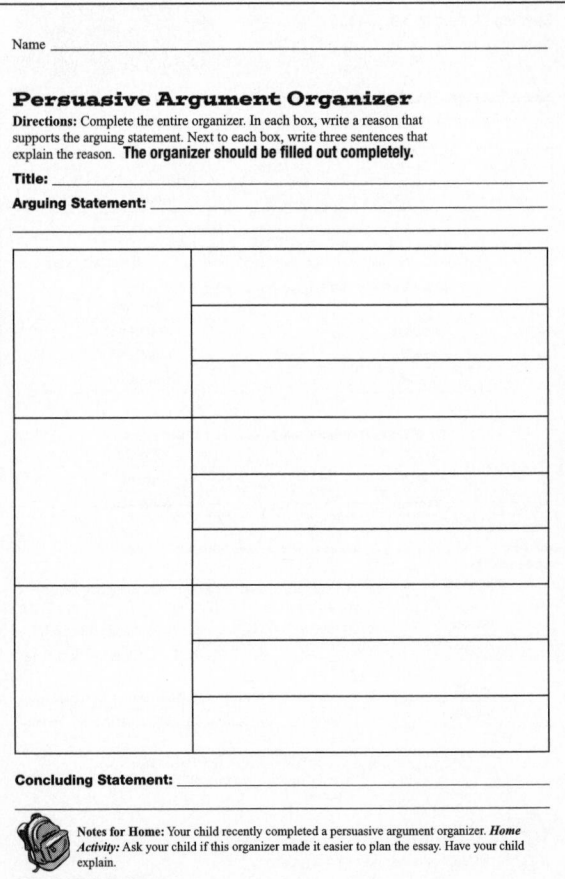

Concluding Statement: ______

Notes for Home: Your child recently completed a persuasive argument organizer. ***Home Activity:*** Ask your child if this organizer made it easier to plan the essay. Have your child explain.

676 Unit 6: Writing Process

Name

Elaboration
Using a Thesaurus

- When you write a persuasive argument, you can elaborate by **using a thesaurus** to find vivid words to replace ordinary words.
- This will make your essay sound more interesting and convincing.

Thesaurus

alive: awake, exhilarated, vivacious
carry: lug, move, haul
cry: howl, whimper, whine
dull: dreary, pale, boring
laugh: howl, giggle, guffaw
tired: fatigued, weary, faint
well: wisely, excellently, favorably

Directions: Elaborate each sentence by replacing the boldfaced word with a word from the Thesaurus box. Rewrite the sentence with the new word, as this example shows.

I felt **tired** after I ran the marathon.
I felt **faint** after I ran the marathon.

Answers will vary. Reasonable answers are given.

1. My dog **cries** when he wants to come inside.
My dog whimpers when he wants to come inside.

2. Washing the car makes me feel **tired.**
Washing the car makes me feel fatigued.

3. We had to **carry** all the groceries upstairs.
We had to lug all the groceries upstairs.

4. Spend your money **well.**
Spend your money wisely.

5. Exercising makes you feel **alive.**
Exercising makes you feel exhilarated.

6. Paint that **dull** looking wall a better color.
Paint that dreary looking wall a better color.

7. The baby **laughed.**
The baby giggled.

Notes for Home: Your child elaborated sentences by adding vivid words. ***Home Activity:*** Take a walk with your child. Give your child sentences that use ordinary words to tell about what you see. Ask your child to change the sentences by replacing the ordinary words with vivid words.

Name

Self-Evaluation Guide
Accept all reasonable responses.

Persuasive Argument

Directions: Think about the final draft of your persuasive argument. Then answer each question below.

	Yes	No	Not sure
1. Did I use the correct form for a five-paragraph essay?			
2. Did I express good reasons that will persuade my reader?			
3. Did I choose vivid words?			
4. Did I use transition words such as *first, next,* and *finally?*			
5. Did I use persuasive words such as *certainly?*			

6. In what ways has your writing improved this year?

7. Write one mistake you made this time that you will avoid the next time.

Notes for Home: Your child wrote and evaluated a five-paragraph persuasive argument. ***Home Activity:*** Ask your child to tell you what he or she likes best about the persuasive argument.

Teacher's Notes

Teacher's Notes

Teacher's Notes

Teacher's Notes

Teacher's Notes

Teacher's Notes

Teacher's Notes